ELECTRONICS FOR COMMUNICATION ENGINEERS

BOOKS by JOHN MARKUS and VIN ZELUFF

ELECTRONICS FOR ENGINEERS

WHAT ELECTRONICS DOES

HANDBOOK OF INDUSTRIAL ELECTRONIC CIRCUITS

ELECTRONICS MANUAL FOR RADIO ENGINEERS

ELECTRONICS FOR COMMUNICATION ENGINEERS

ELECTRONICS FOR COMMUNICATION ENGINEERS

BY JOHN MARKUS AND VIN ZELUFF
ASSOCIATE EDITORS OF *ELECTRONICS*

FIRST EDITION

McGRAW-HILL BOOK COMPANY, INC.

NEW YORK • TORONTO • LONDON • 1952

PREFACE

This book brings to engineers in easy-to-use form the important radio communication, radio broadcasting, television and radar design articles that have appeared in *Electronics* during the past five years. The book is a sequel to "Electronics for Engineers" and "Electronics Manual for Radio Engineers," which similarly made available in convenient reference form the same type of material from earlier issues of this magazine.

For this third book, the new material was carefully selected, checked, edited and condensed to have maximum reference value. The resulting 252 articles were then logically arranged by subject matter into fifteen chapters, so that each chapter constitutes a comprehensive survey of recent developments. Designers, builders and users of electronic equipment will find here the equations, charts, nomographs, tables and other reference data that are so hard to find in loose copies or bound volumes of the original magazine.

Chapters are arranged in alphabetical order so that oftentimes chapter headings alone serve to locate the desired information, as follows: Amplifiers; Antennas; Audio; Cathode-Ray Tubes; Components; Electronic Music; Filters; Measurements; Microwaves; Oscillators; Power Supplies; Propagation; Pulses; Receivers; Transmission Lines; Transmitters.

Worthy of special mention is the chapter on Electronic Music, a relatively new branch of electronics that is today increasing rapidly in importance. Ten significant articles here give design data and circuit details of both commercial and custom-built electronic organs of various types, ranging from the simplest neon-diode systems to complex tone-wheel arrangements that successfully simulate cathedral organ performance. In addi-

tion, much of the material in the Audio chapter is directly applicable to the design and construction of electronic musical instruments.

A specific desired article can be located in four ways —by flipping through the appropriate chapter, by glancing over the article titles listed in the Table of Contents, by looking up the subject of the article in the topical index at the back of the book, or by using the back-of-book author index if the name of the author is remembered. The topical cross-index is particularly valuable, with many articles having as many as ten separate entries to insure quick finding of any desired item.

With the significant work of other engineers collected together in handy cross-indexed volumes, hours and even days of searching through technical literature can be saved. By checking the prior art in a compendium of this type, a problem can be started where others left off rather than from scratch. This reduces the cost of laboratory research and experimentation.

The response of engineers to the predecessor volumes proves conclusively that one article alone, available when needed, is enough to justify a place for books of this type in every electronic design and communication engineer's library.

The engineer authors whose works appear in this volume deserve congratulations for their permanent contributions to the art and industry of electronics.

JOHN MARKUS and VIN ZELUFF

Associate Editors, *Electronics*

New York, N. Y.
February, 1952

CONTENTS

AMPLIFIERS

Gain-Bandwidth Nomograph

Equations involved in design of single-tuned amplifier circuits are incorporated in one large nomograph to speed up design calculations. Shows overall effect of varying the parameters when seeking the most economical tube arrangement for desired gain and bandwidth

By CHESTER W. YOUNG

THE design of vacuum-tube amplifiers involves determining the maximum gain and/or bandwidth using the most economical tube arrangement. The most practical first-approximation calculation for single-tuned circuits such as cascaded synchronously tuned i-f stages was found to be $G_m/2\pi C_t$, and the nomograph on the following page was therefore based on this ratio. The nomograph encompasses all of the interdependent equations used in amplifier design, hence shows the effect of variations in each parameter on the others.

Practical values of G_m and C_t that include the effect of the coupling networks can be found by taking approximately 85 percent of the maximum G_m and 160 percent of the value of C_t given in tube manufacturer's data. This makes the usable gain-bandwidth about 53 percent of the ideal, or roughly one-half. This relationship is found in Table I.

The nomograph solves the following equations:

$$Q = f_o/B \qquad (1)$$
$$A = G_m \times R_L \qquad (2)$$
$$AB = A \times B \qquad (3)$$
$$AB = G_m/2\pi C_t \qquad (4)$$
$$B = 1/2\pi C_t R_L \qquad (5)$$
$$A_{max} = 1/2\pi f_o C_{GP} R_L \qquad (6)$$

where $Q = R \omega C$ = circuit quality, f_o = circuit resonant frequency, B = 3-db bandwidth, A = stage gain, G_m = tube transconductance, R_L = total damping resistance, C_t = total shunt capacitance, A_{max} = maximum usable gain, and C_{GP} = total effective grid-plate capacitance.

Since the bandwidth between two 3-db frequencies of a tuned circuit is equal to the 3-db frequency of a parallel or series R-C circuit, the nomograph can be used also for video types of circuits. Also, as Eq. 5 states that

Table I—Examples of Ideal and Practical Tube Capacitances

IDEAL				
Tube Type	C_g $\mu\mu f$	C_p $\mu\mu f$	C_t $\mu\mu f$	G_m/C_t mc
6AC7	11.0	5.0	16.0	562
6AK5	4.0	2.8	6.8	750
PRACTICAL				
Tube Type	C_{in} $\mu\mu f$	C_{out} $\mu\mu f$	C_t $\mu\mu f$	G_m/C_t mc
6AC7	17.0	8.0	25.0	312
6AK5	6.7	4.4	11.1	378

bandwidth is independent of L, the nomograph ignores L. Use of this nomograph is best illustrated by an example.

If the known values are f_o = 30 mc, B = 1 mc, C_t = 16 $\mu\mu f$, G_m = 5,000, and C_{GP} = 0.0082 $\mu\mu f$, find the values of Q, AB, A, R_L and A_{max}.

Step 1: Align points f_o = 30 mc and B = 1 mc, and read Q = 30.

Step 2: Align points C_t = 16 $\mu\mu f$ and G_m = 5,000, and read AB = 50 mc.

Step 3. Align AB = 50 mc and B = 1 mc, and read A = 50.

Step 4: Align A = 50 and G_m = 5,000, and read R_L = 10,000.

Step 4 (alternate): Since the loading resistance is directly related to bandwidth and shunt capacitance by means of Eq. 5, it may be found by aligning B = 1 mc and C_t = 16 $\mu\mu f$, giving R_L = 10,000 ohms as before.

Step 5: To ascertain whether A = 50 in Step 3 is a stable value of gain, a criterion of feedback through the tube grid-plate capacitance causing oscillation is determined. If the attenuation from plate to grid is set equal to the amplification from grid to plate as the critical value, then the desired gain must be less than the maximum usable gain. The value A_{max} is approximated

1

by dividing R_L by the reactance of C_{GP} and thinking of this attenuation as a negative gain. This holds true when the input and output impedance are the same, as in a multistage syn-chronous tuned i-f amplifier. The reactance of C_{GP} is determined by aligning $f_o = 30$ mc and $C_{GP} = 0.0082$ $\mu\mu f$ and reading $X = 6.5 \times 10^5$ ohms. Now align this value of X and $R_L = 10,000$ and read the maximum usable gain as 65 on the A_{max} scale. This value is greater than the desired gain of 50, so the amplifier is deemed to be stable.

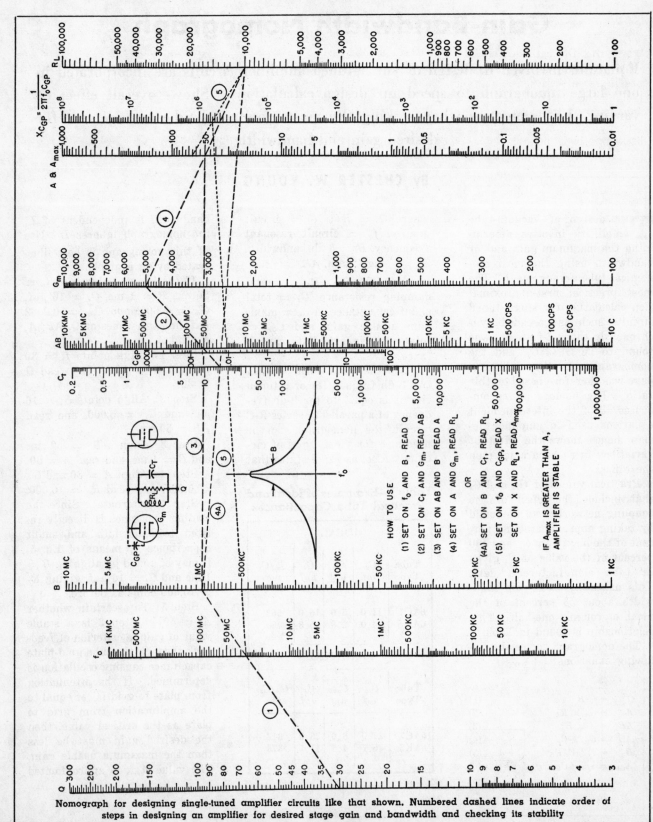

HOW TO USE

(1) SET ON f_o AND B, READ Q
(2) SET ON C_t AND G_m, READ AB
(3) SET ON AB AND B, READ A
(4) SET ON A AND G_m, READ R_L
OR
(4A) SET ON B AND C_t, READ R_L
(5) SET ON f_o AND C_{GP}, READ X
SET ON X AND R_L, READ A_{max}

IF A_{max} IS GREATER THAN A, AMPLIFIER IS STABLE

Nomograph for designing single-tuned amplifier circuits like that shown. Numbered dashed lines indicate order of steps in designing an amplifier for desired stage gain and bandwidth and checking its stability

Cathode-Follower Bandwidth

Nomograph gives upper frequency limit at which bandwidth is 3 db down, in terms of output resistance and total output capacitance of the circuit

By MELVIN B. KLINE

WHILE the cathode follower has come into widespread use in recent years as a major tool of the electronic engineer, and many of its characteristics are well-known, comparatively little has been published about its frequency-handling capabili-ties. A nomograph is given here relating bandwidth (−3 db point), output resistance and output capacitance for cathode-follower operation. Very fast negative pulses or other signals impressed on the grid may not allow the cathode to follow in some instances, due to the time constant of the cathode circuit.

The frequency at which the response is down 3 db is

$$f_{3db} = \frac{1}{2\pi C_k R_o} \qquad (1)$$

where f_{3db} is bandwidth in mc, R_o is output resistance in ohms and C_k is total output capacitance in $\mu\mu$f.

The nomograph is based on this equation. The value of C_k is determined approximately from

$$C_k \cong C_{hk} + C_{pk} + \frac{C_{gk}(C_i + C_{gp})}{C_{gk} + C_i + C_{gp}} + C_s \qquad (2)$$

where C_{hk} is heater-cathode capacitance, C_{pk} is plate-cathode capacitance, C_{gk} is grid-cathode capacitance, C_{gp} is grid-plate ca-pacitance, C_i is input-circuit capacitance, and C_s is the sum of wiring and other capacitances connected externally across the output load. In the case of pentodes C_{gp} can usually be neglected.

The value of R_o can be com-puted from

$$R_o = \frac{R_k}{1 + G_m R_k} \qquad (3)$$

where R_k is the cathode resist-ance and G_m is the transconduct-ance of the tube. The value of R_o can also be obtained from a previously published nomograph.[1]

This nomograph may also be applied to uncompensated R-C amplifiers by replacing R_o with the equivalent output resistance of the amplifier plate circuit. For this case, the nomograph scales can be extended by multiplying the R_o scale and dividing the f_{3db} scale by the same number. The C_k scale then becomes the output capacitance of the amplifier.

REFERENCE

(1) Melvin B. Kline, Cathode-Fol-lower Impedance Nomograph, ELEC-TRONICS, p 130, July 1947.

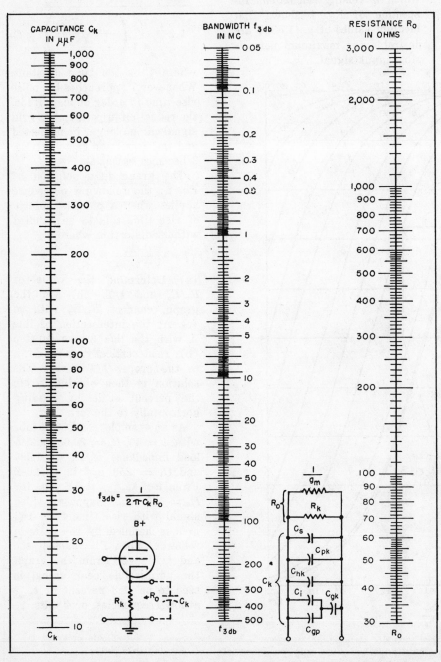

$$f_{3db} = \frac{1}{2\pi C_k R_o}$$

Cathode-Follower Response

Chart gives permissible cathode-follower pulse drive at video frequencies in terms of low-frequency sinusoidal input. Video-frequency overloading and distortion in conventionally loaded circuits originate in output time constant

By RALPH H. BAER

CATHODE FOLLOWERS frequently overload and distort on video signals when designed on the basis of low-frequency formulas. This behavior results from the effect of the time constant associated with the output impedance of the cathode follower and the load capacitance. The usual formula for the peak signal permissible is

$$e_{g_{peak}} = \frac{E_B}{\mu} \left[\frac{1 + \frac{R_k}{R_p}(\mu+1)}{\frac{R_k}{R_p}+2} \right] \quad (1)$$

which is readily calculated. Inspection of Eq. 1 shows that medium values of μ (15-30) are desirable for maximum permissible input signal.

When a video signal with rise time t microseconds is applied to a cathode follower this permissible grid swing is reduced by a factor of

$$\frac{1}{1 + \frac{\mu \frac{R_k}{R_p}}{\frac{R_k}{R_p}+1} \left(\frac{1 - \epsilon^{-\frac{t}{T}}}{\frac{t}{T}} \right)} \quad (2)$$

where T is the time constant. Whenever T approaches the pulse rise time in order of magnitude, the reduction in permissible grid signal can no longer be neglected and the correction factor of Eq. 2 becomes essential.

The graph is a solution of Eq. 2; the following procedure applies when a pulse waveform of rise time t is to be handled without distortion where

$$T = \frac{C_T R_k}{1 + g_m R_k}$$

(a) Determine the value of R_k/R_p and t/T. (b) On the graph, connect R_k/R_p with μ. (c) At the intersection of line A with the line drawn in step (b), read vertically up or down to the proper t/T curve. The solution is then obtained from the percent scale by reading horizontally to the left.

As an example, consider a tube with $\mu = 40$, $R_p = 20,000$ and a load impedance of $R_k = 1,000$ and $C_t = 250$ $\mu\mu$f in parallel. From Eq. 1 $e_{g_{peak}} = 5.6$ volts for $E_B = 150$ volts. Suppose a video signal with rise time $t = 0.42$ μsec is handled by the cathode follower. Then $T = 0.0834$ μsec and $t/T = 5$. From the graph the permissible peak signal is seen to be 72.3 percent of $e_{g_{peak}}$ at low frequencies, or 4 volts.

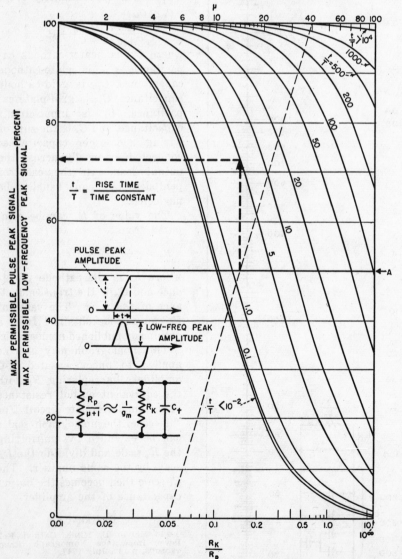

Graphical Solution for Feedback Amplifiers

By LEROY D. BARTER

THE GAIN of any amplifier may be expressed as the maximum gain times a function that shows the variation in the gain.

$$A = \frac{A_m}{P(A)} \qquad (1)$$

where A_m is the maximum gain of an amplifier, $P(A)$ is a complex function, showing both the change in magnitude and phase shift of the gain. In an amplifier with feedback the gain will be

$$A_{fb} = \frac{A}{1 - A\beta} = \frac{\dfrac{A_m}{P(A)}}{1 - \dfrac{A_m}{P(A)}\beta} \qquad (2)$$

$$\frac{A_{fb}}{A_m} = \frac{1}{P(A) - A_m\beta}$$

$$\frac{A_m}{A_{fb}} = P(A) - A_m\beta \qquad (3)$$

Now if $P(A)$ can be conveniently expressed, the gain with feedback can be solved by means of Eq. 3. The remainder of the paper demonstrates the method of finding $P(A)$ and its use.

Single-Stage Amplifier

The gain of a single-stage amplifier can be thought of as containing a gain element that is independent of frequency, within the range considered, and an element that depends upon frequency for its voltage relationships. In Fig. 1A is a single-stage amplifier that may have negative feedback or not depending upon the position of the switch. The gain then is that due to the tube, and the consequent reduction in gain due to the external circuit shown in Fig. 1B. In the normal case the effects of C_1 occur at the lower frequencies while the effects of C_1' occur at the higher frequencies. Hence we may write two equations that will express the variation of gain due to frequency.

$$A_{LF} = \frac{E_{out}}{E_{in}} = A_t\left(\frac{R_1}{R_1 + R_{int} - \dfrac{j}{\omega c}}\right)$$

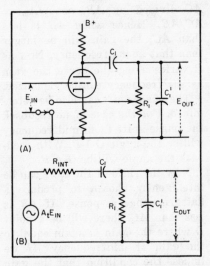

FIG. 1—Simple amplifier in which negative feedback may be introduced

$$= A_t\left(\frac{R_1}{R_1 + R_{int}}\right)$$

$$\left(\frac{1}{1 - \dfrac{j}{\omega C_1(R_1 + R_{int})}}\right)$$

Let $\quad R_{LF} = R_1 + R_{int}$

and let $\quad A_m = A_t\left(\dfrac{R_1}{R_1 + R_{int}}\right)$

$$A_{LF} = A_m\left(\frac{1}{1 - \dfrac{j}{\omega C_1 R_{LF}}}\right) \qquad (4a)$$

$$A_{HF} = \frac{E_{out}}{E_{in}} = A_t\left(\frac{Z_1}{R_{int} + Z_1}\right)$$

$$= A_t\left(\frac{1}{\dfrac{R_{int}}{Z_1} + 1}\right)$$

where $\quad \dfrac{1}{Z_1} = \dfrac{1}{R_1} + j\omega C_1'$

$$A_{HF} = A_t\left(\frac{1}{\dfrac{R_{int}}{R_1} + j\omega C_1' R_{int} + 1}\right)$$

$$= \frac{A_t R_1}{R_{int} + R_1}\left(\frac{1}{1 + \dfrac{j\omega C_1' R_{int} R_1}{R_{int} R_1}}\right)$$

Let $\quad R_{HF} = \dfrac{R_{int} R_1}{R_{int} + R_1}$

and let $\quad A_m = \dfrac{A_t R_1}{R_{int} + R_1}$

$$A_{HF} = A_m\left(\frac{1}{1 + j\omega C_1' R_{HF}}\right) \qquad (4b)$$

Therefore $\quad P_L(A) = 1 - \dfrac{j}{\omega C_1 R_{LF}} \qquad (5a)$

$$P_H(A) = 1 + j\omega C_1' R_{HF} \qquad (5b)$$

Insertion of Eq. 5 into Eq. 3 gives

Low frequency $\dfrac{A_m}{A_{fb}} =$

$$1 - \frac{j}{\omega C_1 R_{LF}} - A_m\beta$$

$$= (1 - A_m\beta)\left(1 - \frac{j}{\omega C_1 R_{LF}(1 - A_m\beta)}\right) \qquad (6a)$$

High frequency $\dfrac{A_m}{A_{fb}} =$

$$1 + j\omega C_1' R_{HF} - A_m\beta$$

$$= (1 - \beta A_m)\left(1 + j\frac{\omega C_1' R_{HF}}{1 - A_m\beta}\right) \qquad (6b)$$

Hence the feedback has the effect of modifying the RC circuits by the feedback factor $(1 - A_m\beta)$. With this new value of RC and the universal gain curves[2] the gain of an amplifier with one pair of RC's in the circuit can easily be determined.

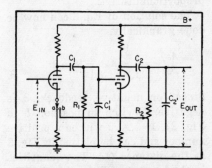

FIG. 2—Two-stage amplifier with optional negative feedback

Two-Stage Amplifier

The usefulness of Eq. 3 is more readily apparent when there are two pair of RC's in the circuit. In Fig. 2 there are two stages of amplification similar to that in Fig. 1. The gain will now be the product of the gain of the two stages. Then for two stages

$$P_L(A) = \left(1 - \frac{j}{\omega C_1 R_{LF1}}\right)$$

$$\left(1 - \frac{j}{\omega C_2 R_{LF2}}\right)$$

Let $S_1 = \dfrac{1}{\omega C_1 R_{LF1}}$ and $S_2 = \dfrac{1}{\omega C_2 R_{LF2}'}$

$$P_L(A) = (1 - jS_1)(1 - jS_2)$$
$$= 1 - S_1 S_2 + j(S_1 + S_2) \quad (7a)$$

$$P_H(A) = (1 + j\omega C_1' R_{HF1})(1 + j\omega C_2' R_{HF2})$$

Let $S_1 = \omega C_1' R_{HF1}$ and $S_2 = \omega C_2' R_{HF2}$

$$P_H(A) = (1 + jS_1)(1 + jS_2)$$
$$= 1 - [S_1 S_2 - j(S_1 + S_2)] \quad (7b)$$

Figures 3 shows a plot of the por-

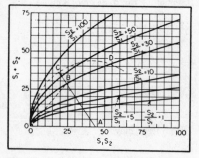

FIG. 3—Curves for graphical analysis of feedback amplifiers

tion of $P(A)$ that is in brackets. Each curve corresponds to a particular ratio of S_2/S_1. They also correspond to a ratio of the RC's since ω will cancel out. For the frequencies above midfrequency $S_1 + S_2$ will be proportional to ω. Then for the low frequencies $S_1 + S_2$ will be proportional to $1/\omega$.

The solution of Eq. 3 can now be done graphically.

$$\frac{A_{mf}}{A_{fb}} = 1 - A_m\beta - [S_1 S_2 \pm j(S_1 + S_2)] \quad (8)$$

Since for negative feedback, β is negative, (switch in position b in Fig. 2), $1 - A_m\beta$ will be a positive number and can be plotted in Fig. 3 as the distance OA. The quantities in the brackets will be the distance OB. Then the value of $P(A)$ will be the vector difference of OB and OA and is equal to AB. In order to visualize what the curves say, draw a circle through O and with the center at A. Then the radius of

this circle will represent the magnitude of the gain at the midfrequency. Since Eq. 3 and consequently Eq. 8 represent the denominator of Eq. 2, the gain at the frequency of B will equal the distance AC divided by AB, or $A/A_m = AC/AB$. Hence when AB is less than AC, the gain will be larger than that at midfrequency. Now as B varies along the curve the gain versus frequency can be visualized.

The phase shift can also be determined. For the case of no feedback the phase shift from midfrequency will be the angle O-1-B. With feedback the angle will be O-A-B.

Now the ratio of the RC's can be intelligently chosen to produce a flat frequency response. If AB is less than AC, there will be a point D where the gain is again equal to the gain at midfrequency. If we impose the condition that the gain in the pass band should not vary more than $\pm m$ percent from the midfrequency gain, the correct ratio of the RC's can be chosen. Since the curves are a family of parabolas this can be done mathematically.

The gain will be a maximum when AB is a minimum. This minimum will be at the point where AB is perpendicular to the parabola. Therefore it is possible to express the minimum AB as a function of S_2/S_1. As this derivation is rather lengthy and outside the immediate interest of this paper, the results only will be given.

$$\frac{S_2}{S_1} = \frac{B}{2}\left(1 + \sqrt{1 - \frac{4}{B}}\right) - 1 \quad (9)$$

$$B = 2(1 - A_m\beta)(1 - (\sqrt{1 - D^2})$$

$$D = \frac{\text{length } AC}{\text{length } AB}$$

Then the point where AB is greater

than AC by m percent will be

$$S_1 S_2 = (1 - A_m\beta)(\sqrt{1 - d^2})$$
$$\left(1 + \sqrt{1 + \frac{1}{d^2}}\right) \quad (10)$$

Equation 9 gives the ratio of the RC's while Eq. 10 gives the magnitude of the RC's which will produce the desired cutoff frequency.

An amplifier was designed, using the circuit in Fig. 2, to have a gain of approximately 10 with a maximum variation of gain with frequency of 5 percent. Also the low-frequency cutoff was to be as near 10 cps as convenient. These strict requirements were necessary for it was to be used in some measuring equipment for the University of Washington Engineering Experiment Station. For these conditions the ratio of the RC's must be 100. The values are shown in Fig. 4. Gain tests were run on this amplifier showing no variation of gain between 20 cps and 10,000 cps, with

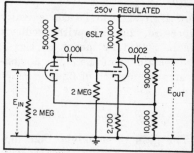

FIG. 4—Two-stage amplifier circuit used to substantiate graphical method

a 10-percent rise at 20,000 cps. This was the frequency limit of the oscillator that was available.

The effect on the gain of any amplifier with negative feedback due to two RC's in tandem, or in general to any two parameters, can be visualized when they are expressed as in Eq. 3 and then plotted as in Fig. 3.

Resistance-Coupled Amplifier Bandwidth

By B. A. LIPPMANN

THE PRACTICE of examining the behavior of resistive amplifier coupling networks by an approximate method of analysis has apparently obscured the fact that the gain characteristic of this circuit is exactly equivalent to a single-tuned circuit. In this article, the equivalence will be proved.

The standard uncompensated resistive coupling network takes the form shown in Fig. 1, where C_1 and C_2 include the tube and wiring capacitances, R_1 is the resultant of the load resistance and the plate resistance of the first tube taken as a parallel combination, and C_m is the coupling capacitor. Ordinarily, $C_m >> C_1$ and $C_m >> C_2$. Where approximate formulas are given, we shall understand them to refer to this condition.

The conventional analysis proceeds by examining the limiting forms the circuit takes at low, medium and high frequencies. For example, at low frequencies C_1 and C_2 are considered negligible and the voltage gain G is determined by considering the voltage divider formed by C_m and R_2 in series. The grid voltage on the second tube is $R_2[R_2 + 1/j\omega C_m]^{-1}$ times the plate voltage on the first tube. Using g for the transconductance of the first tube, its plate voltage is

$$\frac{- gR_1\left(R_2 + \dfrac{1}{j\omega C_m}\right)}{R_1 + R_2 + \dfrac{1}{j\omega C_m}}$$

times the input voltage. The gain G is therefore given by

$$G = \frac{- gR_1 R_2}{R_1 + R_2 + 1/j\omega C_m},$$

so that the low-frequency 3-db point is

$$\omega_1 = 2\pi f_1 = 1/(R_1 + R_2)C_m.$$

At medium frequencies, all three capacitors are considered to have negligible reactances compared with R_1 and R_2 and the effective network is just R_1 and R_2 in parallel. In this frequency range, the gain is a maximum and has no frequency variation.

Finally, at high frequencies, C_m is considered equivalent to a short circuit, so that the network reduces to the parallel combination of the other elements. This network has a falling characteristic with the 3-db point at

$$\omega_2 = 2\pi f_2 = (g_1 + g_2)/(C_1 + C_2)$$

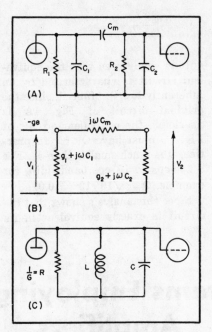

FIG. 1—Resistance-coupled circuit and equivalent

where the conductances of R_1 and R_2 are g_1 and g_2 respectively.

We now show that a straight-forward analysis of the network of Fig. 1A leads to the result that it is exactly equivalent to a shunt combination of R, L and C.

Our problem is to compute $G = V_2/e$ for the admittance network of Fig. 1B. The result is

$$G = V_2/e =$$

$$\frac{- jg\omega C_m}{[g_1 + j\omega(C_1 + C_m)][g_2 + j\omega(C_2 + C_m)] + \omega^2 C_m^2}$$

$$=$$

$$\frac{- g}{\left[\dfrac{g_1C_2 + g_2C_1}{C_m} + g_1 + g_2\right] + j\omega\left(\dfrac{C_1C_2}{C_m} + C_1C_2\right) - \dfrac{j g_1 g_2}{\omega C_m}}$$

We observe that if the coupling network were of the form shown in Fig. 1C, we would have

$$G = \frac{- g}{1/R + j\omega C - j/\omega L}$$

It follows that both networks will have exactly the same gain characteristic if we put

$$G = \frac{1}{R} = \frac{g_1C_2 + g_2C_1}{C_m} + g_1 + g_2$$

$$\cong g_1 + g_2$$

$$L = \frac{C_m}{g_1 g_2}$$

$$C = \frac{C_1C_2}{C_m} + C_1 + C_2 \cong C_1 + C_2$$

The gain characteristic is therefore the same as that of a single-tuned circuit resonant at f_o where

$$\omega_o = \frac{1}{\sqrt{LC}} \cong \sqrt{\frac{g_1 g_2}{C_m(C_1 + C_2)}}$$

The Q and bandwidth Δf are

$$Q = \omega_o RC \cong \frac{1}{g_1 + g_2}\sqrt{\frac{g_1 g_2(C_1 + C_2)}{C_m}}$$

$$\Delta\omega = \frac{\omega_o}{Q} \cong \frac{g_1 + g_2}{C_1 + C_2}$$

To find the 3-db points, we recall that $\Delta\omega = \omega_2 - \omega_1$ and $\omega_o^2 = \omega_1\omega_2$. Solving for ω_2 and ω_1

$$\omega_2 = (\Delta\omega/2) + \sqrt{(\Delta\omega/2)^2 + \omega_o^2}$$

$$\omega_1 = - (\Delta\omega/2) + \sqrt{(\Delta\omega/2)^2 + \omega_o^2}$$

For the two limiting cases,

$$\Delta\omega/2\omega_o >> 1 \text{ and } \Delta\omega/2\omega_o < <1, \text{ we get}$$

$$\left.\begin{array}{l}\dfrac{\Delta\omega}{2\omega_o} < <1; \omega_1 \cong \omega_o - \dfrac{\Delta\omega}{2}\\[2mm]\omega_2 \cong \omega_o + \dfrac{\Delta\omega}{2}\end{array}\right\} \text{error} \cong \dfrac{\Delta\omega}{4\omega_o}$$

$$\left.\begin{array}{l}\dfrac{\Delta\omega}{2\omega_o} >> 1; \omega_1 \cong \dfrac{\omega_o^2}{\omega}\\[2mm]\omega_2 \cong \Delta\omega\end{array}\right\} \text{error} \cong 3\left(\dfrac{\omega_o}{\Delta\omega}\right)^2$$

$$\left.\begin{array}{l}\\\omega_2 \cong \Delta\omega\end{array}\right\} \text{error} \cong \left(\dfrac{\omega_o}{\Delta\omega}\right)^2$$

so that finally,

$$\omega_1 = \sqrt{\frac{g_1 g_2}{C_m\left(C_1 + C_2 + \dfrac{C_1C_2}{C_m}\right)}}$$

$$\left[\sqrt{\frac{C_m\left(g_1 + g_2 + \dfrac{g_1C_2 + g_2C_1}{C_m}\right)^2}{4g_1 g_2\left(C_1 + C_2 + \dfrac{C_1C_2}{C_m}\right)}}\right.$$

$$\left. + 1 - \frac{\sqrt{C_m}\left(g_1 + g_2 + \dfrac{g_1 g_2 + g_2 C_1}{C_m}\right)}{2\sqrt{g_1 g_2\left(C_1 + C_2 + \dfrac{C_1C_2}{C_m}\right)}}\right]$$

$$\omega_2 = \sqrt{\frac{g_1 g_2}{C_m\left(C_1 + C_2 + \dfrac{C_1C_2}{C_m}\right)}}$$

$$\left[\sqrt{\frac{C_m\left(g_1 + g_2 + \dfrac{g_1C_2 + g_2C_1}{C_m}\right)^2}{4g_1 g_2\left(C_1 + C_2 + \dfrac{C_1C_2}{C_m}\right)}}\right.$$

$$\left. + 1 + \frac{\sqrt{C_m}\left(g_1 + g_2 + \dfrac{g_1C_2 + g_2C_1}{C_m}\right)}{2\sqrt{g_1 g_2\left(C_1 + C_2 + \dfrac{C_1C_2}{C_m}\right)}}\right]$$

Or, since $\dfrac{\Delta\omega}{2\omega_o} >> 1$ in the cases of interest to us,

$$\omega_1 \cong \frac{g_1 g_2}{(g_1 + g_2)C_m} = \frac{1}{(R_1 + R_2)C_m}$$

$$\omega_2 \cong \frac{g_1 + g_2}{C_1 + C_2}$$

These results justify the usual approximate analysis for the case $C_m >> \frac{C_1}{C_2}$

For the opposite extreme, $C_m << \frac{C_1}{C_2}$ we get

$$G = \frac{1}{R} \cong \frac{g_1 C_2 + g_2 C_1}{C_m} \qquad \omega_o \cong \sqrt{\frac{g_1 g_2}{C_1 C_2}}$$

$$L = \frac{C_m}{g_1 g_2} \qquad Q \cong \sqrt{\frac{g_1 g_2 C_1 C_2}{g_1 C_2 + g_2 C_1}}$$

$$C \cong \frac{C_1 C_2}{C_m} \qquad \Delta\omega \cong \frac{g_1 C_2 + g_2 C_1}{C_1 C_2} =$$

$$\frac{g_1}{C_1} + \frac{g_2}{C_2}$$

It is easily seen that the equivalent circuit is characterized by an inherently low Q. Indeed, since the original circuit of Fig. 1A is aperiodic, the equivalent circuit of Fig. 1C must have $Q < \frac{1}{2}$. In practice, Q is much smaller than $\frac{1}{2}$. For a 100-cps to 10^6-cps bandwidth, for example, $Q \cong \sqrt{10^2/10^6} = 0.01$.

Since this analysis shows that the circuit is exactly equivalent in its gain characteristic to a single-tuned circuit, it suggests the feasibility of combining this circuit with others in cases where an extremely low Q is required. The point of view taken here also suggests that several of these circuits might be stagger-tuned to produce a wide-band video amplifier without additional compensation. However, since $Q < \frac{1}{2}$, this circuit could only be used as the center stage of an odd number of stagger-tuned circuits.

Tuning Systems Employing Feedback Amplifiers

By PETER G. SULZER

IT IS possible to alter the effective value of an inductance or a capacitance by means of a feedback amplifier. The method is applicable where large variations are required, and is particularly useful where an L-C resonant circuit is to be tuned over a wide frequency range.

Consider an amplifier of voltage gain A having an infinite input impedance and a zero output impedance. An impedance Z is connected between its input and output terminals. With Z_e defined as shown in Fig. 1, it is found that

$$Z_e = \frac{Z}{1 - A}$$

Four conditions can be considered.

$$\begin{array}{ll} -\infty < A < 0 & Z_e/Z < 1 \\ 0 < A < 1 & Z_e/Z > 1 \\ A = 1 & Z_e/Z = \infty \\ 1 < A < \infty & Z_e/Z < -\infty \end{array}$$

If L_e and C_e are the equivalent values of L and C when either one is inserted for Z,

$$L_e = \frac{L}{1 - A} \text{ and } C_e = (1-A) C$$

With the first condition, L is effectively decreased, while C is in-

creased (Miller effect[1]). With the second, L is effectively increased, while C is decreased. The third condition is trivial in this application, while the fourth may produce

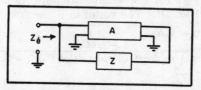

Fig. 1—Feedback amplifier connected for impedance multiplication or division

instablity, and will not be considered here.

It is worth noting that the variations in the equivalent values of the components can be obtained without a serious loss of Q or selectivity. This requires only that the output impedance of the amplifier be kept low, and that its input impedance be high.

The required variation of amplifier gain can be obtained by employing an attenuator or potentiometer or, if desired, by electronic means. Thus it has been possible to tune an L-C circuit over a 30-to-1 frequency range by means of a potentiometer;

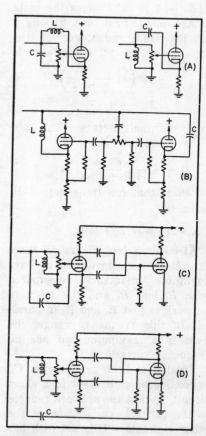

Fig. 2—Simple cathode-follower tuners, A; dual cathode-follower tuner, B; two-stage tuners providing large frequency ratios with good stability C and D

the same frequency ratio was obtained by changing the grid bias of one of the amplifier tubes. Since a potentiometer is a more stable circuit element than a variable-μ tube, better frequency stability will be obtained when using potentiometer tuning. However, electronic tuning is to be preferred when rapid or remote frequency variation is required.

Practical Circuits

Many circuits can be devised using the scheme presented here. Figure 2 contains a few that have been investigated by the writer.

The simple cathode-follower circuits of Fig. 2A produced a frequency ratio of 5 when using a parallel-connected 12AT7. The equivalent resistance inserted in series with the tuned circuit is approximately 100 ohms, which requires that a high L/C ratio be employed to avoid excessive degradation of Q. The dual cathode follower of Fig. 2B provided a frequency ratio of 25. The equivalent

resistance is 400 ohms, which may be undesirable in some applications, particularly at radio frequencies.

Cathode Follower

These three circuits do not employ a large feedback factor to stabilize A; hence relatively poor frequency stability will be obtained when large frequency ratios are used.

The completely degenerative amplifier[2] of Fig. 2C is superior in this respect. In addition, the output impedance may be less than 1 ohm, while the voltage gain may be as high as 0.999, resulting in a frequency ratio of approximately 30. When using a pentode-triode amplifier to tune an oscillator with a frequency ratio of 10, the frequency was constant within 1 percent for plate-supply-voltage variations of ±50 percent.

The circuit of Fig. 2D differs from the previous ones in that A is negative. A frequency ratio of 10 was obtained using a pentode driv-

ing a triode. Larger ratios can be obtained by employing more stages, but instability becomes a serious problem.

Conclusions

The simple cathode-follower circuits are most useful for obtaining wide-deviation frequency modulation at radio frequencies. They should also be useful for tuning radio receivers, although tube noise will be contributed by the amplifier. The two-stage circuits, which are limited to audio or video-frequency applications because of the coupling networks used between stages, have been employed in wide-range, resistance-tuned audio oscillators.

References

(1) J. M. Miller, "Dependence of the Input Impedance of a Three-Electrode Vacuum Tube upon the Load in the Plate Circuit," Bureau of Standards Scientific Paper 351.
(2) Calvin T. Hammack, "Cathode Follower," Report 469, Radiation Lab., MIT, Cambridge, Mass.; also see ELECTRONICS, p 206, Nov. 1946.

Bridged-T Neutralization of Pentode Amplifiers

By H. K. BRADFORD

IN A high-frequency amplifier using a small unbypassed cathode resistor to reduce Miller effect, a modified bridged-T network can be used for neutralization. High and completely stable gain can be realized with this arrangement.

The equivalent circuit (essential elements) may be represented as in Fig. 1A. To complete the bridged T network would normally require additions as in Fig. 1B, which shows R_1, R_2, and C added.

Since there is an essential 90 degree phase shift across C_{PK} there need be no phase shift across R_2 and hence C should actually be a resistor. Rearranging for actual use the circuit is represented as in Fig. 1C.

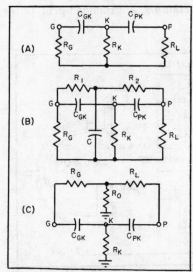

FIG. 1—Modified-bridged-T network may be used to neutralize amplifier with unbypassed cathode

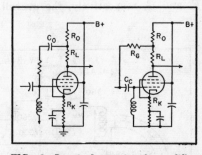

FIG. 2—Practical circuit of amplifier using modified bridged-T neutralization

For the potential generated at P to be completely cancelled at G through the two paths shown, the attenuation must be identical through the two paths and the phase shift must total 180 degrees.

The following relations are needed to make this possible:

$$\frac{R_L}{R_O} = \frac{Xc_{PK}}{R_K} \qquad \frac{R_L}{R_G} = \frac{Xc_{PK}}{Xc_{GK}}$$

$$R_O = \frac{R_L R_K}{Xc_{PK}} \qquad R_G = \frac{R_L Xc_{GK}}{Xc_{PK}}$$

If there is any doubt about the four given values R_o can be made variable to adjust the feedback magnitude exactly. The phase remains within better than 1 degree correct due to the condition of the problem with usual values and the magnitude can be trimmed through wide values with R_o.

Two practical circuits are shown in Fig. 2. Coupling capacitor C_o is added for d-c isolation of the grid. Resistance R_G serves the dual function of grid damping plus feedback.

Fixed-Tuned Broad-Band Television Booster

By ARNOLD NEWTON

THE INHERENT NOISE generated in a receiver sets the ultimate limit to its maximum useful sensitivity. The noise figure gives a measure of the noise contributed by the receiver in excess of the noise generated in the antenna radiation resistance. It is defined as the ratio of the actual available output noise power over the noise power available from a noise-free but otherwise identical receiver. Reducing the noise figure and appropriately increasing the gain is equivalent to raising the transmitted power and hence extending the transmitter service area.

The insertion of a booster is intended to improve the overall noise figure and thus raise the useful gain. If the receiver by itself has a noise figure of F_2 and the booster noise figure and available gain are F_1 and G_1 respectively, the overall noise figure is

$$F = F_1 + \frac{F_2 - 1}{G_1}.$$

A noise figure of approximately 17 db above thermal is characteristic of a poor receiver. About 6 db is the best practical noise figure, the ideal being 3 db when the antenna is matched at the receiver input. In order that the overall noise figure shall approach F_1,

$$G_1 >> \frac{F_2 - 1}{F_1}. \text{ Let } G = 5\frac{F_2 - 1}{F_1} = 50,$$

the voltage gain is then approximately 8. This gain can be obtained over a bandwidth of 40 mc, the width of one complete band. One should therefore be able to cover all the channels in two bands.

First R-F Stage

The noise figure and gain of the first r-f stage are of primary importance. A grounded-grid triode amplifier was chosen for its low noise figure as expressed by

$$F = 1 + \frac{R_g}{R_i} + \left(\frac{\mu}{\mu + 1}\right)^2 \frac{R_{eq}}{R_g}\left(1 + \frac{R_g}{R_i}\right)^2$$

The input resistance R_i due to input loading of a high-frequency triode is large in comparison with the antenna resistance R_g and since usually $\mu >> 1$, the expression for noise figure reduces to $F = 1 + R_{eq}/R_g$ where R_{eq} is equivalent noise resistance of the tube.

The dynamic impedance is $(R_p + Z_L)/(\mu + 1)$. Assuming that $\mu >> 1$ and $R_p >> Z_L$ the dynamic input resistance approaches $1/g_m$, where g_m is the transconductance of the tube. The R_{eq} of a triode is approximately equal to $2.5/g_m$ and the noise figure becomes $F = 3.5 = 5.5$ db.

The input transformer matching the antenna to the tube consists of a single tuned circuit. The dynamic input resistance of the tube shunting the circuit appears like 200 ohms and a tap at the 73-ohm resistance level is provided to terminate the transmission line. A 73-ohm input was chosen because coaxial cable is frequently used in fringe areas to minimize ignition interference.

A balun (balance to unbalance) 300-ohm to 73-ohm transformer for use with a 300-ohm line will be described later.

Interstage Coupling

A double-tuned inductively coupled circuit is used between the plate of the first and the grid of the

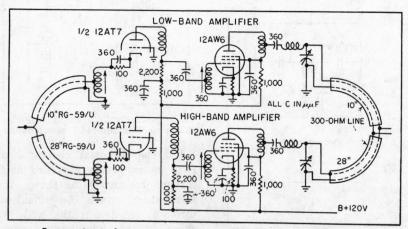

Booster circuit showing use of quarter-wave section crossover network

second r-f amplifiers. Using a 12AT7 and a 12AW6 as the first and second stages respectively the figure of merit based on the estimated total input and output capacitances C_i and C_o is

$$A \Delta f = \frac{g_m}{2\pi\sqrt{C_iC_o}} = 140 \text{ mc}$$

where $g_m = 5 \times 10^{-3}$ mhos, $C_i = 7 \times 10^{-12} F$, and $C_o = 4 \times 10^{-12} F$.

Over a bandwidth of 40 mc it should be possible to realize a gain of 3.5. Accepting a reasonable peak-to-valley ratio, higher gain will result without appreciably impairing resolution, since over any 4.5-mc interval within the transmission band the amplitude variation should be slight. Furthermore, the input circuit being single-tuned, a certain amount of stagger damping is indicated.

The second r-f stage couples into the receiver 300-ohm input resistance. Since the damping resistance is low (300 ohms), wide bandwidth is easily realized. The tuning of this circuit is broad and the overall bandwidth is little affected by its presence. The gain of this stage is approximately 1.5. The voltage step-up in the input circuit is 1.6, so the total gain is approximately 8.

Crossover Network

As two individual bandpass amplifiers are used, the respective inputs and outputs must be either switched or connected through a crossover network. Mechanical advantages and convenience make the latter more desirable. The crossover networks shown in the circuit diagram are of a very simple type.

Two quarter-wave sections connect the two inputs and outputs to the incoming and outgoing lines. For proper rejection, the shorter section leads to the low-band and the longer section to the high-band circuits.

Within the respective bands the loading effect of the alternate amplifier is small owing to its low input impedance and the impedance inversion property of a $\lambda/4$ line. Although these conditions prevail at the midband frequencies only, broadband operation is secured by virtue of the transmission line's low characteristic resistance.

Balun Transformer

The balun transformer for use with a 300-ohm line consists of a $\lambda/2$ section of 73-ohm coaxial line at 65 mc.

When the length of the line is $\lambda/2$ or an odd multiple thereof and terminated in its characteristic re-

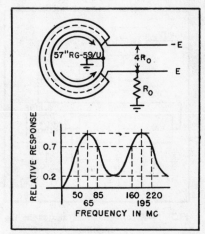

Drawing and response curve of balanced-to-unbalanced transformer made of 73-ohm coaxial cable

sistance, the voltage between center conductor poles is $2E$, either pole voltage to ground being E. The center pole-to-pole resistance is on the basis of equal power $4R_o$, R_o being the line characteristic resistance. The approximate response of a transformer using RG-59/U cable is shown in the accompanying curve.

Utility Video Amplifier

Extended frequency response and double-ended low-impedance output to drive a 75-ohm line and monitor are achieved by use of two feedback pairs in cascade. Wide range of useful applications on program lines is indicated

By E. C. KLUENDER

USE OF FEEDBACK results in some inherent advantages that suggests its incorporation in a utility video amplifier. Feedback assists not only in achieving exceptional amplitude linearity and in extending the high and low frequency responses, but also creates a low-impedance source that lends itself well to driving a 75-ohm line.

Figure 1 shows a simple block diagram illustrating how feedback is employed in an amplifier composed of two feedback pairs in cascade. Overall amplifier gain is controlled by varying the amount of feedback in the first pair. Coupling between the pairs is by means of a large capacitor which results in negligible phase shift for all frequencies concerned.

A schematic diagram is shown in Fig. 2. Two video jacks permit the input to be bridged or terminated. Termination is obtained by inserting a 75-ohm termination plug in one of the input jacks. The input capacitance of the amplifier is 20 $\mu\mu$f. Voltage-type degeneration is fed from the second stage back to the cathode of the first stage, and is adjustable by means of R_6. The low d-c potential existing at the output of the first coupled pair permits the

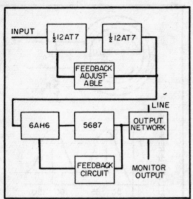

FIG. 1—Arrangement of stages in the amplifier

use of a low-voltage, high-capacitance electrolytic capacitor to couple to the second pair.

The circuit for the second pair is identical with the first, except for components. A very high perveance is obtained in the output stage by connecting the plates of a 5687 in parallel.

The feedback circuit includes an adjustable capacitor C_{14} which provides a frequency compensator useful in adjusting overall amplifier response. A negative 5-volt source is used for grid bias purposes and for bucking out the d-c in the output circuit.

Output Circuit

Point A (Fig. 2) owing to voltage feedback is a very low impedance driving point (sometimes referred to as a zero-impedance point). Due to the reduction in forward gain as frequency is increased, the impedance of point A will rise. The net impedance values are plotted in Fig. 3, while curves A of Fig. 4 and 5 show the resistive and reactive components of this impedance for C_{14} set to maximum capacity.

These curves suggest the use of a series element whose impedance decreases with frequency for feeding a line. Such an element is obtained by using C_{11}, R_{29} and R_{27} in the combination shown in Fig. 2. Making

both R and C adjustable results in a flexible arrangement which has the capability of compensating for the change of impedance of point A.

Figure 6 shows a family of curves for typical settings of R_{29} and C_{11}. The wide range of adjustment is quite evident.

The B curves of Fig. 6 are also plotted on Fig. 4 and 5 where they are added to the curves of impedance at point A. The net resistive component of output impedance is shown as curve C of Fig. 4; the net reactive component of output impedance is shown as curve C of Fig. 5. Note how effectively B compensates for A in each case.

Actual measurements of output impedance for a utility video amplifier are given in Fig. 7 where they are plotted with a greatly expanded scale. This typical curve shows only ±1 ohm variation out to 11 mc. The resulting well-matched source impedance such as this is required for obtaining uniform transmission over coaxial cables without reflections. It also represents a close approach to the ideal driving circuit for telephone lines whose impedance varies widely over the transmission band but which are equalized for uniform response from a 75-ohm source.

The recommendations of a Joint Committee of TV Broadcasters and Manufacturers for Coordination of Video Levels are easily met by the amplifier. This committee's recom-

mendation on Standard Termination Impedances is as follows: "It is recommended that the standard termination impedance for both the sending and receiving ends of a line connected for single-ended operation, shall have a value of 75 ohms plus or minus 5 percent. These figures will apply over the television frequency band below 6 mc but not down to d-c."

Monitor Provisions

The ideal place to monitor an amplifier feeding a line is, of course, across the output of the amplifier. Most amplifiers in use at present cannot drive the double termination resulting from connecting low-impedance monitoring lines across their outputs, and this leads to the incorporation of isolation amplifiers.

Use of isolation amplifiers brings about the possibility of a monitor picture not in accordance with

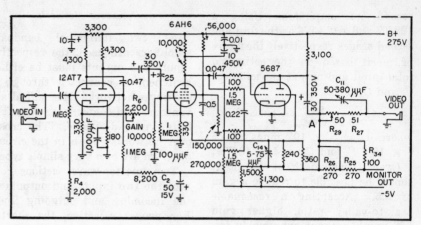

FIG. 2—Complete circuit of one utility amplifier. The low-impedance driving point is designated A, at the right of tube 5687

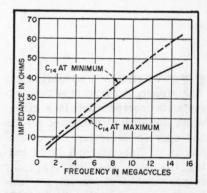

FIG. 3—Plot of point A impedance characteristics

what the line is receiving, both in level and quality. The answer lies in using a line amplifier capable of feeding two lines without introducing a series element capable of failure or extraneous signals. Furthermore, it is desirable that the monitor output have sufficient isolation from the line output to give a true indication of amplifier performance, regardless of changes in line impedance.

The desirable monitor feed characteristics outlined above are achieved by the output circuit employed in this video amplifier. The monitor is fed from point A of Fig. 2, the low-impedance driving point. Resistors R_{25}, R_{26} and R_{34} form a divider for obtaining the required monitor ratios.

For a 1:1 monitoring ratio, the resistors are connected as shown in Fig. 2. For a 2:5 monitor ratio R_{34} is removed; for a 1:5 monitor ratio, the jumper across R_{26} is also removed. No capacitor is employed across these divider resistors in the fashion that C_{11} is used for the line feed, since bandwidth adequate for

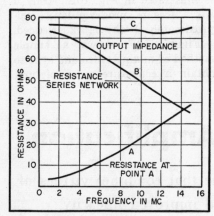

FIG. 4—Resistive components of output impedance

monitoring is obtained without its use.

Isolation Characteristics

For a monitoring ratio of 1 to 1 (equal outputs) the attenuation between the line and the monitor feed is given in Fig. 8. These attenuation figures are obtained by feeding a signal in at the line output jack

and measuring the resultant voltage appearing at the terminated monitor output. The shunting impedance effect obtained due to voltage feedback at point A is evident.

Table I—Impedance Characteristics at Point A

C_{14} Set to Maximum		
Frequency in Mc	Z	$\|Z\|$
1	$3 + j3$	4
3	$5 + j11$	12
5	$10 + j18$	21
7	$14 + j21$	25
9	$20 + j25$	32
11	$26 + j27$	37
13	$33 + j29$	44
15	$40 + j27$	48
C_{14} Set to Minimum		
1	$3 + j5$	6
3	$4 + j13$	14
5	$8 + j22$	23
7	$14 + j29$	32
10	$28 + j38$	47
15	$57 + j26$	62

A 60-cycle hum component appearing on the line output terminal due to ground currents in long coaxial runs would be attenuated by about

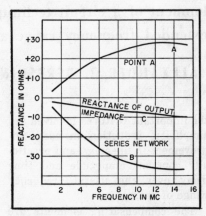

FIG. 5—Reactive components of output impedance

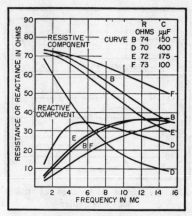

FIG. 6—Family of impedance curves for series networks

34 db; this point is off the curve of Fig. 8. The hum component, as well as other extraneous signals will therefore not appear on the monitor, but rather, the monitor will give a true indication of what the amplifier is feeding to the line.

Figure 9 shows the frequency response of the amplifier connected for a monitor signal equal to the line signal, and operating at unity gain. Two 1.4-volt signals are obtained; the frequency response of the monitor signal is also shown.

The maximum gain available with the connection described above is 2.5. As an optional connection, the 1,500-ohm resistor may be removed giving less negative feedback to the final pair. Such a connection may be used when a greater gain (4 maximum) is desired. Under these conditions the monitor will operate at a 1:5 or 2:5 ratio rather than unity, and signals up to 2 volts may be obtained.

Applications

Figure 10A shows the amplifier feeding a telephone line. The driving impedance illustrated in Fig. 7 is the characteristic especially interesting in this application, also the ability to monitor the outgoing line directly is shown in Fig. 10.

Figure 10B illustrates the ability of feeding two 75-ohm lines from a single amplifier. Three amplifiers are shown feeding six house-monitoring circuits. The use of the amplifier as a buffer is shown in Fig. 10C and 10D.

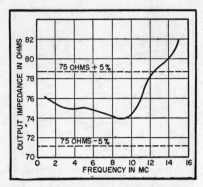

FIG. 7—Output impedance of utility video amplifier

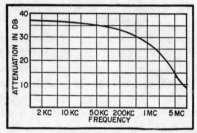

FIG. 8—Attenuation between line and monitor feeds

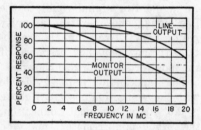

FIG. 9—Frequency response of output to line and monitor

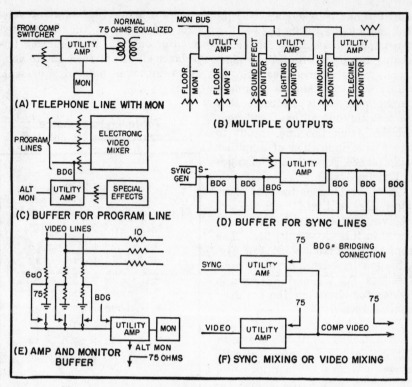

FIG. 10—Typical applications of the video utility amplifier

The amplifier gain controls permit an accurate adjustment of percentage sync and output video level. The method illustrated may also be used to mix two video signals. If a common video signal is fed to the input of the two amplifiers, a 4/3 normal gain and 4/3 normal signal output may be obtained.

A method of obtaining a choice of signals for monitoring without double terminating a program line is illustrated in Fig. 10E. Only a slight loss of program level (approximately 1 db) is experienced.

Figure 10F shows a simple method of mixing video and sync to obtain a composite video picture.

Cathode-Compensated Video Amplification

Theoretical and practical development of a circuit technique that combines virtues of lower cost, simplicity, extended frequency range and improved linearity

By ALEXANDER B. BERESKIN

IT is well known that feedback can be used to modify the frequency, gain and linearity characteristics of amplifiers. The purpose of this paper is to show how feedback, properly obtained in the cathode circuit of a video amplifier, can be used to endow the amplifier with exceptional characteristics. Some of

the important features involved are simplicity, reduction in cost, improvement in linearity, and practically constant amplitude and time delay over the useful frequency range of operation.

The compensating elements are of such values that neither the series inductance of the capacitors nor

the stray capacitance of the inductors has any noticeable effect on the results. These elements are incorporated in a low signal level circuit and do not increase the stray capacitance over that which results with uncompensated operation. The large electrolytic capacitor normally used in the cathode circuit is eliminated, thus increasing the reliability of operation. The total cost of the small mica capacitor and the inductor used for compensation is considerably less than that of the electrolytic capacitor that was eliminated.

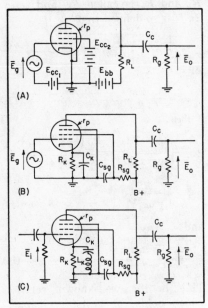

FIG. 1—Basic video amplifier circuit, cathode-biased version employed for determining proper compensation, and practical cathode-compensated circuit

Compensating Procedure

To make proper use of the compensation discussed in this paper the procedure indicated below should be followed:

(A) Use the circuit of Fig. 1B. It is important that the suppressor and screen be returned to ground and not to the cathode.

(B) Determine the stray plate circuit capacitance C_s. This can be done experimentally, if the screen and cathode are perfectly bypassed, by obtaining a gain-frequency curve for some value of R_L close to that which it is intended to use. By using the frequency f at which the gain is down 3 db from the middle frequency value and R_{eq} which is calculated from

$$\frac{1}{R_{eq}} = \frac{1}{R_L} + \frac{1}{r_p} + \frac{1}{R_g} \qquad (1)$$

we get

$$C_s' = \frac{1}{2 \pi f R_{eq}} \qquad (2)$$

and then

$$C_s = C_s' - C_o \qquad (3)$$

where C_o is the capacitance introduced by the measuring circuit.

(C) Determine the middle frequency gain when the screen and cathode are perfectly bypassed to ground and a value of R_{L1} is used such that the gain is down 3 db at the high frequency

$$f_o = \frac{1}{2\pi C_s R_{eq1}} \qquad (4)$$

which is chosen for reference purposes.

Preferably this should be done experimentally, making allowance for the change in the frequency characteristic due to the capacitance introduced by the measuring circuit. The frequency can be computed analytically if g_m is known by using the expression

$$A = g_m R_{eq1} \qquad (5)$$

where R_{eq1} is obtained by substituting R_{L1} in place of R_L in Eq. 1.

(D) Determine the value of R_{eq2} which, when all cathode bypass capacitance is removed, will produce the same middle frequency gain that was obtained in part (C). Use this value of R_{eq2} to determine

$$(1 + g_K R_K) = \frac{R_{eq2}}{R_{eq1}} \qquad (6)$$

This should preferably be done experimentally by measuring the value of R_{L2} required and substituting it in Eq. 1 to get R_{eq2}. A close approximation can be obtained analytically if

$$g_K \cong g_m + g_{c2} = \frac{\delta i_b}{\delta e_{c1}} + \frac{\delta i_{c2}}{\delta e_{c1}} \qquad (7)$$

can be determined. The analytical value obtained in this manner will usually be a little low for it does not take into account the fact that g_m is reduced slightly when a higher value of R_L is used. Additional feedback also results due to the small a-c screen to cathode voltage that will be present. Both of these factors would tend to require a higher value of R_{eq2} than would be given by the analytical expression.

(E) Obtain values of $a/(1 + g_K R_K)$ and f_R/f_o from Fig. 6 for the value of $(1 + g_K R_K)$ given in (D).

(F) The cathode capacitor required is

$$C_K = \frac{a}{(1 + g_K R_K)} \frac{R_{eq2}}{R_K} C_s \qquad (8)$$

and the value of cathode inductor required is

$$L_K = \frac{1}{(2 \pi f_R)^2 C_K} \qquad (9)$$

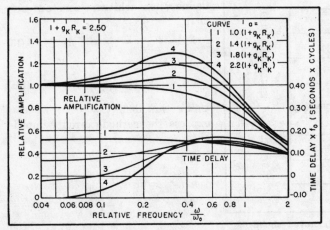

FIG. 2—Effect of variations in factor α when using only a capacitor in parallel with cathode resistor

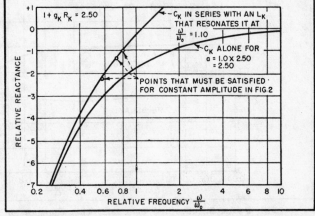

FIG. 3—Relative reactance values required to satisfy requirement of constant amplitude when using only shunt capacitor

(G) Connect the components R_{L2}, C_K and L_K as shown in detail in Fig. 1C.

In a typical amplifier with $f_o = 3.54$ mc and $(1 + g_K R_K) = 2.13$ the required value of cathode capacitor was $C_K = 1,170$ μμf and the required value of cathode inductor was $L_K = 1.13 \times 10^{-6}$ henrys. The amplitude and time-delay characteristics for this amplifier are given in Fig. 8. Additional characteristics of this amplifier will be discussed in the concluding part of this paper. Its low-frequency gain will be that which would have resulted in (C) if infinite cathode bypass capacitance had been used.

Theoretical Development

In an amplifier of the type shown in Fig. 1A the vector ratio $\overline{E}_o/\overline{E}_g$ is known as the voltage amplification or gain and is denoted by the symbol $\overline{A}$. In the middle and high frequency regions this can be expressed as

$$\overline{A} = -\overline{g}_m \overline{Z}_{eq} \qquad (10)$$

where $\overline{Z}_{eq}$ is the parallel impedance of the resistances r_p, R_L, and R_g and the stray capacitive reactance X_s.

If feedback is used and the symbol $\overline{A}_f$ is used to distinguish the voltage amplification with feedback from $\overline{A}$ which is the voltage amplification without feedback, then

$$\overline{A}_f = \frac{\overline{A}}{1 - B \overline{A}} \qquad (11)$$

where $\overline{B}$ is the vector portion of the output to ground voltage fed back in the grid-to-cathode circuit.

The batteries E_{cc1} and E_{cc2} shown in Fig. 1A are ordinarily replaced with the resistance-capacitance combinations shown in Fig. 1B. In this circuit if C_{sg} and C_K are assumed to have zero reactance there is no feedback and then $\overline{A} = -g_m \overline{Z}_{eq}$ as before.

If the parallel combination of r_p, R_L and R_g is called R_{eq} and $\omega_o = 2\pi f_o$ is so defined that

$$\frac{1}{2\pi f_o C_s} = \frac{1}{\omega_o C_s} = R_{eq} \qquad (12)$$

or

$$\omega_o = \frac{1}{C_s R_{eq}} \qquad (12a)$$

then $Z_{eq} =$

$$\frac{R_{eq}(-j\,X_s)}{R_{eq} - j\,X_s} = \frac{R_{eq}\left(-j\,\dfrac{\omega_o}{\omega}\,R_{eq}\right)}{R_{eq} - j\,\dfrac{\omega_o}{\omega}\,R_{eq}}$$

$$Z_{eq} = \frac{R_{eq}}{1 + j\,\dfrac{\omega}{\omega_o}} \qquad (13)$$

and

$$\overline{A} = \frac{-\,g_m\,R_{eq}}{1 + j\,\dfrac{\omega}{\omega_o}} \qquad (14)$$

This is the well-known relation which holds for resistance-capacitance coupled amplifiers in the middle and high-frequency ranges.

If we now assume that the reactance of C_{sg} is still zero while that of C_K is finite, then the flow of alternating plate and screen current through the parallel combination of R_K and C_K will develop an alternating voltage that appears in the grid-to-cathode circuit. In order to specify the cathode-circuit impedance in terms of the previously chosen symbols f_o and ω_o we will define a new arbitrary constant a so that

$$X_K = \frac{1}{\omega C_K} = \frac{1}{a}\,\frac{\omega_o}{\omega}\,R_K \qquad (15)$$

and therefore

$$a = \omega_o C_K R_K = \frac{C_K R_K}{C_s R_{eq}} \qquad (15a)$$

Using this definition of a we can express the cathode circuit impedance as

$$\overline{Z}_K =$$

$$\frac{R_K(-jX_K)}{R_K - jX_K} = \frac{-j\,\dfrac{1}{a}\,\dfrac{\omega_o}{\omega}\,R_K}{1 - j\,\dfrac{1}{a}\,\dfrac{\omega_o}{\omega}} = \frac{R_K}{1 + ja\,\dfrac{\omega}{\omega_o}}$$

$$(16)$$

Since both the screen and plate

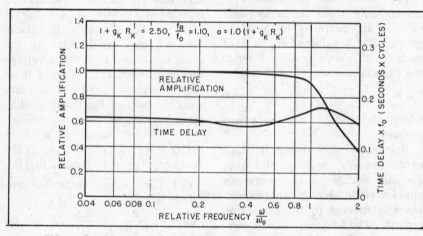

FIG. 4—Amplification and time delay characteristics for circuit constants and conditions of Fig. 3

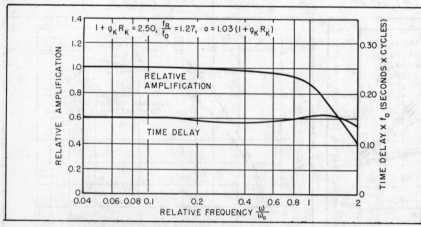

FIG. 5—Amplification and time delay characteristics for improved circuit based on curves of Fig. 6

alternating current flows through the cathode-circuit impedance while only the plate alternating current flows through the plate load impedance it is necessary to define a new term g_K such that

$$\overline{B} = \frac{g_K \overline{Z}_K}{g_m \overline{Z}_{eq}} \qquad (17)$$

Mainly

$$g_K = g_m + g_{c2} = \frac{\delta i_b}{\delta e_{c1}} + \frac{\delta i_{c2}}{\delta e_{c1}} \qquad (18)$$

but as defined in Eq. 17 it will also take care of additional minor factors such as the possibility that g_m itself might change between two conditions of operation and also that there may be other feedback effects due to the small a-c screen-to-cathode voltage. The voltage amplification with feedback is then

$$\dot{A}_f =$$

$$\frac{- g_m \overline{Z}_{eq}}{1 - \left(\dfrac{g_K \overline{Z}_K}{g_m \overline{Z}_{eq}} \right)(- g_m \overline{Z}_{eq})} = \frac{- g_m \overline{Z}_{eq}}{1 + g_K \overline{Z}_K}$$

(19)

If we substitute the values of $\overline{Z}_{eq}$ and $\overline{Z}_K$ obtained previously in this expression for $\overline{A}_f$, then

$$\overline{A}_f = \frac{- g_m \dfrac{R_{eq}}{1 + j \dfrac{\omega}{\omega_o}}}{1 + g_K \dfrac{R_K}{1 + j a \dfrac{\omega}{\omega_o}}}$$

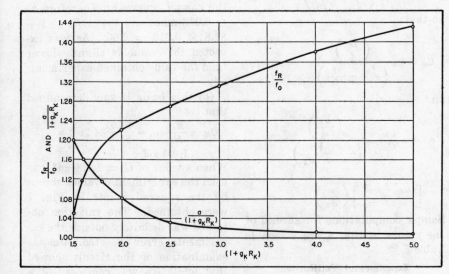

FIG. 6—Computed curves giving satisfactory constants for compensating circuit over a wide range of circuit values

$$= \left[\frac{- g_m R_{eq}}{(1 + g_K R_K) + j a \dfrac{\omega}{\omega_o}} \right] \left[\frac{1 + j a -}{1 + j \dfrac{\omega}{\omega_o}} \right]$$

(20)

Case I: If we let $a = \infty$

$$\overline{A}_1 = \frac{- g_m R_{eq1}}{1 + j \dfrac{\omega}{\omega_o}} \qquad (21)$$

and this of course is the case when the cathode is completely bypassed to ground.

Case II: If we introduce a new value of

$$R_{eq2} = (1 + g_K R_K) R_{eq1} \qquad (22)$$

this will make

$$\omega_{o2} = \frac{\omega_o}{(1 + g_K R_K)} \qquad (23)$$

and then

$$\overline{Z}_{eq2} = \frac{(1 + g_K R_K) R_{eq1}}{1 + j(1 + g_K R_K) \dfrac{\omega}{\omega_o}} \qquad (24)$$

where ω_o is still defined in terms of R_{eq1}. Substituting this value of $\overline{Z}_{eq2}$ in the equation for $\overline{A}_f$ we get

$$\overline{A}_2 = \frac{\left[\dfrac{- g_m(1 + g_K R_K) R_{eq1}}{1 + j(1 + g_K R_K) \dfrac{\omega}{\omega_o}} \right]}{\left[1 + g_K \dfrac{R_K}{1 + j a \dfrac{\omega}{\omega_o}} \right]}$$

$$= \left[\frac{- g_m(1 + g_K R_K) R_{eq1}}{(1 + g_K R_K) + j a \dfrac{\omega}{\omega_o}} \right]$$

$$\left[\frac{1 + j a \dfrac{\omega}{\omega_o}}{1 + j(1 + g_K R_K) \dfrac{\omega}{\omega_o}} \right] \qquad (25)$$

If we also let

$$a = 1 + g_K R_K \qquad (26)$$

then

$$\overline{A}_2 = \frac{- g_m R_{eq1}}{1 + j \dfrac{\omega}{\omega_o}} = \overline{A}_1 \qquad (27)$$

and this is exactly the same vector voltage amplification that we obtained in the original uncompensated case except that now

$$C_K = a C_s \frac{R_{eq1}}{R_K} = C_s \frac{R_{eq2}}{R_K} \qquad (28)$$

and is of the order of magnitude of 0.001 μf instead of being 200 or 300 μf as was required for good low-frequency response in the original case.

Case III: The fact that Case II gives the same vector voltage amplification as the original uncompensated amplifier is interesting, but

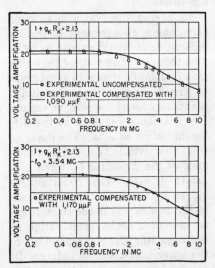

FIG. 7—Experimental verification of Case II and test of accuracy of method

not too useful. It is ordinarily desirable to improve both the amplitude and time-delay characteristics over those that are obtained with uncompensated amplifiers.

If values of a other than those indicated in Eq. 26 are used in Eq. 25 the amplitude and time-delay characteristics shown in Fig. 2 are obtained ($1 + g_K R_K = 2.50$ in this case). It will be observed from these characteristics that a wide range of performance can be obtained.

The ideal characteristic is one in

which both the amplitude and time-delay characteristics are flat over the full range of operation. This requirement cannot be met but a compromise is possible in which one of the two characteristics is made as flat as possible and the other one is allowed to take care of itself.

It will be observed that the higher the value of a, the greater the value of ω/ω_o at which the amplitude characteristic crosses the $A/A_M = 1.0$ value. This would suggest that if we could make the cathode capacitance automatically vary the proper amount with change of frequency, then we could slide from curve to curve in covering the full range of operation. A similar procedure could be used with the time delay but it would probably require different values of a than those necessary for constant amplitude.

Satisfying this variable cathode capacitance requirement is not as difficult as it would appear to be at first thought. The method by which this is done is shown in the curves of Fig. 3. In this figure the circled points represent the relative capacitive reactance required at the different values of ω/ω_o. The lower of the two curves is the relative reactance of the capacitor C_K when $a = 1.0$ $(1 + g_K R_K)$ [the condition required by Case II]. The upper one of the two curves is the relative reactance of a series combination of the capacitor C_{K2} corresponding to the lower curve, and an inductor L_K required to resonate this capacitor at a value of $\omega/\omega_o = 1.10$. The circled points are satisfied very nicely by the series combination of C_K and L_K chosen.

The amplitude and time delay characteristics that result from this choice are shown in Fig. 4. A more satisfactory choice of variables will give the response curves shown in Fig. 5. In this case the time-delay characteristic has been greatly improved with only a slight change of the amplitude characteristic.

The variables for Fig. 5 were obtained from the two curves in Fig. 6. These two curves are the key to

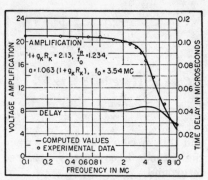

FIG. 8—Experimental verification of Case III

the compensation discussed in this paper and have been designed to produce a time-delay characteristic that will dip approximately four percent to the valley and then rise about six percent to the peak. Either flatter amplitude or time-delay characteristics can be obtained with slight variations in a and f_R/f_o but it is suggested that the response to be expected should be computed in each case.

The simplest procedure for making these computations involves the use of Eq. 25, replacing a by a_{eq} which is developed in the following manner:

If X_C and X_L are self resonant at f_R so that $X_{CR} = X_{LR}$, then at any other frequency the equivalent series reactance is

$$X_{eq} = X_C - X_L = X_{CR}\frac{f_R}{f} - X_{CR}\frac{f}{f_R}$$
$$= X_{CR}\left(\frac{f_R}{f} - \frac{f}{f_R}\right) \quad (29)$$

so that

$$C_{eq} = C_K \frac{\left(\dfrac{f_R}{f}\right)}{\left(\dfrac{f_R}{f} - \dfrac{f}{f_R}\right)} \quad (30)$$

and

$$a_{eq} = a\,\frac{C_{eq}}{C_K} = \frac{a\left(\dfrac{\omega_R}{\omega}\right)}{\left(\dfrac{\omega_R}{\omega} - \dfrac{\omega}{\omega_R}\right)}$$
$$= \frac{a}{\left[\dfrac{\omega_R}{\omega} - \dfrac{\omega}{\omega_R}\right]\left(\dfrac{\omega}{\omega_R}\right)} \quad (31)$$

Sample computations for several of the points in Fig. 8 are shown in Table I.

Experimental Verification

To verify experimentally the theory developed previously, the amplifier circuit of Fig. 1C, using a 6AG7 tube, was set up on a breadboard. The constants used in this circuit were:

$R_{L1} = 2,040$ ohms　　$E_{bb} = 300$ volts
$R_K = 81.8$ ohms　　$E_{c2} = 125$ volts
$R_{sg} = 22,400$ ohms　$E_{c1} = -2.68$ volts

The screen and cathode circuits were bypassed sufficiently well for frequencies above 10 kc and no measurements were made below 100 kc. The experimental frequency characteristic, shown by the curve drawn through the circled points in Fig. 7, was obtained. From this curve it was determined that $f_o = 3.80$ mc and $C_s = 21.0$ μμf.

When the cathode bypass capacitor was removed it was found that a new load resistor $R_{Ls} = 4,440$ ohms was required to produce the same voltage amplification at 100 kc as was obtained previously. Using a value of $r_p = 125,000$ ohms and $R_g = 500,000$ ohms it was determined that $R_{eq1} = 2,000$ ohms and $R_{eq2} = 4,260$ ohms. Therefore

$$1 + g_K R_K = \frac{R_{eq2}}{R_{eq1}} = \frac{4,260}{2,000} = 2.13.$$

Analytically $g_K \cong g_m + g_{c2}$. These values can be obtained from the HB-3 series of RCA Tube Handbooks. For the operating values involved, interpolating between the 100 and 150 screen voltage curves, $g_m \cong 0.010$ mhos and $g_{c2} \cong 0.003$ mhos (obtained from the slope of the e_{c1} vs i_{c2} curves). Therefore $g_K \cong 0.013$ mhos and $1 + g_K R_K \cong 1 + 81.8 \times 0.013 = 2.06$. As was expected this value is slightly lower than the value obtained experimentally.

On this basis it was determined that

$$C_K = \frac{R_{eq2}}{R_K}C_s = \frac{4,260}{81.8} \times 21.0 =$$
$$1,093 \text{ μμf}$$

When a value of $C_K = 1,090$ μμf was used the experimental values shown by the squared points in Fig. 7 were obtained. The variation obtained was definitely outside the experimental error expected. A closer examination of the circuit showed that while R_{L1} was composed of a series combination of two 2-watt resistors, R_{Ls} was composed of a series

Table I—Sample Calculations for Compensated Amplifiers
(Data Plotted in Fig. 8)

Working Equations:

$$a_{eq} = \frac{a}{\left[\dfrac{\omega_R}{\omega} - \dfrac{\omega}{\omega_R}\right]\dfrac{\omega}{\omega_R}} \qquad\qquad \frac{\omega_R}{\omega} = \frac{f_R}{f_o} \times \frac{\omega_o}{\omega}$$

$$\frac{\overline{A}}{\overline{A_M}} = \frac{A}{A_M}\left|\underline{\;\theta\;}\right. = \left[\frac{(1 + g_K R_K)}{(1 + g_K R_K) + j a_{eq}\dfrac{\omega}{\omega_o}}\right]\left[\frac{1 + j a_{eq}\;\dfrac{\omega}{\omega_o}}{1 + j(1 + g_K R_K)\dfrac{\omega}{\omega_o}}\right]$$

$$T_d = \frac{\theta}{360} \times \frac{1}{f} \text{ seconds}$$

Circuit Constants:

$(1 + g_K R_K) = 2.13$, $\dfrac{f_R}{f_o} = 1.234$, $a = 1.063 \times 2.13 = 2.265$

$f_o = 3.54$ mc, $A_M = 20.8$

Quantity					
ω/ω_o	0.03	0.1	0.3	1.0	3.0
ω_R/ω	41.13	12.34	4.113	1.234	0.4113
ω/ω_R	0.0243	0.0809	0.243	0.809	2.430
$\omega_R/\omega - \omega/\omega_R$	41.11	12.26	3.870	.425	−2.019
a_{eq}	2.267	2.280	2.410	6.600	−.4615
$a_{eq}\,\omega/\omega_o$	0.0681	0.2280	0.7230	6.600	−1.384
$1 + j\,a_{eq}\,\omega/\omega_o$	1.0023	1.027	1.237	6.68	1.710
	$\underline{\;3.91°}$	$\underline{\;12.85°}$	$\underline{\;35.85°}$	$\underline{\;81.38°}$	$\overline{\;54.12°}$
$(1 + g_K R_K) + j a_{eq}\omega/\omega_o$	2.1311	2.142	2.245	6.930	2.540
	$\underline{\;1.84°}$	$\underline{\;6.11°}$	$\underline{\;18.79°}$	$\underline{\;72.10°}$	$\overline{\;33.00°}$
$(1 + g_K R_K)\,\omega/\omega_o$	0.0639	0.213	0.639	2.13	6.39
$1 + j(1 + g_K R_K)\,\omega/\omega_o$	1.0020	1.022	1.188	2.352	6.46
	$\underline{\;3.66°}$	$\underline{\;12.03°}$	$\underline{\;32.60°}$	$\underline{\;64.82°}$	$\underline{\;81.10°}$
$\overline{A}/\overline{A_M}$	0.9998	0.9994	0.987	0.875	0.222
	$\underline{\;1.59°}$	$\underline{\;5.29°}$	$\underline{\;15.54°}$	$\underline{\;55.54°}$	$\underline{\;102.20°}$
T_d (microseconds)	0.0416	0.0415	0.0407	0.0436	0.0268
f (mc)	0.106	0.354	1.06	3.54	10.6

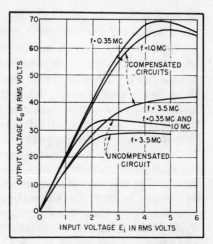

FIG. 9—Experimental characteristics showing improvement in linearity obtained with compensating circuit

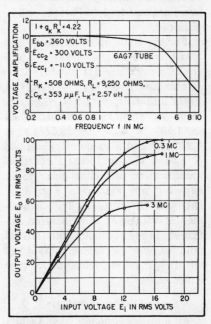

FIG. 10—Frequency and linearity characteristics of amplifier intended for high output voltages

combination of two 2-watt resistors shunted by a ½-watt trimmer resistor. This ½-watt resistor was used to obtain the exact value of R_{L2} that was required. The extra resistor introduced an additional 1.5 µµf in the plate circuit, bringing the total stray capacitance to 22.5 µµf. This in turn reduced f_o from 3.80 mc to 3.54 mc and changed the required value of C_K from 1,093 µµf to 1,170 µµf.

The smooth curve in Fig. 7 shows the theoretical values expected under the new conditions. The circled points represent the experimental data obtained with $C_K =$ 1,170 µµf. The agreement is definitely within the experimental error expected.

Stray Capacitance Effects

In the early stages of the investigation a similar circuit was used with the exception that the suppressor and screen were returned to the cathode instead of being returned to ground. While the theoretical analysis called for approximately 1,000 µµf compensating capacitance, it was found that the experimental value was much closer to 600 µµf.

A more thorough investigation of the circuit showed that the stray cathode-to-plate capacitance acts as though it were multiplied by the voltage amplification and connected from cathode to ground. Most of this capacitance was due to the suppressor which was at cathode potential and the screen which was at cathode potential as far as the operating frequencies were concerned. The measured value of this stray capacitance was approximately 19 µµf and this multiplied by the gain of approximately 21 was equivalent to the missing 400 μμf. This effect could be used to obtain Case II type of compensation with lower values of capacitance than those required for C_K but if Case III type of compensation is used it simply tends to shunt the compensating circuit and make the determination of the proper element values more difficult. For this reason it is suggested that the suppressor and screen always be returned to ground. An additional advantage is that the alternating screen current then flows through R_K, producing additional feedback and requiring the use of $1 + g_K R_K$ instead of $1 + g_m R_K$. Since $1 + g_K R_K$ is greater than $1 + g_m R_K$, additional linearity benefits, which are discussed in detail below, will be obtained.

For the value of $1 + g_K R_K = 2.13$ it is found from the curves of Fig. 6 that proper Case III compensation is obtained when $a/(1 + g_K R_K) = 1.063$ and $f_R/f_o = 1.234$. On this basis we should use values of $C_K = 1.063 \times 4,260 \times 22.5/81.8 = 1,243$ μμf and a value of $f_R = 1.234 \times 3.54 = 4.37$ mc. The theoretical amplification and time delay to be expected are shown in Fig. 8 by the smooth curves. The experimental values of amplification obtained are shown by the circled points. The agreement is well within the experimental error expected.

Additional Advantages

An additional benefit that results from the type of compensation discussed in this paper is in the linearity and voltage-handling capability of the amplifier. Since the compensated amplifier has a larger value of R_L than the uncompensated one, its load line will not be as steep, and therefore larger voltage swings can be expected before either cutoff or positive grid conditions result. In addition to that a considerable amount of negative feedback is present in the compensated amplifier and this tends to reduce the tendency toward nonlinear distortion. These effects are brought out very nicely by the experimental curves in

Fig. 9. It is obvious that in the middle frequency region with compensated operation the linear portion of the curve is more than twice as long as it is for the uncompensated operation. The advantage is lessened for frequencies close to f_o. This is not believed to be too important in video amplifiers intended for television purposes since the high-frequency components of the signal will always have lower amplitude than the middle and low-frequency components.

If it is desired to obtain a large linear range of output voltage the quantity $1 + g_K R_K$ should be made as large as is reasonably convenient. To test this condition the same 6AG7 tube was operated with the following constants:

$$R_L = 9,250 \text{ ohms} \qquad E_{bb} = 360 \text{ volts}$$
$$R_K = 508 \text{ ohms} \qquad E_{cc2} = 300 \text{ volts}$$
$$E_{c1} = -11.0 \text{ volts}$$

In this case the screen grid was operating at its rated dissipation of 1.5 watts while the plate was operating with about 3.5 watts, which is considerably below its rated dissipation. No attempt was made to determine any possible change in stray capacitance that might have resulted. The compensation was calculated on the basis of $1 + g_K R_K = 4.22$ as determined experimentally and $C_s = 21.0$ μμf as found in the original amplifier. The compensating elements used were $C_K = 353$ μμf and $L_K = 2.57 \times 10^{-6}$ henrys.

It can be seen from Fig. 10 that the middle-frequency gain has been reduced to about 10 but the frequency response has not been changed appreciably from the previous case. On the other hand, the linear range of operation, shown in Fig. 10, has been greatly increased. The remarkable thing about this case is that an amplifier which is relatively flat to 3.5 mc and has useful frequency response above 5 mc is able to develop a linear middle-frequency peak-to-peak output voltage of about 200 volts with less than 22 ma combined plate and screen current. Even at

3 mc the linear range is remarkably great.

AN investigation of the factors affecting the input admittance in amplifiers is very important since the input admittance determines to a large extent the loading on the preceding stage. In order to make this investigation, a fictitious test voltage $\overline{E}_T$ is applied in the input circuit of an amplifier such as shown in Fig. 1B. The resulting flow of current from $\overline{E}_T$ determines the input admittance of the amplifier. As shown in Fig. 11 this current flows through three distinct paths, indicated at I_1, I_2 and I_3.

The current I_1 includes all of the currents except those specifically flowing through C_{gp} and C_{gk}. The conductance G_1, the intrinsic input conductance, would effectively be that which would be obtained with a cold tube in the socket. The capacitance C_1, which will be called the intrinsic input capacitance, is not as easily defined or measured but includes the input lead to ground capacitance, the grid to screen capacitance, and the grid to suppressor capacitance. Of course, the intrinsic input conductance and capacitance are modified by the fact that they include distributed as well as lumped effects. The distributed parameters must be taken into account in the analysis.

The magnitude and phase of the current $\overline{I}_2$ will depend on the amplification and phase shift of the amplifier and the magnitude of C_{gp}. This is the ordinary Miller effect which is described in most texts on communications under the heading of input admittance. The input conductance and input capacitance due to the grid-plate capacitance are

$$G_{i_{gp}} = \omega C_{gp} A \sin \theta \qquad (32)$$

and

$$C_{i_{gp}} = C_{gp} (1 - A \cos \theta) \qquad (33)$$

In this case A represents the magnitude of the voltage amplification and θ the phase shift of the plate to ground voltage with respect to the grid to ground voltage. For an uncompensated amplifier with infinite cathode bypass, θ will range from 90 to 180 degrees for capacitive loads and from 180 to 270 degrees for inductive loads. Thus it is seen that capacitive loads tend to produce positive input conductances while inductive loads tend to produce negative input conductances. In the case of the amplifier using cathode compensation, the angle θ can fall outside the limits specified above, but otherwise the two equations apply.

The magnitude and phase of the current $\bar{I}_3$ will depend on the magnitude of C_{gK} and on the vector cathode to ground voltage $\bar{E}_{K-Gnd}$. If the values of $\bar{A}_2$, $\bar{Z}_K$, and $\bar{Z}_{eq}$ from Eq. 25, 16 and 24 respectively are substituted in the expression for $\bar{E}_{K-Gnd}$, the following expression results:

$$\bar{E}_{K-Gnd} = -A\left(\frac{g_K}{g_m}\right)\left(\frac{\bar{Z}_K}{\bar{Z}_{eq}}\right)\bar{E}_T$$

$$= -\left[\frac{-gm\,(1+g_KR_K)R_{eq1}}{(1+g_KR_K)+ja\frac{\omega}{\omega_0}}\right]$$

$$\times \left[\frac{1+ja\frac{\omega}{\omega_0}}{1+j(1+g_KR_K)\frac{\omega}{\omega_0}}\right]\frac{g_K}{g_m}$$

$$\times \frac{\left[\dfrac{R_K}{1+ja\frac{\omega}{\omega_0}}\right]\bar{E}_T}{\left[\dfrac{(1+g_KR_K)\,R_{eq1}}{1+j(1+g_KR_K)\frac{\omega}{\omega_0}}\right]}$$

$$= \frac{+g_KR_K\,\bar{E}_T}{(1+g_KR_K)+ja\frac{\omega}{\omega_0}} \quad (34)$$

If the cathode compensation circuit of Fig. 1C is used then the same equation holds with the exception that a_{eq} from Eq. 31 (Part I) should be used in place of a. Then

$$\bar{E}_{K-Gnd} = \frac{g_KR_K\bar{E}_T}{(1+g_KR_K)+j\,a_{eq}\frac{\omega}{\omega_0}} \quad (35)$$

A loop equation can now be written for the outside loop so that

$$\bar{E}_T - \frac{g_KR_K\bar{E}_T}{(1+g_KR_K)+ja_{eq}\frac{\omega}{\omega_0}} =$$

$$\bar{I}_3\left(-j\frac{1}{\omega C_{gK}}\right) \quad (36)$$

and

$$\bar{Y}_{i_{gK}} = \frac{\bar{I}_3}{\bar{E}_T} = \frac{\omega C_{gK}\,(1+ja_{eq}\frac{\omega}{\omega_0})}{a_{eq}\frac{\omega}{\omega_0}-j(1+g_KR_K)} \quad (37)$$

Rationalizing,

$$\bar{Y}_{i_{gK}} =$$

$$\frac{-\,\omega C_{gK}\,a_{eq}\frac{\omega}{\omega_0}\,g_KR_K + j\omega C_{gK}\left[\left(a_{eq}\frac{\omega}{\omega_0}\right)^2+\right.}{}$$

$$\frac{\left.(1+g_KR_K)\right]}{\left(a_{eq}\frac{\omega}{\omega_0}\right)^2+(1+g_KR_K)^2} \quad (38)$$

Therefore

$$G_{i_{gK}} = \frac{-\,\omega C_{gK}\left(a_{eq}\frac{\omega}{\omega_0}\right)g_KR_K}{\left(a_{eq}\frac{\omega}{\omega_0}\right)^2+(1+g_KR_K)^2} \quad (39)$$

and

$$C_{i_{gK}} = \frac{C_{gK}\left[a_{eq}\left(\frac{\omega}{\omega_0}\right)^2+(1+g_KR_K)\right]}{\left(a_{eq}\frac{\omega}{\omega_0}\right)^2+(1+g_KR_K)^2} \quad (40)$$

As long as $\bar{Z}_K$ is capacitive in nature a_{eq} will be positive and the input conductance due to the grid-cathode capacitance will be negative. For values of frequency at which $\bar{Z}_K$ is inductive in nature a_{eq} becomes negative and therefore this particular input conductance will be positive.

All terms in the expression for the input capacitance due to the grid-cathode capacitance are essentially positive so that this input capacitance will always be positive but will be variable in magnitude.

The total input conductance will be the sum of the input conductances seen by the three currents and may be either positive, zero or negative depending upon the relative values involved. In order to avoid the possibility of high negative values of input conductance, which might result in oscillations, it is desirable to keep the grid-cathode capacitance as low as possible.

In a like manner the total input capacitance will be the sum of the input capacitances seen by the three currents. The input capacitance due to C_{gp} will tend to decrease with increasing frequencies. The input capacitance due to C_{gK} will be $C_{gK}/(1+g_KR_K)$ at low frequencies, attaining a maximum of C_{gK} at f_R (when $a_{eq}=\infty$) and again decreasing to $C_{gK}/(1+g_KR_K)$ at very high frequencies. There is a net tendency towards cancellation of the changes in these two capacitances at frequencies below f_R, although the change will be in the same direction at frequencies above f_R.

Experimental Verification

Proper experimental verification of the input admittance relations would require that the effects due to the various paths be measured individually and then combined to produce the proper total value. The only quantity that can be determined directly with any degree of accuracy is the intrinsic input conductance of the circuit. This is measured with a cold tube in the socket since in this case the C_{gp} and C_{gK} paths introduce practically pure capacitance as far as the input admittance is concerned.

A separation of C_{gp} and C_{gK} from all the other capacitances in the circuit by direct measurement would be quite difficult due to the possibility of multiple paths between the various points. It will be noticed, however, that at the frequency f_R the input conductance due to C_{gK} is equal to zero because

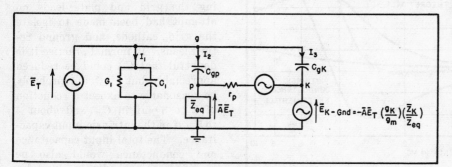

FIG. 11—Equivalent amplifier input circuit for admittance calculations

at this frequency $a_{eq} = \infty$. The remaining input conductance must therefore be the sum of the intrinsic conductance and the conductance due to C_{gp}. Since the intrinsic conductance can be measured directly, the difference between the total input conductance and the intrinsic conductance, at this frequency, will be due solely to the C_{gp} path and therefore we can solve for C_{gp} in Eq. 32. Of course, values of A and θ in this equation must be determined in the manner shown in Table I, part I.

The input conductance due to C_{gp} can now be computed for any other suitable frequency, such as $f_R/2$, at which the input conductance due to C_{gK} is relatively prominent. If the total input conductance for this frequency is measured and the measured intrinsic and computed grid-plate input conductances are subtracted from it, the difference must be the input conductance due to C_{gK}. Using this difference and Eq. 39 the capacitance C_{gK} can be determined.

Experimental data for only two frequencies were required to determine C_{gp} and C_{gK}, but with these values and the experimental intrinsic input conductance the total input conductance can be computed

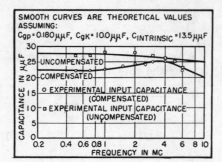

FIG. 13—Theoretical and experimental values of input capacitance

for any frequency. A measure of the accuracy of the method will be the correlation between measured and computed input conductance at frequencies other than the two used to determine C_{gp} and C_{gK}.

The curve for the intrinsic input conductance, shown in Fig. 12, was obtained experimentally. It was found to be the same for both the compensated and uncompensated amplifiers. At low values of frequency it approaches 2 micromhos which is the value of the 0.5-megohm grid leak resistor used. This conductance increases gradually with frequency, reaching approximately 24 micromhos at 10 megacycles.

By the methods described previously for the compensated amplifier, C_{gp} was found to be 0.180 $\mu\mu$f and

C_{gK} was found to be 10.0 $\mu\mu$f. The two smooth curves for input conductances due to C_{gp} and C_{gK} were computed using Eq. 32 and 39 respectively, and were then combined to obtain the theoretical total input conductance curve. Experimental values of total input conductance were also determined and they are shown by the circled points on this diagram. The correlation obtained is very satisfactory and it is believed that the values determined for C_{gp} and C_{gK} are quite accurate.

The intrinsic input capacitance can be determined by measuring the total input capacitance, at any convenient frequency, and subtracting from it the sum of the input capacitances due to C_{gp} and C_{gK}. The total input capacitance can then be determined for any frequency by adding to the intrinsic input capacitance the effective input capacitances due to C_{gp} and C_{gK} at that frequency.

The smooth curves in Fig. 13 are the theoretical input capacitances expected for the amplifier, both compensated and uncompensated, and the circled and squared points are the corresponding experimental values obtained. The correlation appears to be quite satisfactory.

The value determined for the intrinsic input capacitance of the compensated amplifier was 13.5 $\mu\mu$f. The various values of capacitance determined are not believed to be typical of normal practice since the amplifier used was set up on a standard breadboard used for classroom demonstration. Resistors and capacitors were connected to Fahnestock clips and while reasonable care had been exercised in separating the grid and plate leads no attempt had been made to isolate the grid, cathode, and ground return leads. In normal practice it is doubtful that C_{gp} could be reduced appreciably but it would probably be reasonable to expect a reduction of 2 to 3 $\mu\mu$f in C_{gK} and about 4 to 5 $\mu\mu$f in the intrinsic input capacitance. The total input capacitance and conductance would also be modified correspondingly.

In Fig. 14, the theoretical input

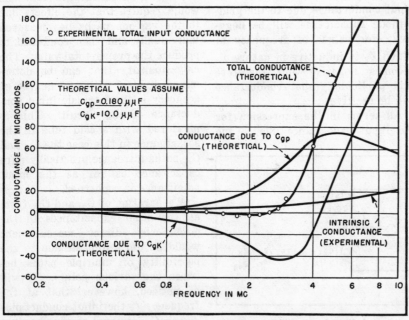

FIG. 12—Input circuit conductance for cathode-compensated amplifier

Table II—Sample Calculations for Input Admittance of Compensated Amplifier (Data Plotted in Fig. 12 and Fig. 13)

Working Equations:

$$C_{i_{gp}} = C_{gp}(1 - A\cos\theta) \qquad\qquad G_{i_{gp}} = \omega C_{gp} A\sin\theta$$

$$C_{i_{gK}} = \frac{C_{gK}\,[(a_{eq}\,\omega/\omega_o)^2 + (1 + {}_gKR_K)^2]}{(a_{eq}\,\omega/\omega_o)^2 + (1 + g_KR_K)^2} \qquad G_{i_{gK}} = \frac{-\,\omega\,C_{gK}\,(a_{eq}\,\omega/\omega_o)\,g_KR_K}{(a_{eq}\,\omega/\omega_o)^2 + (1 + g_KR_K)^2}$$

$$C_i = C_{Intrinsic} + C_{i_{gp}} + C_{i_{gK}}$$

$$G_i = G_{Intrinsic} + G_{i_{gp}} + G_{i_{gK}}$$

Circuit Constants in Addition to Those in Table I:

$C_{gp} = 0.180\ \mu\mu f$, $C_{gK} = 10.0\ \mu\mu f$, $C_{Intrinsic} = 13.5\ \mu\mu f$

$A_m = 20.8\underline{/180°}$

Quantity					
ω/ω_o	0.03	0.1	0.3	1.0	3.0
f (mc)	0.106	0.354	1.06	3.54	10.6
$G_{Intrinsic}$ (micromhos)	2.00	3.00	5.10	9.70	27.0
A	20.8	20.8	20.55	18.2	4.41
θ	178.41°	174.71°	164.46°	124.46°	77.80°
$A\cos\theta$	−20.8	−20.6	−19.8	−10.3	+.93
$C_{i_{gp}}$ ($\mu\mu f$)	3.92	3.89	3.74	2.04	.013
$(a_{eq}\,\omega/\omega_o)$	0.0681	0.2280	0.7230	6.600	−1.384
$(a_{eq}\,\omega/\omega_o)^2$	0.0046	0.052	0.524	43.6	1.92
$(a_{eq}\omega/\omega_o)^2 + (1 + {}_gKR_K)$	2.135	2.182	2.654	45.73	4.05
$(a_{eq}\omega/\omega_o)^2 + (1 + {}_gKR_K)^2$	4.545	4.592	5.064	48.14	6.46
$C_{i_{gK}}$ ($\mu\mu f$)	4.70	4.75	5.25	9.50	6.27
C_i ($\mu\mu f$)	22.12	22.14	22.49	25.04	19.78
$A\sin\theta$	0.576	1.92	5.51	15.00	4.31
$G_{i_{gp}}$ (micromhos)	0.069	0.769	6.59	60.1	51.7
$G_{i_{gK}}$ (micromhos)	−0.112	−1.245	−10.70	−34.4	+161.2
G_i (micromhos)	1.957	2.524	0.99	35.4	239.9

conductance computed for the uncompensated amplifier using $C_{gp} = 0.180\ \mu\mu f$ is slightly lower than the experimental values shown by the circled points. This discrepancy would have been eliminated if 0.10 $\mu\mu f$ had been added to C_{gp} in computing the theoretical input conductance. It is entirely possible that a minor circuit rearrangement could have actually caused this change in capacitance.

The input capacitance and input conductance of the compensated amplifier do not become undesirably excessive in any region of the frequency range considered. Sample computations for some of the points in Fig. 12 and 13 are carried out in Table II.

Comparison With Other Circuits

A basis of comparison among different types of video amplifier circuits can be established on many points, the most important of which are probably: (a) cost, (b) simplicity, (c) disturbance of normal circuit relations, (d) gain, (e) frequency response, (f) time delay, (g) linearity of the output voltage-vs-input voltage characteristic and (h) input admittance relations. Cathode compensation as developed in this paper is superior to other circuits in most of these aspects and is comparable in the rest.

On a cost basis, the circuit with cathode compensation is not only less expensive than any other compensated circuit but is even less expensive than the ordinary uncompensated video amplifier. In an ordinary video amplifier a large electrolytic capacitor is used in parallel with the cathode resistor. Very often this is bypassed by a small paper or mica capacitor which takes over at the higher frequencies at which the electrolytic capacitor

becomes very poor. With cathode compensation the large electrolytic capacitor is discarded, the small capacitor is made the proper size, and an inductor consisting of about ten turns of enameled wire on a quarter-inch Bakelite spool is inserted in series with the small capacitor. A counterbalancing effect might be the necessity of increasing the wattage rating of the load resistor but even this will not overcome the cost advantage of eliminating the electrolytic capacitor.

As far as simplicity is concerned, the ordinary shunt-peaking type of circuit is the only one that compares with cathode compensation. All other circuits require additional elements. In the series peaking circuits a certain division of the stray capacitance is required. If this is not available, then the theoretical curves are not reproduced. Sometimes it is necessary to insert additional capacitance in the circuit in order to obtain this proper distribution. This of course will tend to impair the available frequency response. Adding elements in the plate circuit will also tend to increase the stray capacitance present. This effect was noticed to a slight extent in the experimental case discussed but need not have been present at all if the proper value of resistance had been available.

In all other compensating circuits the impedance of the compensating elements is of the same order of magnitude as the load impedance. In the case of the inductances this results in difficulties due to self-resonance effects which are normally not taken into account. One instance in which this effect is taken into account is in the improved shunt-peaking[1] circuit. In the case of cathode compensation there is never any reason for concern over the stray capacitance of the inductors or the series inductance of the capacitors.

On the basis of gain from a certain tube for a given frequency response, cathode compensation is as good as ordinary shunt peaking and improved shunt peaking but not quite as good as the series peaking circuits which make use of filter circuit characteristics. This however is further modified by considerations as to whether frequency response is limited by amplitude or time delay considerations. On an amplitude consideration basis the series peaking circuits probably have a slight advantage over cathode compensation but this advantage disappears if time delay is used as the criterion of frequency response.

As a matter of fact, video amplifiers intended for television applications continue to have useful output as long as the time delay variations do not become excessive. In the amplifier of Fig. 8 the variation in time delay between the valley and the peak of the curve is of the order of magnitude of 0.004 microsecond. This represents a horizontal distance which corresponds to approximately one-twentieth of the distance between line centers in a television picture. This is certainly a negligible variation in time delay. The only other circuit that even approaches this constant a time delay over such a large frequency range is the shunt peaking compensation in which the inductive reactance at f_o is equal to 35

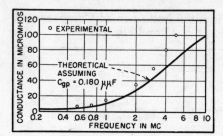

FIG. 14—Input conductance versus frequency of uncompensated amplifier

percent of the load resistance.

On the basis of linearity of output voltage for a given frequency response, cathode compensation is superior to all other circuits in the middle-frequency region and probably as good as any of them at the high-frequency end of the characteristic.

A thorough comparison of the input admittances of the various circuits is not possible because of the lack of data on the other circuits. With cathode compensation the input capacitance is slightly lower than in the corresponding uncompensated amplifier. The input conductance has some elements that tend to make it negative and others that tend to make it positive. A judicious combination of these elements will produce practically zero input conductance over most of the

operating range.

All other video amplifiers are limited in their low-frequency response to some extent by the cathode bypass capacitance used. In the case of cathode compensation, the circuit behaves as though the original uncompensated amplifier had infinite cathode bypass capacitance. Of course the screen bypass and coupling capacitors still have the same effect as they have in any circuit.

There is a possibility that the introduction of additional elements in the plate circuit might make the linearity in the high-frequency region comparable to that obtained at middle frequencies. This possibility has not been investigated up to the present time.

The author wishes to acknowledge the opportunity that he has had for discussing the problems involved in this development with his colleagues and especially with Professor W. C. Osterbrock. He would also like to thank the electrical engineering class of '48 of the University of Cincinnati, for the time they devoted to calculations in his behalf in the early stages of the project.

REFERENCE
(1) A. B. Bereskin, Improved High Frequency Compensation for Wide Band Amplifiers, *Proc. IRE*, p 608, Oct. 1944.

Stagger-Peaked Video Amplifiers

Staggered high-frequency compensation of a video amplifier provides twice the signal from a given amplifier tube in the conventional shunt-peaking circuit, or permits use of a tube having only half the plate-current consumption

By ALLAN EASTON

IT HAS BEEN customary to design a video amplifier so that its power output in response to a sinusoidal input voltage is substantially constant between a high and low cutoff frequency. If the wide-band amplifier is to be used primarily for sine-wave work, or is intended as part of a general-purpose oscilloscope, the conventional design procedure[1] is satisfactory and economical. In the case of video amplifiers which are intended solely for the amplification of pulses or television signals, economies in design can be achieved by the use of staggered high-frequency compensation.

The realization of a desired amplitude-versus-frequency characteristic by means of stagger-tuning a group of individual cascade amplifier stages is well known when applied to tuned amplifiers[2]. In this paper, a similar general principle is applied to video amplifiers.

Characteristics of Video Signal

Figure 1 shows two types of signals for which staggered high-frequency compensation is suitable.

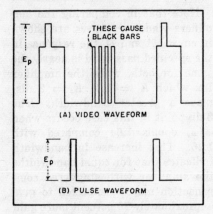

FIG. 1—Types of signals which can be handled by the staggered technique

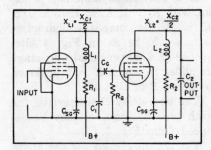

FIG. 2—Capacitances C_1 and C_2 are the result of tube and circuit

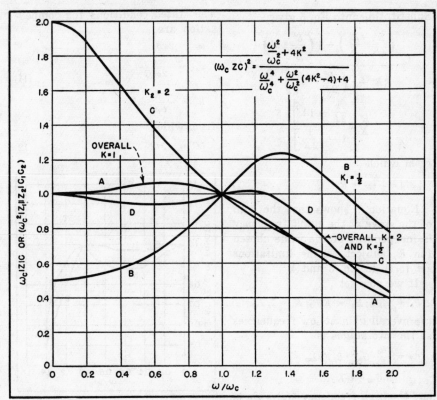

FIG. 3—Amplitude plotted against frequency for several combinations of stages using various values of K

The series of narrow pulses in Fig. 1A is similar to those which result in the narrow wedges in monoscope test patterns. A Fourier analysis of the waveforms of Fig. 1 indicates that while the wave of voltage may have a peak magnitude of E_p volts, no one of the spectral components may be that large; in fact, the higher-frequency components become progressively smaller.

In the case of video signal amplifiers for television receivers, it is customary to specify high-frequency cutoff at about 4 megacycles. However, the signal-frequency components near 4 mc have amplitudes which are only a tiny percentage of E_p. Therefore, it is not necessary for the amplifier which drives the picture tube grid to deliver equal power throughout the entire frequency spectrum.

Most of the signal energy is concentrated at the low and middle portions of the spectrum and very little is ordinarily found near the upper end of the band. The small components require equal amplifica- tion with the lower-frequency components, but do not require as large plate-current swings.

Characteristics of Output Stage

The foregoing qualitative considerations indicate that an amplifier which has constant small signal gain, but a falling power-handling capacity with frequency, will produce a satisfactory picture on the cathode-ray tube. This principle when applied to the output stage of a video amplifier intended for television or pulse signals enables the use of an output-tube plate load resistor of at least twice the size of that dictated by the conventional design procedure.

The proposed approach makes it possible to obtain at least twice as much signal from a given amplifier tube, or, for a given video signal output, to use a tube having at least half the plate-current consumption. The resultant cost of a pulse oscilloscope or of a television receiver might therefore be reduced by a significant amount with no sacrifice in performance.

Design of Video Circuits

An analysis has been made of a pair of video amplifiers employing shunt-peaking compensation and embodying the proposed design principles. Consider the circuit shown in Fig. 2. The gain of this amplifier at low frequencies (neglecting the effects of coupling and screen bypass capacitors) is

$$A = R_1 G_{m1} \cdot R_2 G_{m2} \qquad (1)$$

where R_1 and R_2 are plate load resistances and G_{m1} and G_{m2} are tube transconductances.

At any frequency

$$A = Z_1 G_{m1} \cdot Z_2 G_{m2} \qquad (2)$$

At a particular frequency, f_c, designated as the cutoff frequency, the magnitude of the plate load impedance ($|Z|$) may be made equal to R, the load resistor, when

$$R = X_c \atop X_L = X_c/2 \qquad (3)$$

Now suppose

$$R' = KR = K X_c \atop \text{and } X_L = X_c/2 \qquad (4)$$

Since

$$Z = \frac{X_L X_c - jR X_c}{R + j(X_L - X_c)} \qquad (5)$$

Substituting into Eq. 5 gives

$$Z' = \frac{\left(\frac{R'}{2K} \cdot \frac{R'}{K}\right) - j\left(\frac{R'}{K} \cdot R'\right)}{R' + j\left(\frac{R'}{2K} - \frac{R'}{K}\right)} = \quad (6)$$

$$\frac{R'}{K} \frac{\left[\frac{1}{2K} - j\,1\right]}{\left[1 - j\frac{1}{2K}\right]}$$

from which

$$|Z'| = \frac{R'}{K} = R \quad (7)$$

Equation 7 shows that the gain of the stage at the cutoff frequency is independent of the value chosen for K, subject to the limitations set forth in Eq. 3 and 4.

If we now set

$$R_1' = K_1 R_1;\ R_2' = K_2 R_2;\ K_1 = 1/K_2 \quad (8)$$

the overall gain at low frequencies of the two stages is

$$A_T = \frac{R_1}{K_2} G_{m1} \cdot R_2 K_2 G_{m2} = R_1 G_{m1} \cdot R_2 G_{m2} \quad (9)$$

and the high-frequency (f_c) gain is the same.

The analysis to this point has shown that if the size of the output load resistor is multiplied by a factor K_2 and the size of the input stage load resistance is multiplied by $K_1 = 1/K_2$, the amplifier will have the same gain at low frequencies and at cutoff frequency as an amplifier designed in the conventional manner ($K_1 = K_2 = 1$). The values of compensating inductance and circuit capacitance are identical in both types of designs.

There is no change in the overall gain, but it is possible to drive the amplifier to twice the signal power output without overload when $K_1 = 1/2$, $K_2 = 2$. The first stage pre-emphasizes the higher-frequency components to compensate for the tendency of the second stage to drop off with frequency.

Overall Response

The general frequency response and time-delay characteristic for the above circuits are of interest. The impedance in the plate circuit of either video amplifier is

$$|Z|^2 = \frac{R^2 + \omega_2 L_2}{1 - 2\omega^2 LC + \omega^4 L^2 C^2 + \omega^2 C^2 R^2} \quad (10)$$

The stated conditions for compensation are:

$$\omega_c = 2\pi f_c$$
$$\omega_c L = \frac{1}{2\omega_c C} \quad (11)$$
$$R = \frac{K}{\omega_c C}$$

from which

$$LC = \omega_c^2/2 \quad (12)$$

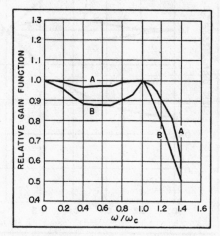

FIG. 4—Curve A shows the overall response of four stages, each having different values of K. Curve B applies to four stages, each having K—1

$$L = \frac{1}{2\omega_c^2 C}$$
$$\omega_c L = \frac{1}{2\omega_c C}$$

The generalized dimensionless impedance function is

$$(|Z|\ \omega_c C)^2 = \frac{(\omega/\omega_c)^2 + 4K^2}{(\omega/\omega_c)^4 + (\omega/\omega_c)^2 (4K^2 - 4) + 4} \quad (13)$$

The phase angle may be determined from

$$\theta = \arctan \omega/R\ [L(1 - \omega^2 LC - CR^2] \quad (14)$$

Substituting the design criteria for L, C, and R gives

$$\theta = \arctan (\omega/\omega_c) \left[\frac{2 - (\omega/\omega_c)^2 - 4K^2}{4K}\right] \quad (15)$$

and

$$\omega_c t = (2\pi/360°)\ (\theta/\omega/\omega_c) \quad (15a)$$

The normalized impedance function of a two-stage video amplifier designed in the conventional fashion ($K_1 = K_2 = 1$) is plotted in Fig. 3, curve A. The corresponding impedance functions for stages having $K_1 = 1/2$ and $K_2 = 2$ are shown in curves B and C, the composite of the two stages results in curve D.

Note that in comparing the amplifiers whose responses are shown in curves A and D, the response in the specified pass band is nearly the same for both, while the amplifier for which $K_1 = 1/2$, $K_2 = 2$ displays a greater bandwidth. The 3-db point in this case occurs when ω/ω_c equals 1.64 compared with 1.46. This increase in bandwidth indicates that for equal bandwidths the amplifier with staggered compensation may be expected to give approximately 20 percent more gain than the conventional shunt-peaked circuit.

If a four-stage amplifier is set up, with $K_1 = 1$, $K_2 = 1$, $K_3 = 1/2$, $K_4 = 2$, the composite characteristic would be as in Fig. 4. Response of a conventional four-stage amplifier in which $K = 1$ is shown by curve B of Fig. 4.

The time-delay characteristic for each type of amplifier may be deduced from Fig. 5.

The circuit chosen for the above analysis was selected not for its excellence as a video amplifier but rather for the ease and simplicity of analysis and demonstration. The method may also be applied to most other types of high-frequency compensation networks, perhaps with a bit more mathematical difficulty.

It has been shown in a qualitative manner than factors of $K_1 = 1/2$ and $K_2 = 2$ should produce no discernible deterioration of amplifier performance principally because the high-frequency components have relatively small amplitudes. Experiment indicates that values of K larger than 2 may be used, but the author has made no extensive mathematical study of this.

Further Applications

An interesting consequence of Eq. 7, which shows that the gain of an amplifier stage at a frequency f_c may be independent of the value of load resistance, is in the use of the circuit as a phase shifter.

While the gain of the circuit at f_c does not change as R is varied, the phase shift certainly does. This can be seen from study of Eq. 15.

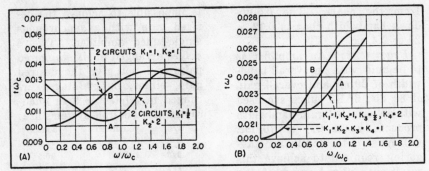

FIG. 5—Time delay of the video amplifiers plotted against frequency

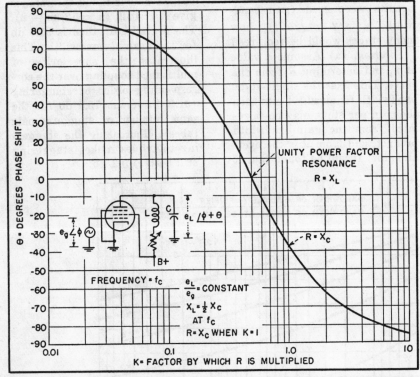

FIG. 6—Effect of load resistance upon phase shift of amplifier at cutoff frequency f_o

Let K be equal to zero ($R = 0$) and $\omega/\omega c = 1$, then θ becomes plus 90 degrees. If K becomes very large (R approaches infinity) θ approaches minus 90 degrees. Thus a variation in R can produce a phase shift which lies between plus or minus 90 degrees. The phase shift is equal to zero when K is 1/2.

Figure 6 is a plot of θ versus K and illustrates the use of this circuit as a constant-amplitude phase-shift network. To obtain a variable phase shift of $n\pi$ radians, it is only necessary to cascade n identical stages.

REFERENCES

(1) Terman, "Radio Engineers Handbook," McGraw-Hill Book Co., N. Y., 1943, p 413.
(2) H. Wallman, Stagger-Tuned Amplifier Design, ELECTRONICS, May 1948.

Stagger-Tuned I-F Design

Chart gives overall bandwidth for 3 db and any fraction of 3 db, for i-f amplifiers having 1 to 500 synchronous or stagger-tuned stages and up to 5 elements per stage

By MATTHEW T. LEBENBAUM

THE BANDWIDTH reduction factor R is here plotted as a function of the number of single or multituned stages n in the amplifier. The family parameter m represents the number of tuning elements in the interstage coupling network when all stages are synchronously tuned; thus, $m = 1$ for a simple RLC tuned interstage, and $m = 2$ for a double-tuned interstage. For a stagger-tuned amplifier, n is the number of n-uples and m is the number of elements in the general n-uple.

Example 1: Assume an amplifier is to have 8 stages using

identical single-tuned interstage couplings. (a) For what 3-db bandwidth must each stage be designed if the overall bandwidth is to be 6 mc? (b) What will be the 0.5-db bandwidth?

Solution. (a) From the curves for $n = 8$ and $m = 1$, $R = 0.3$. Dividing overall bandwidth of 6 mc by this value of R gives 20 mc as the required bandwidth of each stage. (b) If n' stages cascaded give a certain 3-db bandwidth, each stage must be down by $3/n'$ db and n of them will be down $(3/n') n = x$ db at that bandwidth. To determine the x-db bandwidth then, the R factor is determined for a number of stages n' where $n' = n (3/x)$; here n is the actual number of stages and $x < 3$ db. In the case at hand, $n' = 8 \times (3/0.5) = 48$, and $R = 0.12$

from the chart. The 0.5-db-down bandwidth then is 0.12×20 or 2.4 mc.

Example 2: An amplifier is to be built with an overall bandwidth of 20 mc and overall gain of 80 db; 6AK5 tubes are used with an assumed gain-bandwidth product $(g_m/2\pi C_T)$ of 70 mc. (a) What is the minimum staggering required to achieve this result with 12 or less tubes? (b) If equally loaded double-tuned circuits were used (gain-bandwidth = $\sqrt{2}\ g_m/2\pi C_T$), how many stages would be required?

Solution. (a) Assume a value of n, and determine R from the curve. This fixes the single-stage bandwidth required. From this, the gain per stage may be calculated from the gain-bandwidth product, and from this the overall gain. It will be found that it

is impossible to achieve the desired gain with a synchronous single-tuned amplifier. Twelve stages arranged in six staggered pairs will not give the desired gain, either, but 9 stages arranged in triples or 8 in quadruples will. Possible systems are:

n/m	Tubes	db gain
6/2	12	75.5
3/3	9	80.5
4/3	12	102
2/4	8	80

(b) 12 double-tuned interstages give $R = 0.49$ ($n = 12$, $m = 2$). The overall gain then is 91.6 db for the desired bandwidth. This illustrates the superiority of multituned coupling over the corresponding order of staggering (91.6 db versus 75.5 db for the same number of staggered-pair tubes). Increasing the staggering to triples makes staggering still better, 102 db.

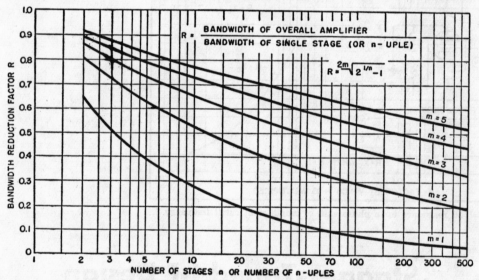

Modified Wallman Circuit with Voltage Feedback

By SHIGEO SHIMIZU

THIS is a report of a new low-noise amplifier circuit. The second stage of the Wallman circuit, which is a current-feedback amplifier, can be replaced by a voltage-feedback amp-

lifier, to form a more convenient circuit. This circuit was developed during a study of a low-noise i-f amplifier of a microwave receiver.

For this purpose, the Wallman circuit (Fig. 1) was generally used for its superiority in terms of noise-figure; but it has some disadvantages, such as difficulty of ad-

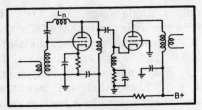

FIG. 1—Normal Wallman circuit with current feedback in second stage

justment, and inconvenience due to the floating cathode of the second stage tube.

The operating expression of the second stage of the Wallman circuit is as follows:

$$i_{p2} = g_{m2} (e_{k2} + i_{p2} Z_{k2})$$
$$i_{p2} (1 - g_{m2} Z_{k2}) = g_{m2} e_{k2}$$
$$i_{p2} = \frac{g_{m2} e_{k2}}{1 - g_{m2} Z_{k2}} \cong \frac{e_{k2}}{Z_{k2}} =$$
$$\frac{(Z_{k2} g_{m1} e_{g1}) + E_{n2}}{Z_{k2}}$$
$$\therefore e_{p2} = Z_{p2} i_{p2} = Z_{p2} g_{m1} e_{g1} + \frac{Z_{p2} E_{n2}}{Z_{k2}}$$

From these equations the facts are clear that, the second stage of the Wallman circuit is a current feedback amplifier and this stage has lower input impedance and lower noise output than a normal grounded-cathode amplifier. It was decided to try voltage feedback in the second stage to achieve the same

benefits that are obtained in the Wallman circuit through the use of current feedback. The resulting circuit (Fig. 2) has the advantage of a grounded cathode in the second stage and easier adjustment due to the use of a pentode. The operating expressions are as follows:

(1) Without feedback

$$e_{p1} = Z_{p1} g_{m1} (E_s + E_{n1})$$
$$e_{p2} = Z_{p2} g_{m2} (e_{p1} + E_{n2})$$
$$= Z_{p2} g_{m2} [Z_{p1} g_{m1} (E_s + E_{n1}) + E_{n2}]$$

(2) With feedback

$$e_{p1}' = e_{p1}/Z_{p1} g_{m1} = (E_s + E_{n1})$$
$$e_{p2}' = e_{p2}/Z_{p1} g_{m1} = Z_{p2} g_{m2}$$
$$\left[(E_s + E_{n1}) + \frac{E_{n2}}{Z_{p1} g_{m1}} \right]$$

where the mean square of E_{n2}

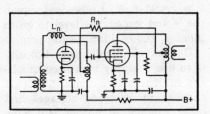

FIG. 2—Modified Wallman circuit permits grounding of second-stage cathode and offers several other advantages

$$E_{n2}^2 = 4 k T \beta$$
$$\left[R_{v2} + R_{p1} + \left(\frac{R_{p1} R_{g2}}{R_{p1} + R_{g2}} \right)^2 \frac{5}{R_{g2}} \right]$$

For the conditions studied—center frequency 50 mc, and a 6AK5 tube connected as pentode

$$E_{n2}^2 = 4 k T \beta (4,300)$$

The converted value of this to the first tube grid is

$$\frac{E_{n2}^2}{(Z_{p1} g_{m1})^2} = 4 k T \beta (43)$$

By comparison of these expressions and expressions of normal Wallman circuit, it is evident that this circuit has an equal noise figure for the case where

$$R_{p1} >> \left[R_{v2} + \left(\frac{R_{p1} R_{g2}}{R_{p1} + R_{g2}} \right)^2 \frac{5}{R_{g2}} \right]$$

and in addition to that, this circuit provides easier adjustment.

Result of the Experiment

In experimenting with this circuit for examination of the foregoing theory, it was found that this circuit (with a center frequency of 52 mc, bandwidth of 10 mc, and employing a 6AK5 tube) had a noise figure of 1.9, as compared to 2.04 for the normal Wallman circuit.

Simplified Q Multiplier

Portion of cathode-follower output is stepped up by passive components and fed back to grid of tube to give extremely high selectivity with absolute stability. Extra parts needed are one tube, one capacitor and two resistors

By H. E. HARRIS

WITH THE RISE of radio navigation, c-w radar, and other systems requiring maximum signal-to-noise ratio, there have grown up in recent years a large number of applications for amplifying systems of very narrow bandwidth. Since the basic limitation on the narrowness of bandwidth which can be obtained in an ordinary tuned amplifier is the resistance associated

with the tuned circuit it uses, it seems logical that one solution to the problem would be the use of an active network to supply energy to the system according to exactly the same laws by which the resistance dissipates it, so that some of the effect would be cancelled out.

The use of such active networks, known, for obvious reasons, as negative resistances, turns out to

be an entirely practical method of raising the Q of a tuned circuit, Ohm's law holds exactly for a negative resistance element, except for sign change, so it is possible to treat it exactly as any other circuit component, even to the extent of combining it with the positive resistances in the circuit.

Consider, for instance, a tuned circuit having an equivalent parallel resistance R. The initial value for Q would be

$$Q_0 = \frac{R}{\omega L} \qquad (1)$$

and suppose there is put in parallel with this tuned circuit an active network having a negative resistance characteristic. The negative resistance can be combined with the positive resistance of the circuit by the usual laws of combination of parallel resistances to give the following relationship for R_{eff}:

$$R_{eff} = \frac{(-R_n)R}{(-R_n)+R} = \frac{R\,R_n}{R_n - R} \qquad (2)$$

which is obviously greater than the original R, corresponding to a multiplication of the original Q by a factor equal to the ratio of the two resistances. In other words

$$\frac{Q_{eff}}{Q_0} = \frac{R_n}{R_n - R} \qquad (3)$$

This Q multiplication can be made arbitrarily large by simply letting R_n approach R.

Practical Systems

A number of systems have been used to secure this negative resistance characteristic, such as secondary emission in a tetrode (dynatron)[1] or the formation of a virtual cathode between screen and suppressor (transitron)[2]. By far the most satisfactory method to date, however, has been the use of positive feedback around a vacuum-tube amplifier.[3,4] This basic method is used in the new circuit proposed here.

Consider an amplifier of gain A and internal resistance R_i such as is represented schematically in Fig. 1A, and assume that positive feedback is introduced through the resistor R_f.

Under the assumption that the input resistance of the amplifier is so high compared to the other circuit resistances that it may be neglected—a condition easily realizable in practice—Kirchhoff's voltage law

The author is now with Magnetic Device Section, Control Divisions, General Electric Co., Schenectady, New York. Work described was done at MIT Research Laboratory of Electronics under U. S. Navy Bureau of Ordnance contract Nord-9661.

can be applied to yield the following equation

$$e_1 = i_1 R_f + i_1 R_i + A e_1 \qquad (4)$$

which can be rearranged to yield

$$Z_1 = \frac{e_1}{i_1} = -\frac{R_f}{A-1} - \frac{R_i}{A-1} \qquad (5)$$

where Z_1 is simply the effective input impedance of the circuit.

This effect is the basis for the increased selectivity of the ordinary regenerative amplifier or detector. Such a regenerative circuit, however, lacks the important characteristic of stability. Referring to Eq. 3 it is seen that appreciable multiplication of the Q is to be had only when R_n is very nearly equal to R. Therefore it takes only a very slight percentage change in R_n, such as would be caused by variations in plate supply voltage, to cause the two resistances to become equal, the Q and impedance level to go to infinity, and oscillations to ensue.

One way to resolve this difficulty is to use a highly stabilized amplifier for the active element so that changes in electrode voltages and other random variations will have little effect upon the gain, and hence upon the negative resistance which is produced. Both Terman[3] and later Ginzton[4] have considered in some detail one such circuit utilizing a highly stabilized two-stage amplifier. It is the purpose of the present paper to describe a much simpler circuit which achieves essentially the same results with

only a single stage. The basis of this circuit is the cathode follower. It has power gain, correct phase relation, and it has very high stability. But, it has less than unity gain. Fig. 1B shows that this drawback can be eliminated by a passive gain element, a transformer. The evolution from this circuit to the practical ones is shown in Fig. 1.

Stability Considerations

The most serious factor limiting the applicability of any positive feedback circuit is the stability. Ginzton[4] described a two-tube circuit; a more general derivation follows:

Consider the circuit shown in Fig. 1F in schematic form. Note that in the special case where $C_1 = \infty$ and $A' > 1$, this circuit reduces to the type of system considered by Gizton, while when $C_1 \neq \infty$, $A' < 1$, it represents the new circuit of Fig. 1E.

The gain of any feedback amplifier can be represented by the equation

$$A' = \frac{K}{1 - \beta K} \qquad (6)$$

In the present case, the gain of primary interest is not that of the tube itself, but rather that from points X-X (Fig. 1F) to the tube grid and through to the output at the cathode. This gain is the product of the active gain A' and what might be called the passive

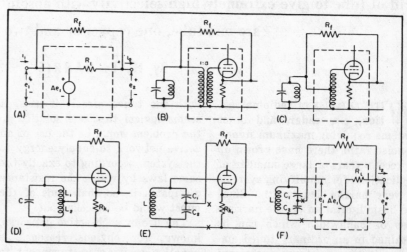

FIG. 1—Simplified circuits showing evolution of single-tube Q multiplier

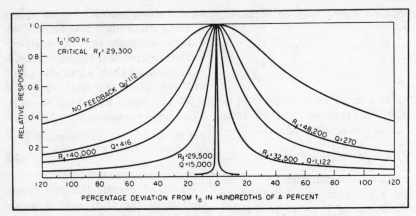

FIG. 2—Curves show selectivity obtainable with Q multiplier. Higher Q values were not tested because of measurement equipment limitations

gain a, or gain contributed by the tapped tuned circuit

$$A = \frac{aK}{1 - \beta K} \qquad (7)$$

where

$$a = \frac{C_2 + C_1}{C_1} \qquad (8)$$

At this point the assumption is made that the output impedance of the amplifier is negligible with respect to the feedback resistor R_f. This is reasonable for an amplifier stabilized with a high degree of negative feedback. Equation 5 for the negative resistance developed across terminals X-X then reduces to

$$-R_n = -\frac{R_f}{A - 1} \qquad (9)$$

or, substituting from Eq. 7 for the actual gain of the circuit

$$-R_n = -\frac{R_f (1 - \beta K)}{a K - 1 + \beta K} \qquad (10)$$

Passing over the details of the derivation, it may be said that this equation is now differentiated partially with respect to the no-feedback gain K, simplified, and rearranged to yield an equation relating the fractional change in the negative resistance produced to the fractional change in the no-feedback gain. That is, an equation of the form

$$\frac{\delta R_n}{R_n} = \frac{1}{k} \quad \frac{\delta K}{K} \qquad (11)$$

where the factor k might be called the stability coefficient of the sys-

tem. In this case the stability coefficient is

$$k = \frac{(1 - \beta K)\,[(a + \beta)\,K - 1]}{a K} \qquad (12)$$

It is apparent that one would like to make the magnitude of this stability coefficient as large as possible. The maximum possible value is found by differentiating again with respect to a convenient parameter —in this case β—and setting the derivative equal to zero. The optimum value of β turns out to be

$$\beta_{opt} = -\left[\frac{a}{2} - \frac{1}{K}\right] \qquad (13)$$

The corresponding value of the stability coefficient is

$$k_{opt} = -\frac{a K}{4} \qquad (14)$$

It is now a simple matter to determine the optimum operating conditions for the circuit

$$\beta_{opt} = -1 \qquad (15)$$

$$k_{opt} = -K/2 \qquad (16)$$

The stability of the negative resistance is merely incidental to the matter of prime concern—the stability of the effective Q. The above results can be related to the Q stability by beginning with Eq. 3 and employing much the same process of differentiating (this time with respect to R_n) and simplifying as in Eq. 10. The result is

$$\frac{\delta Q_{eff}}{Q_{eff}} = -\left[\frac{Q_{eff}}{Q_0} - 1\right] \frac{\delta R_n}{R_n} \qquad (17)$$

Or, combining the two equations

$$\frac{\delta Q_{eff}}{Q_{eff}} = \left[\frac{Q_{eff}}{Q_0} - 1\right] \frac{2}{K} \frac{\delta K}{K} \qquad (18)$$

A number of interesting, facts are apparent from this expression: (1) The stability is independent of the absolute value of initial Q. It is then just as easy to multiply Q from 100 to 1,000 as from 10 to 100. Thus it is important to begin with as high a Q as possible to gain maximum stability. (2) The stability is independent of the frequency, so that the circuit can be used to multiply Q anywhere in the spectrum where the stated assumptions can be met. (3) The higher the Q multiplication, the lower is the stability. For high multiplications this is approximately an inverse relation. (4) The stability increases in direct proportion to the no-feedback gain.

Another Stability Criterion

It seems logical to set up as an important design criterion of a narrow-band amplifier circuit, the amount of change in the no-feedback gain—that is, the change in the g_m with electrode voltage changes, aging, and other possible circuit variations—which can be tolerated without causing the system to break into oscillation.

As a starting point, consider again Eq. 3 for the Q multiplication, and solve this equation for R_n

$$R_n = R \frac{\dfrac{Q_{eff}}{Q_0}}{\dfrac{Q_{eff}}{Q_0} - 1} \qquad (19)$$

From Eq. 3 it is apparent that the point at which oscillations begin will be that point where R_n becomes equal to R. Therefore if R is subtracted from the above expression for R_n, the result will be the absolute value of the change in R_n which can be tolerated without causing oscillations. This can then be divided by R_n, to yield the fractional change in R_n which can be tolerated

$$\left(\frac{\Delta R_n}{R_n}\right)_{tolerable} = \frac{R \dfrac{1}{\dfrac{Q_{eff}}{Q_0} - 1}}{R_n} \qquad (20)$$

or, making use of Eq. 19 again

$$\left(\frac{\Delta R_n}{R_n}\right)_{tolerable} = \frac{Q_0}{Q_{eff}} \qquad (21)$$

But here again the negative resistance is merely a derived characteristic of the circuit. What is really wanted is the permissible change in the no-feedback gain K. It is apparent from the optimum operating conditions which were derived, and from Eq. 10 that the negative resistance can be represented as

$$R_n = R_f \left(\frac{K+1}{K-1} \right) \qquad (22)$$

Then if R_{n1} represents the value of the negative resistance at some particular chosen operating point of the circuit and R_{nc} the critical value of negative resistance at which oscillations occur, Eq. 21 above can be rewritten

$$\left(\frac{\Delta R_n}{R_n} \right)_{tolerable} = \frac{R_{n1} - R_{nc}}{R_{n1}} = \frac{Q_0}{Q_{eff}} \qquad (23)$$

Substituting from Eq. 22 and simplifying, this becomes

$$\frac{R_{n1} - R_{nc}}{R_{n1}} = \frac{2 (K_c - K_1)}{K_1 K_c - K_1 + K_c - 1} \qquad (24)$$

where K_1 is the no-feedback gain at the particular operating point chosen above, and K_c is the no-feedback gain at the critical point.

Now let $K_c = K_1 + \Delta K$. Then

$$\frac{R_{n1} - R_{nc}}{R_{n1}} = \frac{2 \Delta K}{K_1^2 + K_1 \Delta K + \Delta K - 1} \qquad (25)$$

which, by Eq. 21 is equal to $\frac{Q_0}{Q_{eff}}$.

Equating and solving for ΔK gives:

$$\Delta K = \frac{K_1^2 - 1}{\frac{2 Q_{eff}}{Q_0} - (K_1 + 1)} \qquad (26)$$

If this equation is now divided by K_1 the result is the fractional change in no-feedback gain K ($=g_m R_k$) which can be tolerated without oscillations

$$\left(\frac{\Delta K}{K} \right)_{tol} = \frac{1 - \frac{1}{K^2}}{\frac{1}{K} \left(2 \frac{Q_{eff}}{Q_0} - 1 \right) - 1} \qquad (27)$$

In practice, K is almost always kept much larger than 1, and the Q multiplication much larger than a half, so that a somewhat simpler working formula may be obtained:

$$\left(\frac{\Delta K}{K} \right)_{tol} \approx \frac{1}{\dfrac{\dfrac{Q_{eff}}{Q_0}}{\dfrac{K}{2}} - 1} \qquad (28)$$

This is a most interesting expression. For suppose that at some particular operating point a

$$\left. \frac{Q_{eff}}{Q_0} \right|_a = \left. \frac{K}{2} \right|_a \qquad (29)$$

The above equation then goes to infinity, signifying an infinite change in K necessary to cause oscillation. Further, suppose that

$$\left. \frac{Q_{eff}}{Q_0} \right|_a < \left. \frac{K}{2} \right|_a \qquad (30)$$

Then the fractional change in K necessary to cause oscillations is a negative number greater than 1. But this would require a negative gain, which, of course, is impossible in a vacuum-tube amplifier. It can be concluded, therefore, that if at any operating point, the condition

$$\left. \frac{Q_{eff}}{Q_0} \right|_a \lessgtr \left. \frac{K}{2} \right|_a \qquad (31)$$

is met, or, in other words if the circuit constants are adjusted so that the no-feedback gain K ($=g_m R_k$) is always greater than twice the degree of Q multiplication which is desired, there will be no chance of the circuit breaking into oscillation no matter how much the g_m of the tube may change with aging, changes in electrode voltages, shock and so on.

Here, then, is the fundamental contribution of this new circuit. Without any substantial increase in the complexity over the ordinary regenerative system, it has made possible attainment of arbitrarily high Q multiplications, while at the same time retaining the absolute stability of the ordinary amplifier.

Practical Circuit

It is not possible to set down any hard and fast rule as to the magnitude of the $g_m R_k$ product which may be obtained. Experience has shown, however, that with a 6AK5 and a supply voltage of 200 volts, values of about 100 are easily attainable. With higher supply voltages, correspondingly higher values of the $g_m R_k$ product may be realized.

Now suppose that a relatively modest degree of Q multiplication—say 10—is all that is wanted. (This still will allow Q's of the order of 2,000 to 3,000 if a good coil is used). The above equations then become

$$\left(\begin{array}{c} \% \text{ change in} \\ Q_{eff} \end{array} \right) = \frac{1}{5.5} \left(\begin{array}{c} \% \text{ change in} \\ g_m \end{array} \right) \qquad (32)$$

Oscillation impossible

In other words, the percentage change in the Q is only approximately a sixth of the percentage change in the g_m which caused it, and it will be impossible to cause the circuit to oscillate no matter how much the g_m may change with shifts in plate voltage and other circuit parameters.

Even for the relatively high Q multiplication of 100, which would correspond to possible Q's of the order of 30,000, stability is excellent.

$$(\% \text{ change in } Q_{eff}) = 2 (\% \text{ change in } g_m) \qquad (33)$$

100% change in g_m to cause oscillation

This is still well within the practical range of operation, if a power supply of any reasonable regulation is used.

Experimental Results

The curves of Fig. 2 show the results obtainable from a typical circuit of this new type. These curves were taken by applying a variable-frequency, constant-voltage signal to the Q multiplier circuit through an isolating stage and measuring the output voltage as a function of the frequency. The no-feedback curve is a plot of output voltage versus frequency when the feedback circuit was opened, or when $R_f = \infty$ and the circuit was operating as an ordinary cathode follower. The other curves show the effect of reducing the feedback resistor closer and closer to the critical value of 29,300 ohms. The maximum Q value of 15,000 shown was by no means the limit obtainable with the circuit. There was simply no measuring equipment available precise enough to allow a reliable set of data to be taken for higher Q's.

Theory indicates that the shape of the response curve should be un-altered by the Q multiplication. This was checked by plotting data taken for several values of multi-plication on the same graph as the universal resonance curve. In every case the results were identical. This means that these circuits may profitably be cascaded or staggered, using the identical means of calcu-lation as for ordinary resonant circuits.

Experiments have verified the two stability relations. In both cases, the stability turned out to be slightly higher than predicted.

Practical Suggestions

For the convenience of the de-signer, it might be well here to sum-marize a few practical hints which have been discovered in the course of working with this circuit. First of all, for reference, the actual cir-

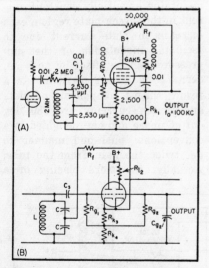

FIG. 3—Practical circuits of single-tube Q multiplier. In B the first triode section serves as the Q multiplier and the sec-ond as a grounded-grid amplifier

cuit used for the preceding experi-mental measurements is reproduced in Fig. 3A.

The exact critical value of the resistance R_f is easily found from Eq. 3. Remembering that the nega-tive resistance is developed across only half of the tuned circuit in this system, Eq. 3 actually becomes:

$$\frac{Q_{eff}}{Q_0} = \frac{R_n}{R_n - R/4} \qquad (34)$$

But R_n is given by Eq. 22. Substi-tuting and regrouping gives

$$\frac{Q_{eff}}{Q_0} = \frac{1}{1 - \dfrac{R/4}{R_f}\dfrac{(K-1)}{(K+1)}} \qquad (35)$$

from which it is apparent that the critical resistance is

$$R_f = \frac{R}{4}\frac{(K-1)}{(K+1)} \qquad (36)$$

For design purposes this value can be taken simply as one-fourth of the tuned circuit impedance. If the circuit is operating properly, oscillations will ensue for all values of R_f less than this value. For $R_f = \infty$ the circuit operates as a cathode follower, and as R_f de-creases toward the critical value, the Q multiplication increases with-out limit.

The actual R_k to be used in com-puting the $g_m R_k$ product is the cathode resistor R_{k1} in parallel with the series combination of R_f and one-fourth of the impedance of the tuned circuit—that is, approxi-mately the cathode resistor in par-allel with one-half the tuned circuit impedance in the multiplier.

The grid biasing connection shown in Fig. 3A is used for the purpose of increasing the $g_m R_k$ product, and hence the stability. Using this arrangement, a large cathode resistor can be used with-out increasing the grid bias exces-sively and thus reducing g_m.

Somewhat higher stabilities are obtained by using pentode as in Fig. 3A, instead of the triode dis-cussed previously. The screen should be by-passed to the cathode.

Otherwise the tube will operate as a triode. If only moderate multi-plications are needed, however, the double triode circuit shown in Fig. 3B may be found useful. Here the first section is used as a Q multi-plier, and the second as a grounded-grid amplifier.

The source impedance should be kept high, either by the use of a series resistor as in Fig. 3A, or by designing the preceding stage for a high output impedance. If high Q multiplications are sought, the ser-ies resistor is preferable, in con-junction with a low output imped-ance for the previous stage.

The phase shift must be kept to a minimum to avoid frequency shift as the Q multiplication is changed.

When the split inductor variation of Fig. 1D is used, the cathode re-sistor R_{k1} may be omitted. This allows about a 2-to-1 increase in stability.

The signal input should be kept relatively low for best results. Ex-perience with the type 6AK5 has shown that inputs much more than a volt or two result in reduced effective Q multiplication due to curvature of the tube characteristic.

It is possible to raise the Q of a coil alone by use of the circuit in Fig. 1D with the capacitor omitted. Use in such a manner suggests a number of additional applications for the circuit.

REFERENCES

(1) F. M. Colebrook, Voltage Amplifi-cation with High Selectivity by Means of the Dynatron Circuit, *Wireless Engineer*, 10, p 69, Feb. 1933.
(2) E. W. Herold, Negative Resistance and Devices for Obtaining It, *Proc. IRE*, 23, p 1,201, Oct. 1935.
(3) F. E. Terman, R. R. Buss, W. R. Hewlett and F. C. Cahill, Some Applica-tions of Negative Feedback with Particu-lar Reference to Laboratory Equipment, *Proc. IRE*, 27, p 649, Oct. 1939.
(4) E. R. Ginzton, Stabilized Negative Impedances, ELECTRONICS, Part I, 18, p 140, Jul. 1945; Part II, 18, p 138, Aug. 1945; and Part III, 18, p 140, Sept. 1945.

Gain-Doubling Frequency Converters

Theory and experimental results for a method of obtaining twice the normal conversion transconductance from pentode mixers. Signal is applied to an inner grid, and No. 3 grid is used in an outer space-current local oscillator. Practical converter circuits for narrow-band broadcast receivers and wide-band f-m receivers are given

By VERNON H. ASKE

IN THE USUAL frequency mixer tube the conversion transconductance is approximately g_m/π, where g_m is the maximum signal grid-to-plate transconductance during the excursion of an oscillator cycle. The possibility of obtaining a conversion transconductance equal to $2g_m/\pi$ was first pointed out by E. W. Herold[1]. In effect, his method involves changing the phase of the signal current 180 deg at the local oscillator frequency rate, using a beam-deflection tube or one having multihumped characteristics. The method to be described here achieves the same gain-doubling result more simply with a pentode mixer.

Analysis

The conversion transconductance g_c of a mixer tube, when considering a small signal modulating a relatively large local oscillator signal of radian frequency ω, is

$$g_c = \frac{1}{2\pi}\int_{-\pi}^{+\pi} g_m \cos \omega t \, d(\omega t) \qquad (1)$$

Solution of this equation does not give maximum conversion transconductance because the negative portion of the cycle subtracts from the positive portion. However, if the integral is observed from $\pi/2$ to $-\pi/2$ only, we obtain g_m/π as the maximum positive limit for conversion transconductance with conventional mixing. These limits are achieved in a triode mixer by imposing sufficient oscillator voltage on the No. 1 grid to cut off the tube during the negative portion of the oscillator cycle. In conventional pentode mixing with the oscillator signal on an outer grid, the same limits are obtained by diverting the space current to an inner grid of the tube during the negative portion of the local oscillator cycle. The goal, however, is to double this transconductance value.

With conventional triode and pentode mixing, the i-f signal is obtained from a tube element that is cut off for half of the tube-operating period. If by some means the sign of the integral of Eq. 1 could be changed for this cut-off half of the oscillator cycle, then the conversion transconductance would be doubled.

Consider a pentode mixer in which the incoming carrier signal is applied to the No. 1 grid and the local oscillator to the suppressor (No. 3) grid. Since a pentode maintains essentially constant current in the screen-plate region, each increase in plate current due to oscillator modulation of the suppressor must be offset by an equal decrease in screen current. As a result, the i-f components of plate and screen currents are 180 deg out of phase and can be added in a conventional push-pull manner to get twice the gain from the tube. Actually, the mere placing of a

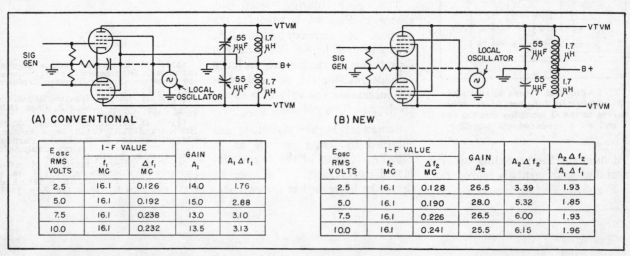

E_{osc} RMS VOLTS	I-F VALUE		GAIN A_1	$A_1 \Delta f_1$
	f_1 MC	Δf_1 MC		
2.5	16.1	0.126	14.0	1.76
5.0	16.1	0.192	15.0	2.88
7.5	16.1	0.238	13.0	3.10
10.0	16.1	0.232	13.5	3.13

(A) CONVENTIONAL

E_{osc} RMS VOLTS	I-F VALUE		GAIN A_2	$A_2 \Delta f_2$	$\dfrac{A_2 \Delta f_2}{A_1 \Delta f_1}$
	f_2 MC	Δf_2 MC			
2.5	16.1	0.128	26.5	3.39	1.93
5.0	16.1	0.190	28.0	5.32	1.85
7.5	16.1	0.226	26.5	6.00	1.93
10.0	16.1	0.241	25.5	6.15	1.96

(B) NEW

FIG. 1—Comparison of conventional balanced push-pull pentode mixer with improved method that places tuned circuit between screen and plate of each tube. Values of components are not necessarily the most desirable for the frequency and bandwidth used

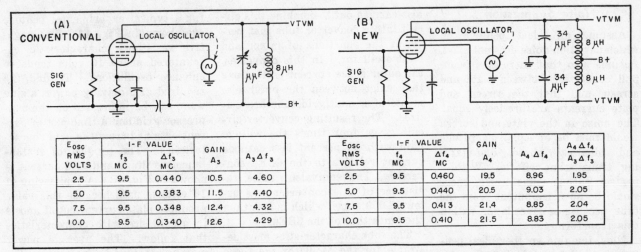

FIG. 2—Comparison of conventional single-tube pentode mixer circuit with improved method that eliminates screen bypass capacitor so tuned circuit is between screen and plate. Values of corresponding inductances and capacitances should be equal as indicated

E_{OSC} RMS VOLTS	I-F VALUE		GAIN A_3	$A_3 \Delta f_3$
	f_3 MC	Δf_3 MC		
2.5	9.5	0.440	10.5	4.60
5.0	9.5	0.383	11.5	4.40
7.5	9.5	0.348	12.4	4.32
10.0	9.5	0.340	12.6	4.29

E_{OSC} RMS VOLTS	I-F VALUE		GAIN A_4	$A_4 \Delta f_4$	$\dfrac{A_4 \Delta f_4}{A_3 \Delta f_3}$
	f_4 MC	Δf_4 MC			
2.5	9.5	0.460	19.5	8.96	1.95
5.0	9.5	0.440	20.5	9.03	2.05
7.5	9.5	0.413	21.4	8.85	2.04
10.0	9.5	0.410	21.5	8.83	2.05

tuned circuit between the plate and screen changes the sign of the integral in Eq. 1 for half of each cycle to give the desired doubling of conversion transconductance.

Verification

Experimental verification of gain doubling with this frequency-mixing process is given in Fig. 1 and 2. Performance of a conventional balanced type mixer is presented in Fig. 1A and results for the new circuit, using the same tubes under the same d-c operating conditions, are in Fig. 1B. The tubes were developmental types with many-turns-per-inch suppressor grids. The oscillator voltage is used as a variable.

Since the voltage gain is inversely proportional to Δf and the two vary with oscillator voltage, the product of these two terms serves as a convenient means of comparison between the two systems. The last column of the tabulation in Fig. 1B indicates the ratio of $A_2 \Delta f_2$ for the new system to $A_1 \Delta f_1$ for the conventional system. These values center about a ratio of 2 to 1, which is predicted from the theory.

As a further check and comparison, the new frequency-conversion method was compared with the conventional method when using a single tube. Data for a conventional single-ended mixer circuit is

given in Fig. 2A, and corresponding data for the new circuit in Fig. 2B. The ratios are again approximately 2 to 1.

The foregoing data were obtained with the suppressor grid operating at zero d-c bias rather than the grid-leak bias that is usually employed. Operating the grid

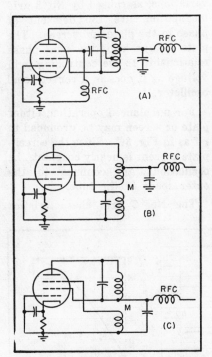

FIG. 3—Balanced and unbalanced oscillator circuits employing new gain-doubling technique

at zero bias results in a much

greater peak g_m and thereby increases conversion transconductance. If sufficient oscillator voltage is impressed, the plate current is swung into saturation and g_c approaches the ideal value of approximately 32 percent of the peak g_m.

Isolation

Another interesting aspect of the circuit is the isolation it offers to signals that tend to pass through the mixer tube at the intermediate frequency. Isolation exists, since any signal on the No. 1 grid produces modulation of the same phase on the screen and plate currents, and will cancel out in the push-pull i-f transformer. This action makes it somewhat difficult to align the i-f by the usual manner of placing the i-f signal on the signal grid of the mixer tube. In this case the signal can better be placed on the oscillator grid. The degree of isolation is determined by the degree of balance in the primary of the i-f transformer and by the transconductance from signal grid-to-plate relative to the transconductance of signal grid-to-screen.

In a pentode we are mainly concerned with shot-effect noise and partition noise. The former is due to time-varying emission from the cathode, and the latter is due to random distribution of cathode current to the positive electrodes in the tube.

Noise Suppression

Assume an ideal pentode in which partition noise does not exist. Assume also that there is a push-pull connection between plate and screen, and that the screen and plate currents are precisely equal. The noise in the plate and screen would then be of equal magnitude and identical phase, disregarding transit-time effects. With a perfect output transformer, there would be no noise output from the tube, because of cancellation within this transformer.

Now, imagine another ideal pentode in which no shot-effect noise exists, but in which partition noise does exist. In this tube any noise variation that takes place in the plate circuit must be accompanied by an equal and opposite noise variation in the screen circuit, since space current is perfectly constant. Thus, if this push-pull connection has in some way doubled the effective transconductance, the equivalent noise resistance of the tube has not changed since the effective noise has also been doubled.

The pentode mixer circuit presented here is actually the combination of these two ideal cases. It therefore has somewhat smaller equivalent noise resistance in the circuit than does a conventional mixer, since the shot-effect noise has decreased while the affect of partition noise remains unchanged.

Converter Tube

In conjunction with this work on the mixer circuit, a program was also carried out to combine this circuit into a converter tube that performs the functions of mixer and local oscillator. In this converter, the outer space current oscillations that exist between the outer elements of a multigrid tube are utilized. The resulting converter circuit gives four times the voltage gain with 30 percent less cathode current relative to the 6BE6 converter. The equivalent noise resistance of this converter was below 18,000 ohms, which is less than one-tenth that of the 6BE6.

The tube characteristics most desirable for the oscillator are those of a pentode whose No. 3 grid-to-plate transconductance is relatively high. This No. 3 grid is used as the control grid, and the plate or screen as the oscillator anode.

The oscillator may be either the balanced or unbalanced type. In the balanced oscillator, shown in Fig. 3A and 3B, the plate-screen coil is center-tapped to r-f ground. This oscillator is suited to a balanced-type circuit since the current variations, as caused by No. 3 grid modulation, are 180 deg out of phase in the plate and screen. The plate voltage holds the same phase relationship to the controlling grid voltage as it does in a conventional oscillator.

For unbalanced operation, either plate or screen may be grounded to r-f as in Fig. 3C. Since the screen-plate current is nearly constant, the oscillations are confined to the outer space of the tube.

The No. 3 grid characteristics for a typical experimental pentode are shown in Fig. 4A. The negative resistance characteristic encountered above 10 volts tends to enhance oscillations. To find the required grid-driving power, a sine wave can be impressed on the suppressor grid and a time plot of current obtained from the grid characteristics. The product of instantaneous voltage and grid current is shown in Fig. 4B. A peak swing of 10 volts is used because this value produces plate current cutoff and is in accordance with characteristics that follow. The average power may be obtained by integrating the instantaneous power curve. The resulting average power is three milliwatts, which is very low and normally will be less than the associated circuit losses.

Converter Design

It is possible to calculate the tickler coil impedance required for a particular application. Suppose an oscillator is to be built at 20 mc in which a tickler coil is placed in the plate circuit to excite a tuned circuit connected to the No. 3 grid, and a total driving power of 15 milliwatts is required. The available exciting power is proportional to the external voltage drop, or in this case the reactive drop across the tickler coil. Then $P_{exciting} = I_{eff}^2 \omega L = 15 \times 10^{-3}$. The effective plate current for the development tubes used is approximately 4 ma. The required tickler coil impedance is then $\omega L = 15 \times 10^{-3}/(4 \times 10^{-3})^2 = 938$ ohms.

These outer space current oscillations may readily be obtained from a pentode as used in Fig. 5 and 6, and the application of a signal to the No. 1 grid will result in a simplified converter. In each circuit, a tickler coil is placed in series with the i-f transformer primary to provide feedback to the No. 3 grid, which is tuned to the local oscillator frequency. In Fig. 5 the screen is grounded for r-f. Figure 6 represents a similar circuit in which the i-f is connected in push-pull between the screen and plate,

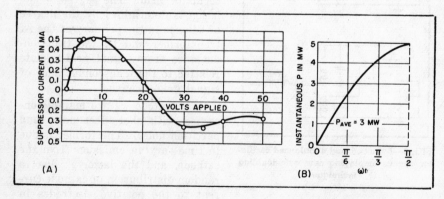

FIG. 4—Characteristic curves for No. 3 grid of typical experimental pentode

and results in increased conversion transconductance.[1] The circuit of Fig. 5 is most useful in narrow-band applications, since the plate resistance in converter use is much larger than the effective plate-screen resistance. Conversely, Fig. 6 is more applicable to wide-band circuits.

The above circuits are operated with zero d-c bias on the suppressor grid. This type of operation is desirable since greater conversion transconductance will result owing to the larger peak plate current. A grid-leak bias on the grid of the oscillator is not necessary with the outer space current oscillator, as it would have little effect on the average current.

It is desirable that the peak swing be sufficient to produce plate-current saturation during the positive excursion of the local-oscillator cycle, and plate-current cutoff during most of its negative excursion, since these are the desired characteristics for maximum conversion transconductance.

Comparisons

The most important characteristics of a converter-type tube are probably (1) conversion transconductance, (2) plate resistance, (3) noise, (4) isolation between signal and oscillator circuits, which is indicative of antenna radiation, (5) voltage gain as a function of wide-range tuning, and (6) automatic volume control, which indicates the cutoff characteristics of a particular tube and any undesirable detuning effects. These characteristics will be discussed in connection with a comparison of the new high-gain pentode converter circuit of **Fig. 5** and a conventional 6BE6 frequency converter for the same narrow-band application (550 to 1,600 kc).

Before making comparative measurements, the oscillator voltage on the No. 3 grid was measured as a function of tuning. The oscillator voltage varied from 19 volts at 1,006 kc (the low end of the oscillator range) to 66 volts rms at the top frequency of 2,056 kc. This wide range of oscillator voltage is undesirable from the viewpoint of oscillator radiation, hence a series R-C circuit was used to load the oscillator. Values of 10,000 ohms and 6.8 μμf discriminate against the higher frequencies as desired to keep the range of oscillator voltage between 11 to 19 volts rms, which is within the practical limits of most converters.

Comparative sensitivity values are given in Fig. 5. With the experimental type pentode, the components were tuned for each individual measurement. The voltage gain was measured from the signal-generator terminals to the secondary of the i-f transformer. The i-f transformer used was designed as an output transformer, and consequently had closer coupling than that usually found in input i-f transformers. With the conventional circuit, plate and screen voltages were 100 volts, and the signal grid was biased to −1.5 volts. The circuit was optimized for voltage gain.

The comparative data shows that greater than twice the voltage gain can be obtained with the pentode with 30 percent less cathode current. The increased voltage gain results from the increased conversion transconductance.

The conversion transconductance of the experimental pentode was approximately 1,200 μmhos. This conversion transconductance is easily determined for this type of operation by measuring the g_m of the signal grid with +10 volts on the suppressor grid, and taking 30 percent of this g_m value as the conversion transconductance. This is accurate to within a few percent.

The effective mixer plate resistance for the new type of operation is approximately three times the value measured for the tube as an amplifier. This value was 350,000 ohms for the development tubes used, as contrasted with 1 megohm for the 6BE6. The conversion transconductance of the 6BE6 is 475 μmhos.

Oscillator Radiation

Radiation back to the antenna from a converter tube depends on the capacitance and space charge coupling between the oscillator grid and the signal grid. In the circuit of Fig. 5, oscillator currents are confined to the outer space of the tube so there is little or no space-charge coupling. The capacitance from the signal grid to oscillator grid of the tube under these conditions is approximately 0.10 μμf, while the corresponding capacitance for the 6BE6 is 0.15 μμf. The relative coupling values from the oscillator to the signal grid at signal frequencies of 550, 1,000 and 1,550 kc are 0.01, 0.07 and 0.13 re-

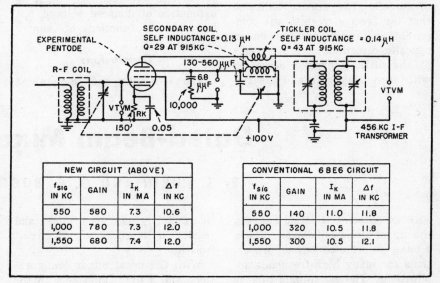

NEW CIRCUIT (ABOVE)			
f_SIG IN KC	GAIN	I_K IN MA	Δf IN KC
550	580	7.3	10.6
1,000	780	7.3	12.0
1,550	680	7.4	12.0

CONVENTIONAL 6BE6 CIRCUIT			
f_SIG IN KC	GAIN	I_K IN MA	Δf IN KC
550	140	11.0	11.8
1,000	320	10.5	11.8
1,550	300	10.5	12.1

FIG. 5—Narrow-band version of new converter circuit, suitable for broadcast band, and comparative performance data on conventional circuit

spectively for the 6BE6 and 0.01, 0.05 and 0.21 for the pentode.

The space-charge coupling within the tube acts with a 180-deg phase shift relative to the direct capacitive coupling voltage. In most converters, these effects are controlled so that they are approximately equal on the broadcast band. This is the reason that the coupled voltage is slightly less with the type 6BE6 in spite of the fact that its capacitance and space-charge coupling are greater.

AVC Action

The action of an avc voltage on the signal grid of the experimental pentode changes the oscillator amplitude as well as the signal-grid g_m. This gives accentuated avc action, and may require a very remote cutoff characteristic for proper operation. Since extensive bias will ultimately result in a reduction of oscillator grid g_m to the point where oscillations will cease, extended avc application (1,000 to 1 reduction of gain) is not possible in this new converter.

In conjunction with avc, it is important to consider the amount of frequency shift that results from its application. To obtain this relative measurement, the gain of the two systems was decreased by the same ratio, and the frequency shift of the oscillator section was measured. The results indicated that the frequency shift was comparable in the two systems, but in opposite directions; the frequency of the 6BE6 converter decreased with decreasing gain and the fre-

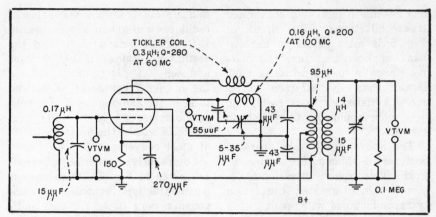

FIG. 6—Wide-band version of new converter circuit

quency of the new converter increased with decreasing gain.

F-M Converter Circuit

Modifications needed in the new converter circuit to meet the requirements of the f-m band are given in Fig. 6. The relatively wide bandwidth permits the use of a push-pull i-f and derives increased gain. At 100 mc the voltage gain from the grid through a double-tuned i-f transformer is 27.5. (The calculated gain of the 6BE6 under similar conditions is one-fourth this value.) The center of the i-f band is 10.7 mc and the bandwidth at the half-power points is 350 kc. The frequency drift of this oscillator circuit was compared with that of a triode in a Hartley circuit and found to be nearly equal. The converter had less frequency shift as a function of filament voltage, but more as a function of supply voltage.

Conclusions

Increased gain can be obtained by using a pentode tube as a converter, with the signal applied to an inner grid and the No. 3 grid used as an outer space current local oscillator. Four times the gain of the type 6BE6 may be obtained by using this less complicated tube, with 30 percent less cathode current. Simple tube construction, high conversion transconductance and low noise characterize this converter. The Sylvania type 5636 and SN1007B tubes are suitable for this application.

The author acknowledges the valuable assistance of B. F. Tyson and James Cooper who supplied measurements that confirmed the theory outlined here and John B. Grund of Sylvania's Emporium division, whose measurements in practical circuits contributed greatly to this project.

REFERENCES

(1) E. W. Herold, Superheterodyne Frequency Conversion Using Phase-Reversal Modulation, *Proc. IRE*, p 184P, April 1946.
(2) E. W. Herold, Superheterodyne Converter System Considerations in Television Receivers, *RCA Review*, p 324, Jan. 1940.

Gated-Beam Mixer

By S. RUBIN AND G. E. BOGGS

THE PROBLEM of isolation between the signal and oscillator circuits in a mixer is often of serious proportions for many high-frequency applications. The gated-beam tube as exemplified by the 6BN6 may be

satisfactorily used as a mixer and results in improved signal circuit isolation.

With the usual mixer configurations and a high impedance in the signal grid circuit, a voltage of os-

cillator frequency on the signal grid may well cause grid-current flow. This will of course alter the tube characteristics. In addition, the oscillator voltage present in the signal circuit may assist in the switching or modulating of the tube and may change the shape of the switching function. If the signal circuit is returned through the avc bus, the oscillator voltage appearing on the signal grid may bias this grid thus reducing the conversion transconductance.

In practice the problems arising from poor isolation between the signal and oscillator circuits are frequently met by maintaining a low impedance in the signal grid circuit. Unfortunately, this is a poor solution, since it may drastically reduce the gain ahead of the mixer.

In tubes where the signal is injected on one grid and the oscillator on another, the coupling between grids is made up of two components, capacitance between the signal and oscillator grid and space-charge coupling. Tubes utilizing the inner grid for oscillator injection have relatively large space-charge coupling at high frequencies and hence are not suitable for applications where good isolation is imperative.

Outer-Grid Mixer

When the signal is applied to the first grid and the oscillator to an outer-grid the combination has come to be known as an outer-grid mixer. This arrangement exhibits a space-charge coupling effect of only $\frac{1}{5}$ to $\frac{1}{10}$ of that present with tubes employing inner-grid injection.[1] It should be noted that with an outer-grid mixer, the voltage induced on the signal grid, due to space-charge coupling between the two grids, adds to the oscillator voltage on the signal grid which is due to capacitive coupling. This is opposite to the effect when using inner-grid injection.

Since the 6BN6 has two rather high transconductance control grids it may be employed as either inner-grid or outer-grid mixer. Maximum isolation is obtained when the tube is used as an outer-grid mixer with the oscillator injected on the third grid. This grid fortunately will not develop a high bias since the grid current is limited by tube design.

The grid-current limiting feature of this tube results in very low os-

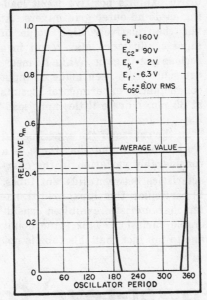

FIG. 1—Switching function characteristic for 6BN6

cillator power requirement and it is found that six to ten volts rms provides adequate oscillator excitation.

A typical switching function for the 6BN6 is shown in Fig. 1. The tube has about a 10-percent improvement in conversion efficiency compared to the 6SA7.

Transconductance

Since grid current in the 6BN6 is limited by the design of the tube, the bias voltage built up on the oscillator grid is very small, resulting in a higher value of peak transconductance. With low bias voltage on the oscillator grid, the magnitude of the grid resistor is not critical within limits. Also, the g_c is practically constant with changing oscillator excitation voltage after a threshold value has been reached, which in this case is about 8 volts.

At 30 mc, with 120 v on the plate and 70 v on the accelerator, the conversion transconductance was lower than anticipated. The low g_c is attributed largely to transit time since raising the plate and accelerator voltages to 155 and 90 v respectively increased the conversion transconductance to 790 μmhos. With a high-impedance input to the signal grid, some loading of the in-

put circuit was observed, as would be expected with outer grid injection. While no input admittance measurements have been made, it would be reasonable to assume that good performance can be obtained with this tube in the lower vhf range.

A typical circuit used during the course of this experimental work is shown in Fig. 2. No special precautions were found necessary, but a metal shield across the tube socket between pins 4 and 5 and pins 1 and 7 is recommended to maintain low capacitance between the two signal grids.

Since the 6BN6 may be employed as an outer-grid mixer, it may be assumed that the method described by Aske[2], where a tuned circuit is placed between the plate and screen, may be used to double the conversion transconductance. If desired the single tube may be used as a converter by using the number 3 grid in an outer space-current local oscillator.

It is interesting to note that

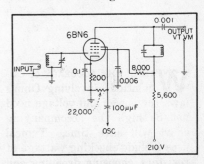

FIG. 2—Schematic diagram of the 6BN6 mixer

above a given supply voltage the conversion gain is essentially constant with increasing supply voltage. Thus in some applications it may be desirable to operate this tube at higher voltages than necessary in order to obtain good voltage stability.

If the 6BN6 is operated at very low voltages, the linearity will suffer. When grid voltages as high as one volt are necessary, the accelerator voltage should be rather high, in the order of 90 v.

Conclusion

The 6BN6 has been shown to

perform well in mixer service. It is one of the very few commercially available high-transconductance tubes for outer-grid injection. The greatest advantage obtained with this tube is the reduced space-charge coupling and low capacitance between control grids. This allows higher frequency operation with a fairly low value of i-f without resulting in excessive values of oscillator voltage appearing on the signal grid.

The tube has a conversion transconductance of approximately 800 μmhos with less cathode current than that taken by many existing pentagrid tubes. In addition the 6BN6 can probably be used in the

gain-doubling circuit of Aske[2] to further increase its utility. The 6BN6 exhibits positive input loading as do all outer grid mixers. At vhf the relatively high value of input conductance may result in a serious loss in gain. While no measurements have been made of input conductance, experimental results at 30 mc indicate little input loading.

In the course of the experimental work it was found that there is a considerable variation in the characteristics between different tubes. In particular, the signal-grid transfer characteristic exhibited considerable variation. This is no doubt due to the fact that this tube is not

tested for this type of service. It may, therefore, be suggested that the 6BN6 could be rated for mixer or converter service by the manufacturer and a portion of these tubes sold for this purpose.

While the 6BN6 makes a very satisfactory mixer for many applications, it is thought quite possible that a gated-beam tube could be developed which would have superior characteristics for mixer applications.

REFERENCES

(1) E. W. Herold, The Operation of Frequency Converters and Mixers for Superheterodyne Reception, *Proc. IRE*. **30**, p 84, Feb. 1942.
(2) V. H. Aske, Gain-Doubling Frequency Converters, ELECTRONICS, 2 , p 92, Jan. 1951.

Graphical Power-Level Computations

Chart relating current, voltage, resistance and power in watts or dbm simplifies numerical calculations. Given any two of these parameters, the other two can be found directly from the chart

By DANIEL C. NUTTING

WHERE THE ACCURACY of calculations involving Ohm's laws for power and voltage need not be high the accompanying chart will save time. Typical uses include checking wattage of resistors, choosing dropping and current-limiting resistors, and comparing power levels at points of different impedances in amplifiers and other circuits.

On the log-log chart the horizontal axis represents resistance and the vertical axis represents power. Superimposed on these coordinates is a similar set of log-log coordinates drawn at 45 deg with respect to the others. These latter coordinates represent current and voltage.

The chart solves equations of the form $wx = y$ and $xy = z$ (or $wx^2 = z$ and $y^2/w = z$).

Given any two parameters, the other two are located at the intersection of the indicated co-

ordinates. For example, if the measured potential across a 20,-000-ohm load resistance is 30 volts, the chart indicates that the load consumes 0.045 watt and draws 1.5 milliamperes.

The auxiliary scale on the right-hand margin of the chart gives the power in terms of decibels with reference to one milliwatt, as is customary in communication measurements.

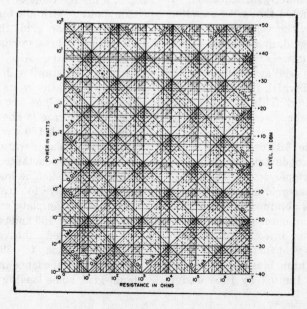

ANTENNAS

How to Select Antenna Towers

A knowledge of mechanical design principles is essential. This article summarizes general practice with respect to self-supported and guyed structures, materials, mounts and footings. Erection and maintenance, factors which affect the choice, are also covered

By WILLIAM SCHWARTZ

ELECTRONIC ENGINEERS are frequently called upon to select structural supports for antennas. Special design is occasionally necessary but in most instances standardized supports are indicated. In either case, selection is facilitated if the engineer has a general knowledge of mechanical design principles, installation and maintenance problems. It is such knowledge that

this paper is intended to summarize.

The maximum strain on most antenna supports is imposed in a horizontal direction by wind; ice coatings create additional gravity loads but their greatest imposition of stress is caused by the increment of area they add to the surface the structure presents to the wind.

The wind pressure on a structure

varies with the square of the wind velocity; calculations based on wind-tunnel data are given below:

Wind Velocity (mph)	Pressure (lb per sq ft)	
	Flat Surface	Round Surface
60	13.3	8.9
70	18.2	12.1
80	23.7	15.8
90	30.0	20.0
100	37.0	24.6
110	44.8	29.8
125	57.9	38.6

The profile or projected area is

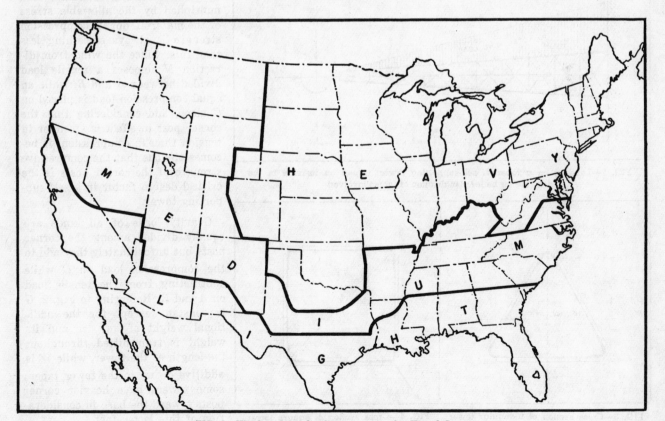

FIG. 1—Wind and ice loading zones in the United States

used for calculations of wind load.

Meteorological records and research have established maximum wind and ice conditions normally to be expected in various parts of the United States. Figure 1 delineates the various wind and ice loading zones. Conservative design practice anticipates the following loadings:

	Ice-Coating (in.)	Wind-Velocity (mph)
Light	0	60
Medium	0.25	70
Heavy	0.50	90

Ice loadings are expressed as radial thicknesses to be added to the projected area of members.

The loading map does not take into account unusual local conditions which may suggest design to a higher or lower wind velocity. In areas subject to hurricanes it is usually best to select towers rated at 90 miles per hour. Hurricanes involve winds having speeds of over 125 miles per hour, but only near the eye or center of the storm; velocities in the periphery are usually below 90 miles per hour. It is therefore sometimes cheaper to replace a damaged structure with a similar structure than to replace with one which would resist the rarely encountered forces which destroyed the original.

Masts and towers are generally rated in terms of pounds of horizontal top load at a given wind velocity, or wind velocity plus a given ice load. An additional figure is often given for the gravity load which may accompany the maximum horizontal load. Thus a tower with a capacity of 200 pounds at 90 mph can be loaded with $6\frac{2}{3}$ square feet of flat surface, 10 square feet of round members, or any combination totaling 200 pounds of wind resistance.

Self-Supporting Structures

Stress analysis of a self-supporting structure is complicated by the fact that it is loaded as a beam and as a column at the same time. Figure 2 shows the loading on a tapered tower; it is turned on its side for better visualization of forces. Shaded area P shows the total wind load on the support structure, usually expressed in pounds per square foot and here represented as increasing toward the base because of longer bracing members and heavier corner posts at the base. The letter T denotes wind load on the antenna, and G and W are the gravity loads of the antenna and tower structures respectively, plus the weight of any ice coating.

Assuming a tower of triangular cross section, the maximum compression load imposed on member C in Fig. 3 occurs when the wind is from direction N. A line parallel to AB and one third up from the base will be the gravity or neutral axis of the section; this line has no theoretical stress. With the wind from N, C is in compression and A and B in tension.

The corner post C is a column; its tensile strength is its net area multiplied by the allowable stress of the material, but its compression strength is always something less than this. Since the wind from direction N imposes a tensile load divided between A and B, while an equal compression load is placed on C alone, and considering that the corner post in effect is stronger in tension than in compression, it becomes obvious that the compressive strength of the corner posts is the critical design factor in a self-supporting tower.

Gravity loads of all kinds are equally divided among the corner posts but unfortunately they add to the compression load on C while subtracting from the tensile load on A and B. Referring to Fig. 2, G is constant except for the additional weight of any ice and its weight is transmitted throughout the length of the tower, while W is additive owing to the tower taper; some towers have heavier corner posts toward the base in consideration of this latter fact.

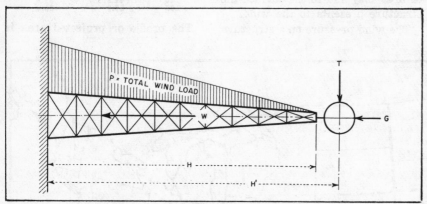

FIG. 2—Loading on a tapered, self-supporting tower, turned on its side in the drawing for better visualization of forces involved

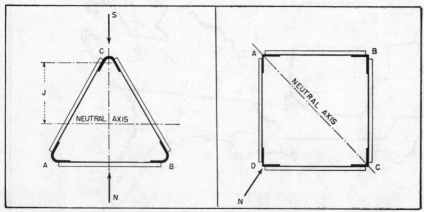

FIG. 3—Cross section of triangular tower   FIG. 4—Cross section of square tower

In the case of square towers P is uniform from top to base of the structure and W increases uniformly instead of geometrically. Maximum stresses occur in a section when the wind is from N as in Fig. 4. The neutral axis is a diagonal, B is in compression, D in tension, and A and C have very little stress.

Guyed Structures

The guyed structure is subject to a different set of stresses, as shown in Fig. 5. The strain taken by each guy is resolved into its horizontal and vertical components for purpose of stress analysis. The horizontal components H_a, H_b, and H_c are equal to the horizontal wind load on half of the sections adjacent to each guy point. The horizontal load on the antenna itself, I, is taken by H_c, and H, the bottom horizontal reaction, is merely half the wind load on the bottom section.

Referring to Fig. 6, $V = H \tan \phi$, and the greater ϕ becomes, corresponding to anchoring the guys closer to the base of the tower, the greater V will become for a given wind load reaction H. In effect, failure of a guyed structure results from wind load stressing the guys to the point where they pull the tower down. Good practice usually has the guys anchored from 70 to 100 percent of their height from the tower base, but some tubular masts, taking advantage of the lower wind resistance of round members, are designed to take the downward pull of guys anchored

closer. Since it is most economical to have all guys in a set anchored at one point, ϕ is usually small for the lower guys.

The summation of all vertical forces at the bottom of the tower, ΣV as in Fig. 5, is the accumulation of gravity loads of the antenna, structure and ice, plus the vertical components V_a, V_b and V_c of all the guy strains. The maximum column load on the corner posts occurs at the bottom of the structure. Since a substantial increment is added at each guy point, many large guyed towers make a change to heavier corner post sections at the guy points. The fact that a structure does not add corner-post material at each guy point, however, does not necessarily mean that it is poorly designed. Changes in corner-post section complicate section splices in some designs and there are economies in keeping the number of different sections to a minimum. Heavier material is often used higher up the tower than stress analysis alone demands.

The wind direction for maximum stress in a guyed tower is different than for a self-supporting one, and is S rather than N in Fig. 3 for a triangular section. Corner-post C again gets the greatest load, in compression, and A and B share an equal tensile load between them. A wind from N will throw the full tensile load on C alone, but the corner post is stronger in tension than in compression.

For the square tower, Fig. 4, corner-post B was in compression in the self-supporting structure; if

guys are added D takes the compression load when the wind is from N and B is in tension. The guys at A and C are slack. A wind normal to any face of a guyed triangular or square tower will not impose stresses as heavy as those just described, because the compressive loads are then divided between two corner posts.

Figure 7 shows how wind pressure on a triangular section between guys stresses it as a simple beam with a uniformly distributed load. With the wind coming from direction N, this results in a compression stress in A. Thus there are three compression loads on A, the beam stress just mentioned, the vertical component of guy strain, and the gravity loads of the antenna and the structure itself plus the weight of any ice. These constitute the maximum loads of any member of the tower, and reach their highest values at the bottom.

Cross-Bracing

The cross-bracing of towers is subject to infinite variation, depending upon decisions of the individual designer. Many combinations of horizontals and diagonals can result in a sound structure, and some successful lighter designs omit either horizontal or diagonal bracing entirely.

In general, and where a structure has both, the horizontals are compression members while the diagonals distribute tensile loads among the corner posts. The corner post is a column unsupported between bracing; the greater the

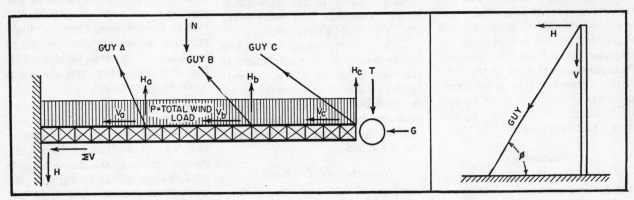

FIG. 5—Loading on a guyed tower, showing vertical and horizontal components   FIG. 6—Guy-angle geometry

length of a bay the heavier the corner post must be, and the bracing must also be heavier. The designer arrives at a compromise between putting his material into corner

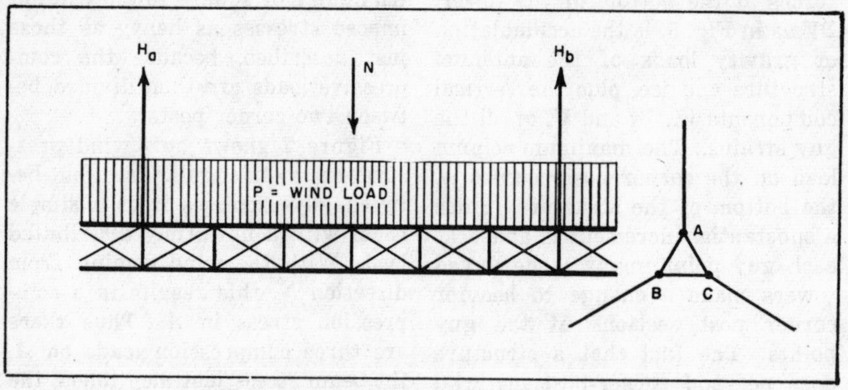

FIG. 7—Wind pressure on triangular tower section between guys

posts or bracing and tries to get a combination which will expose a minimum of area to the wind.

A few successful designs have used wire cable for diagonal bracing, despite the fact that end connections are expensive and cable is subject to stretching.

End connections of rigid bracing usually require that the material be two to three times the diameter of the bolt or rivet in width; this often determines the minimum section which can be used for bracing. Because of corrosion, traditional structural practice has in the past prohibited the use of any section less than ⅛ inch thick, but the tower industry, doing careful stress analysis and using corrosion-resisting materials and coatings, has in many instances safely disregarded this arbitrary minimum. The more massive structures are usually built entirely of standard channels and angles, but lighter towers often use specially formed sections stamped from sheet or extruded in the light metals. Round tubing is an excellent shape for corner posts as well as bracing, since it is equally strong in all directions.

Fastenings

Towers other than the most massive designs are usually factory assembled into sections which are

bolted together at erection. Where rod and tubing are used, factory assembly is generally done by welding; this is highly satisfactory if the welds are sound and are carefully cleaned before galvanizing or painting. The most dangerous type of corrosion starts at improperly cleaned welds.

Factory-driven rivets give little trouble except where they have not been thoroughly descaled before finishing the structure. Bolts and nuts are usually hot-dip galvanized; the nuts are usually retapped slightly oversize after galvanizing to permit easy assembly. Electro-zinc and cadmium plating of bolts and nuts permits their manufacture with closer fits than hot-dip galvanizing, but the difficulty of maintaining quality control, especially in barrel plating, has in some instances in the past made them less uniformly corrosion-resistant. However, electro-zinc and cadmium plate are excellent paint bases; even if the structure itself is not galvanized, plated fastenings are well worth their slight additional cost.

Both self-supporting and guyed towers are subject to substantial vibration in gusty winds. Investment in locknuts or lockwashers of any standard type, plated like the nuts and bolts, is well worth the cost of additional material and erection labor.

Mounts and Footings

Guyed and self-supporting structures are mounted on different

types of footings. The self-supporting tower must be anchored so that each leg footing can resist a tensile pull of high magnitude. Referring to Fig. 2 and 3, this is:

Tensile Pull = $PH/3 \div J + TH' \div J - (G + W) \div$ No. of corner posts. For a given top load capacity and height, a tower with a greater spread at the base will cost more than others but, where soft ground conditions require extensively spread footings, a more economical installation will result from the fact that the tensile forces the base must resist will be less, since the denominator J shown in Fig. 3 is greater. Where a self-supporting tower is used as a vertical radiator, push-pull insulators are usually employed for the legs; Fig. 8 shows how such insulators translate tensile pull on the leg into a compression strain on the porcelain.

The base of a guyed structure is less elaborate, since there are no upward components of force, but the footing, usually a slab of concrete, must be spread over enough ground to distribute vertical loads over an area which can support them without sinking. The slab must resist substantial internal shear stress unless ground conditions permit it to be small in area; it is usually provided with reinforcing bars. The horizontal loads on the base of a guyed tower, being quite small, are taken by a few bolts or anchor rods locating the tower base on its footing. Base insulators for guyed vertical radiators have to be quite substantial to take the downward thrust of the guy strains and gravity loads. However, porcelain has a high strength in compression, so pivot insulators of the type illustrated in Fig. 9 can support even the most massive structures.

Guy anchors require careful investigation of soil conditions and installation. For strains up to a few tons in medium or hard soil, galvanized guy anchors equipped with bearing plates or suitable for use with a deadman buried in the ground are often employed. These are inexpensive and easy to install; even if the largest size cannot support all the guys in a set it is worthwhile providing more than one anchorage if this allows their use. In soft soil, and where guy strains are several tons, concrete footings must generally be designed. Shaping them along the line of average direction of guy pull saves material and labor and the use of a wedge-shaped plate transmitting guy pulls to the anchor allows self-alignment of the guys.

Materials

Steel towers are low in first cost, but their weight is a factor in shipping and erection expense. Even though galvanized they are usually painted periodically in all but quite dry climates; this expense is necessary in any case where the Civil Aeronautics Authority declares a tower to be a hazard to air traffic and requires that it be painted in orange and white stripes for maximum visibility.

Aluminum has become important as a tower material since the development of strong and corrosion-resistant alloys. Having a modulus of elasticity about one third that of steel, an aluminum-alloy tower under load deflects roughly three times as much as a steel tower made to the same design. The alloys used for towers weigh about one third as much as structural steel, and their yield point in tension is about a third higher. In order to reduce deflection, deeper sections are used, but good designs are on the market which are about 40 percent of the weight of a structural steel tower having the same load capacity. They are more expensive than steel structures, but in many cases the additional first cost is offset by savings in shipping and erection.

Stainless steel is the best material for towers from the corrosion standpoint, but is quite expensive. In its annealed state, 18–8 stainless steel has a yield strength about the same as structural aluminum and higher than structural steel. However, most stainless steel used for

antenna-support structures is in the form of tubing, where the cold working accompanying the drawing operations materially raises its strength. Especially where a tower need not be painted, stainless steel towers, like aluminum, effect savings in shipping, erection and maintenance.

Magnesium alloys will undoubtedly play an important part in the future of antenna support structures. Substantially lighter and more corrosion resistant than aluminum, they permit the erection of massive towers with little gear. Research is producing stronger alloys and gradually eliminating detrimental factors such as the susceptibility of magnesium to notch-effect failures.

Phenolic resin-bonded plywood was used for mass-produced masts up to about 100 feet in height during World War II. It has the advantages of low cost, easy erection, low maintenance and the employment of noncritical material. However, it has a shorter life and less load capacity than most metal types and must be lowered when antennas are to be tuned or serviced. Postwar development, particularly in the direction of using fiberglass as a filler material, has improved the quality of this type of product; it is especially useful for testing work and temporary installations where frequent moving of equipment is necessary.

Wooden masts and towers are rarely satisfactory at heights above 50 feet although many up to 250

feet were built in wartime because of the shortage of metals. Design requires great care and flawless materials must be used. The allowable stress being low, sections are bulky and the wind loads consequently quite high.

Selection of Site

Guyed towers require substantial areas for guy anchorage. Installation on a rooftop adds to the height but roof framing must often be reinforced for the tower base and sometimes for guy anchorage as well. One method of anchoring guys on a rooftop of limited area is shown in Fig. 10; alternate methods include running one or more guys to the ground or to another building.

Self-supporting towers require less room for the base, but legal

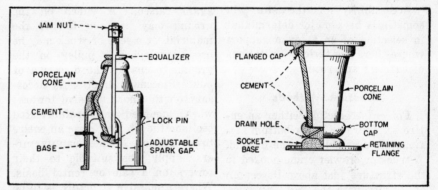

FIG. 8—Support for unguyed tower   FIG. 9—Support for guyed tower

liability exists where the structure might fall onto property owned by others; insurance must be figured into the maintenance cost so sometimes it is cheaper to acquire land around the tower to reduce this charge. Reinforcement of roof framing to anchor a self-supporting structure is usually more costly than for a guyed structure of the same height because of the tensile loads the base must resist, but guy anchorages are eliminated.

Soil conditions should be determined before the selection of a tower to be ground mounted. Soft or swampy ground may dictate the choice of a self-supporting tower with the base spread as much as possible. A guyed structure mounted on soft ground should be as small and light as possible; some of the stainless steel towers made of round tubing are costly but their wind loads are low, their vertical thrust against the ground correspondingly small and the base required less elaborate than for more massive steel units. In temperate or cold climates the footings should go at least below the frost line for safety.

Rock footings are relatively simple. Usually holes are drilled, steel rods with appropriate crossmembers for bonding inserted, and the holes filled with concrete. In the case of the lighter structures, the rod itself can be used as an anchor bolt attached to one leg of the tower. For heavier structures a triangle or square of metal fitting the leg angles of the tower is buried.

Accessibility of the site will sometimes be a major determinant in selection of an antenna support where there are serious limitations of carriers and roads.

Erection Methods

For crane erection, either an entire structure or a few bottom sections are assembled on the ground. A truck or crawler crane hooked to the structure just above its center of gravity lifts the unit and lines attached to the bottom end swing it into an upright position. The crane then lowers it onto the anchor bolts. Crawler cranes capable of

lifting up to ten tons at the end of a 100-foot boom are available in most centers of population in this country, so units up to possibly 200 feet high can be erected by this method. However, great care must be exercised in raising units over 100 feet high, because the guyed units especially are quite limber, and buckling may occur. Rental of cranes is expensive, but the crane is needed only for the minimum hiring period of one day. Gin poles and A-frames can take the place of the crane for smaller units.

For piecemeal erection the bottom section of the structure is erected as a unit. A jib is then attached to one corner post, projecting up more than half the length of the next corner post. This jib is used with a pulley and rope to raise the members of the next bay. After the bay is completed the jib is again raised. A winch on the ground may be used to lift the material, or a jeep or truck may be used, employing a pulley on the ground to change the direction of pull. Piecemeal erection is necessary on the more massive towers; when mounted on prefabricated sections the jib may raise an entire tower section. Some manufacturers supply jibs suitable to their towers on a sale or rental basis. Where a massive structure is to be erected on a rooftop it must be determined whether there is room on the roof to install a hoisting derrick to lift the members or whether

they must be carried up in elevators. These conditions may dictate a maximum size of members, which would control the basic design.

For boom erection many guyed masts are equipped with four sets of guys instead of the minimum three. The boom, which may be one quarter to a third the length of the mast, is attached to the mast base at right angles to it, and the base itself is equipped with a hinge. The mast, including all the guys, is assembled on the ground and the boom is attached in a vertical position. One set of guys is attached to the boom, shortened as necessary. Two sets are attached to their ground anchors. The fourth set, opposite the boom, is attached to a truck or held by manpower. A line fastened to the end of the boom is pulled in the direction opposite the mast, and, as the boom end is pulled down, the mast is raised. At some point near plumb the weight of the boom balances the weight of the mast; beyond this point the mast falls into an upright position and the fourth set of guys opposite the boom must take up their slack and ease the mast into position.

Maintenance

Materials of construction, fastenings, climatic conditions and required length of life determine mantenance requirements.

Painting is the most costly repetitive item and the one most often neglected. Aluminum structures need not be painted unless they are exposed to salt air or industrial fumes corrosive to the metal; in the former case they need painting less often than galvanized steel if a zinc chromate priming coat has been well applied. In dry climates galvanized steel does not need painting either, though both it and aluminum are subject to weathering which may make their appearance undesirable. Galvanizing provides a better paint base than bare steel, as also do Parkerizing and similar chemical treatments for metals.

Bolts are the first parts of a

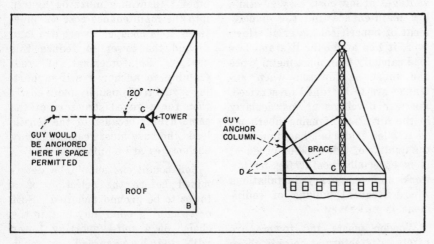

FIG. 10—Use of guy anchor column on rooftop of limited area

tower to show signs of corrosion in most cases, even when painted. Streaks below a bolt head may indicate only the combined effects of rain and dust; nothing need be done about them until wire brushing shows bare metal has been exposed or pitting started. When bolts and nuts begin to rust on an aluminum tower wire brushing and painting will save them.

About six months after a tower has been erected, or after its first winter, all the bolts should be tightened and any showing signs of corrosion painted or replaced. Subse-

quent tightening need only be done once a year, but signs of misalignment or damage should be promptly attended to.

Guys should be adjusted at erection so that the structure is perfectly plumb and straight with all the slack taken out of the guys and all equally taut. Some manufacturers supply guy-tensioning devices based on spring-adjusted turnbuckles, but screw turnbuckles should be provided in addition to these. Guys should be checked four times a year or after severe storms; all wire rope is subject to stretching.

Lighter units generally have bracing handy for climbing, and more massive units are usually provided with a ladder. Where bracing is too widely spaced for climbing, extra horizontals on one face may be provided to form a ladder, or one corner post may be fitted with cantilever climbing rungs.

Tubular masts can be fitted with ladders or rungs attached to clamp rings. These, of course, add to wind resistance. A mast is usually painted by lowering it, or by using a boatswain's chair suspended from the top if it is erect.

Antifading Broadcast Antenna

The service area of a broadcast transmitter within which interference between ground and sky-wave components does not occur can be extended by reduction of high-angle radiation from the antenna.   Use of a sectional mast with an insulator cancels the progressive wave usually found on fabricated towers

By HELMUT BRUECKMANN

THE RECEPTION of a broadcast station in the frequency range 0.5 to 1.6 mc is frequently affected by fading at relatively short distances, especially at night. This kind of fading, which results from interference of ground and sky wave, is observed at distances of about 50 to 100 miles or more. It causes linear and nonlinear distortion at the receiver, sometimes to an extent which completely spoils a high-quality radio program, even with avc in the receiver. This effect is true also for a high-power station, the signal from which is strong enough to overcome r-f noise. As a result, a considerable part of the potential coverage area of many radio stations suffers from poor reception. In order to achieve an undisturbed primary coverage as large as possible, especially at night time, many high-power radio

stations have been equipped with antifading antennas. However, not all of them have been successful.

In 1930, German broadcast stations started to use a single vertical wire or metal rope hung in the axis of a self-supporting wooden tower with a height in the order of half a wavelength and excited electrically at the base. Experience with this kind of antenna in respect to reduction of fading was good. In some cases, the undisturbed night-time primary coverage was increased by 100 percent in area, compared to an antenna with a height of one-quarter wavelength or less. However, the maintenance of the wooden tower proved to be expensive and difficult, and many towers were destroyed by fire or storm. In time they were replaced by self-radiating steel towers which

were fed at the base in the same manner as the one-wire antennas. These steel towers were much cheaper, easier to maintain and less subject to hazards. However, they were disappointing in respect to reduction of fading.

Beginning in 1936, several investigators showed that this effect was due to the progressive voltage-current wave along the tower which is superimposed on the standing voltage-current wave as shown in Fig. 1A. This progressive wave carries the energy which is radiated by each element of the antenna or dissipated by losses. In a thin conductor like the one-wire antenna, the progressive wave is small compared to the standing wave and, therefore, the radiation of the progressive wave is almost negligible. In a thick conductor like a steel tower, this is no longer true. The vertical radiation pattern of a simple vertical antenna with height $H = 0.585 \lambda$ is shown in Fig. 1B, curves 1, 2 and 3, for different values of K.

The distance for which ground and sky wave are equal and, therefore, fading is worst is strongly affected by such modification of the radiation pattern, as illustrated in Fig. 1C. The ground-wave intensity is based on measurements with a certain station as an example. The sky-wave intensity is calculated for perfect reflection from the E-layer as an arbitrary basis of comparison. It is apparent that the distance for which ground and sky wave are equal is reduced considerably with a base-fed mast antenna, compared to a thin vertical radiator, namely from about 135 miles to about 105 miles. This reduction corresponds to a decrease in undisturbed area of 40 percent.

Principle of New Antenna

Around 1940, the author suggested that the shaft of the mast be broken up by an insulator somewhere in its upper part, and that it be excited electrically at this sectional-mast insulator. Although this idea was not in itself new, nobody up to that time had mentioned the advantages of this idea in respect to antifading action.

Disregarding the physical problem of transmitting power to the sectional-mast insulator, by tentatively locating the current source at this point, the basic idea can be illustrated as shown in Fig. 1D. In respect to current distribution, the upper part of the mast works as an open one-wire line and the lower part as a one-wire line terminated by an inductance. According to the flow of energy there is a progressive wave superimposed on the

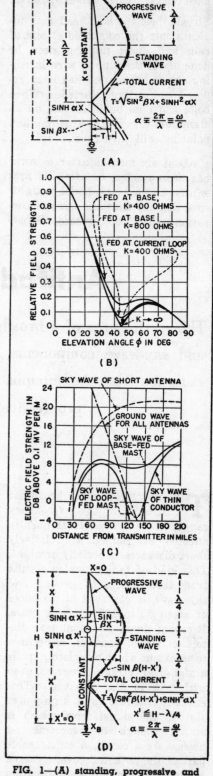

FIG. 1—(A) standing, progressive and total current waves on radiator fed at base, **(B)** vertical pattern of vertical 0.585-wavelength radiator, **(C)** sky and ground-wave field strengths, and **(D)** standing, progressive and total current waves on center-fed radiator

Table I—Characteristics of Antenna Operating at 1,195 kc

	Loop-fed			Base-fed
Length of stub in feet between grounded tap and base of mast	58.7	55.1	52.0	*
Height in feet of the current node above ground	−0.8	8.8	16.8	11
Elevation angle in degrees of null of vertical radiation pattern	90	62	54	65
Gain in db in the horizontal direction due to pattern (calculated)	2.15	2.40	2.61	—
Input impedance in ohms of the coaxial transmission line	$100-j51$	$84+j37$	$27+j35$	*
Antenna efficiency in percent, including matching network	73	67	62	73
Losses in stub in percent of the input power	3	10	12	*
Heat losses in percent along the mast (calculated)	0.7	0.6	0.7	0.7
Losses in percent in coaxial transmission line inside mast	1.4	1.4	4.2	*
Ratio of current in percent at current node and at current loop	——	2.9	2.7	26
Voltage in kv across base insulator	5.9	8.3	10.2	9.5
Voltage in kv across sectional-mast insulator	5.7	4.4	6.9	**
Maximum voltage in kv across coaxial transmission line inside mast	6.8	8.0	13.0	*
Standing-wave ratio in coaxial transmission line inside mast	2.2	2.5	7.9	—

* Disconnected
** Shorted
Voltages are for 100 kw rms unmodulated power input.

standing wave in each part of the mast, traveling upward in the upper part and downward in the lower part. Each of the two progressive waves is, near the current source, about half as strong as in the case of excitation at the base. The radiation components originating from them cancel each other at least partially because of the opposite direction of the progressive waves. For the sake of brevity, this kind of antenna may be called the loop-fed antenna, in contrast to the base-fed antenna.

As shown in Fig. 2, the current distribution in the lower part of the mast depends upon the inductance which is connected between the base of the mast and ground. This means that the vertical radiation pattern can be controlled by varying this inductance. In order to have a pattern suitable for reduction of fading, it is not necessary to have a current loop at the sectional-mast insulator. Actually a current distribution similar to that in Fig. 2B is more favorable because it allows reduction of the total height of the mast, which can be as low as 0.4 wavelength. Since the inductance at the base can be adjusted conveniently, it is possible to adapt the antenna during operation to a change in ionospheric conditions, as it happens, for example, during spring and fall.

A simple way to feed the antenna at the sectional-mast insulator is shown in Fig. 3A. A coaxial r-f cable is wound as a big coil. Its outer conductor is connected between the base of the mast and ground, representing the inductance mentioned above. The inner conductor of this cable is continued through the inside of the lower part of the mast and insulated from it up to the lower end of the upper part of the mast. This continuation of the inner conductor and the mast itself form a coaxial transmission line, with the mast as the outer conductor. A current equal in phase and magnitude and opposite in direction to the current in the inner conductor flows on the inner surface of the lower part of the

mast. No radiation originates therefrom. At the sectional-mast insulator, this current goes around the rim of the mast shaft and continues on the outside surface.

Normally, a tuning and matching network would be introduced at the sectional-mast insulation between the antenna terminals and the coaxial cable. However, in this case it is not necessary. On that part of the coaxial transmission line which is formed by the mast itself and the inner conductor, even a high standing-wave ratio does not matter, both from the standpoints of power losses and break-down voltage of the insulators, because of the great dimensions available.

the base-fed antenna, and by 23 db compared to a simple short antenna. In effect, the loop-fed mast is about equal to, if not better than, the base-fed one-wire antenna in respect to the sky-wave suppression.

The calculated field strength of the reflected sky wave as a function of the distance, when based on the measured pattern, is shown in Fig. 1C. According to this diagram, the undisturbed primary coverage at night time is increased considerably; namely, by about 30 percent in radius or 68 percent in area, compared to a base-fed mast.

Radio Frankfort Antenna

The first broadcast transmitter

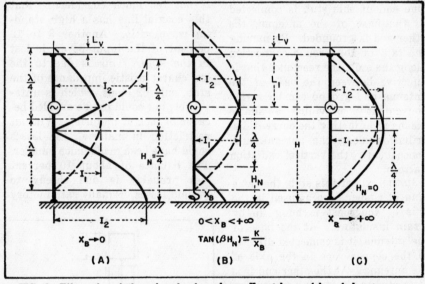

FIG. 2—Effect of variation of series impedance X_B at base of loop-fed antenna on current distribution

Therefore, it is sufficient to have a matching and tuning network at the lower end of the lower part of the mast shaft where it can be operated conveniently. Even more convenient, the matching network can be installed at the grounded end of the coil of coaxial cable.

In order to determine how much the loop-fed antenna actually improves sky-wave suppression, field strength measurements by airplane were made with a 330-foot high antenna model operated at 1,640 kc. For an elevation angle of 43 degrees, the field strength was reduced by about 14 db compared to

which was to have obtained a permanent version of the loop-fed antenna was the 100-kw station in Berlin, Germany. The war prevented this and, instead, such an antenna was erected in 1946 for the 100-kw station in Frankfort-on-Main. Meanwhile, the antenna originally planned for Berlin is thought to have been erected also.

The antenna for Radio Frankfort is a 402-foot steel tower with uniform square cross section. The sectional-mast insulator is at a height of 269 feet so that the upper part of the tower is 133 feet long. The construction of this sectional-mast insulator is similar to that used for station WMAQ.

At the time of the erection in 1947, it was a problem to provide for the necessary inductance between the lower end of the mast shaft and the ground system. This inductance could not be established by a coaxial cable wound into a coil, as indicated in Fig. 3A, because there was no 100-kw cable available. Instead, sections of another mast of identical construction were used to build a kind of short-circuited stub. They are hung up horizontally by strain insulators at a distance of 20 inches above the ground in such a way that they form one big loop with a diameter of 64 feet, as shown in Fig. 3B. One end of this stub is connected to the base of the antenna, the other end is grounded. By moving the tap for the ground connection along the stub, the reactance that is effective between the base of the antenna and ground can be varied conveniently, providing a simple means of adjusting the current distribution along the antenna and, consequently, the vertical radiation pattern.

In the axis of this stub, the same kind of copper rope as used in the axis of the mast is hung up by strain insulators. At the base of the antenna, it is connected directly to the copper rope in the axis of the antenna. At the other end it is connected to a matching and tuning network. In this way the coaxial transmission line represented by the copper rope inside the antenna and the mast shaft is continued to the point where the outer conductor is grounded. In view of the high voltage-rating of this coaxial transmission line inside the stub, there is no danger of flashing over, even with a high standing-wave-ratio. Therefore, the matching and tuning network could be installed outside the mast shaft in a small tuning house.

The actual performance of this antenna was measured for three different settings of the tap for the ground connection on the stub corresponding to three different radia-tion patterns. Some of the results are listed in Table I. A total antenna efficiency of 73, 67 and 62 percent was obtained corresponding to a total loss of 1.4, 1.7, and 2.1 db respectively, a relatively high efficiency considering the inexpensive ground system used and the high frequency of 1.2 mc. Even with these losses, the ground-wave field strength is greater than that of a quarter-wave antenna with an efficiency of 100 percent.

Power Losses

About 1.4 to 4.2 percent of the input power was found to be dissipated in the coaxial transmission line inside the tower. This is not too much considering that this coaxial line has a high standing-wave ratio. Another 3 to 12 percent of the input power is lost in the stub. This is due to the low characteristic impedance of the stub, only 62 ohms, which is unfavorable but could not be avoided because of lack of material. Without restriction in material, the losses could have been made much smaller. The balance of about 10 percent loss probably is due chiefly to ground losses. Equally satisfactory are the voltage ratings of the antenna.

Preliminary field strength recordings at night time, at a distance where the fading with a simple quarter-wavelength antenna at the transmitter previously had been serious, showed that the fading at Radio Frankfort is much smaller than the signal of another station equipped with a quarter-wave antenna located at the same place and with almost the same frequency. Final tests have not yet been made in respect to the area undisturbed by fading.

The new antenna also has advantages in respect to its usable frequency range. Full benefit of its antifading action can be obtained in a frequency range of about ±20 percent of the frequency for which it is designed, without any alteration of the antenna itself, just by properly adjusting the tap for the ground connection on the stub. If the antenna is required to operate at a frequency outside of this range, it can be used as a base-fed antenna with the coaxial cable inside the mast working as a stub, shown in Fig. 3C. With this mode of excitation,

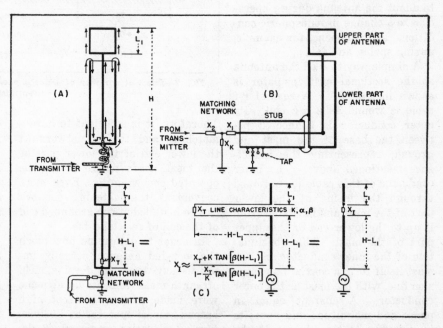

FIG. 3—(A) current flow in loop-fed antenna, (B) loop-fed antenna with matching network outside mast, and (C) equivalent circuit of loop-fed antenna operated as base-fed type

and with a suitable reactance X_r between the inner conductor and the lower end of the mast, the radiation efficiency at low frequencies is higher than with a simple steel tower because its effective height can be increased by making the input impedance of the coaxial cable inside the mast at the sectional-mast insulator inductive. At higher frequencies the sectional-mast insulator can be used to decrease the electrical height of the antenna in order to obtain a more suitable vertical radiation pattern by making

the input impedance of the coaxial cable capacitive. It is also possible to operate the antenna as a simple base-fed mast by short-circuiting the sectional-mast insulator. This possibility may be useful in case of trouble with this insulator.

Acknowledgment is made of the help furnished by Messrs. Gerwig and Graziadei and others involved in the development of the antenna which was carried out under the supervision of the author in the Forschungsantalt der Deutschen Reichspost, Berlin, Germany.

Valuable help in antenna measurements was afforded by Messrs. Haberkant and Behne, employees of Radio Frankfort.

Interest and encouragement were given by R. J. Condon, AMG, and Lt. L. C. Heinzman, then chief engineer of Radio Frankfort.

BIBLIOGRAPHY

Stuart Ballantine, High Quality Radio Broadcasting, *Proc. IRE*, 22, p 564, 1934.
R. F. Guy, Notes on Broadcast Antenna Developments, *RCA Review*, p 39, April 1937.

Tower Carrier Alarm

By KARL NEUWIRTH

THE PURPOSE of the alarm is to alert the operator in case of carrier failure at either tower of the two-tower array.

When normal energy is radiated, the two relays K_1 and K_2 shown in Fig. 1 are held with contacts open by the rectified r-f current fed back from each tower. An abnormal condition anywhere in the transmitter, transmission line or at either tower will cause a decrease in radiated power. Either or both relays will then fall out, causing an alarm bell to ring.

Sometimes static discharges or

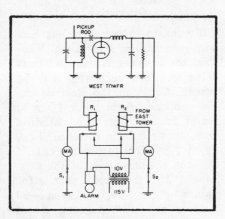

FIG. 1—Carrier-failure alarm used at WNEW. The East tower unit is similar to that used at the West tower

electric storms establish arcs at a transmitter tower gap. These are sustained by the transmitter output and yet are of insufficient proportion to trip the transmitter overload relays. The alarm described will quickly indicate such a condition. The arc is extinguished by cutting the carrier momentarily.

Switches S_1 and S_2 in the diagram are momentary-break types used to test the alarm. The milliammeters indicate visually the strength of current in each tower. The pickup rods are mounted close to the antenna-feed leads.

Directional Antennas for A-M Broadcasting

Simplified and practical method of calculating radiation patterns for two and three-tower arrays when determining coverage and protection. An example is given that provides a convenient check list of the operations involved in plotting a complete pattern

By JOHN H. BATTISON

ALTHOUGH directional antennas have long been in use by a-m broadcasting stations, some engineers regard them with awe, and surround them with an aura of

mystery. Many regard the calculations involved as being beyond their capabilities when, in fact, nothing more than an elementary knowledge of the basic operation of a single

antenna and the ability to perform simple trigonometry is required. It is the object of this article to disperse some misconceptions, and simplify directional-antenna calculations for two and three-tower arrays.

Two-Tower Array

Figure 1 shows the basic diagram for the field at one point caused by two antennas. The nomenclature used to perform the functions is given below, although all engineers do not necessarily use exactly the same symbols for some parameters.

θ_r = angle between reference line R-R' and axis of array
I_1 = current in tower 1
I_2 = current in tower 2
T = ratio of I_2 to I_1 (current ratio for similar towers, or field ratio for dissimilar)
ψ = phase angle of tower 2 with reference to tower 1

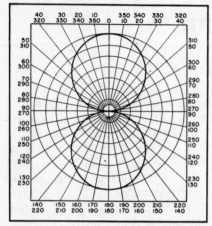

Pattern from two antenna elements of equal height spaced 45 degrees, with equal currents in each element and phase angle of 180 degrees

ϕ_h = phase difference between tower 2 and tower 1 at point P_h
P_h = point at infinity, or such distance that lines drawn from the towers to P_h may be considered parallel (horizontal)
P_v = same as P_h, except above the horizon in vertical plane
α = vertical angle to P_v in space
θ_h = angle between R-R' and line to P_h
S = spacing between towers in degrees (360 degrees equals one wavelength)
θ = angle between axis of array and true north, used when plotting on chart to obtain correct orientation for coverage required and protection
G = height of tower in degrees

When calculating the radiation pattern for a two-tower array, it is usual to number the towers 1 and 2, and to place them at random. "Random" is used in the sense of being an arbitary placement dependent on the whim of the engineer, subject to the dictates of common sense and necessity. In practice, the engineer usually has an ap-

proximate idea of the basic pattern obtainable from certain standard combinations of tower spacing and phasing. From these he can estimate how the final pattern will appear. But eventually the problem boils down to one of trial and error until a pattern is obtained, with reasonable constants, which gives the protection required.

Tower 1 is taken as the reference tower and all quantities are stated with reference to this tower. The reference line R-R' is drawn through tower 1, at random. A point P_h is located on a circle whose center is equidistant between towers 1 and 2, and such a distance that lines joining P_h-tower 1, and P_h-tower 2 may be regarded as parallel (actually the error is so slight that it may be ignored in practice).

Calculation

The basic information has now been presented in a form which enables the designer to see what he is doing and how each step may be taken. Consider the field at P_h. The radiation from tower 1 has to travel farther than the radiation from tower 2 by a distance $S \cos (\theta_r - \theta_h)$. This is also the case if P_h is on the other side of the axis. Line A-A' of the array, that is for values of $(\theta_r - \theta_h)$ between -90 degrees and $+90$ degrees, $S \cos (\theta_r - \theta_h)$ is plus, but when it is between $+90$ and $+270$ $S \cos (\theta_r - \theta_h)$ is negative. This provides the first clue to the manner in which the pattern is obtained, since, depending on the length of the paths to P_h, all signals arriving at P_h will either reinforce or buck each other, thus giving rise to the characteristic pattern for these parameters.

Consider the initial phase difference at the towers. It will be observed that the phase relationship of the fields at P_h resulting from the radiation from towers 1 and 2 is due to the different path lengths. Therefore the tower phase difference must be added to the phase difference to obtain the total phase difference. The total phase differ-

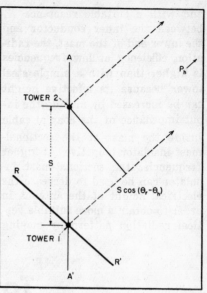

FIG. 1—Basic diagram of field created by a two-tower array

ence between towers is referred to tower 1. If the current in tower 1 leads the current in 2, the phase angle ψ is negative; if it lags in tower 1 then ψ is positive. Thus the total phase difference at point P_h is given by the expression:

$$\phi_h = \psi + S \cos (\theta_r - \theta_h)$$

For the purpose of this discussion it will be assumed that the antennas are identical, although it often happens that due to a desire to use an existing tower in conjunction with a new one, two dissimilar towers will be used. With this assumption the field from each tower is proportional only to the magnitude of the current in the respective towers, and since they are identical the only thing which can cause the fields to differ is a current difference. From this we have a measure of the field strength at P_h in the magnitude of the relative tower currents. Vectorial representation of the component fields by the magnitudes of I_2 and I_1 makes possible the addition of vector I_2 to the reference I_1 at the phase difference angle ϕ_h. A vector I_H is produced, which represents the resulting field strength. In that direction

$$I_H = I_1 + I_2 \angle \phi_h$$

To obtain the antenna pattern necessary to determine the direction of the lobes of radiation of various values it is necessary to compute the field at P_h for all angles from the center of the axis of the array. If $R-R'$ is made to coincide with the axis of the array, only azimuths of from 0 to 180 degrees need be calculated and S cos $(\theta_r - \theta_h)$ then becomes $-S$ cos θ_h. It will also be apparent that in the case of a two-tower array, the

into the antenna will produce a known field strength at one mile. The FCC has incorporated these figures into the Standards of Good Engineering Practice, and so by multiplying the field intensity at one mile produced by one kilowatt, by the square root of the power increase, the assumed rms value for the array will be found. In prac-

grounded and that the current distribution is sinusoidal, then the radiation pattern is given by

$$F = \frac{\cos (G \cos \alpha) - \cos G}{\sin \alpha (1 - \cos G)}$$

where G is antenna height in degrees.

As was done in computing the horizontal patterns, the radiation at any point P_v in the vertical plane is obtained by adding vectorially I_2 and I_1 at the pertinent phase angle, and then multiplying this result by the vertical radiation factor.

Just as for horizontal patterns, the total phase difference of the component fields observed at point P_v is obtained by adding the phase difference caused by the difference in the length of the radiation paths, and the initial phase difference of the antennas.
This is given by

$$\phi_v = \psi_v + S \cos (\theta_r - \theta_h) \cos \alpha$$

As in the case of the horizontal pattern the vectors I_2 and I_1 are added at the phase angle ϕ_v. The resulting vector is then multiplied by F, the radiation factor, and the same conversion factor K as was used in the horizontal pattern. The resulting signal strength at one mile E_v, is plotted in mv per m on polar paper as a vertical section through 90 degrees in the horizontal direction involved.
Thus

$$E_v = I_1 + I_2 \angle \phi_v \times F \times K$$

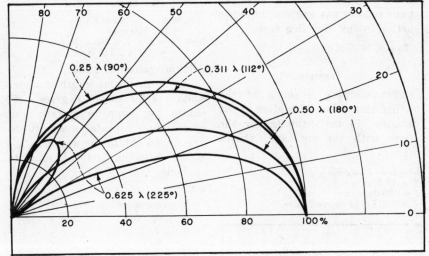

FIG. 2—Vertical radiation patterns of vertical antennas

towers must be equidistant from the center of the circle, and therefore the pattern will be symmetrical. This makes it necessary to compute only one side of the array. These values are now plotted on polar paper and a unit pattern is obtained. Before this can be used directly to compute field strengths at various points it must be converted to absolute field strength E_H.

$$E_H = K \times I_H \qquad K = \frac{\text{Array rms}}{\text{Unit rms}}$$

Value K is a constant which is determined by dividing the rms of the unit pattern into the assumed rms value of the array. The easiest way to do this is to measure the unit area with a planimeter, and convert it to a circle of equal area. The radius is measured in the same units as I_2 and I_1 (used to plot the unit pattern) and divided into the array root mean square value.

General engineering experience has determined over a long period of time that under average conditions of efficiency a given power

tice, the FCC will not usually approve an array below this minimum efficiency. The horizontal pattern is now obtained by plotting the values of absolute field intensity (E_H) for 360 degrees at intervals of 10 degrees (or less in critical directions). From this it can be determined whether the required protection or coverage is being obtained.

Vertical Pattern

The method of calculating the vertical radiation pattern of a two-element array is very similar to that for the horizontal pattern, the only difference being a slight modification of the horizontal method, and the application of the radiation characteristic of a vertical antenna. Most readers are familiar with the fact that a single vertical antenna does not radiate equally in all vertical directions, but, as is shown in Fig. 2, the intensity varies with the angle of elevation above the horizon. If it is assumed that an antenna is operated with its lower end

Three-Tower Array

The method of calculation for a three-tower array is exactly the same as for two towers except that the third tower has to be included in the formulas. Figure 3 shows the basic form for calculating the field at P_h from a three-tower directional array. Tower 1 is the reference tower and is in the center. The same nomenclature as before is used with the addition of the following symbols to take care of the third tower:

I_3 = current in tower 3
T_3 = ratio of current in I_3 to I_1
ϕ_{h3} = phase difference between tower 1 and tower 3

ψ_3 = phase angle of tower 3 with reference to tower 1

S_3 = spacing between towers 3 and 1 in degrees

θ_{r3} = angle between $R\text{-}R'$ and axis of towers 1 and 3

The field at any point will be determined by the magnitudes of the currents in the three towers and their phases. Radiation from tower 1 travels a distance of $S \cos (\theta_r - \theta_h)$ more or less than radiation from tower 2. Also radiation from tower 1 travels a distance of $S_3 \cos (\theta_{r3} - \theta_h)$ more or less than radiation from tower 3. If $(\theta_r - \theta_h)$ or $(\theta_{r3} - \theta_h)$ is between -90 and $+90$ degrees the distance is greater: if $(\theta_r - \theta_h)$ or $(\theta_{r3} - \theta_h)$ is between $+90$ and $+270$ degrees, the distance is shorter.

As in the case of a two-tower array, the initial phase differences must be added to those resulting from the different distances to P_h. Thus the total phase difference with reference to tower 1 from towers 2 and 3 is given by

Towers 1:2 $\phi_h = \psi + S \cos (\theta_r - \theta_h)$
Towers 1:3 $\phi_{h3} = \psi_3 + S_3 \cos (\theta_{r3} - \theta_h)$

If the three towers are similar, adding the vectors for the currents in the three towers at the correct phase angle will produce a vector representing the resultant field strength of the unit pattern I_H

$$I_H = I_1 + I_2 \angle \phi_h + I_3 \angle \phi_{h3}$$

From here on the method is exactly the same as for two towers, with the exception that in all but special cases the pattern is not symmetrical and therefore all values of θ_h from 0 to 360 degrees have to be computed.

The vertical radiation factor F is computed from

$$F = \frac{\cos (G \cos \alpha) - \cos G}{\sin \alpha (1 - \cos G)}$$

The phase difference at point P_v is computed from

Towers 1:2 $\phi_v = \psi + S \cos (\theta_2 - \theta_h) \cos \alpha$
Towers 1:3 $\phi_{v3} = \psi_3 + S_3 \cos (\theta_{r3} - \theta_h) \cos \alpha$
Adding $I_v = I_1 + I_2 \angle \phi_v + I_3 \angle \phi_{v3}$

Then the absolute signal strength at one mile at any angle α above the horizon in any direction θ_h is:

$$E_v = I_v \times K \times F$$

Example

The following example of the method shows the calculation of the radiation in one azimuth for the array with the constants shown below:

$I_1 = I_2 = 4$ amperes
$S = 45$ degrees
$\psi = 180$ degrees
$G = 0.311$ (112 degrees) $G_1 = G_2$

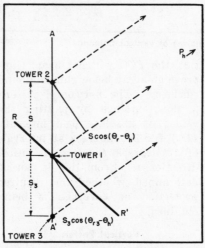

FIG. 3—For calculating the field of a three-tower array, the center tower is used as the reference point

To obtain the unit horizontal pattern, the radiation at every 10 degrees is calculated. For example: suppose $\theta_h = 40$ degrees: $\theta_v = 20$ degrees:
Then

$$\phi_h = \psi + S \cos (\theta_r - \theta_h)$$

Simplifying: $R - R'$ is made to coincide with the axis of the array.

Then

$$\phi_h = \psi + (- S \cos \theta_h)$$
$$= 145.5 \text{ degrees}$$
Now $I_H = I_1 + I_2 \angle 145.5$ degrees
$$= 4 + 4 \angle 145.5 \text{ degrees}$$

Adding vectors $= 2.367$

This is the scalar length of a horizontal vector at 40 degrees. To obtain the complete pattern, this operation is repeated every 10 degrees. To obtain the absolute field at one mile the factor K must be applied.

$$K = \frac{\text{rms array}}{\text{rms unit}} \quad \text{say,} \quad \frac{175 \sqrt{5}}{1.2} = 325$$

Then

$$E_H = K \times I_H = 325 \times 2.4 = 780 \text{ mv}$$
per m at azimuth 40 degrees.

To obtain the vertical pattern (unit) at 20 degrees the procedure is the same except that the vertical formula is used and the vertical radiation factor F has to be calculated from:

$$F = \frac{\cos (G \cos \alpha) - \cos G}{\sin \alpha (I - \cos G)}$$

This is then applied to $I_v \times K$, becoming

$$E_v = I_v \times K \times F$$
substituting: $E_v = I_v \times 325 \times 1.36$
$$= I_v (448)$$

Horizontally Polarized Omnidirectional Antenna

Provides azimuth ratio less than 3 db for frequency range of 2,970 to 3,125 mc with good voltage standing-wave ratio. Vertical pattern has half-power points at 45 degrees, which gives antenna a gain of approximately 2 db over half-wave dipole

By C. BRASSE, JR. AND R. THOMAS

THE ANTENNA described herein was designed for use in the 10-centimeter band, and the particular application for which it was intended required that the azimuth ratio be less than 1.5 db at the center of the band.

To achieve a perfectly omnidirectional pattern in the horizontal plane, with the polarization in this plane, the ideal radiating element should consist of a ring of uniform current. In practice, this type of current distribution may be approximated by means of a number of dipoles, slots, or loops arranged in a circular fashion and equally phased. All three types were considered in connection with the manner in which the elements could be mounted on a ⅞-inch rigid coaxial line, for convenience of manufacture, and it was decided that best results would be obtained through the use of loops as radiators.

Constructional Details

A very rugged feed system for loops can be easily built on the ⅞-inch line by inserting an even number of radial rods equally spaced about the periphery of the coax, alternate rods passing through to the center conductor. Loops are then formed by joining the ends of pairs of adjacent rods, as shown in Fig. 1A, where three loops are arranged on six rods.

This model was constructed by using screws for rods, the ones joining the inner conductor passing through clearance holes in the outer conductor. This feed system can be improved mechanically and electrically by the use of slots as baluns and impedance-matching elements. Figure 2 shows a side view of this configuration, and Fig. 1B shows how the slots permit the proper polarities to be established. In this model, the screws entering the inner conductor are also soldered to the outer conductor, thus forming a rigid support for the entire assembly.

The dimensions of the loops and the resulting current distribution are given in Fig. 1C from which it can be seen that the current is at a relatively high level at the rod ends. Dipoles could be used, but they would have to be longer, and the antenna would not be as mechanically rigid as the quarter-wave loops.

It would of course be possible to use the slots alone as radiating elements, by suitable probe feeding. In this case, however, the depth of the probes is somewhat critical and involves a tedious procedure of adjustment, especially if it is desired to stack two or more sets of elements to increase directivity in the vertical plane. By the use of loops, tuning is easily accomplished by increasing the length of the slots, which should be initially cut slightly less than a half wavelength.

A given set of loops will in general present an impedance which has low resistance and a capacitive reactance, and the negative shunt susceptance contributed by the slots

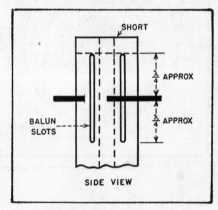

FIG. 2—Side view of configuration giving best results

will serve to match the antenna to the line with a minimum vswr of about 1.5. Increasing the loop perimeter will lower its apparent resistance and will produce a greater departure from a circular

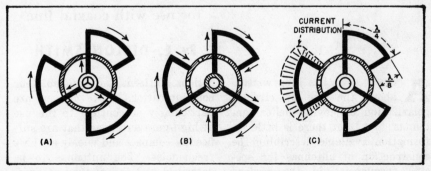

FIG. 1—Configurations shown at B and C are improvements of that shown at A. Addition of balun slots improves electrical and mechanical characteristics

azimuth pattern, due to the shift of current distribution along the loops.

A two- stack array was enclosed in a hollow Plexiglas ball as a simple means of pressurizing the antenna. The upper loops are located ¼ wavelength below the shorted end of the coax, and the lower loops, with feed reversed to obtain proper phasing, are spaced ½ wavelength below the upper set. The vertical pattern has a half-power beamwidth of 45 degrees, equivalent to a gain of approximately 2 db over a half-wave dipole. Figure 3 shows azimuth

patterns taken at 2,970, 3,060 and 3,125 megacycles respectively, and the corresponding azimuth ratios are seen to be 1.25, 1 and 3 db. These patterns were taken on the Bendix automatic pattern-measuring equipment which provides a continuous recording covering a field strength range of 50 db, and incorporates facilities for self calibration in order to insure accuracy at all times.

The vswr characteristics of this antenna are shown in Fig. 4.

Only three loops were required for each element, and the resulting

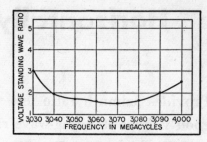

FIG. 4—Curve shows vswr for frequency range. No effort was made to extend range by broadbanding techniques

antenna combines satisfactory electrical performance together. with mechanical simplicity, ruggedness and ease of adjustment.

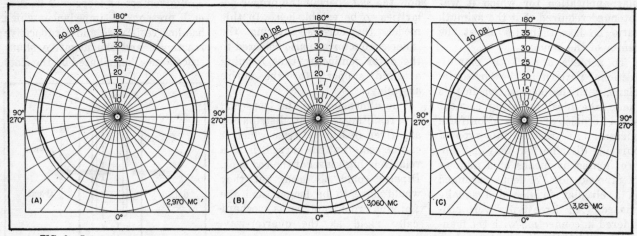

FIG. 3—Azimuth patterns show azimuth ratios of 1.25, 1 and 3 db for frequencies of 2,970, 3,060 and 3,125 respectively

Constructing Helical Antennas

Physically small and mechanically simple antennas with extremely high gain can be built for the 435-mc amateur band and for Citizens Radio on 465 mc. Constructional details for several types are given, as well as dimensions of an impedance-matching transformer for use with coaxial line

By E. DILLON SMITH

A GREAT DEAL has been written about the use of circular polarization employing helical antennas[1, 2, 3, 4, 5] but there is little information available describing the construction of antennas for specific frequencies in the regions most commonly used for communi-

cations. Citizens Radio and amateur communications above 400 mc are particularly susceptible to the use of high-gain antennas that are sufficently compact and wieldy at these frequencies. The antennas to be described and the method of feeding them from coaxial lines have

been proved in practice for the region of 435 mc, as well as for various other frequencies including 465 mc.

Although the type of antenna to be described is in the form of a helix to give end-fire circularly polarized radiation, it is technically nothing more than a long wire antenna. In the design, the turns product nS can be fixed, or the total length of wire nL (in which L is the length of one turn) can be selected. The former method is the more convenient. Right circular polarization was used.

Magnitude of Gain

A circular transmitting antenna operating into a linear receiving antenna can be visualized, for illustrative purposes only, as being about equivalent to two parallel linear stacked end-fire arrays fed in phase. For example, a five-turn helix with a screen is here visualized as a ten-element array in front of a screen. Such a linear array properly designed has a theoretical gain of 26 db over a dipole but is unusual to obtain in practice. A

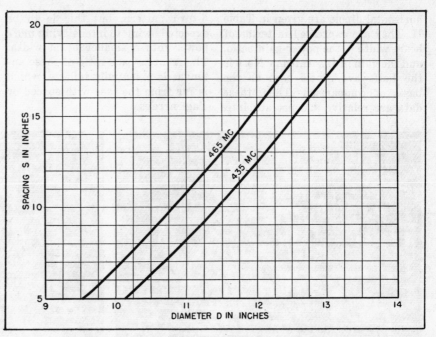

FIG. 2—Design chart for 435 and 465 mc using Fig. 1A notation

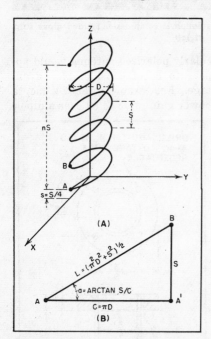

FIG. 1—Geometry of a helical antenna (A) and of one turn of the helix (B)

circular antenna circuit as compared with a linear circuit has shown a measured gain of 18.9 db.

Figure 1 gives the geometry of an antenna of n (five) complete turns wound as a right circular helix of diameter D with turn spacing S. If one complete turn of the helix is developed onto a plane the general dimensions are those given in Fig. 1B. The diameter D and the turn spacing S (or D and the pitch angle a) completely specify the antenna. Practical design curves for 435 and 465-mc antennas are given in Fig. 2.

The antenna works because its dimensions are so chosen that an exciting signal radiated from A (Fig. 1) will arrive at B in proper phase relation with the signal arriving via the wire path L and to be radiated at B to reinforce the A or A' signal.

Specific design data for two single-turn and five five-turn circular antennas are given in Table I. These data follow the notation of Fig. 1 with dimensions taken from the design chart of Fig. 2. The frames for the original one and five-turn antennas were made of redwood.

Because the voltages in the antenna are high, wood frames are not suitable for all-weather high-power operation (more than 1 watt or so) unless well insulated. One ground screen is copper mesh while that for the one-turn radiator is one-inch galvanized mesh. The eight-turn antenna shown in Fig. 3 is mounted on special compression-molded glass strips, resulting in a mechanically strong and electrically efficient design.

In order to match the 130-ohm surge impedance of the antenna to a 53.5-ohm coaxial transmission line there is required an 83.2-ohm transformer. A suggested design for which details are given in Fig. 4 is illustrated in Fig. 5 in exploded, assembled and mounted form. If losses are to be kept at a minimum at these frequencies it is highly important that all transformer internal finish be perfectly smooth, and silver plated. A 5/32-inch center conductor rod must be attached to the receptacle as shown in Fig. 5 This transformer has been used to connect an RG-58/U transmission line to a 435-mc circularly polarized antenna.

Performance Data

The effectiveness of these directive antenna systems was conveniently obtained from the ratio of the power at the terminals of the receiving circular antenna to that at the terminals of a dipole, with the same power applied to the transmitting antennas. This ratio can be expressed as power gain or in decibels.

The results of the performance tests on six circularly polarized antennas compared to a half-wave horizontal dipole are given in Table II. They are expressed in terms of beam width β, the power-gain ratio, and the gain in db. Antenna No. 0 is the half-wave dipole used as the basis of comparison. Thus, these data are relative and not absolute.

5-turn pattern, but this is to be expected owing to intensifying more power into a smaller beam width. The front-to-back ratio of these antennas is essentially infinite, which is far from the case with spaced or Yagi arrays.

sons can be made with the aid of Table II.

Other Applications

These antennas have many additional uses. For the 13 amateur bands from 14 to 21,000 mc, a cir-

FIG. 3—All-weather high-gain antenna for 435 mc giving measured power gain of 246. Insulation is compression-molded glass strip. Method of mounting impedance transformer is indicated at left

Since a horizontal half-wave dipole has a directional radiation pattern its beam width would be descriptive of its ability to radiate power in any given azimuth or horizontal direction. For sake of convenience the beam width, β, is taken as the angle between the points where the power density of the radiation pattern is equal to one-half of the maximum value—the beam angle of half-power points.

It can be shown mathematically, and practically demonstrated, that for a horizontal dipole the azimuth half-power points are plus or minus 39.1 degrees from the maximum, or the half-power beam width is 78.2 degrees. For comparison or reference purposes, the power radiated by the dipole is taken as unity, with all other antennas referred to it.

It should be noted that the beam width of the one-turn helix is 63 percent of that of the dipole, or 49 degrees. As the number of turns increases the beam becomes narrower, the 8-turn antenna being 22 degrees or 28 percent of the dipole.

Characteristics of several antennas are plotted in Fig. 6. A side lobe is shown, for example, in the

Transmission data for two types of circuits are also given in Table II. The first set of data compares the transmission of a wholly circularly polarized circuit with one wherein the transmitting and receiving antennas are both half-wave dipoles. The second compares the transmission from a circular antenna to a dipole, or vice versa.

A well-designed circularly polarized circuit with a one and five-turn antenna on each end will have a power gain of over 75 or 18.8 db as compared to a horizontal dipole circuit, while the one and eight-turn antenna combination will have a power gain of about 250, or 24 db, without constructive or destructive interference.

If both ends of a communications circuit are operated with 8-turn antennas the power gain would then be about 15,849 or 42 db over a dipole circuit. In other words, the equivalent effect of a circular circuit over that of a horizontal dipole circuit with one watt input to the circular transmitting antenna would be the same as 15.8 kw into the dipole. Other similar compari-

cularly polarized antenna would appear to be of considerable advantage. For example, at 14 mc, a power gain of 45 to 80 over a dipole

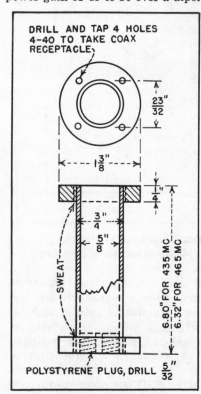

FIG. 4—Detail of impedance-matching unit fabricated from brass

Table I—Sample Antenna Design Data

Antenna Number	1	2	3	4	5	6	7
Fig. Number	—	3	4–7				
S—spacing, in.	4.1	8.1	8.1	10.8	15.3	9.4	12.7
D—diameter, in.	9.8	10.9	10.9	11.6	12.6	10.7	11.4
n—turns	5	1	5	5	5	5	1
s—1st turn, in.	1.0	2.0	2.0	2.7	3.8	2.5	3.0
d—reflector diam, in.	27.2	27.2	27.2	27.2	27.2	25.4	25.4

Table II—Performance Data

Antenna Number	0	1	2	3	4	5	6
Fig. Number	—		3	4–7			5
Turns n	0	5	1	5	5	5	8
Power number (Fig. 8)	0	—	1	—	2	—	3
Half-power beam width β_0	78.2	39	49	35	33	37	22
Ratio β_0/β_h (β_h for doublet)	1.00	0.50	0.63	0.45	0.41	0.47	0.28
Circular vs horizontal circuit							
Power gain	1	10.2	—	74.2	77.6	24.6	246.0
Gain in db	0	10.1	—	18.7	18.9	13.9	23.9
Circular ant to half-wave ant							
Power gain over two half-wave antennas	—	2.6	4.0	18.6	19.5	6.2	49.0
Gain in db	—	4.1	6.0	12.7	12.9	7.9	16.9

can be obtained, depending on tne physical dimensions of the antenna. At the higher frequencies, even higher gains can and have been realized, especially at 2 meters.

In the microwave region, the circularly polarized antenna can eliminate the need for spinning the antennas (this does not refer to conical scan), as is done is some cases for radiation-pattern-gap filling. At the same time, higher gains are realized. This antenna can also replace the dipole used to illuminate a parabolic dish.

The data on five selected circularly polarized arrays are given in Table III. The arrays with three vertically stacked elements materially increase the forward gain, the amount depending on the type of element used, and the vertical beam width is reduced without altering the already sharp horizontal beam. It is highly important, however, that proper feeding of and phasing among the elements in the array be established in order to secure such expected high gains.

REFERENCES

(1) John D. Kraus, Helical Beam Antenna, ELECTRONICS, p 109, April 1947.

(2) H. A. Wheeler, A Helical Antenna for Circular Polarization, *Proc. IRE*, p 1,484, Dec. 1947.

(3) John D. Kraus, Helical Beam Antennas for Wide-Band Applications, *Proc. IRE*, p 1,236, Oct. 1948.

(4) John D. Kraus, The Helical Antenna, *Proc. IRE*, p 263, March 1949.

(5) John D. Kraus, Helical Beam Antenna Design Techniques, *Communications*, p 6, Dec. 1949.

E. DILLON SMITH'S article in the February issue of ELECTRONICS, "Constructing Helical Antennas", deserves commendation for presenting in practical form a new technique of the antenna field.

I was impressed, however, by the exceptionally high values (listed in Table III) of power gain claimed for antenna systems composed of helical arrays as compared to the dipole system. Upon investigation it appears that Mr. Smith obtains these values theoretically by multiplying the measured gain in decibels of an individual helix by the number of elements in the array. This procedure leads to erroneous results.

The gain of an antenna depends only upon its radiation pattern which, in turn, is a function of the spacing and the radiation pattern of the individual array elements. An exact determination of power gain requires an integration process on the radiation patterns; this cannot be done here since Mr. Smith supplies no data on his spacings. An approximate method, developed by Mr. John Ruze of this laboratory, states that the power gain will be slightly less than the value given by

$$G = \frac{27,000}{\beta_h \beta_v}$$

where G is the power gain of the array over that of a half-wave dipole, and β_h and β_v are half-power beamwidths expressed in degrees in the horizontal and vertical planes, respectively.

Using this formula and the beamwidths as given in Table III of the article, the power gain of the various arrays (with a dipole for a transmitting antenna) over that of a pair of dipoles is as follows:

Array No.	1	2	3	4	5
Power Gain	18	33	77	84	105
Gain in Db	12.5	15.2	18.9	19.2	20.2

The system power gain will be in-

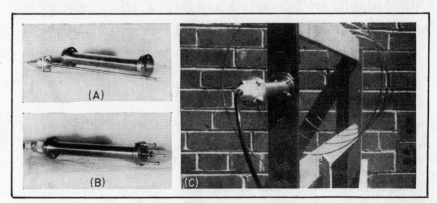

FIG. 5—Unassembled (A), assembled (B) and mounted (C) views of the 83.2-ohm impedance-matching transformer

creased by 6.0 decibels in each case if the single-turn circular antenna is substituted for the transmitting dipole.

In general, the gain of any practical antenna cannot be increased indefinitely without running into the grave obstacles encountered in the design of super-gain systems.

WALTER ROTMAN
Antenna Laboratory
A. F. Cambridge Res. Labs.
Cambridge, Mass.

Table III—Circularly Polarized Arrays

Array Number	1	2	3	4	5
Elements in array					
Vertically	3	3	3	2	3
Horizontally	1	1	1	2	3
Total	3	3	3	4	9
Turns n per element	1	5	8	8	8
Circular vs horizontal circuit					
Power gain	——	5×10^5	1.6×10^7	4×10^9	4×10^{21}
Gain in db	——	57	72	96	216
Circular antenna to half-wave antenna					
Power gain (over pair of half-wave)	63	7.9×10^3	1.3×10^5	6.3×10^6	2×10^{15}
Gain in db	18	39	51	68	153
Beam width in degrees					
β_v, vertical	30	24	16	18	16
β_h, horizontal	49	33	22	18	16

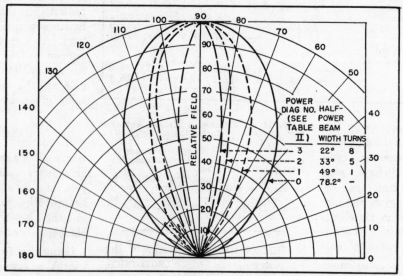

FIG. 6—Power-density field-strength patterns of three antennas (see Table II) for circular polarization, compared with half-wave horizontal dipole

Multi-V Antenna for F-M Broadcasting

Folded dipoles are bent into V's to form a lightweight array that can be mounted atop existing a-m antennas. The array is tuned by extensions on each arm, without seriously changing the impedance match and radiation pattern

By M. W. SCHELDORF

THE MULTI-V ANTENNA is a simple lightweight transmitting array designed for operation in the f-m broadcast band from 88 to 108 megacycles. A basic two-bay design can be attached readily to the sides, corners or top of existing a-m radiators. Additional bays may be added for higher gain.

The radiating portion of the antenna elements takes the shape of a V, or strictly speaking, of a truncated V. This configuration gives a horizontal radiation pattern that is close to circular.

To increase the antenna impedance the folded dipole principle commonly used in receiving antennas is employed. This permits the use of a 51.5-ohm main feeder line. There being no need to feed both

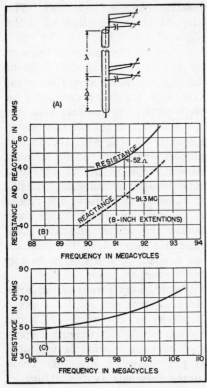

FIG. 1—(A) Circuit of two-element array, (B) driving impedance of one bay with extensions fixed for resonance at 91.3 mc, and (C) resistance of one bay at resonance as it is tuned over the f-m band

halves of the system when the folded antenna principle is used with antennas of low radiation resistance, this technique also reduces the number of transmission lines to half that otherwise required.

Although it is possible to build antennas that will cover the entire f-m band without adjustment, it is necessary to provide adjustments if the array is to be relatively small and light. The complication of these adjustments varies considerably with existing f-m antennas, and in most cases adjustments change both horizontal pattern and impedance. Usually pattern variations are tolerable, but impedance changes need to be counteracted by matching elements or tunable stubs.

With the multi-V one adjustment tunes the antenna to resonance for each frequency in the f-m band without materially affecting impedance values. Tuning is accomplished by extending secondary arms, primary arms remaining a

fixed length determined by the highest frequency of operation. This tuning scheme also has a distinct advantage in connection with the power-handling capacity of the system. In antennas of this general type, where the effective operating length is about a quarter wavelength, the highest voltage occurs at the open end. It is important, therefore, to keep open ends far apart. The diverging arms of the V antenna meet this requirement and provide a safety factor in addition.

In the development of the antenna element, it was found that the condition of horizontal pattern uniformity was possible only by operating at a frequency several megacycles above resonance; in other words, with a positive reactance present in the direct driving impedance. A series capacitor placed in the transmission line just below the end seal unit supplies the proper necessary reactance correction over the band.

Feeding the Array

In connecting two bays of the V antenna, it was necessary to make some arbitrary choices for the sake of simplicity. The widest frequency coverage results when equal-length lines to each bay are provided, and this is commonly done by placing the junction point halfway between them. If the impedances at the junction are higher than the characteristic impedance of the main

line it is best for bandwidth to parallel them. If they are less than this value, it is best to connect them in series. However, this requires a balun and means for reversing the phase of one of the elements. A simpler method is to run one line to the top bay and tap it at the second bay. This scheme effectively places the antenna elements in parallel at the junction point, so such a system is best adapted to driving impedances of values higher than 51.5 ohms (ideally 103 ohms).

The driving impedance inherently varies over the frequency range, and because it is impractical to step up to precisely 103 ohms by means of the folded-dipole principle, a compromise is acceptable and a matcher is utilized to transform the impedance at the junction point to one that averages 51.5 ohms over the frequency range. The resultant schematic diagram is shown in Fig. 1A. Each antenna element has its series capacitor, and the common impedance at the junction point is matched to 51.5 ohms. Note that the feed line is completely isolated for direct currents, permitting an insulation resistance check without disconnection of the elements.

The single-interconnection scheme makes it necessary to feed the antenna with a line one wavelength long between the two bays. In addition, the use of rigid line for this purpose fixes the vertical spacing also at a wavelength. Specifically, due to the reduced velocity

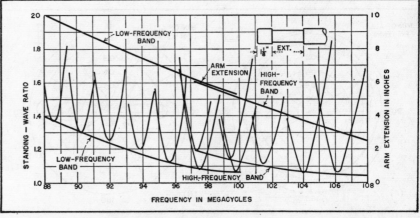

FIG. 2—Standing-wave ratio curves about resonance of antennas when tuned to various frequencies in the band, showing uniform performance

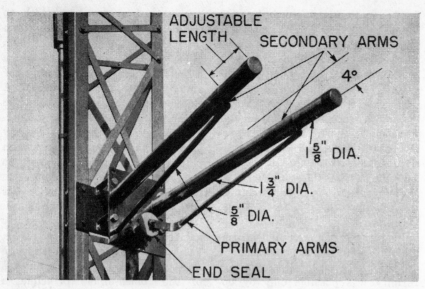

One element of the V antenna, mounted on an existing a-m antenna tower, showing the details of its construction. For usual installations, two elements on a supporting I-beam would be mounted on the top of the a-m tower

of propagation in the lines used (it is necessary to support the inner conductor at regular intervals with a dielectric material), the spacing becomes $K\lambda$ where K is the relative velocity of propagation and λ is the wavelength in free space.

The radiators proper consist essentially of straight pieces of hard-temper copper tubing. Each pair of arms has a $\frac{5}{8}$-inch-diameter fixed length and a $1\frac{3}{4}$-inch-diameter length with a telescoping $1\frac{5}{8}$-inch extension for frequency adjustment. The single excited input conductor is connected to a standard end seal to support its free end.

The two elements are identical but they are attached to the tower differently. The lower bay is fastened rigidly to the tower. The upper bay is held by a set of four straps, which permit vertical movement but prevent horizontal movement. This mounting affords a simple means of allowing for expansion differences in the copper of the interconnection line and the steel of the tower. It also allows the tower to bend without stressing the copper line unduly.

The support for one type V antenna is a steel H-beam so oriented that the well on one side forms a protective enclosure for the trans-

mission line and matcher. The climbing steps are attached to the edges of the flanges on the opposite side, so that unusual freedom for climbing is achieved. Each of the elements has a series capacitor built into the inner conductor of the transmission line just below the end seal. The capacitor consists of a coaxial element with appropriate support insulators. The matcher element consists of an oversized inner conductor and a multiplicity of standard insulators, electrically a quarter-wavelength long and having the proper effective characteristic impedance. The junction line is made in two lengths to suit two frequency bands.

When the extensions of the large radiator arms are set for a given frequency of operation (91.3 mc, for example), the driving impedance of each element is indicated by the curves of Fig. 1B. These curves demonstrate the ability of the antenna to operate over the modulation band with an associated f-m transmitter and transmission line. A family of these curves serves to determine the matcher characteristics, using the values of resonant resistance, of which 52 ohms is representative for 91.3 mc. A collection of the resonant resistance values may be plotted as shown in Fig. 1C. This particular curve indicates that the uniformity is sufficient to permit the construction of just one matcher to cover the entire f-m range. The matcher for

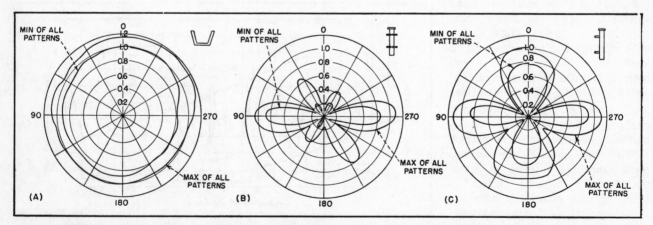

FIG. 3—Horizontal radiation pattern limits (A) show relative independence of tuning adjustment. Vertical pattern limits (B) across V (see insert showing orientation of array) and (C) along V, show somewhat greater variation

the system is therefore designed for a characteristic impedance of 39.8 ohms and is made effectively a λ/4 long at the center of the range.

Measurement of standing-wave ratio on the main feed line is made with the entire antenna mounted well away from reflecting and absorbing surfaces. A series of measurements made over a frequency band, corresponding to fixed positions of the radiator extensions, is of vital importance. Curves of these measurements are shown in Fig. 2. Two corresponding curves showing the necessary arm-extension settings are also given in this figure. The uniformity of the results demonstrates the reliability with which the arms may be set in the factory.

Horizontal and Vertical Radiation

Horizontal field patterns were measured and plotted over the f-m range. The magnitude of the plots was adjusted to give the same radiation in the horizontal plane as an antenna with equal radiation in all directions with a power gain of 1.0. The variations from a circle over the f-m range are so small that the limits can be shown by two curves as in Fig. 3A.

The corresponding vertical patterns are shown in Fig. 3B and 3C. The first is taken perpendicular to the neutral plane and the second is taken in this plane. The difference is due to symmetry for the first case and lack of it in the second.

It might appear that the vertical radiation represented by Fig. 3C would lead to low gain in the horizontal plane, but it should be pointed out that this field is effective in a small solid angle whereas the field in the horizontal direction is effective in a large solid angle. The limit curves also seem to indicate greater variations than those of Fig. 3A, but this is not harmful as it is due to the variation in tilt of the horizontal beam and side lobes as the phase relations between the currents of the two bays vary across the bands.

From the horizontal patterns and two major vertical patterns it is possible to calculate with sufficient practical accuracy the gain of the antenna system, in the horizontal plane, over a dipole antenna. The calculated curves are in Fig. 4.

When the antenna is operated at 93 mc or 103 mc, for which frequencies the junction lines produce exactly in-phase currents at the two

bays, the horizontal beam is precisely horizontal. Below these frequencies the beams tilt downward, and above these frequencies the beams tilt upward. By splitting the f-m range into two bands, as previously mentioned, the tilt has been kept to a low enough value so that the gain is not impaired. Figure 4 also shows curves of beam tilt obtained from the experimental curves.

Because of the wide separation of the high-voltage portions of the radiators, the individual elements are well suited for high-power operation. A conservative rating of 5 kw per bay has been placed on the antenna, although field experience probably will justify a greater power rating.

The writer wishes to acknowledge the able assistance of H. M. Anderson and C. W. Meyer in the development of this antenna.

BIBLIOGRAPHY

(1) Bruce E. Montgomery, A Very-High Frequency Aircraft Antenna for the Reception of 109 Megacycle Localizer Signals, *Proc. IRE*, 33, p 767-772, Nov. 1945.
(2) Lewis Winner, A Report on the Sixth Annual Conference of Broadcast Engineers, *Communications*, 26, p 30-74, April 1946.
(3) M. W. Scheldorf, FM Circular Antenna, *General Electric Review*, 46, p 163-170, March 1943.

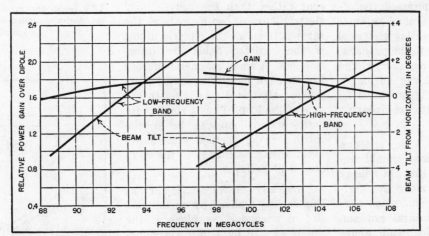

FIG. 4—Changes in radiation patterns shown in Fig. 3 produce slight changes in effective antenna gain, which is mostly due to changes in tilt angle of major lobe of beam. The decreased gain at the edges of the band are chiefly due to this tilt

Flush-Mounted Antenna for Mobile Application

Small annular-slot antenna with the same radiation pattern as a dipole can be built into the metal roof of a car. Theoretical development and experimental results are given for operation at mobile-service and citizens-band frequencies

By DONALD R. RHODES

THE FREQUENCIES initially used for two-way mobile radio were relatively low, so the problem of radiating and receiving signals was usually solved by placing as long an antenna as possible in a convenient physical location. This position was not critical because of the ease with which low-frequency radiation could be diffracted around the conducting surface of an automobile body, and the length was not critical because of the physical impracticability of erecting a vertical rod more than a small fraction of a wavelength in height.

The problem of providing an antenna at the high frequencies in use today is not as easily solved and requires careful consideration of all the influencing factors. As the frequency is increased the effects of diffraction around an automobile diminish, creating electrical shadows,—barriers to the propagation of radio-frequency energy. The antenna dimensions can no longer be chosen arbitrarily but must be part of a systematic engineering design.

Considering that the antenna should have a nearly omnidirectional pattern and that its energy should be directed along the horizon for ground communication purposes, the most natural antenna choice is the vertical stub above ground now being used by police, taxicabs, telephone companies, and others in the 150-mc region. Although a vertical stub on an automobile roof is electrically excellent, its size and appearance leaves much to be desired. Release of the citi-

zens communications band by the Federal Communications Commission will create an additional widespread popular demand for two-way mobile radio systems and the problem of designing a less conspicuous antenna will no doubt present itself.

Fundamental Principles

A short stub antenna mounted above a ground plane can be considered an electric dipole in free space. A small circular-loop antenna may be considered a magnetic dipole on the axis of the loop and has the same radiation pattern as an electric dipole with the radiated electric and magnetic fields interchanged. Furthermore, a circular loop carrying magnetic current rather than the conventional electric current will produce the same pattern as the electric dipole if the radiated fields are interchanged. A small magnetic-current loop can not be distinguished from a short electric dipole lying in the axis of the loop. Thus a small magnetic-current loop can be substituted for the vertical stub above ground with no change in the radiated field pattern.

Physically a magnetic-current loop can be realized by an annular slot in a conducting plane if the slot is excited by a uniform radial electric field as shown in Fig. 1. It has been shown from diffraction theory by Pistolkors[1] that the relative radiation pattern of a narrow annular slot in a perfectly conducting ground plane can be expressed as follows

$$|E_\theta| \simeq kr\, J_1\,(kr \sin \theta)$$

where θ is the angle between the direction of measurement and a line perpendicular to the ground plane, r is the radius of the annular slot, k is $2\pi/\lambda$, and J_1 is the first order Bessel function. This same expression was obtained by Foster[2] for the radiated magnetic field of a cir-

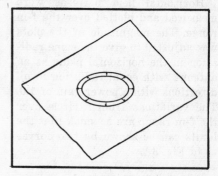

FIG. 1—An annular slot cut in a conducting surface, excited by a uniform radial electric field

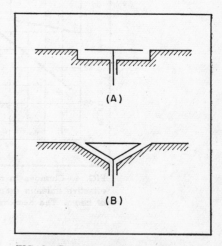

FIG. 2—Cross-sectional view of two possible feed systems for the annular-slot antenna

cular loop with uniform electric current. The relative radiation pattern of a thin wire stub above a perfectly conducting ground is given by the following[3]

$$|E_\theta| \simeq \frac{\cos(kl\cos\theta) - \cos kl}{\sin\theta}$$

where l is the length of the stub. If the slot radius is small the expression for radiated electric field may be simplified by neglecting all but the first term of the expanded Bessel function. Likewise the expression for the electric field radiated from a short stub may be simplified by neglecting all but the lowest-order terms in the expanded sine and cosine functions. For a small slot

$$|E_\theta| \simeq \frac{(kr)^2}{2}\sin\theta$$

and for a short stub

$$|E_\theta| \simeq \frac{(kl)^2}{2}\sin\theta$$

thus we have an exact analogy between the radiated field of a short vertical stub and a small annular slot.

The requirement of a uniform field at the surface of the slot necessitates a symmetrical feed system, the particular feed system used to be determined largely by space limitations and the input impedance desired. Two possible feed systems which can be used to produce a uniform radial electric field at the slot are shown in cross-section in Fig. 2. Both feed systems consist essentially of a radial two-conductor transmission line coaxially fed. Type A has a cylindrical cavity which occupies less space than the conical cavity of type B. However type B provides a more gradual transition of energy from the source to free space and will therefore have a different input impedance. The impedance will depend entirely upon the manner in which the cavity matches the transmission line to the impedance of free space.

Radiation Patterns

To illustrate the analogy between a small annular slot and a short stub above ground for a practical

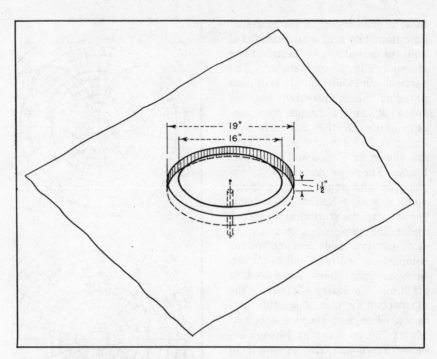

FIG. 3—Sketch showing dimensions of full-scale experimental annular slot. The radiation pattern of this slot was measured at 150 mc and 450 mc

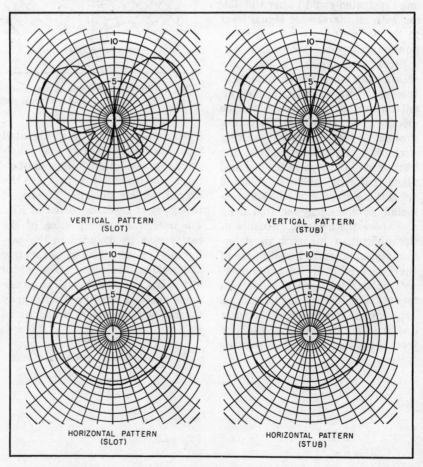

VERTICAL PATTERN (SLOT) VERTICAL PATTERN (STUB)

HORIZONTAL PATTERN (SLOT) HORIZONTAL PATTERN (STUB)

FIG. 4—Radiation patterns in the vertical and horizontal planes of an annular slot and a vertical stub, measured at 150 mc

case, a one-seventh scale model of an automobile roof was constructed and the annular slot of the form shown in Fig. 3 was installed. The vertical and horizontal radiation patterns were measured in free space at model frequencies corresponding to the full-scale frequencies 150 mc and 450 mc and are shown in Fig. 4 and 5, respectively. Then the annular slot was removed and replaced by a short vertical stub. Radiation patterns for the vertical stub were measured under the same conditions as the slot patterns and are shown for comparison in Fig. 4 and 5. It can be seen that there is, indeed, a striking similarity between the corresponding slot and stub patterns. The correspondence is better at 150 mc than at 450 mc because there the slot is small in terms of wavelength. This suggests that a smaller slot than the one illustrated could be used at 450 mc with an increase in signal level in the horizontal plane for a given power input to the antenna.

Since the radiation patterns shown were measured on a model in free space the true pattern of an antenna on an automobile will be modified by reflection from the ground and from other reflecting surfaces. Radiation below the horizon as indicated in the vertical plane patterns will be reflected from the ground and will add vectorially to the energy radiated along and above the horizon. Because of the difficulties inherent in determining the magnitude and phase of energy reradiated from innumerable objects the vertical plane patterns can serve only as an approximate indication of the space distribution of energy radiated from the actual automobile antenna system.

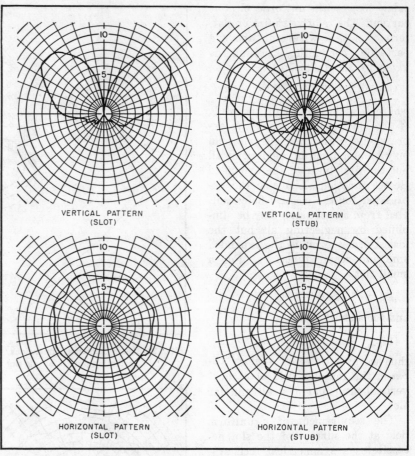

FIG. 5—Radiation patterns in the vertical and horizontal planes of an annular slot and a vertical stub, measured at 450 mc

An antenna of the flush-mounted type should preferably be fabricated by the automobile manufacturer and considered part of the overall vehicle design. If one of the types of feed suggested in Fig. 2 is used, the lower portion of the cavity may be included in the car-top die or constructed separately and welded into place. The width of the slot gap is not critical, so the upper portion of the cavity may assume any convenient proportions.

Fabrication

Several types of dielectric mate-rial are available to fill the cavity and exclude rain, snow and dirt. It is important that a nonconducting paint be used over the slot area to prevent excessive loss of power. The final result should yield an efficient, self-contained radiating system for two-way mobile radio.

REFERENCES

(1) A. A. Pistolkors, Theory of the Circular Diffraction Antenna, *Proc IRE*, p 58, Jan. 1948.
(2) Donald Foster, Loop Antennas with Uniform Current, *Proc IRE*, p 604, Oct. 1944.
(3) Ramo and Whinnery, "Fields and Waves in Modern Radio," John Wiley and Sons, p 433, 1944.

Disguised Antenna Design

TO DISGUISE the transmitting features of the normal police antenna so that it conforms with the appearance and placement of an ordinary car radio aerial, engineers at Ward Products Corporation have designed an antenna whose appearance is identical to that installed on a standard radio-equipped pleasure car. To best accomplish this deception, a standard automotive antenna was modified to give permanent electrical connections at the telescopic joints of the tube assembly.

As a transmitting antenna in 152 to 174-mc use, the 55½-inch whip of

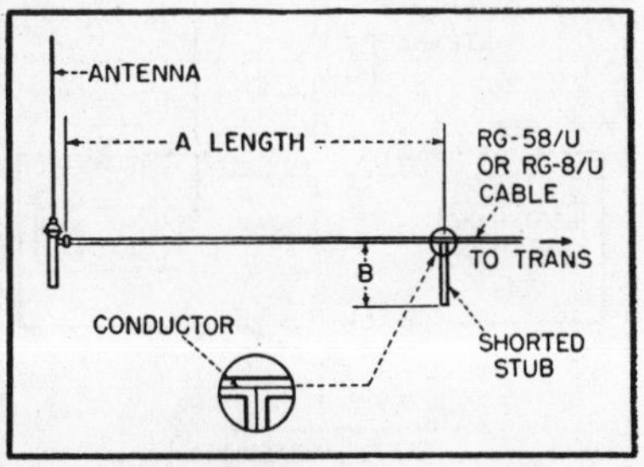

FIG. 1—Dimensions for the stub and line to load the antenna at frequencies from 24 to 50 mc are given in the text

the new antenna operates as a ¾-wavelength antenna and adjusting or loading the antenna is not necessary. However, it is advantageous to bring the Ward SPPB71 antenna as close as possible to the corner post of the windshield. The antenna then operates as an apparent J with the corner post acting as the ¼-wave-length grounded leg. The normal output circuit of commercial transmitters will load to the antenna without difficulty.

For 25 to 50-mc services, the antenna is basically short and it is necessary to load the antenna with a simple stub arrangement to obtain minimum standing wave ratio. The diagram of Fig. 1 illustrates the most convenient loading method.

The basic theory of the loading method is that an antenna less than a ¼ wavelength long presents an impedance at its base of $R - jX_c$ which varies as shown in Fig. 2.

A ⅙-wavelength antenna impedance is thus approximately 15-j100. Connecting a transmission line of $Z_o = 52 + j0$ (RG-8/U) or $53.5 + j0$ (RG-58/U) ohms to the antenna will result in a mismatch and improper loading of the transmitter.

A shorted transmission line stub B less than a quarter wavelength long presents a pure inductive reactance of $0 + jX_L$ ohms. In the SPPB71, moving along the trans-

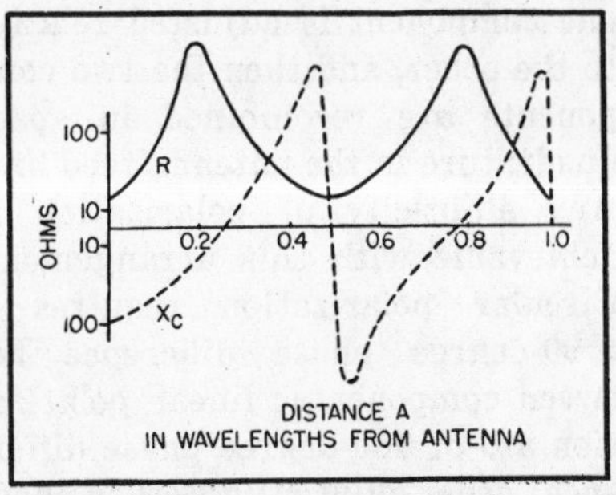

FIG. 2—Variation of impedance at base of antenna as a function of its length

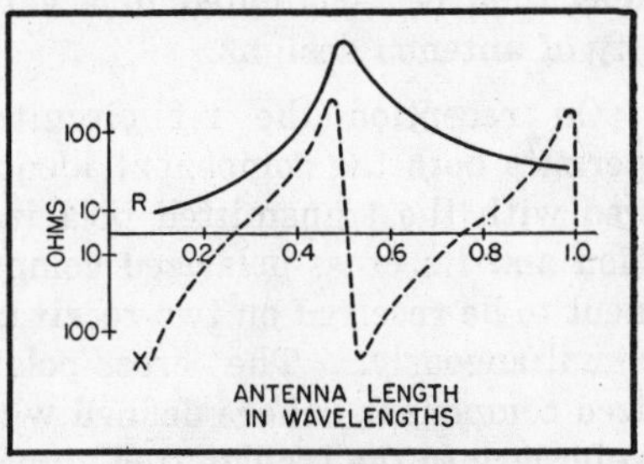

FIG. 3—Variation of R and X° along the transmission line

mission line from the antenna, the values of R and X_c, looking toward the antenna, vary as shown in Fig. 3.

At some point on the line (for example $A = 0.2$), the resistive component of the impedance is equal to the characteristic impedance of the transmission line. At this point, stub B is connected to cancel out the capacitive reactance of the line. In this way the total reactance is brought to zero. From this point, looking toward the antenna, we see an impedance of $52 + j0$ ohms after connecting the stub. Therefore a transmission line connected to the stub network will see a good match with maximum energy transfer.

The following table gives the required lengths for cables A and B of Fig. I.

Loading Chart

Freq in Mc	*A in inches*	*B in inches*
24	60	3
25	56¼	3
26	53⅛	3
27	50½	3⅛
28	47¾	3⅛
29	45	3⅛
30	42½	3¼
31	40	3¼
32	37¾	3⅜
33	35½	3⅜
34	33¼	3½
35	31¼	3¾
36	29	3⅞
37	27	4⅛
38	25	4⅜
39	23	4¾
40	21¼	5
41	19½	5½
42	17½	5¾
43	15	6¼
44	14	6¾
45	12½	7⅜
46	10½	8
47	8½	8¾
48	6¼	9¾
49	3¾	10¾
50	1	12

The output circuits of commercial transmitters will load to the antenna without difficulty.

The polar plot of the antenna radiation pattern indicates the SPPB71 pattern is more nondirectional than the rear or bumper mounted ¼ wavelength whip and less nondirectional than the roof top mounted ¼ wavelength whip.

Microwave Radar Antenna

Special design permits transmission and reception of any specified polarization in search radars, including linear and circular as special cases. Antenna can receive, separately and simultaneously, both transmitted polarization and its cross-polarized component

By HERMAN N. CHAIT

ELIMINATION of certain unwanted radar target reflections is made possible through the analysis of reflected radiation polarization by circular and linear components. In principle this analysis could be accomplished with a plurality of antennas designed to transmit or receive the various polarization components. In practice, however, limitations on space and equipment make it highly desirable to use a single antenna design that is capable of application over a wide range of frequencies. The antenna design described here has the property not only of receiving the transmitted polarization, but also of receiving separately and simultaneously its cross-polarized component.

Previously it has not been possible to use a circularly-polarized search radar system with a single antenna used for transmission and reception, since for most targets the reflected wave will have its sense of polarization reversed and thus will be rejected by the antenna. This present antenna design removes such a limitation and so can be used in a search radar system employing circular polarization. Another advantage in this connection is the possibility of using low power t-r and anti t-r tubes to protect the receiver since receiver and transmitter are on opposite terminals of a hybrid junction.

It is possible to design an antenna with any desired beam characteristics and with either continuously variable polarization or with some chosen fixed polarization. The proper choice of this polarization parameter at a given time may greatly increase the utility of

present-day radar systems.

General Principles

Figure 1 is the block diagram of a system that establishes its polarization characteristics in the r-f transmission line rather than in the antenna proper, and is therefore capable of rather general application. On transmission the power is divided into two equal components in a hybrid junction, the phase of one component is adjusted relative to the other, and then the two components are recombined in space quadrature in the antenna feed line. Any ellipticity of polarization is achievable with this arrangement. Circular polarization requires a ±90-degree phase difference between components; linear polarization a 0 or 180-degree phase difference; other ellipticities, other phase differences. The antenna feed line may then be terminated in a variety of antenna designs.

On reception the r-f circuitry permits both the component identified with the transmitted polarization and its cross-polarized component to be received on two receivers simultaneously. The cross-polarized component is here defined with reference to the transmitted signal. These two components have the same ellipticity ratio, the major axis of their polarization ellipses orthogonal, and their instantaneous E-vectors rotating in opposite senses.

The ability of this system to transmit circular polarization of one sense and then to receive both senses of circular polarization separately and simultaneously is shown in Fig. 2. A generator,

furnishing a voltage $V/0°$, is placed at the right-hand terminal of the hybrid junction (Fig. 2B), which is a magic tee. For purposes of explanation, another generator fur-

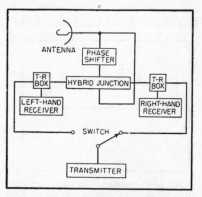

FIG. 1—Block diagram of system that establishes polarization characteristics in the r-f transmission line rather than in antenna proper

nishing no voltage is assumed at the left-hand terminal. Therefore, equal voltages of $0.7V/0°$, in time phase with each other, will appear at equal path distances in the E- and H-plane arms of the magic tee. By adding 90 degrees of phase change to the E-plane path, and arranging the two input terminals to the square waveguide so that they are perpendicular to each other, two voltages equal in magnitude and in time and space quadrature will appear at the antenna.

The signal that is radiated will therefore be right-hand circularly polarized. Similarly, a left-hand circularly polarized signal can be radiated merely by interchanging the two generators, or by adding another 180 degrees of phase change to the E-plane path.

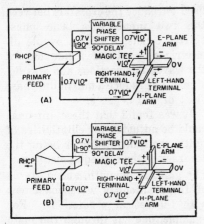

FIG. 2—Reception (A) and transmission (B) of right-hand polarization are illustrated

Reception

Upon reception, the right-hand circularly-polarized component of the incident field induces a voltage at the vertical terminal of the waveguide which is equal in magnitude to, and leads in phase by 90 degrees, the voltage induced at the horizontal terminal. Due to the phase shifter, the two voltages arrive at the E- and H-plane arms in phase and are therefore detected at the right-hand terminal of the magic tee as indicated in Fig. 2A. In like manner the left-hand circularly polarized component of the incident field is received at the left-hand terminal.

To use this same antenna to

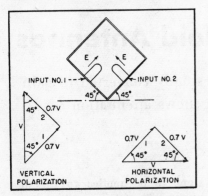

FIG. 3—Operation of antenna when used to transmit and receive linear polarization

transmit and receive linear polarizations, it is necessary that a 0 or 180-degree phase shift be intro-

duced between components. If horizontal and vertical polarizations are desired, the antenna must be so oriented that the input terminals make angles of 45 and 135 degrees with the ground as shown in Fig. 3. Any arbitrarily chosen elliptical polarization can be transmitted and received by a proper adjustment of the phase shift and rotation of the antenna feed.

Whatever component is generated, the component received at the generating terminal of the hybrid junction has the same polarization characteristics as the transmitted signal. For radar type of operation, assuming a single reflection of the transmitted signal from the target surface, the transmitter and receiver of a given linear component are located at the same terminal, whereas the transmitter for a circular component and the receiver for the reflected circular component are located at different terminals of the hybrid junction. It is this fact which excludes the use of circular polarization in radar systems having antennas with one terminal only.

Design Criteria

It was assumed in the previous sections that the transmitted power was divided exactly equally between the two arms and that the two path lengths differed by exactly 90 degrees or by 0 degrees or 180 degrees for circularly or linearly polarized components respectively. In practice a tolerance is put on the polarization characteristics, and it is therefore necessary that design criteria be established. Those for circular polarization are discussed here.

Let the two orthogonal linear components of an electromagnetic field be represented as

$$E_x = A \cos \omega t$$
$$E_y = B \cos (\omega t + \phi) \qquad (1)$$

where A and B are the amplitudes of the components and ϕ the phase angle between them. Then the power ellipticity of polarization can be written

$$e^2 = \frac{P_{max}}{P_{min}} =$$

$$\frac{A^2 + B^2 + \sqrt{(A^2+B^2)^2 - 4\,A^2\,B^2\sin^2\phi}}{A^2 + B^2 - \sqrt{(A^2+B^2)^2 - 4\,A^2\,B^2\sin^2\phi}} \qquad (2)$$

where P_{max} and P_{min} are proportional to the squares of the major and minor axes of the polarization ellipse of this field. When A is equal to B and only ϕ is allowed to

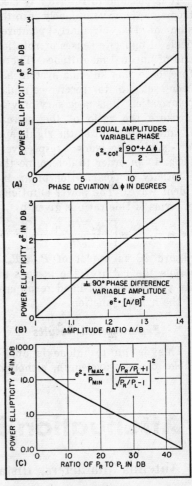

FIG. 4—Curves showing relationship between power ellipticity and other parameters

vary, Eq. 2 becomes

$$\frac{P_{max}}{P_{min}} = \cot^2 \frac{\phi}{2} \qquad (3)$$

For values of ellipticity near circular it is convenient to express the power ellipticity as $P_{max}/P_{min} = \cot^2 \left(\dfrac{90° + \Delta\phi}{2} \right)$, thus showing the deviation of the ellipticity from unity directly in terms of the deviation of ϕ from 90 degrees. Figure 4A is a plot of this relation.

If on the other hand $\phi = \pm 90$ degrees exactly and the amplitudes of the components are allowed to vary, Eq. 2 becomes

$$\frac{P_{\max}}{P_{\min}} = \left(\frac{A}{B}\right)^2 \qquad (4)$$

Figure 4B is a plot of Eq. 4.

Measurement of Ellipticity

It is possible to resolve any electromagnetic wave uniquely into the sum of two circularly polarized fields of opposite senses of rotation and of unequal magnitudes. Therefore, once this antenna system has been set up to receive circular polarization, it is necessary only to measure the ratio of the powers P_R and P_L present at the right- and left-hand receivers respectively (Fig. 1) in order to determine the ellipticity of polarization of an incident wave. The power ellipticity in terms of this ratio is given by

$$e^2 = \frac{P_{\max}}{P_{\min}} = \left[\frac{\sqrt{P_R/P_L}+1}{\sqrt{P_R/P_L}-1}\right]^2 \qquad (5)$$

Figure 4C is a plot of $P_{\max}/P_{\min}$ versus the ratio of the powers at the right- and left-hand terminals of the hybrid junction.

Experimental Results

This design technique is applicable to any wavelength, although the choice of circuit elements is dictated by size or weight limitations. Two such systems have been built, one operating in the 3.2-cm band, the other in the 10-cm band. The two photographs show the 3.2-cm model. The square waveguide used as the transmission line was designed to transmit two TE_{10} modes at right angles to each other but no higher modes. In other words the inner dimension a of the square waveguide satisfied the condition $\lambda/\sqrt{2} > a > \lambda/2$. Waveguides instead of probe couplings were

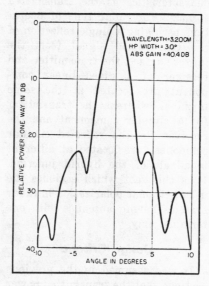

FIG. 5—Power pattern of a circularly-polarized antenna paraboloid 30 inches in diameter

used to reduce the crosstalk between the two input lines. The phase shifter consisted of a movable dielectric slab placed inside one of the waveguide sections and was designed to produce a maximum phase shift of 360 degrees.

It was found that these antennas could be adjusted for ellipticities of unity, the limiting factor being the accuracy of the test equipment used. The gain, beamwidth, and patterns of these antennas were consistent with theoretical predictions. For example, one cut through the main lobe of the radiation pattern of the parabolic type antenna shown was measured for many linear polarizations. It was found that the ellipticity of polarization was no greater than one decibel over the entire portion of the main lobe when the on-axis ellipticity had been adjusted to be less than 0.25 db. Figure 5 shows a typical cut.

Acknowledgment

The author is indebted to L. C. Van Atta and J. I. Bohnert of of Naval Research Laboratory and L. J. Chu of Massachusetts Institute of Technology for their continuous encouragement and stimulating consultations. The author also wishes to acknowledge preliminary work on this project done by S. Topol, formerly of Naval Research Laboratory.

Attenuation Between Paraboloid Antennas

Antenna diameters, distance and wavelength figures are simply converted to gain and loss in db with the table. Algebraic addition shows attenuation

By E. DYKE

THE TABLE provides a convenient means of calculating line-of-sight space attenuation between two paraboloid antennas, but can be used for other shapes and designs if the effective diameter is utilized.

The left-hand column represents the physical quantities shown in the figure and listed below. The corresponding right-hand numerals are equivalent decibel values. The table can be extended since the right column is 20 $\log_{10}$ of the left column. Equation 1 shows the algebraic signs to be applied to the db values. The 93-db constant is a value representative of good design practice.

Space attenuation, $P_r/P_t = -93$ $-S -\lambda +D_r +D_t$ decibels $\qquad (1)$

When D is antenna diameter in inches

S is separation between antennas in miles

λ is wavelength in centimeters

P_r is power received

P_t is power transmitted

Physical Quantities	Gain or Loss in Db
0.1	−20.0
0.5	− 6.0
1.0	0.0
2	+ 6.0
3	+ 9.5
4	12.0
5	14.0
6	15.6
7	16.9
8	18.0
9	19.1

10	20.0
12	21.6
14	22.9
16	24.0
18	25.1
20	26.0
22	26.8
24	27.6
26	28.3
30	29.5
35	30.9
40	32.0
45	33.1
48	33.6
50	34
60	35.6
70	36.9
72	37.2
80	38.1
90	39.1
100	40
120	41.6

140	42.9
160	44.1
180	45.1
200	46.0
250	48.0
300	49.5
400	52.0
500	54.0

Example:

Factor	Dimension	Db
Constant	....	−93
Distance (S)	50 miles	−34
Wavelength (λ)	4.5 cm	+13
Rec. ant. (D_r)	40 in.	+32
Trans. ant. (D_t)	40 in.	+32
Attenuation		−76

Received power P_r can be obtained in dbm by adding the value of transmitted power P_t in dbm to the db value of the attenuation.

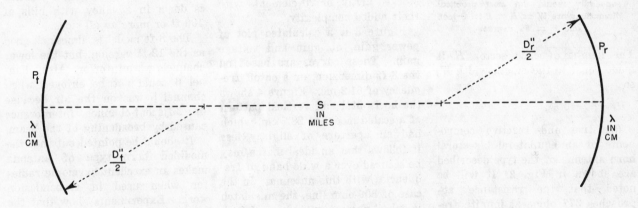

Horn Antennas for Television

Eight-foot equilateral bisectional horn antenna provides over 14-db gain on channel 13 compared with isotropic source antenna. Same performance can be obtained for transmission. Antenna matches commercially available 300-ohm line

By DEAN O. MORGAN

Since horizontally polarized waves are of primary importance (for the reception of television and f-m signals) two of the usual four sides of a horn may be omitted, and the resulting two-sided horn may be fed by direct excitation.

A drawing of this antenna is shown in Fig. 1. This design consists of only two vertical side sectors of the horn. The feed line is connected at the apex of the horn, one conductor being connected to each sector. There are no metallic ties between sectors.

Attenuation to transmission transition being gradual, the approximate cutoff is determined when

$$W_c = 0.5\lambda_c$$

If true unidirectional characteristics are wanted, the flare angle θ should be small. However, a small θ would necessitate a long horn. A good compromise angle of 60 degrees may be used. In this case the dimension B is given by

$$B_c = \frac{W_c}{2 \sin \theta} = 0.5 \lambda_c$$

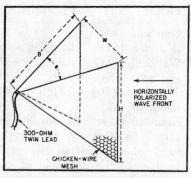

FIG. 1—For reception of channels 2 through 13, where channel 2 is not especially weak, the most practical dimensions are W = H = B = 8 feet, and θ = 60 degrees

The height of each sector H is made equal to the mouth width W, so

$$H_c = W_c = 0.5\lambda_c$$

Resistive and reactive components of an equilateral bisectoral horn antenna of the type described are shown in Fig. 2. It will be noted that the resistance approaches 377 ohms at infinite frequency. The reactive component similarly approaches zero.

Line Match

Since both 300-ohm and 400-ohm line are commercially procurable, frequency down to cutoff (being an ideal match at three times cutoff, or channel 7 and 8).

Dimensions

The actual dimensions used will depend upon the individual problem. For most practical vhf-tv reception, cutoff can be taken as 57 megacycles. For this value of cutoff, $W_c = B_c = H_c = 8.6$ ft. With these dimensions the power gain at 213 mc over an isotropic source is 14.7 db.

Using a slightly reduced size (8 ft) this gain is reduced to 14 db. This is comparable to the gain from 10 dipoles and reflectors in a stacked array, or 20 elements with their added complexity.

Figure 3 is a calculated plot of power gain, db gain and voltage gain. These curves are based on the 8-ft dimension, or a cutoff frequency of 61.2 mc. Figure 4 shows the horizontal and vertical pattern of a scaled model at 28.7 cm, which had an aperture of slightly less it follows that an ideal match may be secured over a wide band of frequencies with this antenna. In the case of 300-ohm line, the mismatch is only 2 percent in power or 0.8 db in addition to the published attenu-

ation loss of the line, when perfectly matched. At cutoff frequency the loss increases to 0.25 percent in power or 1.22 db. Below cutoff the loss increases rapidly due to the decrease in resistance. The use of 400-ohm line would decrease these losses quite a bit from the infinite than 3 times cutoff. Rear radiation is of the order of 1 percent.

Performance

During the course of the experiments, a 12-ft model was erected at Skaneateles, New York. Good pictures and sound were obtained on channels 4 (Buffalo and Schenectady), 5 (Syracuse), 6 (Rochester), 8 (Syracuse), 12 (Binghamton), and 13 (Utica). Other high-gain types failed to produce a usable picture on any channel except 5. This particular location is down in a valley with hills of 100 ft or more an all sides.

The 8-ft model is almost as good as the 12-ft version, but the lower channels were inferior. Also, channel 6 could not be enjoyed when channel 5 was on the air because of adjacent-channel interference caused by broadening of the beam.

It should be pointed out that the modified horn type of antenna makes an excellent harmonic radiator when used in transmission work. Experiments show that the presence of a metal supporting pole does not affect operation, and the

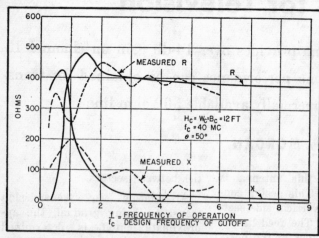

FIG. 2—Universal impedance curves show resistance approaching 377 ohms and reactance approaching zero ohms as frequency increases

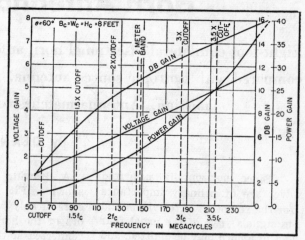

FIG. 3—Curves show calculated gain characteristics (over isotropic point source) for 8-foot 60-degree modified horn antenna

planes may be constructed from wire mesh (chicken wire variety shown in photograph), spline-type construction, woven wire or flat sheets.

Acknowledgements

The author wishes to thank R. B. Dome for his assistance in regard to the fundamental concepts of this antenna. Much advice and helpful hints were also appreciated from

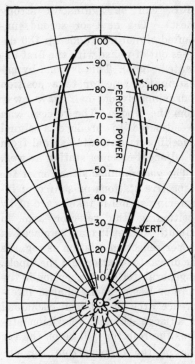

FIG. 4—Directivity patterns for 28.5-cm model (antenna rotated for vertically-polarized signal)

R. E. Fisk and L. O. Krause, associates in antenna development at General Electric, Electronics Park, Syracuse, N. Y.

BIBLIOGRAPHY

R. B. Dome, "Television Principles," Chapter 8. McGraw-Hill Book Co.

W. L. Barrow and F. D. Lewis, The Sectoral Electromagnetic Horn, *Proc. IRE*, p 41, Jan. 1939.

W. L. Barrow and L. J. Chum, Theory of the Electromagnetic Horn, *Proc. IRE*, p 51, Jan. 1939.

D. R. Rhodes, An Experimental Investigation of the Radiation Patterns of Electromagnetic Horn Antennas, *Proc. IRE*, p 1,101, Sept. 1949.

Infinite-Rejection Beam

By W. F. HOISINGTON

IN THE manufacture of high-gain multielement beam antennas, it has not been unusual to be asked for an antenna that would cut out completely a station in back of the beam on the same frequency. One standard 16-element f-m beam showed over 6,000 to 1 power ratio on transmission, but a check of the ratio on reception gave a much lower figure.

Further investigation showed that very strong reflections were present in almost every location tested, and that by moving the beam one-half wavelength in space, front-back ratios both higher and lower than the above figure were obtained. These reflections are the source of television ghosts, and are considerably aggravated by the low f-b ratio of the average television receiving antenna.

The infinite rejection beam (hereafter designated I.R.B.) has three main parts: the receiving element or elements, the reflector or reflectors, and the rejector or rejecting elements. In the economical example shown in Fig. 1, suitable for television reception, the first two parts may consist of a simple folded dipole of proper impedance, a fixed screen or wire reflector in the normal position approximately one-fourth wavelength in back of the dipole, and the rejecting element which is placed in front of the dipole.

Theory of Operation

A desired signal is received from the front on the dipole. The reflector also receives a signal and sends it back to the dipole in proper phase, reinforcing the dipole signal.

This is standard so far, the main requirement for the I.R.B. being that some f-b ratio must be obtained—the higher the better. The unwanted signal, geographically located in back, or at any angle in the back 270 degrees approximately, is also received on the dipole and more or less attenuated by the reflector, depending on design. The rejector now throws a cancellation signal from the unwanted station onto the dipole-reflector beam.

The use of a screen in front of the dipole might seem detrimental to reception but this is not so in any large degree. The almost exact half-wave position in front of the dipole is the worst possible position for reflection action and only drops the desired signal a few db.

The positioning of the rejector is done by any of the usual methods

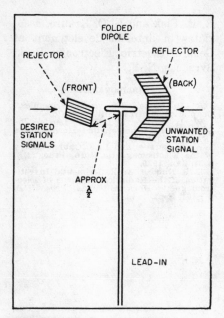

FIG. 1—Basic illustration of the rejector principle applied to a television receiving antenna. Reflector and rejector dimensions are in accordance with conventional antenna practice

for positioning a television antenna against ghosts (one main use of the

I.R.B. can be against a strong ghost). The new, or second, unwanted signal now adds up 180 degrees out of phase with the first unwanted signal. This is done by adjusting the rejector to a position approximately one-half wave away from the dipole. The rejector can be adjusted to produce a signal cancelling an unwanted signal from an adjacent-channel station as well.

The geographical situation of the respective stations or source of interfering signal is taken care of by positioning the rejector arm in azimuth so that it may be placed in proper reflection relation as regards the unwanted station and the dipole. In general, for good reception in the more or less diamond-shaped interference area in between cochannel or adjacent-channel television stations the rejector will be on the far side of the dipole from the unwanted station.

Amplitude of the second unwanted signal is adjusted to equal

that of the first unwanted signal by turning the rejector on its axis so that more or less signal is reflected. This results in cancelling out to zero the unwanted signal. The rejector will even knock out a strong residual or leakage signal in an unshielded receiver or lead-in. This is why the arrangement has been named the Infinite Rejection Beam.

On transmission with a 32-element beam, the I.R.B. will produce an absolute null at any desired angle as long as this is more than approximately 45 degrees from the front center line. This is not unlike the configuration of towers for pattern use on a-m broadcasting. Possibilities exist for same-frequency relay use, but when used on a strong nearby transmitter the receiver null becomes very sensitive to moving objects and acts like a radar for cars and planes. However, on certain mountain locations the I.R.B. may greatly assist relay and similar operations.

Optimum Dimensions for Parasitic Arrays

By L. S. COLE AND W. L. JONES

AT THE PRESENT TIME theoretical results for calculating the performance of parasitic arrays having three or more elements are not available. This led to setting up an experimental unit* which could be used either as a two-element or a three-element array to determine the effects of spacing and tuning on forward gain and input impedance. Figure 1 shows the arrangement of equipment used.

Verification of experimental techniques was accomplished by measuring gain and impedance versus spacing for two-element arrays. The results compare favorably with theoretical results obtained by Brown[1].

For the three-element array each

*This work was done in part under Project No. 11, Engineering Experiment Station, Utah State Agricultural College, Logan, Utah.

parasitic element was tuned, in

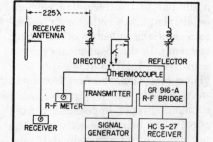

FIG. 1—Block diagram of equipment used in optimizing dimensions for maximum gain of parasitic arrays

turn, for maximum gain at each spacing combination. Results are shown in Fig. 2. In all cases the driven element was fixed at its self-resonant length and maintained at constant power input.

Data on array input resistance R_d and array input reactance X_d are included in Fig. 2A and 2B respectively. These data are useful in obtaining the relative input impedance only, since the impedance of any other array would depend chiefly upon its height above ground.

Corrected Curves

The curves of Fig. 2C are slightly in error because of attenuation in the coaxial line to the array. Therefore the maximum points of the curves of Fig 2C were corrected for known errors and presented in Fig. 2D. Thus Fig. 2D summarizes the final results of gain versus spacing and shows that maximum forward gain is obtained with the reflector spaced approximately 0.15 wavelength and the director spaced 0.3 wavelength.

The corrected gain of this array with conventional spacings (reflector spaced 0.15 wavelength and director spaced 0.1 wavelength) was found to be 6.74 db. Reference to 2D shows that the same array using a reflector spaced 0.15 wavelength and a director spaced 0.3 wavelength had a corrected gain of 8.6 db. Thus greater gain may be obtained by using the wider spacings. However, these spacings give higher input reactance (see Fig. 2B); so impedance matching may be necessary. Figure 2A shows that array input resistance increases with spacing. This is an additional advantage of wider spacings, if the antenna is to be used over a range of frequencies.

REFERENCE

(1) G. H. Brown, Directional Antennas, *Proc. IRE*, 25, p 78, Jan. 1937.

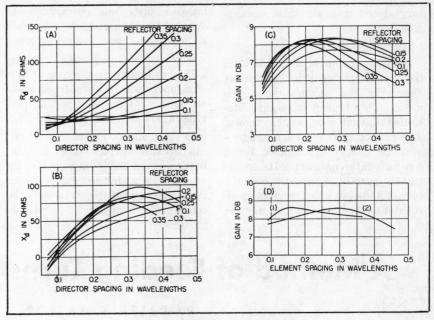

FIG. 2—Resistance and gain curves for various array configurations

Multiple TV Antenna Coupler

By LEONARD MAUTNER

THE PROBLEM OF OPERATING a number of television receivers from one antenna has been with us for a long time, and indications are that it will become more of a problem in the future.

Radio-frequency distribution systems fall into three general classifications:

First, there is the resistor-attenuator scheme which may be useful for a very limited number of sets in a high-signal area. This system has little merit because in an effort to obtain high isolation between sets, one must attenuate the signal so severely that the application is quickly limited in scope.

The second classification involves the use of a single antenna with a central isolation amplifier or a group of individual isolation amplifiers—all employing vacuum tubes to provide the necessary isolation over the tv bands with minimum of introduced loss. The offhand suggestion of a cathode-follower in this

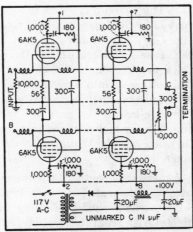

Circuit diagram of four of the eight stages in the eight-position television isolation amplifier for multi-receiver reception with a single antenna

application is, however, an incorrect one. It is not possible to maintain uniform gain characteristics at 216 mc by the use of this technique. The use of a distributed line type wide-band isolation amplifier, however, provides a satisfactory

economical solution. A typical equipment of this type is described below. Such a scheme finds wide application in all but the lowest signal areas, and this solution, when coupled with a wide-band amplifier having a gain of the order of 20 db, then provides an economical solution for nearly all locations.

The third method, which by its nature is the most costly and elegant, involves the use of a separate antenna and channel amplifier for each station. The mixed signals may then be piped at relatively high level around the building proper with bridging take-offs for each of the receivers. In this case it is less difficult to orient the separate antennas to minimize ghost patterns which arise in certain difficult locations due to the large neighboring buildings. However, such a solution with its expensive and complicated terminal equipment is only practical and economical for the largest and most elaborate installations.

Wide-Band Amplifier

A typical example of a wide-band isolation amplifier is the Telecoupler shown in the accompanying diagram. Only four of the eight plate-loaded output stages are shown. The grid circuits in each stage provide the shunt capacitance for a low-pass filter network. Its operation is readily apparent. Using a pair of 150-ohm unbalanced lumped-constant transmission lines for the low-pass filter, one can arrange to drive them back-to-back to provide a 300-ohm input. Alternatively, operating them in parallel provides a 75-ohm input. In the case of 300-ohm operation, each pair of tubes on opposite sides of the line provides a 300-ohm source looking back into their plate circuits. Thus, one can provide outputs from one antenna to four 300-ohm tv sets with an accurate match available. Since the conventional receiver may be considerably unbalanced in its in-put, it is often possible to use the eight 150-ohm outputs to drive eight 300-ohm or 75-ohm receivers.

By removing the termination at the far end of the line, one can add a number of units in cascade, providing more outputs. As many as 24 output lines have been successfully used in practice. Precautions must be taken to make sure that local oscillator radiation from one set with an unbalanced or radiating front end will not radiate back through the system.

A Method of Feeding Turnstile Antennas

By RALPH E. TAYLOR

THE TURNSTILE ANTENNA, as introduced by G. H. Brown,[1] consists primarily of two coplanar half-wavelength dipoles mounted in space quadrature as shown in Fig. 1. The dipoles are fed with r-f currents that are equal in magnitude but phased 90 degrees apart in time. Such an arrangement gives a

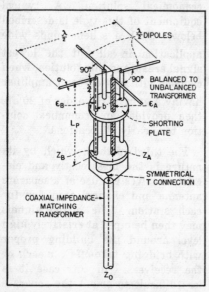

Fig. 1—Schematic drawing showing method of feeding turnstile antenna

nearly circular radiation pattern in the plane of the dipoles. A circularly polarized r-f field vector is radiated in directions normal to the plane of the dipoles.

The turnstile antenna may be considered as essentially comprising four identical, symmetrically-spaced elements, with terminals at the points labeled A, B, C and D in Fig. 2A. The relative magnitudes and phases of the various currents can then be represented by means of the vector diagram shown in Fig 2B. The current I_A leads the current I_D by 90 degrees. Similarly I_C lags I_D, I_B lags I_C, and I_A lags I_B, in each case by 90 degrees. If the dipoles are resonant, the current I and voltage E into a given element are in phase. Coupling between adjacent elements is reduced to a minimum by virtue of the fact that they are at right angles to each other.

A method of feeding turnstile antennas is illustrated in Fig. 1. Phasing is accomplished by feeding the dipoles with separated coaxial feeders having physical lengths which are equal, and electrical lengths which differ by a quarter-wavelength. This is achieved by employing different dielectric materials in the feeders. The physical length is given by the relation

$$L_P = \frac{\lambda}{4(\sqrt{\epsilon_A} - \sqrt{\epsilon_B})}$$

where $\epsilon_A > \epsilon_B$ and λ is the wavelength in free space. ϵ_A and ϵ_B are the respective dielectric constants of the insulating materials in the

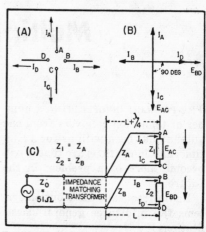

Fig. 2—Radiating antenna (A), vector diagram (B), and equivalent circuit (C) for turnstile antenna

dipole feeders. The sense of rotation of the r-f field vector radiated from the dipoles can be reversed by interchanging ϵ_A and ϵ_B in Fig. 1. The center conductors of the dipole feeders are shown attached to the center conductor of a series, coaxial, impedance matching transformer. A symmetrical T connection is formed.

An equivalent circuit diagram is shown in Fig. 2C. The characteristic impedances of the dipole feeders, Z_A and Z_B, are matched with the respective dipole resistances, R_1 and

R_2. Since the dipoles are resonant, no appreciable standing waves exist in the dipole feeders. Length L represents the electrical length of the ε_B insulator and $L + \lambda/4$ the electrical length of the ε_A insulator. The matching transformer matches the impedance of the parallel combination of Z_1 and Z_B to the characteristic impedance Z_0 of the main feeder line. Antenna currents are prevented from flowing on the outside of the main feeder line by means of a balanced-to-unbalanced transformer shown in Fig. 1. This transformer consists of a high impedance, quarter-wavelength, shorted section of balanced transmission line. It also serves as a rigid mechanical support for the dipoles.

Antennas of the type shown in Fig. 1 are used for telemetering from the V-2 at 1,000 mc. The following parameters were chosen: $\varepsilon_A = 4.6$ (Grade 1137 Lava from the American Lava Corporation), $\varepsilon_B = 2.1$ (Poly F-1114, or Telfon, a du Pont de Nemours product), $Z_A = 51$ ohms, $Z_B = 61$ ohms, $a = 0.30\lambda$ at 1,000 mc, $b = 0.07\lambda$ at

1,000 mc, and $Z_0 = 51$ ohms.

Figure 3A is a plot of voltage

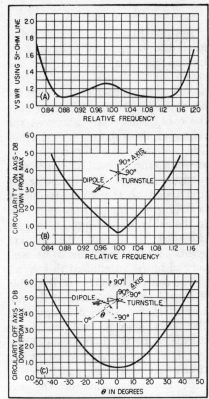

Fig. 3—Typical curves showing operation of antenna using feed system described

standing-wave ratio versus relative frequency. The measurements were made on a 51-ohm coaxial line. The bandpass is 35 percent using a limiting value of vswr (E_{max}/E_{min}) equal to 1.5 to 1.

Figure 3B is a plot of the circularity on axis (eccentricity of the rotating r-f field vector) versus relative frequency. The bandpass is 19 percent for a limiting value of 3 db. These measurements were made with a half-wavelength receiving dipole located in a plane parallel to the plane of the turnstile dipoles. The receiving dipole was spaced approximately ten wavelengths away from the turnstile antenna. It was rotated through 360 degrees about the axis perpendicular to the turnstile dipoles. A comparison was made of the maximum and minimum signals received when the pickup dipole was rotated. This comparison is known as the circularity. Figure 3C is a plot of the circularity versus angle θ in degrees at the center frequency.

REFERENCE

(1) George H. Brown, The Turnstile Antenna, ELECTRONICS, p 14, Apr. 1936.

Coaxial Feed System for Antennas

By JOHN F. CLEMENS

COAXIAL CABLE may be used to feed balanced horizontal antennas without interference, noise pickup or power loss due to unbalanced currents in the outer shield. The familiar delta match is used. The outer shield is bonded to the center of the antenna while a shorted section of cable resonates with the inductive reactance of the system.

Coaxial cable has advantages over unshielded or open-wire line in almost every transmission-line application. Generally speaking, attenuation is lower, making it particularly desirable when the line must be relatively long. For receiving applications the low noise pickup of coaxial cable is a definite advan-

tage. For this reason it is especially suitable for television receiving antenna leadins. Coax is entirely free from weather effects while the ribbon type of line is usually affected by rain and moisture, often deteriorating rapidly from exposure in coastal regions.

No Split Element

A system of coaxial-cable feed for balanced horizontal antennas should find wide application to television and f-m receiving antennas and transmitting antennas such as parasitic beams. The system described has a feature of prime importance in these applications: splitting the driven element is un-

necessary. A feed system which necessitates breaking the antenna is difficult to fabricate since insulating materials of sufficient strength and electrical quality are not available for large self-supporting structures.

A serious problem in applying coaxial feed to a balanced antenna is that of eliminating unbalanced or antenna currents from the outer shield.[1] If present, such currents cause loss of the normal antenna pattern and the low noise pickup feature of coaxial cable. In transmitting, currents on the outer shield may cause feedback, interference or power loss.

The system described achieves

balanced feedline currents as determined by test. In general, a symmetrical system can be relied upon for absence of unbalance effects. The diagram of the system, Fig. 1, discloses almost perfect symmetry.

Delta Match

The impedance between two symmetrically located points on an antenna rises from zero when the points are adjacent, to a very high value when the points are at opposite ends of the antenna. Therefore, in any type of resonant antenna, it is possible to select two points between which the resistive component of impedance is equal to the characteristic impedance of the transmission line. This is the basis for the familiar delta match.[2]

The impedance between two driving points is not purely resistive;

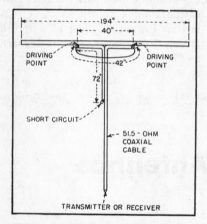

FIG. 1—Driven element of three-element close-spaced array for 29 mc using co-axial feed system

the actual impedance may always be represented by an equivalent series circuit of resistance and reactance. Prediction of the actual input impedance between two driving points is difficult in a parasitic array although approximate formulas are available for the half-wave dipole.[3]

The driving points must be chosen empirically to satisfy the requirement of an equivalent series resistive component equal to the characteristic impedance of the transmission line. Once these points have been determined, the series

reactive component of the impedance may be calculated.

Shield Bonded

Assume that two symmetrically-located driving points have been located on the antenna. If the shield of a coaxial cable is connected to the center of the antenna, no antenna current will flow into the cable since the voltage at the center of the antenna is negligible. The cable may also be run along the antenna since it will act merely to increase its effective diameter. If protrusion of the inner conductor is negligible, no current will flow in the cable. Accordingly, it may be extended to one of the driving points. The shield should be well bonded to the antenna at this point.

The center conductor of the cable is looped past the center of the antenna to the opposite driving point. The coax sees a load resistance paralleled by the inductance of the length of the antenna element between driving points, and in series with the inductance of the extended center conductor. The inductance of both antenna and center conductor can be determined from[4]

$$L = 0.00508 \, a$$
$$\left(2.303 \log \frac{4 \, a}{d} - 0.75 \right) \quad (1)$$

where a and d represent length and diameter of each conductor in inches, and L is given in μh.

The actual equivalent circuit is shown in Fig. 2A where R_p is unknown while L_p, the inductance of the length of antenna between driving points, has been calculated.

The inductance of the extended center conductor, L_2, may likewise be calculated. In Fig. 2B the parallel circuit of R_p and L_p has been replaced by the series equivalent R_s and L_s. In this case, R_s is the characteristic impedance of the line. Inductance L_s may be calculated from

$$X_p = \frac{X_s^2 + R_s^2}{X_s} \quad (2)$$

$$R_p = \frac{X_s^2 + R_s^2}{R_s} \quad (3)$$

$$X_s = \frac{X_p + \sqrt{X_p^2 - 4 R_s^2}}{2} \quad (4)$$

Resistance R_p may be determined likewise if desired.

Resonating Load

Once X_s has been determined the next step is to combine it with the reactance of L_2 and insert a capacitance, C, of such a value to resonate

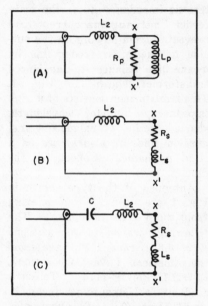

FIG. 2—Equivalent circuits of coaxial feed system show effect of shorted line and distributed inductance

the total inductive reactance as shown in Fig. 2C. A capacitor of capacitance C may be inserted in the center conductor anywhere along its length to obtain an impedance match.

Usually a capacitor is not used because of weather effects. Instead, a length of cable may be used to present the same capacitive reactance. Although a length of either open or shorted cable may be used, the shorted cable is preferable because of its lower loss. If a shorted cable is used the proper electrical length may be computed from

$$X = -j Z_k \tan \theta \quad (5)$$

where X is the desired capacitive reactance. The electrical angle θ may be converted to inches from

$$D = \frac{(32.8) \, (\theta) \, (v_p)}{f} \quad (6)$$

where θ is expressed in degrees, f in megacycles and v_p, the propagation velocity, as a fraction.

The matching section and antenna may be bonded along their mutual length without altering the performance of either.

Allowable Mismatch

The fact that the antenna inductance, L_p, shunts the resistive component, R_p, permits the system to be used when the radiation resistance exceeds the characteristic impedance of the line. A 50-ohm coaxial cable may thus be matched to a free-space dipole having a radiation resistance of 73 ohms.

The cable may be fed inside a tubular antenna element with the center conductor emerging through a hole at one driving point and re-entering the antenna tube at the other driving point.

Experimental Antennas

A test of the system was first made at 300 mc with a close-spaced three-element parasitic array. Instead of the capacitive line section, a small variable capacitor was used. A standing wave ratio of less than 1.5 to 1 was readily obtained. Antenna elements were 3/16 silver-plated brass rods and the feed line was RG-58/U.

The system was next tested on a scaled-up version of the three-element antenna at 29 mc. Spacing from antenna to director was 0.1 wavelength and from antenna to reflector, 0.15 wavelength. The antenna was 194 inches long, the reflector, 204 inches, and the director, 184 inches. All elements were 1 inch in diameter.

With a series variable capacitor and a Micro-Match, two feed points were located 20 inches each side of center. Type RG-8/U cable was then connected as described. The cross lead was formed by 42 inches of center conductor from which the shield had been removed. The cross lead was allowed to sag about three inches from the center of the antenna. The driven element is diagrammed in Fig. 1.

The inductance of 42 inches of wire with a cross-sectional area approximately equivalent to number 14 wire from Eq. 1 is 1.52 μh. The

inductance of the antenna, L_p is 0.862 μh. Reactance X_p is therefore 158 ohms at 29 mc. Reactance X_s from Eq. 4 is 19 ohms. Reactance X_2 is 277 ohms, making the total inductive reactance 296 ohms.

The capacitive reactance required for resonance is 296 ohms. This capacitive reactance was obtained by a 72-inch length of RG-8/U, shorted at one end, as calculated by Eq. 5.

First tests on the antenna were made with the shield of the capacitive shorted section and the driving cable bonded to the antenna and to the metal supporting pole throughout their mutual lengths. On a second antenna the shields were bonded to the antenna at the driving points where the vinyl jacket was removed from the cable but the remainder of the cable was left with the insulation on and merely taped along the antenna and supporting pole. No difference in performance was detectable in the two systems.

Standing-Wave Ratio

The antenna was mounted one wavelength above ground and tested with a Jones Micro-Match. The standing-wave ratio was measured as 1/1 at 29 mc, the resonant frequency of the antenna, rising to approximately 1.5/1 at 28.5 and 30.0 mc.

A question arises as to the desirability of a resonant system for impedance matching such as the length of coaxial cable used to produce capacitive reactance. Reference to Fig. 2C shows that the series resonant circuit includes a resistance of 51.5 ohms. The total series inductive reactance has been calculated as 296 ohms. Thus, the Q of the series circuit is 5.75. Obviously, the feed system is a wideband device compared to the three-element parasitic array on which it is used.

The 29-mc beam antenna was next checked for line current balance. The pattern of the antenna was first measured with a field-strength meter. Maximum radiation was found to be perpendicular

to the antenna elements. An unbalanced antenna will usually show an altered pattern with the maxima occuring slightly off center. The field-strength meter was then positioned a fixed distance from each antenna-element tip in turn and the deflection of the meter was found to be the same in each case. This test indicates that the voltage at each antenna tip is the same. Small incandescent bulbs hung from each end of the antenna showed the same brilliance.

Further Tests

Next, the center conductor was broken close to the first driving point where the conductor emerged from the shield. A receiver connected to the line was now completely dead. The absence of pickup showed that the cable had no signal pickup of its own. Type RG-8/U cable may be used to carry transmitter outputs of two kw or so with the line matched. A standing wave exists in the capacitive shorted line section. Therefore care must be used to select a line of sufficient insulation capacity. For a one-kilowatt transmitter the line current which must flow through the matching section is 4.41 amperes.

The voltage drop across the capacitive section of coax is 1,310 volts. This voltage appears between the inner conductor and the shield of the capacitive matching section at the point where the inner conductor enters the shield. Since RG-8/U has a maximum voltage rating of 4,000 volts rms, it should be adequate for transmitter powers of well over one kilowatt.

REFERENCES

(1) King, Wing and Mimno, "Transmission Lines, Antennas and Wave Guides" p 145, First Edition, McGraw-Hill, New York.
(2) King, Wing, Mimno, "Transmission Lines, Antennas and Wave Guides", p 158, First Edition, McGraw-Hill, New York.
(3) E. K. Sandeman, "Radio Engineering," 1, p 687, John Wiley & Sons, New York 1948.
(4) F. E. Terman, "Radio Engineers Handbook," p 48, First Edition, McGraw-Hill, New York.

Photo Radiation Patterns

Two-dimensional wave interference patterns of two or more radiators of same frequency and polarization can be synthesized quickly and economically by superimposing bullseye patterns photographically.   Examples are shown

By GERHART W. GOEBEL

PHENOMENA of wave propagation, reflection and refraction are best demonstrated by the ripple tank. In cases where the extreme versatility of the ripple tank and its high cost and complexity are not justified, the simple and economical photographic process described may be used. The system provides two-dimension patterns of two or more radiators of the same frequency and polarization.

The image of a wave in a plane normal to the radiator is first drawn in the form of concentric circles centered on the radiating source which appears as a point. The lines represent either a mini-

mum or a maximum; thus they are made equal in thickness to the spaces between them, which represent the opposite wave condition. A photographic negative prepared from the target-shaped drawing is then printed on soft photographic paper with an exposure value of one-half normal. This produces the basic pattern of grey and white.

Pattern Synthesis

In the radiation pattern of two radiators spaced S degrees and having phase difference ϕ (where $S = 0$ and $\phi = 0$), the negative is printed twice with the same exposure. The result is an image of two

grey-and-white patterns superimposed to form a black-and-white pattern as illustrated in (A). The double density of the dark portion indicates reinforcement.

For various phase differences, separate sets of basic patterns are required, with phase angles shown as increased distances from the center to the first grey circle.

The method described is especially useful in helping students visualize the effects of spacing and phase changes on radiation patterns. Extremely vivid illustrative material can be prepared by taking cartoon-type movie exposures of patterns with gradually changing conditions of phase and/or spacing.

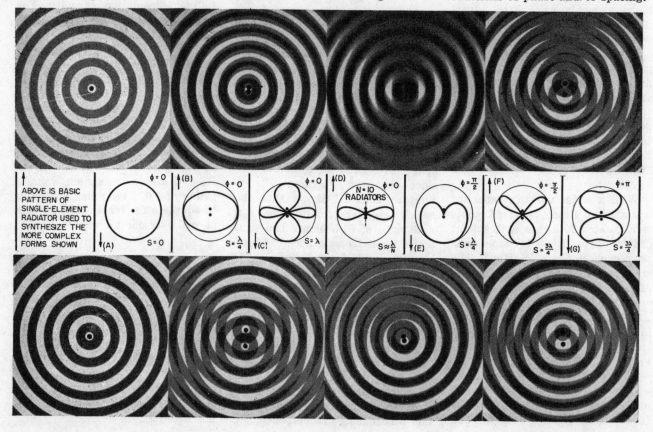

ABOVE IS BASIC PATTERN OF SINGLE-ELEMENT RADIATOR USED TO SYNTHESIZE THE MORE COMPLEX FORMS SHOWN

Pattern Calculator for A-M

Graphical method useful for original design work on a pair of a-m broadcast antenna towers is also particularly applicable if a new pattern or change in frequency is necessary. Requires only dividers and transparent overlay

By GEORGE R. MATHER

THE CALCULATION of directional antenna patterns is often a long and tedious job and is usually at best a laborious exercise in trigonometry. The graphical calculator to be described is readily applicable to two-tower arrays and once the antenna spacing has been established it is a simple matter to observe the change in pattern shape with variations of phasing angle and antenna-current ratios. Although this graphical calculator can be used in original designs its obvious merit is evident when the towers are already installed but perhaps a change in operating frequency is necessitated.

The determination of the shape of a pattern is accomplished by the addition of the field vectors from each of the towers in an array. Figure 1A is a graphical illustration of the geometry involved and is used to establish the notation used.

Development

Tower 1 is used as a reference while tower 2 is considered to be spaced at S degrees from tower 1 with a phase angle of P degrees. Movable point Q is sufficiently remote from the array so that the lines from Q to tower 1 and Q to tower 2 are considered as being parallel. The angle θ is subtended between the line of the towers and a line from the movable point Q to tower 1. Thus for any position of point Q the total phase displacement between the field vectors of tower 1 and tower 2 is T degrees where $T = P - S \cos \theta$.

The resultant field at some angle θ is determined by the use of a vector diagram as shown in Fig. 1B where E_1 and E_2 are proportional to the field of towers 1 and 2 respectively. Note that as the angle θ is varied the phase displacement angle T changes and as a result the posi-

tion of E_2 with reference to E_1 is dependent on the angle θ. Actually the radius vector E_2 describes the arc of a circle.

In Fig. 2 the following relationships become evident. When $T = P - S \cos \theta$, and when $\theta = 0$, $T = P - S$, also when $\theta = 180$, $T = P + S$.

Thus the arc subtended by the rotation of the vector E_2 is $(P + S) - (P - S) = 2S$ degrees. Therefore if the spacing S remains fixed, any such arc whose circumference is calibrated in θ may be used with any combination of current ratio and phasing angle. This calibration of the circumference in θ is also accomplished by solution of the equation $T = P - S \cos \theta$, where θ is the variable.

For purpose of illustration, graphical calculators have been computed for spacing angles 90, 135, 180 and 225 degrees.

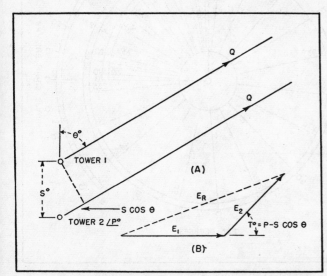

FIG. 1—Basic relationships used in setting up tower equations with spatial relationships shown at (A) and vector addition in (B)

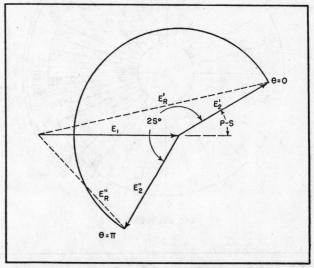

FIG. 2—Vector diagram to show how, if the spacing S between the antenna towers remains fixed, the arc subtended by E_2 can be calibrated in θ

Example

In a determination of the shape of a pattern all that is necessary is a pair of dividers and a transparent overlay sheet. Suppose, for example, we have the following array: $E_1 = 1.0, <0$; $E_2 = 0.5, <+60$; $S = 90$ degrees. Note that the phasing angle minus the spacing angle is equal to $60 - 90 = -30$ degrees.

First a straight line is drawn on the transparency that is then placed in register on the pattern calculator (90 degrees) so that the line passes through the common point of the two vectors and through a phasing − spacing angle of −30 degrees.

From the common point measure a distance to the left on the line that is proportional to E_1. With the common point as center, draw a circle with a radius proportional to E_2.

The resultant for any angle from the tower line is then the sum of the vectors E_1 and E_2, it being recognized that the position of E_2 at any angle is the intersection of the circle described by E_2 with the line representing that angle from the tower line.

The resultant vector will be in the same units as were used for E_1 and E_2.

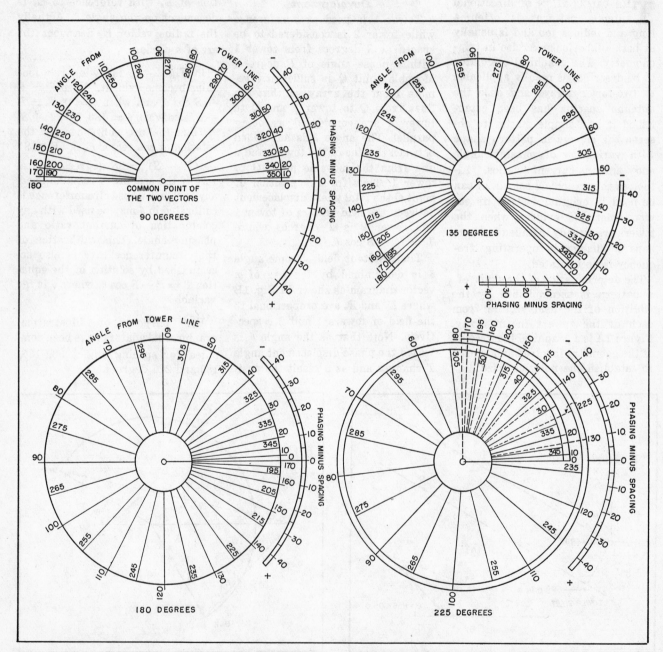

FIG. 3—Patterns can be computed to slide-rule accuracy using enlargements of these calculators. They are given for antenna spacings of 90, 135, 180 and 225 degrees

Antenna Analyzer

Radiation patterns of standard broadcast antenna arrays are produced on the screen of a
cathode-ray tube by an improved electronic computer employing only 38 tubes. Polar
or rectangular presentation of the array pattern can be displayed

By ALVA C. TODD

THE RADIATION EQUATION for
the multielement parallel antenna array does not lend itself
readily to analysis in broadcast antenna radiation pattern problems.
The task of synthesis of an array
to produce a certain desired radiation pattern is much more difficult.
A trial and error process must be
followed and the task is both tedious and time consuming.

To reduce the problem to practical proportions, numerous mechanical computers[1] and electromechanical computers[2] have been
constructed. The mechanical computers have been limited by mechanical complexity to three antenna elements, but no apparent
limit exists for the curve-drawing
electromechanical devices. Any one
of these machines is capable of giving the relative distant field pattern for a given array fed in a
proper prescribed manner.

One of the most recent contributions in the field of antenna array
computer design was made by
Brown and Morrison[3]. They built
an entirely electronic device capable of giving a continuous picture
of the antenna array radiation pattern on the screen of a cathode-ray
tube. With the aid of such a computer, the problem of antenna array synthesis was reduced to dial
adjustment until the desired radiation pattern was observed on the
screen of the cathode-ray tube. The
approximate solution obtained
from the computer then could be
improved to the desired degree of
accuracy by a much shorter trial
and error process.

A similar electronic calculator
that was designed for classroom

antenna array demonstration, as
well as for array analysis and synthesis, will be described.

Control of element parameters is
effected by potentiometer adjustment of direct current and 60-cps
voltages, and by the use of selsyn
control transformers as 60-cps voltage phase shifters. Each dial is
calibrated in terms of the parameter it controls. Provisions are included for polar or rectangular
presentation of the array radiation
pattern.

As was pointed out by Brown and
Morrison, the electronic reproduction of the radiation pattern of an

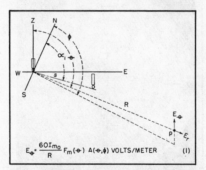

FIG. 1—Simple array consisting of two
parallel elements and equation for distant field

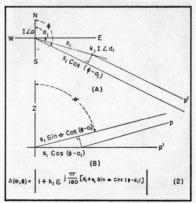

FIG. 2—Horizontal projection of the two-
element array is shown at A and the
ZO p' plane protection at B

antenna array depends upon the
fact that the array factor can be
represented exactly by the magnitude of the sum of a sine wave voltage, representing the field contribution of the reference element, and
a series of phase-modulated sine-
wave voltages, representing the
field contributions of the other elements. Consider an array of parallel elements erected vertically on
a perfectly conducting plane earth
as shown in Fig. 1. The vertical
component of the electric field at
point p, located at distance R (R
very large compared with the wavelength λ) from the reference element is given in Eq. 1, where
$F_m(\theta)$ is the element factor, $A(\phi,\theta)$
is the array factor, R is the dis-
tance in meters to the point of
measurement, θ is the angle from
the top of the element to the point
of measurement, ϕ is the bearing
angle from true north of the point
of measurement, and I_{mo} is the effective value of current in the reference element at the point of
maximum current along the element. The horizontal plane and
ZOp' plane projections of the antenna array are shown in Fig. 2.
If the distance to the point of
measurement is much greater than
the spacing between elements, rays
from the elements to the point of
measurement may be considered
parallel and the array factor for a
two-element array is as shown in
Fig. 2.

The array factor for a five-element array is shown in Fig. 3,
where k_n is the ratio of current in
element n to current in the reference element, δ_n is the phase difference between current in element n

and current in the reference element in electrical degrees, α_n is the azimuth of element n in degrees, and S_n is the spacing between element n and the reference element in electrical degrees.

If the elements are not of equal length, k_n becomes the ratio of the product of the current maximum and the element factor of element n to the product of the current maximum and the element factor of the reference element.

To duplicate the array factor electrically, let the component of the electric field produced by the reference element be represented by the expression of Eq. 6 in Fig. 4. Let the component of the relative electric field produced by element n be represented by Eq. 7.

If five elements are the maximum number to be considered, the sum of the simulating voltages becomes Eq. 8 and expansion of one expression allows the sum of the simulating voltages to be written as shown in Eq. 10. Grouping of terms and substituting as shown, the sum of the simulating voltages becomes Eq. 14.

If $B_n = y_n$, Eq. 14 has an amplitude identical to $A_5(\theta,\phi)$, Eq. 5, and is phase modulated in a very complex manner. If the simulating voltages are combined in a mixing circuit with a bandwidth sufficient to accommodate all significant sideband components, and the resulting sum is applied to a linear detector, the array factor will be simulated by the output of the detector.

Thus to produce a complex voltage whose envelope magnitude simulates the array factor of the multielement parallel antenna array erected vertically on a perfectly conducting plane earth, for arrays with not more than five elements, we require a sine-wave voltage of constant amplitude and frequency, and up to four phase-modulated voltages of arbitrary magnitude and arbitrary average phase, maximum phase deviation, and phase of phase deviation.

Let us again consider the expres-

sion for the phase deviation of the voltage intended to represent the distant field contribution of element n.

$$B_n = \delta_n + S_n\cos(\phi - \alpha_n) \quad (4a)$$

Element current phase angle δ_n must have a range of ± 180 degrees. If spacing S_n between element n and the reference element has a maximum value of 900 degrees, the total phase swing B_n may

be as large as $\pm 1,080$ degrees. Several wide-range phase modulators employing conventional electron tubes have been developed. Systems of phase modulation by Kell[4] and by Day[5] give good linearity over a range of ± 120 degrees. The system due to Day was found to give a somewhat more linear phase-modulation characteristic and a higher output voltage; therefore

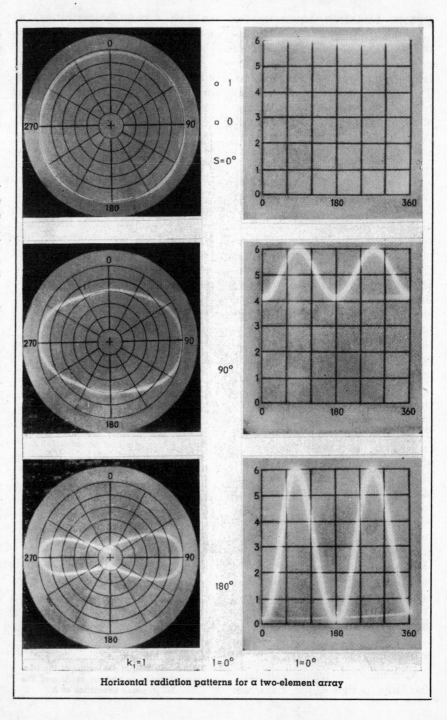

Horizontal radiation patterns for a two-element array

that system was used in the electronic computer. Two tripler-amplifiers in cascade increase the ± 120-degree variation capability to ± 1,080 degrees.

Reference is made to the circuit diagram of the computer unit, Fig. 5. A type 6SJ7 pentode is employed in a modified Pierce crystal oscillator circuit. The quartz plate has a nominal frequency of 100 kc. The circuit is arranged to allow plate current flow during only a very small fraction of the oscillation cycle. A 39,000-ohm resistor isolates the plate from the oscillating circuit. The resulting plate-voltage wave is a pulse about −50 volts high and one-half microsecond wide. The output voltage of the oscillator is applied to a type 6SN7 tube in a differentiator cathode-follower circuit in which the pulse phase is reversed, the pulse width is reduced to a very small fraction of a microsecond, the pulse amplitude is reduced slightly, and the impedance level is reduced to about 450 ohms.

The output voltage of the cathode follower is applied to a pulse bus which feeds the reference-element cascade-tripler amplifier and the four element-phase modulators. Two type 6SJ7 pentodes are employed in the two-stage cascade-tripler amplifiers. The reference-element tripler amplifier introduces a 900-kc voltage of constant ampli-

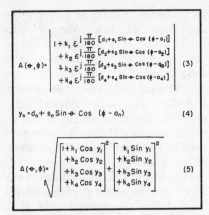

FIG. 3—Array factor for a five-element system

tude in series with the common resonant circuit employed for voltage mixing.

Phase Control

The element-phase modulators use the positive pulse from the pulse bus to key one-half of a 6SN7 in a hard-tube sawtooth oscillator circuit. The time constant of the sawtooth circuit is 2.5 times the wave period; therefore, the resulting sawtooth voltage has a peak value of 0.32 E_{bb} or 70 volts.

A second 6SN7 is employed in a variable clipper-differentiator circuit; the clipper grid is directly coupled to the plate of the sawtooth-generator tube. The cathode bias of the clipper is adjusted to allow grid conduction when the sawtooth voltage rises to 35 volts. Shortly before grid conduction be-

gins, clipper plate conduction produces a sudden drop in clipper plate voltage.

The clipper plate voltage drives a differentiator - phase - reverser which gives a sharp 40-volt positive pulse, the position of which is determined by the clipping level. Fairly linear pulse position variation with clipper cathode-voltage variation was obtained over a range of ± 130 degrees. The average clipping level, which is deter-

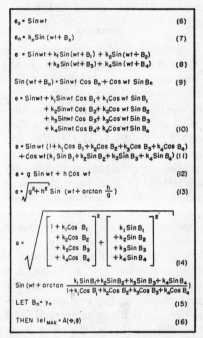

FIG. 4—Equations for simulating voltages for duplicating the array factor electrically

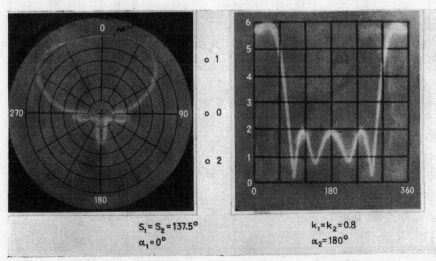

$S_1 = S_2 = 137.5°$
$\alpha_1 = 0°$

$k_1 = k_2 = 0.8$
$\alpha_2 = 180°$

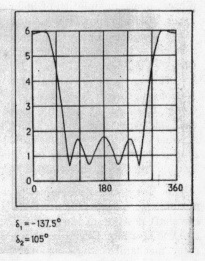

$\delta_1 = -137.5°$
$\delta_2 = 105°$

Horizontal radiation pattern for the WBAA night antenna array. The calculated pattern is shown at right

mined by the d-c cathode potential of the clipper, is made adjustable over a ± 20-degree range, and the dial of the 5,000-ohm wire-wound potentiometer used to control the cathode d-c potential is calibrated linearly in terms of average channel output phase, which corresponds to antenna element current phase, over a range of ± 180 degrees. The two 5,000-ohm rheostats in series with the calibrated potentiometer are used to adjust the 180 and −180-degree phase positions. The control dial is labeled PHASE.

Spacing

Modulation at a frequency of 60 cps simulates variation in ϕ and was achieved by means of a low-gain modulating amplifier, directly coupled to the cathode of the clipper. The second half of the first 6SN7 in the modulator section was used for this purpose. Excitation of the modulating amplifier was furnished by the secondary of a selsyn control transformer whose delta connected primary was excited by a three-phase 60-cps power source in the power-supply unit. The level of the 60-cps modulation was controlled by a 10,000-ohm wire-wound potentiometer in the grid circuit of the modulating amplifier. At the maximum setting of this potentiometer, the position of the modulator output pulse is sinusoidally varied over a range of ± 100 degrees. This corresponds to a crest phase modulation of 900 degrees in the output of the element cascade-tripler amplifier, and therefore the dial controlling the potentiometer is linearly calibrated from 0 to 900 degrees. Crest phase modulation represents the spacing between the element and the reference element; hence the dial is marked SPACING. A series 5,000-ohm rheostat allows initial calibration of the spacing control.

The phase position of 60-cps modulating voltage is controlled by the shaft position of the selsyn control transformer. Deviation between rotor mechanical angle and secondary-voltage phase angle for 6.3

volt, balanced three-phase 60-cps excitation of the primary was found to be very small, and therefore permitted direct phase-shift calibration of the selsyn transformers. The control dials of the selsyn transformers were marked azimuth, as variation in the phase of the 60-cps modulating voltage corresponds to changes in the azimuth of the element α_n.

The output pulse voltage produced by the element phase-modulator drives the control grid of a 6SJ7 pentode operating as a class-C tripler amplifier. The sine-wave

voltage produced across the tripler-amplifier plate parallel-resonant circuit has a center frequency of 300 kc and a phase-modulation crest three times as large as present at the output of the modulator.

The second tripler amplifier is capacitance coupled to the plate of the first and also uses a 6SJ7. The second tripler amplifier performs the function of output voltage control for the element channel. A linear 10,000-ohm wire-wound potentiometer is employed to control the screen grid d-c potential and hence the output voltage. A series 5,000-

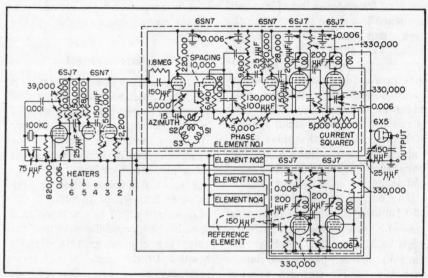

FIG. 5—Circuit of the computer unit for the antenna analyzer

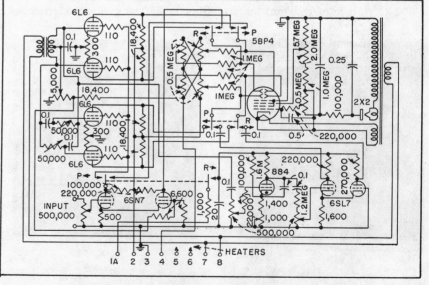

FIG. 6—Circuit of indicator unit mounted on top of front panel

ohm rheostat is provided for initial adjustment.

The output voltage of the tripler
was found to vary almost exactly
with the square root of the screen-
grid voltage; a linear dial calibration was used for the voltage-am-
plitude control, and as the output-
voltage magnitude simulates the
antenna-element current magnitude
(for equal-length elements), the
dial was labeled CURRENT SQUARED.

The secondaries of the second
tripler-amplifier plate transformers
are connected in series and the
combination is tuned to resonate at
900 kc. Although five tripler amplifiers are coupled to a common
900-kc mixing circuit, almost no
cross-channel modulation exists;
the angle of plate-current flow for
the type 6SJ7 pentodes is very
small and therefore their effective
plate resistance is very high.

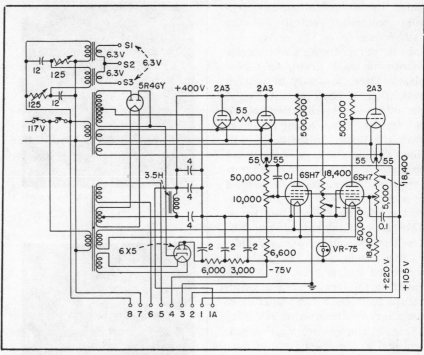

FIG. 7—Power supply circuit includes three-phase 6.3-volt source at top left

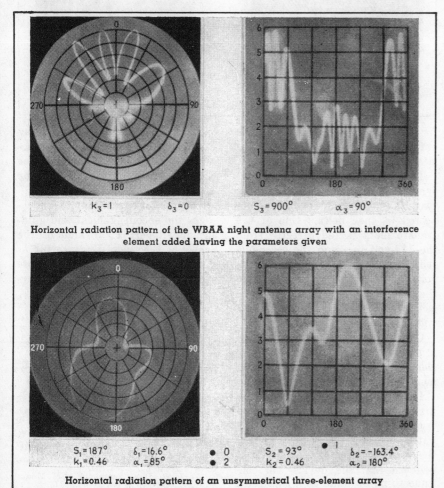

Horizontal radiation pattern of the WBAA night antenna array with an interference
element added having the parameters given

$k_3 = 1$ $\delta_3 = 0$ $S_3 = 900°$ $\alpha_3 = 90°$

● 0
● 1
● 2

$S_1 = 187°$ $\delta_1 = 16.6°$ $S_2 = 93°$ $\delta_2 = -163.4°$
$k_1 = 0.46$ $\alpha_1 = 85°$ $k_2 = 0.46$ $\alpha_2 = 180°$

Horizontal radiation pattern of an unsymmetrical three-element array

The indicator unit occupies the
top chassis of the antenna analyzer.
This unit, Fig. 6, includes a 5BP4
cathode-ray tube and high-voltage
power supply, a linear sweep generator, a computer signal amplifier,
and a polar converter.

If the rectangular presentation
of the antenna-array radiation pattern is desired, the polar-rectangu-
lar switch is placed in the rectangular position. A 6SN7 in a direct-
coupled amplifier circuit increases
the computer output voltage. A potentiometer in the grid circuit permits control of the output signal
voltage.

The computer signal amplifier is
directly coupled to the vertical
plates of the cathode-ray tube.
Direct coupling is necessary to preserve the d-c component of the complex voltage wave that may be
produced by the computer. The 60-
cps linear sweep voltage applied to
the horizontal plates of the cathode-
ray tube is furnished by a type 884
gas-triode sawtooth generator followed by a 6SL7 amplifier.

Means are provided for the initial synchronization of the sawtooth generator and for the initial
adjustment of sweep-voltage ampli-

tude. Double potentiometers provide centering control for the cathode-ray tube. The cathode-ray tube is equipped with a rectangular coordinate scale, drawn on a blue plastic filter, to assist in pattern evaluation. If polar presentation of the antenna-array radiation pattern is desired, the rectangular-polar switch is turned to the polar position. The plate voltage of the linear oscillator and its amplifier is interrupted and screen voltage is applied to a double-balanced modulator circuit employing four 6L6-G tubes. The plates of the cathode-ray tube are directly coupled to the double-balanced modulator. The push-pull connected control grids of the balanced modulators are fed in quadrature from a 6.3-volt transformer secondary by means of a 90-degree phase-shifting network. The control grids are biased to produce plate-current cutoff for a screen voltage of about 20 volts. Screen voltage for the modulator tubes is provided by the computer signal amplifier.

If all antenna current-squared controls are set at zero, and the gain control of the indicator unit is set at about one-third full rotation, a circle will be produced on the screen of the cathode-ray tube. If other elements are introduced, the resulting figure will be more complex if the spacing controls are not set at zero.

The cathode-ray tube is equipped with a polar coordinate scale to assist in pattern evaluation. Sufficient gain has been provided in the unit to permit enlargement of minor lobes in complex array patterns. The polar presentation is not linear enough for computing work, but it is satisfactory for classroom demonstration and for first approximations in array design.

Power Supply

The power unit of Fig. 7 furnishes 6.3-volt 60-cps filament voltage, 6.3-volt 60-cps 3-phase for the four selsyn transformers, 220 volts d-c plate voltage, 105 volts control voltage, and −75 volts bias voltage

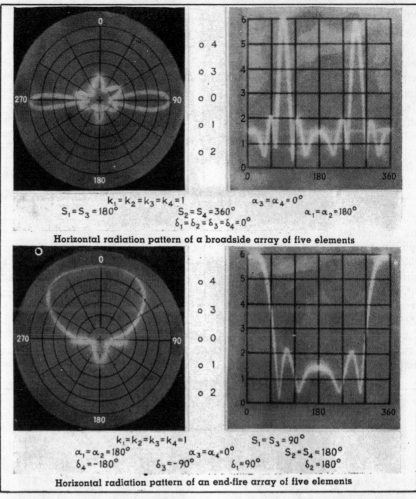

$k_1 = k_2 = k_3 = k_4 = 1$
$S_1 = S_3 = 180°$ $S_2 = S_4 = 360°$
$\delta_1 = \delta_2 = \delta_3 = \delta_4 = 0°$
$\alpha_3 = \alpha_4 = 0°$ $\alpha_1 = \alpha_2 = 180°$

Horizontal radiation pattern of a broadside array of five elements

$k_1 = k_2 = k_3 = k_4 = 1$
$\alpha_1 = \alpha_2 = 180°$ $\alpha_3 = \alpha_4 = 0°$
$\delta_4 = -180°$ $\delta_3 = -90°$ $\delta_1 = 90°$ $\delta_2 = 180°$
$S_1 = S_3 = 90°$ $S_2 = S_4 = 180°$

Horizontal radiation pattern of an end-fire array of five elements

for the computer and indicator units. The rectifier, voltage-regulator section is conventional.

Three-phase voltage for the selsyn transformers is obtained from two 6.3-volt transformers connected in open delta. One of the transformers is fed directly from the 117-volt line and the second is fed through a 60-degree constant-voltage phase shifter connected to the line. Switches provide separate control of filament and plate voltage.

Oscillograms of horizontal radiation patterns are given for two-element, three-element, four-element and five-element arrays.

If the oscillograms of the WBAA night antenna array radiation pattern are compared with the computed pattern, it may be seen that the error is relatively small. It is believed that the device will continue to be of value as a classroom

teaching aid in antenna array study, and that the equipment is accurate enough to be employed for first approximation work by the broadcast-array design engineer.

The writer gratefully acknowledges the encouragement and guidance of Robert P. Siskind of the School of Electrical Engineering at Purdue University, under whose supervision this project was carried forward.

REFERENCES

(1) Alston F. Everest and Wilson S. Prichett, Horizontal-Polar Tracer for Directional Broadcast Antennas, *Proc. IRE*, 30, p 227, May 1942.
William G. Hutton and R. Morris Pierce, A Mechanical Calculator for Directional Antenna Patterns, *Proc. IRE*, p 233, May 1942.
(2) Carl E. Smith and Edward L. Grove, An Electromechanical Calculator for Directional Antenna Patterns, *Trans. AIEE*, (*Elec. Eng.*, Feb. 1943) 62, p 78, Feb. 1943.
(3) George H. Brown and Wendell C. Morrison, The RCA Antennalyzer, *Proc. IRE*, 34, p 992, Dec. 1946.
(4) Ray D. Kell, RCA Laboratories, U. S. Patent no. 2,061,734.
(5) J. R. Day, Serrasoid F-M Modulator, ELECTRONICS, p 72, Oct. 1948.

Improved Antenna Pattern Measurement Facilities

By M. W. SCHELDORF

CHARACTERISTICS OF AN ANTENNA are essentially defined by its two principal qualities, input impedance and radiation patterns. It is generally understood that electrical measurements to determine these characteristics must be made without reflections from structures in the vicinity of the antenna. This is particularly true of pattern measurements where reflected signals contribute to errors in the first order as compared with impedance measurements where these errors appear as second order effects.

Patterns are taken in two ways. In one method, a signal is applied to the antenna under test (rotatable in the plane desired) and the field is measured by a second fixed antenna, (similar to the test antenna but often only a dipole antenna or special directive antenna). In a second method, a fixed field is established by a source antenna and the test antenna is rotated in this field. Measurements are then made of the voltage received. Due to a condition of reciprocity, the results obtained

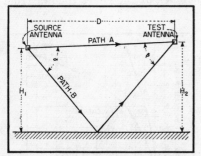

FIG. 1—Ground reflection diagram for test antenna setup

are the same for both methods. When operating at very short wavelengths it is possible to rotate

the test antenna in either a vertical plane or a horizontal plane so as to obtain the commonly accepted standard patterns, but due to ground reflections, it is usually preferable to rotate it in only the horizontal plane, see Fig. 1.

In most pattern tests it is possible to avoid all reflections except the ground reflection and the conditions as indicated in this figure are met. Radiation from one antenna to the other takes place over two general paths, one directly between them, path A, and another by virtue of a ground reflection, path B. Two difficulties result: the signal received will vary anywhere from essentially nothing, due to cancellation, to about double that for path A alone, due to reinforcement; and the pattern as defined by the field at the test antenna, will be a complex combination of the patterns in two planes, differing in altitude by the angle β. Generally the horizontal pattern is desired, so the two antennas must be on the same level reducing H_1 and H_2 and angles α and β to the same value.

It is obvious that the only remedy for the interference is to reduce the radiation along path B to a satisfactory minimum. This may be accomplished in two ways. First, the antenna heights are made as large as possible compared to the separation D. This will reduce the field from path B inversely in proportion. Distance D is usually fixed by the frequency of operation and the size of the antennas by a commonly accepted relationship $D = Kd^2/\lambda$ where K is a value of unity, or greater (depending on the degree of pattern accuracy desired), d is the

aperture of the antennas and λ is the wavelength of operation. Hence the height above ground is no longer a matter of simple arbitrary choice. Secondly, the radiation from the source antenna may be made directive in the vertical plane so that there is relatively little radiation at the angle α.

Testing Large Antennas

Testing of large antennas at low frequencies will be found to require large distances D and consequently large heights above ground. The cover page illustrates a tower structure designed to meet the requirements of these conditions. The tower structure is mounted on skids and is moved about to suit different distances D by means of a bulldozer. The source antenna is mounted on a sliding frame, which may be elevated to the desired height after the antenna has been constructed and attached to the frame at ground level.

The condition of vertical directivity is demonstrated also. The source antenna consists of two vertical rows of folded dipole antennas, four in each row, fed in phase and so spaced as to give the desired horizontal and vertical radiation patterns. No attempt is made to suppress the backward radiation from this antenna, such a procedure being required only when the general space in that direction has possible reflecting surfaces or when a stronger forward field is needed. In the particular setup shown, the antenna separation was 92 feet and the height above ground 28 feet. Measurements were being made in the frequency range 152 to 162 mc.

TV Receiving Antenna Measurements

By KENDRICK H. LIPPITT

TECHNICAL information regarding antenna arrays is needlessly confused by the maze of conflicting performance figures published by some manufacturers.

Measurements made on television receiving antennas using the system of the Technical Appliance Corp. result in a gain figure which takes into consideration not only the true gain of the antenna but also the mismatch loss which occurs into a 300-ohm load.

In this system, the voltage developed across the terminals of a folded dipole terminated in a 300-ohm load is compared with the voltage developed across the terminals of the antenna array being tested, also terminated in a 300-ohm load.

Thirty feet of standard 300-ohm twin-lead line connect the standard folded dipole and the array under test to the measuring voltmeter. A plug arrangement is used at the input to the voltmeter so that neither of the two transmission lines can be connected.

The voltmeter used is an RCA type 301B, a high-frequency field-intensity meter. It has a linear measuring system and is sufficiently stable for gain measurements. The input circuit of the meter was designed to have an impedance of 300 ohms by means of a General Radio bridge, type 916A, and a standing-wave line. For channels 7 to 13 special equipment was built with linear scales.

The zone in which the array is placed for measurement and the half-wave dipole used for reference are not subject to exactly the same signal intensity. Therefore, a television program can not be used to measure the gain of an antenna array because the 6-mc signal level changes as picture detail varies.

A signal generator with stable output connected to an all-channel-type transmitting antenna is the best source of signal for this type

of measurement. It is tunable to any frequency within its range and sends out a signal with a narrow bandwidth. In this way the performance of the antenna over the 6-mc band or over a series of bands may be probed at many points.

Constant field intensity must be obtained in the zone in which the antennas under test are located. Vertical rather than horizontal polarization reduces any discrepancy to a small figure. With vertical polarization, the mutual loading of ground on the antenna is negligible if the antenna is vertical to ground. If an array is horizontal, the mutual coupling may cause a significant change in the operating impedance of the array.

Test Method

In order that the standard reference folded-dipole antenna is in exactly the same field as the antenna under test, the two antennas are placed on a T mast which is rotated to measure front and back ratios of both antennas.

In the gain measurement procedure, the signal generator is tuned to the frequency desired and allowed to stabilize. Next, the antenna array is plugged into the voltmeter and the meter tuned to the frequency of the signal generator and allowed to stabilize. The antenna array is then rotated to the forward position of the T mast and the meter reading recorded.

Finally, the transmission line from the reference folded dipole is plugged into the measuring voltmeter in place of the line from the antenna array without retuning the signal generator or the meter. The reference folded dipole is then swung into the position previously occupied by the antenna array and the meter reading recorded.

With single-channel type antennas, such as Yagi antennas, it is possible to estimate the maximum

gain obtainable from any type array made up of half-wave elements. The chart shown gives the maximum gain available from antenna arrays with various numbers of half-wave elements.

For the same total transmitting power, the power in a single half-wave dipole antenna is twice that in each dipole of an antenna made up of two half-wave dipoles. If the power is cut in half the field produced by the antenna is reduced to 0.707 times its previous value. Therefore, if the voltage from the two half-wave dipoles adds up in phase, 1.4, a 3-db gain is obtained over a single dipole antenna.

In the chart the gain of two elements over one is given as four rather than three db. This improvement is produced by a change in the current distribution on the antenna elements. When elements are spaced close together, as in the conventional Yagi, the current distribution is not sinusoidal. For this same reason, top loading of transmitting antennas is justified where the current distribution is changed to increase the transmitted signal.

The justification for the remainder of the chart follows from

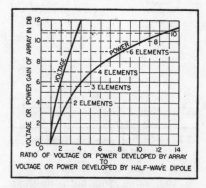

Maximum gain obtainable from antenna arrays with various numbers of half-wave elements. For example, a four-element array is capable of producing a maximum power gain of 5 or a voltage gain of 2.3 which is 7-db gain over a half-wave dipole

the previous reasoning. When the power is divided into two similar antennas, the gain is increased three db over one single antenna.

Over a period of two and one-half years more than 1,000 different antenna arrays have been measured using this technique, from single half-wave dipoles to arrays of sixteen elements. During this period the chart has been accurate and satisfactory.

Wide-Band Amplifier for Central Antenna Installations

By J. B. CRAWLEY

ADDITIONAL AMPLIFICATION is needed in central antenna locations such as display areas of radio stores and final test areas in radio-receiver production to overcome the inherent high noise level produced by street-car lines, neon signs and fluorescent lighting systems. Signal strength of the desired station may also be weak because of steel building structures which decrease signal-to-noise ratio.

This problem has been magnified in recent years because of the increased use of built-in loop antennas in radios. Connecting an outside antenna might work in some cases but in others would offer little improvement.

The circuit shown in Fig. 1 was designed to solve this interference problem. The system consists of an antenna installed as far away from the noise field as possible. It may be a noise-rejecting doublet type or preferably the straight-wire type because most noise is horizontally polarized in contrast to the broadcast signal which is vertically polarized.

Coil construction details for the circuit are as follows: L_1 secondary is made up of 255 turns on 1-in. form in a 2-in. winding space, the primary is 20 turns center tapped; L_2 and L_2' are made up of 213 turns of No. 38 enameled wire on a 1-watt 500,000-ohm resistor and L_3 is made up of 92 turns on $\frac{1}{2}$-in. form in a $1\frac{1}{2}$-in. winding space with the tap

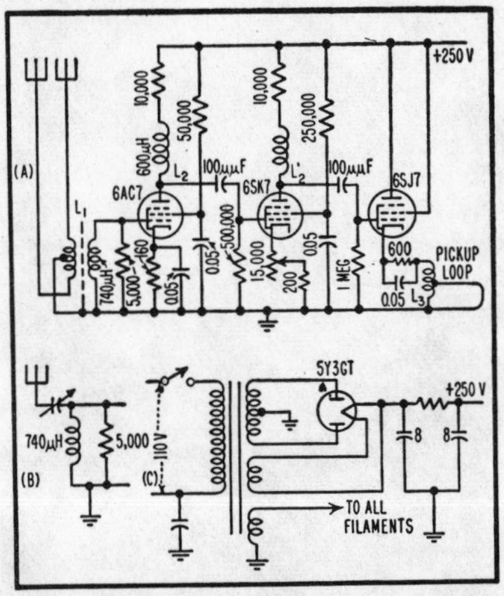

FIG. 1—Circuit of wide-band amplifier with noise-rejecting doublet antenna (A), alternate lead-in for straight-wire antenna (B) and amplifier power supply (C)

37 turns from ground.

The system has a balanced lead-in and an input transformer to the amplifier with a Faraday shield between primary and secondary. The amplifier itself is a two-stage high-gain broad-band amplifier followed by a cathode-follower stage.

Circuit

Design of the amplifier section is similar to the front end of many broadcast sets employing untuned r-f stages. A 6AC7 is used in the first stage to provide high gain. The second stage is a 6SK7 or similar remote-cutoff type. Remote cutoff is necessary because the gain control is incorporated in the second stage and a sharp-cutoff tube

might show nonlinearity with a resultant garbling of signals.

The amplifier is designed to cut off slightly above the broadcast band. By changing the values of the plate resistors and the peaking coils, shortwave coverage may be obtained. However the over-all gain of the amplifier would be less.

To couple the amplifier output to the loop antenna of the receiver or receivers without a physical connection, a low-impedance output loop is used. This stage is matched by a 6SJ7 operated as a cathode follower fed to a single-turn loop.

The output loop may consist of any reasonable length of wire running under a shelf or table near the sets to be operated. It acts as the primary of a coil which inductively couples the signal into the secondary or loop of the receivers.

Care must be taken to prevent regeneration by keeping the input and output wires of the amplifier from running side by side. A wave trap may be installed if a strong local station should tend to overload the amplifier.

Tests made on a five-tube Sentinel radio showed that with the volume control set at normal it was possible to receive six stations fairly well and four others were barely audible. Turning on the amplifier allowed the same set to receive a total of 18 stations without noise.

VHF Dummy Antennas

Three dummy loads for transmitter powers ranging from 25 to 5,000 watts and frequencies up to 160 megacycles are easily constructed. Voltage standing wave ratios are well under 1:1.5 for all types described

By B. E. PARKER

THE INCREASING NUMBER of vhf stations has accented the need for revision of test techniques and equipment designed for operation on the lower frequencies.

At 100 megacycles, a load used as a dummy antenna on the low frequencies may have a reactance several times its d-c resistance, with consequent introduction of a high standing-wave ratio. Standing-wave ratios which do not exceed a ratio of 1:1.5 are generally considered acceptable in the industry and the three dummy antennas illustrated meet this requirement.

The 25-watt unit shown in Fig. 1 handles 25 watts up to 160 mc with a standing-wave ratio under 1:1.3 when properly adjusted.

The 1,000-watt unit, Fig. 2, handles slightly over 1,000 watts at any frequency in the f-m broadcast band with a standing-wave ratio which does not exceed 1:1.3 after the initial adjustment. With reasonable care in building and adjustment it may be adjusted to give a standing-wave ratio under 1:1.1 at any given frequency in the f-m band.

The 5,000-watt unit is illustrated in Fig. 3. It presents a nonreactive resistive load well beyond 160 mc. Standing-wave ratios under 1:1.1 will be obtained up to 160 mc without any kind of adjustment. This is a marked ·advantage in laboratory applications and in factories for testing high-power transmitters.

Each of the dummy loads described has been used by the final test engineers in our f-m department. For 10-watt f-m campus transmitters and communications transmitters, the 25-watt load has

FIG. 1—Low-power dummy antenna consists of a debased 32-volt bulb and a variable capacitor

proven popular, due largely to compactness and ease in connecting to the transmitter under test.

25-Watt Load

The only parts required for construction of the 25-watt dummy load are a 25-watt, 32-volt light bulb, an Amphenol type 83-1SP plug, and a Hammarlund type APC25, 25-$\mu\mu$f capacitor. The 32-volt light bulb is of the popular rural-lighting-system type and is readily available from electrical supply houses in most localities.

The base of the bulb must be removed. A hacksaw, a soldering iron and a pair of diagonal cutters will

do the job nicely without breaking off the two wires. One side of the bulb is soldered directly to the center conductor of the plug. The capacitor is soldered in series with the plug shell and the remaining bulb wire. The rotor connection of the capacitor should connect to the shell. The 25-watt dummy load shown in Fig. 1 has a one-inch length of polyethylene dielectric pushed over the center lead to make the bulb self-supporting. The polyethylene was obtained from a piece of RG8/U coaxial cable.

1,000-Watt Load

The 1,000-watt dummy load has been of real value in field-engineering use and should prove popular because of its portability to stations that experience difficulty in the transmission system from the transmitter up to and including the antenna. When excessive standing-wave ratios are experienced in the transmission-line system, the transmission line may be pulled apart and terminated with the dummy, thus isolating the difficulty to the antenna, isolating unit, or section of coax causing the difficulty.

While the dissipation or power-handling capabilities of this particular dummy load is limited to a little over 1,000 watts, this does not limit its uses to stations of 1,000 watts or less. Most 3-kw f-m transmitters can be reduced in power to a kilowatt by means of transformer taps for the isolation procedure.

To make the 1,000 watt dummy load, ten 100-watt, 120-volt Sylvania light bulbs are connected in parallel by means of three twelve-inch lengths of No. 8 or No. 10 tinned

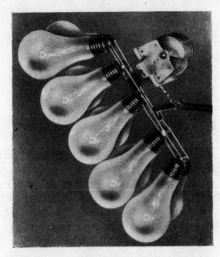

FIG. 2—Ten 100-watt bulbs and a variable capacitor form the 1,000-watt load

copper bus wire. The bulb shells are all soldered to the middle length, with five on each side. The second length of bus is laid across the bulb center-contact point of one row of bulbs and soldered, joining the five bulbs together. The remaining length of bus is laid across the center contacts of the other row of bulbs and likewise soldered.

The two outer rows of bus are joined by a short length of copper strap at least ½ inch wide. This copper strap serves as the connection point for the inner conductor of the coax. A Cardwell variable capacitor is connected, by means of a copper strap, in series with the shells of the bulbs and the outer conductor of the coax. It is paramount that connections be kept short.

The 1,000-watt dummy shown in Fig. 2 has a ten-foot length of RG8/U coax with various adapters attached to assist in connecting to different types of fittings.

5,000-Watt Load

The materials for the 5,000-watt unit are an IRC type LP 51.5-ohm dummy resistor unit and a short length (approximately 14 inches) of 3⅛-inch coaxial cable with end flange attached. Cooling is done by a filtered water flow of five gallons per minute. A rubber hose for carrying the water and the necessary hose fittings and clamps for attaching it to the dummy and the water supply are also required as

shown in Fig. 3.

The type LP resistor slides down into the 3⅛-inch coax with the flange fingers gripping the outer conductor. The lower end of the resistance element is attached to the inner conductor of the coax by means of a 10-32 screw.

The hose carrying the incoming filtered water is connected to the resistor fitting marked INLET. The outgoing heated water is carried off by an additional length of hose to the plumbing drainage system.

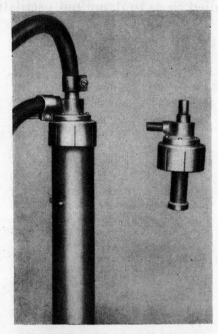

FIG. 3—Complete 5,000-watt dummy antenna is shown at left. The resistive element is at right

A fine-screen wire filter unit may be obtained from a plumbing supply house for insertion in the intake line. The filter prevents abrasive material, practically always present in water mains, from wearing away the thin carbon film constituting the resistive element. Cost of the element is around $70 and the completed dummy should be under $100.

This type dummy load may be increased to 10 kw by using a 3-inch T plumbing fitting and paralleling two 103-ohm type LP units.

Bulb Loads

It would appear that the number of bulbs could be reduced by using bulbs of greater wattage but this

has not been found practical. The larger-wattage bulbs develop hot spots on the filament, destroying it before it can be brought up to brilliance. Also, a type of fluorescence occurs, often accompanied by internal arcing.

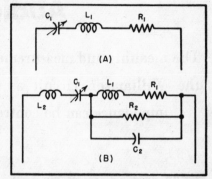

FIG. 4—Basic representation of R, L and C is shown at A. Complexities created by bulb shell and mount are shown at B

The d-c resistance of the bulbs when paralleled and operating at full brilliance figures out to be 14.4 ohms. This is far from the 51.5 ohms desired. Apparently the actual resistance is raised to 51.5 ohms at vhf due to the predominance of skin effect.

Figure 4A is an over-simplified schematic representation of the complex inductance, capacitance and resistance present in bulb-type dummy loads. Resistance R_1 represents the 51.5-ohm resistance in which we are primarily interested; L_1 represents the series inductance due to the filament structure and length; C_1 is the external capacitance added to series-resonate L_1 to the operating frequency and make the load appear purely resistive.

In practice, the complex reactances are more nearly represented by Fig. 4B. Capacitance C_2 represents the shell and lead capacitance in the base of the bulb; R_2 represents the insulating material used in the base of the bulb as well as the losses of the glass filament-supporting structure due to the high lead content used in the glass; L_2 represents the inherent inductance present in even the short external lead lengths used as connections as well as unavoidable inductance present in the capacitor construction.

AUDIO

Audio Amplifier Damping

The meaning and measurement of the damping factor in audio amplifiers are shown, using the Williamson circuit as an example. By means of feedback the amplifier output impedance can be controlled so as to damp out oscillations generated in the load

By ROBERT M. MITCHELL

THE growing interest in transient response of electroacoustical systems necessitates increased attention to the means of controlling amplifier output impedance. However, a more convenient concept is the damping factor, D, which is defined as the ratio of the load impedance, R_l, to the effective generator impedance, Z_o. It will be shown how the damping factor can be controlled through the use of feedback.

If an impedance-matching device, such as a transformer, is placed between the two impedances, the ratio is that obtained with both impedances referred to the same side of the transformer as shown in Fig. 1. Except where stated otherwise, the output impedance and load impedance are assumed to be resistive.

The term damping factor has been applied to this ratio because it is indicative of the effectiveness of the generator in damping oscillations generated by the load. Since it is expressed as a ratio, it will be the same for any output tap on a transformer and is therefore a more convenient characteristic to use than the effective output impedance itself.

The output impedance of an amplifier will be considered to be the ratio of voltage E to current i obtained when the input is short circuited and the voltage E is applied to the output terminals as shown in Fig. 2.

The damping factor may be varied by changing either R_l or Z_o. Since it is usually desired to obtain a given power output from a given tube, it is not practical to change the load impedance. A method that will change the effective output impedance of the amplifier, but will leave the load unchanged is to apply feedback so that the output stage is included in the loop.

Damping by Feedback

Figure 3 shows a basic one-stage feedback diagram, with polarities not indicated to make the diagram general. It will be noted that this

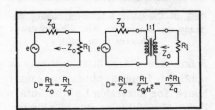

FIG. 1—Damping factor ratio is that with both impedances referred to same side of transformer

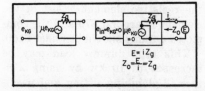

FIG. 2—Conditions under which amplifier output impedance equals E/i

is the so-called voltage type of feedback. If the polarities are such as to make βE oppose e_{in} (assuming

the latter no longer zero) the feedback is negative. For this condition β is considered negative, and the resultant output impedance is less than that without feedback. If the feedback is positive the output impedance is increased. It may be shown that negative-current feedback increases the output impedance, while positive-current feedback reduces it.

It is important that the definition of the original output impedance be clearly understood. If the output impedance without feedback is the plate resistance alone (as in Fig. 3) then this output impedance is changed by the factor $1/(1 - \beta\mu)$, which is not the same factor by which the gain of the stage is changed. If the output impedance without feedback is the plate resistance of the tube in parallel with the load resistance, then the output impedance is changed by the factor $1/(1 - \beta K)$, where K is the stage gain, when feedback is applied. This is the same factor by which the gain is changed. Such a condition would be encountered seldom, if ever, in a loudspeaker output stage, but might arise in connection with an R-C shunt-fed transformer stage. This difference in definition may lead to misunderstanding when different source texts of feedback amplifier design are consulted, unless the distinctions are clearly understood beforehand. In this article, the discussion is confined to the output stage, with the output impedance without feedback being defined as the plate resistance of the output tube in every case.

Most practical amplifier circuits generally comprise more than one stage. In a multistage amplifier it is usually preferable to enclose more than the final stage in the feedback loop, since this, among other things, avoids the requirement of large driving voltages for the final stage. For these conditions the feedback diagram is as shown in Fig. 4.

Multistage Feedback Effects

The results are almost identical to those of Fig. 3, with the exception that the gain K of the intervening stages appears in the factor to increase the effects of the feedback for a given μ and β.

The final equation shown in Fig. 4 is that generally found in textbooks for output impedance of multistage feedback amplifiers. In this form it is not particularly convenient to use for calculation, since it requires a knowledge of the gain of the intervening stages.

A simpler, and more convenient equation may be derived as follows. The damping factor without feedback is

$$D_o = \frac{R_l}{Z_o} = \frac{R_l}{r_p}$$

The damping factor with feedback is

$$D_f = \frac{R_l}{Z_o} = \frac{R_l}{r_p/(1 - \beta K \mu_f)} \quad (2)$$
$$= D_o (1 - \beta K \mu_f)$$

The gain of the final stage is

$$K_f = \mu_f \frac{R_l}{R_l + r_p}$$

Solving for μ_f

$$\mu_f = K_f \left(1 + \frac{r_p}{R_l}\right)$$
$$= K_f \left(1 + \frac{1}{D_o}\right)$$

Substituting in Eq. 2

$$D_f = D_o \left[1 - \beta K K_f \left(1 + \frac{1}{D_o}\right)\right] \quad (3)$$

The amount by which the gain is reduced is

$$1 - \beta K K_f = 1 - \beta K_o$$
where K_o is total gain

That is, if $1 - \beta K_o = 2$, the gain is reduced by 2. Letting this gain reduction factor $= F$, we have

$$D_f = D_o [F - (1 - F)(1/D_o)]$$
$$D_f = F(D_o + 1) - 1 \quad (4)$$

Note that in this final form it is

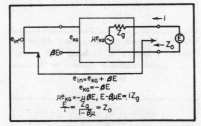

FIG. 3—Output impedance without feedback is represented by plate resistance alone in figure above and in text

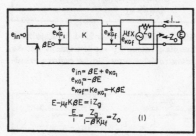

FIG. 4—Conventional concept leading to Eq. 1 above is based on premises illustrated. Equation 4 (see text) is more convenient form

not necessary to know the actual gain of any of the stages, or the feedback ratio, but only the gain reduction and the original damping factor.

For example, it is desired to compute the damping factor obtained in

a push-pull 6L6 amplifier when 20 db of negative voltage feedback is employed.

$$F = 10$$
$$R_l = 5,000$$
$$r_p \text{ (two tubes)} = 45,000$$
$$D_o = 5,000/45,000$$
$$D_f = 10(0.111 + 1) - 1 = 10.11$$

For a push-pull 2A3 amplifier with the same load and the same gain-reduction factor

$$r_p \text{ (2 tubes)} = 1,600$$
$$D_o = 5,000/1,600 = 3.12$$
$$D_f = 10(3.12 + 1) - 1 = 40.2$$

These results show the tremendous changes in output impedance produced by feedback, especially for beam-power tubes. Without feedback the damping factor of the triode amplifier is some 27 times that of the beam-power tubes. With the same amount of feedback applied to each, the damping factor of the triodes is approximately 4 times that of the beam-power tubes. Or looking at it from another point of view, the same amount of feedback produces a 13-fold change for the triodes, but a 90-fold change for the beam power tubes.

Equation 4 has been used to obtain the graph of Fig. 5. In this graph the two curves show changes in damping factor with feedback for typical beam-power tubes and typical power triodes. From this it may be seen that approximately 12 db of feedback is required to make

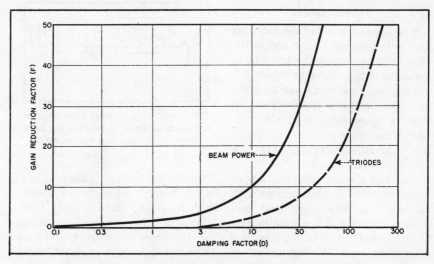

FIG. 5—Curves show changes in damping factor with feedback for typical beam-power and power-triode tubes. Note superiority of triodes

the damping factor of a beam-power tube equal to that of a triode without feedback. It is also evident that the same amount of feedback will always give a greater damping factor in a triode amplifier than in a beam-power amplifier, since the original damping factor of the triode amplifier is greater.

These curves may be used in several ways, although Eq. 4 is so simple that it may be used almost as readily, especially if the following simplifications are made.

The initial damping factor for most beam-power tubes is approximately 0.1, while it is approximately 3 for most triodes. Using these values the following approximate equations, quite suitable for design purposes, are obtained:

For beam power tubes

$$D_f = F - 1 \qquad (4B)$$

For triodes

$$D_f = 4F - 1 \qquad (4C)$$

Both these equations are reasonably accurate when F is equal to or greater than 2 (6-db feedback). For less feedback, Eq. 4 should be used for beam power tubes, while Eq. 4C is still applicable for triodes.

Similar relations may be derived for current feedback, but since this type is relatively little used over the output stage, they will not be derived here.

Measurement

The measurement of the damping factor is generally done indirectly, that is, it is usually the practice to measure output voltages under differing load conditions, and to calculate the damping factor from the results. However, it is equally easy, and often more accurate, to measure it by other methods, which are also described below.

The first method often consists of measuring the output voltage with no load and with rated load, and then calculating D as shown in Fig. 6. This method is satisfactory for amplifiers with low values of D, such as pentode or beam-power amplifiers with little or no feedback.

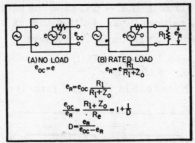

FIG. 6—Method of measuring damping factor by means of no-load and rated-load output voltage shown in bottom equation

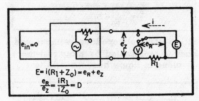

FIG. 7—Simplified method of obtaining damping factor by measurement across series resistor equal to secondary winding

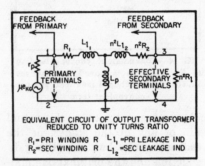

FIG. 8—Limits of the damping factor with feedback obtained from one of two points. See text for discussion

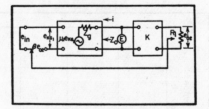

FIG. 9—Effective internal impedance of intermediate stage is reduced by feedback taken from succeeding stage

When the internal impedance is low, as in highly degenerative amplifiers, however, there is very little difference between e_R and e_{oc}. Since the difference of these two terms appears in the denominator, it is possible, when they are almost equal, for an error of a few percent

in either of these terms to produce an error of several hundred percent in the answer.

A more accurate procedure is to use a low-impedance-type a-c bridge. For such measurements the signal-input terminals of the amplifier are short-circuited, the output terminals are connected to the unknown impedance terminals of the bridge, and the bridge balanced as in normal measurements.

An even simpler method, and one quite accurate for damping factors as high as 50 or more is shown in Fig. 7. The input terminals of the amplifier are short-circuited and the output terminals are connected to a generator E in series with a resistance R_l, which is the rated value of the secondary winding of the output transformer. The damping factor is then equal to the ratio of the voltage drops across R_l and across the secondary winding respectively. The generator E may conveniently be the 6.3-volt filament winding of a power transformer. In a highly degenerative amplifier almost all the voltage drop will be across R_l; consequently, it must be fairly high power rating.

When E is 6.3 v a rating of 10 watts will be adequate for almost all situations.

Two points of interest concerning damping factor may be pointed out in passing. First, it can be seen from Fig. 8 that when the feedback is taken from the primary of the output transformer (terminals 1 and 2), the damping factor approaches R_l/R_w as a limit, where R_w is the total winding resistance of the transformer referred to the same side to which R_l is referred. When the feedback is taken from the secondary terminals (3 and 4), however, this limit does not exist, and D can theoretically approach infinity.

Internal Impedance

Second, it is demonstrated below by reference to Fig. 9 that the effective internal impedance of a stage inside the feedback loop is also reduced by negative feedback taken from a succeeding stage.

$$e_{in} = \beta e_{02} + e_{KG1}$$
$$e_{KG1} = -\beta e_{02}$$
$$e_{02} = K_2 E$$
$$E + \mu_1 e_{KG1} = i Z_g$$
$$E + \mu_1 (-\beta e_{02}) = i Z_g$$
$$E + \mu_1 (-\beta K_2 E) = i Z_g$$
$$\frac{E}{i} = \frac{Z_g}{1 - \beta \mu_1 K_2} = Z_o$$

This shows, for example, that overall feedback from the final stage of a class-B modulator will reduce the output impedance of the driver stage as well, thereby contributing to reduced distortion by virtue of this action as well as by its normal distortion-reducing action.

Practical Applications

Although feedback can increase the initial damping factor to a high degree, the values realized in practice are somewhat less than theory indicates. The large damping factors that can be achieved in practical design, however, are well exemplified in the 20-watt wide-range, feedback amplifier shown in Fig. 10. This is the commercial type W-20 Williamson amplifier, in which 20 db of negative feedback is taken over four stages and the output transformer. The damping factor of this amplifier without feedback, measured by the method of Fig. 7, is 2 at 50 cycles (a common value of resonant frequency for high-quality low-frequency type loudspeakers). When 20 db of negative feedback is applied the damping factor is increased to 27, which is only slightly less than the theoretical value of 29 based upon the initial measured value of D_o.

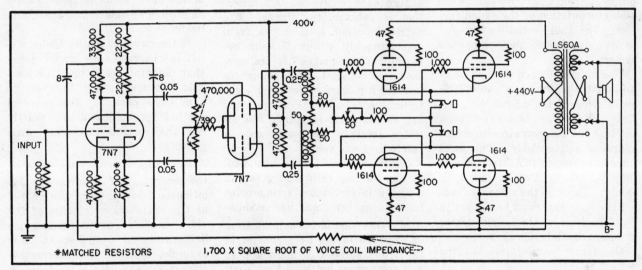

FIG. 10—Circuit diagram of the UTC W-20 Williamson feedback amplifier with damping factor of 27

Simplified Intercarrier Sound

Reduction in number of tubes and tuned circuits is provided by application of the gated beam 6BN6 to the intercarrier sound system of a receiver. Suppression of a-m compares favorably with other f-m detectors as does suppression of ignition interference

By WALTER J. STROH

INTERCARRIER SOUND claims a few advantages over the conventional system in the overall operation of the receiver as well as in the initial design.

The most important benefit of the system is the oscillator stability requirement. The sound subcarrier is dependent only upon the beat between the sound and picture carriers and not the local oscillator frequency, excessive drift of which cannot be tolerated in the conventional system. The trend toward the use of 40-mc i-f makes intercarrier sound extremely attractive since 4.5-mc is far easier to handle than 40-mc, especially in the design of the discriminator or ratio detector transformers.

Keen competition in the manufacture of television receivers demands the utmost in economy and simplicity. With the development of the 6BN6 gated beam tube by Robert Adler[1] of Zenith and its subsequent mass production by the

General Electric Company, an intercarrier sound system embodying increased simplicity and economy can be realized.

In the typical intercarrier receiver, the sound and picture carriers are amplified in a common i-f amplifier. The 4.5-mc beatnote between and sound and picture carriers is detected at the second detector and usually amplified, either in the video stages or separately, before it is separated and fed into an f-m detector. Since the frequency of the beatnote varies directly as the sound carrier, the output of the f-m detector contains the audio modulation of the sound carrier. The audio signal is then fed to a conventional audio amplifier system.

The biggest design problem is to minimize the incidental amplitude modulation of the 4.5-mc beatnote. This problem arises because even the best f-m detector circuits do not suppress a-m entirely. The most important step in this direction was taught by L. W. Parker[2] and R. B. Dome[3]. Through the video i-f channel the bandpass must be shaped so that the level of the sound carrier is approximately 20 db below the peak picture carrier level at the second detector.

A video i-f bandpass characteristic to accomplish this desired sound-to-picture ratio is shown in Fig. 1. The 6-db bandwidth is about

dashed-line curve. The shelf costs an extra tuned circuit, however, and it has been found unnecessary if the slope of the i-f curve is not too steep.

If the sound carrier level is 6 db below the minimum picture carrier level, the amplitude of the beatnote in a linear detector is substantially unaffected by picture carrier amplitude. However, at low levels where the detector is operating according to a square law, the beatnote amplitude varies greatly with sync and video modulation. Therefore, it is desirable to operate the detector at a high enough level so that detection is substantially linear. The detector output level varies from approximately 1.5 to 5 volts between various makes of receivers, assuming a signal strong enough to produce a picture of reasonable entertainment value. For marginal and submarginal reception, the detector level is frequently only a fraction of one volt.

Obtaining the proper sound-to-picture carrier ratio at the second detector is just the starting point in reducing the amplitude modulation. Any nonlinear amplification or overload in the i-f stages or in the video stage will introduce an a-m component on the 4.5-mc beatnote. In the video i-f chain, the last stage is most likely to overload. When overload occurs, the gain of the sound carrier varies with video modulation. To reduce overload

possibilities, the last transformer in a stagger-tuned i-f system should be tuned to the picture carrier side, and all the damping of the stage should be produced by the diode. In so doing, the grid swing required of the last i-f is minimized.

Another place for incidental amplitude modulation to occur is in the video amplifier stage. The video amplifier is a high-level amplifier and must operate with a large grid swing. The transconductance of the stage as a 4.5-mc amplifier will vary with video and sync modulation, especially when the grid is driven hard. This variation causes amplitude modulation of the 4.5-mc beatnote.

If the envelope of the 4.5-mc signal is observed, one would notice that indentations in the 4.5-mc envelope occur during the vertical sync pulse periods. The shape of the indentation would look exactly like the vertical blank and sync pulse.

The depth of the indentation or the percentage of downward modulation is determined by the degree of transconductance change of the video amplifier as the sync pulse drives the grid toward cutoff. For example, in some intercarrier receivers a raspy buzz is produced in the sound when the contrast control is advanced. In these receivers the contrast control is located ahead of the grid of the video amplifier and overload of the amplifier has

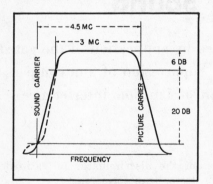

FIG. 1—Required overall response of video i-f stages

3 mc. It would be desirable to have a narrow shelf in the i-f bandpass at the sound carrier so that no slope detection of the sound carrier would occur. This is indicated by the

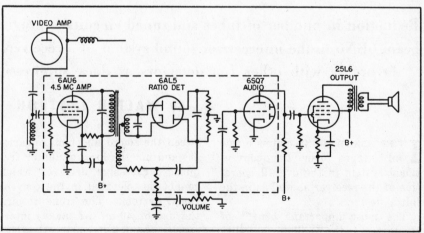

FIG. 2—Circuit most often used for intercarrier sound takes 4.5-mc beat at plate of video amplifier

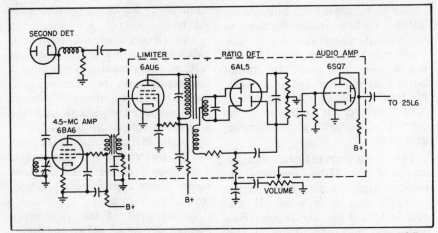

FIG. 3—Alternative circuit takes beat at video detector, requires additional amplifier

occurred as a result of being over-driven.

Intercarrier Buzz

Even though all the proper precautions to minimize amplitude modulation of the 4.5-mc beatnote have been taken in the design of the intercarrier receiver, it is subject to buzzy sound due to transmitter operation. If a transmitter is 100-percent modulated during the white portions of the picture, there will be frequent intervals in which the picture carrier level at the second detector will be zero; and, hence, the 4.5-mc beatnote amplitude drops to zero. The result, of course, is 100-percent amplitude modulation of the 4.5-mc signal, causing what is termed intercarrier buzz.

With a conventional sound system, 100-percent modulation of the picture transmitter does not affect the sound. It is hoped that the broadcasters will soon realize that intercarrier type receivers are becoming a substantial portion of the total number of sets in use, and that they will govern their operation accordingly by limiting the modulation percentage of the picture carrier to 85 or 90 percent.

Figure 2 shows the schematic diagram of an intercarrier sound system of a typical receiver.

The 4.5-mc beatnote is selected from the plate of the video stage by a resonant circuit and is fed to a ratio detector driver tube. The amplified signal is fed into a con-ventional ratio detector circuit using a 6AL5. The audio output is fed to an amplifier stage and then to a power output stage driving the loudspeaker. The portion of the circuit enclosed by the dotted line can be replaced by one tube, the 6BN6, and two single-tuned circuits.

The circuit of Fig. 3 is used in a few commercial receivers. Here the beatnote is taken off at the second detector. The 4.5-mc signal is amplified in two driver stages to make up for the gain lost by not utilizing the video amplifier.

The signal is demodulated in the conventional ratio detector and the audio output amplified in the conventional manner. Again the portion of the circuit enclosed by dotted lines can be replaced by a single 6BN6 tube.

Figure 4 is a block diagram of an intercarrier sound system utilizing a 6BN6 tube. For a tube to perform in this circuit arrangement, it must be a good limiter with a high limiting sensitivity, and it must be an f-m detector with sufficiently high audio output to drive a power stage directly. The 6BN6 gated beam tube fulfills the above requirements.

The schematic of Fig. 5 shows the 6BN6 in an intercarrier receiver performing the functions of a limiter and a discriminator.

The 4.5-mc beatnote from the plate of the first video stage is selected by a transformer whose primary is tuned to resonance at 4.5 mc and whose secondary is untuned and closely coupled to the primary. The first video stage is safe to utilize as an extra gain stage in this circuit because it is operating as a linear amplifier. Also the maximum output of the second detector is limited by agc circuits and the contrast control is located in the second video stage. Therefore the possibility of the first video being driven into an overload condition is eliminated.

The 4.5-mc signal is coupled to the grid of the triode amplifier stage through a small capacitor. This triode amplifier is not neutralized and is highly degenerative by virtue of the voltage feedback ratio determined by the grid-plate capacitance and the $10\text{-}\mu\mu f$ coupling capacitor. Its gain is approximately six. In the plate circuit of the triode is a single-tuned step-up transformer tuned to 4.5 mc. The step-up transformer is placed in the grid circuit so that the grid has a low d-c resistance to ground as required by the 6BN6. The B+ choke has a high impedance at 4.5 mc.

The amplified 4.5-mc signal is fed

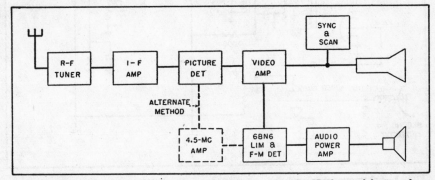

FIG. 4—Block diagram of intercarrier sound system using the 6BN6 gated beam tube

to the limiter grid of the 6BN6 at a level of approximately 5 volts rms. The exact level depends upon the output from the detector, the sound-to-picture amplitude ratio of the transmitted signals, the attenuation of the sound carrier in the i-f amplifier and upon the gain factor of the amplifier stages.

The gain required in the amplifier stage or stages between the detector and the limiter grid of the 6BN6 depends not only upon these factors but also upon the weakest signal or minimum detector output for which satisfactory sound is expected. For instance, assume 0.5 volt for this minimum level. With the sound carrier 20 db farther down, it has an amplitude of about 18 millivolts rms; to bring this up to the limiting level of 1 volt rms requires a gain of 55 times or 35 db.

The circuit shown in Fig. 5 provides a gain of 43 to 46 db. A number of circuit arrangements is possible. Utilizing the video stage should be done with caution, guarding against possible downward modulation. A single pentode amplifier stage between the second detector and the limiter grid might be preferred and would provide sufficient gain.

A-M Suppression

One of the most important characteristics of an f-m detector is its ability to suppress amplitude modulation. In this limiter-discriminator circuit using the 6BN6 the audio output is taken directly from the anode so that ampliture modulation may slip through as a result of spurious plate-bend detection. This tendency is minimized by careful adjustment of the limiter grid bias.

The plate current-grid voltage curve of the 6BN6 resembles a step-function characteristic having an upper and lower knee. If the grid is biased too highly negative, plate-bend detection occurs at the lower knee and the average plate current tends to rise with increased signal. If the grid bias is not negative enough, plate-bend detection of the reverse kind occurs at the upper knee and the average plate current drops with increased signal.

There is an optimum grid bias at which the plate current will stay constant with increased signal. This grid bias point coincides with best a-m rejection. An adjustable control rather than a fixed resistor is placed in the cathode of the 6BN6 to obtain optimum bias because of tube tolerance variations. When the circuit is properly adjusted, the a-m suppression compares favorably with other f-m detectors in commercial use, and the gated beam detector appears to have the edge in suppression of ignition interference where other

circuits are burdened by time constants.

The circuit does not contain a balanced transformer that requires critical adjustment. If the signal impressed upon the limiter grid were 30 percent a-m and 30 percent f-m, modulated simultaneously, the a-m audio component appearing in the audio circuit would be at least 20 db below the f-m component. This holds true for levels of input signal above approximately 1 volt, well below normal.

As a result of the quadrature voltage developed across the tuned circuit in the second grid, f-m detection takes place and the audio information is developed across the 220,000-ohm load resistor.

Discriminator Bandwidth

Figure 6 shows typical discriminator response produced by the 6BN6 with a 4.5-mc center frequency. The most conspicuous difference between this curve and the one for a conventional discriminator is the absence of any sharp curvature beyond the range of normal signal deviations. The harmonic distortion for 25-kc deviation is approximately 2.5 percent.

The bandwidth of the usable portion of the discriminator curve is proportional to the bandwith of the quadrature circuit. Higher L-C ratio in this circuit results in a

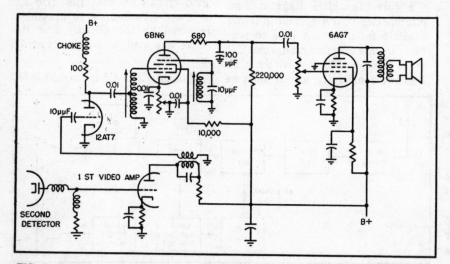

FIG. 5—Schematic of intercarrier sound system with 6BN6 functioning as limiter and f-m detector

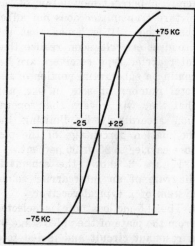

FIG. 6—Typical discriminator response for the gated beam tube

broader curve. Further broadening can be obtained by damping the quadrature circuit with a resistor but this results in impaired audio output and poorer a-m suppression.

The bandwidth can be increased by a better method used in this circuit. A small resistor (680 ohms) is inserted between the anode and the bypass capacitor. The insertion of this resistor has two effects: it damps the quadrature circuit but also supplies more energy to it. As a result, the voltage across the quadrature circuit will stay constant or even rise while the bandwidth is increased. Good audio output and improved a-m suppression result.

The plate bypass capacitor provides the correct amount of de-emphasis.

The stability of the quadrature circuit is important. It should not have excessive frequency drift with temperature and humidity changes. The fixed tuning capacitor across the quadrature circuit, therefore, has a specified temperature coefficient.

Output

The audio output which can be obtained with low distortion is largely a function of the plate supply voltage. In this circuit there is 160 to 170 volts available, and with full 25-kc deviation 15 volts rms audio output is normal with approximately 2-percent distortion. With higher plate voltage and a smaller damping resistor, it is possible to obtain 20 to 25 volts rms audio output with a harmonic distortion of 3 to 5 percent for 25-kc deviation.

With this level of audio output, the usual audio amplifier stage can be omitted and the detector output fed directly into the power tube.

If the transmitting stations could be counted upon to maintain their audio modulation percentage above 30 percent of 25 kc, a 6K6 power tube could be driven to practically full output. But to take care of those times when the percentage modulation of the sound carrier is extremely low, we have chosen to use a 6AG7 power output tube because of its high power sensitivity. A 6V6 or a 25L6 would be sufficient in most cases.

Only three adjustments are necessary. The step-up transformer is tuned for maximum 4.5-mc signal at the limiter grid. The quadrature circuit is tuned for maximum undistorted audio output, and the bias control in the cathode of the 6BN6 is adjusted for maximum a-m rejection.

The intercarrier sound system described has been designed for use in a receiver of highest quality with performance comparable to conventional sound type sets. For receivers where cost is a major consideration, the triode 4.5-mc amplifier may be eliminated by extracting the beatnote from the video amplifier and applying the signal directly to the limiter grid of the 6BN6 through a suitable coupling transformer.

The exact amount of intercarrier gain required between the video detector and the limiter grid of the 6BN6 depends, as has been pointed out, on the sound-to-picture carrier ratio produced in the i-f channel, and on the lowest video signal level at which satisfactory sound is expected. We have found that it is not at all hard to obtain gains of 35 db at 4.5-mc in a pentode video stage by using good circuitry to separate the intercarrier signal from the video frequency band. The main problem remaining in such a circuit is the necessity of avoiding a-m modulation of the 4.5-mc beatnote by the video signals due to overload in the video stage. This is most easily taken care of if the maximum video level is limited by automatic gain control circuits.

The author is indebted to Robert Adler for his valuable assistance and direction in adapting the 6BN6 as the limiter-detector of an intercarrier sound system. He is also indebted to Nathan Aram for his help in the preparation of this paper.

REFERENCES

(1) Robert Adler, The 6BN6 Gated Beam Tube, ELECTRONICS, p 82, Feb. 1950.
(2) L. W. Parker, TV Intercarrier Sound System, *Tele-Tech*, p 26, Oct., 1947.
(3) R. B., Dome, Carrier Difference Reception of Television Sound, ELECTRONICS, p 102, Jan., 1947.

Tunable A-F Amplifier

Variable-frequency circuit used as an oscillator from 200 to 10,000 cycles also serves as a selective amplifier in the same range. For code reception through interference, the device is switched to provide better rejection than a crystal filter

By OSWALD G. VILLARD, JR.

RECENT DISCLOSURE of a simple phase-inverter connection for driving a half-lattice R-C filter of the all-pass type[1] greatly simplifies a variable-frequency circuit useful both as an audio oscillator and as a selective amplifier for rejecting or emphasizing a particular frequency.

This circuit has certain interesting advantages in comparison with the conventional bridged-T, parallel-T, and Wien-bridge methods of accomplishing an equivalent result. It makes practical, for example, an easily-constructed wide-range oscillator in which the magnitude of the feedback voltage is substantially independent of the operating frequency. Thus, it is possible to dispense with special limiting or variable-impedance devices for automatic amplitude control.

When the circuit is used as a rejection network, only one knob need be turned in order to find the null. Inexpensive ganged resistances may be used to change frequency, and frequency ratios of the order of 100 to 1 may readily be obtained without range switching. Finally, the circuit as an oscillator inherently provides a source of quadrature voltage suitable for obtaining a circular sweep on a cathode-ray tube.

Method of Operation

A block diagram of one useful form of this circuit is shown in Fig. 1.

The all-pass-type filter delivers an output voltage whose magnitude is independent of frequency, but whose phase is determined by frequency. The variation of this phase with frequency (that is, the time constant of the network) is adjustable, and this adjustment also has no effect on the magnitude of the output voltage. In Fig. 1A a null will occur when the transmission through each of the parallel circuit branches is equal, and the phase shift through the network is 180 degrees. In Fig. 1B, oscillation occurs when the phase shift of the voltage fed back around the single-stage amplifier is 180 degrees. Consequently oscillations and the null will occur at the same frequency for a given setting of the network time constant.

It is convenient to do the phase shifting in this network in two sections. In Fig. 2 will be found the essential details of one section. Each may be viewed either as an R-C phase shifter of the familiar variety shown in many textbooks, (see Fig. 2A), or as one half of an R-C lattice filter of the all-pass phase-correcting type, as in Fig. 2B. The vector diagram of one section, which shows why the output voltage remains constant as either R, C, or frequency f is varied, is given in Fig. 2C. The phase shift of the output with respect to the input is 2 arctan $2fCR$. The network may be driven equally well by a vacuum-tube phase inverter, or by a transformer.

The special advantage of this particular half-lattice, when used as part of a null bridge or oscillator, is the fact that changing the phase shift by varying R cannot alter the phase-shifter output voltage and consequently affect the completeness of bridge balance or the magnitude of the oscillator feedback. If the corresponding full lattice were used (see the dashed lines in Figure 2B), both resistances would have to be varied in exact synchronism if changes in the magnitude of

the output voltage were to be avoided.

Lattice-Filter Method

Another method of obtaining feedback voltage whose magnitude is independent of frequency or frequency-control setting, and also using an all-pass lattice filter, has been disclosed[2] but is considerably more complicated than the present arrangement because no loss in the all-pass network was permitted. In the present case, greater constructional simplicity is obtained at the expense of a certain amount of amplification.

With the conventional Wien-bridge circuit, two accurately-

ganged capacitors or resistors must be varied to change frequency. If these elements are not in perfect track, the depth of the null will be proportionately reduced, and the feedback voltage will not be constant when the circuit is used as part of an oscillator. Similarly, parallel-T networks which must be varied over a wide frequency range require the accurate ganging of three circuit elements. It is usually necessary, with these circuits, to provide a fine balance control in addition to the coarse frequency control.

Constructional Details

A complete schematic of a typical oscillator-rejection filter device is found in Fig. 3, together with a vector diagram illustrating its operation in rejecting a particular signal. With two phase-shifter stages (V_1 and V_2) it is seen that the null is found when the phase shift

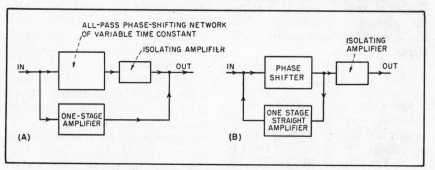

FIG. 1—Block diagram of basic rejection circuit (A) and basic oscillator circuit (B)

through each stage is 90 degrees—that is, when the frequency is such that X_c equals R in Fig. 2C. It follows that the null frequency is inversely proportional to resistance. The same is true of the oscillation frequency.

The gain control P in the grid of V_4 allows adjustment of the depth of the null when the switch S is at the 2, or null, position. Once set for best rejection at one frequency, it is ordinarily not necessary to readjust this control when frequency is changed. When S is set in the 1, or oscillator position, this same gain control P adjusts the amount of feedback. When the feedback is set somewhat below the position at which oscillation occurs, the unit becomes a variable-frequency selective amplifier.

The sharpness of the passband may be controlled by adjusting the amount of feedback. When oscillations are desired, the gain control is set slightly above the threshold of oscillation. Under these conditions waveform will be good and output will not vary appreciably as frequency is changed. Too much feedback causes distortion; too little will make the oscillations unstable and likely to drop out with small residual changes in feedback as frequency is varied.

The only critical circuit components in Fig. 3 are the plate and cathode resistors of the phase inverters. These must be matched very accurately in pairs. The absolute magnitude, of course, is not important. Similarly, the two-to-one ratio between the corresponding resistors of the two tubes need only be approximate. Thus the matching may readily be done on an ohmmeter. For best long-time stability, precision resistors should be used.

It is desirable that the power supply be well-filtered and have a very low output impedance, in order to avoid coupling between the phase inverter stages. Where stability of operation must be maintained in spite of large line-voltage fluctuations, voltage regulation is desirable.

Dial Calibration

In a great many so-called resistance-tuned oscillators, capacitance is varied in order to change frequency. Owing to the effect of the minimum capacitance inherent in variable capacitors, the tuning range obtainable is generally of the order of 10 to 1. By varying resistance in the present circuit, a wide tuning range may be covered in one rotation of the dial. If a straight line frequency-versus-resistance characteristic is desired, the phase-shifting capacitor in Fig. 2A can be replaced by an inductance. However an inverse

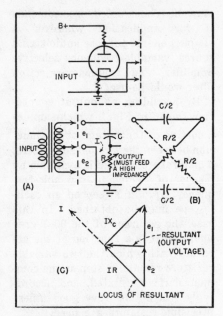

FIG. 2—Phase-shift circuit (A) that can be driven by transformer or vacuum tube; (B) all-pass lattice from which the simple phase-shifter is derived; (C) vector diagram

frequency-versus-resistance calibration is quite practical in many applications. The dual-ganged resistance used in the unit of Fig. 3 is a readily-available Centralab type C-104 which has what is termed a standard audio taper. By taking advantage of this taper, the range

from 200 to 10,000 cycles can be spread out reasonably well on a standard 180-degree vernier dial.

The chief limitation on the upper frequency limit which may be achieved by progressively reducing resistance, in addition to amplifier frequency response, is the loading effect of each R-C phase-shifting network on its associated phase inverter. This upsets the equality of the plate-to-ground and cathode-to-ground a-c voltages, and causes their relative phase to depart from exact phase opposition.

Sharpness of Rejection Band

It is desirable that a frequency-rejection device have as sharp a rejection notch as possible. The circuit described has a performance in this respect which is slightly superior to that of both a Wien and a parallel-T R-C bridge.

A curve of percent response versus frequency is shown in Fig. 4. The parallel-T response curve shown is that of a commonly used and relatively simple type[2] in which two of the resistors and two of the capacitors are identical and the other two elements are half or twice as large. A sharper rejection curve can be obtained by using a more

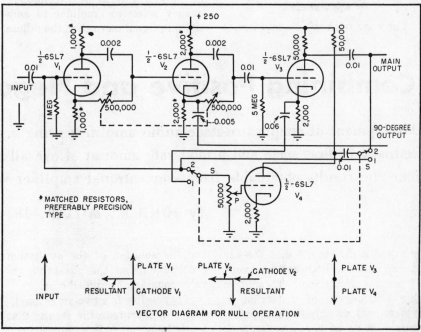

FIG. 3—Schematic circuit diagram and vector diagram for null operation

complex relationship between these elements, but even when this is done the best of several typical cases[9] does not equal the performance of the phase shift bridge.

Discrimination of the phase-shift bridge may be improved by adding

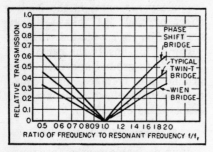

FIG. 4—Relative transmission as a function of frequency rejection

additional phase-shifting sections. With three instead of two, a second null, rather than a maximum of transmission, will occur as frequency approaches either zero or infinity, depending on circuit polarity. With the oscillator connection, there would accordingly be a tendency for simultaneous oscillation at two frequencies. However it is possible that the second oscillation might not prove too troublesome in view of the falling-off in amplifier response at the frequency involved.

Applications

The ease with which this device

may be constructed, recommends it for application wherever a simple general-purpose audio signal source, variable-frequency selective amplifier, and frequency-rejection filter would be useful.

By providing an output connection shown in Fig. 3 which samples a portion of the voltage at the junction between the two phase shifters, a quadrature voltage is available by means of which a variable-frequency circular sweep on an oscilloscope may be obtained. In this case, the accuracy of the 90-degree phase shift is a function of the accuracy with which the two variable resistors remain in step as the common shaft is rotated, and accordingly will not be very good unless precision resistors are used.

This unit is particularly suitable as an accessory for a communications receiver. In phone reception, the frequency-rejection feature may be used to eliminate interfering heterodyne whistles. The sharpness of the rejection slot is, if anything, superior to that of a good crystal filter. For code work, the operator has a choice: he may use the device to reject an interfering code station, leaving the desired signal little affected, or by throwing a switch he may use it as a variable-frequency selective amplifier to amplify one signal more than the others.

The selectivity is continuously variable and may be adjusted to suit.

It is interesting, as this control is advanced, to hear a signal of one particular pitch rise up out of the others simultaneously present. Since the null frequency and frequency of regeneration are the same, it is possible to select and amplify a particular signal, and then by throwing the switch to make it disappear leaving all the others behind.

Acknowledgment

The author is indebted to his colleague, F. W. Clelland, for the suggestion that this oscillator may be used as a source of quadrature voltages. This work is an outgrowth of research for the Watson Laboratories, Air Materiel Command, under Contract W28-099-Ac-131.

REFERENCES

(1) E. W. Rosentreter, Single-Signal, Single-Sideband Adapter, ELECTRONICS, p 124, July 1948.
(2) Valley and Wallman, "Vacuum Tube Amplifiers", Radiation Laboratory Series, 18, 384, McGraw-Hill Book Co., New York, 1948.
(3) Leonard Stanton, Theory and Application of Parallel-T Resistance-Capacitance Frequency-Selective Networks, Proc. IRE, 34, No. 7, p 447, July 1946.
(4) G. Willoner, and F. Tihelka, A Phase-Shift Oscillator with Wide Range Tuning, Proc. IRE, 36, No. 9, p 1096, September, 1948.

Combining Positive and Negative Feedback

Development of simple two-stage audio amplifier using a combination of local positive feedback in first stage and a moderate amount of overall negative feedback to approximate the results obtainable from conventional amplifier with 25 db negative feedback

By JOHN M. MILLER, JR.

IT HAS BEEN PROVED that the ear can detect as little as 0.5 percent of pentode distortion.[1] To achieve this low degree of distortion in typical pentode amplifiers, approximately 25 db of negative feedback is required. This sacrifice in gain,

and the solution of the oscillation problem outside the passband, involve considerable added cost.

It is possible in a two-stage amplifier to approximate the results that would be obtained in a conventional amplifier with 25 db of negative

feedback, by using a combination of local positive feedback in the first stage, and a moderate amount of overall negative feedback. The positive feedback has the effect of increasing the gain of the first stage. The general principle of combined feedback has been known for some time.[2]

The block diagram of a two-stage amplifier with combined feedback is shown in Fig. 1. The inherent voltage gains, with no feedback, of the first and second stages, are represented by A_1 and A_2 respectively, for very small signals; B_1 is the feedback ratio of the feedback around the first stage, and B_2 is the overall feedback ratio, for very small signals. The feedback ratio is defined as the ratio of the voltage fed back to the voltage existing at the point from which the feedback is obtained. These are all complex vector quantities, although their phase angles are likely to be very small in the vicinity of the amplifier band center. In the ideal case where there are no phase shifts, A_1 and A_2 are conventionally considered to be positive, and a feedback ratio is positive when the voltage fed back is in phase with the input.

Feedback Equations

The voltage gain is

$$A = \frac{A_1 A_2}{1 - A_1 B_1 - A_1 A_2 B_2} = \frac{A_1 A_2}{N} \quad (1)$$

N is the vector quantity by which the gain without feedback, $A_1 A_2$, is divided. If B_1 is positive (which would be the case for positive feedback), it has the effect of increasing the gain A; and B_2, if negative, tends to decrease the gain.

A term such as $A_1 B_1$ or $A_1 A_2 B_2$ is known as a feedback factor. In the ideal case it will be a pure positive or negative quantity, but in the practical case, it will have a phase angle that is the sum of the phase angles of the factors involved.

When there is no phase shift in the feedback network itself, the feedback ratio is considered to be a real quantity, and the phase angle of the feedback factor is equal to the sum of the phase angles of the A's involved.

The output impedance Z_2 is

$$Z_2 = Z_L \frac{(1 - A_1 B_1)}{N(1 + Z_L/Z_{p2}) - (1 - A_1 B_1)} \quad (2)$$

where Z_L and Z_{p2} are the load impedance and inherent output impedance of the output stage. It is

seen in the above expression that when the product $A_1 B_1$ is positive, a decrease in the output impedance can result.

The expression for distortion and gain stability is

$$D = \frac{D_1}{N} + D_2 \left(\frac{1 - A_1 B_1}{N} \right) + D_1 D_2 \left(\frac{1 - A_1 B_1}{N} \right) \quad (3)$$

The inherent gain increments D_1 and D_2 in the first and second stages are caused, for example, by a change in applied static or instantaneous signal electrode voltages, or aging of the tube, and D is the resulting overall gain increment. The parameters D, D_1, and D_2 are each expressed as a fraction of A, A_1, and A_2. Equation 3 also holds if D_1, D_2, and D represent nonlinear distortion.

Regeneration and Distortion

For most purposes, optimum performance is obtained by designing so that the product $A_1 B_1$ over the useful range of frequencies is approximately equal to unity. (If the negative feedback were temporarily removed, the first stage would be in a state of critical regeneration, with a gain approaching infinity.) From Eq. 2, we now obtain zero output impedance, and from Eq. 3 we find that the distortion and gain

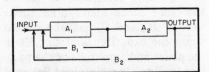

FIG. 1—Notation used for a two-stage amplifier showing two feedback paths

variation contributed by the final stage, including the output transformer, are reduced to zero. From Eq. 1, the gain becomes $1/-B_2$. In an amplifier using negative feedback only, it would be necessary to provide an infinite amount of feedback gain reduction to obtain these results.[3] Very good results can be obtained even when $A_1 B_1$ departs from unity by ±20 percent.

It will be seen from Eq. 3 that if $A_1 B_1$ exceeds 2, the distortion introduced by the output stage will actu-

ally be greater than that which would be produced by omitting the positive feedback entirely. This shows the unsoundness with large feedback factors of the balanced feedback principle, in which $A_1 B_1$ is made equal to $-A_1 A_2 B_2$, (N equals unity), since the distortion and gain variation are greater, though reversed in sign, than if no feedback at all were used.

Oscillation

It is apparent from Eq. 1 that the quantity $(A_1 B_1 + A_1 A_2 B_2)$ is analogous to the feedback factor AB in a conventional feedback amplifier, and may be considered to be the effective feedback factor in determining the possibility of oscillation. Thus we can use Nyquist's[4] and Bode's[5] criteria in analyzing any particular case. If, because of phase reversal in the feedback factor, a positive value of unity is assumed at some frequency, Eq. 1 gives a gain value of infinity, indicating oscillation. If the feedback factor is positive and greater than unity, oscillation will usually result, although there are exceptional cases, known as conditional stability[5], where oscillation does not result. However, in good practice it is customary to design so that the feedback factor never assumes a positive value greater than, say, 0.5.

Since the effective feedback factor $(A_1 B_1 + A_1 A_2 B_2)$ must be held to a value less than plus unity at all frequencies to avoid oscillation, then if $A_1 B_1$ equals plus unity, the negative feedback factor $A_1 A_2 B_2$ must never become zero or positive. This requirement cannot be met; in fact, the asymptotic phase shift in a loop containing a two-stage resistance-coupled amplifier and the primary and secondary of an output transformer is at least 270 degrees at very high frequencies with a resistance load. Thus it becomes necessary to cause $A_1 B_1$ to assume a value other than unity at frequencies where $A_1 A_2 B_2$ is positive. A phase shift must be introduced into the feedback transmission network which, in conjunction with the phase shift in A_1, actually reverses the phase of A_1B_1 at very high and very low frequencies, so that it becomes negative feedback, although its amplitude is then very small. The local feedback factor A_1B_1 may now tend to oppose rather than aid oscillation at extreme frequencies where $A_1A_2B_2$ is positive, although A_1B_1 is still essentially positive and nearly unity throughout the band of useful frequencies.

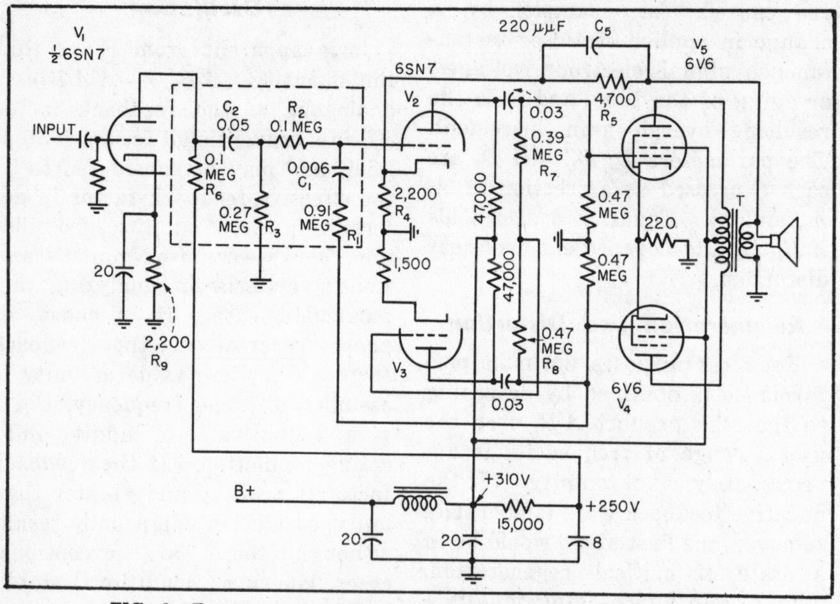

The amplifier of Fig. 2 incorporates positive and negative feedback. It is otherwise conventional, using self-bias throughout, and a highly degenerative self-balancing phase inverter. The output transformer is small, having a $\frac{3}{4} \times \frac{3}{4}$-inch stack. The copper efficiency is about 80 percent.

The overall negative feedback is obtained from the secondary of the output transformer T, and is fed through R_5 to the cathode of V_2. Shunt capacitor C_5 affords some feedback phase correction at very high frequencies. The feedback gain reduction is 9 db, and becomes 11 db with the positive feedback disconnected.

The positive feedback is obtained from the grid of V_4, and is fed through R_1 and C_1 to the grid of tube V_2. The positive feedback voltage is developed primarily across R_2 and C_2, since the plate resistance of V_1 is relatively small, and the input resistance of the grid of V_2 is high. The positive feedback is designed so that, with the negative feedback disconnected, V_2 will be near oscillation or oscillating weakly. Since the voltage gain of the stage V_2 is approximately 10, about one-tenth of the voltage on the grid of V_4 is fed back to the grid of V_2. The resistance of R_1 is therefore made about nine times that of R_2, and C_2 has about nine times the capacitance of C_1. Thus the phase and amplitude of the positive feedback is maintained flat over the range of audio frequencies. Because of the highly degenerative nature of the phase inverter, the balance is not appreciably affected by the additional load of the positive feedback network.

Some phase shift in the positive feedback is obtained at extreme frequencies in the stages V_2 and V_3 due to electrode and stray capacitances, and due to the blocking capacitors. The input capacitance of the grid of V_2 causes a further phase shift, so that the polarity of the product A_1B_1 reverses from positive to negative at extremely high frequencies. The input capacitance of V_2 is primarily dynamic, due to feedback through its grid-plate capacitance[6], at very high fre-

FIG. 2—Two-stage amplifier using combination feedback circuits

Table I—Distortion Figures for Various Combinations of Operating Conditions

Harmonic Distortion — 8 watts into 3.9-ohm speaker load					
Harmonic	Frequency in Cps				
	100		400		1,000	
	%	Db	%	Db	%	Db
2	0.12	58	0.2	54	0.17	55
3	0.09	61	0.24	52	0.32	50
4	0.04	68	0.045	67	0.036	69
5	0.034	69	0.017	75	0.04	68
6	0.002	94	0.003	90	0.02	74
7	<0.001	—	<0.001	—	0.006	84
8					0.006	84
9					<0.001	—
10					0.012	78
11					<0.001	—

Harmonic Distortion—3.9-ohm load				
Harmonic	50 Cps, 5 watts		2 Kc, 4 watts	
	%	Db	%	Db
2	0.7	43	0.1	60
3	0.88	41	0.23	53
4	0.03	70	0.006	84
5	0.08	62	0.02	74
6	0.01	80	0.002	94
7	0.02	74	0.008	82
8	0.004	88	—	
9	0.002	94	—	
10	0.002	94	—	

Percent Harmonic Distortion—8 watts into 3.9 ohms at 100 cps			
Harmonic	No feedback	Negative feedback	Pos-neg feedback
2	0.6	0.07	0.12
3	6.0	2.2	0.094
4	0.15	0.01	0.04
5	0.6	0.08	0.034
6	0.2	0.08	0.002
7	0.2	0.04	<0.001

Percent Harmonic Distortion—8 watts into 3.9 ohms at 400 cps			
Harmonic	No feedback	Negative feedback	Pos-neg feedback
2	1.4	0.3	0.2
3	7.0	2.4	0.24
4	0.6	0.1	0.045
5	1.2	0.08	0.017
6	0.14	0.02	<0.001
7	0.27	0.02	<0.001

Percent Intermodulation Distortion—8 watts into 3.9 ohms, 4 to 1 voltage ratio at 60 and 100 cps

Frequency	No feedback	Negative feedback	Pos-neg feedback
60 Cps			
2 kc	—	—	1.4
7 kc	40	8.0	1.9
12 kc	—	—	2.2
100 Cps			
2 kc	—	6.6	0.52
7 kc	—	5.8	0.84
12 kc	—	6.1	1.0

quencies where the overall feedback is positive or small.

In some designs, it may be necessary to connect a small capacitor from the grid of V_2 to ground, or to use a more elaborate phase-shift network to obtain a sufficiently rapid phase turnover in the local feedback.

At extremely low frequencies most of the local feedback current flows through R_3 instead of through C_2, so that a phase shift is obtained, which together with the phase-shifting action of the 0.03-μf blocking capacitors in stages V_2 and V_3, is sufficient to cause the desired

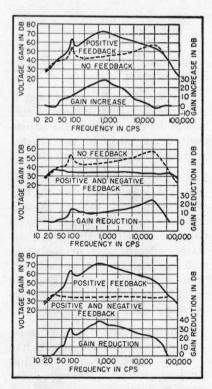

FIG. 3—Amplifier response curves for various types of feedback with 0.5-watt input to a 3.9-ohm loudspeaker load

phase reversal. In practice, the phase reversal frequencies are

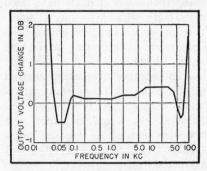

FIG. 4—Voltage regulation in db with 1-volt output into 3.9-ohm loudspeaker load

placed as far outside the desired pass band as good stability permits.

Performance Measurements

Figure 3 permits the determination of the quantities $(1-A_1B_1)$, $(1-A_1B_1-A_1A_2B_2)$, or N, and ratio $(1-A_1B_1-A_1A_2B_2)/(-A_1B_1)$.

Figure 4 indicates a negligibly small output impedance, since the output voltage varies only slightly when the speaker load is disconnected. The regulation of 0.1 db at 400 cycles may be compared with the regulation of 2.7 db that is obtained with the positive feedback disconnected (11 db of negative feedback remaining) or the regula-

tion of 19 db that is obtained with no feedback.

The distortion indicated in Table I would presumably be inaudible even with a wide-range loudspeaker. The intermodulation distortion averages three or four times as much as the harmonic distortion, as would be expected. The table shows that the positive feedback causes a great reduction in distortion.

Design Improvements

The amplifier of Fig. 2 is not represented as being the ultimate in design of a positive-negative feedback amplifier, although it seems probable that most major improvements would involve cost increases.

If the negative feedback could be made uniform over a wider frequency range, the local positive feedback could also be made effective over a wider range. A wide-band output transformer would be helpful. Reducing R_1, R_2, R_3 and R_6 and R_9, and increasing C_2 and C_1, will also be helpful. The grid-plate capacitance of V_2 could be largely neutralized by shunting R_1 with a small capacitor of, say, 3 micromicrofarads. The last two measures would reduce the high-frequency phase shift in the overall

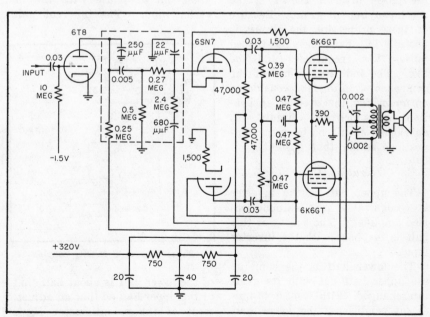

FIG. 5—Complete schematic of a low-cost audio amplifier using combination feedback

feedback that is caused by the Miller effect in V_2. Also, R_7 could be shunted with a small capacitor to reduce the phase shift caused by the grid-plate capacitance of V_3. It would also be desirable to replace R_1 by a network having a rapid phase turnover at ultrasonic frequencies and a small phase shift at audio frequencies.

Low-Cost Amplifier

Figure 5 shows the circuit of an economical amplifier. Type 6K6GT output tubes are used, and the current drain is so low that a 5Y3 rectifier is used at less than its rated operating conditions, and with resistance filtering only. The hum is almost inaudible even in a quiet room, being 67 db below maximum level. In production, the output regulation rarely exceeds ± 0.2 db, and the response is flat over the useful range of frequencies. No production difficulties have arisen, although many many thousands of units have been manufactured, and no special selection of tubes or components has been made. Numerous production units selected at random for test had an average harmonic distortion at 400 cycles of 0.5 percent with 5 watts output. With a shock impulse at the amplifier input, the transient output across the loudspeaker voice coil is negligibly small after the first cycle.

The photograph of this amplifier shows the output transformer to be small. However, the harmonic distortion in the 60-cps output at five watts is only one percent. The 6SN7GT driver-phase inverter is not shown, as it is located on the tuner chassis of the receiver.

Conclusions

In conclusion, it appears that combined positive and negative feedback offers considerable possibility for improved performance in pentode audio power amplifiers, particularly where cost is an important consideration, and when conventional mass-production techniques are used.

REFERENCES

(1) H. F. Olson, "Elements of Acoustical Engineering," Second Edition, D. Van Nostrand Co., Inc., New York, p 488.
(2) F. E. Terman, "Radio Engineers' Handbook," McGraw-Hill Book Co., Inc., New York, First Edition, sec. 5, par. 11.
(3) H. S. Black, Stabilized Feedback Amplifiers, *B.S.T.J.*, Jan. 1934.
(4) H. Nyquist, Regeneration Theory, *B.S.T.J.*, July 1932.
(5) H. W. Bode, Relations between Attenuation and Phase in Feedback Amplifier Design, *B.S.T.J.*, July 1940.
(6) J. M. Miller, Dependence of the Input Impedance of a Three Element Vacuum Tube upon the Load in the Plate Circuit, NBS Scientific Paper 351.

Direct-Coupled Phase Inverter

By E. JOHNSON

DIRECT-CURRENT symmetry and stability of output are obtained from the phase inverter shown in the accompanying diagram. Because of these properties, the circuit is useful in handling flat-topped pulses, low frequencies and the like. The indicated values of the components, although considered optimum for the specific application for which this circuit was developed, should be taken as suggestions rather than absolutes.

Operating Conditions

The upper half of the inverter is recognizable as a cathode-coupled amplifier[1,2]. The output of this half is in phase with the inverter input.

The lower half is the same as the upper half but with its grids interchanged. With respect to quiescent conditions, the lower half of the circuit behaves identically to the upper half. However, the output of the lower half is 180 degrees out of phase with the inverter input. The inherent gain

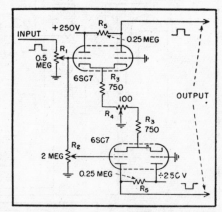

Phase inverter is directly coupled

of the lower half is about half that of the upper half so that an adjustment of the potentiometer R_2 is necessary to equalize the outputs of the two halves. Overall gain of the inverter is controlled by R_1.

Potentiometer R_4 is adjusted to make the d-c output voltage of each half of the circuit equal, the adjustment being made in the absence of signal and before R_2 is adjusted.

The subsequent adjustment of R_2 does not necessitate any further adjustment of R_4, making the circuit very easy to balance. Essentially, each half of the circuit operates independently of the other half so that there is no tendency towards regenerative drifting and critical adjustment that characterize many comparable circuits.

With the typical values of components as shown, the circuit has a voltage gain of about 20 and handles inputs up to two volts without appreciable distortion. Use of 6SN7's would have reduced the gain to about seven. Graphical analysis offers a convenient means of investigating the performance of the circuit and provides a guide for selecting the components[3].

REFERENCES

(1) G. C. Sziklai and A. C. Schroeder, Cathode-Coupled Wide-Band Amplifiers, *Proc IRE*, p 701, Oct. 1945.

(2) K. A. Pullen, The Cathode-Coupled Amplifier, *Proc IRE*, p 402, June 1946.

(3) M. S. Rifkin, A Graphical Analysis of the Cathode-Coupled Amplifier, *Communications*, p 16, Dec. 1946

Stabilizing Gain

Chart simplifies calculations involving fluctuations in gain with and without negative feedback, amount of feedback and sacrifice in gain to obtain required stability

By T. E. KORN

ONE ADVANTAGE of applying negative feedback to low-frequency amplifiers is the stabilization of gain that is obtained. Usually the effects of feedback are calculated from the equation $A' = A/(1 - A\beta)$ where A' is the voltage gain with feedback, A is the voltage gain without feedback, and $A\beta$ is the feedback factor. By converting this equation into logarithmic form and generalizing the reference level, the accompanying chart can be plotted. As used in the chart, A and A' are in db.

Usually the VARIATION OF GAIN WITHOUT FEEDBACK is given in the form of two measured values of A or ΔA corresponding to the extremes of power supply fluctuation, change in tube parameters and other effects. The VARIATION OF GAIN WITH FEEDBACK will generally be given in the amplifier specifications. There will be a REDUCTION IN OVERALL GAIN produced by the feedback, which has to be computed so that the initial gain A can be made large enough to give the required A' after feedback has been applied. The necessary FEEDBACK FACTOR to produce the specified effect may have to be computed, or it may have been obtained already by using the feedback to reduce distortion or output impedance. Although the factors that are given and the ones that are to be found may differ from problem to problem, any two are sufficient to obtain the others from the chart.

Example

An existing amplifier having 5 db more gain than necessary and a measured variation of gain from the normal of −6 db to +4 db is to be stabilized. How much feedback can be used and what will be the resulting stabilization? A loss of 5 db can be tolerated, therefore at this value along the base locate the diagonal line corresponding to the feedback factor; this is 0.8. To find the stabilization, locate the intersection of this feedback factor line with the heavy curve; call it point P. Drop from P to the abscissa and move along the number of db corresponding to the variation of gain without feedback. Return upward to a new intersection with the heavy curve, point P'. The difference measured along the side (ordinate) of the chart between P and P' gives the variation in gain

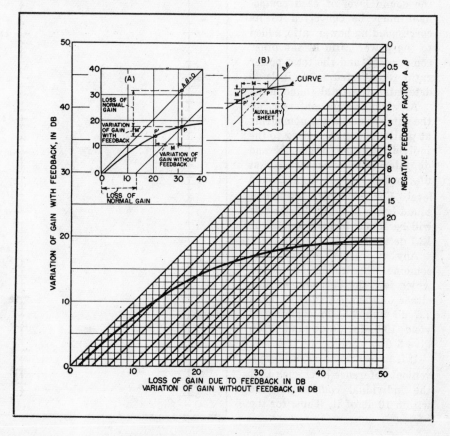

LOSS OF GAIN DUE TO FEEDBACK IN DB
VARIATION OF GAIN WITHOUT FEEDBACK, IN DB

with feedback. For this example the gain will vary with feedback from −3.8 to +2 db. Insert (A) shows construction.

An interesting and usual problem arises when the actual variation of gain and the acceptable variation are given, and the amount of feedback required to produce this stabilization is to be found. Without the chart such a problem entails considerable calculation; with the chart it is simple. As shown in insert (B), the actual and acceptable variations are marked in from the corner of a sheet of paper, forming points P and P'. The edges of this sheet are then kept parallel to the coordinates of the chart and the sheet moved until both P and P' lie on the heavy curve, which they will at one point if the required stabilization is obtainable. Point P is then at the intersection with the required feedback factor. As before, the loss in gain is given at the intersection of this diagonal with abscissa, as in (A).

Combining Sound Levels

Simple nomogram dispenses with the need for log tables, decibel tables or a slide rule when determining the total acoustical power resulting from the combination of two or more sounds

By W. B. CONOVER

TWO OR MORE SOUNDS combine to give a total sound whose acoustical power is the sum of the power involved in the individual components. Since sound levels are expressed in decibels, the sound level of each component must be converted to its corresponding power ratio, added to the power ratio of the other components, and the total power ratio reconverted to decibels to determine the total sound level.

A straightedge intersecting the outer scales of the nomogram at positions corresponding to the individual sound levels db_1 and db_2 intersects the center scale at db_T, which is the total sound level. For example, individual sound levels of 8 and 10 decibels will be found to give a total of 12.1 decibels.

Any two equal sound levels combine to produce a sound which is 3 decibels higher than either of them separately. Thus 7.5 db and 7.5 db combine to yield 10.5 db; 0 db and 0 db give 3 db.

It is necessary to choose a convenient reference level such that the individual components are within 10 db of it. Thus, for the total of 62 db and 67 db, a reference level of 60 db is chosen.

Since the components are 2 and 7 db above this reference, the re-

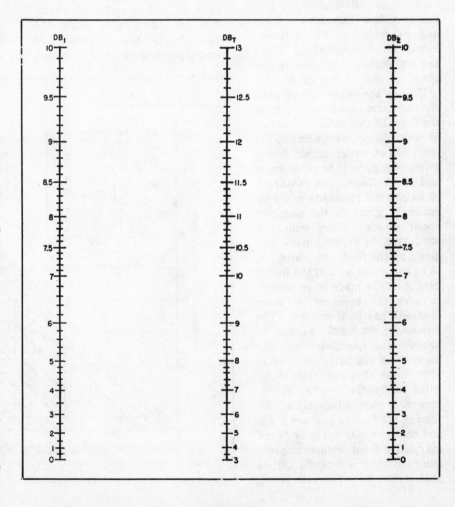

sultant 8.2 db given by the nomogram is added to the reference, giving a total of 68.2 db.

When a difference of more than 10 db exists between two sound levels, the contribution of the smaller may be neglected.

Other Uses

One component of noise can be found when the other component and the total noise are known. This is useful in correcting sound-level meter readings for ambient noise. For example, a sound-level meter shows 64.5 db in the neighborhood of a certain machine when it is operating, and an ambient noise reading of 60 db when the machine is turned off. What is the noise level at the same location due to the machine alone? Choosing 60 db as the reference level, a straight-edge is aligned with 0 db (60-60) on the db_1 scale, and 4.5 db (64.5-60) on the db_T scale, giving a reading of 2.6 db on the db_2 scale. Adding this to the reference level of 60 db results in a noise level of 62.6 db for the machine alone.

When more than two sound levels are to be combined, the total of two components is determined and combined with a third component, the new total combined with a fourth component, and so on. This same process may be employed to determine, in decibels, the rms value of a complex voltage or current wave when its harmonics are expressed in decibels.

High-Fidelity Response From Phonograph Pickups

Basic requirements for high-fidelity phonograph reproduction are discussed briefly. Ways of introducing feedback to compensate for nonlinearity in inexpensive crystal pickups are shown. Includes typical curves for various feedback networks

By ELWIN J. O'BRIEN

ONE CLASSIFICATION of sound divides its components into two groups, pure tones and complex sounds. To be classified as a true high-fidelity sound-reproducing system, an amplifier and its associated components must be capable of reproducing both the pure and the complex sound components exactly as to pitch and intensity, and its output must be free from new frequencies introduced by intermodulation or harmonic distortion in any part of the system.

Intermodulation is defined as the production of frequencies equal to the sum and difference of integral multiples of two or more of the frequencies transmitted to a system. Any resonance in a system will produce nonlinear or intermodulation distortion, unless suitable compensation is provided.

Resonance can occur in any mechanical system containing inertia and elasticity. The effect of a constant driving force applied to an electroacoustic device where resonance is present, such as a crystal pickup, is to produce transient complex vibrations. These vibrations, in the presence of inherent nonlinearity, beat with the periodic vibrations of the music to produce discordant sounds.

Additional transient vibrations, those which produce annoying surface noise, are caused by granular irregularities in records. These random irregularities will produce transient oscillations if there is any

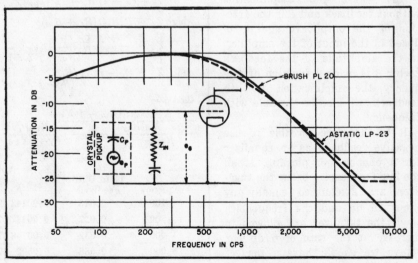

FIG. 1—Relative voltage output curves for typical crystal pickups without feedback, and equivalent circuit for input section of a typical amplifier

resonance in the pickup arm or the pickup itself, and again, in the presence of nonlinearity, intermodulation products will be generated and the surface noise voltages will be increased.

Typical unequalized response curves for two popular crystal pickups as obtained from an ideal lateral test record are shown in Fig. 1 along with the equivalent circuit of the ideal unit. The ideal crystal pickup would be equivalent at audio frequencies to a zero impedance generator in series with a capacitor and would have a frequency response for a constant needle amplitude that decreases at the rate of 6 db per octave. Actually, however, inherent resonance causes high voltages to be generated in the pickup itself and its arm at certain frequencies.

Negative feedback applied to the pickup circuit will reduce this resonance. Each of the two general types of feedback, voltage and current, tend to make the voltage output a replica of the signal voltage, but their effects on the impedance of the circuit are different. Voltage feedback lowers the internal impedance of an amplifier, while current feedback raises the impedance.

Feedback

The voltage amplification with voltage feedback is $A_F = A/(1 - A\beta)$ where A is amplification without feedback and β is the fraction of the output voltage introduced in the input of the amplifier. If the amplitude of the feedback factor β is made a function of frequency, the amplification A_F with feedback will also be variable with frequency.

It is therefore possible to use negative feedback as an equalizer for a phonograph pickup. If all the low frequencies below the turnover are attenuated equally by about 25 db and the frequencies above the turnover are allowed to increase at the rate of 6 db per octave we should have a perfect crystal phonograph pickup equalizer.

Considering the above principle, the phonograph amplifier circuit shown in Fig. 2 was developed experimentally for an Astatic LP-23 or a Brush PL-20 cartridge.

This amplifier, using both voltage and current feedback, includes the pickup impedance in the feedback loop. Calculations for gain and input admittance, using the equivalent circuit shown in Fig. 3, are shown in Table I along with tabulated results for several frequencies. It can be seen that the gain above 500 cycles increases at the rate of about 6 db per octave and, since the amplitude on typical test records drops off at this rate, a flat voltage output would be expected when making frequency response tests.

Input Impedance

Table I shows that the input impedance Z_{IN}, shown dotted in Fig. 3, can be represented by a resistor of approximately 1,500 ohms and a capacitor of approximately 0.5 µf across the pickup, forming a capacitance voltage divider with the capacitance of the crystal pickup (Fig. 3). This nullifies the effect of the crystal capacitance on the grid voltage when used in the normal manner. The output voltage of the feedback amplifier, then, is proportional to the velocity of the modulated groove, making the resultant pickup response equivalent to a magnetic pickup above the turnover point. The increasing variable capacitance with decreasing frequency below the turnover point also produces a constant voltage over this portion of the frequency range. These two effects produce a flat frequency response over the whole range.

The low impedance placed across the pickup also has the effect of damping out any natural resonance in the pickup, causing the needle to follow the groove without extra oscillation. The high damping has the effect of reducing surface noise by preventing the forced natural oscillation of the needle when an irregularity in the record groove has been struck.

In order to appreciate fully the high-fidelity results, a listening demonstration of the circuit is desirable. However, the frequency response must be adjusted by playing a calibrated test record, since

Table I—Calculations for gain, voltage input to second stage, and input impedance, and tabulated results for feedback circuits

Voltage Gain Calculation[1]

$$A_F = \frac{-\mu Z_L}{r_p + (\mu + 1) R_K + (1 + \mu\beta) Z_L}$$

where $Z_L = R_L R_{G2}/(R_L + R_{G2})$
$\beta = Z_G/(Z_G + Z_F)$
$Z_G = -j\, X_{CP} R_{G1}/(R_{G1} - j\, X_{CP})$

and $Z_F = R_F - j\, X_{CC} R_1/(R_1 - j\, X_{CC})$

then $\beta =$
$$\frac{-j\, X_{CP} R_{G1}/(R_{G1} - j\, X_{CP})}{-j\, \dfrac{X_{CP} R_{G1}}{R_{G1} - j\, X_{CP}} + R_F - j\, \dfrac{X_{CC} R_1}{R_1 - j\, X_{CC}}}$$

Input admittance Calculations[2]

$Y_{IN} = Y_F\,[(Y_o + g_m)/(Y_o + Y_F)]$

where $Y_F = 1/Z_F$
$Y_o = 1/R_L + 1/r_p$

and g_m is the transconductance of the tube

$$Y_{IN} = \frac{1}{Z_F} \left[\frac{\dfrac{1}{R_L} + \dfrac{1}{r_p} + g_m}{\dfrac{1}{R_L} + \dfrac{1}{r_p} + \dfrac{1}{Z_F}} \right]$$

Frequency	Gain With Feedback	E_G		Z_{IN}	C_{EQ} in µf
				Voltage and Input Admittance at Amplifier Grid	
100	0.818	0.00143	$\underline{33.8°}$	1,265 − j1,890	0.843
500	0.827	0.00437	$\underline{70.4°}$	1,310 − j466	0.682
1,000	0.832	0.00788	$\underline{78.6°}$	1,230 − j247	0.643
5,000	0.888	0.0592	$\underline{78.6°}$	1,880 − j79	0.4
10,000	1.000	0.118	$\underline{89°}$	1,880 − j32	0.497

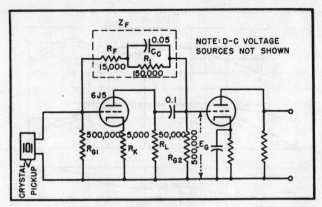

FIG. 2—Typical schematic diagram for phono input circuit employing feedback

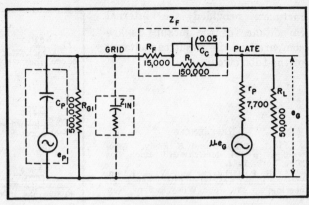

FIG. 3—Equivalent circuit for first stage of amplifier shown in Fig. 2

an adjustment by ear alone, because of listening habits, will seldom give a flat frequency response.

It is possible to equalize almost any of the commercial permanent-sapphire-needle crystal pickups to a flat response over the frequency range of 30 to 10,000 cycles and have only a relatively small amount of noise present. The old model removable-needle types are more difficult to equalize and damp critically because of the increased inertia.

For a typical measure of the flexibility of feedback as an equalizer, the following experimental data are presented:

The original circuit as used with an Astatic HP-36 crystal phonograph pickup using the LP-23 cartridge is shown in Fig. 4A. The

low-frequency boost can be removed by decreasing the value of the 1-megohm capacitor shunt in the feedback network. Fig. 4B shows a similar circuit used with a Brush PL-20 pickup. Both of these circuits, because of the relatively small amount of feedback, can be classed as selective feedback equalizers.

The effect of feedback on a magnetic pickup may be seen in Fig. 4C together with the GE phonograph preamplifier schematic diagram. The solid curve is the normal amplifier response with the GE pickup, while the dotted curve was obtained with the dotted feedback network connected and the 180,000-ohm resistor shorted.

The curves of Fig. 5 show that practically any shape of response

curve may be obtained by a variation of the feedback network. The results shown in 5B were obtained with increased amounts of feedback and can be classed as equalization by control of input admittance.

If the new Astatic QT-j cartridge with removable sapphire needle is used the feedback resistance should be reduced as shown in Fig. 5C. The increased amount of feedback is necessary to remove the 3,000 to 5,000-cycle resonance peak introduced in the pickup to improve the normal frequency response of the cartridge. This boost is not desirable when feedback equalization is used. From these curves it can be seen that the frequency response of the circuit is essentially independent of pickup type or manu-

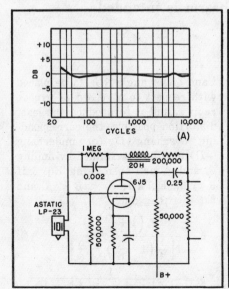

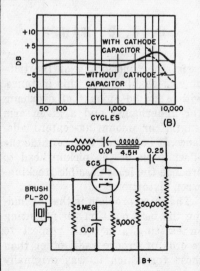

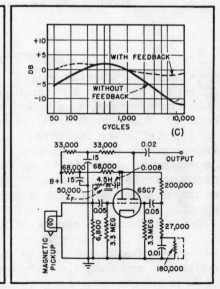

FIG. 4—Input circuits for several popular pickup types using feedback, with associated response curves

facturer, provided the internal capacitance of the pickups is low compared to the input capacitance of the tube circuit.

REFERENCES

(1) J. Millman and S. Seely, "Electronics," p 614, McGraw-Hill Book Co., New York, 1941.

(2) R. I. Sarbacker and W. A. Edson, "Hyper and Ultra High Frequency Engineering," p 430, John Wiley & Sons, New York, 1943.

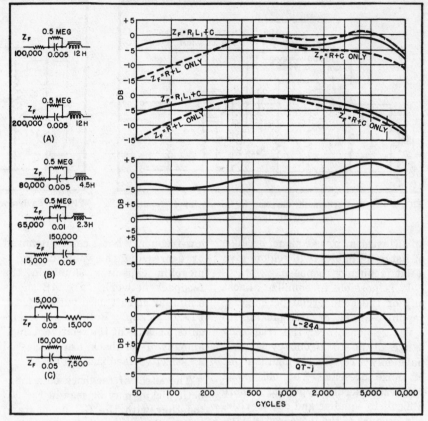

FIG. 5—Typical curves for different types of feedback networks, including one suitable for a magnetic pickup

Pickup Placement

Equations for determining best mounting position for tone arm for use with records having groove radii other than those for which arm is intended

By B. B. BAUER

PHONOGRAPH EQUIPMENT designers are confronted with three distinct problems pertaining to the geometry of phonograph arms.

The first of these is the design of arms to provide the least tracking error distortion on records of given dimensions with an arm of given length, or given distance between mounting centers.

The second problem deals with the design of arms where, as an additional restriction, the arm must overhang or underhang the center of the record by a specified amount, as in record changers, in order to assist the functioning of the tripping mechanism. In this instance, with a stated amount of overhang (or underhang) and a given arm length, or mounting-centers distance, it is desired to determine the offset angle of the pickup head to produce the least possible tracking-error distortion.

The third problem is that of finding the best position for mounting an existing arm with respect to records of groove radii other than those for which it was originally designed.

If an existing arm having length l and offset angle β is to be placed with respect to a record of groove radii r_1 and r_2 to produce the least distortion possible, the corresponding overhang D (or underhang $-D$) may be determined by finding β_o and β_i and then using Eq. 3 if $\beta \leqq \beta_i$, Eq. 4 if $\beta_i < \beta < \beta_o$ and Eq. 5 if $\beta \geqq \beta_o$.

$$\beta_0 = \frac{r_1\left(1 + \frac{r_1}{r_2}\right)}{l\left[\frac{1}{4}\left(1 + \frac{r_1}{r_2}\right)^2 + \frac{r_1}{r_2}\right]} \quad (1)$$

$$\beta_i = \frac{1}{l\left[\left(\frac{1}{r_1} + \frac{1}{r_2}\right) - \frac{r_1}{2}\left(\frac{1}{r_1^2} + \frac{1}{r_2^2}\right)\right]} \quad (2)$$

$$D = \frac{\beta\left(\frac{1}{r_1} + \frac{1}{r_2}\right) - \frac{1}{l}}{\left(\frac{1}{r_1^2} + \frac{1}{r_2^2}\right)} \quad (3)$$

$$D = \frac{r_2}{2}\left(\frac{r_2}{l} - \beta\right)$$
$$\left[\left(1 + \frac{\beta^2}{\left(\frac{r_2}{l} - \beta\right)^2}\right)^{1/2} - 1\right] \quad (4)$$

$$D = \frac{r_1}{2}\left(\beta - \frac{r_1}{l}\right)$$
$$\left[\left(1 + \frac{\beta^2}{\left(\beta - \frac{r_1}{l}\right)^2}\right)^{1/2} + 1\right] \quad (5)$$

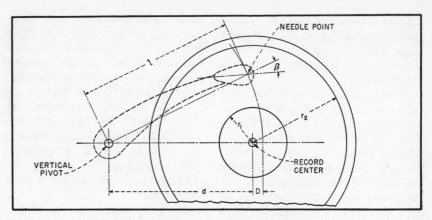

Diagram of typical phonograph layout

If a new arm of length l is designed to provide the least distortion possible with a given overhang D (or underhang $-D$), the corresponding offset angle β may be determined by finding D_o and D_i and then using Eq. 8 if $D \leqq D_i$, Eq. 9 if $D_i < D < D_o$, and Eq. 10 if $D \geqq D_o$.

$$D_o = \frac{r_1^2}{l\left[\frac{1}{4}\left(1 + \frac{r_1}{r_2}\right)^2 + \frac{r_1}{r_2}\right]} \quad (6)$$

$$D_i = \frac{r_1}{l\left[2\left(\frac{1}{r_1} + \frac{1}{r_2}\right) - r_1\left(\frac{1}{r_1^2} + \frac{1}{r_2^2}\right)\right]} \quad (7)$$

$$\beta = \frac{D\left(\frac{1}{r_1^2} + \frac{1}{r_2^2}\right) + \frac{1}{l}}{\left(\frac{1}{r_1} + \frac{1}{r_2}\right)} \quad (8)$$

$$\beta = 2\left(\frac{2D^2}{r_2^2} + \frac{D}{l}\right)^{1/2} - \frac{2D}{r_2} \quad (9)$$

$$\beta = 2\left(\frac{2D^2}{r_1^2} + \frac{D}{l}\right)^{1/2} - \frac{2D}{r_1} \quad (10)$$

If distance d is given instead of length l, find $l = d + D$, and proceed as before.

All linear dimensions are given in inches, and angles are measured in radians.

If a new arm is designed to have a length l and to provide minimum tracking-error distortion over a range of groove radii from r_1 to r_2, optimum offset angle and overhang may be found by using Eq. 1 and Eq. 6.

When d is given instead of l, the overhang D_o may be found from the following equation: $D_o =$

$$\left[\frac{d^2}{4} + \frac{r_1^2}{\left[\frac{1}{4}\left(1 + \frac{r_1}{r_2}\right)^2 + \frac{r_1}{r_2}\right]}\right]^{1/2} - \frac{d}{2}$$

Find β_o from Eq. 1 remembering that $l = d + D_o$.

Versatile Tone Control

Treble and bass frequencies are independently boosted or attenuated in steps to provide 121 different response curve combinations for reproduction of speech or music. Gain at 500-cycle crossover is automatically held constant by switching in cathode followers

By WILLIAM B. LURIE

THE TONE CONTROL described here originated largely with a desire to compensate for the limitations of recording techniques. With it, treble frequencies can be boosted or suppressed, and bass frequencies can be similarly treated independently, all in small steps.

The bass and treble controls each provide sharp rise or fall starting at 500 cycles or any other crossover frequency chosen. Bass control produces no substantial effect above crossover, and treble control produces no substantial effect below.

The rising or falling slope is adjustable in steps of one db per octave up to a maximum of 5 to 7 db per octave. The overall volume level at the crossover frequency is unchanged by applying any bass or treble compensation, or by applying both simultaneously. All frequency-determining components are resistances or capacitances. All curves flatten off above 10 kc and below 25 cycles.

R-C Networks

Selective frequency boost is achieved by attenuating one group of frequencies and readjusting the overall level with flat amplifiers. The basic R-C networks used for this purpose are shown in Fig. 1, along with the networks used primarily for attenuation.

Treble boost (Fig.1A) is obtained with a. bass attenuation network having a gradual drop near the crossover and a sharp flattening off at the lower frequencies. When this curve is slid up the frequency axis until the sharp bend reaches the crossover frequency, it becomes treble boost.

Treble attenuation (Fig. 1B) gives an abrupt drop near the crossover frequency and a smooth flattening off at higher frequencies.

Bass boost (Fig. 1C) is obtained with a treble attenuation network having a gradual drop near the crossover and a sharp flattening off at the higher frequencies. When this curve is in effect slid along the frequency axis until the sharp bend occurs at the crossover frequency, it becomes bass boost.

Bass attenuation (Fig. 1D) gives an abrupt drop near the crossover frequency and a smooth flattening off at lower frequencies.

Any desired crossover frequency may be achieved by selection of resistance and capacitance values for the R-C networks. For example, doubling all indicated resistance values without changing the capacitances will shift the entire curve toward lower frequencies by a factor of two. Doubling all capacitances produces the same effect, while decreasing resistances or capacitances or both shifts the curve bodily toward higher frequencies.

The impedance any network presents may be altered by a factor N, without altering the frequency response curve, by multiplying all resistance values by N and at the same time dividing all capacitances by N.

Complete Circuit

The final tone control circuit is shown in Fig. 2, along with the response curve combinations obtainable and the control switch settings for each. Since all the required compensation cannot satisfactorily be provided in variable form in one network section, composite networks consisting of three such sections in tandem or cascade are used for bass and treble attenuation, with provisions for tapping the composite network at the desired points.

The succeeding sections in any one network increase in impedance by a factor of four or five each time, so that succeeding sections do not furnish loading which would alter the frequency response characteristics of preceding sections.

Because of the nature of the basic bass boost section, the building up of a network from several such sections would add many bulky components. Instead, therefore, a switching arrangement was developed wherein three sections of 1.4, 2.8, and 2.8-db boost per octave were combined successively to give in turn 1.4, 2.8, 4.2, 5.6, and 7-db boost per octave. The same system is employed for treble boost, and the network sections again increase in impedance as they are added.

Two six-pole eleven-position switches are required. The five positions of boost and the five positions of attenuation are wired to one switch for each frequency range, along with a neutral position in which no bass or treble alteration occurs. Continuous control is not provided, but small enough steps make the action gradual as the switches are rotated.

The overall result, then, is to have one switch for bass, giving from 7 db of boost per octave to 5 db of suppression per octave in ten steps, and one switch for treble, giving from 5-db boost per octave to 6-db reduction per octave in ten steps, with no interaction between controls. The words per octave here refer to the number of octaves displacement from 500 cycles.

In order to achieve a constant volume level at the crossover frequency, a stepping gain control was added, ganged to the bass and treble switches, in the cathode circuits of two cathode followers. In this way, the proper amount of input signal is chosen for each position of the selector switch in order that the gain at 500 cycles may remain constant. In practice, this is easily achieveable within one db if care is taken in selecting components.

Cathode Followers

The cathode followers serve the main purpose of transforming a high-impedance input signal down to a low impedance so that the networks may begin at low impedance and build up as described. It has been found that stray coupling between high-impedance networks can seriously alter the ideal frequency response curves. With capacitance values all larger than 400 micro-microfarads, a small unintended coupling capacitance (on a switch wafer, for example) will not produce a noticeable effect on the tone.

Amplification must be provided (not necessarily within the tone control) in order to re-establish the original volume level. At the same

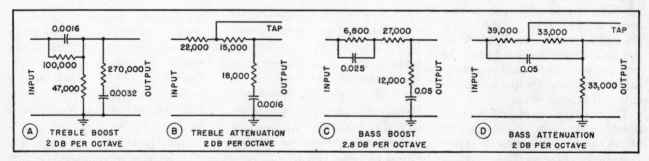

FIG. 1—Typical R-C networks used in tone control for boosting and attenuating audio signals. Taps on attenuation network provide half the indicated effect

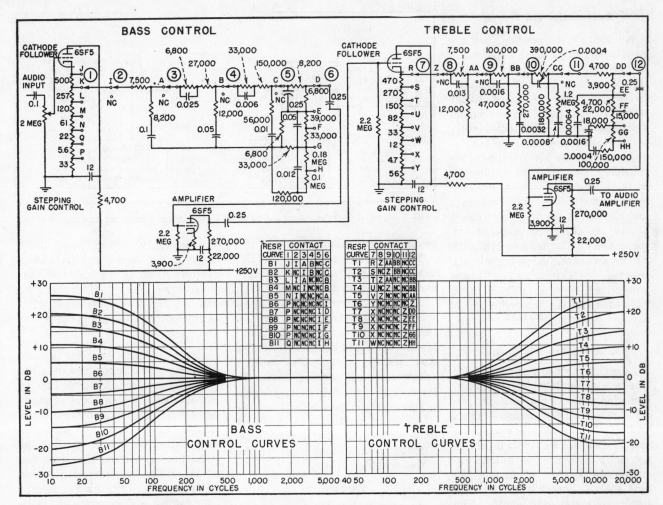

FIG. 2—Complete tone control system. When inserted in an audio amplifier, its overall gain is zero at the 500-cycle crossover frequency. The inset tables give the positions of the contact arms of the two six-pole eleven-position control switches to provide the indicated bass and treble control curves. Treble curves were taken with bass control at B6 (neutral), and bass curves with treble control at T6

time, it is advisable to amplify and then again transform down to low impedance between the bass and treble controls. This serves the added purposes of isolating the bass and treble components electrically and keeping either from operating at too low a voltage level. All these networks are bound to have insertion loss at any frequency, and a total of 40 db of attenuation at 60 or 120 cycles (as provided by bass suppression and treble boost, before re-establishment of the 500-cycle level) could push the signal into the heater-to-cathode hum voltage level.

Amplifier Design

Choice of tubes for this tone control proved somewhat vexing. The 6SL7 twin high-mu triode would have been most convenient, but even a 6SL7W proved to be usually too microphonic, and always too rich in hum introduced through the heater circuit. The 6SN7 does not have enough gain; the 6SC7 has only one external cathode lead. The 6SF5 high-mu triode was found to be available and free from hum in a sufficient number, and so this type was decided upon.

In the amplifier stages, cathode resistors were left unbypassed to make the neutral amplification curve as flat as possible, at the sacrifice of some gain. A total of 12 db more of gain may be obtained by suitable bypassing of these two resistors. All plate supply circuits must be decoupled as shown, and all blocking capacitors must be large enough so that low frequencies are not attenuated.

The input signal level must be low enough so that, after boosting, neither the bass nor the treble signal will overload either level-restoring amplifier. A gain control is therefore provided directly at the input to the tone control. This is not intended as a main gain control for the entire control and program amplifier combination, but as an auxiliary which may be set according to the maximum level of the incoming signal.

In commercial recording, compression takes place before the mechanical limitations of recording techniques produce their tone-modifying effects. Therefore, the tone control should be used before a volume expander. This also lessens the danger of overloading the amplifiers in the tone control.

Construction and Testing

All parts were selected, using a resistance bridge and a capacitance bridge, from stock ½-watt resistors in RMA sizes and stock capacitors. In many cases resistance values were changed slightly from nominal values shown in order to achieve a smooth consistent family of curves.

Assembly may be along lines conventional for low-level audio circuits. Compactness was achieved by wiring virtually all the resistors and capacitors on the two switches before installing the switches on the chassis. The tone control with its two switches, four tubes, a spare selected 6SF5 tube and a 3-tube a-m tuner were assembled on a 9x11-inch chassis, the audio amplifier and power supply being remote.

Checking Response Curves

A testing method was evolved for this type of work, which eliminated disturbing effects due to such factors as voltmeter frequency response, loading, signal generator variations, and distortion. As shown in Fig. 3, an audio oscillator with load resistor was fed to the input of the tone control, across which an electronic voltmeter was placed. The linear db scale on the Ballantine voltmeters simplified measurements since all data could be obtained directly in decibels and plotted immediately; any odd points

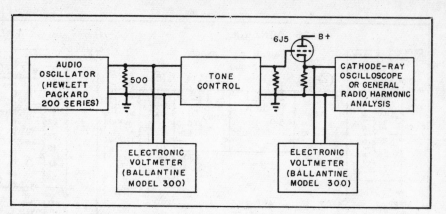

FIG. 3—Method used for testing individual R-C networks and complete tone control system

could be immediately investigated.

Each network was tested individually, after which the entire tone control was tested as a unit.

The output from the last 6SF5 was transformed down to low impedance in an auxiliary cathode follower (6J5) and another voltmeter was placed across the cathode follower cathode resistor. The oscillator was set for 500 cycles, its output set for midscale (10 db) on the input monitor meter, and the input gain control adjusted for midscale (10 db) on the output meter, on the 1 volt scale.

Precautions

Any change in oscillator output as frequency was changed was eliminated by always adjusting the oscillator output control so that the input meter read 10 db. A series of measurements was taken by setting

the frequency, setting the oscillator output, and recording the output reading in db as the treble or bass control was varied throughout its range. The tone control net effect is the output reading in db minus 10.

Great care must be taken in planning this type of measurement since it is easy to overlook a cable lumped capacitance, which will change beyond recognition an otherwise desirable curve. It is also advisable to monitor, on a good oscilloscope or harmonic analyzer, the audio output from the tone control, to avoid recording false readings due to overloading and consequent waveform distortion.

The author wishes to express appreciation to Dr. Hugh F. Gingerich, to whom credit for the basic network design is due.

Background Noise Suppressor

HIGH-FREQUENCY NOISE is bypassed in the absence of high-frequency signals by a reactance-tube circuit, but when desired high-frequency audio signals are present, a disabling network renders the bypassing circuit inoperative. The suppressor can be used to remove record surface noise and noise introduced by the phonograph pickup. Under such conditions, h-f audible noise is constant and readily determined. During reproduction of

quiet passages, noise is objectionable and therefore is suppressed. However, during passages when h-f signals of appreciable amplitude are present, noise is sufficiently below the reproduction level to be unobjectionable. A two-tube circuit acts to suppress background noise during such quiet passages, but to pass desired high frequencies if they are present at amplitudes above the noise level. The circuit is similarly applicable in any audio

channel in which the noise level is constant.

Disabling Circuit

In the accompanying circuit diagram, a crystal phonograph pickup delivers a signal to the output. A circuit associated with the 6SG7 provides capacitive reactance between output and ground, which, in conjunction with series resistor R_1, acts as a low-pass filter. The circuit associated with the 6SQ7 acts to gate the reactance tube, de-

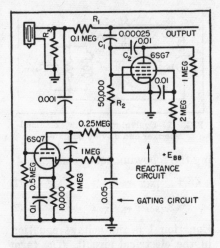

Reactance tube 6SG7 bypasses high-frequency noise. Gating tube 6SQ7 disables the shunting action of the reactance tube when h-f signals are present

creasing its capacitance to ground in the presence of high frequencies to the left of R_1.

A resistance-capacitance divider so proportioned that it passes only high frequencies feeds the grid of the 6SQ7. Likewise the bypassing capacitor for the self-biasing cathode resistor of the 6SQ7 is proportioned to shunt only high frequencies so that the triode is degenerated for low frequencies but amplifies high frequencies. Also the diode-section anode of the 6SQ7 is driven from the triode-section anode through a high-pass resistance-capacitance network. These three high-pass R-C networks pass only frequencies above approximately 600 cps to the rectifier.

The diode section of the 6SQ7 develops a direct-current bias that disables the reactance tube in the presence of high frequencies. To delay the disabling action until the h-f amplitude exceeds the noise level (that is, until wanted signals are present), the cathode resistor of the 6SQ7 is made quite large, the exact magnitude depending on the noise level into the channel. The diode charges a capacitor in the grid circuit of the 6SQ7 to provide a negative biasing potential that reduces the tube's gain in the presence of frequencies above about 600 cps and at intensities higher than the noise level below which quieting is required and in proportion to the amplitude of these signals.

Electronic Low-Pass Filter

Resistance R_1 and vacuum tube 6SG7 constitute a low-pass filter of variable cut-off frequency. Capacitor C_1 is a coupling capacitor, and C_2 is a feedback coupling from anode to grid to enhance the reactive effect of the 6SG7 at higher frequencies. Furthermore, the capacitor between screen and cathode is small so that at low frequencies the gain of the pentode is degenerated by its screen, but at high frequencies the screen is held at ground potential, permitting normal tube gain. The capacitance (as distinguished from capacitive reactance) of the tube is thus a function of frequency.

In addition, the gain of the 6SG7 is controlled by the gating action of the disabling circuit so as to adjust the h-f shunting effect of the tube. The time constant of the grid biasing circuit is relatively short so that disabling bias can be rapidly applied and as quickly removed.

Although the switching action is so fast as to be substantially imperceptible to the human ear, the control action is relatively slow compared to the period of the frequencies being gated so that there is negligible distortion.

Coupling resistance R_2 between the disabling circuit and the reactance circuit serves two purposes. It is made sufficiently small so that the apparent level of the output from the complete suppressor circuit is not appreciably changed as the reactance tube becomes more or less capacitive. In addition, R_2 with C_1 acts as the usual tone compensating network used with crystal phonograph pickups to reduce the midfrequencies in proportion to the reduction of low frequencies provided by resistor R_3.

Should cathode bias be necessary in the reactance tube, the screen bypass capacitor is grounded instead of being connected to the cathode. Furthermore, the cathode bypass capacitor is made small as that at low frequencies there is cathode degeneration. The result is that the impedance of the reactance tube to low frequencies is very high and to high frequencies is quite low in the absence of a disabling bias from the gating circuit. Usual precautions of h-f circuits should be observed in the layout and wiring of the suppressor. (U. S. Patent 2,369,952 granted Feb. 20, 1945 to George F. Devine, assignor to General Electric Co.)

Improving Loudspeaker Response with Motional Feedback

By ROBERT L. TANNER

A FACTOR OF IMPORTANCE in determining the response of loudspeakers, and one usually given insufficient consideration in design, is the effective driving source impedance. The mechanical system of a loudspeaker has the electrical analog[1] shown in Fig. 1. This equivalent circuit is based on the similarity between the differential equations of motion for the loudspeaker and the Kirchhoff circuit equations for the series resonant circuit of the figure. In the analogy the mass of the moving system (cone, voice coil, and air load) is represented by M, the compliance of the suspension by C, and the total dissipation (energy lost in flexing the suspension plus energy radiated) by R. The mechanical constants of the system relate the velocity of motion to the applied force in a manner mathematically identical to the way in which electrical circuit constants relate the current to the applied voltage. It is therefore possible to write the equation.

$$F = Z_{MECH} v$$

where F is applied force, v is velocity, and Z_{MECH} is the mechanical impedance, given in this particular case by

$$Z_{MECH} = R + j\left(\omega M - \frac{1}{\omega C}\right)$$

The force acting on the mechanical system is produced by the flow of current in the voice coil. On the other hand, motion of the voice coil in the magnetic field produces a counter emf in the electrical circuit which can be represented as a voltage drop across a fictitious impedance Z_{MOT} called the motional impedance.

From the electrical point of view

[1] For a demonstration of this and an excellent discussion of electro-mechanical analogues see M. F. Gardner and J. L. Barnes, "Transients in Linear Systems", John Wiley and Sons, New York, 1942, Chapter II.

it is therefore possible to draw an equivalent circuit as shown in Fig. 2. In this figure the amplifier is represented by an equivalent generator E in series with the effective internal impedance Z_i. The loudspeaker is represented by the electrical impedance of the voice coil Z_{vc} in series with the motional impedance. As will be shown, Z_{MOT} is proportional to $\frac{1}{Z_{MECH}}$ and therefore has the characteristics of a parallel resonant circuit. It is convenient to lump Z_i and Z_{vc} into an equivalent driving source impedance Z_e. In general Z_e includes some reactance, but for the frequency range of particular interest the reactance is negligible compared to the resistance and can be ignored.

A more precise understanding of the effects of the electro-mechanical

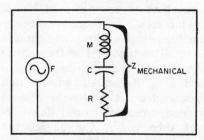

FIG. 1—Electrical analog of loudspeaker

coupling between the mechanical system of the speaker and the electrical circuit of the amplifier and voice coil can be gained by consider-

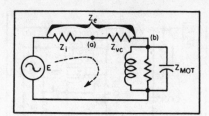

FIG. 2—Equivalent circuit of loudspeaker and driving amplifier

ing the following equations.

$$Z_e i + \frac{Bl\,v}{10^8} = E \qquad (1)$$

$$Z_{MECH} v = \frac{Bl}{10} i \qquad (2)$$

Equation 1 is the voltage equation in the electrical circuit. The term $\frac{Bl\,v}{10^8}$ is the counter emf produced by the motion of the voice coil of length 1 cm in a magnetic field of strength B gauss with velocity v cm per sec. Equation 2 is the force equation of the mechanical system; the term $\frac{Bl}{10} i$ is the force in dynes exerted by the voice coil carrying i amperes. By solving for v in Eq. 2 and substituting in Eq. 1 we have

$$Z_e i + \frac{B^2 l^2}{10^9 Z_{MECH}} i = E \qquad (3)$$

Equation (3) is the basis of the equivalent electrical circuit of Fig. 2. The second term on the left shows that $Z_{MOT} = \frac{B^2 l^2}{10^9 Z_{MECH}}$, and confirms our earlier statement concerning the nature of Z_{MOT}.

Although the effects of the driving source impedance Z_e can be analyzed from the electrical point of view shown in Fig. 3, it is more profitable to make the analysis from an equivalent mechanical point of view. If Eq. 1 is solved for i and the result substituted in Eq. 2 we obtain, after rearranging

$$Z_{MECH} v + \frac{B^2 l^2}{10^9 Z_e} v = \frac{Bl}{10 Z_e} E \qquad (4)$$

This equation serves as the basis of the mechanical equivalent circuit of Fig. 3, in which the driving amplifier is represented as a force source of magnitude $\frac{Bl\,E}{10 Z_e}$ in series with an effective internal impedance $Z_e = \frac{B^2 l^2}{10^9 Z_e}$.

There are several reasons for

Table I—Mechanical and Magnetic Data for Adding Motional Feedback to Amplifier-Speaker Combination for Typical Loudspeakers

Speaker Type	Diameter (inches)	Magnet	Voice Coil Resistance (ohms)	Resonant Frequency (cps)	Effective Mass Including Air Load with Baffle (Grams)	Compliance of Suspension (cm per dyne)	Mechanical Q	Magnetic Conversion Factor $\frac{B^2 l^2}{10^9}$
Cinaud. P8J1	8	6.8 oz Alnico V	6.5	113	9.45	2.1×10^{-7}	15	3.60×10^4
GE S810D	8	6.8 oz Alnico V	3.2	115	9.7	1.98×10^{-7}	9.6	1.38×10^4
Unknown	8	21 oz Alnico III	6.5	118	9.4	1.93×10^{-7}	18	1.82×10^4
Cinaud. P6F1	6	3.16 oz Alnico V	2.95	140	5.50	2.35×10^{-7}	17	6.65×10^3
Unknown	6	1.47 oz Alnico V	2.75	136	3.6	3.78×10^{-7}	12	2.12×10^3

considering the speaker system from the mechanical rather than the electrical point of view. These are first, that speakers of comparable size all have approximately the same mechanical characteristics; second, that the magnetic gap strength and effective driving source impedance are conveniently accounted for because they effect only the element Z_s; and third, that the effects of baffles are most simply considered from the mechanical point of view. For example, a simple enclosure merely increases the effective stiffness and can be considered as a series capacitor in the mechanical circuit.

In calculating the response of a loudspeaker by means of the circuit of Fig. 3 it must be remembered that the radiation resistance of a speaker in an infinite baffle or enclosure increases as the square of the frequency over the range of frequencies for which the speaker diameter is small compared to the wavelength. Most loudspeakers operate in this region for a range of several octaves in the vicinity of the resonant frequency. The low frequency response of a loudspeaker in an infinite baffle has been calculated for several different values of the impedance Z_s, and plotted in the curves of Fig. 4. The curves, which can also be applied to a speaker in a simple enclosure, give response as a function of the frequency relative to the resonant frequency. The magnitude of Z_s is given in terms of X_R, the reactance at resonance of the reactive elements in Fig. 3.

The curves of Fig. 4 indicate how important the impedance Z_s is in determining the response of loudspeakers. Curve A corresponds to a very small value of Z_s, and a mechanical Q of 10 for the speaker. The small value of Z_s might be the result of either a small value for Bl or a large value of Z_e. It is the type of response encountered, for example, when pentode tubes are used in the driving amplifier and no inverse feedback is employed to reduce the effective internal impedance. The pronounced peak in

the response curve is responsible for the poor reproduction of transients which is sometimes described as poor speaker damping. The curves make it obvious that for uniform response and clean reproduction of transients the impedance Z_s should be quite high. This makes it imperative that Z_e be low. Triode tubes, when used in the output stage, provide a source of relatively

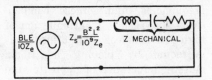

FIG. 3—Equivalent mechanical circuit of loudspeaker and driving amplifier

low impedance, and this is one reason for the traditional preference for triodes. When using triodes the load is usually matched to the tubes in such a manner that the impedance looking back into the amplifier from the speaker is approximately equal to the voice coil resistance. Thus the impedance Z_e is equal to twice the voice coil resistance. By using pentode or beam tetrodes with sufficient negative voltage feedback it is possible to make the effective output impedance of the amplifier small compared to voice coil resistance. Thus Z_e can be made approximately equal to Z_{vc}. In other words, the speaker damping of pentodes with sufficient feedback is twice as good as that of triodes without feedback.

Since ordinary methods never permit the impedance Z_e to be reduced below the value of the voice coil resistance, the maximum value which can be achieved for Z_s is limited by the value of Bl. For speakers with small magnetic structures this maximum value is still too low to result in appreciable improvement in the response obtained with a very high value of Z_e. Even with speakers having the largest magnetic structures supplied in the standard lines, the maximum value of Z_s which can be obtained is still considerably below the optimum value for the speaker in an infinite

baffle. Thus, curve B corresponds closely to the response in an infinite baffle of an eight-inch speaker with a 6.8-oz. Alnico V magnet and a 3.2-ohm voice coil when driven by an amplifier with triodes in the output. It is apparent that optimum response, if achieved by conventional methods, requires the use of an amplifier having sufficient negative voltage feedback to reduce the internal impedance to a negligible value, and in addition, the use of a larger magnet than is obtainable in speakers of moderate cost. Investigation has also revealed that optimum values of Z_s for other baffles require larger magnetic structures than can be obtained in even the more expensive speakers.

The foregoing discussion indicates that a method for increasing the value of Z_s which does not require the use of excessively large and expensive magnetic structures would be of considerable value.

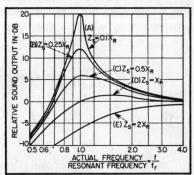

FIG. 4—Relative response of loudspeaker for different values of driving source impedance

The remaining portion of this paper outlines such a method.

Motional Feedback

Optimum response requires that for most speakers Z_e be made smaller than the voice coil resistance. Inspection of Fig. 2 makes it obvious that negative voltage feedback, applied in the customary fashion, cannot reduce Z_e below Z_{vc}. In conventional feedback amplifiers the feedback voltage is taken from point a in Fig. 2 and acts to reduce Z_i only. If a feedback voltage could be taken, instead, from point b, or from directly across the motional impedance, then Z_{vo} would be included in the feedback loop along with Z_i, and Z_o could then be reduced to any desired value. In other words, the feedback voltage must be a motional voltage.

The author has accomplished the result mentioned above in a very simple manner by winding a separate feedback coil of very fine wire over the existing voice coil in a conventional speaker. The voltage induced in this coil by the motion of the voice coil is a pure motional voltage at most frequencies. This voltage, used as a feedback voltage, permits reducing Z_o below Z_{vo}. The method has the additional advantage of including nonlinearities of the cone suspension in the feedback loop and reducing distortion from this cause. Also, by proper design of the feedback coil, nonlinearities due to fringing of the magnetic field are included in the feedback loop and the accompanying distortion reduced with no loss in magnetic efficiency of the speaker.

At very high audio frequencies some difficulty is caused by the mutual inductance between the driving voice coil and the pickup coil. The mutual inductance produces in the feedback voltage a component which is dependent on the induction between the coils rather than on the motion alone. This voltage of induction is very small at most frequencies but becomes quite large at the higher frequencies, and, unless compensated for, results in attenuation of high frequencies. This difficulty is overcome by placing additional mutual inductance of opposite sign between the voice coil and feedback circuits at a point external to the magnetic field. Voltages of induction which are equal and of opposite sign are thus produced in the feedback circuit and cancel, leaving a pure motional voltage as the feedback voltage. It is therefore possible to design as a unit an amplifier-speaker combination, such as the one shown in Fig. 5, of superior performance. Table I, which is included for reference, lists for five typical speakers mechanical and magnetic data necessary to such a design.

In summary, the method presented furnishes a means of achieving excellent performance

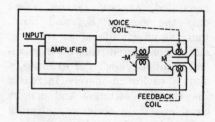

FIG. 5—Block diagram of amplifierspeaker combination with motional feedback compensating mutual inductance

from speakers of low cost. The addition of the pickup coil to the voice coil structure at the time of manufacture should add very little to the cost, and result in negligible change in the mechanical characteristics of the speaker.

Distortion Measurement Device

By PAUL W. KLIPSCH

ALL DISTORTION-MEASUREMENT devices depend on the following elements: a signal to be measured, a means of removing the fundamental of the signal and a measuring or indicating device to reveal the residue or distortion. In this simple form one has essentially a harmonic analyzer.

If a plurality of signals are added for intermodulation measurement, the same basic principle holds with a further means for canceling out the several input signals and examining the resulting output components. These components contain not only the harmonic distortion but also the intermodulation products.

For only occasional measurements of distortion, it is rarely

feasible to spend upwards of $1,000 for the equipment required. However, given a cathode-ray oscillograph, an oscillator, a few items from the usual accumulation around any electronics laboratory and a few hours time, a fair tool can be made up that will give the essential information.

Circuit Arrangement

In Fig. 1 is illustrated an arrangement suitable for determining the harmonic distortion in a single-frequency signal. It is presumed the oscillator is substantially free of distortion otherwise the oscillator distortion must be determined separately. The Wien bridge is adjusted to eliminate the fundamental and the residue is indicated

on a cathode-ray oscilloscope, preferably with a two-stage vertical amplifier.

The bridge may be constructed from a pair of ganged volume controls but due to slack in the shaft it would be better to use a pair of ganged controls with accurate tracking. Passable results were obtained from a pair of carbon volume controls but a lot of headaches disappeared when a pair of precision resistors were substituted.

The particular values of bridge elements were chosen for measuring outputs of low-impedance audio amplifiers at about a 16-ohm level. The bridge as shown will impose negligible load under such circumstances. The variable elements are of such value that wire-wound units are feasible.

The output transformer superposes its own distortion but this occurs after the fundamental has been eliminated and the added distortion is of low order. If the transformer has excessive leakage inductance it will attenuate the higher distortion components. To detect high-order distortion at high frequencies the transformer should be a good one.

In detecting harmonic distortion, the residue after balance will contain all distortion components. The shape of the curve, the sharpness of any kinks and so forth, will indicate the presence of high-order dis-

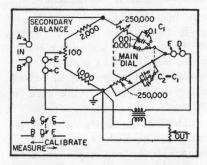

FIG. 1—Wien bridge arrangement for distortion measurement. Arrangement permits both input and output to be grounded and includes calibration means

tortion and the amplitude of the lowest-order harmonic can be measured or estimated.

Without any additions except that of a second oscillator, the device can be used to indicate modulation distortion. The bridge is balanced for one of the frequencies, say the lower, and the envelope of the other frequency examined. A sausage-like pattern indicates the presence of intermodulation and a little calculation will serve to determine the magnitude in appropriate units.

In available components, even precision elements will not track perfectly but mistracking of the variable elements may be compensated for by the variable resistor in the nonreactive arms of the bridge. It has been possible to get a balance of sufficient accuracy to measure

0.3-percent distortion to an accuracy of the order of 5 percent.

The Wien bridge attenuates not only the fundamental (to null) but also attenuates the distortion components to some extent. If considerable precision of the numerical value of distortion is desired it would be necessary to calculate the attenuation of the bridge for one or more of the residue frequencies. Thus, if distortion figures are to be compared with those obtained by other methods of measurement, some corrections may be applicable. If, however, the results are to be comparative and the device described is the only method to be used, one can get a very accurate relative figure of merit without any corrections.

High Fidelity

As this device was built to evaluate audio equipment in the so-called high-fidelity class, a word about measurements of such equipment is in order. Most amplifiers will show fairly low distortion at 400 cycles. The good amplifier is distinguished from the mediocre or poor amplifier by harmonic tests at many frequencies and particularly at extremely low frequencies. As the low C of the pipe organ (C_3) is 32.7 cycles and this should normally be considered as part of the desired spectrum and as power from the C_3 Bourdon pipe is very large, distortion at and below that frequency should be determined. Sometimes wind noise will produce subsonic amplitudes that will cause serious audible intermodulation distortion. It appears that distortion measurements should be made down to frequencies where the response is down 10 db or more. It is at low frequencies where the exciting current of an output transformer creates maximum distortion which will in turn cross modulate higher frequencies.

Not intended to compete with the distortion analyzers which are marvels of speed, accuracy and convenience, the present offering is suggested as a low-cost device for use where occasional distortion data

must be obtained but where the investment in more elaborate equipment is of questionable justification. The device is capable of yielding valuable information and has the advantage that the results are pictorial rather than merely numerical. Qualitative indications of small magnitudes of high-order distortion are evident even in the presence of large quantities of low-order distortion. As it is becoming apparent that a few hundredths of a percent of high-order distortion is more irritating than several percent of low-order distortion, the pictorial representation of the distortion residue may be considerably more valuable than a mere numerical value representing total distortion.

Operation

The signal to be measured is connected to the IN terminals and a cathode-ray oscilloscope, preferably with two-stage vertical amplifier, is connected to OUT terminals.

The bridge is balanced by rotating the main dial while watching the screen. When a minimum is obtained, the secondary balance is adjusted for a further minimum. With a little practice both controls are operated simultaneously to obtain final null of the fundamental. The residue is observed, then the calibration switch is thrown to CALIBRATE position and the calibrated attenuator is rotated until the fundamental is about the same size on the screen as the residue was at the fundamental null. The number of db plus a calculated or estimated correction for pattern size difference is added to give the ratio of the harmonic residue to the fundamental.

In addition to obtaining a numerical ratio between the residue and fundamental, the cathode-ray picture will reveal the presence and order of magnitude of any high-order distortion components. For example a fine whisker-like transient at some part of the cycle might contain mere thousandths of a percent of distortion but be more irritating to a listener than a measured several percent of second or third harmonic.

Beat-Frequency Tone Generator with R-C Tuning

By J. W. WHITEHEAD

THE PRINCIPLES of resistance-capacitance tuning of oscillators may easily be adapted to the design of tone generators using the heterodyne technique. Such a circuit has several advantages over tuned-circuit generators. For example, no difficulty is experienced in covering wide frequency bands with good frequency stability and low distortion and with simple frequency control. Furthermore, there is an extremely low degree of coupling with neighboring components. Remote control of frequency can also be arranged.

Circuit Details

The circuit shows two R-C tuned oscillators feeding the appropriate grids of a hexode mixer. The output from each oscillator is obtained by a suitable tap on the final resistance of each of the phase-shift-ing networks. A refinement (not shown) would be to leave a portion of the automatic bias resistance to each oscillator tube unshunted in order to introduce a degree of feedback for the purpose of limiting the amplitude of oscillation.

Control of the frequency generated by the tube V_1 in the variable frequency section is achieved by altering the effective resistance of one element in the phase-shifting network. This could be done by inserting a normal variable resistance in series with one of the fixed resistances, but here the same effect is secured by varying the grid bias of tube V_2. This tube is a cathode follower, the output impedance of which shunts the center resistance of the phase-shift network. The output impedance is a function of the grid bias on the tube that is controlled by potentiometer R. In short, the frequency of the oscilla-tions generated by the variable oscillator, and hence the resulting tone frequency, is determined by the setting of R.

Potentiometer R may be mounted at any desired distance from the apparatus. The lead from its slider carries no current and can therefore cause no instability, however long it is. The potentiometer dial can be calibrated in frequency.

In practice, both oscillators are set to the same frequency (about 100 kc) with V_2 biased almost to cutoff, but if V_2 has a variable-mu characteristic it need not be biased so far back as might otherwise be necessary.

Instead of a cathode follower for frequency control, a negative-resistance transitron could be used and in this case the magnitude of the negative resistance is a function of the grid bias.

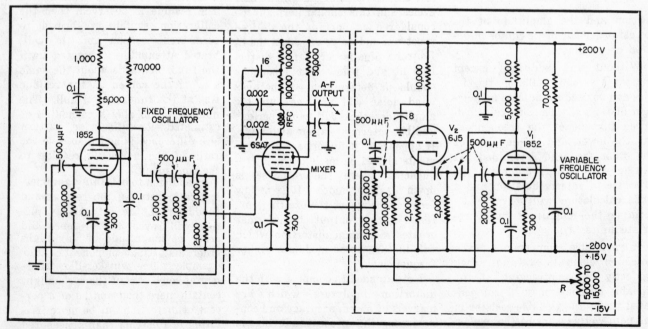

The values shown in the diagram provide oscillator frequencies of about 92 kc and the resulting beat-frequency variation is from a few cycles to over 20 kc. A voltage-regulated plate supply is preferable

Warbler for Beat-Frequency Oscillator

A reactance-tube modulator for use with heterodyne audio oscillator produces frequency deviations of plus and minus ten percent with inputs from 2 to 1,000 cycles. Designed for a flutter generator the circuit has other audio applications

By J. L. FLANAGAN

ACOUSTICIANS and psychologists are often faced with the problem of providing, for experimental purposes, a frequency-modulated or warbled audio tone having negligible inherent amplitude modulation and a variable frequency and degree of modulation.

Common Systems

Experimenters have, in general, met the problem by resorting to mechanical means; probably the most popular method is the use of a mechanically-driven variable capacitor in the tuned circuit of one oscillator of a beat-frequency type audio oscillator.[1] This method is not only cumbersome, but is also subject to restrictions imposed by mechanical tolerances on the accuracy of calibration. The solution to be

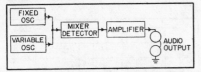

FIG. 1—Simplified arrangement of heterodyne type audio oscillator

described lies in an electronic means of producing the frequency-modulated tone.

There are several methods of frequency modulating R-C phase shift oscillators and obtaining, with the proper design, negligible amplitude modulation.[2,3] Circuits of this nature are employed in subcarrier facsimile transmission. Here, however, we are chiefly interested in the heterodyne-type audio oscillator and shall confine this discussion to it alone.

This work was supported in part by the United States Air Force, under Air Materiel Command contract No. W-19-122ac-14.

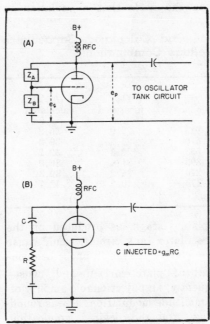

FIG. 2—Basic reactance-tube circuit (A) in which Z_A and Z_B provide 90-deg shift, and capacitive form (B)

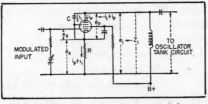

FIG. 3—A type of reactance modulator requiring no avc with little amplitude modulation

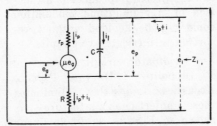

FIG. 4—The linear equivalent circuit derived from the practical modulator shown in Fig. 3

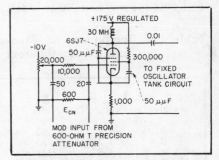

FIG. 5—Final degenerative-type modulator circuit that was built into commercial beat-frequency oscillator

Electronic Frequency Modulator

The reactance-tube modulator offers itself at once for the electrical performance of the task accomplished by the mechanically-driven rotating capacitor. The basic setup of a heterodyne type oscillator is shown in Fig. 1. The frequencies of the beating oscillators are usually in the neighborhood of 200 kc in most commercial types.

By placing a reactance-tube modulator across the tuned circuit of the fixed oscillator and feeding into it the desired modulating signal, a frequency-modulated or warbled audio output is produced. In order that no amplitude modulation be present in the output, the amplitude of the modulated high-frequency oscillator must not vary with the modulating signal. Therefore the a-c component of the plate current in the reactance tube that is in phase with the tank circuit voltage must be kept very small, and must be essentially independent of the modulating signal, in order to give negligible resistive shunting of the tuned circuit.

In considering specific requirements, it should be noted that a normal ear is capable of detecting a difference limen of as low as 2 cps on a 1,000-cps base, under certain conditions of low flutter rates. Thus the modulator must be capable of producing accurately a warbler frequency deviation of as low as ±0.1 percent. In terms of the frequency deviation of the high-frequency oscillator that is modulated by the reactance tube, this frequency deviation is much smaller (±0.0005 percent on a 200-kc base).

$$\frac{R}{1 + g_m R} \ll \frac{1}{j\omega C \ (1 + g_m R)}$$ and the modulator appears mainly reactive.

In the course of the investigation several modifications of this basic circuit were employed to frequency modulate a heterodyne oscillator (a General Radio type 713AS9 and also a type 913). Low-plate-resistance triodes were ruled out at the outset on the basis that a variation in

lowing relations are evident, where the quantities are complex a-c values.

$$e_g = -R\,(i_1 + i_p)$$
$$e_p = X_c\,i_1$$
$$e_1 = X_c\,i_1 + R\,(i_1 + i_p)$$
$$\quad = e_p - e_g$$

The linear equivalent circuit is shown in Fig. 4, from which follows

$$Z\,(\text{injected}) = Z_1 = e_1/(i_p + i_1)$$

$$Z_1 = \frac{X_c\,i_1 + R\,(i_1 + i_p)}{i_p + i_1}$$

$$Z_1 = R + X_c \left(\frac{i_1}{i_p + i_1} \right)$$

$$i_p = i_1 \left[\frac{X_c - \mu R}{r_p + \mu R} \right]$$

$$i_p = i_1 \left[\frac{X_c/r_p - g_m R}{1 + g_m R} \right]$$

$$Z_1 = R + X_c \left[\frac{1}{1 + \dfrac{X_c/r_p - g_m R}{1 + g_m R}} \right]$$

$$Z_1 = R + X_c \left[\frac{1 + g_m R}{1 + X_c/r_p} \right]$$

If $r_p \gg X_c$ (as would be the case for pentodes)

$$Z_1 = R + X_c\,(1 + g_m R)$$

$$Z_1 = R + \frac{1}{j\omega \left(\dfrac{C}{1 + g_m R} \right)}$$

In comparing this modulator with the basic circuit first discussed we note that for the basic circuit

Table I — Comparison of Measured and Calculated Capacitance Injected for Different Voltage Combinations

E_{cn} volts	E_c volts	E_{c2} volts	g_m μmhos	C_{in} measured μμf	C_{in} calculated μμf
0	1.7	62	913	23.0	26.2
2	3.2	85	670	25.5	30.0
4	4.8	110	553	28.3	32.2
6	6.5	130	393	31.4	36.0
8	8.2	150	270	35.2	39.3
10	10.0	170	170	40.2	42.7

The problem then reduces to one of using a modulator that will provide a warbler frequency deviation that may be accurately controlled, measured, and reproduced in the range of ±0.1 to approximately ±10 percent, and which produces less than one-percent amplitude modulation.

Selecting the Modulator

The basic reactance-tube circuit takes the form shown in Fig. 2A, where the elements Z_A and Z_B provide a phase shift of approximately 90 degrees between e_p and e_g.

The nature of the elements Z_A and Z_B is dependent upon whether the tube is to appear capacitive or inductive. In the simplest capacitive form the circuit would appear as in Fig. 2B, where the injected capacitance is approximately equal to $g_m RC$ for high plate-resistance tubes (such as pentodes) as is shown in most any basic electronics text.[4,5]

Actually, taking into account the phase-shift circuit, the injected impedance seen by the tank circuit is equal to

$$\frac{R + 1/j\omega C}{1 + g_m R}, \text{ where in general,}$$

plate voltage, as produced by the oscillator tank circuit, would cause a relatively large in-phase component of plate current and, consequently, an objectionable amount of amplitude modulation. It was found that for the desired application this type of circuit produced in general an overly sufficient amount of frequency modulation and an intolerable amount of amplitude modulation. Using elements of practical size, the sensitivity of the injected capacitance of this type modulator to variations in g_m (or to the modulating signal) was too great for accurate control and measurement of the low deviations. Also, since the resistive component of the injected impedance is a function of g_m, amplitude modulation could not be avoided without resorting to intricate avc circuits.

A modulator circuit, devised by P. Dippolito of Harvard Psycho-Acoustics Lab, that eliminates these objectionable features is shown in Fig. 3. A simple linear analysis of this modulator follows and the impedance relations are derived.

From the above circuit the fol-

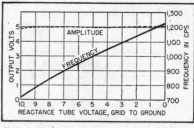

FIG. 6—Static calibration of warbler for 1,000-cps base frequency. Amplitude is essentially constant

$$Z_{\text{inject}} = \frac{R}{1 + g_m R} - j\,\frac{1}{\omega\,C\,(1 + g_m R)}$$

For the degenerative circuit

$$Z_{\text{inject}} = R - j\,\frac{1}{\omega \left(\dfrac{C}{1 + g_m R} \right)}$$

The resistive component injected by the latter circuit is therefore constant for linear operation, and will produce little amplitude modulation. Thus the necessity of complicating the apparatus with avc circuits to obtain the desired amplitude characteristics is foregone. Defining the sensitivity of the injected capacitance to variations in g_m as $\partial C_{inject}/\partial g_m$, we obtain for the respective sensitivities of the basic circuit $C_{inject}/\partial g_m = RC$ and of the degenerative circuit $\partial C_{inject}/\partial g_m = -RC/(1 + g_mR)^2$. The degenerative circuit is considerably less sensitive for given values of R and C, and provides for more accurate reproduction of a given frequency deviation with less accurate measurement of the modulating signal. It should also be noted that the latter circuit has the advantage that the output impedance of the modulating signal source has no effect upon the phase-shift circuit, as might be the case in driving the former modulator.

Warbler Equipment

A degenerative type modulator stage with the circuit elements shown in Fig. 5 was built into a General Radio type 713 beat frequency oscillator, and found to perform exceedingly well. With sinusoidal modulator inputs of 2 to

1,000 cps, a frequency deviation of approximately ± 10 percent was obtained with negligible amplitude modulation. This instrument is

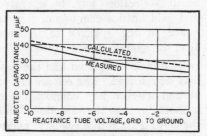

FIG. 7—Graphical comparison of measured and calculated values of injected capacitance

currently being employed as a flutter generator for subjective flutter threshold measurements. It will be noted from the circuit that the screen grid is bypassed only for the r-f oscillator frequency, and not the audio modulating frequency. The purpose in this arrangement was to obtain a variation in g_m with grid voltage which would produce a linear overall frequency variation of the warbler with the input signal. Static calibration curves of this warbler for a 1,000-cps base frequency are shown in Fig. 6.

The injected capacitance of this modulator was measured on a General Radio capacitance bridge Type 716-C, by the substitution method, at a frequency of 200 kc. The injected capacitance was also calculated from the expression obtained in the foregoing derivation. Sample data are shown in the accompanying table and results are plotted in Fig. 7 comparing the measured and calculated values.

Although the circuit has, so far, been used only for producing a sinusoidally frequency-modulated audio tone for subjective flutter measurements, the modulating signal waveform is certainly not limited to sinusoids. The ability of the circuit arrangement to modulate the audio tone with any desired type of wave is counted as a prime advantage.

References

(1) Shower and Biddulph, Differential Pitch Sensitivity of the Ear, *Jour. Acous. Soc. Am.* p 275, Oct. 1931.
(2) Smith and Stanko, Frequency Modulated Audio-Frequency Oscillator for Calibrating Flutter-Measuring Equipment, *Jour. SMPE*, p 309, March 1949.
(3) M. Artzt, Frequency Modulation of R-C Oscillators, *Proc. IRE*, p 409, July 1944.
(4) A. Hund, "Frequency Modulation" McGraw-Hill Book Co., Inc., p 166.
(5) L. B. Arguimbau, "Vacuum Tube Circuits", John Wiley & Sons, p 467.

Simplified Multistation Intercom System

Requires only two wires and ground for complete privacy between any two stations among a maximum of eight stations. The pulse-generating system used for automatic switching can be adapted to remote control by wire, carrier or radio, when power lines are synchronized at transmitters and receivers

By ANDREW W. VINCENT

IN CONVENTIONAL intercommunication systems that do not employ centralized switching the desired talking-circuit path is set up at the calling station when a manually operated selector switch completes a direct-wire connection to the called station. An intercom employing centralized switching ordinarily requires that a circuit first

be established to the switching apparatus; after this the circuit path to the desired station is remotely set up by a manual switch at the calling station.

The cost of the direct-wire system increases rapidly as the service area increases because the multiplicity of wires between stations makes installation, relocation and

servicing difficult. In addition, the extensive wire network increases noise pickup. Central switching, although it eliminates individual station amplifiers and reduces the number of interconnecting wires, usually requires complex central equipment to perform the remotely controlled functions of call, talk, listen and release.

New Central System

The centralized system to be described uses a finder circuit with no line relays, a pulse system for station selection, one audio amplifier, and simple three-position switches at each station. The pulse system employs an inductor and eight different half-wave rectifier combinations to select eight unique positive or negative voltage impulses from a 60-cycle supply.

Up to eight stations can be used. Each station is connected directly to the central unit by three wires, a balanced talking pair and ground. The station units house a p-m speaker, small selenium rectifiers, resistors, a pulse inductor and keys that set up eight different pulse-circuit conditions for station selection and control the talk-listen and re-

lease functions. The keys are three-position lever type with spring return to center.

When a call is made the desired station-selection key is operated and held until a completion tone is heard in the speaker to indicate that the system is not in use. The switching is completed and the key may be released. The release of the station-selector key completes the connections to the amplifier and the calling station is ready to carry the message in the direction of the called station. Operation of the listen key reverses the talking direction, allowing a reply. Operation of the release key releases the system for subsequent calls.

Line Finder Circuit

The glow lamps in Fig. 1 are con-

nected to the *P* wires of each of the balanced pairs extending to each of the speaker stations. The common connection to the glow lamps is in a circuit traceable to ground through the 70-volt transformer winding and the grid circuit of one of the tubes in the bridge circuit.

When the system is idle, the relay contacts complete this circuit in which the 70 volts a-c of the transformer winding is impressed upon each of the *P* station leads through the glow lamps. Since the glow lamp breaks down at and maintains a voltage of about 65 volts d-c, the voltage appearing across the remainder of this circuit will consist of sine-wave tops or pulses as shown in Fig. 2A having effective voltages in these peaks of about 25 volts.

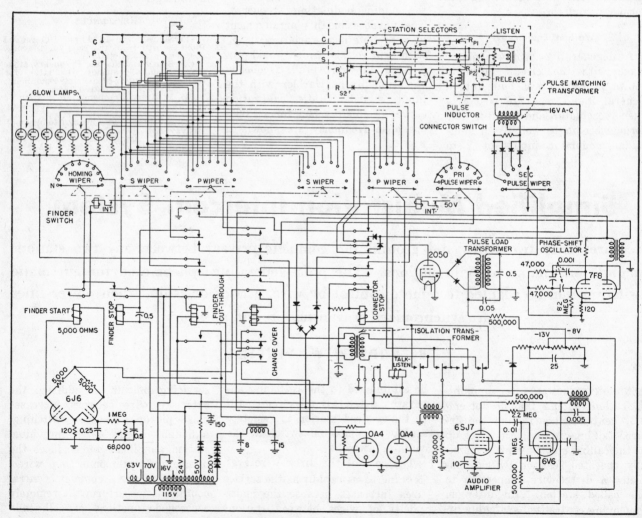

FIG. 1—Wiring diagram of the central station, with connections shown for one substation in dashed box

When the station-selector keys are in the normal position, the station speaker voice coil is connected across the balanced pair P and S. Therefore the line capacitance of

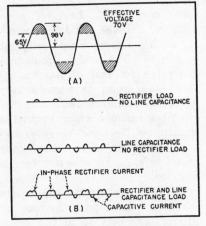

FIG. 2—Voltage and current waveforms available for switching

both the P and S wires to the ground control wire is presented at each of the lines as a capacitance load between the glow lamp and ground, since the speaker impedance is small in relation to the reactance of the line capacitance.

This capacitive load causes symmetrical current pulses to flow in the load capacitor. The time constant of the R-C network in the grid circuit is purposely made long enough so that the d-c grid potential is unaffected and thereby maintains a balance within the bridge circuit.

When the station-selector key is operated at a calling station the speaker is disconnected from the P wire and the load circuit through the rectifier R_{P_1} or R_{P_2} and the pulse inductor to ground is presented to the glow lamp of the calling line. The effect of the rectifier load causes current pulses to flow in the direction in which the rectifier conducts. These rectified pulses cause the R-C circuit at the grid to charge either positively or negatively, thereby unbalancing the bridge circuit which operates the finder start relay and the finder switch. The finder switch, stepping on its own self-interrupting contacts, hunts over the station lines.

Because the rectifier constitutes a resistance load, the rectified current pulses are in phase with the voltage and therefore lag the capacitive current pulses. The connection of the rectifier load on the one calling line controls the bridge circuit even while being shunted by the low-shunt-reactance combination of the other seven line capacitances because the rectifier current component is displaced from the capacitive current component as shown in Fig. 2B.

The finder stop relay is connected between the P wiper of the finder switch and the 24-volt tap of the power transformer. As the finder switch hunts over the lines, the P wiper momentarily connects the finder stop relay to each of the P line wires. When connection is made to the P wire of the calling line, the rectifier load to ground operates the finder stop relay which stops the finder switch and operates the finder cut-through relay which locks up on its own contacts, thereby seizing the link.

The movement of the S wiper from the home position disconnects the 70-volt transformer winding from the glow lamps, thereby disconnecting, by the removal of a sufficient breakdown voltage, the common connection established by the glow lamps to the P line wires. This locks out the other stations from the link by preventing the operation of the finder start relay and also disconnects the unbalanced load on the P line wires, thereby bringing the lines into the balanced condition in readiness for the talking circuits.

Station Selection

The operation of the finder cut-through relay starts the connector switch and connects the P and S wires coming from the calling station, where they are connected to a pulse circuit already set up by the operation of the station-selector key, to the associated central pulse-matching circuit which will stop the connector switch on the contacts of the called line.

The principle of circuit selection utilizes an inductance and selenium rectifiers to break down the 60-cycle power supply voltage into pulses

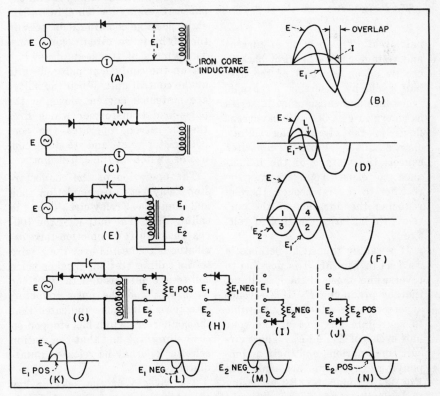

FIG. 3—Combinations of rectifier and inductance connections and their waveforms

that allow 8 selections. The pulse signals are individual, thereby obviating reliance upon combinations of pulses and eliminating testing before the selection is determined.

If an alternating voltage E is fed into an iron-core inductance through a half-wave rectifier, a current I will flow and the voltage E_1 produced across the inductance is the distorted sine wave shown in Fig. 3B. Because of the effect of the inductance in the circuit, the current I and the voltage E_1 is partly carried over into the next

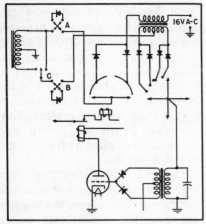

FIG. 4—Talk-listen and release switching circuits

half cycle. This overlap of current and voltage can be brought back to occupy all or any part of the first half cycle by inserting a parallel resistance and capacitance in series as shown in Fig. 3C. When current flows in the circuit, the voltage charge built up across the capacitor cancels the voltage of the inductance and causes voltage across the rectifier to reverse sooner, thereby reducing the duration of the current in relation to the applied voltage E.

If a center tapped inductance is used as in Fig. 3E it is possible to reverse the phase of the E_1 voltage, thereby producing E_2. If a secondary rectifier is added it is possible to segregate any one of the four half cycles of E_1 and E_2. These circuit combinations and their accompanying waveforms are shown in Fig. 3G through N. By reversing the polarity of the primary circuit

rectifier, the current flows during the negative half of the cycle and in the same manner as described above, four more pulses can be generated, occurring during the last half-cycle of the applied voltage E. This pulse-generating circuit can be used for remote-control service over a single pair of wires or to modulate a radio or wire-carrier wave to set up eight different circuit selections, assuming that the same synchronized power source is available at both ends of the connection.

Control Circuits

In the system described, a 3-wire system is necessary for the remote control of the talk-listen and release functions. The three-wire selection circuit used, shown in Fig. 4, is a modification of the basic selection system. The a-c voltage is supplied at the central unit only, thereby making a power connection unnecessary at the speaker station. The diagram shows a simplified circuit of the station switching which, by the operation of the two rectifier reversing switches A and B and the phase-reversing switch C into their eight possible combinations, sets up the eight pulse circuit conditions. The wipers of the stepping switch set up the equivalent pulse circuits at the central unit. When the pulses are matched, current flows in the pulse-load transformer which fires the thyratron, operates the connector-stop relay, and stops the connector switch on the called line.

The operation of the connector-stop relay sets up completion tone and changeover relay circuits on the calling line. The output of the 700-cps phase-shift completion-tone oscillator is connected over the S wire to the calling station, speaker voice coil to ground through the rectifier R_{S1} or R_{S2} and the pulse inductor. The completion tone indicates that the connector switch has stopped on the calling line and that the station selector key may be released immediately.

The release of the selector key operates the changeover relay over

the circuit traceable from the 24-volt power transformer winding through the rectifier bridge circuit and changeover relay winding, the primary pulse wiper of the connector switch, the P wire, the speaker voice coil, back on the S wire and through the output winding of the completion tone oscillator to ground. The bridge circuit prevents the reversal of flux in the changeover relay to allow lock-up operation and introduces into the circuit a rectifier which bucks the station rectifier and thereby prevents operation of the changeover relay before the selector key is released.

The changeover relay disconnects the plate voltage from the tone oscillator, connects it to the audio amplifier and connects the input and output of the audio amplifier to the calling and called lines respectively, thereby completing the talking circuit.

Talk-Listen Circuit

The operation of the listen key at the calling station grounds the talking pair P and S through the bridging center-tapped resistance, thereby operating the talk-listen relay which reverses the amplifier connections to allow a reply from the called station. The current interruptions to the talk-listen relay cause very little disturbance in the amplifier because of the balanced center-tapped connections at the line terminations. The isolation transformer keeps the talk-listen relay current out of the talk-listen switching contacts, thereby preventing switching transients that would be caused by the normal deviations from simultaneous contact closure in a relay with standard adjustment.

Release Circuit

The operation of the release key disconnects the S wire from the speaker voice coil and connects it to ground. The talk-listen relay circuit is completed as in the listen function but the unbalanced current in the isolation transformer causes a transient voltage surge which goes through the input transformer and fires the type OA4 cold-cathode release tube. The OA4 tube supplies current through a differential winding to knock down the cut-through relay which returns the finder switch to the home position on its homing wiper, and interrupts the holding current to the finder-

stop and changeover relays, thereby releasing the system.

The R-C timing circuit fires the other OA4 release tube at a predetermined time after the finder cut-through relay operates unless the talk-listen relay is operated which discharges the capacitor and extends the timing cycle. This feature

releases the system when the calling station is abandoned by the calling party without releasing the system or when there is a circuit failure following the operation of the finder cut-through relay. When a station calls its own line the system is automatically released by the amplifier feedback voltage which fires the OA4 tube.

Voice-Controlled Intercom System

By JOHN R. COONEY

THE PROBLEM of designing an intercommunicating system which does not require manual operation of a talk-listen switch is a rather interesting one, and can be approached in various ways. The system to be described represents a fairly straightforward development which has proved highly satisfactory after prolonged use under typical industrial operating conditions.

The installation and operation is exactly similar to that of the usual simple master-substation system, where the substations consist of simple p-m loudspeakers, except that the caller at the master station is not required to operate a talk-listen switch, the switching being accomplished electronically by the sound of his voice.

As in the case of the ordinary type of system, a remote station may be placed in any kind of location, and answered at almost any distance from the loudspeaker. The master station is expected to be installed in a relatively quiet situation, such as an executive's office, but the requirements for its successful operation are not critical.

After a given substation has been connected by operation of the usual selector switch, sounds originating at the substation are heard normally over the master loudspeaker. However instead of operating a talk-listen switch when he wishes to reply, the home operator has

only to speak (above a certain low threshold level) and the system is instantaneously switched to the outgoing condition, returning to normal immediately after he stops talking.

Although the operator at the master station is expected to be within a few feet of his microphone (a normal situation if he is operating the selector switch anyway), the threshold adjustment can actually be set, in a quiet location, so that he can carry on a conversation as much as 30 feet away from it.

The principle involved in this system is simple, but the actual development of a workable circuit

presented many problems, because of the necessity of precise timing of the sequence of events.

Circuit Details

The circuit details appear in Fig. 1 and the principle of operation is illustrated in Fig. 2 in simplified form.

The system consists roughly of three sections: an out-going amplifier, incoming amplifier, and a control section. The amplifying sections are conventional, except that low-frequency response is intentionally made very poor.

The out-going power amplifier V_1 is normally inoperable because

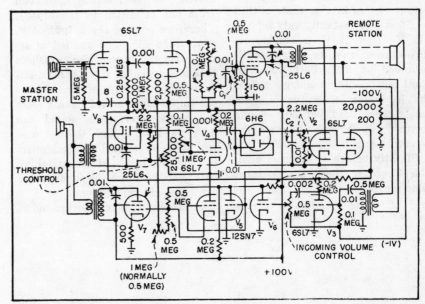

FIG. 1—Complete schematic diagram of automatic intercom system. Tubes in top row comprise outgoing amplifier; bottom row is incoming amplifier (normally on)

its grid is held by the plate of V_2 down to the vicinity of −75 volts. Signals originating at the remote station then appear at the grid of V_3 and are heard over the home loudspeaker. The separate input transformer (or a separate winding on the output transformer of V_1 is necessary, rather than connecting the input of V_3 directly to the plate

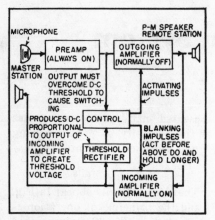

FIG. 2—Simplified block diagram of voice-controlled intercommunication system

of V_1, to prevent plate-supply disturbances from appearing at this high-gain input.

Sounds at the microphone are amplified, and any above a certain level (determined by the setting of the threshold control) are able to overcome the cut-off bias of V_4. The output of this high-μ triode is then rectified and instantly cuts off triode V_2, so that V_1 is quickly returned to operability, at a rate determined by RC. This time constant must be short enough so that the beginning of words is accurately reproduced, yet long enough to avoid a disagreeable thump at the receiving end.

Slightly before V_1 becomes operable (because there are no large time-constants to slow it up) the grid of V_5 (normally cut off) is

driven positive, and the incoming amplifier completely and silently blanked. It is desirable that the blanking operation be complete and as silent as possible, as well as instantaneous; therefore the rather complicated arrangement shown is used.

The plate of V_6 is pulled to ground, making this tube inoperable as an amplifier, and at the same time the direct-coupled grid of V_7 is restrained from going any further negative than ground, so that no click is apparent.

When the sound at the microphone ceases, the negative charge leaks off C_2, V_1 is then instantly blanked, and the clamping of V_7 released shortly thereafter. (As all coupling time-constants are very small, the effect of the heavy overload on V_6 caused by the outgoing signal has been dissipated by the time V_7 returns to operability, so that no disturbances are heard over the loudspeaker.)

Operation

It is obvious that ordinarily sounds issuing from the home loudspeaker would be able to affect the home microphone as well as desired sounds (This would not cause howling as in an ordinary system, but a form of slow motor-boating as the system is periodically switched from one condition to the other). Therefore part of the output of V_7 is rectified (V_8) and applied in series with the normal d-c threshold bias to the grid of V_4. As this additional bias is always proportional to the amplitude of sound issuing from the loudspeaker, such sound can never be loud enough to take control of the system. This mechanism is aided by the slight acoustical lag before sound from the loudspeaker can reach the microphone.

In cases of loud ambient sound at

the remote station, the home station operator has merely to talk slightly louder than the sound issuing at the moment from his loudspeaker to gain instant control at any time. However, it is found that most conversations are necessarily conducted with comparative quiet obtaining at both ends, so that the home loudspeaker is generally practically silent when the home operator wishes to talk.

For example, a machine tool operator at the remote end will always have to shut down his machine, or come closer in order to be able to hear above the din. The talker at the home station can also adjust his incoming volume control to give a level satisfactory for any particular conversation, although this is not usually necessary.

The microphone may be located very close to the home loudspeaker, even in the same cabinet if desired. However, better results are possible if they are separated by a few feet. (A convenient arrangement which has been suggested would be to combine a small microphone with the selector pushbuttons in a compact unit for the desk, while the rest of the equipment could be installed in some out-of-the-way location nearby.)

The system described above was used for a prolonged period in a shipyard, the master station being located in the main office, with substations in a boat-shed, mill buildings, machine shop, blacksmith shop, and an outdoor location; and operation proved completely reliable and highly satisfactory under all circumstances.

In the interests of simplicity, unnecessary details, such as distribution switching and provision for initiating calls from the remote stations have been omitted from the schematic diagram.

Voice-Switched Intercom

Talk-listen switch is eliminated by using four-terminal repeater with flip-flop multi-vibrator that unblocks gated amplifiers alternately 30 times a second. Arriving voice signals stop flip-flop and keep desired channel open without clipping syllables

By RALPH H. BAER

PROPER FUNCTIONING of a fully automatic system for two-way wire transmission of voice-frequency signals depends on the existence of appropriate signals which can initiate switching in the proper direction. Such a system eliminates the need for manual talk-listen switches at the master station or at all substations.

Separate microphones have been used in a number of practical intercommunicators to initiate automatic switching. In these systems the arrival of sound above a minimum threshold level at the microphone provides the control signals. Such devices have given highly satisfactory service in the past.[1,2]

Many experimental automatic intercommunicators have been designed around voice-operated relays similar to the Vodas[3] used in carrier-type telephone systems. In general, these suffer from excessive complexity and maintenance difficulties.

There exists a fundamental difference between terminal conditions in Vodas systems and in intercommunicators. In the first, signal-to-noise ratios are determined by line noise and radio-link interference signals. Rapid break-in operation is highly desirable to approximate the conditions of the normal telephone conversation. A switching arrangement responsive to the syllabic content of speech is therefore indicated.

In intercommunicators, line and equipment noises are usually minimal, but the system must differentiate between ambient acoustic noise and the desired voice signal. In addition, signals at the considerable power level necessary for loudspeaker operation must be handled,

increasing the difficulties resulting from circuit switching transients. Therefore, slower switching speeds than those encountered in the Vodas and in electronically switched carrier systems[4] appear to be necessary.

The admittedly higher first cost of a selfswitching intercommunicator is frequently justified by the conditions under which it is expected to perform. A fully automatic system like that to be described permits a much larger radius of mobility for the participants.

Gated Amplifiers

The diagram in Fig. 1 shows how automatic switching is achieved in an intercommunicator developed for office and industrial use. The two identical channels contain gated amplifiers that are unblocked alternately 30 times per second by a flip-flop multivibrator that feeds the

gated tubes in opposite phase. In addition, each channel has its own control circuit that keeps the channel open if a voice signal reaches it during the 1/60th-second interval when its gated amplifier is unblocked.

In the absence of sounds above ambient level at either speaker, the outputs of the gated amplifiers consist of residual hum and noise signals (approximately 1 volt peak-to-peak) keyed on and off 30 times per second. Normal voice levels at either speaker will therefore appear at the output of the corresponding gated amplifier within a maximum of 1/60th second. These gated-amplifier output signals will normally exceed 5 volts peak-to-peak, and are hence well-suited to initiate the required switching operation since they result from the presence of an adequate sound signal and are simultaneously sense-directed.

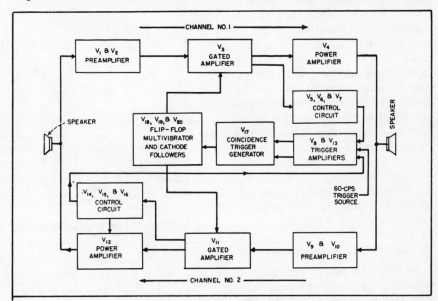

FIG. 1—Twenty stages, some using halves of dual-function tubes, keep either channel open as long as voice signals are present and permit other channel to take over quickly at end of message

In the control circuits, these signals are amplified and rectified, yielding a d-c control voltage which removes the cutoff bias from the output tube and stops the 60-cycle triggers normally applied to the flip-flop circuit. This locks the flip-flop, holding the proper gated amplifier in the on position and permitting sound signals to keep the channel open via its own control circuits. At the same time the gated amplifier in the other channel is held in the off position by the locked flip-flop. Therefore, its control circuit obtains no signal and the power output stage of this channel remains biased beyond cutoff.

Complete plate-current cutoff is required to eliminate residual hum and circuit noise components as well as to prevent feedback through the system and resultant howling during standby conditions, since the output transformer is common to the input of the other channel. It is important that the signal-noise ratio at the output of the gated amplifier be as high as practicable, since a ratio of at least 4 to 1 is required at this point to prevent erratic operation.

A front-panel control is used to reduce the gain of the control circuit signal amplifiers so as to prevent high ambient noise levels at either terminal from locking the system in its direction. With reduced gain it is necessary to raise one's voice at that station, but this is required anyway with conventional intercommunicators to remain intelligible despite the masking effect of the ambient noise.

When voice signals cease in a channel, the d-c output in its control circuit drops to zero, the output tube of the channel is cut off, and the 60-cycle triggers are again permitted to reach the flip-flop, which resumes its keying function.

Operating Requirements

In order to assure reliability of circuit operation the following considerations must be taken into account:

(1) The events originated by the control circuit must be in proper time sequence.

(2) The outputs of the gated amplifiers during their on periods must contain only signals fed by their respective preamplifiers. Thus, the keying signal itself must not appear in the output.

(3) The control circuits must respond rapidly enough to prevent initial syllable clipping due to retarded removal of output tube cutoff bias.

(4) To preserve naturalness of speech, intersyllable response of the control circuits must be slow enough to prevent choppy speech, but sufficiently rapid to permit quick channel reversal after termination of a message.

(5) In their off position the gated amplifiers must be capable of blocking the high-level signals arriving from the preamplifier, whose input is being driven by the output of the other channel.

(6) Despite their relative large number, individual stages should be simple and employ a minimum number of components.

Proper sequencing of events dictates mainly that the flip-flop circuit be locked before the output tube in the live channel is made operative. Also, the flip-flop must resume operation only after the output tube is completely cut off and all transients in the corresponding

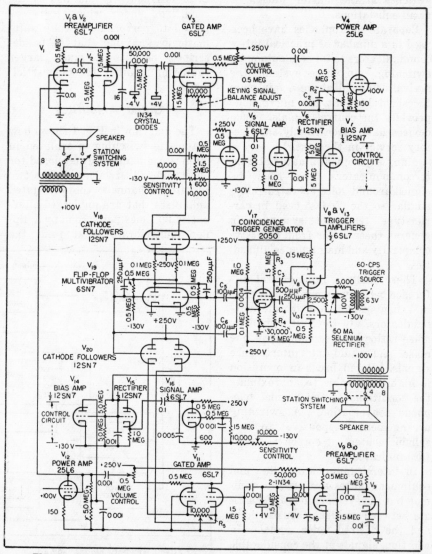

FIG. 2—Amplifiers and control circuits. Power supplies and station-switching arrangements are conventional hence not shown

transformer have died out. In this connection it is important to regulate the rate at which the output tube is biased toward cutoff since this determines largely the character of the resultant transient. Similarly, the rate of response of the trigger signal circuits feeding the flip-flop must be accurately controlled. The initial response may be made nearly instantaneous while the release period must be held within 0.1 to 0.25 second. Lower values decrease the stability of the system and higher values prolong the time taken to reverse direction of transmission after cessation of a message.

In order to prevent the square-wave keying signal from appearing in the output of the gated amplifier, the signal is caused to balance out in the plate circuit of the twin-triode by applying the square-wave keying signals out of phase to the cathodes. Thus no component of the keying signal appears across the plate load of the gated amplifier.

Circuit Details

The complete circuit of the voice-switched intercommunicator appears in Fig. 2. Here it can be seen that the gated amplifiers are driven by the flip-flop through cathode followers to isolate the channels and to make it possible to balance out individually the two gated amplifiers. Semiadjustable controls R_1 and R_5 are provided for this purpose. The stability of the adjustment is such that it maintains balance within 0.25 volt over long periods of time and large line voltage variations. Stability depends only on the characteristics of the gated tube itself and not on those of the cathode followers or

the cathode follower grid signal waveform, provided each cathode follower and its controlled amplifier section are alternately driven beyond cutoff.

The amplitude of the rectangular keying signal between cathode and ground is made approximately 10 volts peak to peak. The gain of the gated amplifier under these operating conditions is thus that of an ordinary cathode-degenerated stage. Reducing the filament voltage of the gated tubes (V_3 & V_{11}) minimizes the hum components developed across the unbypassed cathode resistance. Overall gain of the amplifiers (voice coil to plate of gated amplifier) is 95 db at 1 kc.

Rapidity of response is largely a function of the gain incorporated into the control circuit signal amplifier and of the RC time constants in the control rectifier. Components R_2 and C_2 primarily determine the bias decay and prevent a thumping noise every time plate current is restored.

To prevent gate breakdown by high signal levels, the gated amplifiers are protected by two 1N34 germanium diodes which restrict the input signal to 8 volts peak to peak. Short time constants in the coupling networks prevent the keying signal balance from being affected by the peak clippers. Grid limiting in the preamplifier keeps the signal peaks applied to the clipper diodes below 50 volts.

Trigger pulses for the flip-flop originate in V_8 and V_{13}, whose cathodes are driven by a halfwave-rectified 60-cycle pulse of large amplitude. The resultant square-waves developed across the plate load resistors are differentiated by R_3C_3 and R_4C_4 and applied to the first and

second control element of a 2050 thyratron coincidence trigger generator biased beyond cutoff. The simultaneous arrival of both trigger signals will result in a plate-current pulse whose steep leading edge triggers the flip-flop through C_5 and C_6. Appearance of rectified d-c control voltage at the grids of either V_8 or V_{13} reduces the corresponding trigger signal applied to the thyratron below the firing level. As a consequence the flip-flop maintains its instantaneous equilibrium state until all d-c voltages have disappeared and released V_8 and V_{13}.

A number of experimental models have been built for office intercommunication. They are housed in small cabinets containing the master speaker and a pushbutton arrangement for selection of outgoing lines. In the standby position the incoming amplifier input is grounded, hence plate current in the output tube is cut off and the master speaker is absolutely silent. Provision is made to permit each substation to sound an annunciator at the master to originate a call. The units are powered by selenium rectifiers and simple RC filters. Power supplies and switching arrangements are conventional.

REFERENCES

(1) J. R. Cooney, Voice-Controlled Intercom System, ELECTRONICS, p 118, Sept. 1949.
(2) H. J. McCreary, Electronic Interlocking for Intercommunicators, ELECTRONICS, p 30, Sept. 1941.
(3) L. Wright, The Vodas, *Electrical Engineering*, 56, p 1012, Aug. 1937.
(4) R. C. Fox, F. S. Beale and G. W. Symonds, Voice-Operated Switching of Carrier Systems, ELECTRONICS, p 92, Feb. 1950.

Voice-Operated Busy Signal

CERTAIN special types of telephone networks use voice calling over a single speaker for a multiplicity of lines. The circuit shown in **Fig. 1** enables the party at the called end to identify the particular line on which the voice call is being heard. The system is voice operated, and its sensitivity is such that low-level talking will light an appropriate lamp, but noise will not.

Since voice talking levels rarely exceed + 10 vu (10 milliwatts), and are often as low as − 30 vu (1 microwatt), an amplifier is required; and since line noise will also be amplified, some kind of frequency discrimination is required to prevent false operation. Another design factor is adjustment of release delay time, so that the busy signal will not flash between words or short pauses.

Input resistors R_1 and R_2 assist in providing high input impedance so that the transmission loss caused by bridging the busy signal across the line is small. With no input signal V_2 is biased almost to cutoff by the voltage drop across R_3, and the relay is non-operated. When speech appears on the line, it is amplified by V_1 and V_2. The output signal current of V_2 flows mostly through the combination of C_1 C_2, and R_4, since the relay winding has a very high impedance. The signal is rectified by the copper-oxide

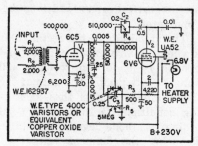

FIG. 1—Voice-operated busy signal operates on low-level speech, but ignores line noise

varistors and appears as a positive charge on the left side of C_3. This charge drives the control grid positive and the resultant increase in plate current operates the relay whose contacts are used to control a lamp or other indicator.

When speech ceases, the charge across C_3 will leak off to ground through the back resistance of the rectifiers and R_5. When the plate current has decreased to the value of current at which the relay releases, the lamp or indicator is extinguished.

The release or holdover time of the relay is governed by the rate of discharge of C_3, which depends primarily on R_5 and the back resistance of the rectifiers. By adjusting R_5, the release time may be varied from approximately three to ten seconds.

Discrimination between noise and signal is obtained by frequency

weighting. This is accomplished in the voice-operated busy signal circuit by attenuating the frequencies below about 300 cycles in the input transformer, and by attenuating frequencies above about 3,000 cycles by by-passing them to ground through a 0.01-µf capacitor. The input transformer is wound on the core of a G-type relay, and has a sufficiently low mutual inductance to suppress the low frequencies and yet have a satisfactory response in the middle voice-frequency range. The frequency response of the voice-operated busy signal is illustrated in Fig. 2.

The circuit described was developed by the Bell Telephone Laboratories for use by the Interstate

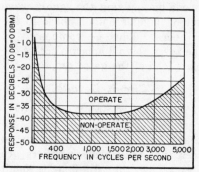

FIG. 2—Frequency response of the voice-operated busy signal

Airways Communications Stations of the CAA. It is presented in somewhat more detail in the Bell Laboratories Record for December, 1949, by E. C. Borman.

Improved Speech Inverter System

Privacy circuit for radio or telephone line employs double modulation of the conversion frequency and is controlled both by the speech input and the average level of speech input. Frequency response is corrected by an R-C equalizer network. Broad dynamic range, low background noise and low distortion are assured

By L. L. KOROS

USERS of wire line, and particularly radiotelephone service, can never be assured complete secrecy of their communications despite laws made for their protection. When circumstances justify the expense of necessary terminal equipment, speech scramblers or inverters are used that make it virtually impossible to decode or unscramble the enroute message without authorization. Owing to the confidential character of such systems the literature gives a very meagre coverage of specific details, although the basic principles have been published.[1]

This article describes an improved speech inverter system employing equipment that is simple in design. In operation, the adjustments to the variable components are not critical and the overall tolerances are fairly broad.

Design Considerations

Common practice in speech inverters is to let the intelligence

* Formerly RCA Victor Argentina, Buenos Aires, Argentina.

flow through a low-pass filter that prevents higher frequencies not essential to the intelligibility of speech from passing into the circuits that follow. The limit is often chosen at 2,700 cps.

The speech frequency band, $f_s \lessgtr$ 2,700 cps, is introduced into a modulator, together with the inversion frequency f_c, which is usually 3,000 cps. There are speech inverters using several inversion frequencies to increase the difficulties for unauthorized reinversion. The method described here can be applied to more complex systems, also.[2] This frequency of inversion is modulated by the intelligence $f_s \lessgtr$ 2,700 cps. The modulator is generally a balanced type. It produces different frequency groups, the more important being $f_c + f_s$ and $f_c - f_s$. The output from the modulator flows through a second low-pass filter with the same frequency limit of 2,700 cps. By this process the $f_c + f_s$ group is suppressed and the transmitted frequency spectrum is 300 to 2,700 cps.

Frequencies lower than 300 cps

produce higher $f_c - f_s$ frequencies than 2,700 cps. They are rejected by the second filter and frequencies higher than 2,700 cps are not introduced into the modulator. The 400-cps frequency in the passband becomes (after modulation and the second filtering process) 3,000 − 400 = 2,600 cps. The 2,600 cps becomes 3,000 − 2,600 = 400 cps. From the lower frequency is produced a higher one and from the higher, a lower one. Thus the frequency spectrum is inverted. The center frequency of 1,500 cps remains as before. This inverted frequency group is transmitted in the normal manner. A radio-frequency carrier can be modulated with the inverted signal, or the inverted signal is sent over a telephone line.

Unscrambling

If at the receiving end the incoming signal is treated in exactly the same manner as the original input intelligence in the sending-end equipment, the inverted intelligence will be reinverted. The inverted intelligence cannot be understood, but the reinverted signal has the same

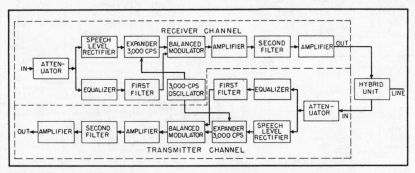

FIG. 1—Two-channel speech inverter showing connection through hybrid unit to line

FIG. 2—Distortion in the speech inverter system used for a complete circuit with three input levels

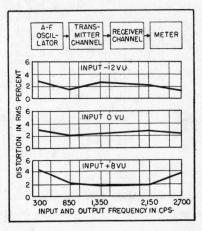

intelligibility as the original input, provided the process of inversion and reinversion has not introduced extreme distortion.

There are several sources of distortion. The internal carrier frequency of 3,000 cps may be present in the output line because it is not balanced out with sufficient accuracy by the modulator or is not suppressed to the necessary low degree by the second filter. In this case, the 3,000 cps introduces a disagreeable background noise. This tone may be mixed with the hum frequency and harmonics of the power supply. The hum level becomes more disturbing in the speech inverter than in a common amplifier because the modulation factor of the intelligence on the 3,000-cps carrier must be low, as will be shown later.

Further distortion is produced by the modulation of the 3,000-cps carrier. In addition to the lower and upper sidebands the $2 f_c = 6,000$ cps and $2 f_s$ frequency groups are frequently present in the output of the modulator circuits. The f_c, $2 f_c$, f_s and $2 f_s$ frequency groups produce cross-modulation frequencies. Many of these cross modulation products are in the passband of the filter and therefore cannot be eliminated; or they are not in the passband but are not suppressed

sufficiently in the second low-pass filter. The $2 f_c = 6,000$ cps and also $3 f_c = 9,000$ cps carrier harmonics contribute to the background noise of the speech inverter.

The inverted intelligence is $3,000 - f_s$. The $2 f_s$ distortion group is in one octave ratio with the incoming intelligence, that is, it is not inverted. The doubling of the input frequency does not impede the intelligibility of the speech. If the level of this distortion is high enough the input direct intelligence can be understood with a common receiver. In this event the purpose of the speech inversion, which is privacy, will not be fulfilled. Furthermore, after passing this tone mixture into a receiver speech-inverter channel, the inverted part of the speech will be reinverted, and the distortion group of double frequency will be inverted. This kind of distortion produces a dissonant effect.

Distortion

Another type of distortion is often produced by detection of r-f fields from the communications transmitter when the speech inverter is near by. The modulator of the speech inverter inherently tends to detect r-f fields. The leakage r-f field carries inverted speech. This signal will be reinverted and intro-

duced again to the transmitter speech input. Heavy distortion, or in some cases regenerative singing, will be produced in this way.

A type of possible distortion is related to the two low-pass filters. It is hard to meet good frequency response because the lowest freqency of maximum attenuation, which is 3,000 cps, must be near the highest passband frequency. The requirements are, however, that 2,700 cps must be transmitted almost without attenuation. The cutoff frequency of the filters must be chosen, therefore, near 2,800 cps. Considerations of economy often make it difficult to use filters with high-Q coils.[3,4] Even expensive coils with Q between 100 and 130 do not give satisfactory results.

The passband of 300 to 2,700 cps can be considered the narrowest possible for speech transmission. If the inadequate frequency response of the filters reduces the transmission of frequencies on both sides of the center frequency of this narrow band and if, in addition, distortion frequencies from the inadequate conversion process are present at a considerable level in the speech output, the intelligibility will suffer seriously.

If the level of the conversion frequency, f_c, be high, the distorting

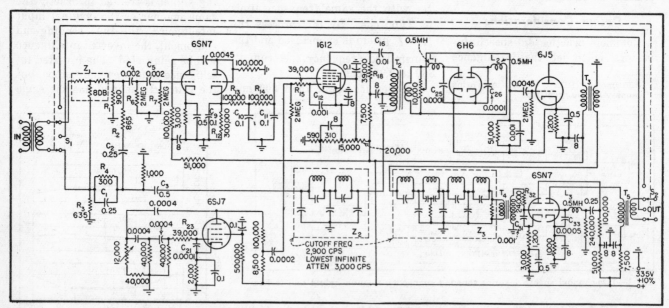

FIG. 3—Circuit diagram of the receiver channel of the speech inverter system

terms of the double intelligence, $2f_s$, and the cross-modulation products between the $2f_s$ and $2f_c$ terms become lower. By increasing the amplitude of f_c, however, the unsuppressed portion of the same and of $2f_c$ and $3f_c$ becomes more disturbing. If more filter sections of the same quality are used to attenuate these frequencies the frequency response in the passband will be worse. The requirement of low distortion is contradictory to the requirement of low background noise. It was recognized as a further difficulty that the level of f_c, which is adjusted to the average speech level, is not sufficient for high speech input level and is excessive for low speech input level or for the case of no speech input. The designer must meet contradictory requirements.

The New System

To reduce the distortions to negligibly low values and to assure a low background noise level an improved system has been introduced. The favorable results are obtained by controlling the level of the conversion frequency. The conversion frequency is modulated by the speech input, as in conventional circuits, but it is also modulated by the average level of the speech input. The frequency response is corrected by an R-C equalizer network.

Figure 1 shows the block diagram of the new speech inverter system. The speech inverter is composed of transmitter and receiver channels. The receiver unit contains the 3,000-cps oscillator; the transmitter unit contains the power supply. All other components for the two channels are identical.

The input attenuator reduces the reactive component of the input channel impedance to an insignificant value. The 3,000-cps oscillator excites the expander. The speech level rectifier controls the 3,000-cps output of the expander. If the speech level rises, the expander feeds more 3,000-cps carrier to the balanced modulator. If the speech level is below a minimum value or if

there is no speech input at all the 3,000-cps signal in the modulator goes down to a low standby level.

This standby level is chosen so low that the residual 3,000 cps and the harmonics of it are better than -50 db below 1 milliwatt at the output of the channel and are consequently inaudible. If the speech level rises, the level of the 3,000-cps tone and the residual of it rises too.

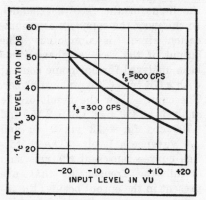

FIG. 4—Conversion and signal frequency levels

Nevertheless, it is not noticeable because it is masked by the speech. Although high-level intelligence is flowing through the speech inverter channel, the 3,000-cps signal and harmonics are still at a relatively low level. As shown in Fig. 2, the rms sum of the remanent 3,000-cps signal, harmonics of it and beats of it with the distortion products of the incoming intelligence remain below a low percentage. The input intelligence will be equalized, and after the first filter, will be fed into the balanced modulator. After the modulator are amplifier stages and a second filter as in the conventional speech inverters.

This speech inverter has no gain or loss. The amplifier stages merely compensate for the losses of the attenuator and equalizer. The normal dynamic range of the input and output is from -12 vu to $+8$ vu, but no excessive distortion can be observed if the speech level on the line rises to as much as $+24$ vu (250 mw). With the expander, the level of f_c will be controlled so that a previously fixed ratio will be assured between the f_c and f_s levels.

It was determined experimentally that an optimum result can be obtained by keeping the level of the 3,000-cps signal at 25 to 30 db higher in the modulator than the level of the intelligence. This level difference assures the lowest distortion due to the $2f_s$ terms and their beat products. The transmitter and the receiver channels may be coupled by a hybrid unit to the telephone line.

Circuit Analysis

The S_1 and S_2 switch system shown in Fig. 3 inserts or removes the channel from the line. This type of switching can be done because the input and output levels are the same. The intelligence, after passing equalizer elements, the function of which is described below, reaches one grid of the 6SN7 double triode and also the input terminal of the two-section filter Z_2. The first section of the 6SN7 works as an amplifier, the second section as a diode rectifier and produces with its filter system (comprising R_{12}, R_{13}, R_{14}, C_9, C_{10} and C_{11}) a fluctuating d-c voltage. This voltage is positive with respect to ground and its value depends on the speech input level. The fluctuation is retarded by the time constant of the filter elements. The optimum value of the time constant is about 0.1 second. The fluctuating d-c voltage more or less neutralizes the negative bias of the type 1612 variable-μ pentode. The first grid of the pentode is excited by the 3,000-cps output of the type 6SJ7 oscillator tube. Into one of the primary windings of T_2 is fed the amplified 3,000-cps tone, the amplitude of which is fluctuating with the speech-input level.

The network R_{13}, C_{16} is designed so that transients, produced by the changes of the plate current of the 1612 tube and which are the consequence of sudden speech level changes, cannot be detected on the secondary winding of T_2. The input filter C_4, R_6, C_5, R_7 prevents frequencies below 300 cps, which are out of the passband, from expanding the 3,000 cps level.

In transformer T_2 the filtered intelligence is added to the fluctuating 3,000-cps carrier frequency. The 6H6 tube acts as a balanced modulator to produce the $f_c + f_s$ and $f_c - f_s$ sidebands. The correct setting of potentiometer R_{28} assures the balance. The predetermined level difference between the 3,000-cps and the intelligence on the plates of the 6H6 in the dynamic range is assured by setting of the bias values and the level of the 3,000-cps excitation on the type 1612 tube.

The level of the 3,000-cps signal on the plates of the 6H6, for very low intelligence input, is higher than 30 db with respect to the intelligence. For very high input it is less than 30 db, but not less than 20 db. Nevertheless, the speech inverter cannot be overloaded by loud speaking. With the most excessive input level the $2f_s$ group cannot become higher than about

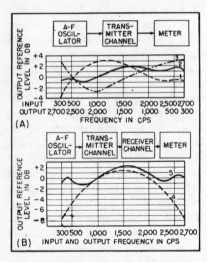

FIG. 5—Curve 1 is response of one channel without equalizer; curve 2 shows response of the equalizer alone; curve 3 is response of one equalized channel. Curve 4 (Fig. 5B) is the frequency response for inversion and reinversion without equalizer; and curve 5 is the same using the equalizer

5 percent of the total; therefore the direct intelligence can never be

understood. Figure 4 shows the ratio of the 3,000-cps level to the input intelligence on the plates of the 6H6 modulator tube.

The modulator is followed by a three-stage conventional amplifier with the second filter Z_3 inserted. To make the measurements illustrated in Fig. 2 two channels are connected in series; the output of the transmitter channel is connected to the input of the receiver channel. In this way the complete communication circuit is simulated. The output of the receiver channel has been analyzed for harmonic content with a GR type 636A wave analyzer. The curves show the result of the analysis at 300, 850, 1,350, 2,150 and 2,700 cps for −12 vu, 0 vu and +8 vu speech levels. The distortion curves represent the rms sum of all the frequencies that are present in the output besides the input frequency. Numerous measurements have demonstrated that the analysis at these frequencies gives a good overall picture of the behavior of the instrument so that the straight-line connections between the measured values is justified. The filters used in the speech inverter channel shown in the schematic have Q's of about 25.

The frequency response of the channel, especially in a complete communication circuit using one transmitter and receiver channel, would not be satisfactory without an equalizer. Resistors R_1, R_2, R_3, R_4 and capacitors C_1 and C_2 form an efficient equalizer system. The circuit is similar to the Wien bridge; no infinite attenuation is produced, however, at any frequency. The peaking tendency of the equalizer at the ends of the passband is compensated by capacitors C_3, C_{25}, C_{26}, C_{31}, C_{33}, inductances L_1, L_2, L_3 and resistor R_{32}. Most of these elements serve also with R_{15}, R_{23}, C_{12} and C_{21} in the cancellation of the r-f

fields from the inverter channel.

Operational Characteristics

The curves in Fig. 5A show effect of the equalizer on one speech inverter channel and those of Fig. 5B on a complete communication circuit of inversion and reinversion. It is important to equalize both channels.

The frequency response can be corrected by pre-emphasis applied to one end of the transmitter channel and to one end of the receiver channel. The pre-emphasis gains are in this case equal to the sum of the losses at both ends of the passband. This method produces an improved overall frequency response, but for radio communication reduces the distortionless modulation range of the radio transmitter. This reduction of the dynamic range of the transmitter will not result or at least to only a low degree, if both channels are equalized individually.

The author wishes to express his appreciation to H. Zuchenbrojt, RCA Victor Argentina and A. Saenz formerly of the same company, for the valuable cooperation in the design work of the speech inverter and in making the numerous measurements needed during the experimental period.

REFERENCES

(1) W. L. Everitt, "Communication Engineering" Second Edition. McGraw-Hill Book Co., p 393, New York, 1937; William W. Roberts, Speech Scrambling Methods, ELECTRONICS, p 108, Oct. 1943.

(2) H. J. Reich, "Theory and Application of Electron Tubes" First Edition, McGraw-Hill Book Co., New York, p 126, 1939.

(3) A. T. Starr, "Electric Circuits and Wave Filters", Second Edition, Sir Isaac Pitman & Sons, Ltd., London, 1944.

(4) J. E. Smith, "Simplified Filter Design", RCA Institutes Technical Press, New York, N. Y.

Automatic Audio Level Alarm

By N. HAGMANN

ONE of the many things to which a broadcast station engineer must pay careful attention is program level and quality. Because rather large variations in level are not easily detected by ear, particularly if the engineer is occupied with other allied work, an automatic alarm system becomes a practical necessity. Such a device is particularly valuable when more than one transmitter carrying the same program material must be monitored.

The audio alarm used at this station is fed through a bridging transformer from the audio source to a 6K6 amplifier stage. This tube feeds into a cascaded diode rectifier, a type 6H6, that separates the diode load circuit from the control circuit. Load resistor R_5 in the cathode of the 6H6 is used to adjust the level of audio to be rectified.

The plate of the same tube feeds the cathode of the second 6H6 section and acts as a d-c separation circuit. The plate of the second section charges a large capacitor that bleeds off through resistors R_6, R_7 and R_8 with R_{11} the controlling element. The grid of the 2050 is connected to the junction of R_6, R_7 and R_{11}. The plate circuit of the 2050 contains the a-c alarm relay. A type 6E5 tuning-eye tube facilitates adjustments for proper level and time delays R_{10} and R_{11}, respectively.

In operation, the 2050 gas tube is made conducting by the rectified signal on its grid stored by the 20-microfarad capacitor. This signal results from the charging effect of the audio input. The proper reference level is set by potentiometer R_{10} that effectively biases the gas tube. Failure of the audio signal, after an appropriate time delay set by R_{11}, results in the relay being de-energized and closing the alarm circuit through its back contacts. A disabling switch in the alarm circuit is useful during symphonic or similar programs in which wide dynamic range is encountered.

The unit can be fed from either audio program lines or the output of an r-f monitor. In the latter case, failure of either the program or the carrier will be detected.

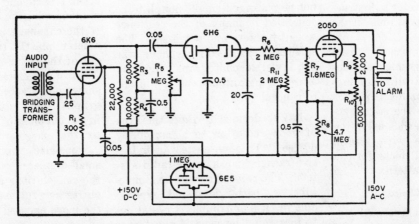

FIG. 1—Diagram of the audio failure alarm. Potentiometer R_{10} sets the level at which the gas tube fires, R_{11} controls time delay between loss of audio and sounding of alarm, and R_5 sets level of audio into the device

Inductive Prompting System

Communications system allows director to cue actors in motion picture scenes without interference to regular sound system. A modulated magnetic field is picked up and demodulated in concealed receivers and conveyed to actors through photographically invisible earphones

By B. H. DENNEY AND R. J. CARR

TWENTY YEARS have passed since the addition of sound to movies eliminated the director's megaphone for prompting actors during the photographing of scenes. In general, producers have relied on extra rehearsal time to take its place. Various tricks have been tried, such as offstage gestures and light signals, but these methods have not been very satisfactory.

There has been a growing demand for a simple radio-type receiver that can be worn inconspicuously on the actor's person. For maximum utility, the ear piece has to be photographically invisible, and the receiver has to be capable of picking up the director's instructions from various positions on the movie set.

Equipment is normally used within sound stages which are unusually well shielded with building-wire screen supporting exterior stucco walls. Inside the stages acoustical control materials are often supported by more wire screen. Pipes, conduits, and ducts form a complex shielding pattern.

Frequency Choice

The radio approach seemed logical. However, at frequencies of 30 megacycles or higher a transmitter's radiation beyond the stage walls would be negligible, but inside the stage the standing-wave patterns would make the use of an efficient automatic volume control or limiter necessary. The efficiency of an antenna worn near the body would be low and variable. Several tubes would be required, so if an estimated fifty receivers were to be built there would be a definite

maintenance problem.

With a lower frequency larger coils and capacitors would be required and, although the standing-wave problem might be less, considerable amplification would be required to overcome the loss caused by the limited antenna size. Radiation beyond the stage walls would probably be troublesome.

Experiments with simple radio receivers at frequencies from 1,500 kilocycles to 460 megacycles confirmed the need of amplification and automatic volume control. However, even if subminiature tubes, printed circuits, and the smallest batteries available were used, a receiver could not be packaged small enough to be concealed in many of the costumes worn by actors and actresses. The smallest hearing-aid earphone was not invisible photographically, and all receiving antennas were difficult to conceal.

It was decided to limit the area of good reception to about 40 by 60 feet. This suggested an inductive rather than a space-radio system. The receivers could be simple, tubeless, batteryless and expendable in case of trouble. Crystal detectors could be used if the transmitter were powerful enough. In this manner the maintenance problem would be limited to one transmitter and its input equipment.

The system finally adopted incorporates a 100-kc transmitter connected to a single-turn loop which surrounds the set area and induces a strong r-f field at all points within the area. Each actor wears a multi-turn loop of wire in which a secondary current flows. This cur-

rent is of sufficient magnitude that when demodulated it is capable of delivering a good output from a hearing-aid type earphone.

The Receiver

The receiver, whose circuit is shown in Fig. 1, uses miniature components mounted on a small terminal card to which the loop is secured and connected. The loop is covered with rubber tubing and the equipment card is covered with an air-drying rubber compound.

The loop-receiver is normally worn around the neck in a plane parallel to the floor, and the small crystal earphone unit is taped or pinned under the clothing. Coupled to the earphone unit, 0.090-inch diameter plastic tubing is brought out of the collar over and down the front of the ear and into the ear as shown in accompanying photographs. The tubing is terminated in a small plastic L which is adapted to the ear canal by means of various-size rubber inserts. The small-diameter tubing blends into the convolutions of the ear and requires careful make-up only across the more exposed neck area.

Strapless evening gowns offered a problem until smaller 6-inch diameter loop receivers were built and concealed in the actress' hair. The output from the smaller-loop receiver is several decibels below the larger 10-inch diameter units but has been satisfactory.

The Transmitter

The r-f section of the 100-kilocycle transmitter, shown in Fig. 2, is push-pull from the crystal oscillator to the class-C output stage. The plate circuit of the output stage is tuned by a variable inductance and a group of fixed capacitors. A variable capacitor for this frequency and for the voltage used would be of an awkward size, therefore the capacitor values are se-

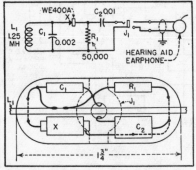

FIG. 1—Circuit diagram and drawing showing placement of receiver parts

lected by a coarse-tuning tap switch. Fine tuning is accomplished by a variometer-type rotor in the electrical center of the inductance. The impedance of the single turn of wire surrounding each different set area changes the effective inductance of the output coil, making it necessary to retune for different loops. This is the transmitter's only critical adjustment.

Audio Equipment

The audio amplifier, Fig. 3, has both a microphone input and a low-gain playback bridging input. Each has its separate gain control. A

tapped control in five 10-decibel steps on the playback input-transformer secondary adjusts for different level playback sources and prevents overloading of the playback input stage. A relay operated from the push-to-talk button on the microphone automatically reduces the playback volume 10 decibels, if desired, when the microphone is used.

Equalization in the plate circuit of the microphone stage improves the intelligibility from the microphone. The microphone is usually held very close to the director's lips as he speaks in low volume, or a whisper. Equalization in the plate circuit of the playback stage has been selected for loudness instead of quality. Attenuating music's low-frequency components by 10 decibels permits a much louder signal to be transmitted without overload.

A switch changes the microphone amplifier stage into a 400-cycle R-C oscillator used for checking the equipment and field strength. The field is uniform enough that receiver volume controls are unnecessary; the audio level is adjusted in the speech amplifier with the class-B modulator plate-current meter serving as a volume indicator.

Storage facilities for the loop-receivers, earphones and attachments and cables and spare parts have been built into the transmitter

dolly which is shown in an accompanying photograph.

Transmitting Loops

The single-turn transmitting loops are placed around the set to be energized at any convenient level from below the floor to 12 feet above the floor. Due to photographic angles and set construction some loops have been used under the floor level for part of the loop and above the floor for the remainder of the loop. Number 10 or 8 wire is used to reduce the resistance and increase the loop current, the value of which will usually be between 2 and 9 amperes.

Circular, square and rectangular loop patterns have been used. The success of the transmitter in covering areas up to 40 by 60 feet with ample volume naturally brought demands for an increased area of coverage. In one long dolly or moving camera scene in an L-shaped area it was difficult to get a strong signal if the loop was run across the diagonal corners of the L. The loop was installed on the margins of the L in the form of block L whose thickness was 20 feet and whose width and length were about 70 and 120 feet.

In a recent picture, one scene required a dolly shot 250 feet long. The camera preceded the actor for nearly 250 feet as he sang a song accompanied by a piano playing outside the stage. The pianist,

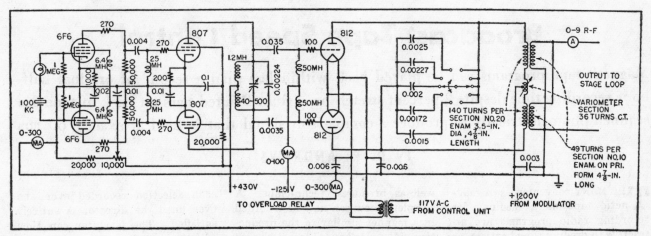

FIG. 2—Circuit diagram of the r-f portion of the 100-kc induction-type transmitter

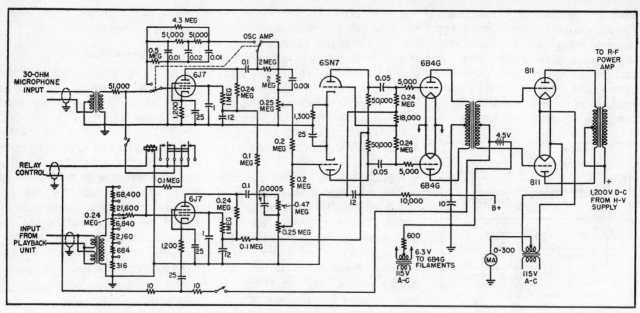

FIG. 3—Speech amplifier and modulator circuit diagram. Equalization is adjusted for loudness rather than for quality

wearing phones bridged across the sound recording system heard the singer; the singer heard the piano music through his concealed receiver, but the sound recording microphone heard only the singer's voice. The orchestra was added later. For this scene two rectangular loops, each 20 feet wide by 125 feet long, were used. They were placed end to end, with a few feet of overlap, properly phased, and connected in parallel. The wire was buried an inch below a dirt surface. An excellent signal resulted.

During the experimental stages of the magnetic-field transmitter design, tests were made whereby the audio signal was applied directly to a transmitting loop while the receivers were used without the demodulating crystal diodes. Such a system worked and certainly was less complex and less expensive than the 100-kilocycle carrier system. However, no method was found to prevent interference with the sound recording system where the unwanted signal was picked up not only in the sound-recording microphone circuit, but also in all low-level audio equipment in the vicinity of the loop.

With the 100-kilocycle system little interference is encountered, although the sound-recording micro-phone and its preamplifier are within the field, because the recording system's response rapidly decreases at frequencies above 15 kilocycles, and the 100-kilocycle signal will only be demodulated in the recording system if an audio stage is nonlinear, or overloaded. If a more than ordinary amount of low-level equipment is used within the field, or there is cable shield trouble, some interference may be heard but it is readily removed by small plug-in filters.

The writers wish to acknowledge the assistance and valuable suggestions of Loren L. Ryder, Director of Recording of Paramount Pictures, Inc.

Broadcast Tape Speed Control

Magnetic-tape programs can be played back within less than a second of original half-hour recording time despite 2-percent stretch or shrink. Printed bars on back of tape are scanned photoelectrically to produce a comparison signal that is held at exactly 60 cps

By D. R. ANDREWS

THE MANY conveniences of magnetic tape as a medium for recording radio programs are attractive to producers and artists, as well as broadcast technicians. A complete show can now be recorded in a manner similar to the production of a Hollywood movie, with each selection recorded over and over until the director is entirely satisfied. The producer can then edit the recordings to produce precisely the type of show he desires. Fluffs may be easily removed and replaced. This practice provides a freedom of expression for the artist that is extremely convenient. During the editing process the show can be carefully timed so that it will be completed without sacrificing valuable commercial time.

To insure desirable continuity, the program must be timed within one second in a half hour. The dimensional stability of plastic-base tape is not sufficient to guarantee that the recorded time will be maintained to such close tolerances during reproduction of the program.

Conditions of temperature and humidity as well as tension affect the physical dimensions of plastic materials. These dimensional changes may increase with time.

Therefore, programs that are shipped to other locations having different climatic conditions or those stored for long periods of time may suffer severely in this respect. In such cases, the time required for reproducing the program may vary considerably from the recording time.

Timing Controls

Several different methods of controlling the playing time of tape recordings have been suggested or tried. One utilizes transverse magnetization to record a reference signal on the tape during the recording of the program.[1] This effect is accomplished by rotating the signal recording head 90 degrees so that the gap is placed parallel to the direction of tape travel. The signal recorded in this manner is reproduced during playback by a similarly oriented head and is used for synchronizing purposes.

A second system[2] makes use of a 14-kc carrier that is modulated with a timing signal. During reproduction, the carrier is filtered from the program signal and after demodulation is used for synchronization.

The system we have developed utilizes optical markings to furnish the timing signal. Since the signal

markings are not magnetic, no unwanted signal is generated in the reproducing head by the additional information stored on the recording medium.

The signal is produced by equally spaced bars, printed on the reverse side of the tape, as they are scanned with an optical transducer. This transducer comprises an extremely simple optical system. A grid, placed directly over the printed side of the tape, consists of a mask with one or more holes to correspond with the markings on the tape. A light source is directed towards the grid and as the tape changes in color beneath the hole in the grid, more or less light is reflected back into a photocell.

Figure 1 shows a cut-away view of a scanner to illustrate the operation of such an optical system. Part of the light from source B goes through the aperture or grid C onto the tape A. The intensity of the light reflected back to the photocell D is partially governed by the color and gloss of the tape surface. The printed markings therefore produce a signal in the photocell whose frequency is directly proportional to the speed of the tape past the aperture.

The signal generated by the motion of the tape must be compared with some standard or reference frequency, which may be obtained from a regular power supply or from a stable clock-circuit power supply. Some large broadcasting studios have the latter to insure the accuracy of clocks used for program timing. Since available clock motors are designed to operate on 60 cps and the NAB standard tape speed is fifteen inches per second, the markings on the tape are placed at four bars per inch. If it is desirable to operate the tape at the secondary standard of 7.5 inches per second, the marking of four bars per inch may still be used to produce a 60-cps signal by means of a frequency-doubling circuit.

Comparing Speeds

Several methods of comparison between reference and photocell

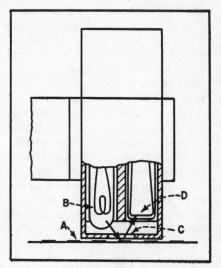

FIG. 1—Light from lamp B reaches photocell D by reflection from tape A

frequencies could have been used. One utilizes a simple beat note for driving the capstan motor. The signal from the photocell is mixed with a signal of twice the reference frequency and the beat note produced will then vary in frequency inversely with the frequency of the photocell signal. This system decreases the error but can never introduce sufficient compensation for complete correction.

A second method uses a two-phase motor as an integrator. The signal from the reference frequency is used to furnish power for one winding of a two-phase capstan motor. The signal furnished by the motion of the tape is amplified to excite the second winding of the motor. If the phase of the current through the first winding leads that of the current in the second winding, the torque of the motor is increased, and conversely, if the phase of the current through the second winding leads that of the current in the first winding, the torque of the motor is decreased. Such a system, however, is an instantaneous or phase-integrating device and does not furnish the time-integrating system desirable for broadcast timing.

Small, fast deviations may produce extremely high percentages of wow. This fact makes it imperative that any correction in speed be accomplished at a very slow rate.

A third method providing a slow time-integrating device may be designed using two synchronous clock motors. One operates from the clock power supply, using no more than 4 watts from this source. A second clock motor operates from the signal generated by the photocell, with rotation counter to that of the first motor. The shafts of the two clock motors are joined by a flexible coupling. As long as the two frequencies governing the speed of the two motors are identical nothing happens, but any difference in the two frequencies causes the frame of one of the motors to rotate with respect to the frame of the second one. This might be described as a simple mechanical differential, which needs no special gears or precision parts.

Capstan Speed Correction

The rotation of the clock frame may be utilized in a number of different ways to obtain correction of the capstan speed. One scheme is mechanically to shift a belt sideways on a tapered pulley. Such a method provides surprisingly accurate correction for timing purposes.

A second mechanical method may be arranged by driving a disk with a friction roller. Speed corrections may be introduced by shifting the roller radially with respect to the disk. The timing with such a system may be controlled very satisfactorily. Such a method is again handicapped with inherent mechanical difficulties that introduce wow in the program material. The precision necessary in the construction of such a device to overcome these difficulties would probably make the cost prohibitive.

Any type of mechanical system is handicapped because the mechanical power developed by standard clock motors is extremely limited.

Overdrive System

The dual clock-motor integrating system may be used satisfactorily by providing an electronic correcting system. One means of doing

this is to have the speed of the capstan slightly more than required to drive the tape at the desired speed. The capstan may then be slowed down to the proper speed by an electronic brake. The power delivered to the electronic brake may be controlled by the rotation produced by the dual clock-motor differential.

There is one serious difficulty encountered in using any type of overdriven system. If, for any reason, it is desirable to record or reproduce tape without synchronization, the machine will be operated at some speed that is higher than normal, making the system incompatible with standard unmarked tape. This incompatibility can be eliminated by driving the capstan with a synchronous motor as shown in Fig. 2. The motor is driven with a power source of variable frequency when utilizing the synchronizing system, or with fixed-frequency power at other times.

The motion of the dual clock-motor differential is used to vary the frequency of a local oscillator having a mean frequency of approximately 60 cps. The signal from the oscillator is amplified with an inexpensive narrow-band power amplifier to drive the capstan motor. A relay is also incorporated so that the input signal to the power ampli-

fier is derived from the local oscillator when the optically marked tape is used. If standard unmarked tape is used, the signal that drives the capstan motor is automatically derived from the clock circuit or other exact reference frequency.

The circuit diagram of the photocell amplifier is shown in Fig. 3. The exciter lamp in the scanning unit must be heated with either direct current or alternating current having a frequency that will not interfere with the operation of the clock motor driven by the signal from the photocell.

Exciter Voltage

Direct current for the exciter lamp might be obtained simply by inserting it in series with the amplifier power supply. However, if such a method is used, it is extremely difficult to filter the power supply sufficiently to eliminate low-frequency feedback effects or motorboating. This difficulty was avoided by using a high-voltage, low-current lamp and connecting it in the bleeder circuit of the d-c power supply.

This particular lamp was designed to be operated with 55 v and 0.047 amp. Many such lamps are now available requiring currents as low as 0.032 amp.

The photocell selected is a lead

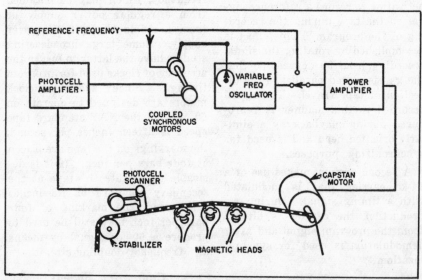

FIG. 2—Block diagram of the final system in which closed-circuit servo operates capstan motor so that signal from tape is exactly 60 cps

sulphide type of small physical dimensions. The glass bulb of the particular one chosen measures only $\frac{5}{8}$ inch long and $\frac{1}{4}$ inch in diameter. Cadmium sulphide cells are available in even smaller sizes (approxi-

operated at half speed or 7.5 inches per sec, the signal is diverted through a frequency-doubling circuit (Fig. 3B). This circuit consists of an amplifier, to regain the losses caused by the other stages;

ance-capacitance filters as well as by a capacitor tuning the inductance of the clock motor itself. Changes in the waveform of the signal are indicated on different sections of the diagram. Signals

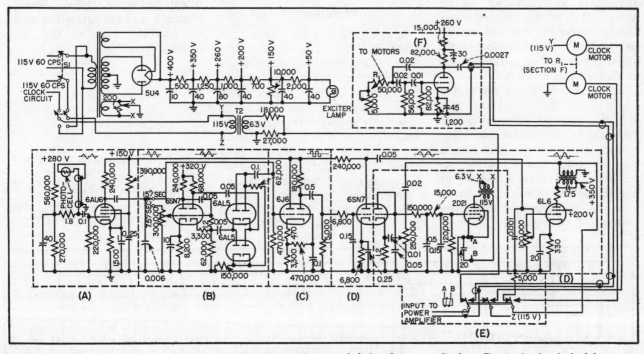

FIG. 3—Complete circuit diagram showing approximate waveforms and their relative amplitudes. Circuits in the dashed boxes are individually described in the text

mately $\frac{1}{4}$-inch cube). The lead sulphide type was chosen also because of its sensitivity at the red end of the visible spectrum.

Since all the better quality plastic-base tapes are coated with ferric oxide, their color is a reddish brown. The markings can be printed on this color with black ink and produce good contrast when scanned with a red-sensitive photocell. If black tape is used with white markings, the contrast is also sufficient with the same photocell.

The lead sulphide photocell has an internal resistance that varies inversely with the light applied to its sensitive area. The circuit requires a voltage supplied through a load resistance or inductance in the same manner as the anode of a vacuum tube.

The output from the photocell is fed to a conventional preamplifier (Fig. 3A). If the tape is being

an isolation stage, to provide balanced input for the bridge; and a full-wave bridge-type rectifier, to provide the frequency doubling. The gain of the amplifier is so adjusted that the output signal has approximately the same level as that of the input but at twice the frequency.

The output from the frequency-doubling circuit or preamplifier, as the case may be, is passed through a limiter or clipper circuit (Fig. 3C). This circuit provides an output of constant amplitude even though the input signal may vary as much as five to one.

The output from the clipping circuit is then amplified sufficiently to operate one of the clock motors (Fig. 3D). Since the signal is changed to approximately a square wave in the clipping circuit, it is necessary to reshape the signal in the amplifier circuits. A nearly sinusoidal signal is provided by resist-

from the photocell and preamplifier are shown for a tape speed of 15 in. per second.

Control Relay

The relay that stops the clock motors and switches the signal for the capstan motor is electronically controlled (Fig. 3E). The coil is in series with the cathode circuit of a thyratron tube and the relay is normally energized. When the grid of the thyratron is biased negatively, the tube is cut off and the relay is denergized.

Bias for the thyratron is furnished by rectifying some of the signal generated by the photocell. The signal is furnished to the diode rectifier through a high-pass filter network from the output of the power amplifier stage. This filter network may be adjusted so the relay will become de-energized as the frequency of the photocell signal approaches 60 cps.

The variable-frequency oscillator (Fig. 3F), furnishing the signal for the capstan motor, uses an R-C circuit of the phase-shift type. Three R-C phase-shifting elements are used, with each unit shifting the phase approximately 60 degrees. One of the resistance elements is varied with the motion developed by the dual clock-motor differential, and so drifts the frequency of the oscillator.

It may be noted that the impedances of the R-C circuits are kept as low as possible. This precaution was used to decrease the possibility of hum pickup in the grid circuit. Any oscillator has a tendency to lock-in on any signal appearing on the grid of the tube. If lock-in occurs, the usefulness of the entire system will be jeopardized.

No circuit is shown for the power amplifier needed to drive the capstan motor. A conventional audio power amplifier may be used or a much simpler narrow-band amplifier could be constructed.

Performance

Repeated timing tests have been made with this synchronizing system. A synchronized tape was recorded with timing markers exactly 15 minutes apart. Reproduction of this tape was again timed. The timer was operated from the same source of power as that furnishing the reference frequency in both cases. The greatest differential between recording and reproducing time in several tests was 0.3 second. This error might be reduced still further at the expense of speed variation or wow. A recovery rate was selected so that any speed changes would occur as slow drift and not be detected as wow.

The curve in Fig. 4 depicts the recovery rate of tape speed after an intentional error that had been introduced into the correcting device by manually rotating the clock-motor differential.

REFERENCES

(1) R. H. Ranger, Sprocketless synchronous magnetic tape, *Jour. SMPTE,* Mar. 1950.

(2) D. G. C. Hare & W. D. Fling, Picture-synchronous magnetic tape recording, *Jour. SMPTE,* May 1950.

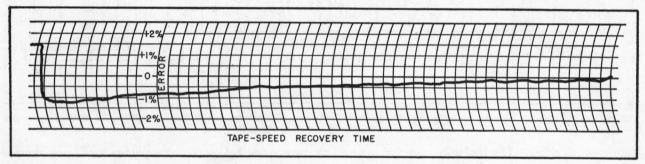

FIG. 4—Recovery time after drastic intentional error was introduced into the system

CATHODE-RAY TUBES

Measurement Method for Picture Tubes

The relationship between screen brightness and input voltage is approximated by a power law, with the exponent 2.2 for the 10BP4 and 2.5 for the 10FP4. The exponents indicate the transfer characteristic when the maximum brightness is also given

By M. W. BALDWIN

IN CONSIDERING the picture tube as a circuit element in a television circuit, it is necessary to know how video signals are transmitted through the tube.

The only characteristic to be considered here is the one relating output amplitude (brightness) to input amplitude (voltage), sometimes called the transfer characteristic. Picture tubes have other important characteristics, chiefly frequency effects associated with spot size and contrast effects due to internal reflections of light, but these may safely be ignored in the method of measurement that follows.

Sample characteristics measured by this method are shown in Fig. 1. The things to note are the large range of brightness values, nearly 1,000 to 1 for the newer tube, and the good fit of the points to a smooth curve. This smoothness is inherent in the nature of the quantity actually measured, namely the logarithmic derivative of the brightness-voltage curve.

This quantity is immune to the small fluctuations, introduced by line voltage variations, that often interfere with direct measurement of brightness and voltage. Also, the process of integrating the logarithmic derivative into the brightness-voltage function is in itself a smoothing operation.

Circuit

The method of measuring the

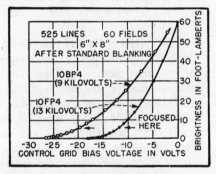

FIG. 1—Sample characteristics of the 10BP4 and 10FP4

logarithmic derivative is shown in Fig. 2. The cathode of the picture tube is connected to an auxiliary circuit carrying an on-off d-c signal controlled by a mechanically operated switch. The amount of signal required on the cathode ranges from about 0.2 volt to about 2 volts.

The control grid of the picture tube is fed, through a suitable coupling capacitor, an all-white composite picture signal of standard form and appropriate amplitude. The usual deflection signals are ap-

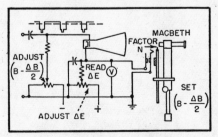

FIG. 2 — Circuit for measuring the logarithmic derivative

plied to produce a normal television raster on the screen. The brightness of this raster is controlled by adjustment of the bias on the control grid.

Incremental changes in screen brightness are made by the cathode signal, poled up so that the screen is brighter when the signal is off. The cathode signal is turned off, and the screen consequently brightened, by a switch at the Macbeth Illuminometer shown on the right in Fig. 2. This action coincides with the mechanical insertion of a light neutral filter into the optical path between the picture screen and the Illuminometer. Opposing factors thus operate on the brightness seen through the Illuminometer eyepiece —the cathode signal acting to increase it, the neutral filter acting simultaneously to decrease it. There is thus a particular value of cathode signal that yields a null result when the neutral filter is moved either into or out of the optical path. Finding that value of ΔE by successive trials constitutes the measurement.

There are two reasons for this particular arrangement: it saves recording time by having the value of ΔE appear on the voltmeter when the neutral filter is in its rest position out of the optical path, and it avoids the possibility of error in ΔE due to cathode current in the picture tube.

When this null condition exists,

the various quantities appearing in Fig. 2 are related as shown in Fig. 3. The screen brightness takes on

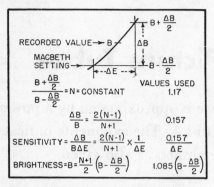

FIG. 3—Relation of quantities shown in Fig. 2 when proper cathode signal is found

two values, $B + (\Delta B)/2$ when the neutral filter is in, $B - (\Delta B)/2$ when it is out, and these two values stand in the constant ratio N fixed by the filter.

What is seen through the Macbeth eye piece is always the lower value. Since neither ΔB nor ΔE is infinitesimal, the exact value of brightness at which their ratio represents the derivative is unknown. However, the overall accuracy of the measurement is not compromised if the arithmetic average B is taken in place of the exact value. The ratio $(\Delta B)/(B\Delta E)$ is then taken to be the logarithmic derivative, and is here called the sensitivity. A higher value of sensitivity requires a smaller value of signal voltage to produce a given visibility of brightness change on the screen.

Sensitivity Curves

Measured sensitivity curves are shown in Fig. 4. The significant aspect is that they are nearly straight lines on this log-log plot. It follows that the derived relationship between brightness and voltage (Fig. 1) may be approximated by a power law, with the exponent 2.2

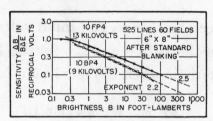

FIG. 4—Measured sensitivity curves are nearly straight lines

for the 10BP4 or 2.5 for the 10FP4. These exponents specify the characteristic of a picture tube concisely and adequately if the maximum usable brightness is also stated.

The slope of a log-log plot of sensitivity against brightness is related in simple fashion to the exponent of the corresponding power law. If the power law is $B = E^n$ and if we take the logarithmic derivative as a good approximation to the measured sensitivity:

$$S = \frac{\Delta B}{B\Delta E} = \frac{dB}{BdE} = nB^{-1/n}$$

then: $\log S = \log n - 1/n \log B$ and the slope of the log-log plot is $-1/n$. The higher the exponent, the smaller the value of the slope. When the exponent is infinite the slope is zero, and in this limiting case the power law becomes an ex-

ponential law:

$$B = a^E$$

$$S = \frac{\Delta B}{B\Delta E} = \frac{dB}{BdE} = \ln a$$

and $\log S$ is independent of $\log B$.

The measured sensitivity curves are integrated by straightforward step-by-step summation of small voltage differences, working downward from the maximum brightness we decide to call usable. Taking the 10FP4 curve in Fig. 1 as an example, we start at 60 footlamberts and make the first step down to 40 footlamberts.

For an average of the sensitivity over this step, take its value at 50 footlamberts, the mid-point. That is, take $(\Delta B)/(B\Delta E)$ to be 0.134 per volt. The brightness step ΔB is minus 20 footlamberts, the average brightness B is 50 footlamberts, and the voltage step ΔE turns out to be -3.0 volts. So we plot the 40 footlambert point 3.0 volts away from the 60 footlambert point, in the negative direction.

The second step is down to 30 footlamberts. At the mid-point, 35 footlamberts, $(\Delta B)/(B\Delta E)$ is 0.156 per volt. For this 10 footlambert step, the second voltage step ΔE is -1.8 volts. The 30 footlambert point is plotted 4.8 volts away from the 60 footlambert point, in the negative direction; and so on down the curve.

The neutral filter is made of two clear microscope cover glasses, comprising four air-glass reflecting surfaces. Its measured visual density is 0.07 (transmission 85 percent, factor $N = 1.17$).

General-Purpose Precision Oscilloscope

Extreme versatility, especially for detailed study of television waveforms, is achieved through use of high-voltage cathode-ray tube, wide-band vertical deflection amplifier, sweep circuit providing a wide range of driven sweep speeds, and a calibrated delay circuit

By R. P. ABBENHOUSE

PRECISE MEASUREMENTS of a wide range of time intervals associated with complex electrical or electronic phenomena are possible with the instrument described in this article. Because of the combination of functions available, it should find wide application in the industrial or academic laboratory for general-purpose development and research.

Suitable combinations of fairly well-known circuits provide, basically, a cathode-ray tube operating at a high accelerating potential, a wide-band vertical-deflection amplifier, a horizontal-sweep generator having a wide range of sweep speeds, a precision delay function, and suitable auxiliary functions for flexibility of operation. In addi-

tion, special provision is made for television applications where it is often of interest or a necessity to determine the precise voltage-time characteristics of the standard television waveform as it is reproduced by television facilities. In fact, the television application was the prime mover in the development of this instrument, while general-purpose applications were a natural outgrowth of the functions that became available.

The primary objective in the development of the instrument was to devise some means for observing television waveforms in greater detail than is possible with ordinary types. It was also considered important to provide as many of the functions as practicable for

tests of television facilities according to the standards of television broadcasting. The detailed observation of television waveforms or small portions thereof requires a suitable wide-band deflection amplifier. Since operation of fast sweeps at low repetition frequencies was anticipated, the use of a high-voltage cathode-ray tube became a practical necessity to obtain a trace of sufficient brightness under such conditions for either visual observation or photographic recording. Then by adding another control knob or two the available functions could be utilized for more general applications in other fields.

The final result of the development program is the instrument shown in the photograph. The indi-

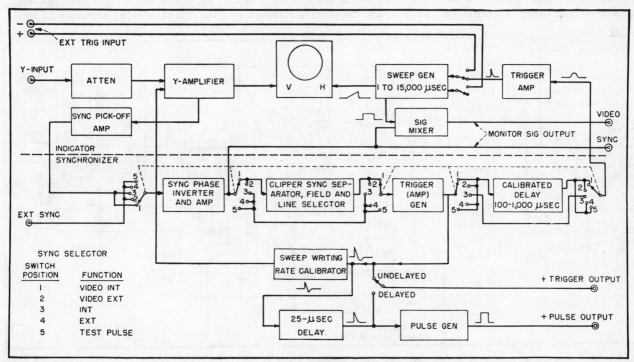

FIG. 1—Block diagram of general-purpose precision oscilloscope. Section above dashed line comprises indicator unit, while that below shows synchronizing circuits

cator unit and necessary controls are mounted at eye level for convenience of operation and viewing.

General Description

A complete description of every detail of the performance specifications is beyond the scope of this article. Rather, the more significant features will be pointed out.

As previously mentioned, the basis of the instrument consists of a combination of a high-voltage cathode-ray tube, a wide-band vertical deflection amplifier, a sweep circuit providing a wide range of driven sweep speeds, and a calibrated delay circuit of suitable precision for maximum utility of the instrument. It is of interest to consider the principal features of this combination. Later in this discussion, the auxiliary functions necessary to make this combination of practical use will be outlined. Figure 1 represents the block diagram of the instrument indicating the nature of these functions and shows them in their proper relation.

The block diagram is seen to be divided into two parts by means of a dashed line. Those blocks above the line comprise the circuits of the cathode-ray indicator unit mounted

in the upper portion of the rack. The cathode-ray tube itself is thus at a convenient level for observation while standing in front of the equipment or while the operator is seated on a standard laboratory chair.

The lower portion of the block diagram comprises the synchronizing facilities providing for various modes of indicator sweep operation. These circuits are located in the next lower portion of the rack panel space at a convenient level for easy operation of controls. All power supplies are in the lower portion of the rack.

The following discussion considers the indicator and synchronizer units separately as delineated in the block diagram shown in Fig. 1.

The cathode-ray tube used in the indicator unit is the type 5RPA[1] and is operated at a total accelerating potential of from 7 to 12 kilovolts, two kilovolts of which are applied between cathode and second anode elements. The positive accelerating potential is obtained from a rectified radio-frequency voltage supply whose output is variable from 5 to 10 kv.

Experimental data shows that, aside from limitations imposed by

the deflection amplifier, the maximum possible visible writing rate for these conditions, using a P2 screen, for example, is better by a factor of approximately 2.5 to 7 as compared to older tube types operating at maximum ratings of 4,400 volts acceleration. The use of a

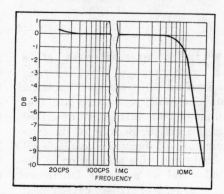

FIG. 3—Steady-state response curve for vertical amplifier

cathode-ray tube with a P2 screen is desirable in this equipment, since it has been found to be suitable as an all-purpose screen when operated at such high accelerating potentials. This is because the P2 screen combines long-persistent characteristics for high-speed low repetition-rate phenomena with high light output efficiency as com-

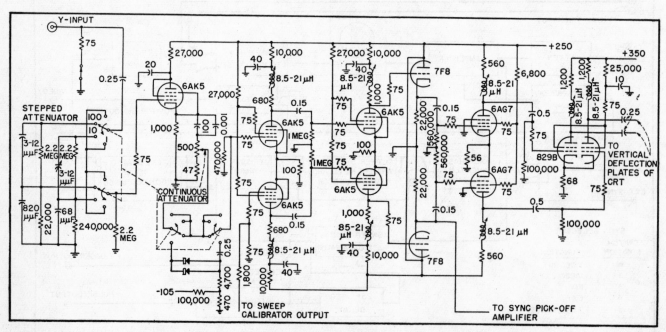

FIG. 2—Circuit diagram of wide-band vertical amplifier which employs shunt peaking adjusted to minimize transient overshoot and nonlinearity of phase shift

pared with other screen materials. For maximum efficiency in photographic recording, however, a cathode-ray tube having a P11 screen is usually used to obtain maximum advantage of such factors as actinic intensity, film sensitivity and film development techniques[2].

Operation at even higher acceleration potentials in this equipment is sometimes desirable and even possible as will be pointed out later, but additional sacrifice must then be taken in deflection sensitivity because of the decrease in deflection sensitivity as accelerating potential is increased.

Vertical Amplifier

The vertical deflection amplifier used in the indicator unit is a conventional push-pull circuit shown in Fig. 2, utilizing an 829B beam tetrode in the output stage. Preceding the output stage are two push-pull 6AK5 stages and a cathode-follower-driven push-pull 6AG7 stage which drives the 829B.

Shunt peaking is used throughout and adjusted slightly below optimum to minimize transient overshoot and nonlinearity of phase shift over the frequency range covered by this circuit. Phase inversion from unbalanced input is accomplished in the first stage with complete balance accumulated in the remaining stages. The first stage is isolated from the input terminal by a high-impedance stepped attenuator of 100 to 1, 10 to 1 and unity attenuation and a cathode follower. The cathode follower feeds a linear gain control arranged so that an additional attenuation of 10 to 1 is obtained at minimum gain. Input impedance is nominally 2.2 megohms shunted by 25 $\mu\mu$f. As a convenience in television applications, the input impedance may be reduced to 75 ohms by means of a toggle switch to match the standard signal distribution lines in a television system.

The performance of this amplifier is such that the minimum rise time that can be observed is 0.04 to 0.045 microsecond. As shown in Fig. 3, sinusoidal response is at-

tenuated 2 db at 10 mc from 1-mc response. Low-frequency response is such that a 20-cps square wave will have a sawtooth distortion of 10 percent or less. This performance is obtained with a gain of approximately 560, resulting in a deflection factor of 0.1-volt rms per inch of peak-to-peak deflection with a total of 12 kilovolts applied to the cathode-ray tube.

Horizontal Sweep

The driven horizontal sweep provides a time base linear to within 5 percent or less over a continuous range of from 15,000 to 1-micro-

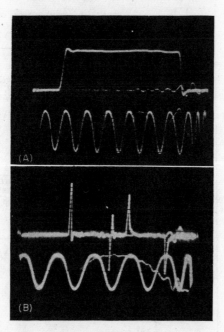

FIG. 4—Oscillograms showing (A) test pulse output with 0.2-μsec calibrating signal and (B) transmission line test with differentiated test pulse and calibrating signal

second duration for four or more inches of deflection. This corresponds to a maximum sweep speed of 4 inches per microsecond. The circuit used is known in some circles as the bootstrap sawtooth generator, and with suitable alteration provides a sweep whose speed may be varied practically continuously over the entire range.

The sweep may be initiated, (as shown in the block diagram of Fig. 1) either externally or internally. External initiation is by means of

a positive or negative trigger signal applied to terminals on the indicator panel suitably connected into the circuit by a panel switch. Internal initiation is accomplished by means of a triggering signal obtained from the synchronizer unit which in turn may be controlled by the signal applied to the vertical-deflection-amplifier input or a signal applied to an external sync terminal on the synchronizer. The sweep starting-time delay through the vertical deflection amplifier, and consequently the synchronizer circuit, is usually not more than 0.5 microsecond, while starting-time delay for direct external sweep triggering is about 0.1 microsecond or less, depending somewhat on trigger rise time.

The problem of signal delay to allow sufficient sweep starting time was considered in the development of the instrument. Because of the stringent requirements of uniform frequency characteristics over the wide response band of the amplifier, such a delay device proved unavailable at reasonable cost.

Synchronizer Unit

The synchronizer unit provides, basically, the function of timing the occurrence of the indicator sweep with respect to a reference time. Essentially two methods of precise timing are available. These consist of a time-calibrating marker oscillator to be described later, and a precision delay circuit delaying the occurrence of the sweep with respect to a reference trigger. This circuit consists of a temperature and linearity-compensated sawtooth generator whose output is compared in amplitude with a regulated d-c voltage[3]. The d-c voltage level is controlled by a 10-turn helical potentiometer having a high degree of linearity. Amplification of the signal resulting from this comparison results in a signal which, when differentiated, is used to trigger the indicator sweep. Two delay ranges are provided; namely 100 and 1,000 microseconds. Time delay between an initiating trigger and the start of the cathode-ray tube sweep is read on a dial controlling the 10-turn potentiometer, and readings are accurate to within plus or minus 0.1 percent full scale. The dial is mounted near the cathode-ray tube on the indicator panel for convenience in operation.

To provide versatility in the control of the sweep-timing functions in the synchronizer unit, certain auxiliary features are available and are described in the following paragraphs.

Internal Triggering

A trigger generator utilizing a blocking oscillator circuit is provided to operate the circuits of the instrument at repetition rates between 120 and 3,000 pps. This circuit, labelled TRIGGER (AMPLIFIER) GENERATOR in the synchronizer portion of the block diagram, may also be used optionally as a trigger amplifier by suitable switching of blocking grid bias. It is preceded by a sync amplifier, and phase selector so that the operation of the circuits may be initiated by external signals of either polarity applied to an external sync terminal or through the vertical deflection amplifier. A trigger from this circuit is available at a front panel terminal and may be either undelayed or delayed 25 microseconds with respect to the generator output. This delay provision is intended for use in so called synchroscope applications where the internal trigger generator is used for initiating or synchronizing purposes.

The operation of the calibrated delay circuit is initiated by the output of the trigger generator, whether used as such or as a trigger amplifier. This circuit thus serves to provide the reference trigger for all subsequent time measurements. The use of the delayed-trigger output results in the possibility of observing before and after a subsequent circuit operation as well as to measure the time duration of such operation by suitable adjustment of the calibrated delay.

For purposes of sweep-speed calibration, a sine-wave-gated oscillator is provided which furnishes

either 10, 1, or 0.2-microsecond intervals in the form of vertical deflections available at any time independently of the normal deflection amplifier input signal. Some care was taken in temperature compensating this circuit to increase its accuracy over long periods. As a result, one-percent accuracy of calibration is obtained.

Television Circuits

A combination of circuits intended strictly for television applications is provided and is shown

plifier. Video content of any line may thus be observed and measured in terms of test-pattern resolution, video i-f transient response and other characteristics not readily displayed by ordinary methods. The exact form of the synchronizing pulses may also be measured to accuracies required by the present Standards of Good Engineering Practice as defined by both the Federal Communications Commission and the RMA.

In this combination of circuits the operations employed to accom-

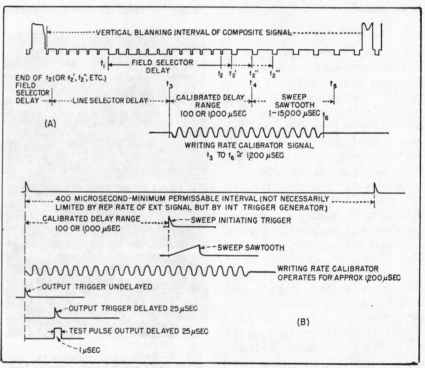

FIG. 5—Time sequence of circuit operation for the two principle types of application (A) Timing television synchronizing and video waveforms, and (B) General purpose timing

on the block diagram (Fig. 1) as CLIPPER, SYNC SEPARATOR, and FIELD and LINE SELECTOR. This combination of circuits, is inserted by means of a sync-selector switch between the sync phase inverter and amplifier and the trigger (amplifier) generator. When the instrument is used in connection with television facilities, either studio or receiving, any one of the 525 horizontal scanning lines of the television raster can be selected for detailed observation in expanded form through the vertical deflection am-

plish the function of line selection in terms of the television composite signal consist mainly of clipping off the video portion of the signal; separating out vertical sync; integrating, amplifying, and differentiating it; triggering a delay multivibrator, a blocking oscillator, and another delay multivibrator; and finally applying the differentiated output of the last-mentioned multivibrator to the trigger amplifier described above. Furthermore, in the application of these multivibrator and blocking-oscillator circuits, use is made of the difference between the alternate and interlaced field signals.

Since the line selector delays the sweep trigger in increments of a scanning line, the calibrated delay circuit is utilized to give continuous and smooth delay over the range of one or more lines. To stabilize the final line selector delay multivibrator against jitter inherent in such a circuit, a suitable amount of composite sync is applied to the timing portion of the circuit. This results in a timing error of only 0.02 microsecond or less, allowing full scale expansion of a pulse such as an equalizer through the sweep-speed control without serious conditions of pattern jitter.

Marker Pulses

As an auxiliary feature for television applications, a marker pulse is available at an output terminal on the indicator chassis which corresponds to the sweep in time. This pulse is mixed with a television composite signal when applied to the vertical-amplifier input terminal. This can be applied to a television monitor with the pulse serving as a marker to indicate the portion of the television video under observation on the horizontal sweep.

A test pulse is also available at a front panel terminal for use in testing amplifier circuits on a transient basis. This pulse is of approximately 1-microsecond duration and has a rise time of something less than 0.02 microsecond, and it is generated by a well-known circuit consisting of two tetrode thyratrons in tandem with a lumped-constant delay line to form the pulse in one of the plate circuits. It is available at 75 ohms or less impedance and variable in amplitude up to 20 volts peak and is initiated by a trigger which is delayed approximately 25 microseconds with respect to the reference trigger.

Figure 4A is an oscillogram of this pulse on a sweep of approximately 1.5 microsecond, with Fig. 4B illustrating one of the many

uses of this pulse. This particular application is a transmission-line test in which the pulse is differentiated and then applied to the line. The leading-edge pip is about 0.07 microsecond wide at 10-percent amplitude. The results shown here indicate a line short-circuited at the far end because of the negative reflection of the leading edge pip to the right of the differentiated trailing edge. The time between the initial leading edge and the first reflection measured at 10-percent amplitude points can then be measured accurately to determine certain electrical characteristics of the line.

All of the above auxiliary func-

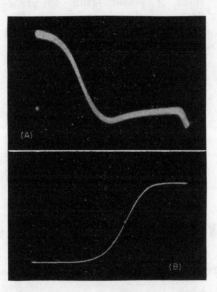

FIG. 6—Voltage waveforms (A) across an electronic photo-flash lamp (15,000-μsec sweep) and (B) voltage rise across same lamp with 10-μsec sweep

tions are suitably combined in the instrument by appropriate switching of various stages.

Applications

Figure 5 shows the time sequence of circuit operation for the two principal types of application of the instrument.

The top portion of Fig. 5 indicates the timing of the horizontal sweep of the instrument with respect to the configuration of the television synchronizing and video waveform. In this case the sync

selector switch in the synchronizer unit sets up a combination of the phase selector; sync amplifier; clipper, sync separator, field and line selector; trigger amplifier (trigger generator operating as a driven blocking oscillator) and calibrated delay.

The sweep calibrator is also optionally available. In effect, the sweep is delayed with respect to a vertical sync pulse and used as a reference point over a range which covers one complete field of the television raster. Either of the interlaced fields may be selected, as previously mentioned, by a circuit which makes use of the half-line difference in time intervals between the last equalizer and first horizontal sync pulse in the two fields. The range of the field selector control is such that at its minimum setting the indicator sweep is triggered at 60 pps, or field frequency; and at intermediate settings the indicator sweep is triggered at 30 pps, or frame frequency. One would expect that at such a low sweep-repetition rate and with the fastest sweep applied to expand a sync pulse (for example, so that only its rise time is displayed), the trace would hardly be visible. However, a trace of sufficient brightness and adequate pattern stability is still obtainable by reason of the high beam-accelerating potential for making photographic recordings. The illustrations shown in this article are reproductions of such photographs. Figure 6B was made at a ½-second exposure using an f 3.5 lens in a camera such as the Du Mont Type 271-A.

This method of observation of the television waveform gives immediate and direct information without recourse to auxiliary equipment, tables, or nomographs.

The lower portion of Fig. 5 indicates the time sequence of circuit operation in general-purpose applications. In this case the sync selector bypasses the television circuits so that the phase selector and sync amplifier feed sync into the trigger amplifier which may now be used as either a driven or free-running blocking oscillator to provide the proper trigger voltage required by subsequent circuits depending on the situation in which it is to be used. Thus the trigger generator, while initiating the operation of the sweep circuit, either initiates the operation of external devices or is initiated, or synchronized, by the external device. If operation of the cathode-ray tube sweep is to be dependent on the signal to be observed, only 0.25 inch of deflection is needed for stable operation. This corresponds to less than 0.07 volt peak-to-peak of signal.

It is to be noted that operation similar to the ordinary oscillograph is possible since the usual internal and external sync provisions are available. However, the calibrated sweep delay is available when the external sync operation is utilized. This system allows for precision time measurement of phenomena up to 1,000 microseconds after some reference signal.

Thus, with the aid of these facilities plus the sweep calibrator, time measurements can be made of small intervals up to the ultimate resolution of the wide-band vertical amplifier and the fastest sweep available. In terms of writing speed, this turns out to be of the order of 20 inches per microsecond.

The usefulness of the instrument can be extended for some applications by applying higher accelerating potentials to the cathode-ray tube. Suitable insulation is provided so that up to 20 kilovolts may be applied by replacing the standard high-voltage power supply with another unit which has a maximum output of 25 kilovolts. In this instrument the voltage should be limited to 20 kilovolts because of a cathode-ray tube rating of 10 to 1 ratio of postdeflection to predeflection accelerating potentials. The brightness of the trace is increased by about four times by doubling the accelerating potential especially for fast single transient observations. This permits reliable photographic recording.

Figure 6 shows two oscillograms of the operation of an electronic photoflash lamp. In this case the delayed output trigger of the Type 280 is applied to the photoflash lamp circuit to initiate its operation. The timing of the circuit operations in the Type 280 is then in accordance with the lower portion of Fig. 5, so that any portion of the voltage wave appearing across the lamp can be positioned on the trace by means of the sweep delay.

The helpful assistance of Horace Atwood, Jr. under whose supervision the project was carried through the development stage is sincerely appreciated. The assistance of Melvin B. Kline in handling some of the work of the synchronizer unit is also acknowledged. Many other valuable suggestions and much other assistance was furnished by other members of the Instrument Engineering Department of the Instrument Division of Allen B. Du Mont Laboratories, Inc.

REFERENCES

(1) I. E. Lempert and R. Feldt, The 5RP Multiband Tube; An Intensifier Type Cathode-Ray Tube for High Voltage Operation, *Proc. IRE*, 34, July 1946.

(2) R. Feldt, An All-Purpose Screen for High Voltage Cathode-Ray Tubes, *The Oscillographer*, Allen B. Du Mont Laboratories, 9, July-Aug. 1947.

(3) V. A. Hughes, A Range Measuring System Using R-C Linear Sweep, Radiation Laboratory Report 540. Also Radiation Laboratory Series, 22, p 277.

Millimicrosecond Oscillography

Pulses as short as 0.5 millimicrosecond can be viewed or recorded through use of high-gain distributed amplifiers and high-vacuum linear-sweep generators. Distributed amplifiers show promise for utilization to 500 mc or higher

By Y. P. YU, H. E. KALLMAN AND P. S. CHRISTALDI

OBSERVATION and measurement of pulses of the order of 10^{-9} to 10^{-10} sec have assumed increasing importance. This paper will discuss some recent oscillographic developments in circuits for measurement of these time intervals.

Development of high-speed sweep circuits[1,2], refinements in reflection systems[3,4,5,6], and waveform analysis using signal delay systems[4] have been described in the literature. This paper is mainly concerned with the development of distributed amplifiers.

The development of amplifiers capable of satisfactory reproduction of signals containing signal components in the order of hundreds of megacycles has been hampered by the limitations imposed by practical values of transconductance, interelectrode capacitances and input loading of vacuum tubes. The suggestion of increasing effective transconductance without increasing shunt capacitance by incorporating a number of tubes into a transmission line network was made many years ago,[8] but only recently[6,9,10,11] has it been utilized to some degree. The principle of distributed amplification appears to be the most promising for use with presently available tubes and components, and a number of practical designs have been evolved.

Distributed Amplifiers

Figure 1 shows the basic circuit

of a distributed amplifier stage. Two artificial transmission lines are connected separately to plates and grids of the amplifier tubes, which become part of the lines. A signal voltage e_g applied to the input terminal is transmitted along the grid line to the grid of V_1, producing a corresponding change in plate current $g_m e_g$, which is transmitted along the plate line. When the applied signal reaches the grid of V_2, a similar change of plate current will be produced in that tube.

If the propagation constants of these two lines are equal, the signal components of plate currents produced by various tubes will arrive at the output terminal at the same time and will add. The usual undesirable effects resulting from paralleling of tube capacitances are thereby eliminated.

When resistor R_1 is made equal to the characteristic impedance of the plate line, signal currents transmitted to the left will be completely absorbed. Similarly, the applied signal e_g will also be absorbed after the grid of V_n when R_2 is made equal to the characteristic impedance of the grid line.

Practical Considerations

For simplicity, both the grid and plate lines can be made of constant-k low-pass T-sections. However, m-derived sections have at least two advantages compared with constant-k sections. First, time delay can be made substantially constant over the entire pass band with less resulting phase distortion. Second, greater shunting capacitance can be used when m is greater than unity. This would permit either greater bandwidth or higher line impedance and correspondingly higher stage gain.

The m-derived network with substantially constant time delay up to two-thirds of the cutoff frequency is known to be that with $m = 1.27$. A typical m-derived section is shown in Fig. 2 together with its equivalents. The negative inductance $-M$ in series with the shunt capacitance C results from the aiding magnetic coupling between the two halves of L.

With L and C defined as in Fig. 2, the characteristic impedance becomes

$$Z_o = \sqrt{\frac{L_k}{C_k}} = \sqrt{\frac{2_m{}^2 L}{(m^2 + 1)\,C}} \quad (1)$$

and the cutoff frequency is

$$f_c = \frac{1}{\pi C_k Z_o} = \frac{m}{\pi C Z_o} \quad (2)$$

The above expression indicates that

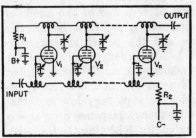

FIG. 1—Basic circuit diagram of a distributed amplifier

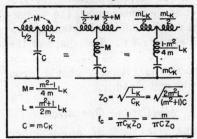

FIG. 2—Typical m-derived section and its equivalents

the cutoff frequency of an m-derived section is m times that of a constant-k section.

Bridged-T networks offer the advantage of more constant characteristic impedance, but this is offset by the need for twice the number of critical circuit elements.

The signals traveling along both the grid and plate lines are subject to losses that will cause considerable attenuation at high frequencies because of the presence of impedance in the cathode circuit and the transit-time effect.

In a distributed amplifier stage the signal at the grid of the first tube is attenuated by these losses once, at the second tube grid twice, and so forth. An analysis assumes that the signal is attenuated by α db in the first section, by 2α db in the second, and so on by $n\alpha$ db in the nth section. The effective sum of all signal components of plate currents is then reduced from $n g_m e_g$ on the output of an n-tube distributed amplifier stage to $g_m e_g (a + a^2 + \ldots + a^n)$, where $a = $ antilog $\alpha/20$. The value of this sum is $g_m e_g a (1 - a^n)/(1 - a)$ and the resulting loss in db is $20 \log a(1 - a^n)/n(1 - a)$. For a typical case of $n = 7$ and $\alpha = 0.6$ db, the resulting loss is 2.5 db.

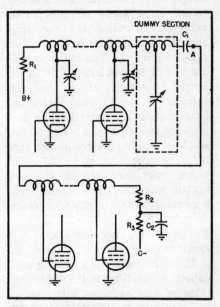

FIG. 3—Method of coupling two stages of a distributed amplifier

Plate Line Losses

Similar consideration may apply to losses in the plate line due to low plate impedance of some tubes, such as the type 6AN5, whose plate impedance is likely to be below 10,000 ohms. The losses so caused, are perhaps 0.5 db per stage.

Because of these losses there is obviously a limiting number of tubes per stage beyond which the amplification of the stage will decrease instead of increase. A mathematical analysis assuming 0.6-db losses per section in both grid and plate lines shows the gain increases very slowly after $n = 8$, becomes maximum when $n = 12$ and decreases thereafter. The effect of coil losses due to skin effect and other factors is small compared with tube losses, about 1 db for 40 sections of 200-ohm networks.

Other factors such as grid and plate-lead inductances result in lowering the amplifier cutoff frequency and in altering the characteristic impedance of the transmission lines. Fortunately, it is possible to minimize such undesirable effects to a small percentage in a well-designed amplifier.

It is important to point out that uniform amplification with respect to frequency variation cannot be obtained in a stage of distributed amplification when the receiving end of the plate line is open. The reasons are: (1) The input impedance of a transmission line is no longer constant if it is not terminated by its own characteristic impedance, thus the line impedance looking at the plates of the amplifier tubes changes as the signal frequency varies; (2) The phase relations between the reflected wave and the signal components of various plate currents change as the signal frequency varies; therefore, they may add at one frequency and subtract at another.

Since the load of an oscillograph deflection amplifier is the deflecting plate of a cathode-ray tube, which is essentially a capacitive load of

not less than 2 $\mu\mu$f, it cannot be connected directly across the terminating resistor of the output line without introducing reflections.

To avoid this undesirable effect, an additional section is used, and the deflecting plates of the cathode-ray tube are connected as part of the shunt capacitance. This capacitance is adjusted so that the total shunting capacitance is equal to that of other sections of the same line.

For amplification of pulses, the transient response of the amplifier is important, particularly the rise time and the percentage of overshoot. In order to minimize the overshoot of a multistage amplifier, it is necessary that the phase distortion be kept very low and that the frequency response drop slowly and steadily, following the Gaussian error curve. If f_1 is the frequency at the 70-percent point of the frequency response curve, the 37-percent point should be located approximately at 1.5 f_1. The shape of the response below 30 percent is not critical, but it also should drop slowly and steadily.

Multistage Operation

The rise time of an amplifier stage is approximately equal to the

ratio of $0.35/W$, where W is the 3-db bandwidth of the amplifier. For n stages, the over-all rise time is approximately equal to the square root of the sum of the squares of those of the individual stages when the percentage of overshoot is negligible. It may be noted here that the effect of an oscillograph amplifier having rise time T_a on a signal pulse having rise time T_p can be estimated from the following expression:

$$T_{\text{resultant}} = \sqrt{T_a{}^2 + T_p{}^2} \qquad (3)$$

Thus a signal pulse with a rise time of 0.01 μsec will appear to be slowed down by 11 percent in an oscillograph amplifier with $T_a = 0.005$ μsec to a resultant rise time of 0.011 μsec.

Since there must always be certain physical distances existing between stages, the inductance of the leads employed for connecting stages affects the response of the amplifier. To overcome this difficulty, additional dummy sections are used. These sections serve as a continuation of the line, with tube capacitances replaced by the increased trimmer capacitances.

Distributed amplifier stages may be coupled directly in order that response may be extended down to

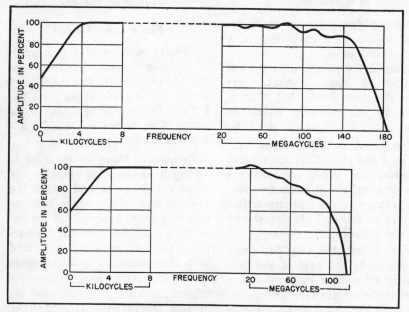

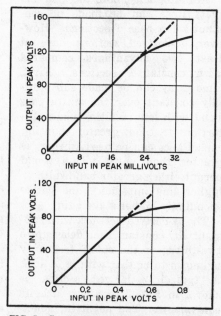

FIG. 4—Amplitude-frequency characteristics of distributed amplifier A (upper curve) and distributed amplifier B (lower curve)

FIG. 5—Amplitude-amplitude characteristics of amplifier A (upper curve) and B (lower)

d-c signals. For such operation, suitable means must be provided to overcome the difficulty of the presence of quiescent plate potential.[12] When d-c response is not required, the arrangement shown in Fig. 3 has been found suitable to allow signals of very low frequencies to pass with the use of standard components and without affecting the response at high frequencies. The physical size of the coupling capacitors should be kept as small as possible in order to avoid difficulties caused by both distributed capacitance and lead inductance of the coupling capacitor.

In Fig. 3, R_1 and R_2 are made equal to the characteristic impedance of the line, C_1 is made equal to C_2, and R_3 is made as large as possible for the type of amplifier tubes used. Under this condition, the impedance to the right of point A essentially equals that to the left except for the existence of a high resistance R_3. Theoretically, the frequency response will be uniform as long as the resistance of R_3 is very large compared with the reactance of C_2. Experimental results show that frequency response can be kept flat to as low as 200 cps even when the line impedance is 200 ohms and the coupling capacitance is only $0.01\mu f$.

Impedance transformation can be secured through the use of a stage of distributed amplification. For such operations the characteristic impedances of grid and plate lines are made respectively equal to the input and output impedances. When the stage consists of more than one tube, the propagation constants of both grid and plate lines should be made identical.

The amplification of a multistage distributed amplifier may be controlled by changing the number of stages or by inserting attenuators. The former may offer the advantage of better frequency response and shorter rise time, while the latter has been proved to be more practical in actual cases, since it minimizes the number of plug-in connections or switches required. While stage gain can also be con-

trolled by variation of grid bias, this method is undesirable because it seriously affects the amplitude-amplitude characteristic, producing nonlinearity.

Results

Two multistage distributed amplifiers are shown in the photographs. Amplifier A consists of six stages, four single-ended stages, a phase inverter, and a push-pull output stage. Amplifier B consists of a single-tube stage used as impedance transformation for coupling to a 50-ohm coaxial cable, a single-ended stage, a phase inverter, and a push-pull output stage.

The individual stages of amplifier A were designed to have their theoretical cutoff frequency at 250 mc and their time delay approximately 1.26×10^{-9} second, while those of amplifier B are at 125 mc and 2.52×10^{-9} second, respectively. The amplitude-frequency characteristics of these two amplifiers are

shown in Fig. 4, and curves showing amplitude-amplitude characteristics of both amplifiers are shown in Fig. 5.

The rise time of amplifier A was measured to be approximately 0.004 μsec and of amplifier B, 0.005 μsec by the use of a special pulse generator capable of producing square pulses of 0.012-μsec duration. The upper curve of Fig. 6 shows the shape of the applied pulse as it appeared on the screen of a cathode-ray tube. The lower curve shows the shape of the same pulse after transmission through a 50-db attenuator and distributed amplifier A. Amplifier A has a gain of approximately 5,000 and is capable of delivering a balanced undistorted output voltage of 130 volts peak to peak. Amplifier B has a gain of approximately 180 and its maximum undistorted output voltage is 85 volts peak to peak, balanced about ground. A tabulation of technical data for both amplifiers

Table I—Technical Data for Distributed Amplifier A

Stages	Tubes	Function	Grid Line Ohms	Plate Line Ohms	Plate Current in Ma	Approx. Gain	Output Volts Peak-to-Peak
1st	8 6AK5's	Preamplifier	200	200	60	4	0.1
2nd	8 6AK5's	Preamplifier	200	200	60	4	0.4
3rd	8 6AK5's	Impedance Transformation	200	125	60	2.5	1
4th	8 6AN5's	Driver	125	125	270	6.5	6.5
5th	2 6AN5's	Phase Invertor	125	125	65	1	6.5
6th	24 6AN5's	Push-Pull Output	125	200	800	20	130
Total	58 Tubes	———	200	200	1.285 amp	5,000	130

Table II—Technical Data for Distributed Amplifier B

Stages	Tubes	Function	Grid Line Ohms	Plate Line Ohms	Plate Current in Ma	Approx. Gain	Output Volts Peak-to-Peak
1st	1 6AK5	Impedance Transformation	50	400	9	2	2
2nd	5 6AK5's	Preamplifier	400	300	45	3.8	6
3rd	1 6CB6	Phase Inverter	300	300	15	1	2.5
4th	14 6CB6's	Push-Pull Output	300	520	210	23	85
Total	21 Tubes	———	50	520	279	175	85

is given in Tables I and II.

High-Speed Sweep Circuits

Since the deflection of the cathode-ray beam is accomplished by a variation of electric field potential between the horizontal deflecting plates, it is necessary to have this field potential changed at a rate dv/dt such that the spot will move at the required speed. For instance, a type 5XP cathode-ray tube operating with a second-anode potential of 4 kv and an intensifier potential of 25 kv requires approximately 300 volts change in electric field potential for one inch of horizontal deflection. The capacitance between these two plates, including wiring capacitance, is approximately 15 $\mu\mu$f. The current required for a sweep speed of 400 inches per μsec becomes $I = C\ dv/dt = 2$ amperes. This result indicates that a tube with high current capacity is required in a high-speed sweep circuit.

The requirement of high current capacity suggests immediately the use of a thyratron but time jitter is then produced on the screen of the cathode-ray tube. Furthermore, it is difficult to operate gas-tube sweeps at repetition rates above 10,000 or even 5,000 per second because of the relatively long time required for deionization.

If a high-vacuum tube is considered for use as a switch tube it will be required to conduct between successive sweeps in a conventional circuit. For high sweep speeds it becomes difficult to find a vacuum tube that can pass 2 amperes of plate current and that has interelectrode capacitances and lead inductances small enough for the highest sweep speeds desired.

A vacuum-tube sweep circuit in which the switch tube is normally cut off and conducts only during the time of sweep is shown in Fig. 7. In this circuit the switch tube V_5 is a vacuum tetrode type 4X150A. The lead inductances and interelectrode capacitances of this tube are quite small, yet its peak current capacity is over 2 amperes. If the

repetition rate is kept under 100,-000 per second, forced-air cooling of the tube is unnecessary.

Use of Tetrode

The reasons for using a tetrode instead of a triode as a switching

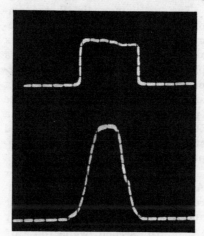

FIG. 6—Waveform of 0.012 μsec test pulse applied directly to vertical deflecting plates of cathode-ray tube (upper waveform) and same pulse after transmission through a 50-db attenuator and amplifier A (lower waveform)

tube are: (1) The input capacitance is substantially smaller because Miller effect is greatly minimized by the presence of a screen grid. This enables the sweep speed to become higher and simplifies somewhat the requirements of the trigger circuit. (2) Constant plate current can be obtained when the potential at the screen is made to

rise or fall by the same amount as that at the cathode. Constant plate current is very important when linear sweep is required. In the circuit of Fig. 7 the potential at the screen of the switch tube is made to follow that of the cathode by the use of coupling capacitor C_4.

Before the application of an input trigger pulse, all tubes are cut off. This results in low plate power consumption and permits the use of circuit components of low power rating.

When a trigger pulse is introduced to the grid of V_1, plate current flows and a positive pulse is introduced at the grid of V_2 through magnetic coupling in transformer T_1. Tube V_2 operates as a blocking oscillator. The time constant of R_1C_1 determines the width of the pulse produced by this blocking oscillator. The pulse is taken from the third winding of transformer T_1 to the grid of the cathode-ray tube for beam gating and to the input terminal of the delay cable for triggering the second blocking oscillator V_3 and V_4. Use of the delay cable was found necessary in order to have the beam on at the instant when the sweep voltage starts. The time delay introduced by the cable of Fig. 7 is about 0.02 μsec. Components C_2 and R_3 are employed as a differentiating circuit.

The time constant of $C_3\ R_5$ deter-

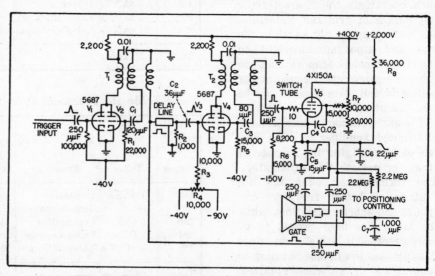

FIG. 7—Schematic diagram of high-speed sweep circuit

mines the width of the rectangular pulse on the grid of V_5. Normally, tetrode V_5 is cut off, the voltage across capacitor C_6 is equal to about 2,000 volts and the voltage across C_5 is zero. During the pulse, the grid-to-cathode potential of V_5 is driven to zero or even slightly positive. Capacitor C_6 is discharged by the plate current of V_5 and capacitor C_5 is charged by the plate and screen currents of the same tube.

Since the screen-to-cathode voltage of V_5 is kept constant by the use of coupling capacitor C_4, both plate and screen currents are expected to be essentially constant during the pulse, thus permitting substantially linear sweep voltages to be developed across C_5 and C_6.

The value of C_5 is slightly larger than that of C_6 because the current flowing to C_5 is larger than that

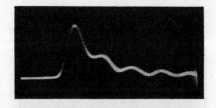

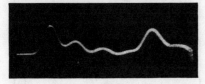

FIG. 8—Upper curve shows a 5×10^{-10} second pulse displayed on a sweep generated by the circuit of Fig. 7. Lower curve is the same pulse and its reflection produced by a 30-inch open-circuited stub of RG-58/U cable

flowing out from C_6. After the pulse, tube V_5 is cut off, capacitor C_5 discharges through R_6 and capacitor C_6 charges through R_8. The sweep speed can be changed by varying capacitors C_5 and C_6.

Experimental Results

Experimental results show that the circuit can generate a balanced sweep voltage of about 1,500 volts peak to peak. The maximum sweep speed obtainable is over 800 inches per μsec when the sweep voltage is

applied to the horizontal plates of a type 5XP cathode-ray tube with its second anode at 2,000 volts and

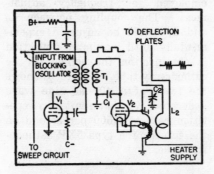

FIG. 9—Schematic diagram of high-frequency timing signal generator

third anode at 14 kilovolts. The speed is reduced by one-half when the second anode voltage is increased to 4,000 volts and the third anode is increased to 29 kilovolts. The sweep speed may be increased to 1,200 inches per microsecond when the sweep voltage is applied to the vertical deflecting plates of the cathode-ray tube.

The amount of time jitter is not more than the width of a normal trace on the cathode-ray tube and is estimated to be less than 0.0001 μsec. Departure from linearity was found to be less than 5 percent. The starting time from the instant of input trigger to the beginning of the sweep voltage is estimated to be 0.045 μsec. The maximum repetition rate is over 100,000 per second. The total consumption of plate and screen power is under 10 watts average.

Results of employing this sweep circuit to view a pulse signal of 0.5 millimicrosecond duration are shown in the curves Fig. 8. This pulse was generated by a circuit developed by the Purdue Research Foundation for the United States Air Force and the Signal Corps. The oscillations at the trailing edge of the upper pulse curve of Fig. 8 were produced by the pulse generator itself, since it employs the principle of reflection to generate narrow pulses. The lower curve of Fig. 8 shows the results of connecting a 30-inch open-circuited stub of RG-58/U coaxial cable at the signal

deflecting plates. This arrangement will allow an accurate calibration of the time axis. Since RG-58/U coaxial cable has a characteristic impedance of 53 ohms and a capacitance per foot of 28 $\mu\mu$f, the time delay will be 1.5 millimicroseconds per foot. Thus the time between the two major peaks of the lower curve of Fig. 8 is 7.5×10^{-9} second. The waveform of the pulse as shown may differ from the true waveform because of transit time effects in the cathode-ray tube and the frequency characteristic of the coaxial cable.

In order to calibrate the speed of the sweep, either a sine-wave os-

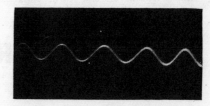

FIG. 10—A keyed 400-mc timing signal with a 2,500 prf. generated by the circuit of Fig. 9

cillator that oscillates at some known frequency or a pulse generator that produces sharp pulses at some known repetition rate can be employed to produce timing marks as vertical deflection. For sweep speeds of 400 inches per μsec, sharp pulses with rise times of less than 0.1 millimicrosecond would be required. Such pulses are difficult to generate and to apply to the deflecting plates or the control grid of the cathode-ray tube because of the leakage capacitances and inductances of all commercial circuit components involved. On the other hand, sine waves at frequencies of 1,000 mc or lower are comparatively less difficult to produce and to apply since the undesirable effects can generally be eliminated by the use of appropriate resonant circuits.

Synchronization of the timing signal to the sweep voltage is another important problem to be considered. For reasons described previously, the jitter should be less than 0.25 millimicrosecond in order to produce a satisfactory trace with a sweep speed of 400 inches per μsec. It was found that a plate-pulsed oscillator can be arranged to satisfy these requirements.

Timing Signal Generator

The schematic diagram of such a circuit is shown in Fig. 9. In this circuit, the first blocking oscillator provides a trigger pulse to the sweep circuit and at the same time serves to trigger the second blocking oscillator V_1. The output from the third winding of transformer T_1 provides the plate current needed for oscillator tube V_2. The heater of V_2 is raised above a-c ground potential by the use of a choke wound on the lower half of

coil L_1. This is necessary because the cathode of V_2 is above a-c ground potential. Capacitor C_2 is employed for frequency adjustment. The coupling between L_1 and L_2 should be adjusted experimentally until maximum deflection is obtained on the screen of the cathode-ray tube. Figure 10 shows the trace of a 400-mc sine wave generated by this circuit at a repetition rate of 2,500 per second on the screen of a type 5XP cathode-ray tube.

REFERENCES

(1) D. F. Winter, "Winterscope or Fast Sweep Synchroscope", Report 1001, Radiation Laboratory, MIT, 1946.

(2) Soller, Starr and Valley, "Cathode-Ray Tube Displays", McGraw-Hill Book Co. Inc., New York, 1948, p 288.

(3) I. E. Lempert and R. Feldt, The 5RP Multiband Tube: An Intensifier-Type Cathode-Ray Tube for High-Voltage Operation, Proc. IRE, 34, p 432, June 1946.

(4) J. V. Lebacqz, Short-time Oscillography, Proc. NEC 13, p 68, 1947.

(5) A. V. Haeff, U. S. Patent 2,064,469.

(6) M. Newman, R. P. Featherstone and P. S. Christaldi, A Cathode-Ray Oscillograph with 100-Megacycle Bandwidth, Proc. NEC. 4. p 445. 1948.

(7) J. R. Pierce, Traveling Wave Oscilloscope, ELECTRONICS, 22, p 97, Nov. 1949.

(8) W. S. Percival, British Patent 460,562.

(9) E. L. Ginzton, W. R. Hewlett, J. H. Jasberg and J. D. Noe, Distributed Amplification, Proc. IRE, 36, p 950, August 1948.

(10) F. Kennedy and H. G. Rudenberg, 200-Mc Traveling Wave Chain Amplifier, ELECTRONICS, 22, p 106, Dec. 1949.

(11) W. W. Horton, J. H. Jasberg and J. D. Noe, Distributed Amplifiers, Practical Considerations and Experimental Results, Proc. IRE, 38, p 748, July 1950.

(12) Y. P. Yu, Cathode-Follower Coupling in D-C Amplifiers, ELECTRONICS, 19, p 99, August 1946.

Aids to CRO Display of Phase Angle

By L. FLEMING

AUDIO-FREQUENCY NETWORKS are commonly measured in terms of transmission level versus frequency, without particular reference to phase angle. The use of the ordinary elliptical Lissajous figure on a cathode-ray oscilloscope screen suffers from the drawback of poor precision, and difficultly in conveniently determining the phase angle in degrees from measurements made on the elliptical display. Where the amount of work to be done justifies the fairly large cost, a direct-reading phase meter or a Z-angle meter is ideal[1,2,8]. Sulzer has described an instrument[3] for use in conjunction with a cro

to give vectorial display of voltages in the form of radial lines. Wideband phase splitters[4,5] are employed to derive a circular sweep from one signal, and Z-axis modulation of the cro is obtained from both.

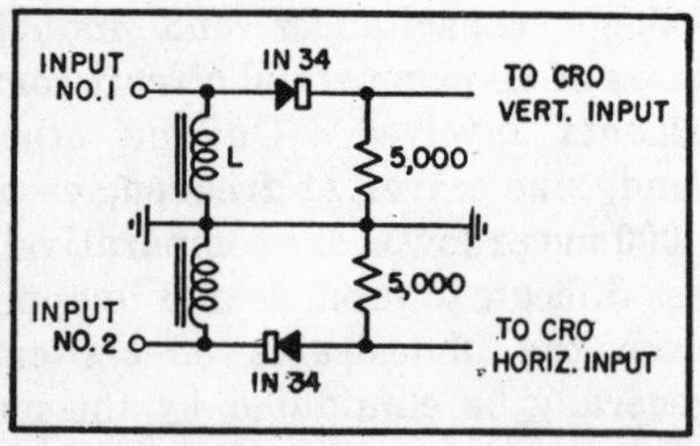

These devices are all somewhat complex. Where only occasional measurements are made, one may look for a simpler instrument. Such simple devices can be built in at least two ways, without using any tubes. The principle involves half-wave clipping of one or both signals, or sharpening into pips.

Half-Wave Clipping

A simple arrangement of considerable utility is shown in Fig. 1. The positive half of one sine wave is clipped off, and the negative half of the other, by means of two identical circuits. One output is fed to the horizontal input of a cro, and the other to the vertical input. The two voltages appear alternately. The resulting display is an L-shaped figure when the two voltages are in phase, as shown in Fig. 2. When the phase angle is between 0 and 90 degrees, the display takes

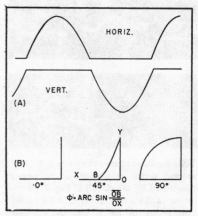

FIG. 2—Oscilloscope voltages and resulting display for circuit shown in Fig. 1

the form of a shelf-bracket, due to the difference between trace and retrace paths of the beam. In this range between 0 and 90 degrees, the lengths of the two legs of the L measure the relative amplitudes of the respective input voltages. The phase angle is measured by the location of the intercept of the fillet along the horizontal leg of the L. As indicated in Fig. 2, the sine of the phase angle is equal to the intercept distance OB divided by the

FIG. 1—Half-wave rectifier circuit for displaying phase angle between two sine waves as shown in Fig. 2

length of the base line *OX*.

This display is ambiguous about 0 degrees, that is, it will not distinguish between lead and lag. Above 90 degrees the legs of the L shorten, and the figure is not readily interpreted. Its value is in the measurement of small angles, less than about 60 degrees, and its accuracy is greater for the smaller angles.

In order for clipping to occur accurately at the zero line, the d-c resistance on the source side of the rectifiers must be low compared to the load resistance. Inductances L (Fig. 1) are shown for this purpose. For work between about 50 and 10,000 cps these inductances may be ordinary radio replacement type filter chokes, of 15 henrys or so.

Sharpening Into Pips

Another useful accessory in indicating phase is a differentiating network that sharpens one of the two signals into pips. The pip breaks at the positive-going zero-axis crossing of the voltage wave in the circuit illustrated, Fig. 3. This circuit is intended to operate out of a source such as an audio oscillator, supplying 10 volts or more with a source impedance of a few hundred ohms or less. The first crystal rectifier clips off the negative halves of the wave. Following the crystal load resistor are two R-C differentiators C_1R_1 and C_2R_2, each with a back-connected shunt

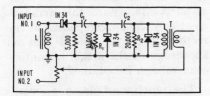

FIG. 3—Tubeless circuit for converting sine waves into pips for crt indication of phase angle between two signals

rectifier to permit only the positive pips to appear in the output. The transformer *T* (a standard 500 to

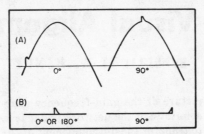

FIG. 4—Typical phase-angle indication using pip method. In A a saw-tooth sweep is used—in B sweep in sinusoidal

500 ohm audio unit) is a convenient means for mixing the pips with the other signal.

The pips so derived are mixed or added directly with the other signal and fed to the vertical input of a cro. The display consists of a sine wave with a pip superimposed on each cycle at a location dependent on the phase relation between the two voltages. Figure 4 illustrates the type of figure obtained. Since the pips start at the positive-going zero-axis crossing, the occurrence of pips at this point on the composite wave indicates zero phase angle. This type of display is unambiguous all the way to 360 degrees.

A differentiator of this sort, unfortunately, has a large signal loss. With a 10-volt input, the height of the pips, by the time they have been made suitably short, is only about 50 millivolts. Hence the comparison voltage should be adjusted in level to around 0.5 volt or perhaps less. The upper frequency limit of Fig. 3 is about 3,000 cycles, due to the difficulty in obtaining sharp pips with such a simple tubeless circuit. The time constants of the differentiators are usable over a frequency range of about 2 to 1. For the range 250 to 500 cps the best value for C_1 is 0.002 μf, for C_2, 0.001 μf. For other frequencies the capacitances should be varied accordingly.

The true zero-axis crossing point is announced by the left-hand or leading edge of the pip. If the pip is a bit long, the crest and the trailing edge should be ignored.

At a gain in simplicity of operation and a loss in clarity, the cro connections may be changed to give the type of display illustrated at the bottom of Fig. 4. Here, instead of the internal sweep of the cro being employed, one of the sinusoids is used to provide horizontal deflection. The pips obtained from the other signal are fed to the vertical input. When the phase angle is zero, the leading edge of the pip will appear at the middle of the horizontal line. With lagging or leading angles, the pip will move to the right or left. The loss in clarity lies in the ambiguity of this display about 180 degrees.

An attractive possibility for phase measurement lies in the scheme of sharpening both signals into pips, using one pip to trigger the sawtooth sweep of a cro, and applying the other pip to the vertical cro input. The display would consist of a horizontal line carrying a pip, and the position of the pip along the line would be a direct linear measure of the phase angle. The accuracy would depend entirely on the linearity of the cro sweep and the relative shortness of the retrace time.

REFERENCES

(1) J. Kritz, A Precision Phasemeter for Audio Frequencies, ELECTRONICS, p 102, Oct. 1950.

(2) Florman and Tait, An Electronic Phasemeter, *Proc. IRE*, 37, p 207, Feb. 1949.

(3) P. G. Sulzer, Vector Voltage Indicator, ELECTRONICS, p 107, June 1949.

(4) D. G. C. Luck. Properties of some Wide-Band Phase-Splitting Networks, *Proc. IRE*, 37, p 147, Feb. 1949.

(5) R. B. Dome, Wide Band Phase Shift Networks, ELECTRONICS, p 112, Dec. 1946.

(6) Hilary Moss, Cathode Ray Tube Traces, p 66, pub. by Electronic Engineering, 28 Essex St., London, Sept. 1949.

(7) Samuel Sabaroff, Technique for Distortion Analysis, ELECTRONICS, p 114, June 1948.

(8) E. O. Kretzmer, Measuring Phase at Audio and Ultrasonic Frequencies, ELECTRONICS, Oct. 1949.

Baseline for Visual Alignment Systems

By ELLIOTT A. HENRY

ACTIVITY in the television field has stimulated interest in sweep-frequency generators and visual alignment systems. The time saving and ease of adjustment inherent in visual systems outweigh the initial cost of equipment and the difficulty in making accurate gain measurements. Precise gain measurements, as well as a more accurate picture of the gain-frequency characteristic of the amplifier or net work, may be obtained if a reference of zero voltage (baseline) is provided on the cro screen.

The baseline may be obtained by blanking the return sweep within the sweep generator or by blanking the input of the vertical amplifier of the cro. As the majority of sweep generators do not incorporate internal blanking, and as physical or electrical considerations present conversion problems, the latter method is to be preferred.

While electrical blanking, obtained by keying one of the cro amplifier stages, might be used, it will not produce satisfactory results as the d-c component of the rectified

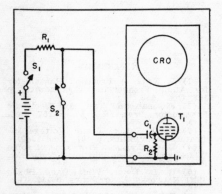

FIG. 1—Simplified circuit using battery to charge capacitor

wave will be lost in coupling to the cro and a d-c component, equal to the plate voltage difference of the keyed stage, will be added and appear on the cro screen. Since it is necessary, to produce an accurate

picture of the gain-frequency characteristic of the network under test, to transfer the d-c component of the rectified wave to the cro screen and since this is readily accomplished by periodically restoring the cro vertical amplifier to its zero operating condition, mechanical blanking was chosen.

Basic Operation

For an explanation of the transfer of the d-c component, reference is made to Fig. 1. With switch 2 open, when switch 1 is closed, with the battery polarity as shown, C_1 charges through R_1 and R_2. The direction of current flow makes the grid of T_1 go positive and the cro spot to move upward. When C_1 becomes fully charged, current ceases to flow and the grid returns to its static value. The spot returns to its former position and nothing further happens as long as conditions remain unchanged.

Now if switch S_2 is momentarily depressed, C_1 will be discharged through R_2 while the battery will be protected by R_1. The direction of current flow is now such as to make the grid of T_1 go negative and the cro spot to move downward. Therefore if S_2 is made to operate rapidly and to have equal off and on time, the pattern obtained will be a series of square waves, the magnitude of which will be an absolute proportionality to the battery voltage as C_1 has had a charge alternating between zero and full battery voltage.

By substituting the load of the linear diode detector for the battery, adjusting switch S_2 on-time to 180 degrees of the modulation cycle, and providing a means of phasing the start of S_2 on-time, either the up or down sweep may be blanked and the baseline, equivalent to zero voltage, obtained.

Resistor R_1 should have a value at least four times greater than the diode load resistor to prevent the

discharge of the diode capacitor during switch S_2 on-time. Switch S_2 must be capable of very fast action and have very low contact resistance. A relay with the mercury-

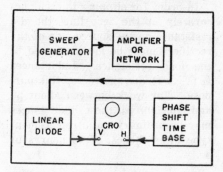

FIG. 2—Conventional circuit for single image alignment

wetted type contacts is recommended to provide the clean baseline and fast action required.

Single Image Alignment

A common arrangement for single image alignment is shown in block form in Fig. 2. Here the sweep generator uses sinusoidal modulation and a sinusoidal time base is used to produce a linear frequency-time pattern. With the modulation and time base voltages in phase, a single image will be seen, assuming no distortion, with the up and down sweeps coinciding at all points. With this arrangement only the a-c component of the rectified wave is viewed and no knowledge of the actual instantaneous voltage is obtained.

The practice of using a sweep-width very wide in comparison to the pass-band of the network under test to obtain two points of assumed zero voltage (F_{max} and F_{min}), may lead to a false picture of the gain-frequency trace. A more accurate picture of the steady-state characteristic of the network under test is obtained by using a narrow sweep-width and the baseline for accurate gain measurements.

Figure 3 shows the blanking unit in block form connected to the common arrangement of Fig. 2. The

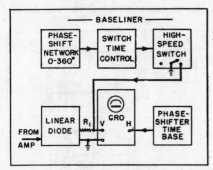

FIG. 3—Addition of the Baseliner provides zero reference trace

phase-shift network in the Baseliner is adjusted to make the switch ON time start with either F_{max} or F_{min}. The switch time control is used to adjust the switch ON time to exactly 180 degrees.

With single-image alignment, the procedure is the same as where no blanking is used. With double-image alignment, the blanking is not used until alignment is complete. After alignment is complete the blanking is used and one image disappears, being replaced by the baseline. Absolute gain measurements may then be made.

External input connections allow

the use of any switch rate from one to sixty cycles. As the switch contacts are single-pole double-throw, the unit may also be used as a high speed mechanical switch (up to 60 cps) to replace an electronic switch. It is most advantageous where one or more of the signals to be switched has a d-c component that it is desired to preserve.

REFERENCE

(1) Frantz, The Transmission of a Frequency Modulated Wave Through A Network, *Proc. IRE*, Mar. 1946.

Fast Sweep Circuit

Designed for study of extremely short-duration phenomena, the oscilloscope described has a maximum sweep speed of 100 inches per microsecond, obtained from a simple thyratron circuit. Three methods of calibration are employed

By N. L. DAVIS AND R. E. WHITE

IN ATOMIC STUDIES, the scintillation counter has assumed great importance. With these counters it is now possible to detect the incidence of single alpha or beta particles or single-gamma quanta upon certain types of crystals. When particles strike the crystal, minute fluorescent light flashes are produced.

The use of a multiplier phototube makes it possible to convert these tiny flashes to voltage pulse waveforms, a much more convenient form for recording and studying. The voltage waveforms produced are, however, of extremely short duration and the problem of displaying them in sufficient detail to allow accurate study and counting presents a considerable problem in design of high-speed oscilloscopes. In the field of digital computers there is an increasing requirement for high-speed operation. Such operation demands the use of short-duration pulses. For the observation of such pulse voltages, a fast-

sweep oscilloscope is required.

For use in the type of problems mentioned an oscilloscope with the

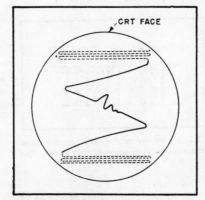

FIG. 1—Stable delayed sweep is provided by modified raster scan

following characteristics has been developed: The frequency response is uniform to 265 megacycles. It is possible to observe either single traces or recurrent traces to a repetition rate of 5,000 cycles. The unit has a maximum sweep speed of 100 inches per microsecond (0.01 μsec per inch) with several sweep

ranges reaching a maximum sweep length of 25 microseconds. A low-impedance keying pulse is provided for keying external circuits under examination. A variable delay between the external keying pulse and the oscilloscope is available which may be varied from 0 to greater than 3 μsec.

Requirements

The first three specifications place severe requirements on the cathode-ray tube and its circuitry. The tube must be capable of producing traces of very high brilliance, and the transit time of the electron beam through the deflection plates must be sufficiently low to permit the required frequency response. The performance of the cathode-ray tube on both of these factors is improved by the use of very high accelerating potentials.

Two DuMont crt types are designed for high-speed oscilloscope applications. A few of the pertinent characteristics of these two tube types are compared in the accompanying box. For the oscilloscope to be described, the 5RP-A satisfies the required brilliance and frequency limits and was used because of its immediate availability.

Sweep Circuitry

With an accelerating potential of 20,000 volts on the 5RP-A tube, a deflection sensitivity of approximately 0.005 inch per volt may be expected. For five inches deflection approximately 1,000 volts of sweep voltage is required. If the fastest sweep (100 inches per μsec) is considered, a voltage slope of 20,000 volts per μsec must be developed for a sweep wave form.

Two general methods of generating suitable sweep voltages were investigated: modified raster scan using vacuum tubes, and sweeps generated by hydrogen thyratrons.

The modified raster scan produces the presentation shown in Fig. 1. To develop this scan, a two-megacycle oscillator is keyed to provide either sine-wave sweeps or a series of linear sawtooth sweeps. The cathode-ray tube is then unblanked during the interval under investigation. Coinciding with the unblanking pulse, a small expansion sweep voltage is applied to the vertical deflection system so that several consecutive sweeps become distinguishable. This corresponds to a raster type of scan in that several sweeps may be made available at a given time.

One advantage of this type of sweep is that it provides stable delayed sweeps with no stable delay-pulse generation required. The time jitter of any sweep depends only upon the variation in the amplitude and frequency of the two-mc basic oscillator.

The jitter in the delay of the unblanking pulse used in this system does not result in time jitter in the trace itself, but is seen as fluctuations in the end of the interval being examined. This method works quite satisfactorily for sweeps longer than 0.5 μsec. Above this speed, the generation of steep

voltage slopes demands higher currents than can be conveniently obtained from vacuum tubes.

The rate of rise in volts per second of voltage across a capacitor is

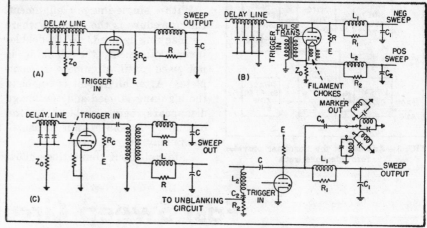

FIG. 2—Balanced and unbalanced sweep circuits for hydrogen thyratrons

equal to the current divided by the capacitance.

$$\frac{i}{c}\left(\frac{\text{amperes}}{\text{farads}}\right) = \frac{dV}{dT}\left(\frac{\text{volts}}{\text{seconds}}\right)$$

If the sweeps are developed over the lowest possible capacitance consisting of the output capacitance of the sweep generator tube in parallel with wiring and cathode-ray tube capacitances, the current

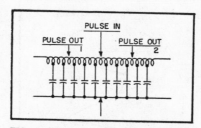

FIG. 3—Two-output delay line for initiating action observed and later, the scope sweep

which must be handled becomes objectionably high to be handled by a vacuum tube. For example, given a minimum capacitance of 30 $\mu\mu$f and a rate of rise of 20,000 volts per μsec, the current becomes 0.6 ampere.

In addition, the amount of cross coupling from one deflection plate to the next right-angle plate increases as the capacitance from plate to ground is lowered. This is

due to the capacitance divider formed by the capacitance to ground and the plate-to-plate capacitance of the cathode-ray tube. If the capacitance from the deflection plate to ground is deliberately made as high as 100 $\mu\mu$f to minimize cross-coupling effects, the current is increased to two amperes. This magnitude of current leads to the selection of a gas-filled tube such as the thyratron as a sweep generation source.

Several variations of the basic circuit for the development of sweeps through the use of a hydrogen thyratron are possible. Figure 2A shows one form such a circuit may take. The tube may be a 2D21, 2050, 3C45, 4C35 or others.

This circuit operates as follows: with the thyratron in an unfired condition, the pulse-forming network is charged to voltage E

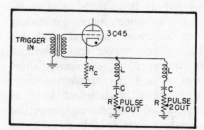

FIG. 4—Jitter is avoided by taking two outputs from cathode of thyratron

through resistance R_c. When the trigger pulse is impressed upon the grid of the thyratron, the tube conducts and the voltage at the plate of the gas tube falls very rapidly to a voltage 20 to 50 volts above ground depending upon the tube used.

The charged line then discharges through the series circuit of Z_o and the thyratron. This produces a negative square pulse across Z_o of

CRT Characteristics

Direct interelectrode capacitances	K1030	5RP-A
Deflection plate D_1 to D_2	0.52	1.8
Deflection plate D_3 to D_4	0.39	1.5
Maximum ratings		
Anode 2 to final intensifier	30,000 v	22,000 v
Typical deflection factor	128	140±20 percent

amplitude $E/2$ and length equal to twice the delay of the line, providing an unblanking pulse. The sharp drop at the plate is integrated by the RLC circuit to provide a substantially linear sweep voltage approximately equal to the supply voltage.

Associated with single-ended sweeps on electrostatic cathode-ray tubes there is an effect known as deflection defocusing which appears as progressive defocusing from start to end of the sweep. To correct this situation, two methods of producing balanced sweeps have been investigated. One method is illustrated by the circuit shown in Fig. 2B. The circuit is similar in operation to that previously described. When the thyratron is triggered, the cathode of the gas tube rises rapidly to a voltage $V/2$. In this way, C_2 charges to $V/2$ through L_2 and R_2 to provide a positive linear sweep approximately equal to $V/2$. Capacitor C discharges from V to $V/2$ to provide a negative sweep approximately equal to $V/2$. A positive square pulse of amplitude $V/2$ is developed across Z_o so that an unblanking pulse may be obtained from the circuit.

Another method of obtaining balanced sweeps employs a transformer. In this circuit, Fig. 2C, the cathode of the gas tube is grounded, eliminating the necessity of filament chokes and the pulse transformer for keying purposes. Here the unblanking pulse is obtained across Z_o and the sharp voltage step at the plate is capacitively coupled to the phase-inverting transformer. The voltage step is integrated from the secondary of the transformer to develop balanced sweeps. The linearity of these sweeps depends upon the frequency response of the transformer.

With the 5RP-A tube, deflection defocusing is not very serious and because of the possible simplification of circuitry, the single-ended sweep circuit shown in Fig. 2D is now used in this oscilloscope. The sharp voltage drop at the plate of the gas tube is integrated by $L_1R_1C_1$ to provide the sweep output.

The sharp voltage drop is also coupled by C_4, a very small capacitor, to one of several tuned circuits in the grid circuit of the cathode-ray tube where a damped train of oscillations suitable for intensity markers is generated. The L_2, R_2 and C_2 components produce a negative voltage pulse from which an unblanking pulse of sweep duration is formed.

Delay

When using an oscilloscope having high sweep speeds, the difficulty of maintaining the sweep in coincidence with the signal is considerable. To obtain a good presentation, the jitter should be kept less than one line width. This naturally applies to recurrent phenomena only since jitter from one sweep to the next is not recorded if individual sweeps are being photographed. Consider the case of the fastest sweep described, namely, 0.01 μsec per inch. Allowing for a spot size of 0.05 inch, this demands a jitter less than 500 $\mu\mu$sec for recurrent sweeps.

To obtain coincidence of sweep and signal, means must be provided to delay the sweep over the interval being examined. In the past, some variation of the circuit shown in Fig. 3 has been used. In this circuit a pulse is developed and fed into a delay line. This pulse traveling along the delay line is picked off at two points. A pulse with one delay is used to initiate the action to be observed, and a pulse at a second delay is used to initiate the oscilloscope sweep. These delays are so chosen that the transient to be observed occurs in the desired portion of the oscilloscope sweep.

An investigation of the keying characteristic of thyratrons has shown that with a d-c heater supply, a keying pulse supplied from a low-impedance source can provide stable keying of a thyratron on a comparatively slow voltage slope. By decreasing the amplitude of this low-impedance pulse, the delay in firing the thyratron is increased.

Figure 4 shows a suitable source of low-impedance keying pulses. In this circuit two low-impedance pulses are obtained simultaneously from the same thyratron, thus assuring that no jitter exists between them. One pulse is used to trigger the thyratron sweep tube while the other is used to trigger the thyratron to be observed.

The values of L and C can be switched to furnish a rough adjustment of the delay in firing. For fine adjustment the amplitude of the keying pulse is changed by varying R. By means of suitable adjustment, the sweep tube and the tube under observation can be keyed simultaneously.

With this general type of circuit negligible jitter delays to 10 μsec have been obtained. To do this the values of L and C are such as to produce an approximate half sine-wave pulse of length equal to 20 μsec. By suitable compensation within the gas-tube circuit as well as changes in the design of the thyratron the stable delay interval may be increased.

Calibration

The high-speed sweeps described were calibrated by several methods to find one accurate method suitable for both visual and photographic use.

Perhaps the most accurate

method tried consists of using a crystal-controlled transmitter as a timing-wave source. The timing wave is applied to the vertical deflection plates and single-trace photographs taken. It has the disadvantage of not being synchronized with the sweeps and cannot be used to measure time directly when viewing recurrent phenomena.

A third method consists of ringing an inductance to produce a train of damped oscillations. This method is easiest to apply since a thyratron having high-current capabilities can be used for generating the oscillation. With the 3C45 the physical size of the tube appears to limit the frequency of oscillations to about 60 mc.

The oscilloscope is housed in a four-foot cabinet with component parts placed in three levels. The crt gun and deflection section are enclosed in a mu-metal shield to prevent magnetic fields from influencing the beam. The front of the tube is maintained at the final intensifier voltage by means of a copper band encircling the tube. To prevent corona and provide physical support for the tube, a Lucite collar is fastened to the front panel and supports the front of the cathode-ray tube. A sheet of $\frac{1}{8}$-inch Lucite protects the observer from the high voltage. The high-voltage bleeder for obtaining the proper voltages for the intensifier elements consists of half-watt 1.8-

megohm resistors wound in a spiral groove cut into a polystyrene rod to minimize corona effects. The total resistance is 100 megohms so that a 200-microampere meter may be used with the bleeder to read 20 kilovolts at full scale.

The limits on bandwidth and sweep speeds encountered in this oscilloscope are not a function of the circuitry. The frequency limitation is imposed by the cathode-ray tube and may be extended by a factor of four with use of the K1030 type tube. The available writing rate then becomes much greater and the circuitry may be extended to provide sweeps of much higher writing rates.

Linear Sweep Generation

By DAVID SAYRE

THE CONSTANT-CURRENT triode circuit can be made the basis of two linear sweep generators, one to generate a negative-going sweep and the other to generate a positive-going sweep. These circuits are accurate, reliable, easy to design and very economical.

Mathematical analysis indicates the desirability of using a high-μ tube. It is also desirable to use a tube with a short grid base, to minimize the effect of tube change on the exact cathode voltage and hence on plate current. The 6SL7 meets both these requirements very well.

Negative-Going Sweeps

If the constant current is made to pass through a capacitance C, as in Fig. 1, a negative-going linear sweep is formed at the plate; as long as the switch is closed the plate will be at E_{bb} volts and i_p will flow through the switch. When the switch is opened i_p must flow through C. The rate of change of voltage at the plate is $-i_p/C = -E_{cc}/RC$ volts per second. For the

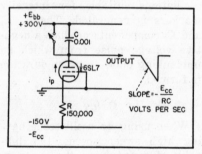

FIG. 1—Basic negative-going linear sweep generator

values of Fig. 1 the sweep thus falls at the rate of 1 volt per microsecond. By proper choice of these values sweep speeds much faster or much slower than this can be obtained. The sweep will continue until it has dropped to about 50 volts, or until the switch is closed again. At the end it will be falling about 2 percent slower than at the start.

Electronic Switch

For most applications the chief difficulty of this circuit is the switch. If the sweep is to run continuously the simple arrangement

of Fig. 2 may be used. Here V_2, which acts as the switch, is turned on very hard momentarily by the incoming pulses and each time rapidly raises the output voltage to 300 volts. Since under such circumstances a section of a 6SN7 can conduct 100 ma or more, the duration of the pulses need be only $i_p/100$ (i_p in ma) of the duration of the sweep. For $i_p = 1$ ma a duty

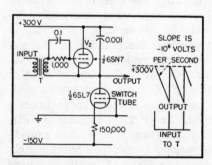

FIG. 2—Practical continuously-running negative-going linear sweep generator, using pulse input to actuate electronic switch

cycle of 99 percent is easy to obtain.

During the sweep run-down, V_2 is cut off by grid-current bias accumulated across the grid RC network. Transformer T can be any pulse transformer. Usually there will be a blocking oscillator elsewhere in the circuit, in which case V_2 can simply be driven from the third winding on the blocking oscillator pulse transformer.

Positive Going Sweep

To obtain a positive-going sweep one must put C in the cathode circuit of the constant-current triode as in Fig. 3. This, however, causes the sweep to appear on the cathode; to keep the current constant, the sweep must be placed on the grid also. This is accomplished by C'. No current can be allowed to pass through C', however, for any such current would alter the current through C itself. For this reason the grid is returned to ground not by a resistor but by diode V_3, which is cut off all during the sweep.

As long as the switch is closed current i_p flows through it. When it is opened the current is diverted into C and the sweep rises at a rate of $i_p/C = E_{cc}/RC$ volts per second. The sweep will continue until the cathode of V, has risen to within about 50 volts of E_{bb} or until electronic switch V_2 is closed again by an input pulse.

With the values indicated, the positive-going circuit is suitable for generating a 250-volt linear sweep with a slope of 1 volt per microsecond. If the sweep is to run continuously the grid of switch tube V_2 should simply be supplied with short positive pulses. If single sweeps are required a negative gate of the desired duration must be supplied.

Comparison with Other Circuits

The positive-going circuit contrasts favorably with the ordinary bootstrap linear sweep generator. However, in the bootstrap circuit the charging current for C must flow through C' and both must be recharged after each cycle. Higher duty cycles are therefore easily obtained with the positive-going circuit. For the same reasons C' in the bootstrap version must be larger than C by a factor of 10 or more, whereas in the circuit of Fig. 3 it can be as small as 0.001 μf.

The two linear sweep generators described may properly be termed precision circuits. They are suitable for such applications as linear time-modulation, the measurement of short time-intervals as in radar ranging, and the generation of linear functions in electronic com-

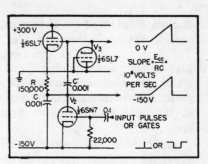

FIG. 3—Practical positive-going linear sweep with switch tube

puters. Their accuracy is intermediate to those of the two principal methods now employed, the bootstrap and the Miller feedback circuits, being slightly better than the former and slightly poorer than the latter.

It is a characteristic of both these circuits that their output impedance is almost purely capacitive. Consequently the circuit which they are intended to drive may present an input admittance which is capacitive with no harmful effects other than a decrease in the slope of the sweep, but may not present a resistance without some differentiation of the sweep occurring. In this respect these generators resemble the bootstrap circuit but are inferior to the Miller feedback circuit, which has a low output impedance and can drive any type of load.

Inexpensive Picture Generator

With interlacing, effective resolution of better than 450 lines in both directions is achieved with a conventional picture tube as the light source of a flying-spot system. Circuit details and discussion of alternative arrangements are included

By J. R. POPKIN-CLURMAN

THE PICTURE GENERATOR to be described achieves economy by using the basic circuits of a television receiver and employing the flying-spot scanner principle.

The synchronizing signals for initiating the flying-spot sweeps are derived from any standard RMA generator source. These signals

can be readily obtained by abstracting the composite synchronizing pulses from a broadcast television signal as received from any television station.

The generator will also operate on a 262-line noninterlaced basis or with a simple interlacer circuit should a standard RMA signal not

be available. The effective resolution of the generator is better than 450 lines in both vertical and horizontal directions if interlacing is used.

The description to follow applies equally well to the unit which can be built or for modification of an existing standard tv broadcast set.

A block diagram of the picture generating system is shown in Fig. 1. The first unit contains the sweep, high-voltage and blanking circuits which are necessary to provide a raster for the cathode-ray tube used at the light source for the flying spot.

Light from the raster is sent from the crt face through the picture, which is a transparency, and is then picked up by a multiplier phototube. The signal is then amplified in a video amplifier whose frequency response is corrected for the phosphor decay characteristics of the flying-spot cathode-ray tube. The signal is then passed through a video phase splitter which allows either positive or negative transparencies to be used. Following the phase splitter is a mixer stage, which adds blanking pulses to the video and then feeds a clipping stage. These circuits are shown in Fig. 2.

The output of the clipping stage is a composite video picture suitable in every respect for either modulating a signal generator or feeding the video section of another television set, providing synchronizing is available. Careful adjustment of the receiver's hold controls will sometimes allow the blanking impulses to be used for sync. However, separated RMA sync pulses derived from the receiver may be added to the blanking to give an RMA composite sync video signal.

Sweep Chassis

The blanking is derived from the television receiver or the sweep chassis of Fig. 3. This chassis is conventional in most respects except for the interlace generator. Greater care than is normal for a television set is taken to preserve the linearity of the horizontal and vertical sawtooth currents generated. For those not wishing to use the exact complement of tubes shown, equivalent tube types may be readily substituted; for example, in place of the 12AU7, 6SN7 tubes may be used. A 6W4 may be used in place of the 5V4 damper tube.

For even greater linearity in the horizontal sweep, a bootstrap 6AS7 in the circuit of Fig. 4 can be used. For the 6BG6 tube a single 6CD6 or 807 tube may be substituted. For the 6SN7 vertical deflection amplifier a 6V6, 6K6, 6F6 and similar types may be used. Instead of the blocking-oscillator circuit for the sawtooth generators, multivibrators or gas tubes will operate equally well. The RCA synchrolock horizontal oscillator and afc circuit would also provide significant improvement in performance.

The higher-than-normal voltage for the second anode is obtained by wrapping an additional filament winding (made from RG 59/U or RG 62/U cable without the shield) around the coil of the horizontal output transformer to supply the pulse-doubler rectifier tube. The horizontal output transformer is a standard RCA type 211T1 or equivalent.

The second-anode voltage to the crt is made as high as is consistent with the ability of the tube to withstand the voltage and with the available power in the sweep circuits to produce a raster of adequate size. The higher the voltage the smaller the raster spot size, the better the resolution, and the better the signal-to-noise ratio of the final derived video signal. A voltage of 18,000 to 20,000 volts has been used with the 10FP4 tube. Any of the tubes having the special P15 phosphor will give even better resolution.

Practically any cathode-ray tube will produce pictures when used for flying-spot scanner service. However, certain phosphors are very difficult to compensate for electrically. The green P1 phosphor is an example of such a type. The P2, P4, P7, P11 and P15 phosphors are all quite suitable.

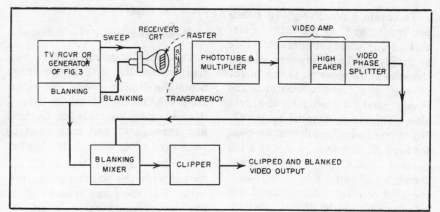

FIG. 1—Stages of the picture-generating system. The video output can feed the video stage of a conventional receiver or modulate an r-f signal generator

Surplus P7 radar tubes make fine inexpensive flying-spot scanners; however, those types of P7 phosphors which have a heavy deposit of the long-peristence material cause a shadow or grain in the picture. The trace of the blue phosphor is the most useful one in the P7 screen. Most of the 7FP7 and 12DP7 tubes did not show too annoying grain structure. The P4 phosphor tubes could be adequately compensated to give pictures having better than 450-line resolution. The 5WP15 tube provides beautiful 700-line definition when the video amplifier bandwidths are extended to over 10 megacycles. The P15 phosphors also produce a very good picture-signal-to-noise ratio. Because of the extra-high voltage associated with the flying-spot tube it has been found that magnetic deflection tubes lend themselves most suitably in this application. Signal to noise for P4 screens is better than 36 db.

Blanking Circuit

The blanking is derived by differentiating the vertical and horizontal sawtooth current sweeps. A 1N34 rectifier is used across one of the isolating resistors to improve the rise time of the horizontal blanking pulse. No attempt is made to limit the blanking pulses fed to the grid of the flying-spot-scanner cathode-ray tube, as they are negative and any amplitude greater than beam cutoff does not affect the operation of the system. The voltage

pulses present at the secondary of the horizontal output transformer are already of the proper shape and polarity for blanking.

Blanking voltages may also be obtained from other portions of the circuit than are indicated in Fig. 2. The integrated vertical pulse present at the input to the vertical

sawtooth generator may be used, or in those receivers of the RCA type 630, the vertical pulse boost in the plate circuit of the second sync amplifier may be used while the horizontal sync pulses may be used for blanking. The blanking connection to the crt grid is shown in Fig. 5, which also shows how

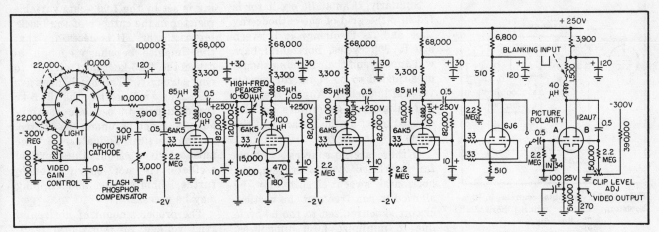

FIG. 2—Phototube and video amplifier circuits. Phase-splitter tube 6J6 permits either a positive or a negative transparency to be transmitted. Plate decoupling resistors of stages after the first can be 50,000 ohms

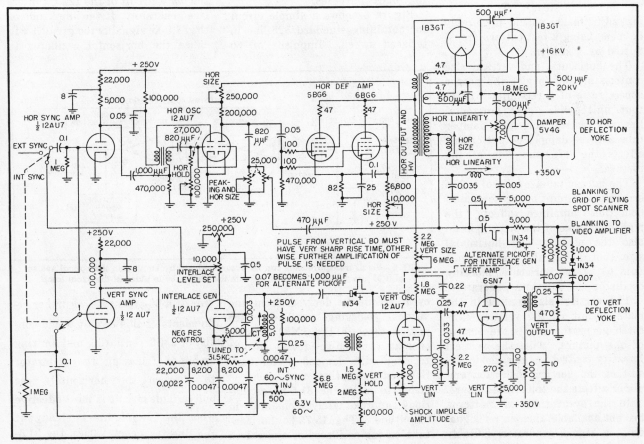

FIG. 3—Sweep chassis contains deflection circuits, interlace generator and voltage doubler for 16-kv output

35-mm transparencies may be transmitted.

For initial adjustment, a video signal from a television receiver tuned to a station is fed into the grid of the picture tube instead of the mixed blanking pulses. The sync accompanying the picture is

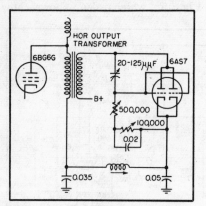

FIG. 4—All variable controls in this bootstrap circuit adjust horizontal linearity

fed into the external sync input. The hold controls are adjusted until the picture is steady. The following adjustments should preferably be made using a test pattern transmitted by a station.

The horizontal and vertical size controls are set to give the proper aspect ratio of three units high to four units wide. The horizontal linearity resistor across the damper tube and the damper output circuit affects the left-hand side of the picture.

The horizontal size control in the screen grid circuit of the horizontal deflection amplifier affects the right-hand side of the picture, as do also the peaking and horizontal size controls in the plate circuit (pin 6) of the horizontal blocking oscillator and sawtooth generator.

The vertical size control in the plate circuit of the vertical sawtooth generator affects the bottom of the picture, while the vertical linearity control in the cathode circuit of the vertical deflection amplifier affects the top of the picture.

In the event that test patterns are not available, then an r-f signal from a signal generator, suitably amplified, may be fed into the grid

of the flying-spot crt and to the sync input. If the frequency is in excess of 150 kilocycles and is synchronized as a harmonic of the horizontal sawtooth generator, a series of vertical black and white bars will appear on the face of the tube. For proper linearity, these bars should have equal spacing.

Similarly, if an audio oscillator is fed into the grid of the cathode-ray tube and its frequency is between 600 to 900 cycles, horizontal bars will appear and their spacing should be adjusted to be equal for proper vertical linearity. Any of the commercial grating generators can also be used to set up the linearity of the sweeps.

If there are no sources available for interlaced sync operation, the horizontal sweep circuit may be allowed to run free and the vertical circuit synchronized to the 60-cycle line to minimize hum difficulties. This will give a 260-line noninterlaced sweep, which may be adequate for many purposes.

Figure 6 shows a simple circuit for obtaining standard 525-line interlaced sweep. Impulses of 60-

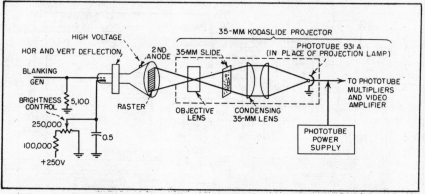

FIG. 5—Small transparencies can be accommodated by employing the optical system of a 35-mm projector backwards, with the phototube in place of the usual lamp

cycle frequency derived from the vertical blocking oscillator are passed through the 1N34 crystal, causing a 31.5-kc tuned circuit to ring with damped oscillations. Sufficient negative resistance is added to make the 31.5-kc oscillations approximately constant in amplitude. The 15.75-kc horizontal blocking oscillator or syncrolock oscillator can then be synchronized

by two-to-one countdown.

By adjusting the 31.5-kc tuned circuit, interlace is readily obtained. The amount of negative resistance given this circuit is controlled by the 5,000-ohm variable resistor in the cathode of the 12AU7 interlace generator.

The amplitude of the initial ringing is set by the 1,000-ohm variable resistor in the cathode of the blocking oscillator. It is necessary that this impulse be sharp enough to cause the 31.5-kc tuned circuit to ring strongly. Too much negative resistance will cause the 31.5-kc tuned circuit to oscillate continuously and not be under the control of the vertical oscillator. If the pulse derived from the vertical oscillator is not sharp enough, further amplification and clipping may be necessary.

The proper amount of horizontal sync voltage for horizontal oscillator control is obtained by adjustment of the two potentiometers in the plate circuit of the 12AU7 interlace generator. If the amplitude of the 31.5-kc signal is too great it will cause the horizontal oscillator to

tear at a 60-cycle rate. Further refinements of this circuit would consist of a differentiating and limiting amplifier following the generator to sharpen the horizontal sync pulses. This circuit is most effective when the 60-cycle line is steady; if the line frequency varies, the 31.5-kc circuit will have to be readjusted.

Construction

All of the circuits involved in the chain from the phototube through the mixer and clipper should be built with the same care normally taken for a high-gain i-f amplifier for a carrier frequency of 6 mc. The components should be well

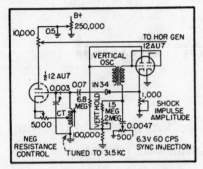

FIG. 6—Circuit of interlace generator for obtaining 525-line interlaced sweep

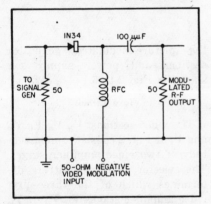

FIG. 7—Simple modulator circuit for adding video to an r-f generator

nected to the grid of the flying-spot scanner and to the blanking mixer in the video amplifier; a transparency is next taped on the face of the cathode-ray tube. The intensity control of the crt is then adjusted for the brightest possible raster that can still be focused.

The video gain control is advanced until a video output signal is obtained. This video signal should be examined by means of another television receiver or on a monitor screen. Should there be spaced from the chassis, and the stages isolated from each other. The first few stages operate at rather low levels and unless this portion of the unit at least is well shielded there may be considerable

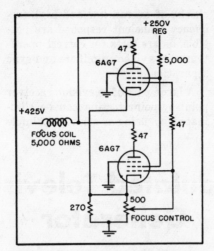

FIG. 8—Regulation of focus coil current is provided by this circuit

pickup from local broadcasting stations and others.

The phototube should be well shielded against both r-f and light pickup. Foil or thin sheet, or a proper-size can, should be placed over the phototube and grounded. A slot approximately the size of the window area of the phototube (that portion inside the tube covered by a sawtooth wire screen) should be cut in the foil or sheet in order to allow light passing through the transparency to be picked up by the phototube.

A regulated supply of 250 volts and 65 milliamperes should be used for the video circuit. A negative regulated voltage should also be used for the phototube supply. Load resistors for the dynode stages of the phototube can be wired directly to the pins of the socket.

A phase-inverter stage having equal outputs of opposite polarities is also useful should a negative instead of a positive transparency be used. Positive transparencies are preferred in this system because the noise generated in the phototube is proportional to the brightness of the light and hence any noise or snow present will be less pronounced in the lighter portions of the picture. Thus, if a positive is used to make the picture, the noise is much less visible than with a negative, where the highlights of the negative on reversal become

dark areas on the resulting positive picture, showing noise in the dark areas.

The peaking coils shown will equalize the response to greater than 5.5 megacycles. Should conventional 4.5-mc video peaking coils be used, the resolution will suffer slightly. The bias for the video tubes can be derived from a small battery. Alternatively, the bias may be derived from a negative voltage source and brought down to the proper values by voltage dividers.

Adjustments

After the linearity has been properly set, the blanking is recon-streaking or long smear tails following the picture, the high-frequency peaking capacitor, C in Fig. 2, should be adjusted until these effects disappear. A sharp white or black outline following an object for a short distance is removed by adjusting the flash phosphor compensator, R in Fig 2.

The video gain control is adjusted until the proper picture contrast is obtained on the monitor. These adjustments are readily and quickly made.

A further improvement in the system may be secured by using a Kodaslide projector in reverse by focusing an image of the crt raster upon a 35-mm transparency and then picking up the light passed through the transparency with a condensing lens. The phototube is mounted where the projection lamp was formerly placed. The same precautions about shielding apply here. Figure 5 shows this setup. If it is desired to transmit opaque information, then the raster of the flying spot must be projected by a lens on to the opaque material to be transmitted, and the light from the opaque material then picked up by the phototube. This is a full application of the old flying-spot method.

Figure 7 shows a simple modulator circuit for modulating any signal generator or r-f source.

Figure 8 is a circuit for automatic regulation of focus, which might be used in more elaborate designs.

Applications

Complete picture signals for the final testing of any television receiver are available in the absence of a broadcast tv signal. Complete checks of overall low and high-frequency transient response are possible, as are tests for correct operation of the video amplifiers and sync separation.

A large part of television receiver point-by-point testing can be eliminated by using a series of simple test pictures which are specially prepared to show up television receiver faults. These special pictures would have dark and light backgrounds for showing how d-c restorers or d-c-coupled video amplifiers behave.

Picture-Modulated Television Signal Generator

Circuit data and performance characteristics of a signal source for production testing of receivers at points remote from telecasting stations. A mixing pad permits the combination of picture, sound and noise signals to simulate actual conditions

By ALLAN EASTON

THIS paper describes the design features and performance characteristics of a signal generator, uniquely suited for television receiver measurements in that it is capable of providing a signal of known amplitude on one of the twelve commercially allocated channels and is capable of being fully modulated by a standard RMA composite video signal. The picture-modulated generator can be used by television receiver manufacturers far removed from television broadcasting stations to test production receivers with picture signals free from noise, ghosts, and interference.

The block diagram of the generator in Fig. 1 shows the following stages:

(1) A video amplifier section whose function is to amplify a small video signal so that it has sufficient amplitude .and proper polarity to operate the modulator. Multiple inputs have been provided to enable rapid selection of any one of three different video signals. The amplifier also provides a mixing channel so that synchronizing signals may be added to one or all of the video waves or two video waves may be added together for a composite display.

(2) The modulator which inserts the video intelligence on the r-f carrier in the approved fashion; that is, zero carrier corresponding to 100-percent modulation of white signals.

(3) The crystal controlled r-f oscillator which generates an unmodulated signal and precisely determines the picture carrier frequency.

(4) The multiplier chain which multiplies the oscillator frequency up to the actual picture carrier frequency.

(5) The power amplifier to amplify the modulated carrier and couple to the attenuator.

(6) The mutual inductance attenuator which provides continuously variable output from 6 db below one volt (0.5 volt) to below 120 db below one volt (1 microvolt).

(7) The output matching box which incorporates the terminating resistors and attenuator level-indicating crystal.

(8) The metering circuit, used to measure the rectified attenuator output and calibrate the attenuator.

Simplified circuit diagrams of the picture-modulated generator sections and power supply are shown in Fig. 2 to 6.

Video Circuit

The video sections, V_2, V_3, V_4, V_5, and V_6 of Fig. 2 consists fundamentally of two video amplifier stages. The selector switch S_1 setting determines which of the three first video amplifier stages V_3, V_4, or V_5, are connected through to the second video amplifier stage V_6. An additional tube V_2 is included to enable the adding of synchronizing pulses or an additional video signal to the others, if desired.

The selector switch setting also determines which gain control potentiometer R_{42}, R_{43}, or R_{44}, is effective in altering the transconductance of the sync amplifier, V_2. Since each of the four first amplifier tubes also have individual gain controls, the modulation depth and black level for each video signal can be preset, and pictures switched readily without further adjustment of any operating controls.

The two video stages are compensated by a modification of simple shunt peaking[1] to insure uniform high-frequency gain to beyond 4.5 mc. The low-frequency response of the amplifier is sufficient to transmit the vertical retrace region of the video wave with less than two-percent droop.

A parallel resonant cathode trap is included in the cathode circuit of V_6 and is tuned to 4.5 mc to attenuate the 4.5-mc video components which might otherwise appear in the sound channel and would result in undesired interference in the receiver output. The cathode trap causes a discontinuity in the amplitude and phase characteristic of the video amplifier; since this is similar to that introduced at the television transmitter or at the receiver, it produces no unusual distortion.

The type of gain control indicated was chosen with regard to the nature of the video signal desired. Where pulse-type signals, those unaffected by amplitude nonlinearity distortion, are used a screen grid voltage control is specified. This control enables a large range of input signals to be employed. However, with signals where the linearity of the video amplifier must be maintained, the degenerative cathode resistor type of control is indicated. This type of gain control has limited control capabilities because of circuit capacitances and required bandwidth, in this case about 10 db of control.

Maximum gain of video amplifier channels 2 and 3 containing V_4 and V_5, is approximately 23 db (14 times) whereas the maximum gain of the other channels is about 29 db (28 times). Thus for channels 2 and 3 a minimum signal of about 0.4 volt peak to peak is required fully to cut off the modulator tube.

The input impedance of the amplifier channels was made high so that the picture-modulated generator might be connected to a terminated line without causing appreciable loading. This makes easier multiple operation of generators from a single line.

Modulator Circuit

The output of the video amplifier connects to the suppressor grid of

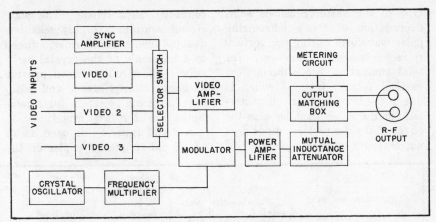

FIG. 1—Block diagram of picture-modulated generator

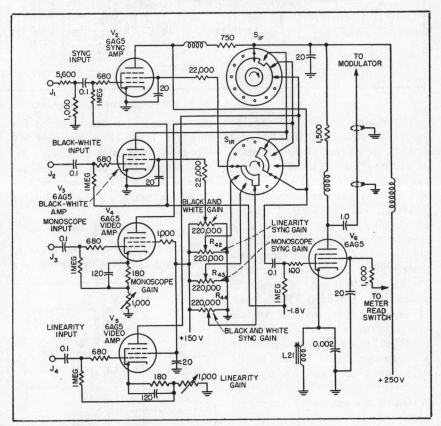

FIG. 2—Video section of the generator

the 6AS6 modulator tube V_9 shown in Fig. 3. The r-f signal is impressed on the control grid and the modulated energy appears in the plate circuit. The 6AS6 tube is specially designed for mixer or modulator service in that the grid-plate transconductance is capable of control by the suppressor-cathode potential in a manner which is reproducible from tube to tube. A d-c restorer diode V_8 connected to the suppressor insures

that the synchronizing signal peaks are held at zero potential as illustrated in Fig. 7.

The video polarity on the suppressor grid of the modulator tube is such that sync tips produce 100 percent carrier, while the white portions of the video waveform cause reduction of the carrier to approximately 7 percent. The d-c restorer serves to clamp the sync tips to zero bias regardless of picture content. Unfortunately, this type of d-c restorer causes some degradation of the synchronizing pulse waveform during the vertical retrace interval. However, the total amount of droop during the vertical retrace interval which is due to the low-frequency characteristic of the video amplifier plus the effect of the d-c restorer diode does not exceed 5 percent.

connected as a triode. The plate circuit contains a highly selective, double-tuned transformer, tuned to a harmonic of the crystal oscillator. The circuits shown provide adequate multiplication and adjacent harmonic rejection for a multiplication of at least nine times.

A 6AG5 tube, V_7, is used as an additional frequency tripler on the

stagger-tuned pair. The second circuit is the fixed coil of a mutual inductance attenuator which is resonant near the picture carrier.

The composite r-f transmission characteristic from modulator grid to the output terminals is shown in Fig. 8. for operation on channel 13. The total 3-db bandwidth is about 9 mc.

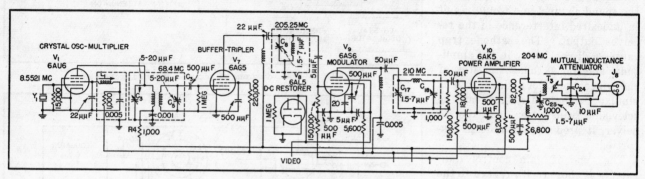

FIG. 3—Modulator and r-f circuits

The modulation linearity of the modulator tube is sufficiently good so that no appreciable compression of white values will occur providing the carrier level is not reduced below about 7 percent of maximum. There is, however, a small amount of clipping of the synchronizing tips by the d-c restorer. Thus a signal which contains approximately 28 percent sync, instead of the usual 25 percent, is needed to produce the standard RMA signal. If separate synchronizing signals are used in conjunction with V_9, no difficulty will be experienced. If a composite signal is fed to the video input, the amount of sync in the video waveform should be adjusted at the synchronizing generator.

Frequency Multiplier

The modulator grid is fed from the multiplier chain which develops the required r-f voltage at the picture carrier frequency. The frequency-determining element of the frequency multiplier chain is crystal Y_1 operating between 7 and 9 mc depending upon the channel desired. Tube V_1 in Fig. 3 is a combined crystal oscillator and frequency multiplier. The control grid, screen grid and cathode are

generators which are designed for channels 7–13. For channels 1–6 this stage is used as a buffer.

Approximately one volt of r-f voltage at the picture carrier frequency appears on the modulator grid.

Output Amplifier

The modulator plate connects to a resonant circuit which is one of a

The picture carrier is situated in such a manner that the upper sidebands are faithfully transmitted whereas the lower sidebands are progressively attenuated. However, for all practical purposes for use with commercial television receivers, the picture-modulated generator is essentially double sideband. The shape of this transmis-

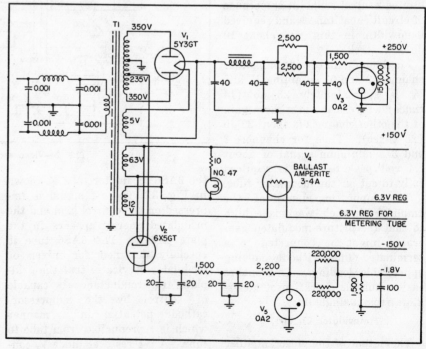

FIG. 4—Complete power supply circuit for the generator

sion characteristic is somewhat modified when the attenuator is set for maximum output but is still satisfactory.

Power amplifier tube V_{10} couples into the mutual inductance attenuator.[2] A balanced plate circuit with C_{25} forming one of the balance capacitors and the circuit capacitance on the 6AK5 side forming the other, is used. This balanced condition is essential if the output of the attenuator is to be balanced with respect to ground.

Figure 9 shows a cross section of the attenuator indicating the position of the fixed and movable coils. The ratio of the voltage induced in the movable coil at a distance X inches from the fixed coil to that induced at a distance $(X + d/2)$ inches is 16 db. If the diameter of the cylinder is one inch, then the attenuation will be 32 db per inch of travel. Approximately 120 db of attenuation is provided in the attenuator shown.

The movable piston has a gear rack attached to it which is driven by means of a pair of split gears actuated by a shaft from the front panel. The attenuator dial is directly calibrated in db attenuation. A movable zero slider is incorporated to aid in setting the reference point.

Coupling Unit

By means of the output coupling unit, shown at the left of Fig. 5, the balanced signal from the attenuator cable is delivered to the r-f output jack on the front panel. Located in this unit is the METER READ SWITCH S_2 and the circuitry necessary for conducting the d-c measuring voltage of the output-level measurement system from the output lead to the output-level metering circuit. In the coupling unit and output head are the circuits for enabling both the r-f output signal and the d-c output-level measuring voltage to be carried by the same output cable.

Output Head

The output head is connected to the R-F OUTPUT JACK on the front

panel by a three-foot length of RG-22U balanced twin conductor cable. The output head contains a terminating network with the following nominal output impedances: 10 ohms unbalanced to ground, 50 ohms unbalanced to ground, 20 ohms balanced, and 100 ohms bal-

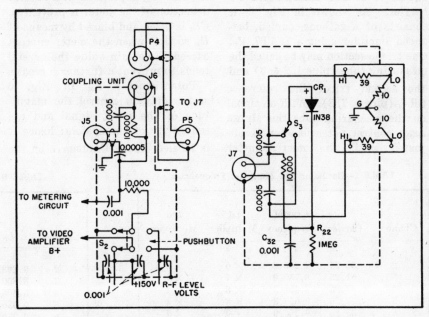

FIG. 5—Output coupling unit, left, and the output head circuit

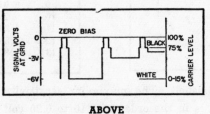

ABOVE

FIG. 7—Waveform at suppressor grid of modulator tube showing the effect of the d-c restorer on sync tips as scene brightness varies

RIGHT

FIG. 6—Output metering circuit

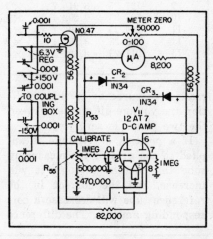

anced. The maximum output voltage across the 100-ohm output resistance is 0.5 volt rms.

Also located in the output head is a crystal rectifier CR_1, a 1N38 connected in a peak voltmeter circuit with R_{22} and C_{32}. This crystal can be connected by switch S_3 to either side of the line in the output head to indicate the magnitude of the

output voltage. This enables measurement of the actual output voltage under load as well as the open-circuit voltage. The positive d-c voltage developed across R_{22} is carried by one of the conductors of the output cable to one side of the METER READ SWITCH S_2 of the

coupling unit. When the switch button is depressed the video amplifier is disabled and the d-c measurement voltage is connected to the metering circuit. Thus the attenuator output level is set with no modulation on the carrier, eliminating the possible errors which might be caused by different picture content. The modulator circuits are designed so that eliminating the video signal has a negligible effect on the amplitude of the picture carrier.

Output Level Meter

The output level meter is designed to indicate the output voltage level of the unmodulated r-f carrier. As shown in Fig. 6, it consists of a cathode-coupled, balanced amplifier using a 12AT7, V_{11}. One triode section may be called the measuring tube (pins 1, 2 & 3) and the second triode the reference tube, (pins 6, 7, 8). With no signal on the measuring tube the METER ZERO control potentiometer is adjusted until the microammeter

of potential between the two plates is then a measure of the applied grid voltage.

To protect the meter from accidental overload of either polarity two 1N34 crystal rectifiers CR_2 and CR_3 are connected in a novel manner between the two plate circuits. Crystal CR_2 is poled so that reverse deflection of the meter is prevented. CR_3 is poled and biased by means of R_{53} so that when the meter current exceeds a certain value the crystal tends to prevent a further increase.

Potentiometer R_{55} in Fig. 6 serves only to control the magnitude of the input signal and the sensitivity of the system; hence it is labeled METER CALIBRATE on the

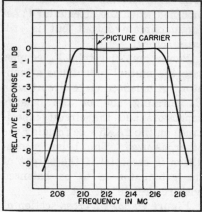

FIG. 8—Composite r-f transmission characteristic

Shielding and Leakage

Great care has been exercised in

TABLE I—Oscillator and Multiplier Frequencies

Channel	Picture Carrier	Crystal Frequency	1st Multiplier	2nd Multiplier
	mc	kc		
2	55.25	9,208.3	×6	×1
3	61.25	8,750.0	×7	×1
4	67.25	8,406.3	×8	×1
5	77.25	9,656.3	×8	×1
6	83.25	9,250.0	×9	×1
7	175.25	8,345.3	×7	×3
8	181.25	8,630.9	×7	×3
9	187.25	8,916.7	×7	×3
10	193.25	9,202.4	×7	×3
11	199.25	8,302.1	×8	×3
12	205.25	8,552.1	×8	×3
13	211.25	8,802.1	×8	×3

TABLE II—Coil and Alignment Frequencies

Channel	L_1	C_3 and C_5	C_8	C_{17} and C_{18}	C_{25}
	kc	mc	mc	mc	mc
2	9,208.3	55.25	55.25	54	60
3	8,750.0	61.25	61.25	60	66
4	8,406.3	67.25	67.25	66	72
5	9,656.3	77.25	77.25	76	82
6	9,250.0	83.25	83.25	82	88
7	8,345.3	58.42	175.25	174	180
8	8,630.9	60.42	181.25	180	186
9	8,916.7	62.42	187.25	186	192
10	9,202.4	64.42	193.25	192	198
11	8,302.1	66.42	199.25	198	204
12	8,552.1	68.42	205.25	204	210
13	8,802.1	70.42	211.25	210	216

reads zero current; in this condition the voltage difference between the two plates is zero.

If a positive d-c voltage is applied to the grid of the measuring tube the current through it will increase, and the current in the reference tube will decrease a corresponding amount. The difference

panel. The maximum sensitivity is in the order of 0.16 to 0.20 volt for full-scale deflection.

Picture-modulated generators have been designed and constructed for channels 2 to 13 inclusive. Tables 1 and 2 indicate the frequencies involved.

providing good shielding and r-f filtering to enable the use of picture modulated generators with sensitive receivers. It is possible, as a result, to attenuate completely, so that no trace of a picture signal remains on the most sensitive television receiver which has been available for test. The generators

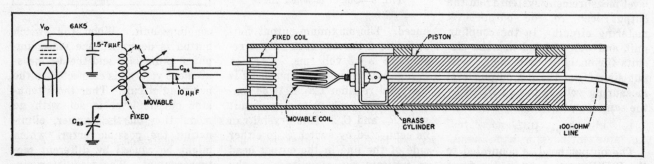

FIG. 9—Construction details of the mutual inductance attenuator

have been tested for r-f leakage through the power cables, chassis openings, and around the covers with sensitive communication receivers and have shown no discernible leakage.

The effective shielding has been accomplished by carefully filtering every power lead which enters or leaves the chassis in several stages. All circuits which carry r-f or have r-f fields have been carefully compartmented.

Another factor which tends toward low radiation and leakage is the absence of a high-level oscillator at the picture carrier frequency. The high-level oscillator operates between 7 and 9 mc and consequently does not affect the television receiver.

Setting Modulation Depth

The setting of the several video signal controls to obtain the standard depth of modulation can

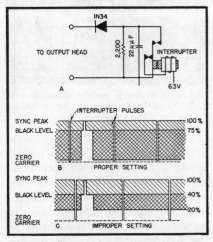

FIG. 10—Circuit of interrupter for estimating the position of zero carrier level. By adjustment of the gain controls of the generator, the modulation depth and the black level may be set according to RMA and FCC standards. Acceptable setting is shown at (B) and incorrect setting indicating excessive sync gain and inadequate video gain is shown at (C)

be accomplished by the following procedure. The equipment required in addition to the video source for modulating the picture modulated generator includes a wide band, high-gain oscilloscope, a mechanical buzzer-type interrupter and a

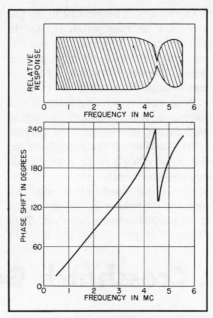

FIG. 11—Overall amplitude and phase versus frequency characteristic

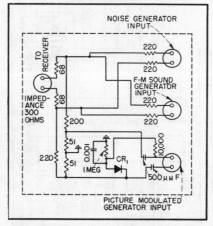

FIG. 12—Mixing pad for combining an f-m sound signal with the video channel

crystal rectifier, video detector circuit.

The circuit and an illustration of the type of display are shown in Fig. 10. Here the rectifier circuit is connected across the output terminals of the output head. The output from the detector is connected to the vertical plates of the oscilloscope; the horizontal sweep set to 30 cps and synchronized with the power line.

The interrupter periodically short circuits the output from the detector so as to indicate the zero carrier level of the signal from the generator. The pattern on the oscilloscope appears as shown as a

replica of the video modulating waveform with periodic spikes extending down to zero carrier level. In general the spikes will not be synchronous with the video signal and horizontal sweep.

To set modulation depth adjust the video and synchronizing signal gain controls until the video signal plus the sync peaks are equal to about 93 percent of the peak signal observed on the screen of the oscilloscope. The black level adjustment is made by proportioning the relative amounts of sync and video signals.

Overall Performance

The overall amplitude and phase versus frequency characteristic is shown on Fig. 11. The curves were taken with a Hazeltine phase curve tracer.[3] The swept video was connected at the video input jack and the output signal recovered across a 2,000-ohm load resistor of a crystal detector connected across the r-f output terminals. In this manner the fidelity of the entire unit including the video, r-f, and coupling circuits can be evaluated.

A resume of the performance specifications is as follows:

Operating frequency range—One channel

Output level—0.5 v to below 1 μv

Output impedance—10 ohms unbalanced; 50 ohms unbalanced; 20 ohms balanced; 100 ohms balanced

Video polarity—black positive

Video input level—0.4 v to 1.2 v peak to peak

Frequency accuracy—50 kc of nominal picture carrier

Spurious frequencies—at least 44 db below picture carrier

Attenuator balance—the unbalance to ground between two halves does not exceed 0.5 db

Power drain—110 watts at 117 v 60 cps

Modulation depth—adjustable, zero to about 93 percent

Sound Channel

The instrument has been used with standard RMA signal generators manufactured by RCA and

Telequip Corp. In addition to the monoscope, several video patterns have been used, among which are: black and white signal, linearity bar pattern, step wave, camera signals and signals taken off the air by a television receiver.

In normal use of the instrument, an f-m signal generator operating on the proper sound carrier frequency is an important accessory. Figure 12 is a circuit diagram of a mixing pad which enables mixing of sound, picture and noise signals to simulate the actual television transmission. The picture input has a crystal rectifier which is used in place of the output coupling box for measurements of picture carrier level. The insertion loss of the system is approximately 9 db.

With receivers using intercarrier sound, a small amount of phase modulation of the picture carrier by the action of the modulator on the tuned circuit in its grid circuit may be observed.

The phase modulation may be reduced by means of input admittance variation compensation. This consists of an unbypassed cathode resistance in the 6AS6 cathode. The size varies between 25 and 100 ohms depending on the channel.

REFERENCES

(1) F. E. Terman, "Radio Engineers Handbook," McGraw-Hill Book Co., p 413.

(2) D. E. Hartnett and N. P. Case, The Design and Testing of Multirange Receivers, *Proc IRE*, **23**, p 578, June 1935.

(3) B. D. Loughlin, A Phase Curve Tracer for Television, *Proc IRE*, **29**, p 107, Mar. 1941.

Television Crosshatch Generator

LINEARITY ADJUSTMENTS in television receivers may be expedited by the use of a relatively simple crosshatch generator, the circuit of which appears in the accompanying diagram. This unit blanks the electron beam at regular intervals to form 12 horizontal and 16 vertical lines on the screen of the picture tube. Since the generator is connected directly to the receiver being adjusted, test pattern distortion errors introduced in camera chains and transmitters are avoided.

The generator has sufficiently low power requirements to allow the necessary voltages for its operation to be taken from the receiver being tested without undue strain on the components of the receiver power supply.

The number of lines is adjustable, but the 12 to 16 ratio has been found

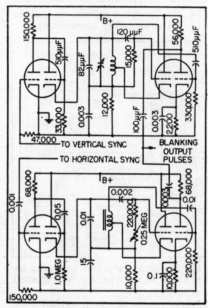

FIG. 1—Circuit diagram of crosshatch generator. Type 12AU7 tubes are used throughout

FIG. 2—Crosshatch pattern obtained with properly adjusted receiver using crosshatch generator

to be most convenient for most linearity adjustments. Thus the proper aspect ratio, as well as both horizontal and vertical linearity adjustments, may be made easily and accurately. Philco Corporation is responsible for the development of the instrument.

Single-Frame TV Photography

By M. DISTEL AND A. GROSS

IN ENDEAVORING to record a remotely situated, random, short-duration visual phenomenon, an experimental closed-circuit television system was arranged to transmit the scene to the picture tube where it could be photographically recorded. Since the time of occurrence of the event was not predictable, an electronic triggering scheme was tried which would enable the film camera to monitor the screen continuously. The camera shutter was opened and the screen maintained dark except when triggered to brightness by the event itself, thus capturing the image on film. The alternative to this, of course, would be the obviously less economical method of operating a motion picture camera continuously in anticipation of the event.

Trigger System

The effectiveness of the electronic triggering scheme depended upon a number of things. The camera and television receiver had to be in a light-tight enclosure to prevent fogging of the exposed film. Triggering the kinescope picture on and off had to be accomplished by sequential application of the proper bias voltages to the kinescope control grid. In trial, a single-shot multivibrator, triggered by the event by means of an auxiliary photocell in the television camera, generated a square pulse of duration equal to the average television frame period. This pulse was used to gate the cathode-ray beam.

It was found that the vertical oscillator of the 40-frame-per-second television scanning system would, over a period of days and under changing temperature conditions, vary approximately within one cycle per second about a frequency in the range 39 to 46 cycles per second. Rather than modify the television synchronization generator system to remedy this difficulty, it was decided to control the timing circuit which gates the kinescope cathode-ray beam. It

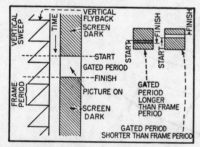

FIG. 1—Samples of banding occurring in single-frame television photography

was necessary to find some solution since, within a few hours after adjustment, the photographs taken would invariably cover slightly more or slightly less than the single frame required, resulting in undesirable banding as illustrated in Fig. 1. To overcome this defect in the photograph it is necessary that the on period of the picture, initiated at any time during a given frame, extend to exactly the equivalent point in the succeeding frame.

Circuit Details

The circuit, which was evolved from various designs and selected as the simplest satisfactory solution, comprises a single-shot multivibrator whose pulse width is a function of grid bias, and an analog counter circuit whose output voltage is proportional to the input frequency, in this case the television frame frequency. Figure 2 shows a block diagram of the system.

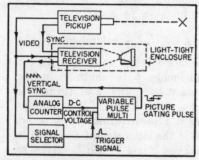

FIG. 2—System for gating one frame of a television receiver whose vertical scanning frequency is not constant

The television pickup feeds both video and sync signals to the receiver. The signal selector is used to derive a trigger pip from the event which is fed to the variable-pulse multivibrator where it initiates the picture gating pulse. The analog counter is the control circuit for the multivibrator, and makes the multivibrator pulse vary in width to compensate for the drift of the frame frequency of the television system.

Figure 3 shows the complete schematic of the multivibrator and counter. To the counter circuit is fed a portion of the output of the vertical oscillator. The counter produces a voltage proportional to the frequency of the vertical oscillator. A negative counter was used in this case so that an increase in frequency causes a drop in average plate current of V_4. Thus the output voltage drops with an increase in frequency. For the type of controllable multivibrator selected, this effect was necessary so that the pulse width would decrease with an increase in frequency. For cases where an increase in frequency

must give a wider output pulse, a positive counter circuit may be used.

Counter Design

In the design of the counter circuit, whether positive or negative, the time constant $R_1 C_2 \gg 1/f$ where f is the frequency to be measured, and $C_2 \gg C_1$ with C_1 being kept very small.

The d-c output voltage of the counter is equal to:

$$\frac{E_a f R_1 C_1}{1 + f R_1 C_1}\left(1 - \frac{1}{2 f R_1 C_2}\right)$$

where E_a is the peak applied voltage and f the frequency, and R_1, C_1 and C_2 are as shown in the schematic of Fig. 3.

For the values shown in Fig. 3 a variation from 39 cycles per second to 46 cps will give a voltage change of 2.5 volts.

The multivibrator was so designed that for a change of -2.5 volts on the control grid the output pulse of the multivibrator decreases from 25,380 microseconds to 21,300 microseconds. This compares fairly well with the requirement of 25,640 microseconds for 39 cps, and 21,740

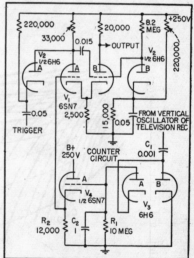

FIG. 3—Vertical scanning frequency variation from 39 to 46 cps will give a voltage change of -2.5 volts for controlling gating time

microseconds for 46 cps.

Since the counter is sensitive to amplitude as well as frequency, it is important that the input to the counter be limited to constant amplitude signals. Where amplitude variation is anticipated, a limiter stage should be placed ahead of the counter.

COMPONENTS

Television I-F Coil Design

By JEAN HOWARD FELKER

VARIOUS nomographs, charts, and calculators are available for the calculation of the inductance of coils, but most of these graphical aids do not cover the range of values of interest to the designer of coils for television, f-m, and radar i-f frequencies. The accompanying nomograph has been designed to fulfill this need. Unlike other coil nomographs, it gives in one operation the number of close-wound turns required to get a desired inductance.

The nomograph is based on a modification of H. A. Wheeler's inductance formula[1]

$$L = \frac{r^2 n^2}{9r + 10l} \text{ microhenrys} \quad (1)$$

where r is the radius of the coil in inches, l its length in inches, and n the number of turns. In close-wound coils, l is a function of n. Substitution of nd, where d is the diameter of the wire in inches, for l in Eq. 1 gives an

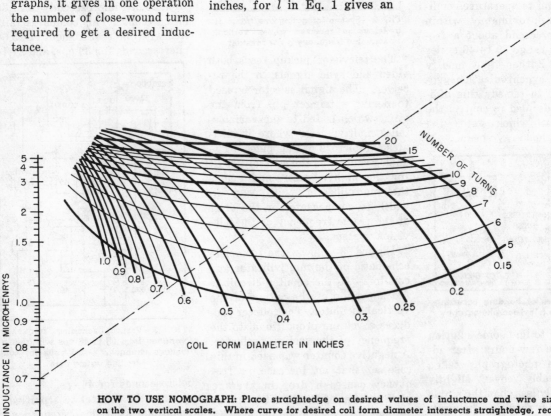

HOW TO USE NOMOGRAPH: Place straightedge on desired values of inductance and wire size on the two vertical scales. Where curve for desired coil form diameter intersects straightedge, read required number of turns on other set of curves

Example: How many turns of number 30 wire are required on a 0.25-inch diameter coil form to obtain 0.7 microhenry? Run straightedge between 0.7 on lefthand vertical scale and 30 on righthand side of righthand vertical scale, as indicated by thin dashed line. Trace upward along 0.25 diameter curve to straightedge, and read 10 turns as value of other curve passing through this intersection

equation which can be solved for n to give

$$n = \frac{10dL + \sqrt{100d^2 L^2 + 36r^3 L}}{2r^2} \quad (2)$$

The complexity of Eq. 2 accounts for the unusual structure of the nomograph and indicates the computational labor avoided by its use.

D. Pollack[2] has shown verification for the formula $L = N^2 D/(102\ S + 45)$ microhenrys, where D is the diameter of the coil in centimeters, N is the number of turns, and S is the ratio of the length of the coil to its diameter. Changing the centimeter dimensions of D in Eq. 3

to inches and employing Wheeler's symbols gives $L = r^2n^2/(8.85\ r + 10l)$, verifying Eq. 1.

REFERENCES

(1) H. A. Wheeler, Simple Inductance Formulas for Radio Coils, *Proc IRE*, p 1,398, Oct. 1928.
(2) D. Pollack, The Design of Inductances for Frequencies Between 4 and 25 Megacycles, *Electrical Engineering*, Sept. 1937.

Bifilar I-F Coils

Improved noise immunity because of low grid time constant and economy in production due to the elimination of several components are achieved by use of bifilar coils between stages of stagger-tuned i-f amplifiers. Detailed analysis is given

By S. R. SCHEINER

BIFILAR COILS as interstage coupling devices in stagger-tuned amplifiers[1] provide a number of desirable features in addition to those of the conventional coupling system.

A bifilar coil may be defined as a transformer having as close to unity coupling as physically possible. The construction of a typical bifilar coil for use in the television i-f range from 21 to 26 mc is illustrated in Fig. 1. The coil shown is wound on a 0.292-inch O.D. Bakelite form using No. 30 wire with heavy formvar insulation.

The two windings are formed simultaneously, so that any turn on winding A is adjacent to two turns on winding B, thus insuring a high degree of coupling between coils. Measurements indicate a coefficient of coupling of approximately 90 percent. The insulation on the two windings is generally colored differently for convenience in wiring. The bifilar coil is tuned by a single iron core inside the form.

The use of bifilar coils in a typical television i-f system is illustrated in Fig. 2. This circuit represents a low-cost system employing only two i-f amplifier tubes and designed for a 3-db bandwidth of 2.2 mc and a 6-db bandwidth of approximately 2.65 mc. The three bifilar coils are labeled T_1, T_2 and T_3 in Fig. 2. The

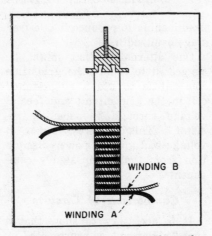

FIG. 1—Construction of bifilar coil

individual tuning frequencies and stage loading are based on the values determined by design formulas for an ideal stagger-tuned triple, and modified as required by practical considerations.

A similar amplifier using single-tuned coils and coupling capacitors is shown in Fig. 3.

Economics

Comparison of Fig. 2 with Fig. 3 indicates that the use of a bifilar coil eliminates the necessity for a coupling capacitor in each stage. The added cost of winding the extra coil and providing the required insulation is approximately one cent. This is several cents less than the cost of an ordinary coupling capacitor, so that an appreciable cost saving is provided by the bifilar coil system.

An r-f choke is employed in Fig. 3 to feed B voltage to the last i-f tube plate, and the tuned-circuit coil is connected from video detector cathode to ground. Here, the resistance in series with the i-f

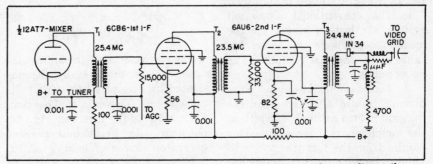

FIG. 2—Circuit of staggered two-stage i-f amplifier using bifilar coupling coils

plate must be low to avoid excessive drop in B voltage, and the resistance across the video detector load must be low to maintain diode detector efficiency. In this circuit, the use of a bifilar coil effects a further economy by eliminating the need for the r-f choke.

A second important advantage resulting from the use of bifilar coils is the improved noise immunity because of the low impedance in the i-f grid circuits. In the conventional amplifier illustrated in Fig. 3, where the d-c grid return is through the load resistor, an appreciable time constant in the grid may result. Noise pulses of sufficient amplitude to draw grid current will develop a charge on the coupling capacitor, and this charge will maintain bias on the tube until it can leak off through the grid resistor.

If bias is developed, the stage gain will be reduced after each noise pulse until the bias returns to normal. Severe noise may be sufficient to drive the tube to cutoff. The effect on the picture is that each noise pulse which modulates the carrier toward the black level is not itself very noticeable, but is followed by a white tail which is very objectionable.

In Fig. 3 the grid of the last i-f stage has a time constant of approximately 3.3 microseconds. The active time for one horizontal line is approximately 53.3 microseconds, so that severe noise would produce noticeable white streaking. When bifilar coils are employed, the grid time constant is virtually zero, so that the effect of noise on the picture is only to produce the black specks caused by noise modulation.

In the conventional single-coil system, the last i-f stages are the most susceptible to this effect because of the increased amplitude of noise pulses.

It becomes increasingly more difficult to use a resistor for the d-c grid return as the bandwidth of the amplifier is narrowed. This results from the fact that the individual stage loading, as prescribed by stagger-tuned design formulas,

becomes less as the bandwidth is narrowed. Hence, the grid time constant becomes increasingly larger and the noise performance progressively poorer unless a bifilar coil or an additional choke is employed.

A higher i-f frequency would result in a longer grid time constant, since the increased tube transit time loading will necessitate less fixed loading to produce the desired stage bandwidth.

One alternative that might be suggested to reduce the grid time constant is to use a single-tuned coil in the grid circuit and feed B voltage through the loading resistor. This requires higher B voltage and greater power dissipation from the power supply components.

Comparison of Circuits

It is necessary to show that a tuned bifilar coil, as represented by Fig. 4A, is electrically equivalent to the single-tuned circuit of Fig. 4B, provided :—

$$L = \sqrt{L_1 L_2} \qquad (1)$$

$$C = \sqrt{\frac{L_1}{L_2}} C_1 + \sqrt{\frac{L_2}{L_1}} C_2 \qquad (2)$$

$$\frac{1}{R} = \frac{1}{\sqrt{\frac{L_2}{L_1}} R_1} + \frac{1}{\sqrt{\frac{L_1}{L_2}} R_2} \qquad (3)$$

The equivalence of these two circuits can be most easily demonstrated by several successive applications of Thevenin's Theorem. Figure 5A is the same as Fig. 4A redrawn with a constant current generator source of energy added. If we consider the internal and load circuits to the left and right

of terminals 1 and 2, then the equivalent circuit according to Thevenin's theorem will be as shown in Fig. 5B where

$$E_A = \frac{i_o}{j\omega C_1} \qquad (4)$$

$$Z_A = \frac{1}{j\omega C_1} \qquad (5)$$

If we apply Thevenin's theorem

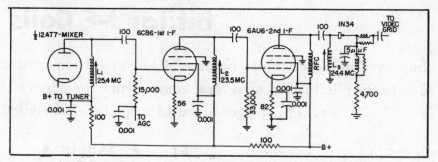

FIG. 3—Circuit of conventional single-tuned staggered stages

to Fig. 5B, the equivalent circuit illustrated in Fig. 5C is obtained, where

$$E_B = \frac{E_A R_1}{R_1 + Z_A} \qquad (6)$$

$$Z_B = \frac{1}{\frac{1}{R_1} + \frac{1}{Z_A}} \qquad (7)$$

One more application of Thevenin's theorem results in Fig. 5D, where

$$E_c = \frac{-j\omega M E_B}{Z_B + j\omega L_1} \qquad (8)$$

$$Z_c = \frac{\omega^2 M^2}{Z_B + j\omega L_1} \qquad (9)$$

$$e_2 = \frac{i_2}{\frac{1}{R_2} + j\omega C_2} \qquad (10)$$

$$i_2 = \frac{E_c}{Z_c + j\omega L_2 + \frac{1}{1/R_2 + j\omega C_2}} \qquad (11)$$

Substitution and simplification will result in Eq. 12 provided k, the coefficient of coupling, is set equal to unity so that $M = \sqrt{L_1 L_2}$.

$$e_2 = \frac{-i_o}{\sqrt{\frac{L_1}{L_2}} \frac{1}{R_1} + \sqrt{\frac{L_2}{L_1}} \frac{1}{R_2} + j\omega \left(\sqrt{\frac{L_1}{L_2}} C_1 + \right.}$$
$$\cdots \qquad \overline{\left. \sqrt{\frac{L_2}{L_1}} C_2 \right) + \frac{1}{j\omega \sqrt{L_1 L_2}}} \qquad (12)$$

But Eq. 12 is recognizable as the equation for the response of a single-tuned circuit with the values set forth as in Eq. 1, 2 and 3.

In other words, a single-tuned circuit whose constants are so defined will be electrically equivalent to the bifilar coupling scheme. Hence, the bifilar coil will have the same selectivity curve as the equivalent single-tuned circuit and can be treated as such in the design of stagger-tuned amplifiers.

For the special case of a 1 to 1 transformer, $L_1 = L_2$, Eq. 12 becomes:

$$e_2 = \frac{-i_o}{\frac{1}{R_1} + \frac{1}{R_2} + j\omega\,(C_1 + C_2) + \frac{1}{j\omega L}} \quad (13)$$

This is the equation for a single-tuned coil of inductance $L = L_1 = L_2$, having the same input and output loading and capacities as the bifilar coil. In other words, a 1 to 1 bifilar coil will produce the same selectivity curve and the same gain bandwidth factor as a single-tuned coil with the same capacitances and loadings.

If we consider once more the general case where L_1 is not equal to L_2, Eq. 12, then it can be shown that by selection of a proper ratio between L_1 and L_2, an improvement in gain-bandwidth factor over a single-tuned coil can be obtained provided the circuit input and output capacitances are unequal.

Consider the circuit in Fig. 6 where the coupling is 100 percent. Capacitance C_2 is greater than C_1 in the circuit. Let

$$A = \frac{N_1}{N_2} = \sqrt{\frac{L_1}{L_2}}$$

The stage gain from grid to grid is given by

$$\text{Gain} = \frac{g_m R_1}{A} \quad (14)$$

and the bandwidth by

$$\Delta f = \frac{1}{2\pi R_1 C_{eq}} = \frac{1}{2\pi R_1\left(C_1 + \frac{C_2}{A^2}\right)} \quad (15)$$

then

$$\text{gain} \times \Delta f = \frac{g_m}{2\pi A\left(C_1 + \frac{C_2}{A^2}\right)} \quad (16)$$

Equation 16 will be a maximum when

$A\left(C_1 + \frac{C_2}{A^2}\right)$ is a minimum which occurs

when $\dfrac{d}{dA}\left[A\left(C_1 + \dfrac{C_2}{A^2}\right)\right] = 0 \quad (17)$

$$C_1 - \frac{C_2}{A^2} = 0 \quad (18)$$

$$A = \sqrt{\frac{C_2}{C_1}} \quad (19)$$

That is, maximum gain-bandwidth product will be obtained from such a coupling scheme when the turns ratio of the transformer is set equal to the square root of the capacitance ratio. Substituting this value in Eq. 16,

$$\text{Max gain} \times \text{BW} = \frac{g_m}{2\pi\,(2\,\sqrt{C_1 C_2})} \quad (20)$$

Compare this with the gain-bandwidth product for a single coil given by

$$\text{Gain} \times \text{BW} = \frac{g_m}{2\pi\,(C_1 + C_2)} \quad (21)$$

When $C_1 = C_2$, the equations are equivalent and no advantage results from the bifilar coil. But if C_1 and C_2 are not equal, a bifilar coil will possess an advantage since $2\sqrt{C_1 C_2}$ will be less than $C_1 + C_2$.

If $m = C_2/C_1$, the advantage of a properly designed bifilar transformer over a single coil becomes greater as this capacitance ratio is increased. In an unpublished paper, H. Goldberg has shown the following relationship to exist between m, the circuit capacitance ratio and the gain-bandwidth advantage over a single-tuned circuit. These results can easily be checked by Eq. 20 and 21.

m	Gain-Bandwidth Ratio
2.0	1.060
2.5	1.110
3.0	1.155
4.0	1.250
5.0	1.340
15.0	2.005

The above analysis indicates that of two tubes designed to have the same figure of merit, the one possessing the greater inequality between input and output capacitances is the better tube, since it is possible by proper design to secure a higher gain-bandwidth product.

Turns Ratio

In a television i-f amplifier stage, the ratio between input and output capacitance depends primarily on the tube types employed. The capacitances contributed by tube sockets, leads, and coils can be minimized by careful design, but nothing further can be done. Tubes such as the 6CB6 and 6AG5 have a higher ratio of input to output capacitance than the 6AU6, but even their use would not provide a value of m greater than 2.

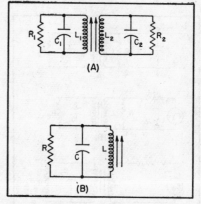

FIG. 4—Bifilar coil A is electrical equivalent of single-tuned coil B

An increase in gain of only six percent could be obtained by increasing the turns ratio on the bifilar coil. To wind such a transformer is obviously more difficult and more expensive. Further, as the turns ratio is made larger, it becomes increasingly more difficult to maintain a high degree of coupling between coils. For these reasons, it has generally been found more feasible to use a 1 to 1 bifilar coil for interstage coupling in commercial television receivers.

In the output stage, however, a bifilar coil with a step-up turns ratio provides a very convenient method for transforming the video diode load until the operating Q of the last i-f circuit is correct. Here it is not possible to obtain the optimum value of gain-bandwidth product since the diode load resistor is determined by considerations of video response. If R_D represents the diode load resistor, the equivalent loading across the i-f tuned circuit is approximately

$$R_{eq} = \frac{R_D}{2\eta} \qquad . \quad (22)$$

where η is the efficiency of rectification[2].

In the circuit of Fig. 2, the diode load resistor, as determined by video design limitations, is 4,700 ohms. A practical value of diode efficiency is 50 percent. Then, by Eq. 22, the loading on the last tuned circuit is equivalent to 4,700 ohms. The bandwidth of this circuit, if a 1 to 1 transformer or a single coil

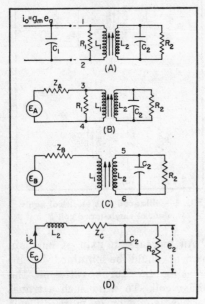

FIG. 5—Successive applications of Thevenin's theorem shows that single-tuned and bifilar-coupled circuits are equivalent

is employed, will be given by

$$\Delta f = \frac{1}{2\pi R C_T} \qquad (23)$$

where C_T = total input plus output capacitance, R = total equivalent shunt loading and the gain is given by $g_m R$.

In a typical practical amplifier C_T is equal to approximately 10 $\mu\mu f$. Then $\Delta f = 3.4$ mc.

The particular i-f system shown represents a stagger-tuned triple of over-all 3-db bandwidth equal to 2.2 mc. Stagger-tuned design formulas indicate that the broadest individual circuit shall have a 3-db bandwidth of 2.2 mc. The problem

is not to obtain maximum gain × bandwidth, but to devise some means of narrowing the bandwidth from 3.4 mc to 2.2 mc, and then to obtain as much gain as possible with that bandwidth.

In Eq. 23 R and C_T are the parameters over which we have some control. The most obvious method for narrowing the bandwidth is by adding fixed capacitance. But Eq. 23 and the gain equation show that the effect will be to narrow the bandwidth without increasing the gain.

However, it is possible to narrow the bandwith by some matching device, and increase the gain somewhat at the same time. If a bifilar coil is employed, Eq. 3 indicates that the diode loading resistance is multiplied by $\sqrt{L_1/L_2}$. The tube plate loading is simultaneously reduced by a factor $\sqrt{L_1/L_2}$ but the plate loading resistance is so large that this effect is unimportant.

If the capacitance on the plate side of T_3 in Fig. 2 equals 8 $\mu\mu f$ and that on the diode side equals 2 $\mu\mu f$, then the equivalent capacitance for Fig. 4B according to Eq. 2 is given by $C = 8N + 2/N$ where $N = \sqrt{L_1/L_2}$ and by Eq. 3 $1/R = 1/(4,700N)$. Therefore

$$\Delta f = \frac{1}{2\pi \times 4,700 N \times \left(8N + \frac{2}{N}\right) 10^{-12}}$$
$$= 2.2 \times 10^6$$
$$N = \sqrt{1.68} = 1.30$$

That is, if the primary and secondary inductances have a ratio of 1.68 to 1, the video diode load will be transformed to produce the desired bandwidth of 2.2 mc. Then the gain = $g_m R = 1.30 \times 4,700\ g_m$.

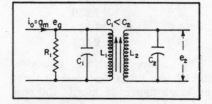

FIG. 6—Circuit with unequal capacitances and coupling of 100 percent

Hence, an increase in gain of 30 percent over that obtainable by

adding shunt capacitance is realized through use of a bifilar coil.

The same impedance step-up, and consequent increase in gain, could be obtained by use of a suitable tapped coil or capacitance divider, but the bifilar coil is the simplest and most economical scheme.

Impedance Transformer

There are several other instances in the design of stagger-tuned i-f amplifiers where the use of a bifilar coil as an impedance transformer is desirable. For example, when the transit time loading of the tube itself becomes almost as large as the desired loading, the bifilar coil provides a simple means of decreasing this loading. One disadvantage of appreciable tube loading is poor noise immunity. Another disadvantage is that this loading varies between tubes, and therefore cannot be relied on to provide uniformity in production.

A bifilar coil enables the tube impedance to be stepped up and the circuit loaded with a close tolerance resistor, assuring uniformity of response. As mentioned previously, a narrow bandwidth and a high i-f frequency both result in the tube loading becoming appreciable. It is even possible in some amplifier design for the tube loading to exceed the desired circuit loading unless some step-up is employed.

Another instance where the circuit loading may exceed the required loading dictated by design considerations is the plate loading of a triode mixer. Here again, a bifilar coil of proper turns ratio may be employed to step up the mixer plate impedance, so that a fixed loading resistor can be used to insure circuit stability.

The bifilar type of construction lends itself most readily to a close wound assembly. Hence, the coil Q obtained is not as high as a space-wound single coil, but Q's of the value of 70 are obtained with no difficulty, and this is sufficient for most applications.

As the turns ratio between windings is increased, the difficulty of obtaining coupling approaching 100 percent is also multiplied. Also, the winding process itself becomes more difficult and expensive. All of the previous derivations were based upon the assumption that 100 percent coupling existed between the coils. If a high degree of coupling is not present, the bifilar coil is no longer equivalent to a single-tuned circuit, so that more than one resonant frequency may result. Coils having a step-up ratio as high as 1.30 to 1 have been tried with no difficulties.

A final limitation of the use of bifilar coils is the fact that they preclude the usual method of neutralization of grid to plate capacitance.

Where the i-f is high, and the stage gain and grid to plate capacitance large, it may be necessary to provide neutralization of the grid-to-plate capacitance to avoid the dis-symmetry of the response curve resulting from feedback. In an i-f amplifier, this neutralization is usually provided by choice of a proper value of common plate screen bypass capacitor that enables balancing a capacitance bridge which prevents the feedback of output voltage (plate to screen) to the input terminals (grid to ground). Hence, the plate voltage is prevented from coupling back to the grid and the tube grid to plate capacitance is

effectively neutralized.

When a bifilar coil is employed, the r-f voltage developed across the bifilar coil primary is effectively shorted across one leg of the bridge by the bifilar secondary and the balance is no longer maintained. In other words, the screen of the tube is effectively grounded by the secondary of the transformer, so that neutralization by this method is impractical.

REFERENCES

(1) G. E. Valley, Jr. and H. Wallman, "Vacuum Tube Amplifiers," Ch. 4, McGraw-Hill Book Co., New York, 1948.
(2) F. E. Terman, "Radio Engineering," Third Edition, p 504, McGraw-Hill Book Co., New York, 1947.

Determining Form Factors of I-F Transformers

By WILLIAM C. VERGARA

THE DEGREE OF COUPLING of a conventional i-f transformer can be determined readily by measuring the bandwidths at two levels of attenuation and computing the ratio of these bandwidths. This ratio is directly related to the coupling factor of the transformer and is plotted in the accompanying graph to facilitate the determination.

Development of Method

The selectivity characteristic of the circuit shown on the graph is given by the well known (see for example J. E. Maynard's treatment in ELECTRONICS, p 15, Feb. 1937) relation given at the top of the graph with the terms as defined. The assumptions on which this relation was derived limit its validity to the practical case where only frequencies close to resonance are of interest; that is (1) the Q's are constant for all frequencies close to resonance, (2) the Q's are sufficiently high so that the inductive and capacitive reactances are equal and parallel and series resonances

occur at substantially the same frequency, (3) there is no feedback in the associated vacuum tube circuit and (4) the tuned circuits are coupled by pure reactance.

This relation (at the top of the graph) can be solved for s giving the result shown on the graph. This expression relates the departure from resonance s to the coupling factor b and the attenuation factor u.

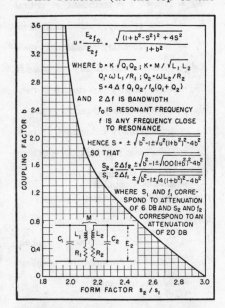

Transformer coupling can be determined simply from this chart and measurements at bandwidth at two levels of attenuation from the response at resonance

graph) can be solved for s giving the result shown on the graph. This expression relates the departure from resonance s to the coupling factor b and the attenuation factor u.

The factor s and therefore the bandwidth can be computed for any level of attenuation by substituting the appropriate value of u. Let s_1 be defined as the bandwidth factor corresponding to an attenuation of 6 db below the response at the resonant frequency; u is then equal to 2. Similarly, s_2 corresponds to an attenuation of 20 db for which u is 10.

Substituting these values of u and writing the ratio s_2/s_1 gives the final equation presented on the graph. This equation is plotted as the curve of the graph and is used in determining the coupling factor of a transformer.

Using the Graph

The ratio s_2/s_1 equals the ratio of the bandwidths at 20 and at 6-db attenuation. The coupling factor b

can be determined for a particular transformer by measuring s_2/s_1 and then reading the corresponding value of b from the graph.

The choice of 6 and 20-db levels for the bandwidth measurements was made arbitrarily for ease and accuracy of performing the measurements.

Measure Coupling Coefficient in Tuned R-F Transformers

By S. G. FELDMAN AND M. GOLDSTEIN

IN THE DESIGN of proximity-coupled double-tuned transformers, the measurement of the coupling coefficient in terms of critical coupling has been a tedious process producing less than accurate results. The measurement can be simplified to a great extent by application of the equations resulting from the analysis of double-tuned transformers.

Proximity coupling in double-tuned transformers usually consists of the resultant of inductive coupling and distributed capacitive coupling as shown in Fig. 1A. The more common methods of measuring the amount of coupling present

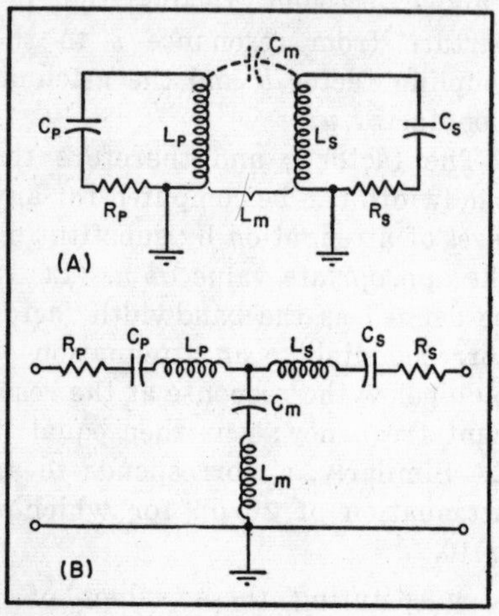

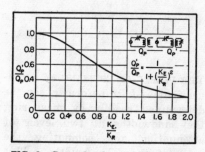

FIG. 1—Basic diagram showing contribution of inductive and distributed-capacitance coupling

usually determine the inductive component and neglect the other on the assumption that the capacitive coupling component is very small through proper design. This assumption is erroneous as it introduces a variable parameter that

often results in unaccountable non-uniformity among mass-produced transformers. The following method will measure the composite effect of both types of coupling, and evaluate the result in percent of critical coupling.

Application and Measurement

Referring to the equivalent circuit of a proximity-coupled double-tuned transformer in Fig. 1B, analysis of the circuit results in the following equation:

$$\frac{Q_P'}{Q_P} = \frac{1}{1 + (K_E/K_R)^2} \qquad (1)$$

where the following terminology has been used

K_L = coefficient of inductive coupling
K_C = coefficient of capacitive coupling
$K_E = K_L - K_C$ = effective coefficient of coupling
$K_R = 1/(Q_P Q_S)^{1/2}$ = coefficient of critical coupling
R_p = series primary resistance at resonance
R_s = series secondary resistance at resonance
R_P' = effective series primary resistance at resonance
C_P = series primary capacitance at resonance
C_S = series secondary capacitance at resonance
L_P = series primary inductance at resonance
L_S = series secondary inductance at resonance
$Q_P = \omega L_P/R_P$ = primary Q without secondary coupled
$Q_S = \omega L_S/R_S$ = secondary Q without primary coupled
$Q_P' = \omega L_P/R_P'$ = effective primary Q with secondary coupled
$L_M = K_L/(L_P L_S)^{1/2}$ = inductive coupling component
$C_M = (C_P C_S)^{1/2}/kc$ = capacitive coupling component
f = resonant frequency
$\omega = 2\pi f$

Equation 1 has been plotted for values of K_E/K_R up to 2, thus developing Fig 2.

Interpretation of Eq. 1 indicates that Q_P'/Q_P is a function of composite coupling in percent of critical. Therefore, to evaluate Eq. 1 all that is necessary experimentally is to measure Q_P'/Q_P. With the aid of Fig. 2, the amount of effective coupling present in percent of critical can be readily determined.

One of the more simple methods to evaluate Q_P'/Q_P is as follows:

FIG. 2—Curve for determining coupling coefficient in percent of critical coupling

Using a Q-meter or equivalent circuit, resonate the primary winding at the proper frequency with the secondary winding open, or shorted, or detuned, so as not to affect the primary Q (Fig. 3A). Note the Q reading as being equal to Q_P. Then tune secondary winding to resonance by an indication of minimum response in primary Q reading (Fig. 3B). Interaction between primary and secondary will require a number of resettings of primary resonance for a maximum Q reading. The adjustments should be continued until no further interaction is noted. The new reading obtained is Q_P'.

Examples

Example 1. On the Q-meter Q_P reads 80; Q_P' reads 40. Thus,

Q_P'/Q_P equals 0.5. From Fig. 2, K_E/K_R is equal to 1.0, or the transformer is critically coupled.

Example 2. On the Q-meter Q_P reads 70; Q_P' reads 20. Thus, Q_P'/Q_P equals 0.35. From Fig. 2, K_E/K_R is equal to 1.35, or the transformer is over-coupled. To obtain the most accurate results, certain safeguards and precautions should be included in the measurement technique. The shunting effect of plate resistances and input grid resistances of tubes must be simulated by an equivalent resistor across each tuned circuit. The transformer shield can should be used and also grounded. The secondary winding should be properly oriented as to phase relationship. In making measurements on a transformer that is thought to be over-coupled, the reading for Q_P' must be considered in the light of a double-humped response curve. Variation of the signal frequency source will indicate the resonant point as being a minimum lying between two maxi-

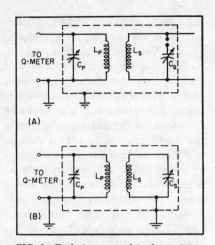

FIG. 3—Techniques used in determining coefficient of coupling with Q-meter

mum indications at frequencies slightly removed from the resonant frequency.

Conclusion

Although this paper is intentionally restricted to the measuring of the percent of critical coupling pre-

sent in a double-tuned transformer, it may also be applied to other types as well. For instance, taking the case of an untuned primary coupled to a tuned secondary transformer, Q_P'/Q_P may be evaluated with the Q-meter method by assuming the tuned winding as being the primary. Then Q_p will be the reading obtained with untuned winding open-circuited, and Q_P' will be obtained by loading the untuned winding properly with a resistor simulating the desired input matching impedance. The ratio Q_P'/Q_P thus obtained will indicate the amount of coupling present from Fig. 2 in percent of optimum coupling, where optimum coupling is equivalent to the condition of maximum transfer of power.

Likewise, though all the above equations are derived in percent of a reference term, their absolute magnitudes can be obtained readily, in most cases, by evaluating the reference term.

Graphical Iron-Core Reactor Design

By MORTON R. WHITMAN

REACTOR DESIGNERS are usually plagued by the mutually hostile requirements of speed and an optimum balance of the parameters involved in the design of reactors which carry both direct and alternating currents.

An optimum balance means the use of readily available parts and standard production techniques, a minimum of material in construction, low operating noise level and good thermal and insulation characteristics.

The principal difficulty in this problem arises from the nonlinearity of the magnetic material used in core structures. This makes impossible the derivation of an explicit formula which could give accurately say, the size and weight of a specified reactor. The purpose

here is to suggest empirical techniques for doing these things.

Model theory offers a useful approach to this problem. It generalizes the results obtained on a sample and makes possible, in effect, the extrapolation of the data so obtained. The precision of data obtained in this way depends on how accurately a unit holds to scale with this sample, or prototype. Nevertheless, even if the scale factor is omitted from consideration, the results are significant from a design point of view.

An important result of the kind discussed is the relation: weight equals kLI^2 where weight is that of either core iron or total core and coil weight (adjustment of the constant k can be performed to suit one requirement

or the other since in a line of geometrically similar reactors the winding weight will be a relatively fixed percentage of total core and coil weight); L is the inductance, and I is the direct current in the winding. An alignment chart is presented in Fig. 1 to expedite use of this relationship. The chart is not intended to give actual design figures but can be made to do so by reference to the data on an arbitrarily selected prototype unit and appropriate vertical displacement of the axes. Greatest accuracy can be secured by choosing as prototype a unit somewhere in the desired range of size and weight.

A second relation gives the weight in terms of the time constant, L/R, of the reactor. Here, R is the simple ohmic resistance of the winding—L/R equals $KW^z/3$. The form of this equation makes graphical representation very simple. Measurements of the time constant and the weight on a single unit are used as the co-ordinates of a point on log-log paper. A straight line drawn through this point with a slope equal to $\frac{2}{3}$ completes the graph. A typical curve is shown in Fig. 2.

The curves must be used with caution since generally they are

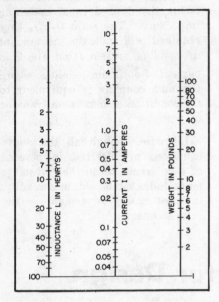

FIG. 1—Alignment chart which may be altered to give actual design figures by reference to data on an arbitrarily selected prototype unit and appropriate vertical displacement of vertical axes

valid only when conditions of similarity to the prototype are maintained. Varying insulation requirements, cooling considerations and other considerations introduce error. Nevertheless, the curves are useful for estimating purposes and for reducing the number of steps in the preliminaries to actual design.

Filter reactors for use with polyphase rectifier systems operate at considerably lower excitation levels than corresponding single-phase systems for the same output voltage. Since permeability is an increasing function of the excitation up to some maximum characteristic of the material used, the polyphase filter reactor will in general be different from the single-phase unit. The difference will not be so large, however, that the charts will not be of some use for both.

An illustration of the use of the curves will be given here. Assume we wish to design a reactor of 5 henrys at 1 amp d-c. The insulation level, excitation and thermal characteristics will be neglected to illustrate the technique.

From Fig. 1, the weight will be 47 pounds. From Fig. 2 the time constant will be 0.46. Hence, the nominal resistance will be 5/0.46 or approximately 11 ohms. On the basis of the information now available the required lamination size is

readily determined.

A square center leg cross-section will give minimum length of turn for the winding for a given cross-section area so that using minimum copper weight as a criterion the lamination size may be picked out from a table of lamination sizes and weights per square stack. Since the resistance is known, the number of turns in the winding may be readily determined in terms of the mean length of turn for the core size chosen. The design may then be refined by consideration of the factors which have been omitted up to this point. In most instances only relatively slight changes will be required.

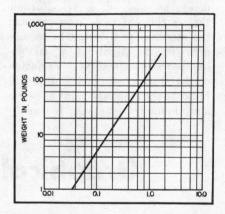

FIG. 2—Design curve for finding weight of a single reactor unit from the reactor time constant, L/R

Wideband Series-Parallel Transformer Design

By VINCENT C. RIDEOUT

SERIES-PARALLEL tuned transformers may be used to match a low-impedance transmission line to a higher impedance line (Fig. 1A), or to give a flat-band connection between a low-impedance line and the capacitive input or output of an amplifier (Fig. 1B). Maximally-flat-response formulas are based

upon a filter theory approach which uses the fact that the series-parallel transformer may be put into the form of a half-section constant-k band-pass filter plus an ideal transformer. The bandwidth Δf_c between cutoff frequencies f_1 and f_2 of the constant-k filter becomes the bandwidth between one-db points on

the corresponding transformer. Let f_m be the geometric mid-frequency. We then have

$$f_2 - f_1 = \Delta f_c \equiv \Delta\omega_c/2\pi \qquad (1)$$
$$\sqrt{f_1 f_2} = f_m \equiv \omega_m/2\pi \qquad (2)$$

The design formulas for a maximally-flat transformer of the form shown in Fig. 1 may be expressed in terms of $\Delta\omega_c$, ω_m, the generator (or

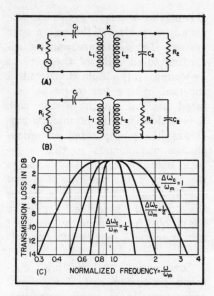

FIG. 1—Series-parallel transformers and normalized response curves for various bandwidth-to-midfrequency ratios

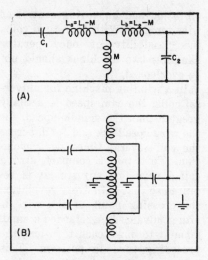

FIG. 2—Series-parallel transformer in equivalent-T form is shown in (A). Inductive coupling (B) must be used in balanced-to-unbalanced transformers

load) resistance R_1 and the input (or output) capacitance C_2.

$$C_1 = \Delta\omega_c/\omega_m{}^2 R_1 \quad (3)$$
$$L_1 = [1 + (\Delta\omega_c/\omega_m)^2] R_1/\Delta\omega \quad (4)$$
$$R_2 = 1/\Delta\omega_c C_2 \quad (5)$$
$$L_2 = 1/\omega_m{}^2 C_2 \quad (6)$$
$$k = M/\sqrt{L_1 L_2} = \frac{\Delta\omega_c/\omega_m}{\sqrt{1+(\Delta\omega_c/\omega_m)^2}} \quad (7)$$

The amplitude response of this transformer is geometrically symmetrical about f_m, with a loss curve given by $p = 1 + \frac{1}{4}(\Delta\omega/\Delta\omega_c)^4$ where $\Delta\omega$ is the bandwidth between any two points of equal loss. In Fig. 1C loss curves are plotted against normalized frequency for three values of the ratio $\Delta\omega_c/\omega_m = (f_2 - f_1)/\sqrt{f_1 f_2}$.

EXAMPLE: A matched input transformer is to be designed to connect a coaxial line ($R_1 = 50$ ohms) to the first tube (a 6AK5, $C_g = 8.5\ \mu\mu f$) of an amplifier. One-db points are to be at $f_1 = 80$ mc and at $f_2 = 120$ mc. The design formulas give:

$$\Delta\omega_c = 2\pi\,(120-80)\ 10^6 = 2.51 \times 10^8 \text{ rad/sec}$$
$$\omega_m = 2\pi\sqrt{120 \times 80} \times 10^6 = 6.15 \times 10^8 \text{ rad/sec}$$
$$C_1 = 13.27\ \mu\mu f$$
$$L_1 = 0.2325\ \mu h$$
$$R_2 = 468 \text{ ohms}$$
$$L_2 = 0.311\ \mu h$$
$$k = 0.378$$

It may be preferable to build the T (or π) equivalent of the transformer as shown in Fig. 2A. Since $M = k\sqrt{L_1 L_2} = 0.102\ \mu h$ in our example, $L_a = 0.130\ \mu h$ and $L_b = 0.209\ \mu h$. It is obvious that certain designs may call for a negative L_a or L_b and so cannot be built in equivalent T (or π) form. In the case of balanced line inputs a construction such as that shown in Fig. 2B may be used.

Coil-Winder Nomograph

Methods of winding reliable universal, interleaf and bobbin coils for electronic equipment, and instructions for constructing a nomograph that shows minimum coil-lot size at which an automatic winder becomes more economical than a manual machine

By CARL E. SULLIVAN, JR.

ELECTRICAL COILS, vital parts of any radio or tv set, undergo continual redesign either to improve performance or to cut costs. The decision of the production engineer as to how coils should be wound, what machines should be used, and how the machines should be set up becomes more and more vital as military requirements call for both short and long runs of entirely new coil designs. With the pool of skilled manpower dwindling

rapidly, the attractiveness of automatic coil-winding machinery increases correspondingly.

Fortunately, most of the coils used in radio, television and communication receivers use one of the following three types of construction: (1) Universal or lattice-wound coil; (2) interleaf coil; (3) bobbin coil.

The universal coil is by far the most familiar to the electronic engineer. This coil is recognized by

its open, self-supporting structure and the geometric pattern of the multi-strand Litzendraht wire lay. This geometric pattern is the secret of the coil's high Q, high inductance and minimum resistance. Typical applications are for peaking coils, traps and flyback transformers in television receivers.

The interleaf coil, characterized by insulating layers of paper or acetate sheet between layers of wire, is used in power transformers, audio output transformers and filter chokes. It is generally used with a laminated iron or steel core and for these applications is square or rectangular in shape.

The bobbin coil, least used for radio and tv, is simply a single random winding in a flanged paper or plastic bobbin. Its purpose is to supply a controllable magnetic field, as in the focus coil of a tv receiver.

Winding Universal Coils

Machines for winding universal coils require accurate construction because these coils are self-supporting, depending solely on their construction for strength. The wire must be laid down in an accurate predetermined pattern that varies with the size of the wire, the diameter of the tube and the turns.

The average universal coil contains about 700 turns. As winding machines run between 700 and 1,000 rpm, winding time is seldom longer than 1 minute. On the other hand, the time required to handle or prepare the coil while on the machine is comparatively long, and each operation must be repeated for each individual coil.

To obtain maximum productivity, the largest coil multiple physically possible should be used. For universal coils, common practice is to wind four in multiple (four coils at a time). An additional advantage of a large coil multiple is that it permits a more flexible choice of speeds. Generally, after removing the completed coils from the machine the operator has a finishing operation to perform on each coil during winding of the next set.

Assuming a unit time for this operation of, say, 30 seconds, the operator would be busy for 2 minutes between sets with a four-coil multiple, but only 1 minute with a two-coil multiple. With the larger multiple, therefore, it is possible to wind at half the speed of the two-coil multiple and achieve the same productivity.

Lower speed is a definite advantage for it reduces maintenance on the machine and improves the quality of the winding by reducing vibration and improving control of wire tension. With high-turn coils, the possibility of one operator handling two machines should not be overlooked.

In a winding machine for universal coils, the cam speed is actually greater than the spindle speed, for the wire goes back and forth across the coil several times per revolution. To obtain a compact, strong coil a very fine adjustment is required so that with every revolution the crossing point of the wire is either advanced or retarded a small amount to make each turn lock the preceding turn in position. This amount is approximately equal to the size of the wire being wound. The device which controls this spacing is called a gainer. Its correct setting can be determined only by trial and error, for there are so many variables. The gainer adjustment is stepless and permits winding a coil for any degree of compactness, but there is only one setting which will give the electrical and dimensional requirements of any one specification.

Manual Interleaf Machines

In manual winding machines for interleaf coils, the interleaf paper is inserted by the operator at the completion of each layer. In automatic machines, the interleaf paper is inserted automatically by the machine without stopping the arbor. The manual machine is the more popular because it is simpler, more flexible and less expensive. However, each machine has its own merits and field of application.

The manual machine is designed for simplicity, a minimum of adjustments and low cost. Coils are wound in multiples up to thirty on arbor-supported paper tubes 16 to 30 inches long, and wide sheets of insulating paper are inserted by the operator between each wire layer. Upon completion, the stick is marked, removed from the machine, then cut into individual coils on a band saw.

An electric motor operating through a friction clutch drives the arbor or spindle, and this in turn drives the traversing mechanism, usually a leadscrew, through a gear system. The gears are selected according to the size of the wire to be wound. Adjustable stops control reversal of the leadscrew as dictated by the length of the coil. Recent development of manual machines has concentrated on quick-change mechanisms so that a female operator can quickly change the setup of the machine to a new specification. This feature makes the manual machine especially adaptable for producing coils of few turns and in small-lot quantities.

Commercial coil-winding concerns producing coils for several users, usually in small quantities, are mostly equipped with manual machines because of their extreme flexibility. Generally, however, they have a few automatic machines for high-production stock items.

Automatic Interleaf Machine

Equipment manufacturers who wind their own coils are predominantly equipped with automatic machines, as their runs are long. The automatic machine can be run at higher speeds, up to 2,500 rpm, as the paper is inserted at full speed, whereas the operator must slow down while inserting manually. Furthermore, since the entire winding operation is automatic, the operator can perform some finishing operation during winding.

The automatic machine is more expensive and inherently more complex than the manual. Setup time, too, is longer on automatics when changing over from one coil specification to another.

Choice of Machine

A production engineer fortunate enough to have both manual and automatic winding equipment at his disposal must always analyze each coil specification closely and decide where production would be less costly—on the hand-fed machines or on the automatics. A nomograph of the type shown in Fig. 1 can be worked up for any specific plant to aid in determining whether or not it would be economical to place a coil on an automatic machine. Handling time on the machine when the wire is not running is the variable that depends on the individual plant and the abilities of its mechanics.

The curves shown are for two different ratios of handling times, designated for convenience as class A and class B. Usually a plant will make two or even more distinct types of coils having different handling times, and here one set of curves is needed for each type on the nomograph. If desired, the curves can be designated more specifically by type names such as *Output, Type 1* or *Reactor, Type 5*, as being more descriptive of the types of work being run by the particular concern.

Once the nomograph has been drawn, its use is simple. Merely trace across from the desired value of coil turns to the appropriate upper curve, trace down from there to the corresponding lower curve, then trace across to the right-hand scale and read the minimum economical lot size for an automatic machine.

Winding Bobbin Coils

Machines for winding bobbin coils are the simplest of all in construction. Since the flanges of the bobbin support the coil, a precise lay of wire is not required and a gainer mechanism is unnecessary. A wide range of traverse speeds is required, but fine regulation is not. Generally, winders for bobbin coils are of the single-spindle variety with but one coil being wound at a time.

Sometimes two or more single-spindle units are ganged together on a machine to operate with one common traverse mechanism. The three-spindle arrangement lends itself to extremely high operator and machine efficiency, for winding speed can be so adjusted that winding time equals twice the handling time. Two spindles of the machine are always running while the operator tends the third. Just as she finishes at one spindle the next goes down and is ready to be tended. With this system, one coil is obtained for every handling time. The primary rule to follow when placing a coil on this machine is to minimize the amount of handling to be done at the machine. These machines are fitted with special motors and tensions to enable high winding speeds (5,000 rpm), and every effort should be made to take full advantage of this feature. These machines can be purchased with spindles in any multiple up to six, depending on the type of coil to be run.

This discussion has been limited to general over-all considerations pertinent in any plant, in an effort to clarify somewhat the problems facing the coil production engineer.

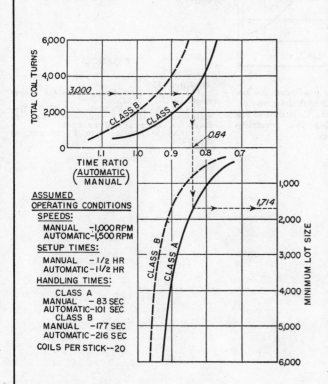

FIG. 1—Example of nomograph that can be prepared for any plant to determine whether automatic or manual winding machines are more economical for a particular job. In construction steps given below, values in parentheses are those for plant and coil used as example in nomograph

(1) Find average winding speeds for automatic (1,500 rpm) and manual (1,000 rpm) winding machines

(2) For one representative coil (3,000 turns), find handling time (total time on machine with wire not running, including taping, inserting taps and other hand work) per stick for the automatic (101 sec) and manual (83 sec) machines

(3) For same coil, find winding time (total turns divided by speed) for automatic (120 sec) and manual (180 sec)

(4) Add handling and winding times to get total time for automatic (221 sec) and manual (263 sec)

(5) Divide total time on automatic by total time on manual to get time ratio (0.84)

(6) Repeat steps 2, 3, 4 and 5 for the same type of coil having different turns, and plot resulting time ratio values against turns to get upper curve (500 turns gives 1.07 ratio; 6,000 gives 0.77)

(7) For first coil (3,000 turns) find difference in total time per stick (263 — 221 = 42 sec) as time gained on automatic per stick of 20 coils

(8) Find setup time (total time to readjust machine to new coil specification) for automatic (1½ hours) and manual (½ hour). Take difference (1 hour or 3,600 sec) and divide by time gained per stick on automatic (42 sec) to get 85.7 sticks as break-even point. Multiply by coils per stick (20) to get minimum lot size (1,714 coils) at which use of automatic machine is justified

(9) Repeat steps 7 and 8 for coils having different turns, and plot minimum lot size against time ratio values to get lower curve of nomograph (500 turns gives beyond-infinity lot size; 6,000 turns gives 705 coils minimum lot size)

Resistor Behavior at High Frequencies

VARIOUS types of resistors exhibit different characteristics when operating in the region above ten megacycles, depending on their physical size, nature of resistance element and physical location. The analysis of an isolated resistance element was first considered by Howe[1] and later by Hartshorn[2]. It has been found that experimental values compare quite well with theoretical values.

The experimental equipment used in determining the behavior of resistors at high frequencies includes two G-R resistance bridges, a Measurements Corp. signal generator, and a Hallicrafters SX-42 receiver which served as the detector. Various values of resistors between 50 and 77,000 ohms were measured, and their equivalent resistances calculated by Hartshorn's method.[2]

It was found that for standard types, the equivalent resistance of a resistor decreases more rapidly with frequency for high d-c value resistors than for low-value resistors. For the same value of d-c resistance, the smaller the physical size of the resistor, the better are its high-frequency characteristics.

The carbon type proved to be superior to composition for high-frequency work, but both of these types are inferior to resistors made with a carbon coating on an insulator. Wire-wound resistors are too reactive for use as resistors above about 10 mc. For resistors whose construction permits analysis by Hartshorn's calculations, the experimental and calculated values conform within 10 percent. Thus it may be concluded that the equivalent resistance of almost any resistor under one megohm may be predicted with fair accuracy from Hartshorn's curve, shown above. The falling off of resistors of greater d-c value may be explained qualitatively by combining this and the Boella effect.

The Boella effect[3,4] theory states that the molecules of the resistance element are separated by minute insulators which form capacitors. This is, however, strictly a qualitative theory and would be extremely difficult to analyze on a quantitative basis. This effect may be neglected for values less than one megohm; higher values contain much more nonconducting material in their composition, thereby giving rise to an increased number of the minute capacitors mentioned above.

This experimental verification of the theoretical characteristics of resistances at high frequencies was described by George R. Arthur and Samuel E. Church of Yale University in a research report for the U. S. Signal Corps and presented orally by H. L. Krauss, also of Yale, at the 1950 IRE National Convention.

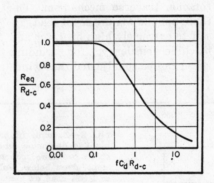

Hartshorn's curve for predicting the behavior of resistors at high frequencies. Distributed capacitance C_d is that of the isolated resistor plus the proximity effects

REFERENCES

(1) G. W. O. Howe, *Wireless Engineer*, 12, June 1935.
(2) L. H. Hartshorn, *Wireless Engineer*, 15, July 1938.
(3) O. S. The Behavior of High Resistances at High Frequencies, *Wireless Engineer*, 12, p 303, June 1935.
(4) Mario Boella, Alta Frequenza, 3, Apr. 1934.

Temperature-Compensating Capacitor Nomograph

Gives directly with one setting of a celluloid triangle the capacitance values required when two temperature-compensating capacitors are paralleled. Solves problem of compensating a tuned circuit when a single capacitor having the required temperature coefficient is not available

By THOMAS T. BROWN

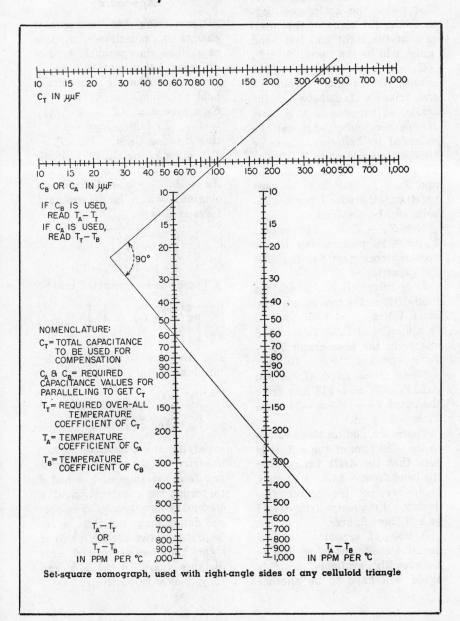

NOMENCLATURE:

C_T = TOTAL CAPACITANCE TO BE USED FOR COMPENSATION

C_A & C_B = REQUIRED CAPACITANCE VALUES FOR PARALLELING TO GET C_T

T_T = REQUIRED OVER-ALL TEMPERATURE COEFFICIENT OF C_T

T_A = TEMPERATURE COEFFICIENT OF C_A

T_B = TEMPERATURE COEFFICIENT OF C_B

Set-square nomograph, used with right-angle sides of any celluloid triangle

ONE of the most common ways of compensating for the effect of temperature coefficients of coils or capacitors on the frequency of a tuned circuit is by the use of ceramic capacitors of large negative coefficient in parallel with the normal mica or air-spaced capacitor. The values of these components are usually estimated by proportion and trial and error to get an overall temperature coefficient of zero. The accompanying chart gives these values directly.

To use the chart, set a triangle or set square to join two known values on two parallel scales. Then move the triangle back or forward along the line of intersection until its right-angle edge cuts the third value on the other scale. The unknown value is then read off where this edge cuts the remaining scale; i.e., each side intersects two values. A setting of three values on one edge is not valid.

The algebraic sign of an unknown value obtained from a vertical scale will be the same as that of the known value on the other vertical scale.

The range of the chart can be readily extended by multiplying the scales by factors of ten in any of the following four ways: all four scales, two parallel scales, top horizontal and right vertical or lower horizontal and left vertical pairs of scales.

Example 1

A fixed-frequency oscillator is tuned by a 400-$\mu\mu$f capacitor to 2 mc. The coil has a temperature coefficient of +40 parts per million per degree C, and it is required to compensate this to zero drift. Capacitors rated at

+20 ppm and −220 ppm are available. What are the values required?

Solution. $C_T = C_A + C_B$. $T_T = -40$ ppm, $T_A = +20$, $T_B = -220$ and $C_T = 400$, so that $T_A - T_T = +60$ and $T_A - T_B = +240$.

With one of the right-angled sides of a set-square or triangle on the nomograph, join the point 60 on the $T_A - T_T$ scale with 240 on the $T_A - T_B$. Now advance the perpendicular edge of the set-square until it cuts the C_T scale at 400 $\mu\mu$f, still keeping the other two points intersected, and read the required value of C_B as 100 $\mu\mu$f at the intersection on the C_B scale. The required values are thus a 100-$\mu\mu$f capacitor with −220 ppm temperature coefficient and a $400 - 100 = 300$ $\mu\mu$f capacitor with +20 ppm coefficient, connected in parallel.

Example 2

In a particular wave analyzer, the low-frequency waveform is heterodyned by an oscillator working between 500 and 550 kc, and the harmonic components of the modulated wave are separated by a crystal filter. It is desirable to have this oscillator free from frequency variation due to changes in ambient temperature. The tuning capacitor to be used has a range of 50 to 300 $\mu\mu$f with the low-temperature coefficient of +20 ppm. The coil is wound on a ceramic form and has a coefficient of +80 ppm.

Since only a 10-percent frequency sweep is required, it will be necessary to pad out the capacitor to reduce the capacitance sweep to 20 percent; at the same time this capacitor can be used to provide temperature compensation. A 950-$\mu\mu$f unit in parallel with the variable capacitor gives a sweep of 1,000 to 1,250 $\mu\mu$f providing slight overlap at the ends of the scale. Exact temperature compensation is to be provided at the center of

the band, which is 1,125 $\mu\mu$f.

Solution. Let $C_T = 1,125$ $\mu\mu$f, $C_A = 950$ $\mu\mu$f, $C_B = 175$ $\mu\mu$f, and $T_B = +20$.

The overall coefficient of the capacitor combination to compensate for the +80 ppm of the coil will be given by $T_T = -80$, and therefore $T_T - T_B = -100$.

Multiplying scales C_T and C_A by a factor of 10, with 112.5 $\mu\mu$f on the C_T scale joined to 95 $\mu\mu$f on the C_A scale by one edge of a right-angle triangle, the other edge is advanced to intersect 100 on the $T_T - T_B$ scale, whence $T_A - T_B$ is read as 118. (Note that since the scales are logarithmic, the signs of the products of the right and left hand scales will be the same; thus $T_A - T_B = -118$ since $T_T - T_B = -100$. Should the corner of the triangle fall between the scales, as happens in this case, the perpendicular edge can be extended by bringing a rule or another triangle up to it. Scales C_A and $T_T - T_B$, and scales C_B and $T_A - T_T$ may only be used together, otherwise incorrect results will be obtained.)

Now $T_A - T_B = -118$, so that $T_A = -98$ ppm, which is the required coefficient for the 950-$\mu\mu$f capacitor.

It is interesting to check the total drift at the two ends of the band. When $C_T = 1,250$ $\mu\mu$f, $C_A = 950$ $\mu\mu$f and $T_A - T_B = -118$ and from the nomograph $T_T - T_B = -90$ and $T_T = -70$ ppm.

When $C_T = 1,000$, $C_A = 950$ $\mu\mu$f, $T_A - T_B = -118$ and from the chart $T_T - T_B = -114$ and $T_T = -94$ ppm.

Therefore, adding these values to the +80 ppm of the coil, it is seen that the drift varies over the band from −14 to +10 ppm, being zero at the center frequency. Frequency drift would be half these figures.

A 950-$\mu\mu$f capacitor with a negative coefficient of 98 ppm is not readily available, so this again will have to be another

parallel combination of two capacitors. Since a silvered mica capacitor is generally a more stable component than a ceramic capacitor, it will be better to use a large mica capacitor with a low positive coefficient and a small ceramic with as large a negative coefficient as is available. Assume this to be −680 ppm, and that of the silvered mica to be +20 ppm. Then $T_A - T_B = 700$ and $T_A - T_T = 118$, and from the nomograph $C_B = 100$ $\mu\mu$f (ceramic) and $C_A = 950 - 160 = 790$ $\mu\mu$f (mica).

Appendix

Considering the incremental change in capacitance of two capacitors in parallel having different temperature coefficients, the following relationship holds: $C_A = nC_B = [n/(n+1)] C_T$, where $n = (T_B - T_T)/(T_T - T_A)$. By taking logs and putting $x = \log C_T$, $y = \log (T_A - T_B)$ and $z = \log C_B$, four simultaneous equations of the form $Ax + By + Cz + D = 0$ are obtained, which in determinant form are

$$\begin{vmatrix} 1 & 0 & 0 & -\log C_T \\ 0 & 1 & 0 & -\log (T_A - T_T) \\ 0 & 0 & 1 & -\log C_B \\ 1 & 1 & -1 & -\log (T_A - T_B) \end{vmatrix}$$

These can be converted into

$$\begin{vmatrix} \log (T_A - T_B) & 1 & 1 & 1 \\ \log (T_A - T_T) & 0 & 1 & 1 \\ \log C_T & 1 & 0 & 1 \\ \log C_B & 0 & 0 & 1 \end{vmatrix}$$

and are now in standard determinant form

$$\begin{vmatrix} f(a) & g(a) & 1 & 1 \\ f(b) & g(b) & 1 & 1 \\ f(c) & g(c) & 0 & 1 \\ f(d) & g(d) & 0 & 1 \end{vmatrix}$$

satisfying the conditions of colinearity of the coordinates of any four variables a, b, c and d to permit the construction of a set-square nomograph. The second determinant can thus be interpreted as two vertical pairs of logarithmic scales spaced unit distance apart, in the x, y and jx, jy planes respectively.

Adjustable Temperature-Coefficient Capacitor

IN SOME special radio-frequency circuits where a high degree of thermal stabilization is crucial, a capacitor with an adjustable temperature coefficient of capacitance may serve a vital purpose.

Commercially available fixed capacitors may be used in conjunction with high-quality inductors to produce tuned L-C circuits with some degree of thermal stability if proper care is taken in selecting compensating capacitors. In those cases where further refinement in frequency stabilization is necessary, it may well be advisable and practical to use a capacitor with a constant total capacitance and an adjustment shaft which will allow a wide variety of temperature coefficients to be selected at will. Such a capacitor should allow temperature coefficients (T-C values) over a rather large range and provide both positive and negative T-C values.

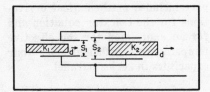

FIG. 1—Basic idea of adjustable temperature coefficient capacitor

The principles upon which a capacitor of this type may operate are illustrated by Fig. 1. Two parallel capacitors are coupled electrically and mechanically so that a change of the amount of dielectric in one capacitor is accompanied by a compensating (opposite) change in the second capacitor. The dielectric constants K_1 and K_2 and plate geometrics are chosen to keep the total shunt capacitance constant. Assuming that the mechanical displacements d and the corresponding changes in effective electrode areas are the same for both capacitors, the total shunt capacitance will

remain constant when

$$\frac{K_1}{S_1} = \frac{K_2}{S_2}$$

where S_1 and S_2 are the plate separations corresponding to K_1 and K_2.

Since a capacitor may be made in which two different dielectrics contribute to the total shunt capacitance, two materials with different temperature coefficients of dielectric constant may be selected. If the materials have coefficients of opposite sign, a capacitor of this type may be designed to have an adjustable T-C value over a wide range—possibly even passing through a condition of zero T-C.

The reliability of the ceramic trimmer type of adjustable-T-C capacitor leaves much to be desired. This type of capacitor ordinarily employs fired-on silver electrodes and a ceramic-to-silver rubbing contact acts to bring more or less of the active dielectric into the circuit. Mechanical abrasion effects often act to deposit small amounts of the silver electrodes on ceramic surfaces which should be ground flat and kept clean. Thus, erratic capacitance variations are often observed when such capacitors are used in circuits where a large number of capacitance adjustments are necessary. For many trimmer-capacitor applications relatively few adjustments are needed and variable ceramic capacitors given satisfactory service.

The temperature coefficients of many variable ceramic capacitors are difficult to control adequately. These T-C inconsistencies often arise as a result of the relatively high-K materials used as a dielectric. In many cases, inconsistencies are found in T-C and Q values of these capacitors as a result of moisture being trapped between rotor and stator elements even for capacitors employing only moderately

high-K dielectric materials. It thus appears that for the maximum degree of consistency the variable-ceramic capacitor type of construction should be avoided in favor of an air-capacitor arrangement.

It will be shown how a (fixed capacitance) variable-T-C capacitor can be designed without involving the difficulties inherent in any solid-dielectric variable capacitor of the ceramic-trimmer variety.

Proposed Capacitor

A four-element combination of capacitors can be made in such a way as to provide an equivalent capacitor which will maintain a constant total capacitance and provide an adjustable value of T-C. The adjustable elements of this device can be air-dielectric capacitors, thus avoiding the difficulties encountered with ceramic-dielectric capacitors. In this scheme four capacitors are connected in series-parallel as shown in Fig. 2. One element in each series leg is a variable air-dielectric capacitor. These two capacitors C_x and C_y are mechanically coupled so that, when they vary with respect to each other in accordance with a predetermined law, the equivalent capacitance (of the four-element combination) remains constant.

If the series capacitors C_1 and C_2 have vastly different T-C values, their individual effects in producing an equivalent T-C depend upon the relative amplitudes of C_x and C_y. For example, if the T-C of C_1 is positive and the T-C of C_2 is negative the total circuit will have a positive or negative T-C depending upon the contribution to the total by C_x or C_y. With this arrangement a capacitor can be designed which will be capable of maintaining its capacitance and yet be adjustable in T-C from a relatively large positive value to a relatively large negative value.

It is apparent intuitively from a study of Fig. 2 that for the widest latitude of variation in T-C, C_x and C_y must have the largest possible range of adjustability. In addition, it may seem fruitful to reduce the

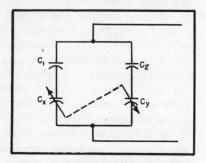

FIG. 2—Schematic representation of arrangement for obtaining continuously variable temperature coefficient capacitor with constant value of capacitance

magnitudes of C_1 and C_2 to an absolute minimum and yet maintain large T-C values for these elements. This procedure introduces difficulties, however, since capacitors having small capacitances and large T-C values are less predictable in the practical case. This results from the fact that these elements often employ relatively high-K materials which carry into any electrical circuit some undesirable instabilities.

For our purposes it appears to be most conservative to select a circuit of the kind proposed, such that

$$C_x = C_y = C_1 = C_2 = C$$

where C_x and C_y are the nominal (mid-range) values of capacitance for the respective variable air-dielectric capacitors. For this case it can be shown that the condition for constant equivalent circuit capacitance is given by

$$\Delta C_x = \frac{-\Delta C_y}{1 + \dfrac{\Delta C_y}{C}}$$

where

$\Delta C_y =$ any change in C_y made to change the equivalent T-C value, and

$\Delta C_x =$ the corresponding change in C_x necessary for a constant-capacitance condition.

This equation describes the conditions for tracking (maintenance of a constant equivalent capacitance) in a capacitor of the proposed design. If a parallel-plate construction is to be used, one air-dielectric capacitor can have linear capacitance variation with shaft rotation. In such a case the other variable capacitor would have to be designed with plates shaped in accordance with the tracking equation. A further refinement would involve plate shaping to make the two variable air capacitors identical in contour.

The total capacitance per unit volume for a capacitor of this type will ordinarily be about one-fourth that of a conventional air-dielectric

capacitor. The fixed capacitor elements of the proposed four-capacitor combination can be fixed ceramic capacitors which will add a negligible volume to the total. The air capacitors, however, must be individually set to their mid-values (in order to allow a T-C variation in two directions),

In some circuitry problems it may be possible to use the general scheme described without going to any effort to achieve mechanical tracking through the use of a common shaft or drive mechanism. A simple four-capacitor network can be employed and capacitance constancy indicated by a frequency-measuring technique. The network will be applicable to the individual circuit where it is used but no simple T-C characteristics can be attached to it unless the capacitance tracking condition is satisfied. Such a network will have the advantage of using only commercially available components and may find some application in critically stabilized L-C circuits.

The information presented here was taken from NRL Report 3689, by John A. Connor. The original report includes mathematical derivations for the tracking equation and for an expression for the effective temperature coefficient of four capacitors in series parallel.

Checking Crystals

By P. O. FARNHAM

MAINTENANCE and repair of military aircraft radio communications equipment in large quantities has evolved a means of checking crystals with a fundamental frequency in the region between 6 and 13 mc are considered. The equipment, the frequencies and the procedures can be modified slightly to include many other applications.

The equipment is arranged as shown in Fig. 1. Outputs at 10, 100 of 1,000-kc intervals can be selected

at will from the substandard of frequency. Each of the receivers is equipped with a beat-frequency oscillator that can be turned off if the receiver is used as a detector for beats from two other signal sources.

Direct frequency calibration is provided on the tuning dials of the receivers and the two tunable oscillators. Headphones and an output meter are used to indicate beat-frequency output from a receiver.

Before making measurements, the

1,000-kc crystal frequency of the substandard (5th harmonic) is checked against the 5-mc standard frequency signal from WWV by feeding both these signals to receiver 1 tuned to 5 mc. The 100-kc substandard intervals are next checked with receiver 2 in the beat-frequency condition. Beats should be observed only at each 100-kc scale line of the receiver dial.

With receiver 2 set nearly to zero beat on an even 100-kc mark (for example, 8 mc) the 10-kc intervals are then switched on in the substandard. The same beat frequency should be observed. As the receiver is tuned slowly towards 8.1 mc, it should be possible to count ten beats. Leaving the receiver near zero beat at the tenth count, the

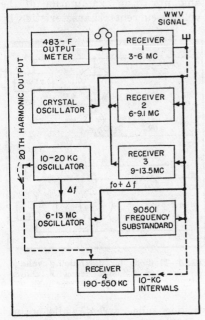

FIG. 1—Complete setup of receivers and oscillators for crystal calibration

100-kc interval is again switched in from the substandard. The beat frequency tone remains the same.

Measurement Method

The method of measurement of crystal oscillator frequency can be most clearly followed with a numerical example. Receiver 2 is used for crystal frequencies from 6 to 9 mc, receiver 3 for crystal frequencies from 9 to 13 mc. Assume that the

frequency indicated on the nameplate of the crystal is 7,361.1 kc, which will be called f_c. Using receiver 2, set the 6–13 mc oscillator accurately to the substandard 10-kc harmonic that lies somewhere between 10 and 20 kc below f_c.

In this example, the oscillator will be set to 7,350 kc and this frequency will be called f_o. The 10–20-kc oscillator is then turned on to modulate the 7,350-kc output and produce an upper sideband output adjustable from 7,360 to 7,370 kc.

The frequency of the 10–20-kc oscillator will be called Δf. The value of f is adjusted to produce zero-beat in the receiver output between the crystal and the upper sideband frequency of the 6–13 mc oscillator. The true crystal frequency f is obtained by adding the values of f_o and Δf.

The output-meter is used as a zero-beat indicator when bringing the 6–13 mc oscillator to zero beat with the desired 10-kc harmonic of the substandard. To establish the modulation frequency Δf of the 10–20-kc oscillator it is necessary to beat the crystal frequency and the modulated output of the 6–13-mc oscillator together in receiver 2.

The 10–20-kc oscillator is tuned approximately to 11.1 kc (for this case the value of f_c-f_o). Near this setting and with the receiver gain reduced to prevent pickup of an undesired sideband output ($f_o + 2\,\Delta f$) a relatively clean beat output tone of low frequency should be obtained from the receiver. This signal corresponds to pickup of the desired sideband output ($f_o + \Delta f$). It is distinguished from pickup at the undesired sideband by being free of

extra, high-frequency beat components.

The receiver should be tuned to maximum beat output and then the 10–20-kc oscillator adjusted for zero-beat output using the output meter. If this reading of Δf should come out 11.65 kc, this value will then be added to 7,350 (f_o) giving an actual crystal frequency f of 7,361.65 kc. The error ($f-f_c$) based upon the value stamped on the crystal holder will then be $+ 0.55$ kc or the percentage error will be $+ 0.00748$ percent.

If the actual crystal frequency f should be such that zero-beat setting of the 10–20 kc oscillator lies off its tuning range, it will be necessary to re-establish the setting of the 6–13-mc oscillator.

Suppose the actual crystal frequency f had been 7,359.3 kc instead of 7,361.65 used in the example. It would then be necessary to tune the 10–20-kc oscillator to a Δf value of 9.3 kc.

Since this value is not attainable, f_o (the 6–13-mc oscillator) must be reset to a new lower value of 7,340 kc. The value for Δf will then be 19.3 kc.

Similarly, if the actual crystal frequency were much higher than its nameplate value, it would then be necessary to reset the 6–13-mc oscillator to a new higher value of 7,360 kc. In either case, the actual frequency of the crystal is given by $f = f_o + \Delta f$.

Receiver 4 is used as a detector for beats between the substandard 10-kc intervals and the 20th harmonic of the 10–20-kc oscillator when it is desired to check the frequency calibration of the latter unit.

Tester for VR Tubes

By STEPHEN S. PESCHEL

VOLTAGE-REGULATOR tubes frequently light up or glow when they are not functioning properly—not stabilizing the voltage at the load

terminals. When used to stabilize an oscillator circuit for instance, they may flash on keying without going out, and give all outward ap-

pearances of working properly, but in reality they may be loafing on the job. Where voltage-regulation of the order of 1 percent may be needed, tests may disclose an actual regulation of 5 percent. Where such tubes are used in the series-type of electronically-regulated power supply for voltage reference, it is also important to use VR tubes that work properly.

With very rare exceptions new VR tubes, when operated properly, do stabilize voltages within the limits stated in tube handbooks. However, accidental current over-loads will impair their operation, and frequently make them entirely useless as regulators. Unless the gaseous discharge or glow changes to an arc discharge and actually burns the tube completely, the tube may appear to glow normally. Some sort of a checker is needed to test these tubes.

Reviewing theory briefly, VR tubes are specially constructed gaseous glow tubes which maintain a rather constant voltage drop when current through them is varied over quite a range. A fundamental voltage-stabilizing circuit using a VR150 is shown in Fig. 1. The limiting resistor is

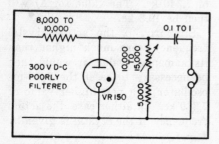

FIG. 1—Fundamental voltage - regulating circuit using VR150

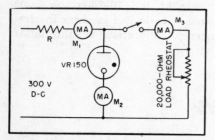

FIG. 2—Experimental setup for demonstrating filtering action of VR tube

necessary to limit tube current to a safe value. The resistance is generally selected to permit maximum

permissible current thru the VR, say 30 ma, with load disconnected. Its value is calculated by dividing tube current into the voltage difference (supply voltage less tube drop). In the above example, $R = (300 - 150/30$ ma $- 5,000$ ohms.

The supply voltage should be higher than the starting voltage, which is generally about 30 percent higher than the operating voltage. A high supply voltage calls for a high limiting resistor, which aids regulation.

Referring to Fig. 1, with no load (switch open) and R adjusted for maximum permissible current thru the VR150, say 30 ma, obviously both milliammeters, M_1 and M_2 will indicate the same current of 30 ma. With load rheostat set at full 20,000 ohms and the switch closed, M_3 will indicate the load current of 7.5 ma, M_2 will decrease from 30 to 22.5 ma, and M_1 will read the sum of M_2 and M_3 or 30 ma. As the rheostat is slowly cut out, M_3 will increase at the same rate as M_2 decreases, until the VR tube goes out. Then M_1 and M_3 will read the same, and M_2 will be zero.

The more commonly used VR tubes will regulate to within 1 to 3 volts out of 105 or 150 volts, when tube current is varied between 5 and 30 ma. At smaller current variations, voltage regulation will naturally be better.

Since VR tubes will regulate against very rapid current fluctuations, they will also regulate against a-c ripple voltage, which may be likened to a periodic current variation. The use of VR tubes on a poorly filtered power supply frequently produces results ordinarily obtained through the use of an additional section of filter. The filtering action of VR tubes may be easily demonstrated by a simple experiment, Fig. 2.

With all load resistance in the circuit, and the VR tube glowing, a faint hum may be heard in the phones. As the 10,000 to 15,000-ohm rheostat is decreased, a point will be reached where the glow will

disappear, at which time the hum in the phones will increase considerably. Measurements with any a-c vtvm capable of reading a few milli-volts will show approximately a hundred-fold reduction in ripple, when measured across the power supply and then across the VR tube.

One method of checking VR tubes amounts to an examination of the voltage-current characteristic by

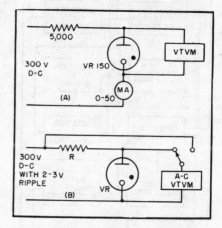

FIG. 3—Methods for determining voltage-current (A) and hum-reduction (B) characteristics of voltage-regulator tubes

varying tube current while noting the change in voltage drop across the tube, Fig. 3A. While the current is varied between 5 and 30 ma, tube drop may change from 153 to 150 volts. Unless a large, open-scale voltmeter is used it may be difficult to see this small change. Greater accuracy may be obtained by inserting a fresh B battery of 135 volts in series with the voltmeter and in opposition to normal current flow, to buck out all but some 15 volts. A low-range vtvm may then be used, when a differential of 2 or 3 volts will be more readily noticeable.

The second method of checking VR tubes takes advantage of the fact that the filtering action of the tube goes hand in hand with regulating ability. An average VR105, for instance, regulates better than the average VR90; it also attenuates ripple better. A simple circuit, Fig. 3B, illustrates this type of VR tube checker.

A VR tube checker with a small

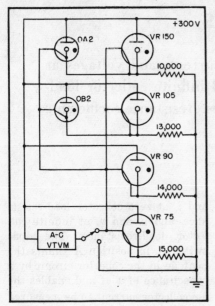

FIG. 4—Circuit diagram of simple VR tube checker. Use is made of internal jumpers to complete circuits

self-contained power supply was constructed, and more than 100 various VR tubes were checked to demonstrate its usefulness. As shown in the schematic of Fig. 4,

a separate socket for each type was installed. Advantage was taken of the built-in jumper within the tubes to complete both the power circuit and the metering circuit. Limiting resistors were adjusted to pass exactly 15 ma thru any type of VR tube during test.

Only one tube was tested at one time, by plugging it into the appropriate socket, and reading the hum in millivolts on a Ballantine a-c vtvm. The double-throw pushbutton enabled reading the power supply hum voltage ahead of the VR circuit. Since the power supply hum voltage remained constant at 2.25 volts, the push button was not often used.

The results of these comparative checks which are listed in Table I, show that good tubes had low ripple and were constant in the value of ripple. Defective tubes showed a high ripple and in addition some of these had wide fluctuations in ripple output, in one case 30 to 80 mv. This last group was seen to flicker,

due to periodic changes in the areas where the glow took place.

Some of the tubes tested, particularly the OA 2 series, were defi-

Table I—Results of Tests on 100 VR Tubes

Tube Type	Good Tubes (mv hum)	Best Tubes (as low as)	Bad Tubes (as high as)
OA2	25 mv	18 mv	80 mv
VR150	19 mv	12 mv	45 mv
OB2	11 mv	7 mv	25 mv
VR105	13 mv	10 mv	23 mv
VR90	36 mv	28 mv	60 mv
VR75	17 mv	15 mv	24 mv

nitely known to be defective, as they were removed from equipment for that reason. Most of these had been overloaded considerably, which accounts for the high average ripple in the OA2 series.

The rest of the averages bear out tube handbook data, particularly that the VR105, and its miniature counterpart, the OB2, appear to be most efficient.

Precision VR Tube Tester

WHEN an unusually constant voltage is desired, careful selection of VR tubes is necessary as these tubes vary noticeably in their operating characteristics. A simple circuit for predetermining the reliability of VR tube performance is shown in the diagram.

Ideally, the voltage drop across the VR tube is constant throughout its rated current range; however, many tubes do not give a uniform regulating characteristic. Small transients caused by line variations or other reasons result in changes in voltage drop across the tube with consequent changes in regulated output. These results are virtually independent of tube age, and new tubes are sometimes among the worst offenders.

Thus to test VR tubes properly, it is necessary to examine each tube over its entire operating cur-

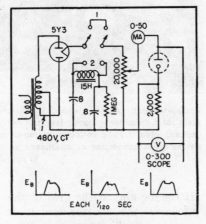

Circuit for testing VR tube over its operating current range

rent range, while employing a sensitive detecting device to indicate voltage variations.

The tube selector circuit has been developed by O. B. Rudolph and

described in *Rev. Sci. Inst.*, May, 1950. By throwing the switch to position 2, a well-filtered d-c output will be obtained which can be used for preheating the tube undergoing test if desired and also for checking firing voltage which will be indicated on the voltmeter. With the switch in position 1, pulsating d-c voltage will be applied to the tube for precision checking of the overall voltage-current characteristic.

The milliammeter indicates rms current and care should be exercised to prevent the peak value of the current from exceeding 40 ma.

Shown in the illustration are three of the various types of oscilloscope traces which have been obtained from different tubes. The trace at left is ideal and the only one acceptable for many applications.

Testing Transistors

Simple test circuit using two pentodes gives direct currents and voltages at operating point, corresponding a-c values for zero and infinite collector load-resistance, and current and voltage amplification values. Resistance coefficients are then easily calculated

By K. LEHOVEC

SINCE the transistor is now commercially available from different manufacturers, a simple method for testing which still yields rather extensive information becomes of wider interest.

If all a-c components are sufficiently small, a linear relation holds between the alternating current i_e through the emitter and the alternating current i_c through the collector on one hand, and the a-c voltage emitter-base v_e and the a-c voltage collector-base v_c on the other hand:

$$v_e = R_{11}\,i_e + R_{12}\,i_c$$
$$v_c = R_{21}\,i_e + R_{22}\,i_c \qquad (1)$$

The four coefficients, R_{11}, R_{12}, R_{21} and R_{22}, may be used to describe the operation of the transistor at a particular operation point, given for instance by the direct currents.[1] The coefficients are practically independent of frequency up to several hundred thousand cycles.

In Table I some of the most important circuit qualities of the transistor are expressed in terms of these coefficients. A convenient method of measuring the coefficients is described. It is hoped that it may contribute to the establishment of a standardized method for test and characterization of transistors.

Test Circuit

The characteristic feature of the test circuit is the use of a pentode in the emitter circuit and a pentode in the collector circuit, both operating in the saturation range. Thus the direct current through emitter and collector can be adjusted independently of the emitter impedance or the collector impedance of the

transistor by a proper bias voltage at the grid of the pentodes. By modulation of the grid voltage of the pentode in the emitter circuit, an alternating current $i_e = 100$ microamperes rms. at 5,000 cps is produced. This current is usually found to be sufficiently small so that distortion of the sine wave by the transistor may be neglected.

If the d-c bias at the grid of the pentode in the emitter circuit is changed, a small adjustment of the a-c grid voltage may be needed to keep the a-c emitter current constant. That can be avoided by using two pentodes in parallel in the emitter circuit, one as adjustable d-c current generator and the other as fixed a-c current generator.

For the calculation of the coefficients it is sufficient to measure v_e

and i_c at zero collector load-resistance, and v_e and v_c at infinite collector load-resistance. The dpdt switch S_2 in position A shunts the pentode in the collector circuit by a capacitance of 1 μf and enables the a-c collector current to be measured at practically zero a-c load resistance (the collector impedance is of the order of 20,000 ohms).

Complete equipment for testing transistors. Left to right: Electronic a-c voltmeter; vtvm for d-c emitter voltage; test unit, with transistor on three-terminal panel in foreground; vtvm for d-c collector voltage; audio signal generator. Jacks on test unit permit quick connection of additional precision meters and experimental connections to pentode grids

With switch S_2 in position B, the pentode in the collector circuit is shunted by the capacitance in series with a 5-megohm resistance. This avoids sudden charge currents of the capacitance after changes in the switch position and provides a practically infinite a-c load resistance in the collector circuit.

Equipment Used

The test setup includes an electronic a-c voltmeter to measure the a-c components, a vacuum-tube voltmeter for the d-c emitter voltage, a vacuum-tube voltmeter for the d-c collector voltage and an audio signal generator which is connected internally to the grid of the pentode in the emitter circuit. The transistor is placed in a holder constructed to ground automatically the emitter and the collector input if the transistor is taken out.

The a-c components are measured on the same a-c voltmeter by throwing the appropriate switches. All a-c components are measured on the same range (10 to 100 millivolts) of the electronic a-c voltmeter by means of proper voltage dividers included in the test circuit.

Presentation of Results

It is convenient to arrange the measured values in the form shown in Table II. The first or left-hand group contains the direct currents and voltages, which describe the operation point. The second group contains in the upper line the alternating currents and voltages at zero collector load-resistance and in the lower line the corresponding values for infinite collector load-resistance. The third group gives the current amplification at zero collector load resistance and the voltage amplification at infinite collector load resistance. The fourth group contains the four coefficients, which are calculated from the a-c components in the second group according to

$$|R_{11}| = (v_e/i_e)_\infty$$
$$|R_{12}| = [(v_e)_\infty - (v_e)_0]/(i_c)_0$$
$$|R_{21}| = (v_c/i_e)_\infty$$
$$|R_{22}| = (v_c)_\infty/(i_c)_0 \qquad (2)$$

The above equations follow immediately from Eq. 1 if first $(i_c)_\infty$ and then $(v_c)_0$ are set equal to zero.

In Table III, numerical values obtained on a commercial Bell Telephone Laboratories germanium transistor are given in the arrangement of Table II.

For a quick test, one is often more interested in the maximum

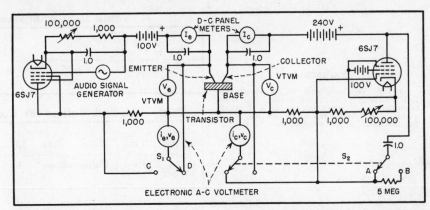

Test circuit for transistors. Batteries are used throughout, with on-off switch in heater circuit. Collector and emitter leads are automatically shorted to base when transistor is removed

Table I—Important Circuit Qualities of Transistors

(1) Short-circuit stability .... $\delta = \dfrac{R_{12}}{R_{11}} \dfrac{R_{21}}{R_{22}} < 1$

(2) Input impedance .... $R_{11} - \dfrac{R_{12} R_{21}}{R_{22} + R_L}$
(collector load-resistance is R_L)

(3) Output impedance .... $R'_{22} - \dfrac{R_{12} R_{21}}{R_{11} + R_g}$
(external resistance in emitter circuit is R_g)

(4) Power amplification .... $\dfrac{R_{21}^2}{R_{11} R_{22}} \dfrac{R_L}{(R_L + R_{22})} \dfrac{1}{(1 - \delta + R_L/R_{22})}$
(output power/input power)

(5) Maximum current amplification .... $\dfrac{R_{21}}{R_{22}}$
(zero load)

(6) Maximum voltage amplification .... $\dfrac{R_{21}}{R_{11}}$
(infinite load)

The following values refer specifically to $\delta < 1$ and a load resistance matched for maximum available power amplification:

(7) Load resistance matched for maximum power amplification .... $R_{22} \sqrt{1 - \delta}$

(8) Input impedance at maximum power amplification .... $R_{11} \sqrt{1 - \delta}$

(9) Maximum power amplification .... $\dfrac{R_{21}^2}{R_{11} R_{22}} \dfrac{1}{(1 + \sqrt{1 - \delta})^2}$

(10) Insertion gain at maximum power amplification .... $\dfrac{R_{21}^2}{4R_{11}^2} \dfrac{1}{(1 + \sqrt{1 - \delta})^2}$

(11) Insertion gain (at maximum power amplification)/maximum power amplification .... $\dfrac{R_{22}}{4R_{11}}$

(12) Current amplification at maximum power gain ...... $\dfrac{R_{21}}{R_{22}} \dfrac{1}{1 + \sqrt{1 - \delta}}$

(13) Voltage amplification at maximum power gain .... $\dfrac{R_{21}}{R_{11}} \dfrac{1}{1 + \sqrt{1 - \delta}}$

current amplification and the maximum voltage amplification than in the resistance coefficients. It is then an advantage of the circuit that the maximum current amplification is obtained without further calculation from the a-c collector current at zero collector load-resistance.

Table II—Arrangement of Measured Values

I_e I_c	i_e	$(v_e)_o$	$(i_c)_o$	0	$(i_c/i_e)_o$	$|R_{11}|$ $|R_{12}|$
V_e V_c	i_e	$(v_e)_\infty$	0	$(v_c)_\infty$	$(v_c/v_e)_\infty$	$|R_{21}|$ $|R_{22}|$

Table III—Test Values for Commercial Germanium Transistor

0.5 ma 2.0 ma	100 μa	18mv	132μa	0	1.32	420 ohms	182 ohms
0.13 v 22.5 v	100 μa	42mv	0	3.1v	74	31,000 ohms	23,500 ohms

REFERENCE

(1) W. Bardeen and W. Brattain of Bell Telephone Laboratories used this representation of transistors in a lecture given in October 1948 in Princeton, N. J. for the local AIEE section.

ELECTRONIC MUSIC

Gas-Diode Electronic Organ

Chains of sawtooth tone generators using 10-cent neon lamps are synchronized to master oscillators for frequency control. Undesired harmonics are removed with tone filters to give five octaves of organ-like music with two vibrato stops and six tone-color stops

By ROBERT M. STRASSNER

ELECTRIC-KEYBOARD musical instruments may be classified into two main groups according to their means of tone production: (1) electromechanical generators; (2) electric-circuit generators. Mechanical systems are either rotary or vibratory. Both means have been used to modulate electrostatic or magnetic fields or beams of light. Electric circuit types have employed both vacuum and gas-tube oscillators as tone generators.

Designers of new instruments have either imitated existing instruments or have devised completely new pleasing tonal qualities and controls. However, one of the greatest complaints against electric instruments is that they are generally too perfect, and therefore unnatural. Variation is the essence of musical expression and variations in pitch, loudness, tone color

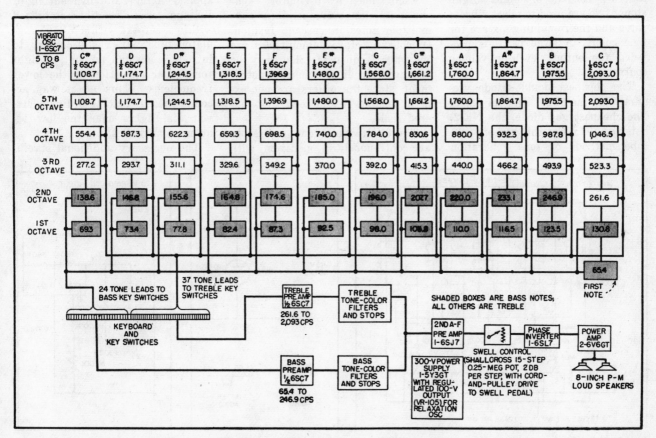

FIG. 1—Arrangement of stages in complete organ. Frequency value in cycles is given for each master oscillator (top row) and each of the 61 synchronized NE-2 neon-tube relaxation oscillators comprising the five octaves. Shaded boxes represent bass notes

and vibrato should be within easy control of the musician. On the other hand, too many controls confuse or discourage the performer. In general, new instruments should be easily operated by masters of similar existing instruments.

It was required to develop an organ-like electronic instrument that would retail for $800, whereas the cheapest all-electronic organ then available sold for about $3,000. Since mechanical economies in the design and construction of the console and keyboard would classify the equipment as a toy rather than a musical instrument, it was necessary to retain the standard form of the other low-priced organ-like instruments. The main savings were effected in parts and production costs, with minimum sacrifice in performance. A standard organ keyboard of five octaves or 61 notes covering the range from C 65 to C 2,093 cycles is used. The controls consist of eight organ stops; two are used to select vibrato rates and the remaining six are for tone color. A swell pedal is provided for output level or volume control.

The cheapest double-triode vacuum tube, the 6SC7, lists for $2.00. The cheapest gas diode, the NE-2, lists for 10¢. For this reason, gas-tube methods of tone generation

were thoroughly investigated. As it happens, the sawtooth waveform of the gas-discharge relaxation oscillator has a high harmonic content, permitting wide variation in tone color by removing the undesired harmonics with suitable filters. The main difficulty was, of course, with frequency stability.

Actual Design

The block diagram of the complete instrument is shown in Fig. 1. The twelve separately-tuned master oscillators generate continuously the twelve frequencies for the highest of the five octaves provided. For each master oscillator there is a chain of sawtooth tone generators, the first of which is synchronized to the fundamental frequency. Only these harmonic-rich sawtooth generators feed the preamplifiers and tone-color filters; the master oscillators serve only for frequency control and are not heard.

Each master oscillator synchronizes its corresponding submultiple notes in cascade fashion. Of course, octave submultiples are the only frequencies that may be synchronized in a musical instrument, since the others are not exactly related in the equally-tempered scale.

The 61 sawtooth tone generators are continuously in operation, with

all their output leads terminating at the keyboard switches. Twenty-four of the generators feed the bass preamp, and the remaining 37 feed the treble preamp. When the musician depresses one or more keys, the corresponding key switches send the tonal combination to the treble and/or the bass preamp. Stops at the control panel select the desired combination of tone color. The bass and treble tone-color filters then separately modify the upper and lower portions of the keyboard and inject their combined outputs at the second preamp grid. The input level to the phase inverter is controlled by a step potentiometer operated by the foot of the performer. The signal continues through the power amplifier to the dual-speaker combination.

The main factors affecting the frequency stability of gas-discharge oscillators were found to be applied voltage and incident light. Voltage was readily stabilized within 2 percent with a VR105 regulator tube. It was necessary to introduce a small amount of light for proper operation at the lower frequencies. This effect was accomplished by placing ordinary six-volt dial lights near the low-frequency gas diodes.

The necessary additional stabili-

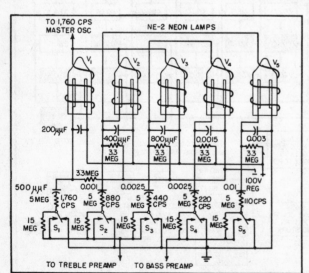

FIG. 2—Example of octave divider chain. For 6-note C chain, sync signals are injected in slightly different order so that the two lowest notes (most difficult to control) are triggered

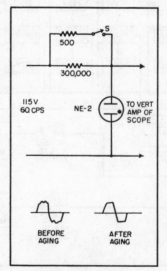

FIG. 3—Neon-lamp test and aging circuit for improving stability of sawtooth oscillators

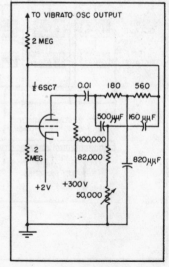

FIG. 4—Typical master oscillator circuit, with component values for the 1,760-cps chain

zation was obtained by subjecting the tubes to a small electrostatic field at the controlling frequency. By using a portion of the output from one oscillator whose frequency was already under control to synchronize another at a submultiple frequency, octave divider chains were developed. Three or four turns of hookup wire provided sufficient coupling for reliable control within plus or minus 10 percent of the free-running frequency.

Figure 2 shows a typical octave-divider chain. The charging capacitors for the first three stages are connected so that the output voltage to the treble preamplifier approaches −100 volts according to the relation:

$$V = 100\,(1 - e^{-t/RC}) \qquad (1)$$

The time for discharge is extremely short compared with the time required for the voltage to increase from the extinction voltage V_e to the ignition voltage V_i, so that the free-running frequency of oscillation is mainly a function of the difference between these two voltages[1]. Substituting V_e and then V_i for V and taking the reciprocal of the difference between the two corresponding values of t, the frequency of oscillation becomes

$$f_o = \frac{1}{RC\,\ln\left(\dfrac{100 - V_e}{100 - V_i}\right)} \qquad (2)$$

This expression is approximate because V_e and V_i are themselves affected by frequency, incident light, temperature and magnitude of the discharge current.

At the point of ignition, in the first three stages, the output voltage rises very quickly to +100 volts. The last two tubes in the chain, V_4 and V_5, are connected so that a positive-approaching sawtooth is produced. It was found that the steep time rise at the point of discharge in the negative sawtooth is much more effective in controlling the positive-sawtooth generators than other combinations. Because the lowest frequencies are the more difficult to control, the last two tubes in the

chain are both controlled by the steep negative sawtooth. The first three tubes in the chain, V_1, V_2 and V_3, are controlled directly by the master oscillator.

The charging resistance was adjusted to about 3.3 megohms in all cases. This value represents a compromise between higher values, which would be more unstable against temperature variations and would limit the discharge current, and lower values that operate the tube too near the border between oscillation and continuous glow. For all other factors remaining constant, Eq. 2 shows that if R is increased, C must necessarily be reduced if frequency is to remain constant. A reduction in C means less energy storage in the capacitor and therefore less discharge current. If R is too low, the charging current will be so high that the tube is unable to extinguish at the completion of capacitor discharge, which results in continuous glow.

Switches S_1 through S_5 are mechanically linked to the playing keys. When in the up position, these switches ground the outputs of all unplayed oscillators and also parallel the 15-meg resistors from grid to ground of the preamps, giving 0.625 meg and 0.405 meg respectively at the bass and treble inputs. As a key is depressed and the ground connection removed, a

28-db loss of available oscillator output for bass notes and 31-db loss for the treble is momentarily sent to the preamps. When the key has completed $\frac{2}{3}$ of its stroke, the 15-meg resistor is shunted, thereby allowing playing level. In this manner the loud transient click that would otherwise be present has been almost completely eliminated.

Despite these precautions against transients, key switches with silver alloy contacts caused considerable clicking. Evidently these high-impedance circuits were extremely sensitive to the slightest oxide coating at the contacts. Even the best silver forms a slight coating under normal conditions. The final switches were formed from Nichrome V wire. Clicking was unnoticeable and these switches have maintained their characteristics for a long period of time.

After the first experimental model had been in use for several months, a few oscillators drifted out of their range of control. It was determined that an aging process within the tubes had taken place. It was observed that the glow in troublesome tubes was irregular and unevenly spread over the electrode area. When these tubes were tested as positive and negative peak clippers in the circuit of Fig. 3 (switch S open), they failed to produce square and symmetrically

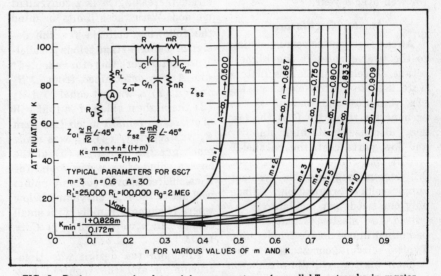

FIG. 5—Design curves for determining parameters of parallel-T networks in master oscillators

208   ELECTRONICS FOR COMMUNICATION ENGINEERS

clipped sine waves. When the switch was closed for several seconds, allowing about 200 ma to flow, the glow started unevenly but gradually spread over the entire area of both electrodes. At the completion of this spread, the switch was opened because continued application of this high current overheats the electrodes and destroys their photosensitive coating. After proper aging, the wave is always symmetrical and squarely clipped. Uniform characteristics throughout the remainder of their life were thereby assured. The experimental model has remained in synchronism for well over a year.

Master Oscillators

At the frequencies corresponding to the twelve notes in the highest octave, twelve stable oscillators were used to control eleven chains of five notes and one of six to account for the extra C at the low end. Because of its high stability and low parts cost, the parallel-T circuit was chosen. Stabilities of 0.1 percent are possible without supply-voltage regulation. Since only one triode per oscillator is required, two master oscillators may be housed in one double triode tube. Typical circuit constants of the A-chain master oscillator are shown in Fig. 4.

To aid in determining the parallel-T network parameters, the curves for Fig. 5 were plotted from equations already derived[2]. This presentation assumes zero generator impedance and infinite load impedance. Therefore, the network open-circuit input impedance Z_{o1} should be much greater than the generator impedance R_L' and its short-circuit output impedance Z_{s2} should be much less than the load impedance R_g in order that the network balance conditions be least disturbed. After stage gain A has been determined by the tube and load resistor selected, n as a function of A for various values of m may be read directly from the curves.

For sustained oscillation, network attenuation K must be less than stage gain A. If there is no loading on the network and constants are to exact tolerance, K could be taken equal to A. This is, of course, impossible and for reliable operation, K should not be more than one-half A. In most of the literature on the subject, m is taken equal to one. [3,4] It should be noted that increased selectivity as well as decreased K occurs as m is increased.

The more common method of increasing selectivity is to increase A only. With high-mu triodes the upper limit on A is about 35, so that if additional selectivity is desired, increasing m is a convenient method. With these limits in mind the following criteria for the design of a single-stage triode parallel-T oscillator were therefore adopted: (1) A was determined from μ, R_L and r_p; (2) K was set equal to $A/2$; (3) the highest value of m that will allow Z_{s2} to remain much less than R_g was selected; (4) Z_{o1} was made much greater than R_L'; (5) at the chosen value of m, n was found for K calculated above; (6) only points well above the K_{min} curve and below where K changes rapidly with small changes in n were used; (7) $C = 1/\omega R$.

Although the design was time-consuming and the required low-tolerance components are expensive, the production cost per oscillator is less than for other types and stability is comparable with a laboratory standard.

Vibrato Oscillator

Vibrato in most musical instruments is produced by combined frequency and amplitude modulation. However, a rather pleasing effect may be obtained from frequency modulation alone. Figure 6 shows the vibrato oscillator, which is a standard four-section phase-shift variety.[5] Frequency is adjusted to about six cycles per second and is controllable at the stop tabs by simultaneously varying two of the 1-meg resistors in the phase-shift network. Oscillator output is injected through the 2-meg resistors shown in Fig. 4 to the grids of all

master oscillators. The extent of the frequency swing or vibrato depth is determined by the amplitude of the injected voltage.

Tone-Color Stops

The raw sawtooth waveform from the tone generators could hardly pass for music because of its improper harmonic distribution. After this sawtooth has passed through filter circuits that alter its harmonic structure, many pleasing tonal effects are obtained.

The highest note on the keyboard of this instrument is the 32nd harmonic of the lowest. A low-pass filter designed to remove certain harmonics of the treble notes would have negligible effect on bass notes. In like manner, another low-pass filter with a much lower cutoff point would be very effective in coloring bass notes and yet completely at-

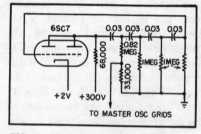

FIG. 6—Vibrato oscillator circuit. Output frequency is approximately 6 cps

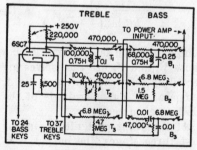

FIG. 7—Bass and treble tone-color filters, each using half of the 6SC7

tenuate the treble section. If uniform tone color were required, a separate filter for each tone color of each note would be needed. However, few instruments have the same tone color throughout their range.[6,7] A satisfactory tonal balance was obtained by splitting the keyboard at middle C (261 cycles). Two filter sections were provided.

The 24 notes below middle C were routed to bass stops or filters and the 37 above to treble stops. When a bass note is played and a bass stop is closed, a tone is produced that in pitch is determined by the note played, in color is designated by the stop closed and is at a level depending on the setting of the swell pedal. Figure 7 shows circuit constants of the tone color unit. One filter in each section is a resonant band-pass type designed to act as a formant-producing element. (Formants are caused by boosting partial tones around a particular resonance frequency.) The others are ordinary R-C networks. These combinations produce horn, string and reed effects. Large amounts of insertion loss were deliberately incorporated in each network in order that output level would be noticeably increased as more stops were closed.

Choice of Speakers

The distortion of the 8-watt amplifier used was held to a minimum consistent with parts cost, but best speaker performance (oddly enough) was realized with one of the least expensive combinations tested. The final choice was a pair of 8-inch p-m speakers, one with a hard cone resonating at 150 cycles and the other soft for a 75-cycle resonance. When these were operated in parallel, their reciprocal damping effects appeared to reduce overall resonance and distortion to a low degree. An 8-watt test signal that produced objectionable distortion in a 25-watt high-fidelity speaker supplied by a prominent manufacturer was easily handled by the 10-watt combination used. The dual system was also chosen because it allowed a more uniform dispersion than could be realized from even a large single speaker.

Conclusions

It was pointed out that the purpose of this project was to design a low-cost, easily-operated organ-like instrument. Low manufacturing cost was accomplished by using inexpensive tone generators whose tiny size lend themselves to small identical subassemblies. Pleasing tone color was the main standard of performance. To this end, comments on the results of listening tests by many musicians and engineers have been most gratifying. Provided reasonable care is exercised in the selection of capacitors and resistors in the parallel-T networks, the instrument should remain in tune indefinitely. Eight organ stops provide 196 combinations of tone color. Any person able to play keyboard instruments can play this instrument with little or no practice.

REFERENCES

(1) H. J. Reich, "Theory and Application of Electron Tubes," p 454, McGraw-Hill Book Co., New York, 1944.
(2) H. S. McGaughan, Variation of an RC Parallel-T Null Network, *Tele-Tech*, p 48, August 1947.
(3) W. G. Shepherd and R. O. Wise, Variable Frequency Bridge-Type Frequency-Stabilized Oscillators, *Proc. IRE*, p 256, June 1943.
(4) A. E. Hastings, Analysis of a Resistance Capacitance Parallel-T Network and Applications, *Proc. I.R.E.*, p 126, March 1946.
(5) L. Stanton, Theory and Application of Parallel-T Resistance Capacitance Frequency Selective Networks, *Proc. I.R.E.*, p 447, July 1946.
(6) S. K. Lewer, "Electronic Musical Instruments," *Electronic Engineering*, 1948. This monograph has an extensive bibliography and lists American and British patents.
(7) B. F. Miessner, Electronic Music and Instruments, *Proc. IRE*, p 1,427, Nov. 1936.

Electronic Organ

Keyboard controls 167 Hartley oscillators designed for grid-circuit keying and high stability of tuning. Separate loudspeaker channels minimize Doppler-effect distortion at cone. Power amplifiers have low intermodulation distortion

By T. H. LONG

IN the organ-type electronic musical instrument to be described, each note of the keyboard corresponds to a Hartley oscillator arranged to provide a sinusoidal fundamental, devoid of harmonics, and a pulse signal that is rich in harmonics. Twelve additional oscillators provide an octave extension of the treble on the swell (upper) manual.

The various voices are derived from mixer circuits that mix the fundamentals and pulse signals in the proper proportions and subject the resultant to appropriate frequency-discriminating circuits to produce the desired formant. The outputs of the several mixers associated with any division of the organ (swell, great, or pedal) are mixed through buffer amplifiers. The resultant signal from each division is further amplified to recover the mixing loss and is passed through the volume control associated with the expression pedals.

The expression pedal controlling the volume of the swell manual voices also controls some of the pedal voices by means of a separate potentiometer having a range of control which is less than the range used on the manual voices. This compensates for reduced sensitivity of the ear at low sound levels in the pedal tones and maintains a satisfactory balance between these voices in the pedal division and those in the swell division over the complete range of the expression pedal. The other pedal voices are handled similarly on the expression pedal used for the great manual.

Following the expression pedals the outputs of the three organ divisions may be mixed together or kept separate as the installation may require. For a small room all three outputs may be mixed at the input of a power amplifier. For installations requiring more than one loudspeaker the signals from the pedal voices are amplified and fed to one or more pedal loudspeakers while the signals from the manual voices are either mixed into a common power amplifier and loudspeaker system or are fed into two separate systems.

The lowest frequency available in the pedal oscillators is the musical note C_1 (32.703 cycles per second). The lowest frequency produced by the manual oscillators is one octave higher, or 65.406 cycles per second. It has been found desirable to use separate power amplifiers and loudspeakers for the manuals and for the pedals. Power input to the pedal loudspeakers is limited by the cone excursion at the lowest frequency and the power input to the manual loudspeakers tends to be limited by the power-handling capacity of the voice coils.

This separation of loudspeaker channels practically eliminates the distortion inherently produced by the Doppler effect when medium or high frequencies are being radiated by a cone that is simultaneously executing low-frequency vibrations of appreciable amplitude. The further separation of the signals from the manuals, though not so necessary, does contribute to the elimination of this distortion that has long been associated with electronic instruments when played at high sound intensities, and also lends to the space effect that is highly desirable especially in large installations.

Oscillators

The Hartley type of oscillator with grid circuit keying was selected for a number of reasons: (1) such an oscillator provides a dependable tone signal generator that produces transient and steady-state

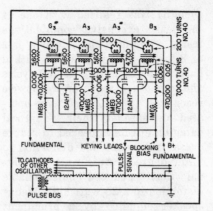

FIG. 1—Circuit of typical four-note oscillator chassis

effects in an independent fashion comparable to the tone generators generally used in the production of orchestral, vocal, or pipe organ music; (2) the oscillator can be

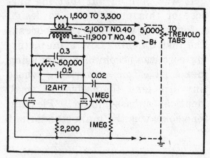

FIG. 2—Tremolo oscillator circuit

keyed with the simplest type of switch and permits use of conventional pipe-organ couplers; (3) the oscillator can be produced and maintained at a reasonable cost.

Oscillator design requirements included: (1) high stability of tuning, especially with time and with temperature variations: (2) good keying characteristics for natural attack and release of tone; (3) satisfactory tremolo having the proper amount of amplitude, frequency, and quality change to compare with the tremolo or vibrato generally used in vocal music or by orchestral instruments; (4) proper and uniform tonal qualities with adequate amounts of natural harmonics available; (5) easy tunability; (6) simple, inexpensive construction.

The resulting oscillator, using half of a twin triode, is assembled on a four-note chassis as indicated

in Fig. 1. The organ described here has 167 oscillators. Of these, 32 are associated with the pedals (notes C_1 to G_3), 61 are in the great division (C_2 to C_7), 73 are in the swell division (C_2 to C_8), and a special type of low-frequency oscillator is used as a source of tremolo frequency. The fundamental tone signals generated in the tank circuits are mixed in series for a given rank of oscillators, and the pulse signals are parallel-mixed.

The oscillator circuit constants are so chosen that plate and heater voltage variations will not appreciably affect tuning of the oscillators. The oscillator plate supply is, however, taken from a voltage-regulated source in order to provide a source having a low apparent impedance. This eliminates a tendency that would otherwise exist for the several ranks of oscillators to synchronize when the same note is played in each or to lock in exact octave relationship when octaves are played. This synchronization, if permitted by a sufficiently large common impedance in the plate voltage source, would seriously reduce the grand celeste or chorus effect that depends upon independent tone generators.

Tremolo Oscillator

The tremolo oscillator circuit in Fig. 2 feeds approximately 5 volts of low-frequency signal into a 1,500-ohm resistance. The tremolo frequency is adjustable through the range of 4.7 to 6.5 cycles per second by a resistance control.

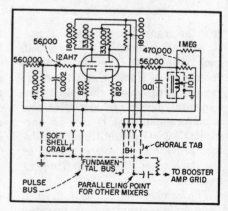

FIG. 3—Great soft string tab and chorale mixer circuit

Mixers

The mixers are single-stage amplifiers that mix the proper amounts of fundamental and pulse signals together and determine the formant for the proper tonal character of each voice. Each voice is controlled from a conventional tablet switch on the console. This switch short-circuits the grid of any mixer to ground when the voice is not wanted. The output circuits of the mixers associated with one division are paralleled. The circuit of a typical mixer chassis which includes two mixers, soft string, and chorale is given in Fig. 3.

The coupler arrangement, as applied to the A_3 keys of the great and swell manuals and the A_2 key of the pedals, is shown in Fig. 4. The oscillators are keyed by grounding the keying leads either directly or through the tremolo generator output. Any key is able to control several oscillators through appropriate couplers. Tremolo can be obtained in either manual independently of the other manual, since the manuals have independent keying busses.

When the swell-division oscillators are keyed from the great manual they sound with the voices set up for the swell manual, which may be quite different from those selected for the great manual. The same considerations apply when the great oscillators are keyed from the pedal clavier through the great to pedal coupler. However, there is no provision for tremolo to the pedal oscillators since tremolo in the low-frequency range is not desirable. The block diagram in Fig. 5 shows the substantial independence of the swell, great, and pedal organs.

Loudspeakers and Power Amplifiers

The loudspeaker and power amplifier problems associated with this electronic musical instrument are

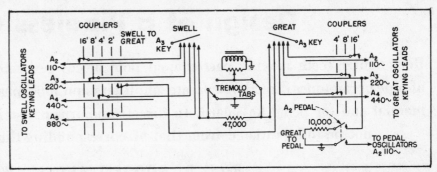

FIG. 4—Typical coupler circuit, with keying details for one key in each manual and one pedal key

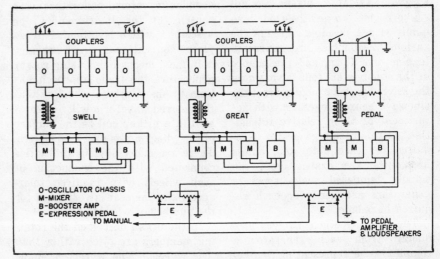

FIG. 5—Block diagram of model 2A, showing substantial independence of swell, great, and pedal organs. Most of the oscillators have been omitted here

almost unique since substantial amounts of power must be delivered with low distortion at frequencies down to 32 cycles per second. Much less intermodulation can be tolerated in an electronic organ than in more conventional applications. Music that is quite acceptable at low intensity levels will become intolerable at high levels if the usual harmonic distortion is permitted.

The power amplifiers were designed to have harmonic distortion below one percent at full power output. Great care was used in the choice and arrangement of loudspeakers. The manual loudspeakers are provided with diffraction devices that satisfactorily spread

the high-frequency components of sound energy through a large horizontal angle. This arrangement avoids the beaming effect that is undesirable in organ music, without the energy loss and time lag that would be associated with diffusion of the high-frequency sounds by bouncing them off the ceiling.

Acknowledgments

Important contributions to the development of this electronic organ were made by Messrs. L. B. Greenleaf, E. L. Kent, S. L. Krauss, R. T. Bozak, S. W. McKellip, J. R. Ford, R. G. Campbell, W. J. Harness, and A. W. Harrison.

Design of a Pipeless Organ

Rectangular teeth moving past shaped pole pieces generate desired complex waveforms of pipe organ tones directly. Separate amplifiers and loudspeaker systems are used for each manual and for pedal keyboard. In direct-comparison listening test, performance could not be differentiated from that of corresponding three-manual pipe organ

By J. D. GOODELL AND E. SWEDIEN

TWO BASICALLY DIFFERENT approaches to synthesized tone qualities are possible. In one the various frequencies are generated in sinewave form, and the timbre of the steady-state tone is varied by the selection of harmonics from the sinewave source together with adjustment of their relative intensities. In this case a generator is required for each note, and, unless harmonics are drawn from the equally tempered scale, separate generators are used for each required harmonic.

The second method involves producing from each generator a complex wave representing the resultant of the fundamental and harmonic structures of the musical tone. Each stop corresponds to a complete set of generators in a manner exactly analogous to a rank of pipes. If the instrument is intended specifically to produce pipe-organ effects, this characteristic is essential. As a consequence, the complex waveform generators were chosen for the instrument to be described, which is intended to replace conventional large organs.

In most mechanisms using rotary generators the basic approach has been to shape a tone wheel so that the desired waveform will be generated in a pickup coil as the surface of the wheel moves past a pole piece. There are many obvious difficulties connected with the production of such wheels with required tolerances, and the cost is very high for the number of wheels needed.

In the organ described the rotating members are pitch rather than tone wheels. The wheels resemble conventional gears with teeth (vanes) distributed symmetrically around the periphery. The pole pieces of the pickup coils are shaped to produce the desired waveform. A number of pole pieces together with corresponding patterns are shown in Fig. 1.

There are many advantages in this system, not the least of which is the fact that a single pitch wheel may be used in conjunction with several coils and pole pieces oriented around its periphery to generate various waveforms. Pitch wheels with 1, 2, 4, 8, 16, 32 and 64 teeth respectively are assembled on a single shaft so that each wheel corresponds to a successive octave of a single note. The shaft itself is made of non-magnetic stainless steel, and the spacers between the pitch wheels are of brass to avoid coupling between the circuits.

A total of twelve shafts with seven pitch wheels on each shaft produce all the fundamental frequencies of an organ keyboard. In order to generate the fundamentals corresponding to the 4-foot, 2-foot and 32-foot pipe pitches for various stops played in the top or bottom octaves of the keyboard respectively, it is necessary to add one or more pitch wheels to each shaft.

Each set of coil and pole piece as-

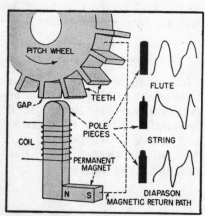

FIG. 1—Method used for generating complex waveforms directly by shaping pole piece so air gap varies as each tooth moves past, and examples of waveforms

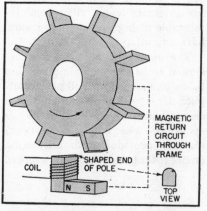

FIG. 2—Area-scanning method of generating complex waveforms, wherein air gap is constant but magnetic reluctance varies as each tooth moves past

Pitch-wheel assembly that determines frequency of one note in scale over range of seven octaves. Wheels have 1, 2, 4, 8, 16, 32 and 64 teeth respectively

semblies generates a complete keyboard of corresponding waveforms. The output from the coils may be connected to one or more manuals of the organ. The only limitation on the number of stops that may be obtained in this manner is the physical dimension of each coil assembly by comparison with the outside circumference of the pitch wheels.

The complete generator assembly for a two-manual organ has twelve complete tone-wheel assemblies in the lower bank, corresponding to the complete organ keyboard fundamentals. Each tone wheel in this bank has four associated coil and

ity than is achieved with the usual tremolo. This is one of the features of this design that contributes to its ability to conform to pipe-organ characteristics. Few pipe organs include more than a string celeste stop, but with the design described a flute celeste is not costly in comparison to adding a complete set of pipes in a pipe organ.

Tremolo Effect

Synchronous motors are used to drive the main pitch-wheel shafts through a flexible spring coupling. On the end of the main driveshaft in the lower bank is a flywheel. Suspended from above and resting

tion in load is absorbed by the spring coupling, momentarily slowing down the angular velocity of the main drive shaft and all the pitch wheels by a small amount.

When the overload is removed (as the eccentric rotates away from the magnetic structure) the spring coupling feeds the energy back into the system as a pulse that overshoots slightly, since it is not critically damped, and the angular velocity of the pitch wheels is increased beyond normal for an instant. The pickup coils see this as a variation in pitch that is alternately below and above normal, at a rate that is adjusted by the period of the

Drive system for pitch-wheel assembly (bench test setup). Tuning is done by sliding entire assembly so rubber-tired wheel shifts along surface of cone-shaped wood drive wheel. Changing diameter of drive wheel changes fundamental frequency

Closeup of pitch-wheel assembly, showing how coils (in rectangular shield boxes) and shaped pole pieces are distributed around periphery of each toothed wheel to get different complex waveforms and hence tones at each freqency

pole-piece assemblies corresponding to flute, diapason, string and trumpet basic tone colors.

The upper bank of twelve complete tone-wheel assemblies includes only two sets of coil assemblies, corresponding to a flute and string tone color. The upper bank is tuned slightly sharp with respect to the lower bank and represents the celeste stops. This corresponds exactly to pipe-organ practice in which a separate rank of string pipes is tuned slightly sharp to provide a beat that sounds to the ear much like a vibrato, although the result is appreciably richer in qual-

against this flywheel is a lever arm, with an electromagnet attached to the end just below the flywheel and with its pole piece facing an eccentric steel wheel that is driven by the main drive shaft. This is the mechanism used for obtaining a tremolo.

When the tremolo electromagnet is not energized, the lever arm simply places a small constant load on the drive shaft through friction against the flywheel. When the electromagnet is energized it is periodically attracted to the eccentric wheel so that the pressure of the lever arm is increased. This varia-

eccentric wheel to be between six and seven cycles per second. The extent of the variation in pitch is determined by the amount of energy supplied to the electromagnet. This is adjustable over a relatively wide range with a control on the console.

In this connection it is noted that there are two basic types of vibrato, one being amplitude modulation and the other frequency modulation. The frequency-modulation method is the more desirable of the two, but in many instruments is difficult to obtain with accuracy. The tremulant described may be set to produce any desired result and it is exceptionally stable in operation.

Method of Tuning

The drive system employs a simple arrangement for tuning the individual sets of pitch wheels. Spaced suitably along the driveshaft are cone-shaped wood wheels. On each side of each cone-shaped wheel is a pitch-wheel assembly, suitably oriented so that its rubber-tired drive wheel contacts the cone-shaped wheel at the correct angle.

The pitch-wheel assemblies are mounted to the base board through slots with adjustable pressure bolts so that they may be easily moved with relation to the cone-shaped wheels on the main driveshaft. The speed that they are driven depends on the size of the cone and the portion of the cone contacted by the rubber drive wheel. This permits rapid tuning of the instrument and maintains tuning over long periods of time without sensitivity to temperature variables or line voltage variations within wide limits.

The entire pitch-wheel assembly is adequately shock mounted. Stability of drive requires careful attention to the mechanical reactances and resistances involved, and dynamic balance of the entire system is essential.

Scanning Methods

The waveform may be scanned either by shaping the pole piece in accordance with the instantaneous gap as in Fig. 1, which is termed profile scanning, or by the area scanning method where the gap distance is constant but the area of the pole piece is varied, as in Fig. 2.

With the profile-scanning method the effect of a given variation in the shape of the pole piece is inversely proportional to the width of the gap. It is also true that a deep sharp cleft in the pole piece does not have its full effect on the result because of fringe effects from the sides of the tooth to the steep sides of the cleft. Thus, very high harmonics are likely to be obscured, the design of the pole piece becomes critical and the dimensions of all the units in the system must be kept to a minimum.

With the area-scanning method the gap distance is a constant and the very high harmonic structures are easier to control.

The profile-scanning method is used in current designs for reasons of economy in production costs and because it has been found possible to achieve entirely satisfactory basic organ tones with this orientation. In elaborate organs where very brilliant solo reeds are required, it is entirely practical to combine the two systems.

Pole-Piece Design

A rigorous and complete mathematical expression for predicting the dynamic flux patterns in a system of this kind in terms of the shape of the pole piece is completely impractical, if not impossible. Developing a pole piece to produce a desired voltage waveform may be approached as a first approximation by mathematical and graphic methods, however. This approximation turns out to be remarkably close to the end result, and the final touching up of the profile is accomplished on the basis of rationalizations and intuitive concepts resulting from laboratory experience.

In plotting the initial curve most of the constants and small variables are neglected and the reluctance of the gap is considered to be the only function of first order importance. The procedure is indicated in Fig. 3.

On a listening-test basis, the plotted first approximation for a pole-piece profile will usually come very close to the quality of tone for the complex waveform originally selected for synthesis and analyzed into its sine wave components. A number of small factors, such as the fact that the tooth leaving the gap is still producing some changes in flux when the approaching tooth enters the gap, are compensated for by minor modifications of the profile.

For any given profile the higher-order harmonic content will be de-

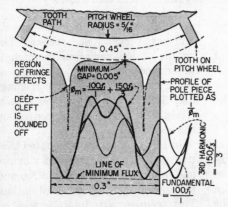

FIG. 3—Details of combined mathematical and graphical procedure for designing shaped pole piece to generate desired complex waveform of an organ tone

Mathematical Basis; The desired complex voltage waveform can be expressed in terms of its sine wave components as

$$E = A \sin \omega t + B \sin 2\,\omega t + C \sin 3\,\omega t + \ldots\ldots\ldots \tag{1}$$

Since E is proportional to $d\phi/dt$, the flux ϕ is obtained by integration as

$$-\phi = \frac{A}{\omega} \cos \omega t + \frac{B}{2\omega} \cos 2\,\omega t + \frac{C}{3\omega} \cos 3\,\omega t + \ldots\ldots\ldots \tag{2}$$

where A, B and C are the percentages of harmonics in the voltage waveform. Phase angles can be neglected because of the insensitivity of the ear to phase shift and unnecessary constants can be eliminated, giving for the required relative maximum flux amplitudes the simple expression

$$\phi_m = \frac{A}{1} + \frac{B}{2} + \frac{C}{3} + \ldots\ldots\ldots \tag{3}$$

Graphical Design Procedure: Draw portion of tooth wheel. Draw path of tooth face (dotted). Draw pole-piece width, making it approximately two-thirds of space between teeth on wheel. Analyze desired waveform to determine relative amplitudes of harmonics. Draw fundamental so one cycle fills width of pole piece. Draw sine wave for each harmonic (only third harmonic used in example), and add to get ϕ_m. Harmonics may be shifted in relative phase to fundamental to get simplest pole-piece profile. Assume flux is inversely proportional to reluctance and hence to dimensions of gap. Measure maximum flux values with reference to minimum flux line, and plot points across edge of pole piece at distance from tooth path based on inverse ratio of respective flux values.

veloped in inverse ratio to variations in the size of the gap actually established with the assembly completed. This may be used to advantage by spacing the pole piece intended to reproduce relatively pure sine wave flute tones as far as is practicable from the pitch wheels. Conversely, a trumpet pole piece may be deliberately moved in closer than planned in the initial design in order to increase its brilliance. The choice of gap for various stops is also somewhat dependent on the relative amplitude desired.

Balance of the output from various frequencies is partially accomplished by varying the number of turns on the coils. For example, a flute stop coil for the lowest frequency will require 6,500 turns of number 43 wire, while the upper register coils for the same stop will be wound with only a few hundred turns of number 39 wire.

The required shift in relative dimensions of pitch wheels and pole pieces is accomplished at the lower frequencies by making the diameter of the pitch wheels smaller and by increasing the size of the pole piece. At the higher frequencies the wheel size may be increased and the pole piece reduced.

At the low-frequency end only the portion of the pole piece that projects beyond the coil is enlarged. This permits holding coil dimensions constant, to simplify physical construction of the assemblies.

Output-Circuit Arrangements

The output circuit is designed so that all stops for an entire keyboard are brought to a single preamplifier input. This is schematically indicated in Fig. 4. Series resistors R_1, R_2, R_3, R_4 are used for isolation and to balance the output from various notes within a stop as well as between various stops. The resistor values range from 50,000 ohms to 1 megohm.

The key connections operate attenuators on bus-bar contacts. The circuit is designed so that the outputs from all the coils are grounded except when a key is depressed.

This is essential in order to eliminate crosstalk between the circuits and requires somewhat unconventional methods.

In pipe organs the attack of the tone is modified by the discrete interval of time required for the valve to open and for the standing waves to be established in the pipe. There are many possible methods of obtaining control over the attack of the tone.

An experimental attack-controlling action used transformer coupling, with a separate transformer for each key. The primary was stationary and the secondary was moved physically by the key action so that the coupling was gradually increased as the key was depressed. This type of action has the advantage of eliminating any possibility of clicks or other noises when the key is actuated. It has the disadvantage of being expensive to produce in satisfactory form because of coupling between circuits and such problems as obtaining adequate high-frequency response from such transformers.

In the practical organ design, the attack is controlled by attenuators carefully designed for long life and lack of noise. This type of action makes the instrument touch-sensitive, and it is possible for an experienced performer to use this feature

to advantage. Careful attention to the design of this action, both mechanically and electrically, probably contributes more to the simulation of actual pipe organ effects than any other single feature. If an organist is not told in advance that this instrument generates the tones electrically, he will often have to be shown the generators before he will believe it.

Additional Tonal Variations

Since all of the generators are connected to all of the keyboards through conventional stops on the input side but are fed into separate preamplifiers at the output of each keyboard, it is possible to modify still further the tone colors available and to maintain the effect of adding ranks of pipes. For example, the output of the swell manual may be fed through a flat preamplifier while the great organ is fed through a preamplifier with a pronounced rising high-frequency characteristic. Thus, although the same generator sources are used for both manuals, the stops on the great organ will be markedly more brilliant than those on the swell manual.

By using separate power amplifiers and loudspeakers for each manual, the effect obtained is analogous to doubling the number of

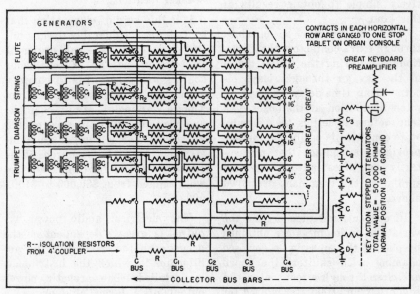

FIG. 4—Simplified schematic illustrating generator and control-circuit design principles employed in Mastertouch pipeless organ

available stops. Actually the flute stops with relatively small harmonic content will not be greatly affected by this procedure. In practice, therefore, the number of stop timbres available is increased only by approximately half in this manner. The results are entirely comparable in listening observations to adding ranks of pipes in a pipe organ.

The characteristic of a tone is modified not only by its harmonic content and the attack but also by its relative average loudness. Thus, a diapason tone generator may be fed to the same manual through two stop tabs and a distinct modification obtained by introducing a constant attenuation in the circuit of one tab only. There are innumerable permutations and combinations possible through circuitry of this kind, including octave couplers and couplers between manuals.

"On"-Effect Variations

There are many pipe-organ stops and musical instruments where the character of the sound is greatly dependent on fundamental and harmonic-content fluctuations at the start of the tone before it settles into a steady state. This is particularly true of such stops as the French horn and the gedeckt flute. The design of the action and key contact arrangements make it relatively simple to obtain results of this kind.

"On" effects may be obtained through extra contactors that function only during the initial travel of the key, or through relays incorporating time-delay releases. A pitch fluctuation at the onset of a tone before it settles to a steady-state condition is easily obtained by providing a contact that momentarily energizes an arrangement similar to the tremulant described above.

In conventional pipe organs the variations in loudness are obtained by placing the pipes in an enclosed chamber with shutters that open and close through a foot control. In this organ an attenuator is used for this purpose, controlled by a shoe

identical to those used in pipe organs. This arrangement permits precise control over the loudness and provides a dynamic range from the threshold of hearing to full organ.

A separate vernier control is provided for the pedal organ so that the organist may adjust the relative level from the pedal stops in accordance with the character of the music. This is comparable in many ways to providing additional pedal stops.

Amplifiers and Loudspeakers

In all installations a separate preamplifier and power amplifier channel are used for each manual and for the pedal keyboard. In elaborate installations one or more individual stops may be fed through separate channels. Each channel feeds a separate loudspeaker system so that a stop that appears on two or more manuals, even though it is derived from the same source, speaks from different loudspeakers often placed in different locations. Thus, even though the characteristics of the amplifiers are the same, the sound of a string when played on the great manual will be appreciably different than when played on the swell manual because of the difference in loudspeakers and the acoustic conditions of the loudspeaker locations.

It is this kind of elaboration that contributes considerably to the ability of a relatively small organ of this design, so far as tone color sources are concerned, to compete with very large pipe organs from a price standpoint. As an example, a recent installation was quoted at $18,000 for a three-manual instrument in a large church. Pipe organ quotations for comparable results ranged from $60,000 to $100,-000.

The electrical audio power required is greatly dependent on the acoustic characteristics of the auditorium in which the instrument is installed. The acoustic power output of a large pipe organ is greater than most people realize. In

general, it is desirable to be able to produce with full organ a minimum of 100 decibels above the reference threshold as measured with a commercial sound-level meter in all listening locations.

The peak power from organ music is in the lowest pedal octave. In an effort to produce satisfactory pedal tones without duplicating the peak power output of a pipe organ, it is not uncommon to use 16-foot stops that are rich in harmonic structures. This simulates the loudness subjectively observed but falls far short of achieving the full deep foundation tone of a real 16-foot pipe.

Perhaps the most important pedal stop is the 16-foot bourdon (a relatively pure flute tone). To produce it from a loudspeaker system at full pipe organ level requires carefully designed enclosures and exceptionally clean power amplifiers. In a typical church installation where the seating capacity was around 1,500 and the reverberation time relatively low, 100 watts of electrical audio power fed to five efficient loudspeaker systems (consisting of a total of 130 loudspeakers) was required for satisfactory results.

The only really satisfactory subjective criterion of performance in audio work is direct comparison. In the installation described above it was possible to make such a comparison with a three-manual pipe organ having eighteen ranks of pipes. The test was made with fifteen observers. All but two of the observers were critical listeners thoroughly familiar with pipe-organ tonal attributes, either by virtue of being professional organists, engineers who had participated in the installation, or because of an interest in organ music.

The test was made entirely on the basis of whether the observers could differentiate between the instruments. A few bars of music were played twelve times on each organ using various stops. Flute, diapason and string stops were used separately and in combination.

Several of the engineers admitted that their judgments included an intimate knowledge of characteristics in the organs that had little to do with the quality of the tone. Even with this added factor, no single score was high enough to be significant of anything except the close similarity in the basic character of the instruments.

BIBLIOGRAPHY

G. T. Winch and A. M. Midgley, Electronic Musical Instruments and the Development of the Pipeless Organ, *The Journal of the Institution of Electrical Engineers*, June 1940.

E. Meyer and G. Buchmann, Abhandlungen der Preussischen Akademie der Wissenschaften, 1931.

J. D. Goodell and B. M. H. Michel, Auditory Perception, ELECTRONICS, July 1946.

J. D. Goodell, Special Loudspeaker Systems, Part II, *Radio and Television News, Radio-Electronic Engineering Edition*, June 1949.

Converts Piano to Organ

NOVEL musical arrangements are now made possible by an electronic converter that attaches to a piano so that it becomes three instruments, a piano, an organ, or a piano-organ combination.

The conversion of the piano is accomplished by clamping a key switch frame across the keyboard so that plungers make contact to the keys. Operation of the keys in the normal piano technique then actuates the switches to close the appropriate circuits of organ tone generators connected to an audio amplifier and loudspeaker system in an adjacent cabinet.

The sources of all tones are 12 cascade generators. The circuit of one of these is shown in the diagram. Each cascade has five stages of 12AX7 twin triodes. Each cascade supplies the tones for the octavely related notes over the range of the instrument (for example, the C cascade supplies all the C tones and the C# cascade all the C# tones). There is one output from each stage of all cascades, thus providing a tone coverage of 60 notes extending from C1, 65 cycles, through B5, 1,976 cycles.

On each cascade the 12AX7 twin triode nearest the tuning coil is both the master oscillator and a reactance tube. The master oscillator triode is an inductively tuned electron-coupled oscillator having a sawtooth output waveform. The other triode is a reactance tube across the master oscillator tank circuit. Each master oscillator is the highest frequency generator on its cascade, and its output is used

for the top octave of the range, C5 to B5.

Frequency Dividers

The four remaining tubes on each cascade are simple slave multivibrators, each locking in and oscillating at one-half of the frequency of the one driving it. The master oscillator drives the first multivibrator, which in turn drives the second, and so on, down the line, to produce the five tones, each an octave apart.

If a tube or one of its associated parts should fail, the indication is a drop in pitch of the note concerned.

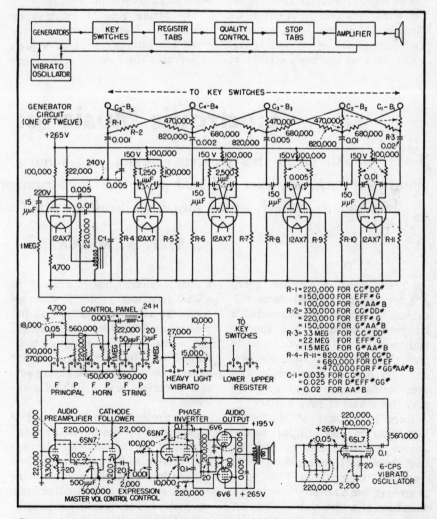

Circuit of multivibrator tone generators, audio amplifier, control panel and vibrato oscillator of the electronic piano-to-organ converter. The block diagram shows the sequence of functions

All the lower octavely related notes will also be out of tune.

As the slave multivibrators are capacitively coupled and driven, any change in the tuning of the master oscillator, by moving the tuning coil core, will also tune the multivibrators directly. The reactance triode grid is driven by the output of the vibrato oscillator to frequency modulate the master oscillator, to produce vibrato.

Except for slight differences in the values of some of the components, all 12 cascades are similar.

The control panel that clamps to the front of the piano contains the register, vibrato, and tone-quality selector switches. It also contains the tone-control components and the expression control.

The register selector switches select either the bottom register, C1 through C3, or the upper register, C#3 through B5, by connecting collector bars on the key switches to the tone-quality selector switches.

Following the register selector switches, the notes played pass through the tone selectors, namely principal, horn, and string. From the tone selectors the notes played go to the amplifier input.

The principal tone is obtained by means of an RC filter comprised of an 18,000-ohm resistor and a 0.05 μf capacitor, which attenuate the higher-frequency components of the generated sawtooth waveform.

The horn tone is obtained by passing the generated signal through an LC filter. The filter consists of a 24-henry coil and a 0.003-μf capacitor, and is peaked at approximately 600 cycles. The horn is augmented by borrowing some of the principal tone through a 560,-000 and 220,000-ohm resistor.

The string tone is obtained by passing the signal through a very small capacitor shunted by a high resistance. The f string is produced by using a 50-$\mu\mu$f capacitor and 1-megohm resistor. The p string uses a 20$\mu\mu$f capacitor and a 2-megohm resistor.

The 8-watt audio amplifier is conventional, using a master volume control after the preamplifier stage and an expression control after the cathode follower.

The vibrato switches select either heavy or light vibrato. The vibrato oscillator is a 6SL7 twin triode, one triode of which is a phase-shift oscillator. Its frequency is determined by the three 220,000-ohm resistors and the three 0.05-μf capacitors in the grid circuit. The second triode is a buffer amplifier between the vibrato oscillator triode and the reactance tubes on the cascade generators.

The instrument was developed and produced by engineers of the Lowrey Organ Division of Central Commercial Company of Chicago.

Electronic Music for Four

Novel "wobble organ" has separate soprano, alto, tenor and bass oscillators and a common power pack, amplifier and loudspeaker. The instrument plays anything from barbershop ballads to Bach with a pleasing vibrato quality from which it gets its name

By L. A. MEACHAM

AT one time or another, every musically inclined communications engineer has connected a laboratory oscillator to a speaker and twiddled the frequency dial to play himself a tune. But did anyone ever provide four people with four oscillators, so that they might play like a barber-shop quartet?

Here is a facet of electronics which up to now, so far as the author has been able to discover, has been left unexplored. The question occurred to him while searching for a novelty to entertain members of a glee club at their annual party. The results of preliminary research (conducted in the author's cellar, since it was not an official company project) were received so enthusiastically that improved models were designed (in the same cellar), playing techniques were improved, and concert experience was obtained before several surprised and delighted audiences.

The present state of the art is represented by the "wobble organ" described in this article. It uses inexpensive radio parts, and offers interesting possibilities for home recreation of the participation kind, as well as for various entertainment fields involving large groups.

The four players sit around a card table. In front of each player is a small "playing console". On the floor near the table is a cabinet containing a power supply, an amplifier, and a speaker.

Each console contains a thyratron sawtooth oscillator, with suitable control circuits and a simple waveform-shaping network which emphasizes or suppresses various harmonics in the complex sawtooth wave and thus affords a distinctive and different tone quality for each player. The physical arrangement of a console is shown in Fig. 1. The main control device is the "wobble arm", carried on a potentiometer shaft which extends through the sloping front. This control is designed to vary the pitch over a range of about 2½ octaves (about 6-to-1 in frequency). The range is at least that of the human voice, and in the present model is located differently on the frequency spectrum for each console, so that the four of them cover the vocal ranges of soprano, alto, tenor and bass respectively. (A male quartet model could be obtained merely by changing capacitance values.) The pitch control, or wobble arm, is operated by the right hand of the player in relation to the musical scale designations on the sloping scale quadrant. These designations need be used only as a rough guide, but they are of great value even to an experienced player in making rapid and accurate changes over large musical intervals, and they are indispensable to a beginner.

Operation of the tone source or oscillator is not continuous; each console can be turned on and off at will by the individual performer. The four consoles are normally silent. Oscillation is started by a slight downward pressure of the player's left hand on the knob at the left front of the console. This pressure closes a contact applying plate voltage to the oscillator. Thus the player may use a "portamento" between notes (leaving the tone on) or "detache" (momentarily interrupting it) as desired. The volume of sound delivered by the individual console to the common speaker is also under the control of this same knob, which may be turned as well as pressed by the player's left hand. The rotation can be calibrated in musical symbols, *pp*, *p*, *mp*, *mf*, *f*, and *ff*, indicating different degrees of loudness from pianissimo to fortissimo, but in the present model this is left to the musical taste of the player and only *p* and *f* are marked as rough guides near the opposite ends of the range. The switch action mentioned above is obtained very simply by mounting the potentiometer near the free end of a flat cantilever spring, the fixed end of which is screwed to the underside of the console top. A downward motion of about 3/32-inch brings the free end into electrical contact with a fixed metal contact that also limits travel.

One other control, a tuning adjustment to compensate for such variables as temperature and aging, is required, as in almost any other musical instrument. This tuning knob is initially adjusted by the player's left hand while the corresponding wrist presses down the "on" knob and his right hand aligns the wobble arm with a scale mark (such as middle C) corresponding to the pitch of the reference source to which he wishes to tune.

The present consoles are made of ⅜-inch plywood, with scale quadrants of ⅛-inch pressed hardboard. Each scale quadrant is made removable to facilitate storage, being mounted in slides at its edges. A simple catch is provided to support the free end of the wobble arm when not in use. The bottom of the console is made removable for access to component parts.

The layout of the speaker cabinet is conventional, the only novel feature being the provision of storage space for the four consoles, two at each side of the loudspeaker.

Circuits

Complete schematics are given of the consoles in Fig. 2 and the power supply and amplifier in Fig. 3. The thyratron relaxation oscillator in each console is of the type commonly used in oscilloscope sweep circuits, with the variable timing resistance used for the main pitch control and the grid bias for tuning. Different timing capacitors and waveform-shaping networks are shown (terminals *A*, *B*, *C*) for the respective consoles. When the consoles are plugged together a common shielded path is formed from the networks to the amplifier input.

The use of a 1-megohm logarithmic potentiometer in series with a fixed 10,000-ohm resistor for each frequency control provides a relationship between shaft angle and musical pitch which is substantially linear over a resistance range of 16,000 to 450,000 ohms, with a slope of about 30 degrees per octave. Accordingly, each half-tone occupies 2.5 degrees and each whole tone 5 degrees. The wobble arm

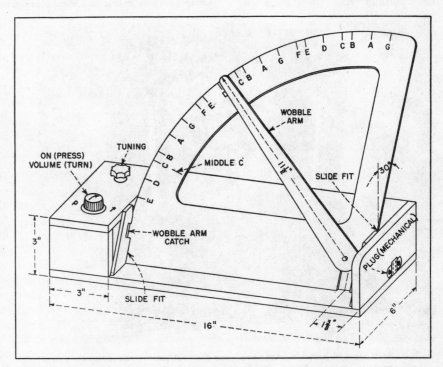

FIG. 1—The bass console. Others are similar mechanically except for calibration of the scale quadrant and placement of interconnecting plugs

swings over more than 75 degrees, giving the desired 2½ octaves, and is set on its shaft so that the minimum total resistance actually used is 75,000 ohms. The potentiometer should have a molded carbon element or equivalent so as to minimize effects of mechanical wear on scale calibration.

A voltage divider across the 150-volt supply (resistors R_1 and R_2 in Fig. 2) is arranged to hold the plate of the thyratron at about 40 volts above cathode potential while the "on" contact is open. The tube does not conduct in this condition, because its firing point for normal tuning is designed to be near 80 volts. The effect of the bias is to make the d-c potential at point A, while the oscillation is off, substantially equal to the d-c component of the sawtooth wave at the same point when it is on. Figure 4 shows how the bias eliminates a starting transient in the sawtooth wave as it is delivered to the input of the shaping network. If present, the transient would give a noticeable thump at the beginning of each note, particularly if the volume were turned up until excessive initial voltage rise overloaded the

final stage of the amplifier.

A voltage-doubling selenium-rectifier type of power supply (Fig. 3) delivers 100 milliamperes at 250 volts, and two voltage regulators are arranged in series to provide

stable plate and bias potentials. This regulation is quite important, not only to avoid fluctuations of pitch with line voltage, but to keep the four consoles independent of one another in spite of the fact that

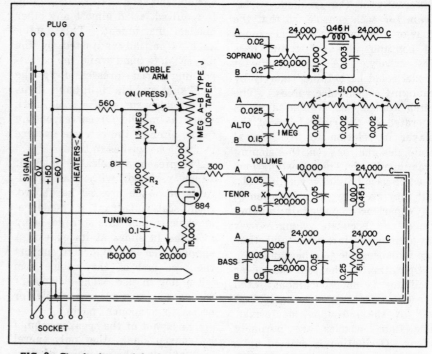

FIG. 2—Circuit of one of the four consoles, in this case the tenor console. The other three are identical electrically except for timing and waveform-shaping networks. Component-part values and circuits are shown for the soprano, alto and bass units

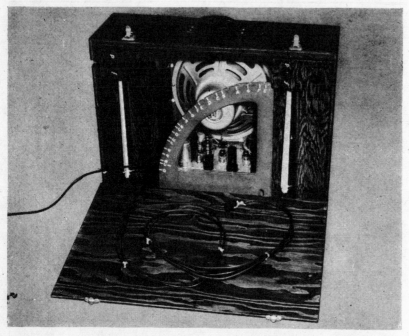

Rear view of portable case containing the wobble organ's common power supply, speaker and amplifier, with the four individual consoles knocked down and stowed away

their mean plate currents change as they are started and stopped or as their pitches are varied.

The audio amplifier is conventional; it includes a volume control, allowing the over-all instrument to be adjusted to a room of any size.

Playing Techniques

Several interesting facts have developed from playing and experimenting on this instrument. First, although steady tones, without vibrato, are desirable in some kinds of music, a much more live effect can be obtained by wobbling the pitch control smoothly through a small range above and below the position of true intonation. This corresponds to the vibrato used in playing a violin or trombone, or occurring naturally in the human voice. All who have learned to play thus far agree that a vibrato of small extent (less than a quarter tone peak-to-peak) and at a rate of about 4 or 5 per second is desirable. This motion, as may be guessed, accounts for choice of the name wobble organ.

To allow the player's right hand to produce vibrato with a comfortable wrist motion the notes should be spaced well apart on the dial. A spacing of about one inch per whole tone appears to be a reasonable minimum. This figure, taken with the potentiometer calibration of 5 degrees per whole tone noted earlier, leads to a figure of about one foot for the length of the wobble arm.

It may be noticed in Fig. 1 that the scale quadrant (in this bass console) is calibrated with high notes toward the left and low notes toward the right. This comes about because logarithmic potentiometers having a left-handed taper are not commonly stocked in suitable sizes. Although players quickly become accustomed to this arrangement, it has been found that most of them would prefer to have the scale reversed to match the convention of the piano keyboard.

Experience has been obtained both with family groups playing for their own entertainment, and with quartets well rehearsed for public performance. Some solo work has also been done using a single console with piano accompaniment. In every case enjoyment and recreation value have been strikingly evident. Even two professional symphony players who took part in one of the quartets were highly entertained and,

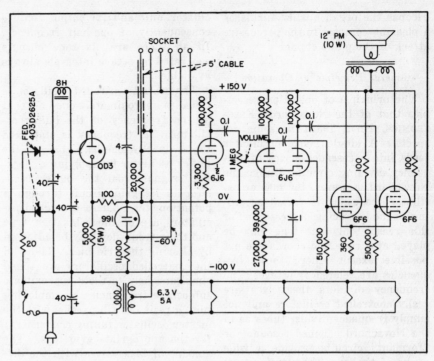

FIG. 3—Circuit of the common power supply, amplifier and loudspeaker unit

incidentally, behaved like the amateurs in that they played awkwardly at first but improved very rapidly.

The music used has varied from simple "rounds" and folk songs to Bach chorales. Although no suggestion is intended that the wobble organ may ever join the ranks of the serious musical instruments, nevertheless it can do things with Bach that are actually rather satisfying. It has a voice-like quality, and yet overcomes certain vocal restrictions. The soprano never strains for high passages, the alto cannot possibly run short of breath,

the tenor never cracks and the bass has power at his command for his very lowest note.

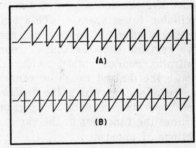

FIG. 4—Waveform at point X of Fig. 2 at start of oscillation (A) without bias derived from the bleeder R_1 R_2 and (B) with the bias

Solovox Principles

By FREDERICK D. MERRILL, JR.

FOR many years there has been a need for a really small, compact, portable musical instrument which would permit single tone solo performance with versatility of timbre, pitch range and tone envelope. Although such a device would prefer-

ably use a standard keyboard playing technique, conservation of width necessitates cutting down the number of keys. Early commercial models in this field received scant attention because either a new playing technique had to be learned or the

range in timbre was too limited.

The Solovox manufactured by Hammond Instrument Company represents a new approach to this problem. Although it may be played independently, the combination with a piano is particularly appropriate because the organ quality furnishes a pleasing contrast to the percussive attack of the piano strings.

General Principle of Operation

The principle of operation resembles that of the Novachord (ELECTRONICS, Nov., 1939) in some respects. A single master oscillator feeds into a cascaded series of frequency dividing circuits. Unlike the Novachord, however, the master oscillator frequency is varied according to the key being depressed. For this reason only one tone may be played at a time and chords are not possible except where these frequencies are related by octaves. The frequency dividers themselves are really controlled oscillators and not simply frequency divider tubes as in the Novachord. Tuned resonant or "formant" circuits provide a wide range of timbre. The attack or envelope is regulated by the grid bias variation of the control tube when a key is depressed. There are only three octaves of keys available but nevertheless six octaves in pitch range are present since five divider oscillator tubes operate. This represents a spread of 65.4 to 3951 cps. The register controls (bass, tenor, contralto, soprano tablet switches) choose the desired range or ranges of frequency at which the instrument operates. The block diagram outlines the functions of the various sections of apparatus.

The Generator Section

The frequency of the master oscillator is adjusted to any of the twelve chromatic tones of the highest octave range of the instrument (2093 to 3951 cps) by depressing any of the 36 keys. The actual octave pitch at the loudspeaker may be the same as the master oscillator or one or more octaves lower, depending on the number of divider stages chosen jointly by the key octave position and the register control.

The first controlled oscillator (buffer) is stabilized by the master oscillator and operates at the same frequency. Each succeeding tube is essentially a frequency dividing os-

cillator unit and its output tone is consequently of one-half frequency. In all there are six tone outputs separated by octave intervals always available.

The second controlled oscillator is tuned to approximately one-half that of the frequency of the buffer oscillator. Its frequency is stabilized to be exactly one-half that of the buffer oscillator by applying a "locking" signal from the buffer oscillator to its grid circuit through a potentiometer. These controlled oscillators are of the relaxation type and their frequency may be adjusted by altering the grid bias. Thus, all the controlled oscillators are tuned simultaneously to their approximate sub-octave frequencies by employing tuning resistors (in parallel with the master oscillator tuning condensers) for the appropriate grid bias. The amount of bias varies with the different keys.

The oscillators all operate at their top pitches when no key is depressed. When a key other than *B* is depressed, all oscillators simultaneously shift to the frequencies corresponding to the key. The master oscillator is accurately tuned by the tuning condensers and the controlled oscillators by the tuning resistors.

The particular oscillator output which the loudspeaker reproduces is determined by a second contact under each key, called the control contact. Three relays are connected to the respective control contacts of the keys in the separate upper, middle, and lower octaves. Each relay has a contact to connect the grid of the preamplifier tube to the desired oscillator through the register controls. For example, if the "Soprano" control is actuated, and the *G* key in the middle of the keyboard depressed, then the tuning contact under the key will tune all the oscillators to the *G* tones of the various octaves and the control contact will operate the middle octave relay. This relay completes a circuit from the output of the second controlled oscillator through a register control resistor to the middle octave relay contact, and then to the preamplifier tube. Thus, the register controls

shift the pitch range of the keyboard as a whole to four different positions. In addition, by simultaneously depressing two or more of these controls, a composite tone will be heard consisting of the outputs of several oscillators sounding simultaneously in their octave relations.

Other contacts associated with each of the relays serve to prevent undesirable tones from occurring when two keys are depressed simultaneously in adjoining groups. If two keys are depressed within one of the three octave groups then the lowest pitched of the two will be automatically selected for sounding through the speaker.

There are two main divisions to the timbre control methods. First there is a "mute" tube which operates nonlinearly to suppress the sharp curvature of the input signal waveform, and thus weakens the higher overtones. When this more mellow timbre is not desired, the mute switch is used to by-pass the signal around the tube.

The second section of the timbre control circuits alters the frequency characteristics of the amplifier. The "Deep Tone" switch allows a condenser to by-pass the highs. The "Brilliant Tone" switch connects an inductance between high side and ground so as to furnish a comparatively low impedance path to ground for the low frequencies, resulting in their removal from the following stage. "Full Tone" retains both the high and low frequency components. The "First Voice" and "Second Voice" consist of resonant circuits tuned to respectively the 500-cps zone and the 1000-cps zone. These tone control circuits are connected in series so each may be used independently of the others. This timbre control method relies on the extreme richness of harmonics from the output of the preamplifier tube.

Envelope Control

Complete control over the tone envelope is not provided in this instrument. However, the tone onset may be adjusted to slow or fast, the former being used particularly for the organ, orchestra wind instrument and string simulation. The rate of decay cannot be adjusted except by using the knee operated volume control. There is provision made to eliminate decay transient thumps.

A gradual buildup of the volume from an individual tone to produce an organ or wind instrument effect is obtained as follows. The control contacts under the playing keys serve to remove the cutoff bias from the control tubes as well as to operate one of the three relays. This is brought about by dropping the bias to below cutoff for these variable mu control tubes. The time constant of the grid-cathode circuit slows up the tone beginning and ending, so as to eliminate loudspeaker keying clicks. To speed up the attack a 0.1 μf condenser connected between the control tube cathodes and grids may be disconnected by operating the "fast attack" switch.

The Vibrato

The vibrato effect is produced by a small piece of powdered iron moving in and out of a coil connected to a tap on the master oscillator tuning coil so that the oscillator frequency varies. The iron itself is supported by a magnetically driven reed which is first set into motion when the volume control lever is pulled forward in starting the instrument.

Volume Controls

There are two volume controls provided in the instrument. The first limits the maximum volume obtainable from the instrument and is located under the keyboard compartment so that adjustment may be made for the particular room being used. Normally it is not operated during the playing of the instrument. A knee swell used by the player for volume expression moves a switch connected to seven fixed resistors. These form a part of a voltage divider circuit which varies the grid bias to the remote cutoff control tubes, so as to change the gain.

Tuning

The Solovox is tuned once to put it in agreement with the piano or other instruments it is accompanying and no additional retunings are necessary. Since but one master oscillator is used, the entire operation is accomplished by adjusting the frequency of the master oscillator alone by turning a knob located on one corner of the tone cabinet. This results in moving a powdered iron core in or out of an inductance in the master oscillator circuit. The controlled oscillators can also be readjusted to correct pitch should one attempt to alter the master oscillator greatly from its normal frequency, but this is seldom necessary.

An interior view of the generator and amplifier chassis as well as the loudspeaker cabinet is shown in the accompanying photograph. The large round container at the left protects the relays from dust, etc. This assembly is so shallow that it may be attached to either side of an upright piano or to the bottom of a grand piano.

In the belief that the instrument would find particular application with pianos to provide a wind instrument solo part, the keyboard with the associated control tablets is designed to be attached to the front edge of the piano as shown in the illustrations. The lowest C is placed opposite the middle C of the piano so that the thumb of the right hand can play the Solovox and the remaining fingers simultaneously depress the piano keys for accompaniment similarly as is often done by organists.

The wide range of tone colors, frequency, and organ-like attack with optional vibrato provide a small solo keyboard instrument of great versatility.

Readers are referred to United States Patents: Re 20,831; Re 21,137; 2,099,204; 2,117,002; 2,142,-580; 2,203,432; 2,203,569 for background information on this electronic musical instrument.

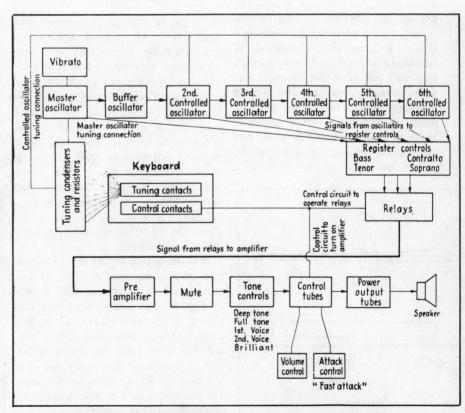

Block diagram of the electrical circuits of the Solovox. The keys control the frequency of the master oscillator and controlled oscillators, whereas the tone tablets connect various tone-modifying auxiliary amplifiers and filters

Design for an Electronic Reed Organ

Electrostatic pick-up directly from the reeds of a conventional inexpensive pneumatic harmonium, using the method employed in electronic pianos, makes it possible to enrich the tone, increase the volume range and provide new timbres

By FREDERICK D. MERRILL, JR.

NEARLY every radio experimenter with a love for music has dreamed of having a fine pipe organ installed in his own home, if only the instrument were not so expensive. It is possible, however, to construct an electronic organ giving beautiful tones at a small fraction of the prohibitive cost of commercial instruments. Such an instrument may be constructed with the familiar reed organ as a foundation. Several different timbres can be controlled by stop buttons, the tone is truly organesque, and even the deep pedal tones may be reproduced. The usual reed sounds are much improved by electronic amplification.

Any reed organ may be made electronic by the simple method of threading a machine screw through the reed cell near the tongue. The screw acts as an electrostatic pick-up member. With only one rank of reeds the greatest practical variation is from bass and treble tone, but two ranks, pitched an octave above and below a third rank, permit a wide pitch and timbre range. Figure 1 illustrates a typical reed. Figure 2 shows the reed equipped with pick-up screw for converting the mechanical vibrations of the reed tongue into minute electric currents.

Reed organs are obtained very cheaply from music stores. Churches sometimes have an old unused one lying around. It is unnecessary to purchase a new one since second-hand ones can easily be found with a little searching. The better ones have several banks of reed cell blocks as well as pedal keys and swell pedal.

The Pick-up System

There is one pick-up screw for each reed. All pick-up screws are connected by a five mil diameter steel piano wire which fits tightly inside the thread of the screw, forming a full loop. The preferred screws are hexagonal headed brass, flat end, of diameter a little larger than the tongue width. The hexagonal head permits adjustment with an open ended wrench or pliers. The brass diminishes corroding and the flat end advantage is illustrated in Fig. 4. A concave or convex shape reduces the effective capacity between screw and tongue.

It is important to line up the screw and tongue accurately. This is accomplished by a special tool shown in Fig. 5. The left side of tool (as shown in the side elevation) is the same size as a reed base. The right side has three holes for marking the drilling point in the reed cell for the pick-up screw. The tool fits into the cell and a scriber marks through the hole, onto the outside wood. This operation is carried out with the top covering the reed block removed from

instrument so that the drilling will be feasible. During the drilling the reeds are removed from cells to prevent injury to them. All wood splinters and dirt must be removed before the reeds are again inserted for blowing. Should a speck of dust lodge between reed tongue and its slotted base, it can be removed by sliding a thin piece of paper under tongue.

For the long low frequency reeds, the preferred pick-up point is about two-thirds the distance from the base towards the tip. With the medium frequency reeds the distance is increased to about three-quarters, and in the high frequency reeds the pick-up screw is located right at the tongue tip. There is a small change in timbre as the pick-up screw is moved along towards the tip but this is relatively useless as a timbre variation method. For the lowest octave or two the output from a single pick-up screw may be too low. The output may be increased by employing two or three screws along the

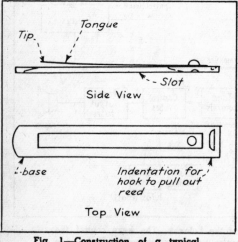

Fig. 1—Construction of a typical pneumatic reed

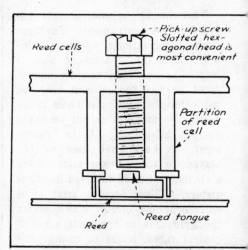

Fig. 2—Reed equipped with electrostatic pick-up

tongue length.

It is well to lacquer the screw end heavily so that any chance contact between tongue and screw will not produce a loud "pop" in the loudspeaker. The reed bases are connected together by a pair of fine steel wires imbedded in the felt and running the length of the bank in back of the bases.

Diminishing the Residual Acoustic Tone

Since the organ will be operated with the pedal controlling the volume of sound coming from loudspeaker, it is desirable to lessen the direct output sound from the reeds themselves. If this is not carried out, the direct reed tone will produce a timbre different from that coming from the loudspeaker, when the gain of the amplifier is reduced. A felt-lined box covering the reeds will help. To permit air to pass into the box, several holes or slits are cut in the wood and the air allowed to suck through the felt.

Electrostatic Shielding

Electrostatic shielding must be provided to prevent stray fields from getting into the pick-up lines and causing hum. The cheapest material is gold or silver paper obtainable from stationery stores. One may also apply Aquadag, a colloidal graphite diluted in alcohol, with a paint brush. The resistance to ground when dry should not exceed 50,000 ohms. Con-

centrated Aquadag paste may be obtained from Acheson Oildag Corp., Port Huron, Michigan. The shielding is applied to the outside of the small box covering the reed banks. If the instrument has the entire amplifier and loudspeaker within the same console as the reeds, then it will probably be necessary to shield the a-c cords inside the cabinet. If one listens to the loudspeaker for hum while a lamp cord carrying alternating current is moved around the console, the effectiveness of the shielding may be judged.

For reed organs already equipped with draw knobs or tabs for timbre control, it is simplest to retain that system although other electrical methods are available and will be explained later. The pneumatic system operates solely by a long wood strip surfaced with leather, pivoting down over the air inlet.

Several precautions may be necessary to prevent the movement of this strip from generating noise. When the leather surface strikes against the reed cell partitions and reed bases a loud thud may be heard from loudspeaker. This undoubtedly arises from the agitation of the leather dielectric in the electrostatic field, generating static fields which feed electric impulses into the amplifier. If the leather edge farthest from the reed base and nearest to hinges is painted with Aquadag and grounded, most of this noise will disappear. Another loudspeaker noise occurring

when this wood strip is moved may resemble a rattle or scratching. This can come from the brass hinges supporting the movement of the strip and is cured by scraping a little of the lacquer off each hinge half and joining with a flexible wire by soldering. It must be emphasized that any intermittent metallic contact in the electrostatic pick-up field or grounding and shielding circuits is liable to generate noise. The prevention consists in making the contact positive at all times.

The limitation of the pneumatic stop control system lies in the difficulty of adding the electric timbre control to the draw knob motion. One may, of course, have separate bass and treble tone control potentiometer knobs. But with this pneumatic strip, the bank of reeds is either contributing 100 per cent electric output or none; there is no variation possible between those extremes.

The Pick-up Amplifier

Approximately 100 db gain is needed in the amplifier, with an input resistance of two megohms. The frequency range depends at its lowest limit on the lowest frequency reed used. The upper limit is about 6000 to 8000 cps. Of course, it is useless to have available a lower frequency limit than that the loudspeaker is capable of reproducing. The coupling of harmonium reeds to the air is extremely inefficient for frequencies below 100 cps and it is

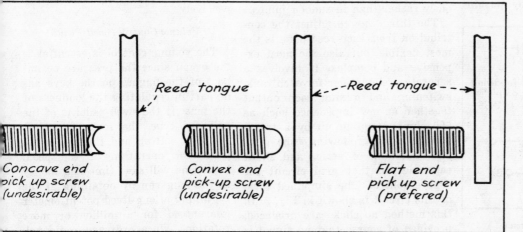

Fig. 4—Three types of screws ends. The flat end provides the highest voltage pick-up because of greater capacitance

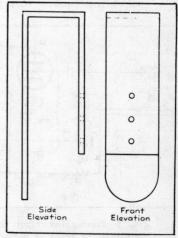

Fig. 5—Tool for locating drilling points for pick-up screws

here that the electronic equipment may be made to out-perform conventional reed organs greatly by giving deep, rich bass tones. Remembering that the standard pitch of middle C is 261 cps and that of the A above, 440 cps, one can easily compute the lowest frequency on the instrument. Doubtless it will be 87, 43, or about 30 cps, depending on the reed ranks found in the instrument. An amplifier of not less than 15 watts undistorted power output, such as that given by a pair of type 2A3 tubes in push pull, should be used for good bass reproduction.

The amplifier must be free of perceptible cross modulation lest difference-frequency components mar the clarity of tones when playing. With beam power tubes in push pull, for example, unless about fifteen per cent inverse feedback is employed, the chordal distortion in the treble renders the performance unsatisfactory.

A typical pre-amplifier input circuit is shown in Fig. 6. It is much easier to construct a hum-free amplifier by having the pre-amplifier on one chassis and the power amplifier on another chassis. High impedance shielded cable leads may cause hum unless the shielding is insulated from ground except for the single connection to the one common grounding point.

Organ Stops Controlled by Electrical Methods

It is usual with pipe organs to select the desired stop by pushing

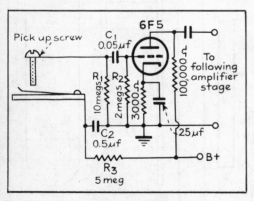

Fig. 6—Preamplifier input circuit. Care must be taken to protect the grid circuit from extraneous fields

down a rocking tab or pulling out a knob. The pneumatic system has already been described. Two electrical methods will be explained below.

One may adjust the output signal from a given bank of reeds by varying the polarizing voltage on the bases, as shown in Fig. 7. To eliminate switching clicks a filter time delay arrangement must be included, as indicated by the resistors R_3, R_4, C_2 and C_3. Unfortunately, with full gain setting of a high power amplifier, the necessary time delay must run into seconds to eliminate all traces of clicks. If the switching could take place gradually, such as by slowly increasing pressure of a metallic conductor on soft aquadagged felt (the resistance would start at several megohms and gradually drop down to about 25,000 ohms) the time delay of the filter could be short to prevent click, but the design of such a multi-contact slowly closing switch does not appear practical for simple construction. Short circuiting the amplifier or loudspeaker during shifting of the polarizing voltage has no advantage since this method itself also brings in a click. A potentiometer may be useful for setting the polarizing voltage as a timbre control means, but this will not allow fast shifting of quality where there are pre-set combinations involving three reed banks and bass and treble tone controls. With the potentiometer, however, clicks will be negligible, since the voltage is varied continuously rather than in sudden jumps.

The third way to adjust the contribution from each reed bank is the most flexible, but also the most expensive and complex. It involves a separate pre-amplifier for each rank, switching and mixing each output together at low impedance such as 500 ohms, stepping up by a transformer to the following tube grid, and switching of series and shunt capacities in that grid circuit for timbre control. The simplified form of this circuit is shown in Fig. 8. In this method no clicks are produced, provided of course that no signal is being fed into the input during the switching.

The switch itself is of the interlocking type so that when one button is pushed in, another already in automatically releases. Assuming that the instrument contains three reed ranks and provision is to be made for bass, treble, and volume control, there will be six single pole single throw switches, or twelve blades in all, operated by one button. At least six and preferably twelve button sections are desirable for setting up as many different combinations. Several manufacturers of

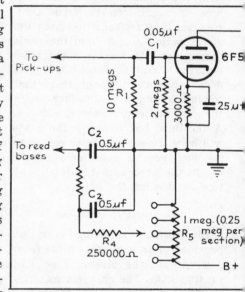

Fig. 7—Method of varying the electric output from each bank of reeds. The polarizing voltage applied to the reed bases is varied by R_5

radio push button tuning switches can furnish the desired unit inexpensively.

Volume Control Swell Pedal

The volume control is essential to the organ since the pressure or impact of the fingers on the keys has no part in regulating the loudness of the tone. If the swell pedal is of the balanced type, the foot can adjust the gain setting and then leave the pedal for operation of the pedal keys. One will save time and money in the long run by obtaining at the beginning a long-lived potentiometer guaranteed for a million or more rotations, since ordinary radio volume controls invariably become noisy after a little usage. There are several now on the market that may be obtained for less than two dollars.

A pre-set volume control in front of this potentiometer in the pre-amplifier common channel is necessary to avoid turning the gain beyond the point at which overload and distortion appears in the loudspeaker.

Choice of the Loudspeaker

A twelve-inch loudspeaker is the smallest that can be recommended for adequate volume and the 15-inch electro-dynamic is preferred. The low frequency pedal tones can only be reproduced with a large baffle plane, infinite baffle arrangement (sound absorbing back) or bass reflex. Resonant sound chambers for accentuating the bass have the undesired weakness of dulling the stridency of tones and lengthening the damping period, but some economical compromise must be effected between deepness of bass and brilliancy of treble. Trained ears will quickly detect a synthetic bass which lacks real strength in the fundamental, or perhaps one should say the sense of feeling detects the deficiency, since the bass tones are felt as much as they are heard.

No organ would be complete without a tremulant, which introduces a low-frequency variation in volume. The most obvious way to arrange this is to vary the amplifier gain at a periodic rate between six and twelve times a second, and thus the loudspeaker volume rises and falls. A superior scheme would raise and lower the frequency of all the notes along with a change in their volume. This may be brought about in the familiar Doppler effect by arranging a single paddle to move to and fro in front of a loudspeaker. Alternate pulses push out the air and pull it in so that the frequency fluctuates as well as the volume. The pivot axis is towards the base of the celotex board.

With many reed organs there is already a pneumatic provision for tremulant by rapidly opening and shutting the air equalizer chamber.

Installation of Amplifier and Loudspeaker

The amplifier and loudspeaker are preferably placed within the organ console if space permits this. In any case, the pre-amplifier section should be inside the organ to keep the lead from pick-up screws to input short. It is best to have that lead formed of high-voltage auto ignition cable to insure against leakage noises. To eliminate loading the pick-up system with the dead capacity of shielding for this lead, no shielding is used unless it is necessary to prevent a-c hum. At this highly sensitive input, the insulation resistance must be high—at least a hundred megohms. Ordinary tape insulation is unsatisfactory and all leakage paths should have a full inch length.

Accessibility of all parts warrants careful consideration. Where separate channels are used for preamplifiers, the outputs can be arranged with detachable plugs.

Voicing of Pick-up Screws

Having connected all the electric parts, one next proceeds to the voicing or adjustment of pick-up screws for uniform loudness from the loudspeaker. The first stage of this rough adjustment can take place by blowing a reed in normal manner while the screw is threaded in until a buzzing indicates contact is being made with vibrating tongue and then the screw is backed off a full turn.

The first precaution is to hold down adjoining bass keys and observe, when they are suddenly released, whether sharp clicks come from loudspeaker. If disagreeable noises do result, then the reed tongues are slapping against the screws so the latter must be backed off farther. When all such thumps have been eliminated by checking with various key combinations, then one can start to drop down the volume of the louder reeds to balance with the softer ones all over the keyboard. The extreme bass and treble may

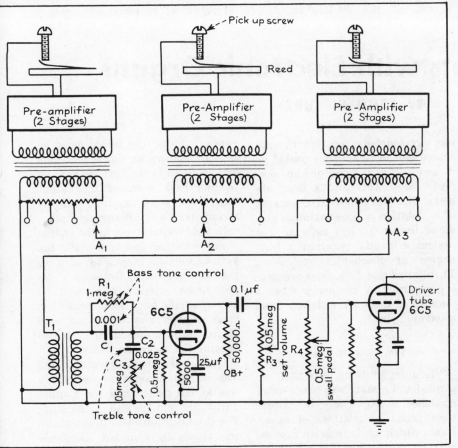

Fig. 8—Simplified circuit showing separate two stage pre-amplifiers (6F5 and 6C5 tubes) for each bank

be a little weaker than the middle region but that is unimportant if there is no abrupt shift in volume going from one key to another. An a-c voltmeter across the voice coil furnishes the most convenient indication for volume equality, although the ear must be the final judge. Each rank of reeds is voiced separately before their outputs are combined.

Setting up the Stops

If there are already stop draw knobs on the console, these may be marked 16 feet, 8 feet, and 4 feet, and this designation refers to the frequency of each set of reeds. For the 8-foot stop depressing the middle A key gives the expected tone frequency of 440 cps. The same key with the 16-foot stop gives the octave below and the 4-foot stop the octave above middle A.

In this case there are seven stops which can be quickly set up: (1) 16 feet alone; (2) 8 feet alone; (3) 4 feet alone; (4) 16 feet and 8 feet together; (5) 8 feet and 4 feet together; (6) 16 feet and 4 feet together; (7) 16 feet, 8 feet, and 4 feet together. Other combinations take into consideration the bass and treble tone controls. A general objective is to determine the thinnest timbre (rich in upper harmonics) and the thickest timbre (strong fundamental and weak in overtones) and divide the stops between these extremes. Another desirable pair of stops is (1) strong volume treble section tapering down to weak bass section; (2) the reverse. Also the 16 feet, 8 feet, and 4 feet stops may be combined in percentages other than 100 or zero when the separate channel mixing system is used. It is impractical to give more specific directions on setting up the timbres since tastes and the instrument itself vary so much. That is, one instrument may have just one bank of reeds while another may have a half dozen or more.

To aid setting up the timbres, one button of the switch should be selected to throw on manually operated controls for each reed bank, the bass and treble tone controls and volume control. Thus one may mix the tones at will and use this arrangement to compare with the stops previously set up. The six knobs of the potentiometers (assuming separate channel system for inputs) may be inside the console, or left outside for the musician playing the finished instrument to modulate from one timbre to another in continuous fashion rather than to break up the tone continuity by pushing another button to obtain a different timbre.

The loudspeaker volume output for a given gain setting should be about the same for all the stops, since the swell pedal can cover the full range from minimum to maximum undistorted amplifier output.

It is hoped that this general description will be found sufficiently clear and complete to enable the experimenter to carry out the construction of an electronic organ.

Experiments with Electronic Organs

By JOHN H. JUPE

EXPERIENCES in the construction of various electronic organs are related by S. K. Lewer in *Electronic Engineering* for September, 1944. He was confronted by a choice of (a) complex waveforms, analyzed by the keyboard controls into the various tones required; or (b) sine waves, synthesized by the keyboard controls into the various tones.

He chose (a) and decided that an electrostatic method of generation was best for the amateur because cutting and shaping metal electrodes is easier than winding large numbers of electromagnets or setting up precision optical systems, and because time delay resistance-capacitance circuits provide easy means of controlling tone etc. This original choice has been confirmed by later experiments.

The first experimental generator was a gramaphone record with equi-spaced tinfoil waveforms pasted on it and using a fixed pickup electrode. Both this and a later all-metal disc were discarded because of modulation or tone variation produced by mechanical defects. The system evidently required a high degree of mechanical precision. There were also difficulties concerning accuracy of frequency when a number of discs were driven from a common shaft.

Vibration Methods

Vibratory systems were then examined and a start was made using stretched wires, where the vibrations produce variations of capacitance which are translated into oscillatory voltages across a high resistance. To generate sustained (organ) tones, the wires must be kept in continuous vibration. This was achieved in the first instance by feeding back some of the output from the final a-f amplifier into the string itself and arranging a magnetic field transversely to the string.

For selecting and converting the various tones, a second set of pickups was provided. Brass or phosphor bronze wires were found to be quite satisfactory and small bar magnets about two inches long were placed on each side of the wire to provide the magnetic fields.

Quite pure tones were obtained provided the maintaining electrode was at the center and the magnet ⅓ distant from the end of the wire. The chief difficulty was in maintaining absolutely constant amplitude of vibration, due to minute pickup and amplifier changes.

Later, a method of maintaining the strings with low pressure air jets was thought promising but it failed above about 800 cps.

Used Reeds

Attention was then given to vibrating reeds as variable capacitance elements, with reeds taken first from a harmonica and later from an American organ. Forty reeds, covering 32-2000 cps in five octaves, were assembled and at first, direct acoustic output was difficult to silence, particularly at the higher frequencies. Cotton wool provided a reasonable solution to this problem. Key click filters were also necessary and by suitably choosing the values, could be made to provide "attack" controls as well.

Continuously operated reeds were satisfactory but there was a slight background roar, i.e. stray pickup from all reeds simultaneously. The war stopped experiments but there have been some later ones using an undulating change of capacitance to produce a frequency change in an oscillator instead of a current change in a resistance. In the opinion of Lewer, this system merits further careful consideration.

Argument for Electronic Music

By SIDNEY T. FISHER

MUSICAL THEORY, where it touches on the intervals employed in harmony, is in a state of great confusion. The scale universally used for keyboard instruments, the Tempered (diatonic) Scale, inadequately translates musical conceptions, and its weaknesses should be recognized. The Just (diatonic) Scale is in full accord with the spirit of music and the letter of physical laws, and in the light of modern instrumentalities, could now be adopted. Electrical musical keyboard instruments can be designed in a practical form to play the Just Scale in all keys. These are some of the conclusions to be drawn from the facts to be outlined, but it is first necessary to understand scale structure from the musical standpoint.

"Just"-scale musical instruments have been under consideration by investigators for many years and in recent years a number of articles have appeared in musical journals on this subject. Such instruments, due to anomalies in scale structure, have been considered by most authorities as being impossible from a practical standpoint. They have thus become to be regarded by musicians as an ideal to be sought after but impossible of practical attainment. This article has for its object the description of practical instruments whose scale frequencies bear exact harmonic relationships to one another, to the end that maximum harmoniousness may be achieved.

Scale Structure

Tones separated by discrete pitch intervals are a universal tradition in modern Western music. An octave of seven notes is usually employed and this is the diatonic scale.[1] In addition, in accordance with an almost universal tradition, five additional intervals are inserted, which break up the five larger intervals of the seven-note scale. Most music—particularly music by the classic masters—is written in the seven-note scale. This scale has its most familiar embodiment in the piano and it is not an exaggeration to say that the keyboard mechanism of the piano has been made the basis of the modern system of music. The scale can be conveniently thought of as it appears on the piano keyboard. If we take the note C as the starting note for an octave, then the seven notes of the diatonic scale are played by the white digitals and the five additional tones which divide the larger intervals of diatonic scale are played by the black digitals.

The scale obtained by playing the white notes of the piano in sequence, commencing with C, is called the key of C major, or the natural key. Other keys then are obtained by playing a series of notes, commencing with the key note, which have the same sequence of intervals: tone, tone, semi-tone, tone, tone, tone, semi-tone.

It is advisable to guard at the outset against a common misconception; this is the idea that scales were made first, and music afterwards. Scales are made in the process of creating music. If music consisted only of single-note melodies, the requirements to be met by a scale would allow the widest latitude in choosing the intervals. Modern Western music, however, employs harmony as its most important feature, and it is necessary therefore that certain groups of notes of our scale, sounded simultaneously, should form harmonious chords.

Chords and Harmony

The physical criterion for harmoniousness in a chord is that the ratio of the frequencies of its component tones may be expressed as the ratio of small integers. The smaller the integers the more marked is the consonance. The application of this law to the diatonic scale fixes the intervals *between* the notes as seen in Fig. 1.

Note:	C	D	E	F	G	A	B	C
Ratio:	1	9/8	5/4	4/3	3/2	5/3	15/8	2
Name:	Unison	Second	Third	Fourth	Fifth	Sixth	Seventh	Octave
Interval	9:8	10:9	16:15	9:8	10:9	9:8	16:15	

Fig. 1—The 7-note Just Scale in the key of C (the natural key). This is fundamental in Western culture, and is the idealized form of the scales in actual use

In the first line are the letter names of the notes of the scale, in the key of C, in the second line are the ratios of their frequencies to the leading note, and in the third are the musical names of the intervals obtained by sounding together each of the notes of the scale with the leading note. These intervals form a version of the diatonic scale called the Just Scale. The fourth line shows the frequency ratios between adjacent notes. It will be noted that three sizes of intervals exist, those represented by pitch ratios of 9:8, 10:9 and 16:15. The two large intervals, 9:8 and 10:9 are called a tone, and the smallest interval, 16:15, a semi-tone.

Three triads or groups of three notes are considered the foundation of the system of harmony. These chords are the triads having frequency ratios 4:5:6 formed with their lowest note a fifth below the key note, on the key note, and a fifth above the key note. In the octave shown above, these triads are CEG, FAC, and GBD, giving the arrangement of Fig. 2. These three triads define every note in the diatonic scale and fix the ratios at the values listed above.

The Tempered Scale

It is apparent that none of the possible ways of setting up a scale —progressions by fifths (frequency ratio 3:2), by fourths (frequency ratio 4:3), or by thirds (frequency ratio 5:4)—will give the octave note, since all these ratios are prime to one another. The ex-

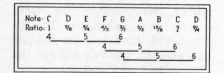

Fig. 2—The three major triads (triad chord = of three notes). These are the chief foundation of harmony as employed in Western music

tremely complicated treatment of diatonic scale structures that exists in musical literature is brought about solely by the fact that the tone sources of traditional instru-

ments cannot be adjusted in frequency to form a new scale for each key change. Figure 3 shows the difficulty graphically.

The Tempered Scale[6] (Scale of Equal Temperament) is universally used today for keyboard instruments and therefore nominally by all musicians. It is based on the simple arrangement that an octave is divided into twelve equal intervals of a semi-tone, each of which, therefore, has a frequency ratio of the 12th root of two. This scale has the great virtue that it permits modulation without limitation. In music, modulation means a change in key, i.e., an overall shift in frequency.

This is shown graphically in Fig. 4. It has the disadvantage that many of the harmonic intervals are quite inaccurate. Fortunately, the interval of a fifth (nominal frequency ratio 3:2) is very close and this is the most important interval in harmony. However, the intervals of a third and a sixth, which are also of frequent occurrence, are very poor, being about a third of a semi-tone too large. The Tempered Scale, therefore, presents the disadvantages that many subtle effects in music which depend on variations in consonance of different intervals, are largely obscured by the fact that intervals which should sound quite consonant, such as thirds, are somewhat dissonant.

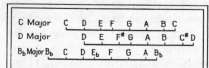

Fig. 3—The effect of changing key in the Just Scale is to shift the frequencies of some of the notes; this is necessary because of the unequal intervals. Logarithms of the ratios are plotted

By virtue of its make-up, the Tempered Scale has the same harmonic intervals in any key. In the Just Scale, when an instrument is tuned in one key, the harmonic structure is changed perceptibly for the other keys, if the instrument is not retuned. In the Tempered Scale a change of key means

only a change of pitch. The graphical comparison of the Tempered and Just Scale intervals is shown in Fig. 5.

Helmholtz's Views

The shortcomings of the Tempered Scale have been familiar to musicians and physicists alike since it was first adopted. Helmholtz in 1860 pointed out its serious defects and suggested that in a generation or two the Tempered Scale might have a very marked effect on our acuteness of appreciation for harmony. It appears that his predictions have been fulfilled to a large extent and that the return of a strict perception of harmony is only possible by replacing the Tempered Scale with the Just Scale.

Helmholtz's comments on the differences between the Tempered and the Just Scales are worth quoting because they outline clearly the reasons leading up to the work described in this paper. They show that the deficiencies of the Tempered Scale have been fully recognized, as has been the excellence of the (7-note) Just Scale. And yet until the present, no practical solution has been obtained for the application of the Just Scale to keyboard instruments.

The following excerpts are from the 4th English edition of Helmholtz's "Sensations of Tone":

"As regards musical effect, the difference between the just and the equally tempered intonations, is very remarkable. The justly intoned chords, in favourable positions . . . possess a full, and, as it were, saturated harmoniousness; they flow on, with a full stress, calm and smooth, without tremor or beat. Equally tempered chords sound beside them rough, dull, trembling, restless. The difference is so marked that everyone, whether he is musically cultivated or not, observes it at once. . . .

"It must not be imagined that the difference between tempered and just intonation is a mere mathematical subtlety without any practical value. That this difference is really very striking even to unmusical ears is shown immediately by actual experiments with properly tuned instruments. . . ."

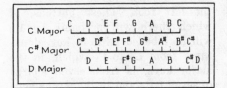

Fig. 4—The effect of changing key in the Tempered Scale is simply to shift the pitch of the music. No readjustment of the scale intervals is involved. Logarithms of the ratios are plotted

It must be realized that the Tempered Scale has been adopted solely because it will permit changing into different keys without any change in the structure of the music. Since the intervals in the Just Scale are unequal, if a modulation from one key to another is to be made, then of necessity the scale must be readjusted so that it can maintain the exact sequence of intervals in the key. With conventional keyboard instruments, this is not possible and the Tempered Scale is the only practical solution.

At various times, proposals for new keyboards have been made. A complication of the keyboard is not a practical approach to the problem because of the considerable difficulty it adds to the work of the performer. It is, however, the only possible approach to a solution in the case of traditional instruments.

Electronic Instrument Possibilities

With the introduction of electrical methods of producing musical tones we have, for the first time, the facility offered to us of key changes which will be strictly harmonious on an instrument tuned in the Just Scale. This is true only because the frequencies of the tone generators of electrical instruments can be instantaneously and accurately readjusted.

That complications will be introduced into an electrical musical instrument by the use of the Just Scale is demonstrated by Fig. 3. It is seen that a digital on the keyboard must have access to a considerable number of slightly differ-

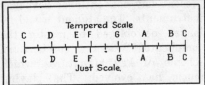

Fig. 5—Comparison of Tempered and Just Scale intervals. Logarithms of the ratios are plotted

ing frequencies if exact harmonic ratios are to be preserved in all keys. In conventional instruments, this is an insurmountable obstacle. It has been judged so by Helmholtz, and all other writers in·the field.

Electrical musical instruments are not new in themselves, but the idea of tuning them in the Just Scale and providing means by which this scale can be adjusted correctly for each key signature appears to be original. It is entirely credible that such an invention will make a profound impression on musicians. Development of practical forms of instruments appears to be of importance. One of the most obvious ways to approach the problem is to take a highly-developed existing instrument such as the Hammond (Electric) Organ and redesign it in such a way as to make this proposal workable.

The Hammond Organ[2] consists of a number of rotary generators driven from a single synchronous motor. There is one generator for each note of the keyboard plus some extra generators for harmonics that lie beyond the keyboard range. All these generators produce tones which lie almost exactly on the Tempered Scale.

It should be noted that the Hammond instrument in its harmonic make-up differs from conventional pipe organs because all the frequencies used in the synthesis of any musical quality lie in the Tempered Scale; in other words, natural harmonics are entirely suppressed and tempered harmonics are substituted. This avoids the serious clash that occurs in conventional pipe organs between natural harmonics and tempered fundamentals which lie very close together. In no

other instrument, to the author's knowledge, are tempered harmonics used, and while the results may not be immediately perceptible to the lay ear, the characteristic harmoniousness of the Hammond Organ, which becomes apparent after some familiarity with it, must be ascribed to this basic improvement.

Hammond Organ Modifications

The application of the Just Scale to the Hammond Organ[3] or to other instruments of this general character, is carried out as follows: The tone wheels and gears are changed so that the frequencies of the generators lie on the Just Scale. The motor is coupled to the main drive shaft through a 15-position gear set, including 15 magnetic clutches. Thus the drive can be at any one of 15 speeds, depending on which clutch is operated, and the speed may be instantaneously changed by operating any other clutch. The clutches are operated from a row of 15 pushbuttons arranged along the base of the instrument and intended to be actuated by the left foot. These pushbuttons are marked with key signatures from C# to C♭ and (including the natural key) permit playing in 15 major and 15 minor keys. This appears to be adequate for practically all music now existent.

Operation

When the pushbutton for the key of C is operated—that is, the natural major key—the motor speed is such that middle A is 440 cycles per second and all other tones on the keyboard are exactly in the Just Scale. The instrument then can be played in the key of C in the Just Scale. There is no question of the use of tempered or natural harmonics. A number of additional generators must be added in each octave to take care of some harmonics of notes other than the key notes.

If it is wished to changed the instrument so that it can be played in the key of E, then the pushbutton marked "E" is depressed. This will release the "C" clutch and operate the "E" clutch and the speed of the main drive shaft will be changed to 5/4 of its former speed. The instrument will therefore be raised in pitch in the ratio of 5/4 and upon playing on the white notes as before, i.e., in the key of C major, the instrument will sound in the key of E. Since all the harmonics and added generators are changed in the same ratio, the organ is still in the Just Scale and this scale is correctly tuned for the key in which it is being played.

It will be noted that except for accidentals, in major keys the performer need only learn to play on the white notes. The instrument then always plays as though the music were in the natural key and it sounds in the key corresponding to the pushbutton which is operated.

Each pushbutton would be labelled with the key signature. For instance one of the pushbuttons—that for the key of D, say—would be labelled "D—2♯ major". To each of these pushbuttons would be wired a small illuminated indicator with the same label as the pushbutton. These indicators would be mounted in a row between the two manuals so that the organist is always aware of the key to which his instrument is tuned.

A Transposing Instrument

It will be seen that this organ is a transposing instrument and that existing music could not be readily played on it unless it were written in the key of C. All organ music would have to be transcribed to this key, with the key signature in which it is to sound marked separately. Minor keys would have to be transcribed to the naturally corresponding minor. The key-signature indication could very well take the form of an added note below the bass staff and, as far as the performer is concerned, would be simply one more note to be played, which he could play with his left foot. To avoid confusion with bass notes, the keynote names could be used.

Such an instrument as this would be learned much more readily than

present day conventional keyboard instruments. The student would no longer be obliged to master the complicated and cumbersome scheme of key signatures which music has evolved. The playing position of his hands on the keyboard would never be changed and the black notes would only be necessary for accidentals or for minor keys. The student, therefore, would devote the major part of his energy to the artistic development of his music rather than to the mastering of the mere mechanics of notation.

That such an instrument could not be put into use immediately is fully appreciated; that an instrument of this general character should eventually become widely used is, however, maintained. A sufficient interval of time must elapse to permit the transcription of a large amount of existing music into the natural key before such a scheme could be of much use. The ultimate advantages are beyond argument. Such a transposing instrument is readily evolved from a Hammond Organ or similar device because of the simple nature of the mechanism for speed changing. It will be apparent that the transposing feature can be readily applied also to the instrument to be described next.

Altering the Novachord

Another instrument which is adaptable practically is the Hammond Novachord'; this is typical of all instruments which obtain their tones from vacuum-tube oscillators. In the Novachord, twelve oscillators forming the top twelve notes of the keyboard are employed, and all other tones are obtained through a frequency-dividing and harmonic-generating system. The addition of an elaborate control system allows waves of any general character to be produced. The instrument, not being restricted to steady-state tones as is the Hammond Organ, will, with reasonable accuracy, imitate most of the conventional instruments. Using this sort of an instrument as a basis, the author would suggest a new instrument

tuned in the Just Scale as follows:

A row of pushbuttons will be provided along the base of the instrument intended to be operated by the left foot. These buttons, of which there will probably be 15, will be labelled with 15 key signatures from C♯ to C♭ which, in the major keys, is from seven sharps to seven flats and in the minor keys from four sharps to ten flats. Each of these pushbuttons will operate a 12-contact relay and the circuit is so arranged that only one relay can be operated at a time. Above the manual appear 15 illuminated signals which indicate which relay is operated. To each of the 12 contacts of each relay is wired a small capacitor and these are the tuning capacitors of the 12 oscillators.

When any relay is actuated, therefore, the 12 oscillators are adjusted to frequencies corresponding to the 12 capacitors that are cut into the circuit. Since all other tones on the instrument are derived from the 12 tones of the top octave, it follows that all the frequencies on the keyboard are governed by each pushbutton.

This instrument can be made a transposing instrument such as the organ already described, if the tuning capacitor is chosen of such a value as to step the whole octave upwards or downwards by a uniform amount as different relays are operated. It can also be arranged to be played exactly as conventional instruments are played by merely adjusting the frequencies of the notes of the octave so that for any desired key the frequencies will occur in the correct sequence. We should find ourselves with an instrument which is played exactly as a piano or an organ is played today, but which will sound in the Just Scale. It will be possible on this instrument to have an additional pushbutton which would tune the instrument in the Tempered Scale if for any reason this were desired, as for example, in order to play chromatic music.

Amplifier Considerations

One of the design difficulties in

electrical and electronic musical instruments is that the nominal power rating of the amplifier-loudspeaker system, which is based on negligible distortion for a sine wave, cannot be approached when complex waves formed from many harmonic components in random phase relation are transmitted. This reduction in power output is due to the possibility at any instant of the amplitudes of all the components adding arithmetically, so that the voltage or current peak is the arithmetical sum of all the components, while the loudness of the power output is only the root-mean-square sum.

In an instrument tuned to the Just Scale, such as either of the two described, it is possible to fix the phase of all the components of a tone so that the peak amplitudes of all the waves could never add up at any instant. Even in an instrument tuned in the Tempered Scale this is worth doing, since the octave components, that is the sub-harmonic, and the second, fourth and eighth harmonics, are exactly correct and a precise phase relation can be maintained.

REFERENCES

(1) Fisher, S. T., "Electrical Production of Musical Tones", Jour. of the Soc. Mot. Pic. Eng., Mar., 1939.
(2) Hammond, L., U. S. Patent No. 1,956,350.
(3) Fisher, S. T., U. S. Patent No. 2,273,768.
(4) Hammond, L., U. S. Patent No. 2,126,682.
(5) Fisher, S. T., U. S. Patent No. 2,293,499.
(6) Fisher, S. T., "An Engineer Looks at Music."—Jour. Eng. Inst. of Canada, Oct., 1942.

Tone Source for Tuning Musical Instruments

By EARL L. KENT

THE SIMPLE AND ACCURATE tone-producing device shown in the accompanying photograph was designed to fill a need in the rapid tuning of the musical instruments in bands and orchestras.

The tuner produces a continuous tone with adjustable tone intensity, frequency and timbre. A frequency

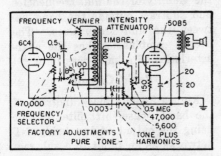

Circuit diagram of electronic tuning tone source

vernier is provided on the back of the instrument so the director may select his frequency standard any-where between 435 and 445 cps. Two tones are selectable by the frequency selector on the front panel giving either A or B♭. The semitone relationship is retained irrespective of the setting of the frequency vernier. In other words, when the desired frequency is selected for A, the switch for changing the output note to B♭ automatically sets in the proper interval or half note.

A timbre switch enables the director to select either a flute-like tone or a reed-like voice that is rich in harmonics, depending upon which tonal character is better for the musicians tuning to it. This switch makes it possible to take the signal from the tank circuit by way of the secondary winding in a relatively pure form, or from the plate current circuit in a pulse form that contains high harmonic content. The tank circuit is tuned to the fundamental frequency of the oscillator so the voltage produced across it is approximately sinusoidal.

The volume control provides adjustment of the sound level to suit the room and ambient sound conditions. Sufficient volume is available for use with a large group of musicians.

In designing the instrument special care has been taken to provide the extreme stability required of tuning devices with changes in temperature, line voltage and tube life. The instrument drifts about 0.06 percent after 5 minutes warm-up, and after 15 minutes returns to its original frequency. A 5-percent fluctuation of line voltage will cause about 0.09-percent change in frequency. A 0.06-percent change in frequency is about 1/100 of a half tone.

FILTERS

Phase-Shift Band-Pass Filters

Double bridged-T network using readily available components provides good band-pass characteristic at minimum expense. Usable bandwidth depends on allowable dip between null points of the individual bridged-T networks

By D. H. PICKENS AND J. N. VAN SCOYOC

ANYONE who has conducted laboratory investigations within a given frequency range has at some time or another felt the need for an easily constructed band-pass filter. The presence of undesired signals such as a-c hum and random noise near the frequency region of intelligence-bearing signals has led to an extensive investigation of net-

works which will eliminate these undesirable frequency components. The object of this paper is to describe the operation of a band-pass filter which employs components normally found in all laboratories, and which does not involve any complicated calculations in its design and construction. This type of filter may in many cases be used in place of the more conventional type filters with their complicated and specialized components.

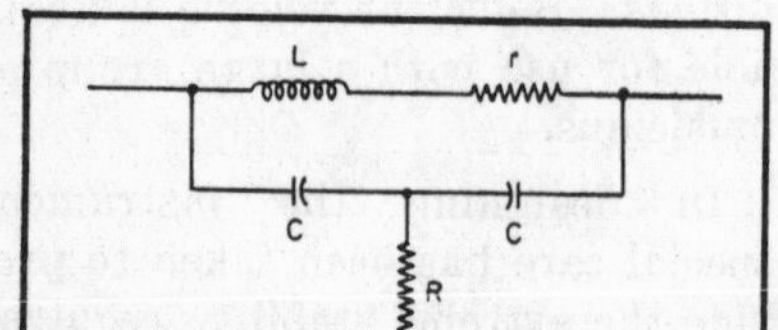

The basic circuit of the phase-shift filter is a combination of conventional bridged-T networks. The circuit diagram for a bridged-T network is shown in Fig. 1A. Figure 1B shows the attenuation characteristics of bridged-T networks and clearly illustrates the effect of Q on the frequency response of the network. An analysis of the network will yield the expression for the null frequency f_0 and the condition for an absolute null in terms of the network parameters.

$$f_0 = \frac{1}{2\pi}\sqrt{\frac{2}{LC}}$$

$$R = \frac{1}{r\omega_0^2 C^2}$$

The latter equation expresses the conditions for null.

Figure 1C is a generalized phase-shift characteristic for the bridge-T network. It will be noticed that the sign of the phase shift changes as the frequency passes through the null frequency of the network. It is this characteristic that makes it

possible to combine the output of two bridged-T networks to form the attenuation characteristic of a bandpass network. If the outputs of two similar bridged-T networks, whose null frequencies are separated by a given increment, are combined in such a manner that the output of one network is subtracted from the other, the phase relationship between the two outputs is such that they will add in the vicinity of the null frequencies and subtract outside the band between the null frequencies. The overall combination has the characteristics of a band-pass filter.

Basic Circuit

Figure 2A is a block diagram of the basic phase-shift filter circuit using the output of two bridged-T networks as an input to a subtraction circuit. Each of the two T sections has its own Q, null frequency and transfer function β. The derivation of the transfer function for the composite circuit is a lengthy and complex process and no time will be devoted to its derivation. The resulting transfer function is shown in Fig. 2B. This expression shows that the transmission characteristic of the phase-shift filter is a function of Q and the null frequencies of the two T sections.

Differential combination of the output of the two T sections which make up the active branch of the

FIG. 1—Phase shift introduced by a bridged-T network changes in sign as frequency passes through null frequency

phase-shift filter may be accomplished in many different circuits. Several of these circuits will be discussed in detail in a later section of this paper. Basically, these circuits may be grouped in two general

the combining circuit used. The gain characteristic of the cathode-coupled circuit used as a subtraction circuit in these tests was such that the input to one tube had to be

cathode-coupled subtraction circuit will be discussed in greater detail in a later section of this paper.

Figure 6 is a family of attenuation curves obtained by increasing the frequency increment between the null frequencies of the two bridged-T sections. This was accomplished by decreasing the capacitance in one section and resetting the value of the resistance to give an absolute null. The null frequency of one T section was held constant at 1,800 cps. It will be noticed that as the bandwidth is increased, by increasing the separation between the null frequencies, the output decreases in the passband. This characteristic of the phase-shift filter is similar to that of the conventional tuned coupled circuit. Further investigation revealed that as the bandwidth is increased for a given center frequency this dip in the passband will increase to a point where the circuit is no longer usable as a filter with a single passband.

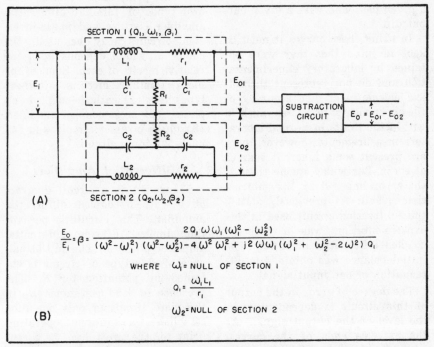

FIG. 2—If the output of a bridged-T network is subtracted from that of a similar network whose null frequency is close to that of the first, the phase relationship between the two outputs is such that they will add near the null frequencies and subtract outside the band between the null frequencies

classes: (1) direct subtraction circuits, and (2) phase inversion and addition circuits.

Figure 3 is a block diagram of a phase-shift filter in which the desired output is obtained by direct subtraction of the outputs of the two T sections. Figure 4 shows the block diagram of the method in which the phase of the input to one T section is inverted and the outputs of the two T sections are put into a summation circuit. The difference between the two transmission characteristics of the T section is then obtained by direct addition of the two signals, one of which has had its phase inverted.

Experimental tests were conducted on a phase-shift filter utilizing two air-core speaker field coils as the inductances in the two T sections. Figure 5 is the circuit diagram of the tested circuit, showing

attenuated by potentiometer R so that the output represented the true difference between the input signals. This characteristic of the

Passband Dip

Before any attempt is made to design a phase-shift filter, the degree of dip in the passband which can be tolerated must be established. This amount of dip is dependent upon the particular application of the filter. Primarily, though, it must be remembered that

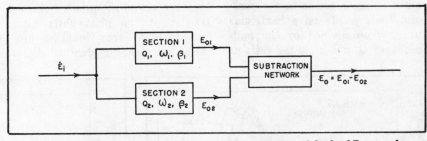

FIG. 3—Direct subtraction method for combining outputs of bridged-T networks

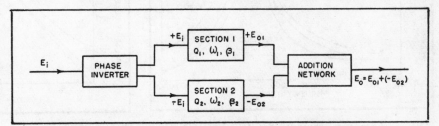

FIG. 4—Phase-inversion—addition type of phase-shift filter

limitation of the amount of allowable dip also places a limitation on the maximum bandwidth that may be used. Some median must be established between the width of the passband and the output dip in this passband. Again, this choice will depend on specific applications.

Figure 7 is a family of experimentally obtained universal curves which may be used to determine the allowable bandwidth for a given output dip within the passband. As a matter of choice the curves were obtained for arbitrarily chosen output dips of 3 db, 1.5 db and 0 db. Knowing the midfrequency and the Q of the coils at this frequency, these curves may be used to establish the maximum bandwidth that may be used. The design process

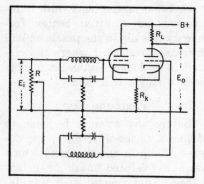

FIG. 5—Phase-shift filter and cathode-coupled subtraction circuit

to be followed is as follows: The values of the abscissa at the passband limit points on a particular curve, when divided by the midfrequency Q, will yield the ratio of

the bandwidth to midfrequency. Knowing the midfrequency, the allowable bandwidth may then be established. The reverse of this process may be used to determine the value of Q necessary to obtain a given passband with a given output dip.

In using these curves it must be kept in mind that they were obtained by laboratory experimentation and do not represent theoretical calculations. The accuracy of the experimental processes was held within the limits of normal laboratory measurements; however, there are present some inherent sources of error. Particular among these is the error imposed by the subtraction circuit. As previously stated, the subtraction circuit used in this experimentation was a cathode-coupled differential amplifier. The initial balance was obtained by attenuation of one input signal.

The degree of error in the output of this circuit is dependent upon the level of the output signal. At the extreme ends of the curves, where the frequency is quite a distance from the midfrequency, the output level became very small so that the error in initial balance of the cathode-coupled circuit became more prominent. At these removed points on the curves, the curve represents more the unbalance and distortion in the amplifier circuit than the actual attenuation characteristic of the phase-shift filter. This residual error would be minimized by cascading identical stages.

To prevent this type of error from becoming of such magnitude as to diminish the utility of the filter circuit, a subtraction circuit whose initial balance can be effected to a very fine point must be used. Several types of familiar differential amplifier circuits and phase-inversion circuits may be used, the choice of which depends upon the relative merits of each. Some of the more familiar circuits of these types are: (1) cathode-coupled amplifier, (2) cross-coupled amplifier, (3) phase-inverter circuit, and (4) push-pull input circuit.

Differential Amplifiers

Figure 8A is a circuit diagram of a cathode-coupled differential amplifier. This circuit is perhaps the simplest of the differential amplifier circuits. The initial balance of this type of circuit is obtained by potentiometer R. The presence of load resistance R_L in the plate circuit of only one tube establishes a different operating point for the two tubes. As a consequence, the gain from the grid of V_2 is always greater than that of V_1. To offset this difference of gain, the input signal to the grid of V_2 must be attenuated by means of potentiometer R until zero output is obtained with a common input.

Figure 8B is a circuit diagram of a cross-coupled differential amplifier. This circuit affords the highly desirable features of low sensitivity to hum and large dynamic range of input signals, with an output

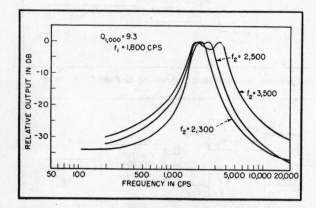

FIG. 6—Attenuation characteristics for phase-shift filter using air-core coils

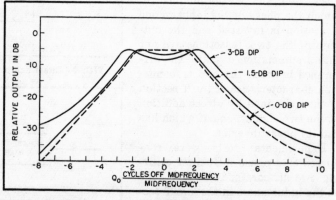

FIG. 7—Universal curves for phase-shift filters derived from experimental data

that is proportional to the difference between the two input signals. The tubes V_1 and V_4 are connected as cathode followers, with the cross coupling between V_2 and V_3 providing phase inversion. The input voltage of V_2 is the difference between the output voltages of V_1 and V_4. The input voltage of V_3 is equal to this same voltage but opposite in phase. The output voltages of V_2 and V_3 will then be proportional to the difference between the impressed voltages on V_1 and V_4 but opposite in phase. The overall output will then represent the difference between the two input signals if any degree of symmetry in tube or circuit parameters has been maintained.

To offset any dissymmetry in the circuit, potentiometer R has been inserted. The initial balance of the circuit may be effected by varying R to a point where zero output is obtained with the same signal applied to V_1 and V_4. Since the circuit conditions previously described exist whether the input signal is impressed on both V_1 and V_4, this circuit may be used as a push-pull input stage or a balanced phase inverter.

Figure 9 is a circuit diagram of a phase-inverter subtraction circuit. Its operation is based upon the fact that the plate and cathode voltages of a tube are 180 degrees out of phase with each other. If the plate and cathode resistance of V_1 and V_2 are of equal magnitude then identical inputs to both V_1 and V_2 will produce voltages across the plate of V_1 and the cathode of V_2 which are equal and opposite. When an initial balance is obtained by means of R_0, the output voltage E_0 will be proportional to the difference between the two input voltages E_{i1} and E_{i2}.

A system utilizing a balanced center-tapped transformer represents the simplest means of obtaining two equal and opposite voltages.

Choice of Circuits

The choice of which circuit to use as a combining circuit in the phase-shift filter is dependent upon the relative merits of each. Perhaps the simplest method is one utilizing the balanced push-pull output from a transformer. The use of this circuit depends solely upon its availability since the design and construction of such a transformer contributes much complication.

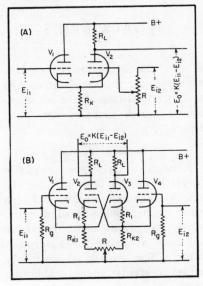

FIG. 8—Cathode-coupled (A) and cross-coupled (B) differential amplifier circuits

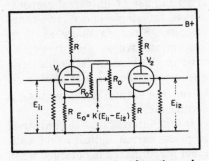

FIG. 9—Phase-inverter subtraction circuit

The ease of design and construction of the phase-inverter circuit seems to indicate a high degree of utility; however, it must be pointed out that any difference between the resistances used in the plate and cathode circuit will result in an error in the output signal.

The cathode-coupled amplifier is the median between circuit complexity and performance as a differential amplifier. This circuit, involving two tubes, performs very well as a part of the phase-shift filter. The experimental processes conducted in this investigation indicated that the initial balance of the circuit could be made to the degree of approximately —50 db.

The versatility of the cross-coupled amplifier and its adaptability for use as either a phase inverter or a differential amplifier makes its use very desirable. The condition of initial balance may be effected quite easily. Its low susceptibility to hum and large dynamic input characteristic are also indicative of its utility. The objectionable feature of this circuit is the physical size of the circuit wherein four tubes are required. Again the choice between performance and circuit complexity is an arbitrary one and rests with the particular function to which the filter is applied.

Summary

The similarity of the phase-shift filter's attenuation characteristic to that of the tuned coupled circuit seems to indicate its most important possibility. The performance of specific tuned coupled circuits can be approached to a satisfactory degree by use of a phase-shift filter. In doing so, the complex problems of coil design and coupling factors are eliminated. The simplicity of the phase-shift filter with respect to the tuned coupled circuit, in view of their similar attenuation characteristics, is an argument somewhat in favor of its use. The authors feel that the advantages of this circuit are more pronounced in the audio-frequency range.

The phase-shift filter, with its lack of complex design and construction procedure, lends itself to many applications. At first glance it may appear that an even better performance could be obtained by use of m and k type filters; however, the use of such filters involves an extensive design procedure and many components of specific values. Calculations have shown that if the same number of components were used in cascaded sections of the phase-shift filter its performance would approach that of m and k type filters.

Design of Absorption Traps

Universal response curves show the ratio of the response of a tuned circuit to which a trap is coupled to the response without the trap for typical values of attenuation and trap-circuit frequency separation.   Nomograph permits rapid determination of coupling factor

By JACK AVINS

THE PROBLEM of obtaining attenuation at critical frequencies arises frequently in the design of amplifiers employing tuned circuits. One widely used method of obtaining this attenuation is by means of absorption traps.

The type of absorption trap analyzed in this paper consists of a circuit tuned to the rejection frequency and coupled to a tuned circuit which is fed by a constant-current source such as a pentode tube. An analytical expression is derived to show the attenuation introduced by the trap and its effect on the variation in amplification with frequency. This information is presented by universal curves which show the ratio between the response obtained with a trap to the response obtained without the trap, as a function of the following parameters: (1) the rejection at the trap frequency, (2) the generalized frequency separation between the trap and the circuit to which it is coupled, and (3) the ratio between the Q of the trap and the Q of the circuit to which it is coupled.

Application

A typical application is found in the design of video intermediate-frequency amplifiers of television receivers which employ staggered tuned circuits as coupling elements. In these receivers rejection at the accompanying sound carrier frequency and at the picture and sound carrier frequencies of the adjacent channels is frequently obtained by means of absorption traps which are inductively coupled to the staggered tuned circuits. The universal response curves presented show the effect of the absorption traps on the response over the pass band as well as the magnitude of the after response which impairs the skirt selectivity.

Response Curves

Although universal response curves have long been used for the simple resonant circuit and for synchronous double-tuned circuits, analogous curves heretofore have not been available for absorption traps. The universal response curves presented here enable the same simplification in the design of absorption trap circuits as results from the use of universal response curves for single and double-tuned circuits. Since as many as three absorption traps are frequently used in the video intermediate-frequency amplifier of a television receiver, the saving in design time is significant.

It is of interest that the universal response curves indicate that optimum performance is obtained when an absorption trap is coupled to a

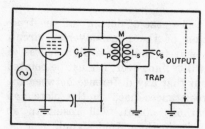

FIG. 1—Circuit diagram and equivalent circuit of a typical amplifier employing an absorption trap

circuit which is relatively close in frequency. A misconception that the circuits should be widely separated has led to the design of some amplifiers having relatively high distortion of the pass band and high after responses for a given rejection.

Determination of Response Ratio

A typical circuit employing an absorption trap is shown in Fig. 1. The amplifier plate load consists of the tuned circuit L_pC_p which is inductively coupled to the trap circuit L_sC_s. In addition to the simple inductive coupling shown in Fig. 1, it is possible to use other forms of coupling such as high-side capacitive coupling. As with synchronous double-tuned circuits, results are equivalent in the narrow-band case.

The effect of the trap on the overall response is conveniently expressed by determining the ratio of the response with the trap to the response without the trap. This ratio is particularly convenient in applying the results to the design of stagger-tuned amplifiers. It permits the conventional procedure to be followed in the design of the staggered circuits and the effect of the traps can then be added to determine the overall response.

Definition of Terms

The following terms are defined:

f_p = resonant frequency of the primary

f_s = resonant frequency of the trap

$\delta = (f - f_s)/f_s$ = fractional detuning with respect to trap

$\delta_1 = (f_p - f_s)/f_s$ = fractional detuning of primary with respect to the trap

$p = 2Q_p\delta$ = generalized fractional detuning

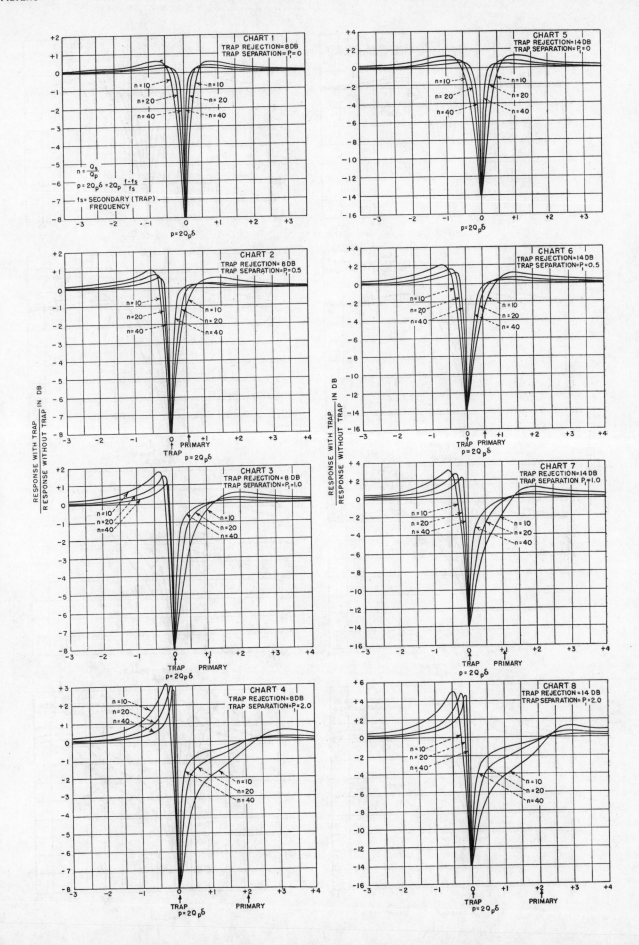

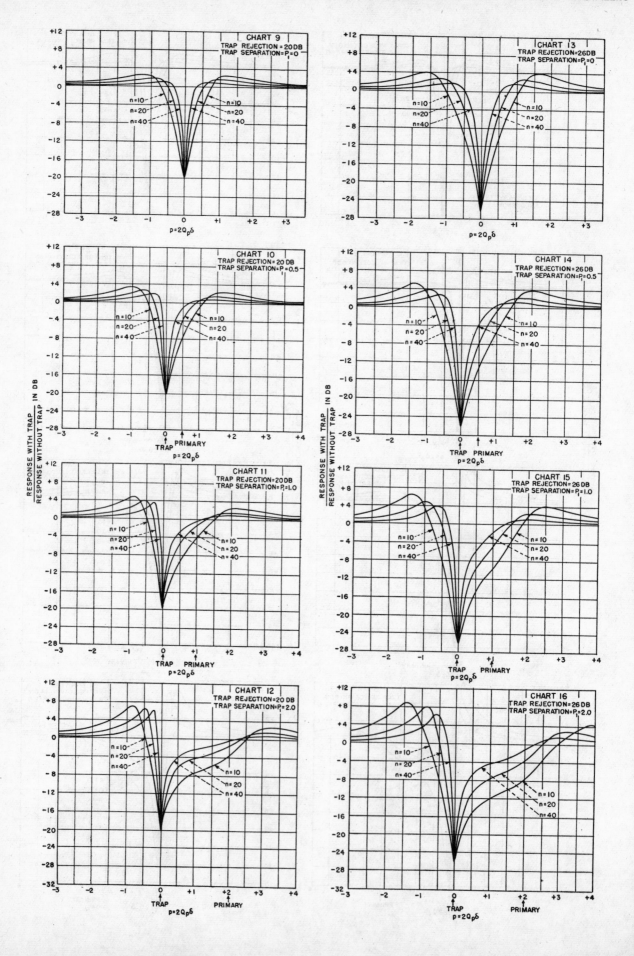

$p_1 = 2Q_p\delta_1$ = generalized fractional detuning of primary with respect to trap

$\alpha = 4\pi^2 f_s^2 M^2/R_p R_s$ = (coupling/critical coupling)^2

$n = Q_s/Q_p$ = trap Q/primary Q

R = desired attenuation at the trap frequency

If $2\delta \ll 1$, it can be shown that the impedance reflected by the trap is $\alpha/(1 + n^2 p^2) - j\,\alpha\,np/(1 + n^2 p^2)$

It can further be shown that the effect of the trap can be represented as a function of three parameters by the following expression:

$$\frac{\text{Response with trap}}{\text{Response without trap}} =$$

$$\left[\frac{1 + (p - p_1)^2}{\{1 + \alpha/(1 + n^2 p^2)\}^2 + \{p - p_1 - \frac{}{}}{\alpha\,np/(1 + n^2 p^2)\}^2}\right]^{\frac{1}{2}} \quad (1)$$

The three parameters are p_1, n, and R as previously defined.

The coupling factor α is related to the attenuation introduced by the trap at its resonant frequency by the equation $(1 + \alpha)^2 = R^2 (1 + p_1^2) - p_1^2$. As is to be expected the value of the coupling factor depends not only on the desired attenuation but on the generalized tuning separation p_1.

The analytical solution (Eq. 1) may be expressed in a more useful form by plotting the response ratio for suitable values of the three parameters.

Representative Charts

The families of curves shown in Charts 1 to 16 are the result of plotting Eq. 1 as a function of p for representative values of the parameters: frequency separation p_1, attenuation at the trap frequency R, and Q ratio n.

Four values of p_1 are chosen; these are 0, 0.5, 1.0, and 2.0. The curves for $p_1 = 0$ show the response for the limiting case as the frequency separation approaches zero. The curves for $p_1 = 0.5$ correspond to the trap being tuned to the frequency at which the response of the primary by itself is 90 percent of

its maximum response. Similarly, $p_1 = 1.0$ corresponds to the 70.7 − percent point and $p_1 = 2.0$ corresponds to the 44.7 − percent point.

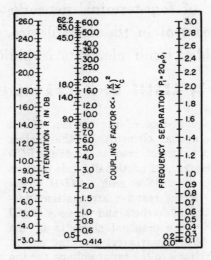

FIG. 2—Nomograph for determination of coupling factor between absorption trap and tuned circuit

These values cover the range normally encountered in the application of absorption traps.

Curves are drawn for four values of the attenuation R. These are $R = 8, 14, 20,$ and 26 db, corresponding to an attenuation of from 2.5 to 20 times in voltage ratio.

For each value of p_1 and R, curves are drawn for three values of n: $n = 10$; $n = 20$; and $n = 40$. These values of the ratio between the secondary and primary Q correspond to the values encountered in the design of stagger-tuned amplifiers at television intermediate frequencies.

A decibel scale is used in plotting the response ratio to permit the effect of several traps to be determined by addition of the individual response ratios. The overall response is then determined by the addition of the total response ratio curve to the response obtained in the absence of the absorption traps. Care must be taken to combine the curves with respect to an absolute frequency scale.

The response curves are all plotted on the basis that the trap or secondary frequency is lower than

the frequency of the circuit to which it is coupled. If the opposite is true, the curves still apply provided the positive direction of the p frequency scale is reversed. The desired response is then the mirror image of the response shown in the charts.

Nomograph for Coupling Determination

The coupling factor

$$\alpha = \frac{\omega_s^2 M^2}{R_p R_s}$$

is related to the attenuation introduced by the trap at its resonant frequency by the equation

$$(1 + \alpha)^2 = R^2(1 + p_1^2) - p_1^2 \quad (2)$$

As is to be expected, the value of the coupling factor depends not only on the desired attenuation but also on the generalized tuning separation p_1.

A nomograph constructed from this equation to enable the rapid determination of α, when p_1 and R are known, is shown in Fig. 2.

To determine experimentally the coupling corresponding to a given value of α, the trap is initially tuned to the same frequency as the primary. The coupling is then adjusted until the response R' drops to $1/(1 + \alpha)$ of the original response.

Conclusions

The universal response curves presented in Charts 1 to 16 significantly reduce the labor required to solve problems involving absorption traps. An examination of these curves reveals that so far as the circuit design permits, it is desirable to have the frequency separation as small as possible; and a high trap Q is desirable.

It is clear that neither the L/C ratio of the primary nor the L/C ratio of the trap have any effect on the response of the circuit, provided the proper coupling is used. In general the value of trap inductance is determined so as to obtain the maximum Q consistent with a convenient physical coil size.

Filter Characteristics for the Dynamic Noise Suppressor

Analysis of the cascaded pair of four-terminal networks that form the basis for high- and low-frequency response control in the Scott device. Effect of reactance tubes as variable circuit elements is indicated

By LESLIE G. McCRACKEN

The dynamic noise suppressor basically consists of two four-terminal networks connected in cascade, each network dynamically controlling the high-frequency and low-frequency response of the audio amplifier, respectively. Each network, in turn, consists of a few lumped parameters, all dissipation-less, together with a variable reactance, the value of which depends on the relative signal level. We shall now consider each of the four-terminal networks, investigating them in the manner of conventional filter theory.

For a four-terminal network comprised of two impedances, Z_1 and Z_2, as shown in Fig. 1, the attenuation function can be expressed as the inverse hyperbolic cosine of the square-root of the product of the diagonal elements of the matrix usually referred to as the *ABCD* matrix.[2,3] Functionally, this relation is $\gamma = 8.686 \cosh^{-1} (AD)^{1/2}$ where γ is the reactive attenuation function in decibels, and where A and D are the diagonal elements of the *ABCD* matrix relating the output voltage to the input voltage for the four-terminal network. Now, if we consider what A and D are for Fig. 1A, we find that the attenuation function is

$$\gamma = 8.686 \cosh^{-1}[1 + (Z_1/Z_2)]^{1/2} \text{ decibels} \quad (1)$$

Considering the four-terminal network shown in Fig. 1B, we may write Z_1 and Z_2 as

$$Z_1 = \frac{j\omega L_1}{1 - \omega^2 L_1 C_1}$$

$$Z_2 = j\omega L_2 + (1/j\omega C)$$

If these values are substituted in Eq. 1 the attenuation function becomes

$$\gamma = 8.686 \cosh^{-1} \times$$
$$\left(1 + \frac{-\omega^2 L_1 C}{(1 - \omega_2 L_1 C_1)(1 - \omega^2 L_2 C)}\right)^{1/2} \text{db} \quad (2)$$

Inspection of Eq. 2 reveals that the attenuation function versus frequency will have, in general, the shape indicated in Fig. 2A. There are two points of infinite attenuation, the frequencies for which we shall designate as f_{c1} and f_{c2}, where the subscripts 1 and 2 refer to the parameter subscripts responsible for the frequencies of infinite attenuation. Furthermore, there is a definite pass band, since this network under consideration is a stop-band filter, and has a critical frequency f_o that designates the edge of the pass band. Finally, we shall define the frequency of minimum attenuation lying between f_{c1} and f_{c2} as f_m. It is merely a matter of algebra and some differential calculus to find these critical frequencies in terms of the network parameters, expressed as follows

$$f_{c_1} = (1/2\pi)(1/L_1 C_1)^{1/2} \quad (3a)$$

$$f_{c_2} = (1/2\pi)(1/L_2 C)^{1/2} \quad (3b)$$

$$f_o \cong (1/2\pi)(1/L_1 C)^{1/2} \quad (3c)$$

$$f_m = (1/2\pi)(1/L_1 L_2 C_1 C)^{1/4} \quad (3d)$$

Immediately, one notes that of the two frequencies yielding infinite attenuation, one will be constant regardless of the variations of the variable reactance for the capacitor C (Fig. 1B), while the other frequency of infinite attenuation shifts for variations in the reactance of capacitor C. It is this variation that is of paramount importance in

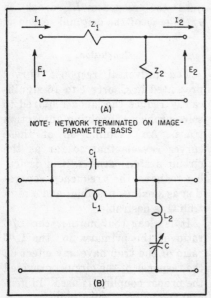

FIG. 1A—Four-terminal network with generalized series and shunt arms

FIG. 1B—A stop-band filter

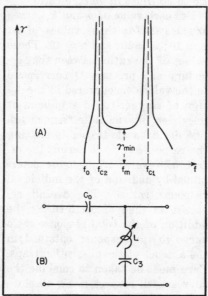

FIG. 2A—Attenuation function of stop-band filter vs frequency

FIG. 2B—High-pass filter

the dynamic noise suppressor, for by dynamically altering the value of capacitance C, one may achieve a variable stop-band filter; and, by careful selection of components, one may achieve a characteristic approximating that of the human ear.

For the four-terminal network considered it is possible to find the minimum attenuation in the range of frequencies between f_{c1} and f_{c2}.

$$\gamma_{min} = 8.686 \cosh^{-1} \times$$
$$\left(1 - \frac{\omega_m^2 L_1 C}{\left(1 - \frac{\omega_m^2}{\omega_{c_1}^2}\right)\left(1 - \frac{\omega_m^2}{\omega_{c_2}^2}\right)}\right)^{1/2} \text{db}$$

where:

$$\omega_m = 2\pi f_m$$
$$\omega_{c_1} = 2\pi f_{c_1}$$
$$\omega_{c_2} = 2\pi f_{c2}$$

The minimum attenuation will be least when the critical frequencies f_{c1} and f_{c2} are widely spaced, say in a ratio f_{c1}/f_{c2} greater than 10. When this condition obtains, the minimum attenuation in the stop band reduces to approximately

$$\gamma_{min} = 8.686 \cosh^{-1} [1 + (L_1/L_2)]^{1/2} \text{ db} \quad (4)$$

Increasing the ratio L_1/L_2 will raise the minimum attenuation in the stop band, so that the dynamic noise suppressor should be designed with a favorable L_1/L_2 ratio.

Connected in cascade with the four-terminal network above is a high-pass filter of the configuration shown in Fig. 2B. This network is simpler to analyze, and the resulting attenuation function is

$$\gamma' = 8.686 \cosh^{-1} \times$$
$$\left(1 + \frac{C_3}{2C_o (1 - \omega^2 L C_3)}\right)^{1/2} \text{db} \quad (5)$$

where L will now be the variable parameter dependent on signal

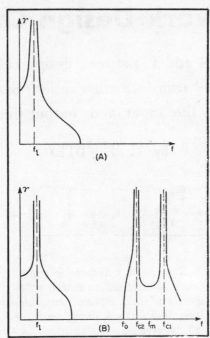

FIG. 3A—Attenuation function of high-pass filter vs frequency

FIG. 3B—Attenuation of overall network as function of frequency

level. The equation above indicates a resonant attenuation peak which will shift when the L parameter is varied; this peak of infinite attenuation will occur at a frequency f_x, which is

$$f_x = (1/2\pi)(1/LC_3)^{1/2}$$

The characteristic curve for this high-pass filter is shown in Fig 3A. Here, we note that the slope of the attenuation function vs frequency changes gradually, whereas the slope of the characteristic curve for the stop-band filter changed very abruptly. These characteristics resemble those obtained for a con-

stant -k filter and a repeated derivation m- derived filter, respectively.

Combined Networks

The overall response of the combined four-terminal networks is shown in Fig. 3B. If we now permit the L and C parameters to vary linearly as functions of signal level, we note that the bandwidth of the overall circuit changes rapidly in the high-frequency region and slowly in the low-frequency region.

Utilizing the signal level to change the grid bias on reactance tubes in the dynamic noise suppressor, where the reactance tubes replace the variable elements in the networks, and adjusting the circuit to conform to the characteristics of the human ear, we are able to obtain the optimum signal-to-noise ratio that is possible from the given sound source. Sound is used loosely here to correspond to the impressions on disc recordings or the signal at the output of the detector in an amplitude-modulation receiver tuned to an amplitude-modulation station.

We may conclude from the discussion above that there is good theoretical evidence to support H. H. Scott's statements that the dynamic noise suppressor will improve a sound system if it be properly designed.

REFERENCES
(1) H. H. Scott, Dynamic Noise Suppressor, ELECTRONICS, p 96, Dec. 1947.
(2) E. A. Guillemin, Communication Networks, John Wiley and Sons, Inc., 1935, p 70.
(3) Ref. (2) p 169.

Network Design Charts

Time-saving universal T, pi and L network design charts covering all normally encountered phase shifts and transformation ratios. Scale multiplying factors are eliminated by normalizing the input and output impedances being matched

By T. U. FOLEY

THE PROBLEM of matching arbitrary impedances to a given transmission-line impedance is common throughout the radio industry. The accompanying charts permit simultaneous solution of matching reactance limits over a range of both phase shift and load resistance. To make the plots universal, it was necessary to normalize to a one-ohm or one-mho transmission line. If the practical line is other than one ohm, it will be necessary to normalize R_2, so that $R_{2n} = R_2/R_1$. Using this value of R_{2n}, enter the chart along this line to the appropriate value of phase shift and interpolate between plotted values of loci, obtaining Z_{1n}, Z_{2n} and Z_{3n} in turn on the three charts. To obtain Z_1, Z_2 and Z_3, simply multiply Z_{1n}, Z_{2n} and Z_{3n} by actual line impedance.

Example 1. Assume a T network is required to match a 35-ohm load to a 50-ohm transmission line with a phase shift of 80 degrees.

(a) $Z_o = 50$ $R_2 = 35$ $\beta = 80°$
(b) $R_{2n} = 35/50 = 0.7$
(c) Enter chart Z_1 at $R_2 = 0.7$ and follow to $\beta = 80°$
(d) Read $Z_{1n} = +0.67$
(e) $Z_1 = j\,50 \times (+0.67) = +j\,33.5$ ohms
(f) Similarly, on chart Z_2 find $Z_{2n} = +0.725$
(g) $Z_2 = j\,50\,(+0.725) = +j\,36.25$ ohms
(h) Similarly, on chart Z_3 find $Z_{3n} = -0.85$
(i) $Z_3 = j\,50\,(-0.85) = -j\,42.5$ ohms

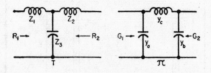

Example 2. Assume a π network is required to match a 35-ohm load to a 50-ohm transmission line with a phase shift of 80 degrees.

(a) $Z_o = 50$, $R_2 = 35$, $\beta = 80°$
(b) $G_o = 1/50 = 0.02$ $G_2 = 1/35 = 0.0286$ $G_{2n} = 0.0286/0.02 = 1.43$
(c) Enter chart Y_a at $G_2 = 1.43$ and follow to $\beta = 80°$
(d) Read $Y_{an} = +1.03$
(e) $Y_a = j\,0.02\,(+1.03) = +j\,0.0206$ or $Z_a = 1/Y_a = -j\,48.5$ ohms
(f) Similarly, on chart Y_b find $Y_{bn} = 0.96$
(g) $Y_b = j\,0.02\,(+0.96) = +j\,0.0192$ or $Z_b = 1/Y_b = -j\,52.1$ ohms
(h) Similarly, on chart Y_c find $Y_{cn} = -1.22$
(i) $Y_c = j\,0.02\,(-1.22) = -j\,0.0244$, or $Z_c = 1/Y_c = +j\,41$ ohms

Example 3. Assume an L network is required to match a 12.5-ohm load to a 50-ohm transmis-

sion line. (Note that in the case of an L network, we cannot specify both phase shift and load resistance since when one is specified the other is fixed.)

(a) $Z_o = 50$ $R_2 = 12.5$
(b) $R_{2n} = 12.5/50 = 0.25$
(c) (If R_{2n} is less than 1, enter chart Z_1; if R_{2n} is greater than 1, enter chart Z_2)
(d) Enter chart Z_1 at $R_2 = 0.25$ and follow to locus of zero reactance
(e) Read $\beta = 60°$, $Z_1 = 0$
(f) Enter chart Z_2 at $R_2 = 0.25$ and follow to $\beta = 60°$
(g) Read $Z_{2n} = +0.43$
(h) $Z_2 = j\,50\,(+0.43) = +j\,21.5$ ohms
(i) Similarly, find $Z_{3n} = -0.58$
(j) $Z_3 = j\,50\,(-0.58) = -j\,29$ ohms

All of the above illustrations have assumed lagging networks. Reversing the sign of each reactance arm changes from lagging network to leading network.

To extend the technique to cover a range of phase shifts over a range of load resistances, the principles of the preceding illustrations pertain. In this case, however, the point plot be-

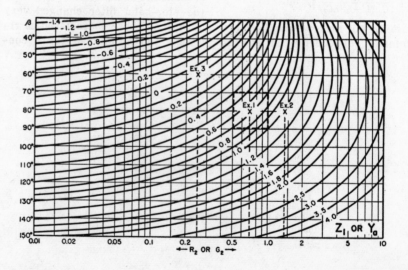

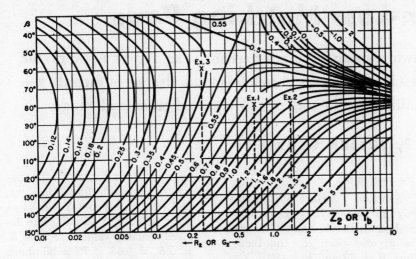

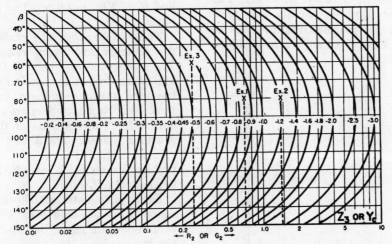

comes a rectangle about the design center. A rectangular template can be made on transparent material to permit evaluation over a range of ±10 degrees from design-center phase shift. Simultaneously, it would cover a 2 to 1 load resistance variation. Other rectangles can be made easily to cover any range of phase shift and load resistance variation.

Example 4. Since the range technique is essentially the same as the point technique, a single illustration will suffice: Assume a T network is required to match a 35-ohm nominal resistance to a 50-ohm transmission line over a resistance range of 2 to 1 centered on 35 ohms and over a phase shift range of 70° to 90°. Following the technique of Example 1, center the rectangle at

$R_2 = 0.7$ and $\beta = 80°$ on chart Z_1. Read limits of $Z_{1n} = +0.39 \rightarrow 1.0$. Then

$$Z_1 = j\,50\,(+0.39 \rightarrow +1.0) = +j\,19.5 \rightarrow +j\,50\text{ ohms}$$

Appendix

Referring to Fig. 1 and 2, equations for reactance arms of T and π networks are:

$$Z_1 = -j\,\frac{R_1 \cos \beta - \sqrt{R_1 R_2}}{\sin \beta} \quad (1)$$

$$Z_2 = -j\,\frac{R_2 \cos \beta - \sqrt{R_1 R_2}}{\sin \beta} \quad (2)$$

$$Z_3 = -j\,\frac{\sqrt{R_1 R_2}}{\sin \beta} \quad (3)$$

$$Z_a = +j\,\frac{R_1 R_2 \sin \beta}{R_2 \cos \beta - \sqrt{R_1 R_2}} \quad (4)$$

$$Z_b = +j\,\frac{R_1 R_2 \sin \beta}{R_1 \cos \beta - \sqrt{R_1 R_2}} \quad (5)$$

$$Z_c = +j\,\sqrt{R_1 R_2}\,\sin \beta \quad (6)$$

These equations may be normalized in terms of R_1 by substituting

$R_{2n} = R_2/R_1$, leaving

$$Z_{1n} = \frac{Z_1}{R_1} = -j\,\frac{\cos \beta - \sqrt{R_{2n}}}{\sin \beta} \quad (7)$$

$$Z_{2n} = \frac{Z_2}{R_1} = -j\,\frac{R_{2n}\cos \beta - \sqrt{R_{2n}}}{\sin \beta} \quad (8)$$

$$Z_{3n} = \frac{Z_3}{R_1} = -j\,\frac{\sqrt{R_{2n}}}{\sin \beta} \quad (9)$$

$$Z_{an} = \frac{Z_a}{R_1} = +j\,\frac{R_{2n}\sin \beta}{R_{2n}\cos \beta - \sqrt{R_{2n}}} \quad (10)$$

$$Z_{bn} = \frac{Z_b}{R_1} = +j\,\frac{R_{2n}\sin \beta}{\cos \beta - \sqrt{R_{2n}}} \quad (11)$$

$$Z_{cn} = \frac{Z_c}{R_1} = +j\,\sqrt{R_{2n}}\,\sin \beta \quad (12)$$

Equations 10, 11 and 12 can be put on an admittance basis as follows:

$$Y_{an} = \frac{1}{Z_{an}} = -j\,\frac{R_{2n}\cos \beta - \sqrt{R_{2n}}}{R_{2n}\sin \beta}$$

$$= -j\,\frac{\dfrac{1}{G_{2n}}\cos \beta - \sqrt{\dfrac{1}{G_{2n}}}}{\dfrac{1}{G_{2n}}\sin \beta}$$

$$= -j\,\frac{\cos \beta - \sqrt{G_{2n}}}{\sin \beta} \quad (13)$$

$$Y_{bn} = \frac{1}{Z_{bn}} = -j\,\frac{\cos \beta - \sqrt{R_{2n}}}{R_{2n}\sin \beta}$$

$$= -j\,\frac{G_{2n}\cos \beta - \sqrt{G_{2n}}}{\sin \beta} \quad (14)$$

$$Y_{cn} = \frac{1}{Z_{cn}} = -j\,\frac{1}{\sqrt{R_{2n}}\,\sin \beta}$$

$$= -j\,\frac{\sqrt{G_{2n}}}{\sin \beta} \quad (15)$$

Comparing Eq. 13, 14 and 15 with Eq. 7, 8 and 9, it is seen that the equations for a π network on an admittance basis are identical to the equations for a T network on an impedance basis. Solving for R_{2n} in Eq. 7, 8 and 9 gives

$$R_{2n} = (Z_{1n}\sin \beta + \cos \beta)^2 \quad (16)$$

$$R_{2n} = \left(\frac{1 \pm \sqrt{1 - 2Z_{2n}\sin 2\beta}}{2\cos \beta}\right)^2 \quad (17)$$

$$R_{2n} = (-Z_{3n}\sin \beta)^2 \quad (18)$$

Equations 16, 17 and 18 were used to calculate points on curves Z_1, Z_2 and Z_3 by holding Z's fixed for each locus, ranging β over 30° to 150° and solving for R_{2n}.

Minimum-Loss Matching Pads

Simple nomograph gives the two resistance values needed in an L-type network for matching unequal impedances with minimum power loss, and also gives directly the amount of loss in db. Multiplying factors are easily used to extend ranges

By JOSEPH C. BREGAR

A TWO-RESISTANCE network for matching two unequal impedances provides proper matching with a minimum of power loss. The accompanying nomograph solves for the resistance values needed.

Example 1. Match a 72-ohm line to a 52-ohm line with a minimum of power loss. Determine the loss in db.

Solution. Adjust a straightedge to connect 72 on the R_a scale and 52 on the R_b scale (R_a must be greater than R_b, and therefore $R_a = 72$ and $R_b = 52$). The intercept on the db loss scale shows the matching-pad loss as 5.1 db. Next, adjust the straight-edge at right angles to the loss line and through the 5.1-db point, and read the X and Y values as $X = 0.53$ and $Y = 1.9$. The desired resistor values are then $R_1 = XR_a = 0.53 \times 72 = 38$ ohms, and $R_2 = YR_b = 1.9 \times 52 = 99$ ohms.

The scale ranges are chosen for common impedance values. The nomograph may be used for any values by the application of the same multiplier to the R_a and R_b scales. No multipliers are required for the loss scale or the X and Y values. The X and Y values are applied to the original problem values of R_a and R_b in determining R_1 and R_2.

Example 2. Match a 3,000-ohm source to a 600-ohm load with a minimum of loss. Determine the loss.

Solution. A convenient scale factor is 1/10. Applied to the problem values, R_a becomes 300 and R_b becomes 60. Connect these points with a straightedge and read the pad loss as 12.5 db. Next, read the X and Y values as 0.89 and 1.12 respectively. Applying these values to the original problem impedances of 3,000 and 600 ohms gives $R_1 = 0.89 \times 3,000 = 2,700$ ohms and $R_2 = 1.12 \times 600 = 670$ ohms.

The matching of impedances of more than 30-to-1 ratio involves high power losses, and other types of coupling networks are employed. For impedance matching when power loss is unimportant and the ratio of impedances is more than 30-to-1, the X and Y values approach 1; then $R_a = R_1$ and $R_b = R_2$ for proper matching.

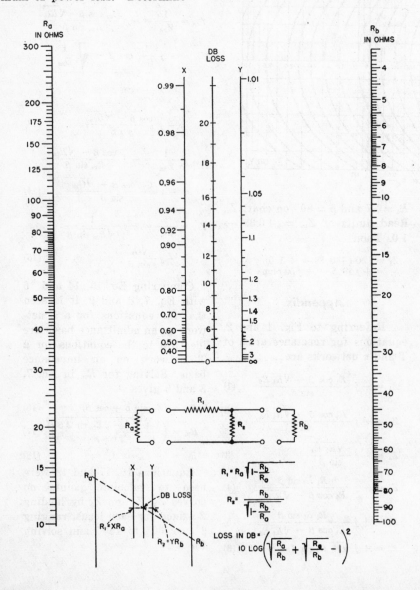

$$R_1 = R_a \sqrt{1 - \frac{R_b}{R_a}}$$

$$R_2 = \frac{R_b}{\sqrt{1 - \frac{R_b}{R_a}}}$$

$$\text{LOSS IN DB} = 10 \log\left(\sqrt{\frac{R_a}{R_b}} + \sqrt{\frac{R_a}{R_b} - 1}\right)^2$$

Universal Equalizer Chart

Modification of familiar Smith chart consolidates on one time-saving plot all positive-value solutions to the two general equations for series, shunt and bridged-T audio equalizers

By D. A. ALSBERG

THE single chart in Fig. 1 replaces as many as eleven conventional equalizer charts, yet gives all solutions containing positive resistances or conductances for the commonly used equalizer structures of Fig. 2.

The chart is derived by applying to the two general forms of equalizer equations (Eq. 10 and 11 in Fig. 2) the bilinear transform

$$u + jv = (1 + \zeta)/(1 - \zeta) \qquad (12)$$

where ζ is a complex number. This transforms the conventional rectangular grid of u and v to a set of orthogonal circles, all of which pass through the point $\zeta = +1$, and the circle $u = 0$ is identical with the unit circle in

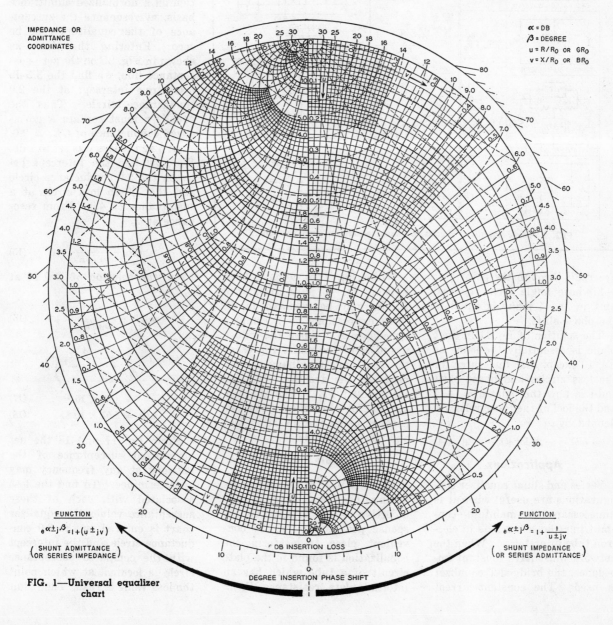

IMPEDANCE OR
ADMITTANCE
COORDINATES

α = DB
β = DEGREE
$u = R/R_0$ OR GR_0
$v = X/R_0$ OR BR_0

FUNCTION

$e^{\alpha \pm j\beta} = 1 + (u \pm jv)$

$\left(\begin{array}{c} \text{SHUNT ADMITTANCE} \\ \text{OR SERIES IMPEDANCE} \end{array} \right)$

DB INSERTION LOSS

DEGREE INSERTION PHASE SHIFT

FUNCTION

$e^{\alpha \pm j\beta} = 1 + \dfrac{1}{u \pm jv}$

$\left(\begin{array}{c} \text{SHUNT IMPEDANCE} \\ \text{OR SERIES ADMITTANCE} \end{array} \right)$

FIG. 1—Universal equalizer chart

the ζ plane. This grid of orthogonal circles representing the u and v coordinates is identical to the grid of the familiar Smith chart.

Solving Eq. 10 in the ζ plane, the lines of constant insertion loss become circles centered on the point $\zeta = -1$ and whose loci are defined by

$$\alpha \ (db) = -20 \log |(1 + \zeta)/2| \quad (13)$$

The lines of constant phase shift

generator is a special case of the shunt equalizer and is particularly useful in electron tube stages which behave substantially like constant-current generators, such as pentodes. One specific use is to compute the effect of shunting parasitic capacitances on the gain and phase of an electron tube stage. In this case the parasitic shunt reactance would be considered Z_2.

3,000 ohms and works into a load of $R_r = 1,000$ ohms, as in Fig. 2B. The shape of curve A suggests use of a parallel-tuned circuit shunted by a resistance in the case of a series equalizer. With three independent elements in the equalizer, three independent parameters may be chosen. As first parameter we choose to tune the circuit to $\omega_0 = 10$ kc. As second parameter we choose to make the equalizer loss exactly 3.5 db at 10 kc, and as third parameter we decide to match exactly the excess gain of 1 db at $\omega_1 = 5$ kc.

Proceeding with the computation on a normalized admittance basis, at resonance the susceptance of the equalizer must be zero. Entering the chart as shown in Fig. 2C on the zero-susceptance line, we find the 3.5-db loss circle intercept at the 2.0 conductance circle. Thus the equalizer must contain a normalized conductance of $GR_0 = 2.0$.

At 5 kc the loss was set to 1 db. We now find the intercept between the 2.0 conductance circle and the 1.0-db loss circle at a susceptance of 4.0. From resonance at ω_0.

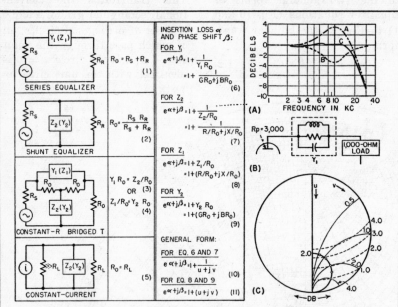

FIG. 2—Basic equalizer circuits, pertinent equations, and example

are radii through the point $\zeta = -1$ whose angle from the real axis in the ζ plane is equal to the phase shift.

The solution of Eq. 11 in the ζ plane is essentially the same as Eq. 10 except that the center for the loss circles and phase shift radii is now the point $\zeta = +1$ and the loci of the loss circles are defined by

$$\alpha \ (db) = -20 \log |(1 - \zeta)/2| \quad (14)$$

Applications

Series and shunt equalizer configurations are useful when it is unnecessary to maintain constant impedance, such as in electron tube interstages. When the network must have constant impedance, the bridged-T equalizer is used. The constant-current

While Eq. 1 to 9 have been written for a pure resistance R_0, R_0 may be replaced in all these expressions by a complex impedance Z_0. Then the values u and v in the chart represent the real and imaginary components of the fraction Z/Z_0 or the product YZ_0. The chart is also useful when measuring impedance using the insertion loss and phase principle.

Example of Use

Curve A in Fig. 2A represents an amplifier response curve. The objective is to flatten the response peak at 10 kc. A convenient place to perform the equalization is found in the plate circuit of a tube which has an internal plate resistance $R_p =$

$$\omega_0 CR_0 - \frac{1}{\omega_0 L/R_0} = 0 \quad (15)$$

From the solution of Eq. 10 at ω_1

$$\omega_1 CR_0 - \frac{1}{\omega_1 L/R_0} = 4.0 \quad (16)$$

then

$$CR_0 = \frac{4}{\left(\omega_1 - \frac{\omega_0^2}{\omega_1} \right)}$$

$$= 4.25 \times 10^{-5} \quad (17)$$

$$L/R_0 = 5.97 \times 10^{-6} \quad (18)$$

From Eq. 17 and 18 the net normalized susceptance of the network at any frequency may be determined. To find the loss associated with each of these susceptance values the equalizer chart is entered on the 2.0 conductance circle and the intercept with the computed susceptance circle is located, at which point the loss value is read. The result is plotted in curve B on Fig. 2A, and the resulting net transmission characteristic is plotted as curve C.

Assuming curve C to be adequately flat, the actual element values of the equalizer are found: From Eq. 1, R_o is 4,000 ohms.

Substituting this in $GR_o = 2.0$ gives 2,000 ohms for $1/G$. From Eq. 17, C is 0.0106 μf. From Eq. 18, L is 23.9 mh.

Equalizer Design Chart

Bass and treble attenuation or accentuation of two types of R-C equalizers for audio-frequency circuits are easily determined from the graph. Curves sketched from the chart resemble those computed laboriously point by point

By CHARLES P. BOEGLI

FOUR USES OF THE GRAPH are demonstrated by the examples. The entire range of characteristics is related to the quantity a, which is defined for each type of equalizer in Fig. 1 and 2.

An equalizer is to provide a treble drop of 3 db per octave beginning at 1,000 cps, operates from a source resistance of 33,000 ohms.

Solution. For 3 db per octave, $a = 0.33$. $R(1 - a) = 33,000$ whence $R = 49,300$ and $aR = 16,300$. From the graph, $f_1'/f_1 = 1.72$ so that $f_1' = 1,720$ cps. At this frequency $X_c = 49,300$ ohms, or $C = 0.0019$ μf. The high-frequency turnover is 1000/0.111 = 9,000 cps and the high-frequency level is down 9.6 db.

Find characteristics of equalizer consisting of series resistance of 48,000 ohms followed by shunt of 18,000 ohms and a 0.001 –μf capacitor in series.

Solution. Total $R = 66,000$ ohms. At f_1', $X_c = 66,000$ ohms, or $f_1' = 2,400$ cps; $a = 0.273$ for which the graph shows a treble attenuation of 3.4 db per octave with $f_1'/f_1 = 1.63$; $f_1 = 1,470$ cps. Other data from the graph are the high-frequency turnover (14,200 cps) and the high-frequency level (down 11.3 db).

An equalizer for treble accentuation of 4 db per octave be-

ginning at 5,000 cps is terminated by a 100,000-ohm grid resistor.

Solution. For 4 db per octave, $a = 0.20$. $R/(1 - a) = 100,000$

whence $R = 80,000$ ohms and $R/a = 400,000$ ohms; $f_1 = 5,000$ cps so $f_1' = 7,450$ cps and $f_2' = 37,250$ cps. Capacitor C has a reactance of 80,000 ohms at

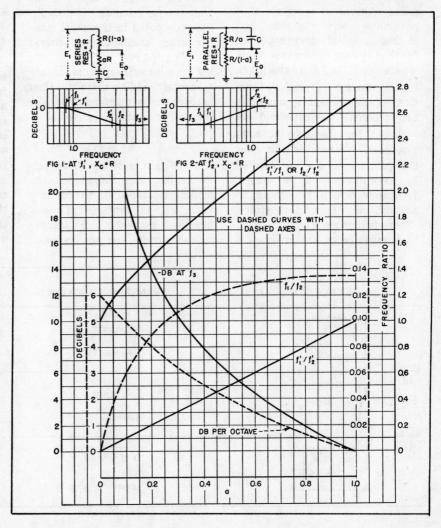

FIG 1–AT f_1', $X_c = R$

FIG 2–AT f_2', $X_c = R$

37,250 cps; $C = 53$ μμf.

Find the characteristics of an equalizer consisting of a series impedance of a 250-μμf capacitor paralleled by 1.5-megohms, this series impedance being followed by a shunt resistance of 222,000 ohms. This equalizer has been recommended for use with crystal pickups for commercial constant-velocity pressings.

Solution. Parallel resistance R is 193,000 ohms; f_2' is then 3,250 cps. Furthermore, $193,000/(1 - a) = 222,000$ whence $1 - a = 0.87$ and $a = 0.13$. The equalizer provides 4.7 db per octave treble boost with f_1' at 422 cps and f_1 (the turnover frequency) at 313 cps. The low-frequency drop is 17.7 db.

As attenuation in db per octave decreases, the frequency range over which the equalizer is effective narrows.

Transfer Functions for R-C and R-L Equalizer Networks

By E. W. TSCHUDI

THE accompanying tabulation of transfer functions or the ratio of output to input voltage (E_o/E_i) is the result of attempts to determine the electrical equivalent network of a pneumatic servo system and to find a satisfactory equalizer for that system. The phase angle ϕ between E_o and E_i is also given in the tables. Transfer functions of the elementary networks are common knowledge and are included for the sake of completeness. Wherever possible the gain curves are represented by asymptotes and the corner frequency which is the intersection of these asymptotes. Where two or more corners exist, they must be of the order of a decade apart in order that the gain curve may be represented by asymptotes. When it is desired to compute the actual gain, p should be replaced by $j\omega$ in the transfer function and the amplitude computed in the usual manner for complex quantities; squaring the real and then squaring the imaginary components separately, adding them and then taking the square root of the sum. For example in No. 1,

$$A = \sqrt{\frac{1}{1 + T^2 \omega^2}}$$

and the gain is 20 log A. In networks including inductance, the ohmic resistance of the inductance, R_L, is represented as a practical necessity. Phase response curves are not included since it is comparatively simple to compute the phase angle at several representative frequencies. In general the phase angle is positive when the associated gain increases and negative when the gain decreases (attenuation).

The inclusion of phantom shunt impedances in No. 1 and 8 indicates the transfer functions are not affected by their presence. The values of T_a and T_b in the corner frequencies of No. 4 and 6 are the roots of the quadratic expressions in the denominators of these transfer functions. They are different from the two time constants T_1 and T_2 that are, respectively, the products of R_1C_1 and R_2C_2.

NETWORK	TRANSFER FUNCTION	GAIN CURVE
(1)	$\dfrac{1}{1+Tp}$ $\phi = -\tan^{-1} T\omega$	 6 DB/OCT (LOW PASS)
(2)	$\dfrac{Tp}{1+Tp}$ $\phi = 90° - \tan^{-1} T\omega$	 6 DB/OCT (HIGH PASS)
(3)	$\dfrac{1}{1+3Tp+T^2 p^2}$ $\phi = -\tan^{-1} \dfrac{3T\omega}{1-T^2\omega^2}$	 12 DB/OCT

NETWORK	TRANSFER FUNCTION	GAIN CURVE
(4)	$$\frac{1}{1+(T_1+T_2+R_1C_2)p+T_1T_2p^2}$$ $$\phi=-\tan^{-1}\frac{(T_1+T_2+R_1C_2)\omega}{1-T_1T_2\omega^2}$$	
(5)	$$\frac{1}{3+2Tp}$$ $$\phi=-\tan^{-1}\frac{2T\omega}{3}$$	
(6)	$$\frac{T_1T_2p^2}{1+(T_1+T_2+R_1C_2)p+T_1T_2p^2}$$ $$\phi=180°-\tan^{-1}\frac{(T_1+T_2+R_1C_2)\omega}{1-T_1T_2\omega^2}$$	
(7)	$$\frac{T^3p^3}{1+5Tp+6T^2p^2+T^3p^3}$$ $$\phi=270°-\tan^{-1}\frac{(5-T^2\omega^2)T\omega}{1-6T^2\omega^2}$$	
(8)	$$\frac{Tp}{1+3Tp+T^2p^2}$$ $$\phi=90°-\tan^{-1}\frac{3T\omega}{1-T^2\omega^2}$$	
(9)	$$\frac{Tp}{1+3Tp+T^2p^2}$$ $$\phi=90°-\tan^{-1}\frac{3T\omega}{1-T^2\omega^2}$$	SAME AS 8
(10)	$$\frac{Tp}{1+3Tp+T^2p^2}$$ $$\phi=90°-\tan^{-1}\frac{3T\omega}{1-T^2\omega^2}$$	SAME AS 8
(11)	$$\frac{Tp}{1+3Tp}$$ $$\phi=90°-\tan^{-1}3T\omega$$	
(12)	$$\frac{1+Tp}{1+2Tp}$$ $$\phi=\tan^{-1}T\omega-\tan^{-1}2T\omega$$	
(13)	$$\frac{1+Tp}{1+2Tp}$$ $$\phi=\tan^{-1}T\omega-\tan^{-1}2T\omega$$	SAME AS 12
(14)	$$\frac{(1+Tp)^2}{1+3Tp+T^2p^2}$$ $$\phi=2\tan^{-1}T\omega-\tan^{-1}\frac{3T\omega}{1-T^2\omega^2}$$	

NETWORK	TRANSFER FUNCTION	GAIN CURVE
(15)	$$\frac{1+Tp}{2+Tp}$$ $$\phi=\tan^{-1}T\omega-\tan^{-1}\frac{T\omega}{2}$$	
(16)	$$\frac{k(1+Tp)}{(1+k)+kTp}$$ $$\phi=\tan^{-1}T\omega-\tan^{-1}\frac{kT\omega}{1+k}$$	
(17)	$$\frac{1+Tp}{2+Tp}$$ $$\phi=\tan^{-1}T\omega-\tan^{-1}\frac{T\omega}{2}$$	SAME AS 15
(18)	$$\frac{1+Tp}{3+Tp}$$ $$\phi=\tan^{-1}T\omega-\tan^{-1}\frac{T\omega}{3}$$	
(19)	$$\frac{(1+Tp)^2}{2+5Tp+T^2p^2}$$ $$\phi=2\tan^{-1}T\omega-\tan^{-1}\frac{5T\omega}{2-T^2\omega^2}$$	
(20)	$$\frac{1+3Tp}{2+5Tp+T^2p^2}$$ $$\phi=\tan^{-1}3T\omega-\tan^{-1}\frac{5T\omega}{2-T^2\omega^2}$$	
(21)	$$\frac{k(3+Tp)}{3(1+k)+2kTp}=\frac{k[9(1+k)+2k\omega^2T^2+3(1-k)j\omega T]}{9(1+k)^2+4k^2\omega^2T^2}$$ $$\phi=\tan^{-1}\frac{T\omega}{3}-\tan^{-1}\frac{2kT\omega}{3(1+k)}$$	j-TERM NEGATIVE FOR k>1 ZERO FOR k=1 POSITIVE FOR k<1 $$A=k\sqrt{\frac{9+T^2\omega^2}{9(1+k)^2+4k^2T^2\omega^2}}$$
(22)	$$\frac{R_2(1+T_1p)}{(R_1+R_2)+(R_1T_2+R_2T_1)p}$$ $$\phi=\tan^{-1}T_1\omega-\tan^{-1}\frac{(R_1T_2+R_2T_1)\omega}{R_1+R_2}$$	
(23)	$$\frac{R_2(1+3T_1p)(1-T_2p)}{(3R_1+2R_2)+R_2(3T_1-2T_2)p-3T_2(R_1T_2+R_2T_1)p^2}$$ $$\phi=\tan^{-1}3T_1\omega-\tan^{-1}T_2\omega-\tan^{-1}\frac{R_2(3T_1-2T_2)\omega}{3R_1+2R_2+3T_2(R_1T_2+R_2T_1)\omega^2}$$	
(24)	$$\frac{R_2[1+(2T_1-T_2)p+T_1(T_1-2T_2)p^2-T_1^2T_2p^3]}{(2R_1+R_2)+(R_1T_1+3R_2T_1-R_2T_2)p+(R_2T_1^2-3R_2T_1T_2-2R_1T_2^2)p^2-T_1(R_1T_2^2+R_2T_1T_2)p^3}$$ $$\phi=\tan^{-1}\frac{(2T_1-T_2+T_1^2T_2\omega^2)\omega}{1-T_1(T_1-2T_2)\omega^2}-\tan^{-1}\frac{[R_1T_1+3R_2T_1-R_2T_2+T_1(R_1T_2^2+R_2T_1T_2)\omega^2]\omega}{2R_1+R_2-(R_2T_1^2-3R_2T_1T_2-2R_1T_2^2)\omega^2}$$ (LEADING ANGLE)	
(25)	$$\frac{R_L+Lp}{R+R_L+Lp}$$ $$\phi=\tan^{-1}\frac{L\omega}{R_L}-\tan^{-1}\frac{L\omega}{R+R_L}$$	

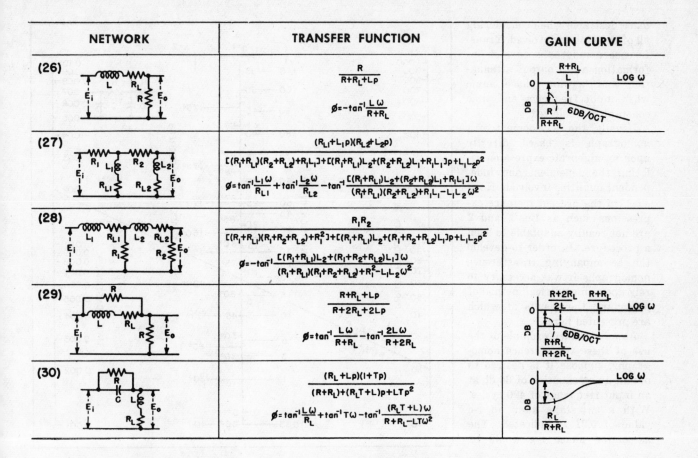

NETWORK	TRANSFER FUNCTION	GAIN CURVE
(26)	$$\frac{R}{R+R_L+Lp}$$ $$\phi=-\tan^{-1}\frac{L\omega}{R+R_L}$$	
(27)	$$\frac{(R_{L1}+L_1p)(R_{L2}+L_2p)}{[(R_1+R_{L1})(R_2+R_{L2})+R_1L_1]+[(R_1+R_{L1})L_2+(R_2+R_{L2})L_1+R_1L_1]p+L_1L_2p^2}$$ $$\phi=\tan^{-1}\frac{L_1\omega}{R_{L1}}+\tan^{-1}\frac{L_2\omega}{R_{L2}}-\tan^{-1}\frac{[(R_1+R_{L1})L_2+(R_2+R_{L2})L_1+R_1L_1]\omega}{(R_1+R_{L1})(R_2+R_{L2})+R_1L_1-L_1L_2\omega^2}$$	
(28)	$$\frac{R_1R_2}{[(R_1+R_{L1})(R_1+R_2+R_{L2})+R_1^2]+[(R_1+R_{L1})L_2+(R_1+R_2+R_{L2})L_1]p+L_1L_2p^2}$$ $$\phi=-\tan^{-1}\frac{[(R_1+R_{L1})L_2+(R_1+R_2+R_{L2})L_1]\omega}{(R_1+R_{L1})(R_1+R_2+R_{L2})+R_1^2-L_1L_2\omega^2}$$	
(29)	$$\frac{R+R_L+Lp}{R+2R_L+2Lp}$$ $$\phi=\tan^{-1}\frac{L\omega}{R+R_L}-\tan^{-1}\frac{2L\omega}{R+2R_L}$$	
(30)	$$\frac{(R_L+Lp)(1+Tp)}{(R+R_L)+(R_LT+L)p+LTp^2}$$ $$\phi=\tan^{-1}\frac{L\omega}{R_L}+\tan^{-1}T\omega-\tan^{-1}\frac{(R_LT+L)\omega}{R+R_L-LT\omega^2}$$	

Transference Nomographs for Low-Pass Iterative Filters

Figures for attenuation at the prescribed frequency allow r-c constant to be read off. Phase angle for this and for other frequencies between 10 and 1,000 cycles is quickly determined as a second step

By E. W. TSCHUDI

THE USE of low-pass iterative filters requires the proper choice of r-c time constant and number of iterative stages to attain a specified attenuation at a selected noise frequency while at the same time attenuation throughout the pass band is held within a prescribed maximum. A knowledge of the amount of lagging phase angle at several input frequencies for any selected iterative filter is also of vital importance. To determine these

several quantities from the transfer function of one or more iterative filters can be a laborious procedure. For example, the transfer function of a four-stage filter is

$$\frac{E_o}{E_i} = \frac{1}{1+10Tp+15T^2p^2+7T^3p^3+T^4p^4} \quad (1)$$

where $T = RC$ and $p = j\omega = j2\pi f$. The attenuation resulting from such a filter is given by

$$A_{db} = 20 \log \times \left[\frac{1}{(1-15T^2\omega^2+T^4\omega^4)^2+(10T\omega-7T^3\omega^3)^2}\right]^{\frac{1}{2}} \quad (2)$$

and the phase angle by

$$\phi = \tan^{-1}\frac{10T\omega-7T^3\omega^3}{1-15T^2\omega^2+T^4\omega^4} \quad (3)$$

If by the aid of Eq. 2 a value of the time constant T is found that will result in satisfactory attenuation at a noise frequency ω_n, one still would not know if a three-stage filter might not be more desirable when considering all of the factors involved. Transference nomographs furnish information as to output attenuation and lagging phase angle when input frequency and time constant are selected.

Usually, the development of a nomograph is based directly upon an algebraic expression relating the dependent and independent qualities involved. However, in the present instance expressions such as Eq. 1 and 2 are not readily adaptable to such a procedure. In order to develop the accompanying transference nomographs it was necessary to rely upon an empirical method of procedure, the results of which are presented here.

As an extended example of the use of these transference nomographs, suppose it is desired to obtain an attenuation of 60 db at an input frequency of 400 cycles. With a two-stage filter an r-c value of 0.01 is indicated. The associated phase lag would be

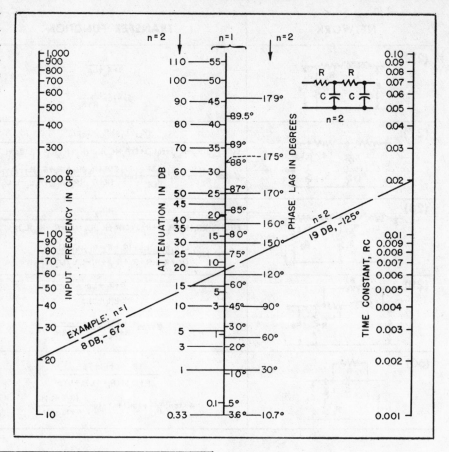

173 degrees. This filter would then produce an attenuation of about 6 db at a frequency of 10 cycles with an associated phase lag of about 73 degrees.

With a three-stage filter, an r-c value of 0.004 is indicated to produce 60 db at 400 cycles with an associated phase lag of 241 degrees. This time constant will produce between 4 db and 5 db at 10 cycles with an associated phase lag of 65 degrees. With a four-stage filter, an r-c value of 0.002 is indicated for 60 db down and would result in a phase lag of 285 degrees at 400 cycles. At 10 cycles the attenuation would be about 4 db with a phase lag of about 60 degrees. The final choice of the number of stages to be used would be dictated by circuit performance requirements.

Since the output of a filter, as given by its transfer function, is applicable only when the filter is isolated, values taken from the

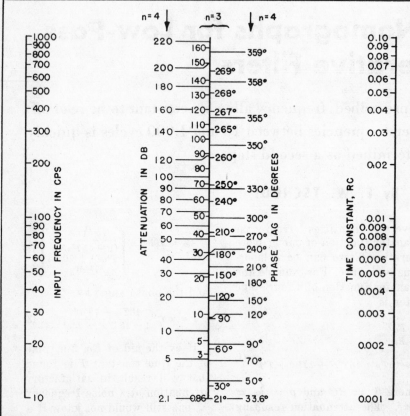

nomographs should be applied in an actual circuit including the filter only when that filter is separated from the balance of the circuit by an isolation amplifier, or by a transducer if the filter is part of a servo loop. In all other cases the balance of a circuit loads the filter and thereby alters its transfer characteristics.

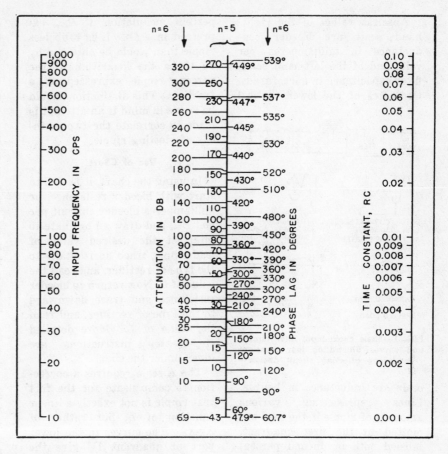

Choke-Input Filter Chart

For given bleeder current, chart gives optimum values of L and C, resulting output ripple and resonant frequency, and magnitudes of four significant transients for nine combinations of single-phase and polyphase rectifier circuits with various power input frequencies

By REUBEN LEE

PREVIOUS charts for choke-input filters give the ratio of choke reactance to capacitor reactance or the LC product needed to attenuate the ripple to the required level, but individual values of L and C are not thereby determined. Where regulation is important, L and C must have definite values to avoid capacitance effect, or the tendency for the d-c voltage to rise at light loads.

For the circuit of Fig. 1 it can be shown that

$$R_1 = (X_L - X_C)/P_A \qquad (1)$$

where R_1 is maximum bleeder resistance to prevent voltage rise, X_L is choke reactance at fundamental ripple frequency, X_C is capacitor reactance at fundamental ripple frequency and P_A is peak amplitude of fundamental ripple frequency in the rectifier output, which depends on the type of rectifier.

Attenuation in this filter can be expressed by

$$\frac{P_A}{P_R} = \frac{X_L - X_C}{X_C} \qquad (2)$$

where P_R is the peak ripple amplitude in the load. Combining Eq. 1 and 2 gives $X_C = R_1 P_R$, and therefore

$$C = \frac{1}{\omega R_1 P_R} = \frac{1}{R_1}\left(\frac{1}{\omega P_R}\right) \qquad (3)$$

Description of Chart

For a given rectifier, filter capacitance C thus depends only on the bleeder resistance and percent ripple. Once capacitance is fixed, the minimum inductance is also fixed; these are the values plotted on the chart.

Abscissa values of the right-hand scale are bleeder conductance in milliamperes per volt; and of the left-hand scale, filter capacitance in microfarads. Ordinates of the lower vertical

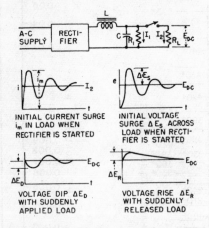

FIG. 1—Basic choke-input filter circuit, and curves illustrating four transient conditions affecting circuit design

scale are inductance in henrys. Lines representing various amounts of ripple in the load are plotted in the first quadrant, labeled both in db and percent ripple. In the second quadrant, lines are drawn representing different types of rectifiers and supply line frequencies. A similar set of lines is shown in the fourth quadrant.

Two orthogonal sets of lines are drawn in the third quadrant. Those sloping downward to the right represent resonant frequency of the filter L and C and also load resistance R_L. The other set of lines is labeled $\sqrt{L/C}$, which may be regarded as the filter impedance. It can be shown that the transient properties of the filter are dependent upon the ratio of $\sqrt{L/C}$ to R_L.

Ripple is plotted in two ways. Percent values are rms ripple voltage in the load divided by d-c voltage output E_{d-c}, according to the IRE standard definition; db values are equal to 20 $\log_{10}$ $(rms\ ripple)/0.707\ E_{d-c}$. Instruments for measuring hum normally read the db value, which is the noise-to-signal ratio for 100

percent modulation of E_{d-c}, expressed in −db. It is 3 db less ripple than would be obtained by 20 times the logarithm of the percent ripple expressed as a fraction. This distinction should be borne in mind if an attempt is made to correlate the two methods of plotting ripple.

Use of Chart

In using the chart, it is well to start with bleeder resistance, or milliamperes bleeder current per volt E_{d-c} and draw an ordinate to intersect the desired value of load ripple, trace horizontally to the type of rectifier, and read the value of C. Now return to bleeder resistance and trace downward to the type of rectifier, and read the value of L. More detailed step-by-step instructions are given under the chart.

The L scale requires a correction to compensate for the fact that ripple is not exactly a linear function of L, but rather of X_L-X_C. The curves in the lower part of quadrant IV give the amount of correction to be added when the correction is greater than 1 percent.

Bleeder current given is the minimum necessary for continuous current from the rectifier. Steady-state peak ripple current is read directly on the same scale.

The third quadrant has a series of lines labeled f_r, and the intersection of L and C thereon indicates the resonant frequency of the filter. It should be no higher than the value given in the small table in quadrant IV in order to avoid excessive ripple in polyphase rectifiers due to supply-line phase unbalance.

If the supply voltage is suddenly impressed, or if the load varies suddenly, the filter is subject to transients. The bottom scales of quadrant III give the magnitudes of the four transients indicated on the curves in Fig. 1.

Swinging Choke

If the choke in the filter swings

to S times the full-load value in henrys, the regulation is improved considerably without affecting the full-load ripple. The chart may still be used for this case with certain corrections. At least this is true for the single-phase full-wave rectifier, which is where the swinging choke is used most commonly. The swinging choke requires less bleeder current for a given number of henrys at full load, but capacitance C is not appreciably affected.

Since use of the chart starts with bleeder current, it is necessary to multiply the capacitance obtained from the chart by the ratio S, but to it must be added nearly the same percentage the chart gives in the curve of corrections for L.

The value of L obtained by projecting the bleeder current downwards is the maximum or swinging value. It must be divided by S to obtain the full-load value. Transient conditions may be approximated closely by using the full amount of capacitance in the filter and the full-load value of henrys in the choke. Peak ripple current is dependent on the full-load value of henrys and is therefore S times the bleeder current.

Shunt-tuned Choke

If the filter choke is parallel-tuned to the fundamental ripple frequency, the ripple and regulation are less than they would be with an untuned choke. The inductance of the choke is held as constant as is practicable from bleeder load to full load, so that approximately the same ripple is obtained at all loads. With practicable tolerances on choke inductance and tuning capacitance, the choke impedance is effectively increased 3 to 1, hence $R_1 = (3X_L - X_C)/P_A$, and the ratio (P_A/P_R is equal to $(3X_L - X_C)/X_C$. Combining gives $X_C = P_R R_1$, and the chart can be used directly for capacitance C. The values of inductance, however, must be divided by 3 in order to obtain the actual henrys in the choke. This lower value of henrys and the capacitance C across the load determine transient condi-

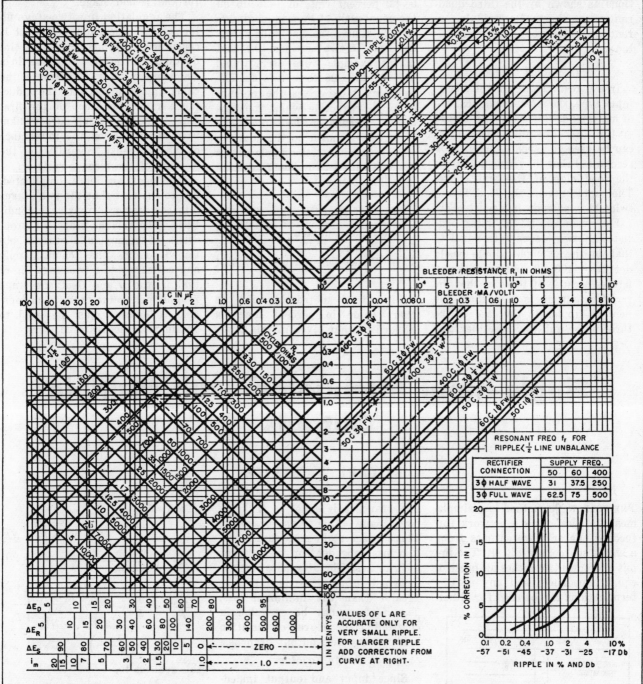

1. Assume suitable value of bleeder resistance or bleeder current I_1 in ma per volt of E_{d-c}. This is also steady-state peak ripple current in ma.

2. Trace upward on desired bleeder ordinate to intersect desired value of load ripple, and from here trace horizontally to the left to diagonal line for rectifier and supply frequency used. Directly under read value of C.

3. Trace downward on same desired bleeder ordinate to intersect diagonal line below for rectifier and supply frequency, and read value of L.

4. From desired ripple value, determine correction for L on graph at lower right, and add indicated correction to value of L.

5. Using corrected value of L and next standard value of C, find intersection in third quadrant and read maximum resonant frequency f_r.

6. Using same values of L and C as in 5, read value of ratio $\sqrt{L/C}$.

7. Under intersection of $\sqrt{L/C}$ with load resistance R_L read values of the four transients.

Example (shown dotted):
Three-phase full-wave 60-cycle rectifier; $E_{d-c} = 3,000$ v; $I_2 = 1$ amp; $I_1 = 96$ ma; load ripple $= -50$ db

Solution:
Bleeder ma/volt $= 0.032$
$C = 4.5$ μf (use 5 μf)
Scale value of $L = 0.78$ h; corrected value $= 0.82$ h
Resonant frequency $= 75$ cycles
Load resistance $R_L = 3,000$ ohms
$i_m = 7$ $I_2 = 7$ amp; $\Delta E_S = 79\%$; $\Delta E_D = 12\%$ $\Delta E_R = 15\%$

tions as shown by the third quadrant of the chart. Peak ripple current is limited by tuning capacitance.

Two-Stage Filters

In a two-stage filter of the choke-input type, the most economical use of material occurs when both stages of the filter are alike. The chart can be used for such filters if it is recognized that the ripple is that on the load side of the first choke. The ripple across the load is not twice this amount in negative db.

For example, if the filter consisted of two stages both equal to that in the example, ripple would not be − 100 db, but some lower figure, because of the fact that the rectifier output is less than 100 percent ripple. In the case of the three-phase full-wave rectifier this

is 4.2 percent rms, or −25 db on the usual ratio of hum to maximum signal. Hence the net hum across the load, if two sections like that in the example were used, would be − 50 db − 25 db = − 75 db. The following table gives the amount of ripple reduction which must be applied to each of the three kinds of rectifiers shown on the chart in order to arrive at the ripple across the load with a two-stage filter having like sections.

Type of Rectifier	db	rms
Single-Phase Full-Wave	3.5	0.47
Three-Phase Half-Wave	12	0.18
Three-Phase Full-Wave	25	0.04

Instead of subtracting db, the chart value in percent may be divided by that given in this table,

for the second stage.

The regulation in a two-stage filter, as far as capacitance effect is concerned, depends upon the inductance of the first choke as in a single-stage filter. Therefore the chart applies directly to the inductance and capacitance of the first stage. The peak ripple current likewise depends upon the inductance of the first choke, regardless of the location of the bleeder resistor.

Transients are more complicated, due to the fact that the two stages interact under transient conditions. The various transient properties of voltage and current obtained from the chart apply approximately to a two-stage filter; that is, the L and C of one stage roughly determine them. Considerable refinement must be used to obtain more accurate answers.

Single-Input Attenuators with Multiple Outputs

By CARL W. ULRICH

THE FOLLOWING method is a simple means of designing a network for feeding one or more outputs from a single source, see Fig. 1. The input and output branches all present equal impedances and any of the terminations can be used for either

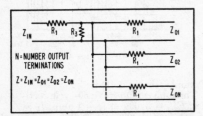

FIG. 1—Attenuator network for feeding one or more outputs from a single source

an input or an output. Thus a network designed to feed three outputs from one input can also be used to feed two inputs to two outputs or three inputs to one output.

The insertion loss between any

two branches is equal to that between any other two branches. There is a certain minimum insertion loss dependent on the number of branches. The attenuator can be designed for any loss, equal to or greater than the minimum loss. This feature may be of value in controlling the degree of isolation between any two output branches.

Design Equation

Since input and output impedances are equal

$$\frac{E_{in}}{E_{out}} = \text{Log}_{10}^{-1} \frac{\text{db loss}}{20} = B$$

Insertion loss in db = $20 \log_{10} \frac{E_{in}}{E_{out}}$ =

$20 \log_{10} B$

$$Z_{in} = Z = R_1 + \frac{\left(\frac{R_1 + Z}{N}\right) R_3}{\frac{R_1 + Z}{N} + R_3} =$$

$$R_1 + \frac{R_3 (Z + R_1)}{Z + R_1 + NR_3}$$

From which,

$$R_3 = \frac{Z^2 - R_1^2}{Z - NZ + R_1 + NR_1}$$

$$\text{or} \quad \frac{Z^2 - R_1^2}{(N + 1) R_1 - (N - 1) Z} \quad (1)$$

$$\frac{E_{out}}{E_{in}} = \frac{1}{B} = \frac{\frac{R_3 (Z + R_1)}{Z + R_1 + NR_3}}{\frac{R_3 (Z + R_1)}{Z + R_1 + NR_3} + R_1}$$

$$\left(\frac{Z}{Z + R_1}\right)$$

this reduces to,

$$R_1 (Z + R_1) = R_3 (BZ - Z - R_1 - NR_1)$$

substituting for R_3 the value obtained in Eq. 1

$$R_1 (Z + R_1) = \frac{Z^2 - R_1^2}{NR_1 + R_1 - NZ + Z}$$
$$(BZ - Z - R_1 - NR_1)$$

or

$$R_1 = \frac{(B - 1) Z}{B + 1} \quad (2)$$

The condition for minimum possible loss is realized when $R_3 =$

infinity. This condition is obtained when the denominator of Eq. 1 = 0.

Equating the denominator to 0 and substituting for R_1 the value obtained in Eq. 2

$$(N + 1) \frac{(B - 1) Z}{(B + 1)} - (N - 1) Z = 0$$

$$B - N = 0, \quad B = N$$

This means that the minimum possible loss is obtained when $B = N$. If B is less than N, R_3 will be negative and not physically realizable. If B is greater than N, R_3 will be positive and have a finite value. Therefore B may be equal to, or greater than N and the minimum possible insertion loss in db $= 20 \log_{10} N$

Pad Design

To design a pad using this method, determine the minimum insertion loss for the desired value of N

output terminations.

Suppose $N = 4$, then minimum insertion loss in db $= 20 \log_{10} 4 = 20(.602)$ or 12 db

The pad may now be designed for any value of insertion loss equal to or greater than 12 db. Suppose a loss of 20 db is desired and $Z = 600$ ohms.

Then, $B = \log_{10}^{-1}\left(\frac{20}{20}\right) = 10$

$$R_1 = \frac{9}{11} (600) \text{ or } 490.9 \text{ ohms}$$

and $R_3 = \frac{600^2 - 490.9^2}{5(490.9) - 3(600)} = 181.8 \text{ ohms}$

For the special case where minimum loss is desired $B = N$ or 4

and $R_1 = \frac{3}{5} (600)$ or 360 ohms

$$R_3 = \frac{600^2 - 360^2}{5(360) - 3(600)} = \text{infinity}$$

Thus it is evident that for the

minimum loss condition, when $B = N$, resistor R_3 can be eliminated.

Another special case occurs when $N = 1$. If B is also 1 then $R_1 = 0$ and $R_3 = $ infinity, and a direct connection is indicated without a network.

For any other value of B greater than 1, R_1 can be determined as before by means of Eq. 2.

Equation 1 reduces to

$$R_3 \doteq \frac{Z^2 - R_1^2}{2 R_1} \text{ or } \frac{Z^2}{2 R_1} - \frac{R_1}{2}$$

It is believed that this method involves less computation for T pads having equal input and output impedances.

To convert to balanced attenuators simply use $\frac{R_1}{2}$ on each side of the terminations instead of R_1 on one side.

Wien-Bridge Network Modifications

By R. ZUIDHOF

To DETERMINE the influence of the stray capacitance in shunt with the series resistor in a Wien-bridge network such as used in a-c bridges, resistance-capacitance oscillators and selective amplifiers[1], an attempt was made to find an expression for the frequency and the ratio of the impedances with an extra capacitance C_s placed in the circuit. Eight modifications of the Wien network were derived. Three of them showing interesting properties appear in Fig. 1.

From Fig. 2 the influence of the capacitance C_s on the frequency can be determined when C_1 equals $C_2 = C$. However C_s also has some influence on the impedance ratio. When in an R-C oscillator tuning is done by means of a variable capacitor, the stray capacitance C_s may have a harmful effect when the variable capacitor has its minimum value. Both frequency and impedance ratio will be affected if the value of C_s forms an appreciable

part of the value of the variable capacitor in its minimum position.

In a resistor-switching oscillator with three or more ranges[2,3], the stray capacitance will probably not be the same on all ranges. Therefore at the high-frequency end the scales will not properly coincide.

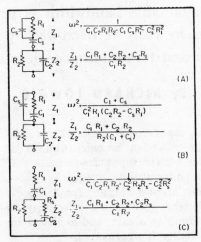

FIG. 1—Three modifications of the Wien-bridge network

The effect of C_s on the impedance ratio manifests itself in the output voltage, which will not remain constant. By means of a second capacitance C_s in shunt with C_1 however, this ratio can be made constant. When C_1 is made $C + C_s$, $C_2 = C$ and R_1 equals $R_2 = R$, the impedance ratio becomes

$$\frac{Z_1}{Z_2} = \frac{(C + C_s) R + CR + C_sR}{(C + C_s)R}$$

$$= 2 = \text{constant}$$

The formula for the frequency now becomes

$$f = \frac{1}{2\pi R \sqrt{C^2 - C_s^2}}$$

As can be seen, C_s has an opposite effect on the frequency from C and this property can be used to extend the frequency range.

When on all ranges trimmers C_s are placed over R_1 and C_1, the oscillator can be completely trimmed, so that the scales properly coincide and even the phase shift in the amplifier on the higher frequencies can be compensated.

The output voltage can also be made constant over the whole range by means of the trimmers. Of course the resistors of all ranges must have the proper ratio and also the ganging of the variable capacitor has to be correct.

Fig. 3A presents the most general form of the first modification. It can be shown that for a constant impedance ratio x must be equal to yz and when this condition has been fulfilled, Z_1/Z_2 will have the constant value $y + 1/z$.

When a Wien-bridge network is designed for optimum frequency stability[4], this property will be useful.

Trimming can also be done according to the modification shown in Fig. 1B. If R_1 and R_2 are both made equal to R, $C_1 = C$ and $C_2 = C + 2C_s$ the impedance ratio $Z_1/Z_2 = 2$ and

$$f = \frac{1}{2 \pi RC}$$

which is the formula of the original Wien bridge. The factor $2C_s$ may consist of the amplifier-input capacitance only and the trimmer C_s must then be half of this capacitance.

Figure 1C shows an interesting property. The values of the compo-

nents can be chosen such that tuning can be accomplished by variation of one circuit element only. When C_1 and C_2 are both made C, $R_1 = R - R_s$ and $R_2 = R$; the impedance ratio becomes

$$\frac{Z_1}{Z_2} = \frac{C(R - R_S) + CR + CR_S}{CR} = 2$$

thus Z_1/Z_2 is a constant, and

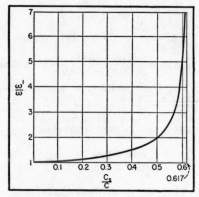

FIG. 2—Influence of capacitance on frequency

$$\omega^2 = \frac{1}{C^2 (R^2 - 2RR_S - R_S{}^2)}$$

From Fig. 3B it can be seen how this is brought into effect. However in practice the output does not remain constant and a good sine wave can only be obtained over a small range.

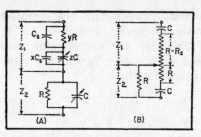

FIG. 3—Trimmers provide frequency and output-voltage control

For the influence of R_s on the frequency variation a similar curve as in Fig. 2 can be drawn. It can be seen from this curve and calculations, that a very slight variation of R_s above a certain value gives a large frequency variation, therefore the selectivity deteriorates rapidly. With a differential variable capacitor a similar solution can be obtained for Fig. 1B.

REFERENCES

(1) F. E. Terman, "Radio Engineers' Handbook" McGraw-Hill Book Co., p 503 and p 904, New York 1943.

(2) W. Noel Eldred, Generator for A-F Measurements, *F-M and Television*, p 31, June 1949.

(3) Charles F. Lober, A Wide-Range Test Oscillator, *QST*, p 40, May 1946.

(4) H. A. Whale, Optimum Conditions for an R-C Oscillator, ELECTRONICS, p 178, Feb. 1948.

Lattice-Type Crystal Filter

Crystal filters of the type described can easily be made for any frequency at which good crystals are obtainable. The attainable bandwidth is proportional to the center frequency, but can be made wider by coils or narrower by capacitors. Requirements for crystals, capacitors and terminating devices are not stringent

By RICHARD LOWRIE

THE selection of an intermediate frequency for a low-frequency, wide-range superheterodyne receiver presents many vexing problems. If a frequency below the low-

The work described was performed at Melpar, Inc., Alexandria, Va., for Air Materiel Command under contract AF33-(038)-3581.

est input frequency is chosen, image rejection becomes difficult at the higher input frequencies. If an intermediate frequency above the highest input frequency is chosen, good skirt selectivity is difficult to obtain, and oscillator instability is aggravated.

A recent design of a receiver to

cover the 100 kc to 1.75-mc range in the smallest practical volume met this dilemma, not by the use of two different low intermediate frequencies, one for the low band and one for all other bands, as is now standard practice, but by the use of an intermediate frequency higher than the highest input frequency.

Oscillator instability, it was believed, could be cured by taking adequate pains, but the high intermediate frequency chosen to eliminate bulky i-f transformers required special attention to the skirt selectivity problem. The potential simplicity of the lattice-type crystal filter led to its trial in this application, despite warnings in the literature on the subject that construction of such units for frequencies as high as 0.5 megacycle was fraught with difficulties. The success obtained, once a good source of crystals was discovered, has been most encouraging.

The filter described below is a band-pass filter centered at 2 mc with a pass band of approximately 4,000 cycles. This is effectively a highly selective voice filter, but the bandwidth may be altered for other applications. The design of such a filter is fairly simple, but several practical details must be given attention to assure a good response.

Design Theory

A lattice circuit is used to obtain a symmetrical curve and maximum selectivity. A schematic of the circuit is shown in Fig. 1. The frequency of the series-arm crystals is 2,000.0 kc while that of the shunt arm crystals is 1,997.5 kc. The pass band extends from 1,997.5 kc to 2,001.5 kc. Although the difference between the series resonant frequencies of the two crystals is 2,500 cycles, a bandwidth of twice this, or 5,000 cycles, may theoretically be attained when they are used in a lattice circuit. The practical band-

width is about 80 percent of the theoretical maximum.

Figure 2 shows the reactance curves of two crystals whose series resonant frequencies are 2,500 cycles apart. When these crystals are in the arms of a lattice, balance is obtained at the points where the reactances are equal in magnitude and of the same sign. This occurs at points A-A. Zero attenuation or complete lack of balance occurs when one crystal is capacitive and the other inductive, such as in the region B to C. From the reactance curves, a plot of the attenuation versus frequency can be drawn as shown by the dashed lines when the crystals are in a lattice circuit. For a uniform attenuation in the pass-band region, the parallel-resonant frequency of the lower-frequency crystal must be the same as the series-resonant frequency of the higher-frequency crystal. The parallel-resonant frequency may be lowered by placing a small trimmer capacitor in parallel with the crystal. Trimmer capacitors also allow the shape of the attenuation curve to be varied outside the pass band. High-rejection peaks are possible; or a gradually widening curve may be obtained if the greatest attenuation is desired at frequencies far from resonance.

For any one crystal, the separation of the series and parallel-resonant frequencies is a function of the series and shunt capacitances of the crystal. Since the series capacitance is fixed by the series-resonant frequency, it is customary to specify the shunt capacitance.

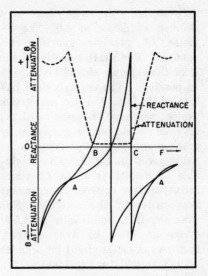

FIG. 2—Reactance curves (solid lines) for crystals in the lattice network and the attenuation curve shown by a dashed line

The bandwidth is given by the formula $BW = f_r c / C_o$, where c is the series capacitance, C_o is the shunt capacitance, and f_r is the series-resonant frequency. This formula is developed from the equivalent circuit of Fig. 3. The parallel resonant frequency is

$$f_p = f_r + \Delta f = 1/2\pi \ (LC^1)^{1/2} \quad (1)$$
$$\text{where } C^1 = cC_o/(c + C_o) \quad (2)$$
$$\text{and } L = 1/(2\pi f_r)^2 c$$

From Eq. 1 and Eq. 2

$$1/C^1 = (f_r + \Delta f)^2/(f_r)^2 c \quad (3)$$

$$\frac{(f_r + \Delta f)^2}{(f_r)^2} = \frac{C}{C_o} + 1 = \left(1 + \frac{\Delta f}{f_r}\right)^2 \quad (4)$$

From Eq. 4, $c/C_o = 2\Delta f/f_r \quad (5)$

or $\qquad \Delta f = f_r c/2C_o \quad (6)$

The bandwidth is twice Δf

$$BW = f_r c/C_o \quad (7)$$

Equation 7 gives the theoretical maximum bandwidth. The ratio of C_o/c is about 138 for a —18.5-degree X-cut crystal, and about 250 for an AT cut. A wider bandwidth may be obtained with a smaller ratio. However, a crystal cut for a low ratio may not satisfy the requirements of temperature stability, spurious response or Q.

Practical Design

The crystals used were accurate to within ±20 cycles and were free of spurious resonances within 50 kilocycles of resonance. The use of

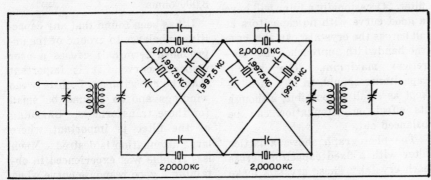

FIG. 1—Circuit for the 2-mc filter using eight crystals

split-plating crystals was not deemed advisable at 2,000 kc because of possible spurious responses. For sharp selectivity, the Q of the crystals should be as high as possible. The crystals used had a Q of 130,000. For a conservative design, resonant frequencies of the crystals should not be separated by much more than 40 percent of the value given in Eq. 7. The attainable bandwidth is about 1.6 times the separation between the resonant frequencies of the crystals. For example, if a bandwidth of 1,500 cycles at 1,000 kc were desired, then two crystals might be ordered at 999 kc and two at 1,000 kc for each lattice. The pass band will then extend from 999 kc to about 1,001 kc if no external capacitance

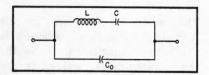

FIG. 3—Equivalent circuit of the crystal as evaluated in the equations

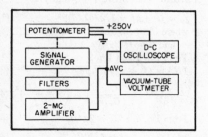

FIG. 4—Test equipment used to adjust the filter. The potentiometer and signal generator are driven simultaneously by hand

is added. From Eq. 7, the C_o/c ratio necessary for a bandwidth of 1,500 cycles is 667. Since c is fixed, if the crystal C_o/c is 250, additional capacitance will have to be added in parallel with the crystal in order to reduce the bandwidth. (A wider bandwidth can be obtained by using a coil with each crystal, as shown by Mason[1]). This capacitance is also necessary to adjust the shape of the curve at the larger values of attenuation. If the bandwidth cannot be reduced enough without harming

the selectivity, crystals with narrower frequency separation should be used. The frequency, temperature, and spurious response requirements determine the cut of the crystal. The cut determines the C_o/c ratio, which fixes the attainable bandwidth.

The capacitors used across the crystals must have a very high Q for sharp selectivity. Ceramic or mica capacitors are satisfactory, but some of the less expensive variable ceramics are not. After the shape of the attenuation curve has been adjusted with trimmer capacitors, the capacitors can be measured and replaced with fixed capacitors. The values are not critical.

Test Setup

If an oscilloscope is used in a test setup as shown in Fig. 4, the process of trimming the crystals and then installing fixed capacitors can be accomplished for a filter in a half hour. The frequency control on the signal generator of the test setup is geared to a 10-turn potentiometer that supplies a voltage proportional to signal-generator frequency for horizontal deflection. The avc voltage is used for vertical deflection. A P7 screen in the oscilloscope permits observation of the trace left by the slowly moving spot and permits hand cranking of the signal-generator tuner.

A fairly wide range of adjustment of the attenuation curve may be obtained with only two trimmer capacitors across adjacent bridge arms. This simplifies the adjustments and makes a more compact filter. Occasionally a filter will have a good curve with no capacitors at all across the crystals. In this case the bandwidth approaches the theoretical maximum. The wiring capacitance should, in any case, be kept as small as possible, although its effect on attenuation can be balanced out.

The photograph shows a lattice filter with a fixed capacitor across each crystal. These crystals make neat, small packages. A fixed and a variable capacitor are shown to the

left of the filter box. On the right, two views of a sealed crystal unit are shown.

The correct value of terminating impedance has been determined by trial to be about 8,000 ohms, which may be obtained by using series resistors or a tuned circuit. Either the input or output of the filter must be free from ground. The best results using two filters occur

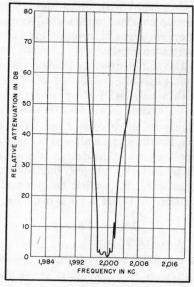

FIG. 5—Selectivity curve for a typical crystal filter

when the input and output terminals are both isolated from ground by double-tuned transformers as shown in the circuit of Fig. 1. The transformers also serve to keep insertion losses low. The resonant impedance of these transformers was designed to be approximately 8,000 ohms.

It has been found that any capacitive unbalance to ground of the ungrounded terminals causes a poor response curve. It is important that the capacitances both between windings and to ground be small for these transformers. Shielding of the filter is important where large attenuation is desired. Much less trouble was experienced in obtaining a good response curve when transformers were used instead of resistors. However, the transformers must be tuned to the center of the pass band.

If two filters are used in series, a transformer between the two gives a flat pass band that is somewhat narrower than when the filters are coupled directly together. Direct coupling gives pass-band irregularity of 2 to 3 db, which may be partially smoothed out by an H-pad if use of a transformer is not desirable. An occasional sharp peak in the pass band is probably due to the crystal pairs not being of exactly the same frequency. The crystals should be held to a frequency tolerance of at least 0.001 percent.

A typical frequency response of the two-section filter is shown in Fig. 5. The bandwidth is 3,900 cycles in the pass band and is 12,000 cycles at 60-db attenuation. A maximum attenuation of 80 db was measured before the curve began to widen rapidly. The voltage insertion loss, including that of the transformers, was not greater than 10 db for a two-section filter.

The main effect that a 115-degree C heat test had on the curve was an overall narrowing of about 400 cycles. Zero temperature coefficient capacitors were used in the filter.

This filter was designed to give good adjacent-channel selectivity in a receiver using an intermediate frequency of 2,000 kc. Other applications for such a filter are numerous. The frequency need not be limited to 2,000 kc but could be made considerably higher or lower if desired.

J. R. Schulman was in charge of the design of the receiver using this filter, T. F. Burke did preliminary filter design and consulting, and W. G. Tuller suggested the crystal-filter approach. The Reeves-Hoffman Co. cooperated in designing the required crystals to make them free of spurious responses.

REFERENCES

(1) W. P. Mason, "Electromechanical Transducers and Wave Filters", D. Van Nostrand Co., Inc., Second Edition, p 258.
(2) Paul K. Taylor, Single Sideband Crystal Filters, ELECTRONICS, p 116, Oct. 1948.

MEASUREMENTS

Measuring Phase at Audio and Ultrasonic Frequencies

Phase difference between two periodic signals is compared in a flip-flop circuit. The average current is read directly in degrees of phase on a calibrated meter. Possible applications include measurement of phase shift in feedback amplifiers, from screen-grid degeneration in a pentode stage, and in simulated antenna arrays

By ERNEST R. KRETZMER

PERIODIC SIGNALS are characterized by the parameters of amplitude, frequency and phase relative to some time reference.

Measurement of amplitude and frequency, at audio and ultrasonic frequencies, can be carried out rather easily, but accurate measurement of phase has proved much more difficult and has consequently been neglected in many applications where it could provide useful information. In contrast to amplitude and frequency, phase is a relative concept—that is, one is generally interested in the phase difference between two periodic signals.

A variety of methods has been used to measure phase difference. The most familiar of these is the display of Lissajous figures on the screen of a cathode-ray oscilloscope. These patterns, obtained by applying one signal to the horizontal deflection plates, the other to the vertical deflection plates of the cro, indicate the phase difference between the two signals; for example, a straight line indicates 0 or 180 degrees, while a circle indicates 90 deg. Another method, also using a cro as an indicating device, employs an electronic switch to produce a superposition of the two signals on the screen, so that the phase difference can be scaled off directly.

Other cro methods, not so widely known but capable of greater accuracy, make use of a circular sweep derived from one of the two signals. One such scheme, devised by K. S. Lion[1], is illustrated. The circular sweep, ordinarily of very small diameter, is expanded momentarily by each of the two signals being compared; the geometrical angle between the two spikes thus produced is the unknown phase

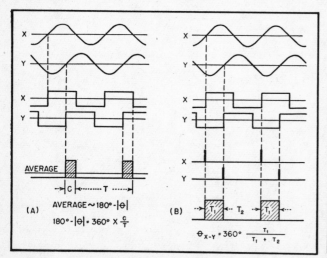

FIG. 1—Direct-reading methods of phase measurement

$$\text{AVERAGE} \sim 180° - |\theta|$$
$$180° - |\theta| = 360° \times \frac{c}{T}$$

$$\theta_{X-Y} = 360° \frac{T_1}{T_1 + T_2}$$

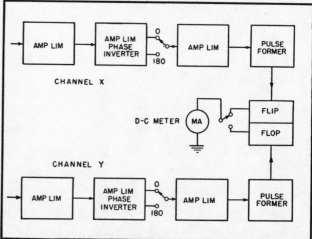

FIG. 2—Block diagram of direct-reading flip-flop meter

angle. More than two signals can have their relative phases displayed simultaneously.

Schemes not requiring a cathode-ray oscilloscope fall into two classifications: null methods, requiring a balancing operation, and direct-reading methods that produce a direct phase-angle indication on a meter. As an example of the former, amplitude and phase of one of the two signals can be changed until it completely cancels the other. The required phase shift is then read from a calibrated dial. The use of ordinary phase-shift networks would render the calibration frequency-sensitive, but by adding a quadrature component to one of the signals it is possible to obtain the necessary phase shift independently of frequency, over a finite frequency range.[2] Apart from the inconvenience of the balancing operation, this null method has the disadvantage of requiring sinusoidal signals.

Two practical methods that give direct meter indications of the phase difference between two signals X and Y are illustrated in Fig. 1. The signals (which need not have sinusoidal waveforms or equal magnitudes) are converted to square waves whose edges coincide with the zero-axis crossings of the original signals. In Fig. 1A, these two square waves are fed to a gate tube that produces a current pro-

portional to the fractional overlap of the positive portions of the square waves. Similarly, the overlap between the positive portions of square wave x and the negative portions of square wave y, or vice versa, can be measured by means of a diode and a d-c meter. In any case, the meter reading is proportional to the magnitude of the phase difference, or its supplement, and is ambiguous to the extent that one cannot distinguish between the angles θ and $360 - \theta$.

The ambiguity of the overlap method is avoided in the case of the flip-flop method, illustrated in Fig. 1B. Here, the two square waves X and Y are used to form pulse trains X and Y, respectively. Each X pulse triggers a flip-flop circuit into the flip position, for a time interval T_1 until the next Y pulse arrives and triggers the circuit into the flop position, for a period T_2, and so on. It is clear that the angle by which signal X leads signal Y is directly proportional to the fraction $T_1/(T_1 + T_2)$, and hence to the average current through the X side of the trigger circuit. Conversely, the angle by which Y leads X corresponds to the fraction $T_2/(T_1 + T_2)$ and hence to the average current through the Y side of the trigger circuit. The remainder of this paper will be devoted to this flip-flop method. It was patented in 1945,[3] and other workers have since

experimented with this as well as with the overlap method.[4,5]

The Flip-Flop Method

Figure 2 shows a block diagram of an instrument employing the flip-flop method for measuring the phase difference between two periodic voltages. Two identical channels, X and Y, handle the two signals, X and Y, respectively. The principal operation performed in each channel is the limiting-amplifying process by which the signals are converted into square waves. The first three stages serve this purpose. The second stage is, in addition, a phase inverter that makes it possible to reverse the signal polarity. If the signal has evenly spaced zero-axis crossings, such a reversal represents a phase shift of 180 degrees. The square wave in each channel is fed to a pulse former, which, in effect, differentiates the positive-going edges. The resulting pips are fed to a flip-flop circuit. A d-c meter measures the average current through either side of the

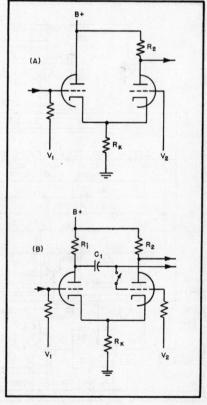

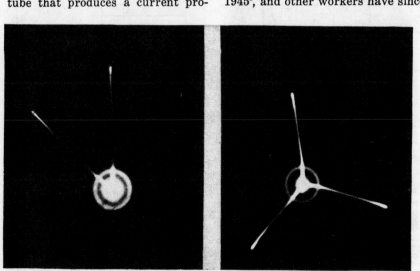

Oscillograms showing a method of phase measurement employing a circular sweep

FIG. 3—Cathode-coupled clipper circuits

circuit, allowing the meter to read either the angle θ or the angle $360 - \theta$. This switching arrangement, together with the phase-reversing switches, permits any angle to be transposed into the first quadrant (0 to 90 deg), so that the meter scale can be expanded by a factor of four if increased meter sensitivity is desired.

Although the block diagram of Fig. 2 appears straightforward, severe problems are encountered in the design of an instrument combining simplicity with accurate readings that are independent of input amplitude and frequency over wide ranges.

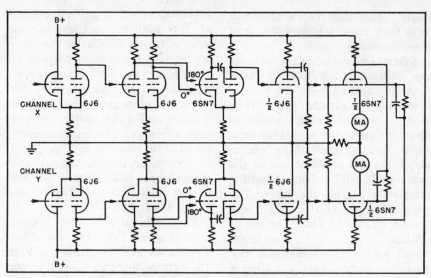

FIG. 4—Simplified circuit diagram of the direct-reading phase meter

Square-Wave Generation

The most difficult operation is the formation of square waves from the original signals, since the square-wave edges must coincide exactly with the zero-axis crossings, regardless of signal amplitude and frequency. Most instruments constructed in the past have made use of cascaded pentode-diode combinations. Such extensive amplifier-limiter stages are neither simple, nor do they answer the requirements of wide frequency band and large amplitude range as well as might be expected. A circuit that appears better suited for the present application is the cathode-coupled clipper,[6] the basic form of which is shown in Fig. 3A. The grid of the right-hand triode is returned to a fixed positive voltage, V_2. The signal is applied to the grid of the left-hand triode that is also returned through a high resistance to a fixed positive voltage, V_1. For small input signals, the

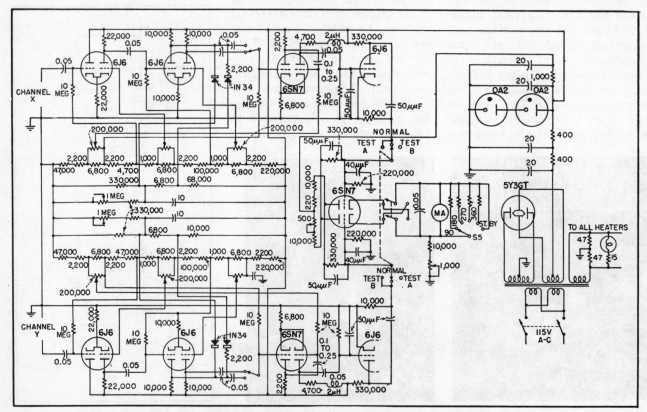

FIG. 5—Circuit of a commercial model of the direct-reading phase meter

circuit acts as a linear amplifier. However, if the instantaneous signal voltage goes below a certain value (a few volts below V_1), the left-hand triode cuts off, and above a certain value (a few volts above V_1), the right-hand triode cuts off. Thus, both the positive and negative limiting results from one or the other tube's being cut off, and very good limiting symmetry can therefore be attained. Like a cathode follower, the cathode-coupled circuit has high input impedance and can handle a large range of input voltages without drawing grid current. It has other useful advantages, illustrated in Fig. 3B. First, by inserting the resistor R_1 in the plate line of the input triode, one obtains a phase inverter, the usefulness of which was pointed out in the discussion of the block diagram (Fig. 2). The limiting action at the plate of the input triode is not exactly the same as at the plate of the output triode, but by means of a type IN34 germanium crystal diode it can be made very nearly the same. A second useful modification is obtained by connecting a capacitor C_1 as shown. This addition makes the circuit regenerative without destroying its controllability and results in an output square wave with edges of short rise and decay times limited only by stray capacitance.

Elementary Circuit

A simplified circuit diagram of a complete phase meter in Fig. 4 shows close correspondence to the block diagram. Three cascaded limiter-amplifier stages are cathode-coupled types, the first stage being in the basic form, the second modified to provide phase reversal if desired, and the third stage being regenerative so as to insure very steep square-wave edges. The fourth stage in each channel is a triode followed by an r-c differentiator. The triode has a high load resistance but a low plate resistance, so that it reacts rapidly only to the positive going square-wave edges—producing large negative pulses of

0.5-μsec duration at the differentiator output.

These pulses mark the positive-going zero-axis crossings of the original signal (either channel X or channel Y), unless the phase-reversing switch is in the 180-deg position—in which case the pulses mark the negative crossings. The flip-flop circuit, triggered alternately by pulses from channels X and Y, is an Eccles-Jordan type. The average current through either half of the circuit is measured in the cathode-to-ground lead; although two separate meters are shown for the sake of simplicity there is actually only one that can be switched into either side. A recording instrument may be connected in series with the meter if the phase angle is to be recorded continuously.

The complete circuit diagram of a commercial phase meter is shown in Fig. 5. The meter-scale switch provides four different full-scale ranges in addition to the test position in which the full-scale adjustment is made. An electrical zero adjustment is not required, since zero phase angle means no conduction through the triode containing the meter. There is a small region of uncertainty in the immediate vicinity of 0 degree, because the two pulses coincide and confuse the trigger circuit. Changing the position of either phase-reversing switch remedies this condition.

Practical Performance

The performance of the commercial instrument is substantially independent of signal amplitude and frequency over wide ranges. With amplitudes between 1 and 170 peak volts and frequency between 20 cps and 100 kc, the error would not exceed 3.5 degrees if the meter were perfectly linear. Since the meter is accurate only within 1 percent of full scale, the total maximum error is 3.5 degrees plus 1 percent of full scale. The instrument functions even with input amplitudes down to 0.1 or 0.2 volt, and frequency as low as 3 to 5 cps. Decreasing the

amplitudes generally reduces the stability rather than the accuracy while decreasing the frequency does cause a gradual reduction in accuracy. At 10 cps, the maxium error is 6 degrees plus 1 percent of full scale. A similar gradual decrease in accuracy occurs at the high-frequency end, beginning at 20 kc, only if the two phase-reversing switches are in opposite positions, in which case the maximum error reaches 6 degrees plus 1 percent of full scale at 40 kc. In normal operation, the switches are in identical positions and the accuracy does not change appreciably with increasing frequency up to more than 100 kc.

Since the flip-flop method measures the phase difference as the fractional time between zero-axis crossings, the measurement has a definite meaning, regaraiess of the signal waveform. Exceptions may occur in extreme cases of distortion in which the signal crosses the zero axis more than twice during one period, but such cases are rare and unimportant.

Asymmetrical Signals

The zero axis, as a result of a-c coupling in the limiter-amplifier stages, is the average of the a-c component of the signal. Consequently, if a sinusoidal signal has either its positive peaks or its negative peaks limited, the resulting signal is not only asymmetrical but its zero-axis crossings are no longer evenly spaced because the zero axis has been shifted. In such a case, changing the position of either phase-reversing switch will not alter the reading by 180 degrees, inasmuch as opposite zero-axis crossings are not 180 degrees apart. The phase meter affords a means of detecting such asymmetry with greater sensitivity than a cathode-ray oscilloscope. For example, it is a simple matter to ascertain that the positive and negative half-periods of the square waves produced by some commercial square-wave generators are generally unequal. The phase meter can readily be used to determine the duty factor of a train of pulses as well as the time delay between two pulse trains, provided that the repetition rate is not too high and the pulses are not too short.

R-F Phase Measurements

All methods of audio-frequency phase measurement can be used to measure the phase difference between radio-frequency signals, as in the testing of broadcast antennas, by taking advantage of the heterodyne principle. If both signals are heterodyned into the audio frequency band by means of a common heat oscillator, their phase difference will be preserved. The required converter stage could be added to each of the two channels with relatively little complication. A preferable solution may be to precede the phase meter with a separate unit containing heterodyne stages and amplifiers. Both audio and r-f phase measurements can then be made at low (millivolt) input levels.

Applying the Phase Meter

A typical problem in which the direct-reading phase meter finds a useful application is that of phase shift in feedback amplifiers. Figure 6 shows plots of phase shift versus frequency (from 10 cps to 100 kc) obtained in approximately ten minutes by means of the phase meter described. The three curves are for various degrees of feedback,

ranging from zero to critical feedback. The amplifier tested contains two triode stages and a transformer, resonance in the transformer being responsible for the peculiar phase variation at 30 kc

Another example is the measurement of phase shift resulting from screen-grid degeneration in a single pentode stage. Accurate computation of this phase shift, even with a good knowledge of the tube characteristics, is not a simple matter, although the phase meter affords an easy way of measuring it. The phase shift plotted versus frequency, for various degrees of screen-grid bypassing, is shown in Fig. 7. Both the magnitude and phase angle of the gain can also be plotted on polar coordinates.

A most interesting and important application of the direct-reading phase meter occurs in acoustics. Arrays of phased loudspeakers, used to simulate directive antenna arrays, contain hundreds of small speakers whose phase characteristic must be within certain tolerances over a wide band of audio frequencies. The test setup for these loudspeakers is shown in Fig. 8, together with a plot of phase shift versus frequency. It contains the speaker, an anechoic chamber, a dynamic microphone, and two transformers whose resonances are evident in the plot. A linearly

increasing component of phase shift results from the chamber whose length, expressed in wavelengths, is directly proportional to frequency. Practice has shown that, by cro methods, only 3 to 5 speakers can be tested in one day, while up to 60 can be tested per day by means of a direct-reading phase meter.

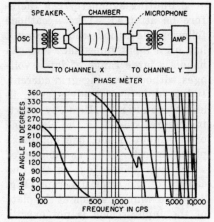

FIG. 8—Phase shift versus frequency for an electroacoustical system used in testing loudspeakers

Some applications require the testing of hundreds of speakers, so that, several months' work is reduced to a week's work.

Acknowledgment

The phase meter described was developed for the Technology Instrument Corporation, Waltham,

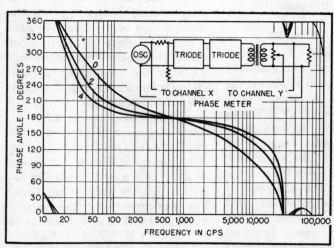

FIG. 6—Phase shift of an amplifier for various degrees of inverse feedback over a wide band of frequencies

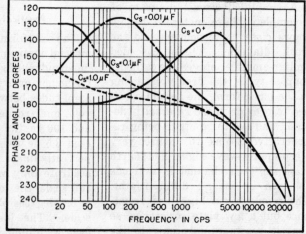

FIG. 7—Phase shift in a pentode stage with various degrees of screen bypassing when screen resistor is 240,000 ohms

Massachusetts. The writer wishes to express his appreciation to Mr. L. E. Packard of that company for his help in the development.

REFERENCES

(1) J. Goodman, unpublished BS thesis, Electrical Engineering Dept., MIT, 1943.
(2) J. R. Ragazzini and L. A. Zadeh, A Wide-Band Audio Phasemeter, National Convention, IRE, 1949.
(3) J. E. Shepherd, U. S. Pat. 2,370,692.
(4) Harold Goldberg, Direct Reading Phasemeter, *Bendix Radio Engineer*, p 4, April 1946.
(5) E. F. Florman and A. Tait, An Electronic Phasemeter, *Proc. IRE*, p 207, February 1949.
(6) L. A. Goldmuntz and H. L. Krauss, The Cathode-Coupled Clipper Circuit, *Proc. IRE*, p 1172, Sept. 1948.

Measuring Vector Relationships

Imaginary and real components of an unknown voltage in terms of a reference voltage are indicated directly over a frequency range of 8 cycles to 500 mc. Other applications include study of phase delay in amplifiers, wave filters and attenuators

By Y. P. YU

VECTOR RELATIONS of alternating voltages over a wide frequency range, from 8 cycles to 500 megacycles, can be measured by means of the instrument to be described. In most applications, the operating principle is based essentially on the vector theory of addition and subtraction. The operating principles underlying two frequent applications, measurement of the phase angle between two given voltages and measurement of complex components of an unknown voltage, will be discussed.

Phase-Angle Measurement

Figure 1 shows a block diagram of the instrument as it is used for the measurement of the phase angle between two given voltages, E_1 and E_2. Variable attenuators R_1 and R_2 are used for adjusting the amplitudes of E_1 and E_2. Phase inverters P_1 and P_2 are capable of producing a constant phase shift of 180 degrees over the entire range of operating frequency.

When terminals 4 and 8 are connected to terminals 1 and 6 respectively, output meter V will read the vector difference of E_1' and E_2'. If the absolute amplitudes of E_1' and E_2' are made equal by adjusting R_1 and R_2, the reading E_o on the output meter may be expressed as

$$E_o = E_2' - E_1'$$
$$= |E_1'| (\cos \theta + j \sin \theta - 1) \qquad (1)$$

where θ is the phase angle between E_1 and E_2. The absolute magnitude of E_o may be written as

$$|E_o| = |E_1'| \sqrt{(\cos \theta - 1)^2 + \sin^2 \theta}$$
$$= 2 |E_1'| \sin \frac{\theta}{2} \qquad (2)$$

For simplicity, the magnitude of $|E_1'|$ is made equal to one volt dur-

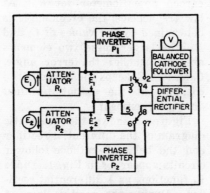

FIG. 1—Block diagram of the Vector-lyzer

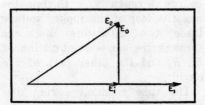

FIG. 2—Vector diagram used in connection with measurement of complex components of an unknown voltage

ing adjustment of attenuator R_1, whereby the term $|E_1'|$ may be omitted in Eq. 2, and

$$|E_o| = 2 \sin \frac{\theta}{2}$$

The output meter may be calibrated to indicate directly the phase angle in degrees between any two voltages. For instance, a meter with full-scale sensitivity of two volts will read 60 degrees at its center and 180 degrees at full scale.

The distribution of readings on a meter face is an important factor in the design of measuring instruments. A linear-scale meter which has a guarantee of one percent error at full scale would produce an error of 10 percent at one-tenth full scale. Sinusoidal distribution of meter readings is a desirable feature since the percentage accuracy of readings is nearly uniform over the entire scale.

Where the two voltages under consideration are nearly opposite in phase, the accuracy of reading can be greatly increased by introducing a phase shift of 180 degrees to either one. This is done with phase inverter P_1 or P_2. A second scale starting with 180 degrees at its normal zero position is established.

Without altering the value of any circuit element the full-scale sensitivity may be increased to any value between 0 and 180 degrees or between 180 and 360 degrees by increasing the value of $|E'_1|$.

The principle underlying this feasibility can best be explained by referring to Eq. 2. As the phase angle θ of this equation decreases, the magnitude of the resultant voltage $|E_o|$ may be held constant if the amplitudes of the input voltages increase accordingly. This in turn keeps the indication on the output meter unchanged, since it is energized by the resultant voltage $|E_o|$.

If it is desired to increase the full-scale angular sensitivity of the instrument from 180 degrees to 60 degrees with the voltage sensitivity of the output meter remaining at 2 volts, R_1 and R_2 are readjusted so that the magnitudes of $|E_1'|$ and $|E_2'|$ will be two volts instead of one volt. After this readjustment the angular sensitivity of the output meter will be increased by three times.

Measuring Complex Voltages

The instrument is a simple and convenient device for direct indication of the imaginary and real components of an unknown voltage in terms of a reference voltage. The block diagram of Fig. 1 may also be used to explain the operating principle underlying this application.

In Fig. 1, E_1 and E_2 are assumed to be the reference and unknown voltages respectively. Attenuator R_2 is adjusted to give zero attenuation so that E_2' will be equal to E_2. Attenuator R_1 is adjusted until the deflection at the output meter reaches a minimum with terminals 4 and 8 connected respectively to terminals 1 and 6. To represent this condition, a vector diagram is drawn in Fig. 2 for voltages E_1', E_2, and E_o. Symbol E_o denotes the reading on output meter V, which is also the potential developed across terminals 1 and 6 when the meter is correctly calibrated.

Since these three vectors form a right triangle, the diagram indicates that E_o is equal to the imaginary component of E_2 and that E_1' is equal to the real component of E_2. The output meter will read directly the imaginary component with terminals 4 and 8 connected to the positions shown in Fig. 1 and read directly the real component when terminal 8 is connected to terminal 5.

If the phase angle between the unknown voltage and the reference voltage is greater than 90 degrees but less than 270 degrees, the above method of measuring complex components still is useful when E_1' is shifted 180 degrees with respect to E_1 by inserting phase inverter P_1.

High-Impedance Attenuator

The attenuator circuit shown in Fig. 3 is designed to minimize phase-distortion difficulties encountered with conventional volume controls at high frequencies. The triode is arranged as a cathode follower to provide a high input impedance and to allow the resistance of the potentiometer at its cathode to become very low. The first feature is essential for many practical applications while the second helps to minimize the error caused by the stray capacitances of the potentiometer.

Experimental results show that the maximum error introduced by the circuit of Fig. 3 is less than 2 degrees at 2.5 mc with a 1,000-ohm carbon potentiometer for R_4. At low frequencies, the error angle is determined by the values of C_2 and R_5—the larger these two elements are, the smaller the error angle. Capacitor C_2 keeps the d-c potential constant at the output terminal during adjustment.

Figure 4 shows the schematic diagram of the differential rectifier and the balanced cathode-follower circuits appearing in Fig. 1. Diode V_1 functions as a differential rectifier. During the positive loop of the applied voltage, C_1 and C_2 charge through V_1. During the negative loop of the applied voltage these two capacitors discharge through the series combination of R_1, R_2 and the other part of the circuit.

The time constant during discharge is made very large compared with that during charge, and therefore the sum of the average potentials across C_1 and C_2 is only slightly less than the peak value of the positive loop of the applied voltage. Resistors R_1 and R_2 are used to isolate both input terminals from the other part of the circuit. Both input terminals can be connected to points which are above a-c ground potential.

Triodes V_2 and V_3 function as a balanced cathode follower. The impedance between points C and D looking into the cathode follower is $R_3/(1 - A)$, where A is the gain of the cathode follower. This impedance becomes very large compared with R_3 when A approaches unity. In practice, the value of $R_3/(1 - A)$ can be conveniently made equal to 100 megohms or higher if R_3 is chosen to be 10 megohms. This high impedance makes it possible to operate the instrument at frequencies as low as a few cycles since the time constant $[C_1C_2/(C_1 + C_2)]$ $[R_3/(1 - A)]$ determines the lower limit of the frequency response.

Another feature of the circuits described is good stability. This is achieved by the use of balanced arrangement. Physically, R_5, R_8, V_1-V_2 and V_3-V_4 perform as four arms of a balanced bridge in which R_5 and R_8 correspond to the ratio arms, V_1-V_2 to the unknown arm and V_3-V_4 to the standard arm.

VHF Operation

With available circuit elements and technical knowledge it is extremely difficult to construct a variable attenuator which will produce negligible or constant phase shift from 10 to 500 mc while also having a high input impedance. It is equally difficult to construct a high-impedance network which will introduce a constant phase shift over this range.

Figure 5 shows the basic circuit of the instrument when it is used at high frequencies. In this circuit, rectification is performed by the probe which consists of a germanium crystal, two capacitors and two resistors. The resonant frequency of the probe can be made very high, over 700 mc, when care is taken during construction. Potentiometer R_4 is used for panel zero adjustment. Before operation the variable arms of potentiometers R_3 and R_9 are set at their extreme right positions.

In order to explain the operation of this circuit, consider the case of measuring the phase angle between two given voltages. Assume that symbols E_1 and E_2 represent the two given voltages and the magnitude of E_1 is smaller than that of E_2. The procedure for handling various controls is as follows: (1) Connect input terminal 6 to ground and connect terminals 4 and 5 to terminals 1 and 2, respectively. Adjust potentiometer R_3 until a half-scale deflection is obtained on the output meter. This step serves to adjust the sensitivity of the instrument so that a full-scale deflection will occur if the phase angle to be measured is 180 degrees. (2) Connect terminal 4 to ground and terminal 6 back to terminal 3, then adjust potentiometer R_0 until a half-scale deflection is again obtained on the output meter. This step serves to adjust the zero indication of the instrument so that the output meter will read zero when the two input voltages are in phase. (3) Connect terminal 4 back to terminal 1. Now enter the reading of the output meter into one of the curves of Fig. 6 and find the answer on the X axis. If the absolute magnitudes of both input voltages are equal, the phase angle can be read directly on the output meter and it is possible to omit both the second step and the use of the curves of Fig. 6.

To explain the operating principle, an expression for the voltage E_o developed across terminals 1 and 6, which is also the reading on the output meter, is written as follows:

$$E_o = E_2 - E_1 = |E_1|(n \cos \theta + j\, n \sin \theta - 1) \quad (3)$$

where $n = |E_2|/|E_1|$ and θ is the phase angle between E_1 and E_2. The absolute amplitude of E_o is

$$|E_o| = |E_1|\ \sqrt{n^2 + 1 - 2n \cos \theta} \quad (4)$$

Equation 4 indicates that $|E_o|$ varies from $(n-1)\,|E_1|$ to $(n+1)\,|E_1|$ as the angle θ varies from zero to 180 degrees. Thus the maximum variation is $2\,|E_1|$ which is independent of the ratio n. This rela-

tion is very important in using the instrument at high frequencies.

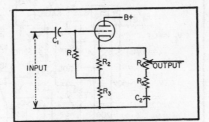

FIG. 3—Basic circuit diagram of the attenuator for audio and radio frequencies

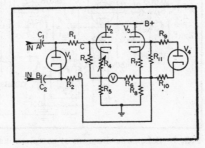

FIG. 4—Differential rectifier and balanced cathode follower

Assume that θ_1 is the reading of the output meter and θ is the true phase angle between E_1 and E_2. Since the scale of the output meter is calibrated in degrees for the case when both input voltages have equal amplitude, we may write

$$2\,|E_1| \sin \frac{\theta_1}{2} = |E_1| \left[\ \sqrt{n^2 + 1 - 2n \cos \theta} - (n-1)\right] \quad (5)$$

In Eq. 5, the term at the left is obtained by substituting $n = 1$ into Eq. 3, while the term at the right is derived from Eq. 4 and the fact that a voltage with amplitude equal to $(n-1)\,|E_1|$ is balanced out from the output meter during the second step of adjustment. By rearrangment of terms, Eq. 5 becomes

$$\cos \theta = 2 \left(1 - \sin \frac{\theta_1}{2}\right)\left(1 + \frac{1}{n} \sin \frac{\theta_1}{2}\right) - 1 \quad (6)$$

Graphical representation of Eq. 6 is shown in Fig. 6.

Complete Instrument

A simplified circuit diagram of the complete instrument is shown in Fig. 7. Essentially the instrument is a combination of the follow-

ing elements: two variable attenuators, two phase inverters, a differential rectifier, a balanced cathode follower, a high-frequency probe, an automatic relay circuit and a regulated power supply. Duo-triodes V_1 and V_3, having a transconductance of approximately 10,000 micromhos with both sections connected in parallel, are employed as cathode followers in the attenuator circuits, permitting the use of low-resistance potentiometers R_1 and R_2 for adjustment.

Two single-stage degenerative amplifiers using pentodes V_2 and V_4 are employed for phase inversion. When switch S_4 is at the position marked BINDING POST, duodiode V_6 and duo-triode V_7 are connected respectively as a differential rectifier and a balanced cathode follower similar to those described in the early part of this paper.

The high-frequency probe consists of a germanium crystal, two resistors and two capacitors. When switch S_4 is at the position marked PROBE, the balanced cathode follower is connected to the probe for operation at high frequencies. Potentiometer R_5 is inserted for panel zero adjustment when the probe is in use, otherwise potentiometer R_4 is used alone for the same purpose.

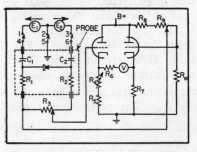

FIG. 5—Circuit diagram of the Vectorlyzer for operation at high frequencies

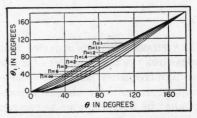

FIG. 6—Curves used in conjunction with the high-frequency probe

This arrangement was found necessary in order to avoid initial rush of pointer movement during zero setting. Switch S_3 is used for sense identification. If voltage V_1 lags V_2, the turning of switch S_3 will cause the meter reading to increase since an additional phase angle is added to voltage V_1.

During operation, when switch S_1 or S_2 is turned from the position shown in Fig. 7 to the position marked 0° or the position marked DIRECT, a sudden large variation in potential difference may develop across capacitors C_3 and C_4. This variation in turn causes a heavy transient current to overload the output meter. The operation will be interrupted until the charges on C_3 and C_4 return to the steady-state condition. This condition may take as long as several minutes to establish since the input impedance of the balanced cathode follower is very high, over 100 megohms. The heavy transient current may even damage the output meter in some cases unless an automatic relay circuit is added to the instrument.

The relay circuit embodies a triode V_5, which normally operates slightly above its cutoff, an R-C circuit of proper time constant and an electromagnetic relay of which the action is controlled by the plate current of the triode. When switch S_1 is turned to the position marked 0° from the position shown in Fig. 7, C_1 is short circuited and C_2 with zero initial charge is connected across the grid and cathode of triode V_5. The plate current of V_5

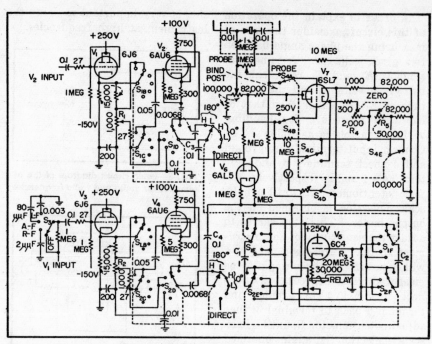

FIG. 7—Schematic diagram of complete instrument. Duo-triodes V_1 and V_3 are employed as cathode followers in the attenuator circuits

rises abruptly and the relay in its cathode circuit is energized immediately. Capacitor C_2 charges through R_3 and the potential at the grid of V_5 decreases exponentially toward zero.

The relay will be deenergized again as soon as the plate current of V_5 decreases to a certain value. The energizing of the relay serves to short-circuit the input terminals of the balanced cathode follower and to disconnect the output meter. The charges on C_3 and C_4 will reach their steady-state condition in a much shorter interval and the pointer of the output meter will

stay at its zero position until the steady-state condition has been established if a proper time constant is chosen for R_3C_2. During the next switching action that includes the turning of switch S_1 to its original position or the position marked DIRECT, or the turning of switch S_2 to the position marked 0°, C_2 will be short-circuited and C_1 will be connected across the grid and cathode of triode V_5. The relay operates and the process repeats.

The author wishes to acknowledge that the instrument described was developed for the Advance Electronics Company.

Phase Meter

By E. O. VANDEVEN

THE PHASE METER is a device that measures the phase angles of a low or high frequency polyphase voltage supply. Essentially this is accomplished by developing on the screen of a cathode-ray oscilloscope a circular sweep at the polyphase supply

frequency. Each phase voltage of the polyphase supply is then separately amplified, clipped, differentiated and again amplified.

In the output of each phase amplifier are pulses which are established in time by their respective

phase voltage. These pulses are mixed and applied to the Z-axis amplifier of the oscilloscope to intensity modulate the circular trace, causing a dark or bright spot to appear for each phase voltage. The angular displacement between the spots is then a measure of the angular displacement between corresponding phase voltages. The phase angles can be read by calibrating the oscilloscope screen radially in degrees.

A block diagram of the phase meter is shown in Fig. 1. One phase

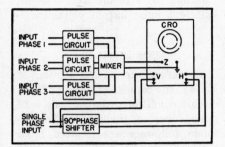

FIG. 1—Block diagram of phase detector

of the three-phase supply is applied to a device which shifts the phase by 90 degrees. This is done, since to obtain a circular sweep it is necessary to apply to the horizontal and vertical amplifiers voltages of the same frequency but separated in phase by 90 degrees. The pulse forming and mixing circuits are also indicated.

The phase meter was developed

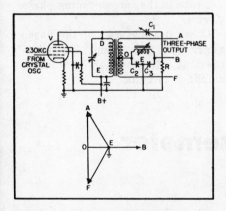

FIG. 2—Single-phase to three-phase transformation circuit and phase diagram

for work with the 2H21 phasitron tube, used to generate crystal-controlled f-m. The phasitron has three-phase r-f applied to the deflector electrodes. A crystal oscillator at approximately 230 kilocycles is the signal source. This single-phase voltage is transformed to three-phase by employing a modified Scott transformer connection.

The single- to three-phase transformation circuit, with the associated phase relationships, is shown in Fig. 2. Amplifier tube V supplies a transformer load, the secondary of which is center tapped. Secondary voltage, AF, is shown vectorially on the phase diagram. The OB vector, displaced 90 degrees from AF, is obtained by shifting the phase of the primary voltage DE by 90 degrees. Since DE and AF are in phase, vector OB is then 90 degrees from AF.

Resistor R is essentially connected from B to E which is part of a tuned circuit. Therefore by detuning the tuned circuit slightly from the resonant point the reactance from B to E can be made to appear inductive. This inductive reactance is in series with C_1, and by proper adjustment of these two parameters the voltage BE will be displaced from the supply voltage DE by 90 degrees. By properly establishing the ratio of C_2 to C_3, the point E is selected along the OB vector. Point E is grounded providing a neutral point for the balanced three-phase system.

For the phasitron to operate with minimum distortion it is necessary that the exciter supply phase voltages of equal magnitude and angular displacement. The phase meter was developed to facilitate the adjustment of the exciter supply for perfect three-phase output.

Circular Sweep

Figure 3 shows the circuit used to obtain circular sweep. The single-phase, 230-kc signal feeds a pentode amplifier. The amplifier plate circuit has a tuned transformer which, when resonated, gives a 90-degree phase shift between primary and secondary. Proper adjustment of the secondary tuning capacitor is accomplished by observing the pattern on the c-r tube. When this capacitor, and the horizontal and vertical gains, are correctly set, the result will be a circular trace on the cro screen.

The pentode amplifier is run class A and with an unbypassed cathode resistor. This is to minimize dis-

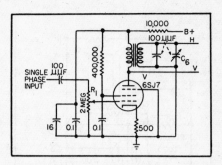

FIG. 3—Circuit of circular sweep generator

tortion of the voltages applied to the vertical and horizontal amplifiers. The cro amplifiers must also have low distortion, or it will be impossible to obtain perfect circular sweep. Circle size is controlled by R_1.

One of the pulse-forming circuits is shown in Fig. 4. Phase voltage is applied to V_{1A}, a cathode follower. This tube transforms from high-impedance input to low-impedance output across L_1.

Operation

Accuracy of the meter depends more than anything else on the coupling circuit between V_{1A} and V_2, and the operation of V_2. The voltage developed across L_1 is at least 30 volts rms. Therefore the grid of V_2 swings from minus 50 volts to 50 volts plus, less the drop across R_3C_3. The tube begins to conduct when the input voltage rises to approximately -4.5 volts. When it reaches zero volts, grid current begins to flow, resulting in a voltage drop across the grid resistor.

The output of V_2 therefore is a pulse whose leading edge is very steep. It is important that this leading edge be definitely established in time with respect to the phase input voltage.

Tube V_2 is directly coupled to L_1, since a blocking capacitor would have a discharge time constant which would develop grid bias on V_2 and change its operating point with respect to the phase input voltage. Filter R_3C_3 has a time constant which is short compared to the period of one cycle. Thus, as the voltage across L_1 rises from its peak negative value, V_2 should begin to

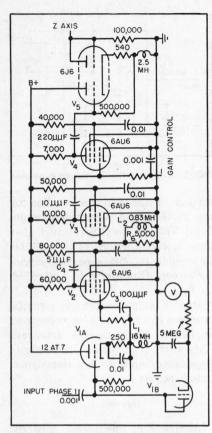

FIG. 4—Pulse generator for one phase

conduct at a point determined entirely by its cutoff potential.

If the magnitude of the phase voltage is varied, this point will shift slightly, which is part of the inherent error of the device. If all phase voltages are varied by the

same amount however, no net error should result. All operating points will have shifted by the same amount and in the same direction.

C_4 and R_6L_2 constitute a differentiating circuit, the voltage on V_3

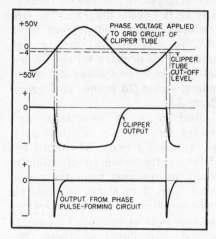

FIG. 5—Phase relations in pulse-forming circuit

grid consisting of narrow positive and negative pulses. Since V_3 is zero biased, its grid presents low impedance to the positive pulses and high impedance to the negative ones. In the output, positive pulses predominate.

Tube V_4 is an amplifier-inverter, biased beyond cutoff. The pulses are also narrowed in this stage. Output of V_4 is applied to V_5, a cathode follower. The negative pulses developed

oped across the cathode-follower load impedance cannot be fed to the Z axis input directly. If this were done the cathode-follower loads of all phase circuits would essentially be in parallel. When one cathode follower were pulsing the remaining two would present excessive loading. The result would be insufficient pulse output voltage.

Circuit Isolation

Therefore the second section of V_5 is diode connected. Under these circuit conditions, the cathode load impedances of the inoperative cathode followers are isolated from the load impedance of the one that is operating.

Tube V_{1B} is diode-connected to form part of a peak-reading voltmeter circuit. The meter is calibrated to read rms phase voltage.

Figure 5 shows the phase relationship between the sine wave input to the phase circuit and the output pulses appearing at the Z-axis input to the cro. The leading edge of each pulse is determined by the cutoff point of the first clipper tube in the corresponding phase circuit.

Other possible uses of the phase meter principle include the measurement of phase shift through amplifier circuits.

Single-Tube Audio Phasemeter

By JOSEPH A. VANOUS

A PHASEMETER is described, which is capable of measuring phase difference between two sinusoidal voltages from 300 cps to 100,000 cps. Angles from 1 to 180 degrees are measurable with an accuracy of better than 1 degree. No preliminary adjustments for frequency are necessary with this meter.

A unique property of the magnitude of the sum and differences of two alternating current voltages makes the operation of this phase-

meter possible. In operation, the phasemeter is connected across the phase-shift network. After two calibrations, the sine or cosine of half of the phase angle is measured directly. The principal value of the inverse function is found in a table of trigonometric functions. Multiplying this value by 2 will produce the phase angle in degrees.

Principle of Operation

Several other types of phase-

meters employ cascaded amplifier-limiter stages which supply square waves to the indicating circuits[1, 2]. Circuit simplicity is achieved by making a comparison between two sinusoidal waves directly.

The phasemeter consists of two low-impedance generators connected by an impedance of 2Z. The voltage at the centertap of the connecting circuit is measured by an a-c voltmeter as shown in Fig. 1A. The two voltages have the polarity

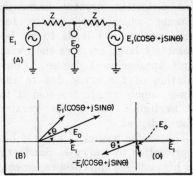

FIG. 1—Basic circuit and vector diagrams showing basis for two-tube audio - frequency phase measuring device

shown where E_1 is the voltage at generator 1, and $E_1 (\cos \theta + j \sin \theta)$ is the voltage at generator 2. The two voltages have the same magnitude but differ by an angle θ which is the phase angle. Assuming the voltage E_0 is measured by a high-impedance voltmeter drawing negligible current, the following equation can be written

$$E_1 - E_1 (\cos \theta + j \sin \theta) = i (2Z) \quad (1)$$

$$i = \frac{E_1 - E_1 (\cos \theta + j \sin \theta)}{2 Z}$$

$$E_0 = E_1 - i Z \quad (2)$$

Substituting Eq. 1 for i in Eq. 2

$$E_0 = E_1 - Z \left(\frac{E_1 - E_1 (\cos \theta + j \sin \theta)}{2 Z} \right)$$

$$= \frac{E_1}{2} (1 + \cos \theta + j \sin \theta)$$

Solving for the absolute magnitude of the voltage measured at E_0

$$|E_0| = \frac{E_1}{2} \sqrt{(1 + \cos \theta)^2 + (\sin \theta)^2}$$

$$= \frac{E_1}{2} \left(2 \sqrt{\frac{1 + \cos \theta}{2}} \right)$$

$$\text{cosine } \theta/2 = \left(\frac{1 + \cos \theta}{2} \right)^{\frac{1}{2}}$$

$$|E_0| = \frac{E_1}{2} (2) \cos \theta/2$$

$$|E_0| = E_1 \cos \theta/2$$

If the generator voltages are calibrated equal and unity in value, then the voltmeter will read the cosine of $\theta/2$. The vector diagram in Fig. 1B shows the relationship of the voltages for an arbitrary phase angle θ.

If generator 2 is reversed 180 degrees in phase the voltage E_0 will equal

$$|E_0| = E_1 \sin \theta/2$$

This can be proved by following a mathematical procedure identical to the one outlined above. The corresponding vector diagram is shown in Fig. 1C.

By calibrating the generator voltages at one volt, the voltmeter will read the cosine of $\theta/2$ or the sine of $\theta/2$ directly. A table of trigonometric functions will convert these readings to half of the phase angle. Multiplying this angle by two will produce the phase angle.

Equipment

The two low-impedance generators of Fig. 1A for measuring the the cosine of $\theta/2$ consist of cathode followers as shown in Fig. 2. Outputs of the cathode followers are connected in series by an impedance composed of two blocking capacitors and two resistors. The resist-

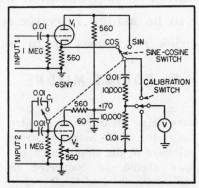

FIG. 2—Phasemeter circuit diagram shows function of sine-cosine switch

ors are identical in value to provide a center-tap. The reactances of the blocking capacitors are also equal to produce an equal impedance both sides of center-tap. Reference to the derivation will reveal this as an initial condition.

Cathode followers were employed to provide an impedance transformation from a high input impedance to a low output impedance. It is desirable to have a high input impedance to prevent the loading of the measured network, and to

prevent any additional phase shift by this loading. A low output impedance allows calibration of the voltmeter without excessive cycling.

A 180-degree phase reversal for measurement of the sine of $\theta/2$ is accomplished by obtaining the output from the plate of V_1. The switch labeled SINE-COSINE performs this operation.

The input to each tube consists of a blocking capacitor and a grid-leak resistor. Identical components are used to prevent a phase difference at the grids in addition to that being measured while measuring the cosine of $\theta/2$. When the output of V_1 is taken from the plate for the measurement of the sine of $\theta/2$, the reactance of the filter capacitor becomes significant at the low frequencies, and creates a spurious phase shift. This unwanted phase shift is canceled by introducing an opposite phase shift at the grid of V_2 by decreasing the reactance of the R-C circuit.

The rate of change of the sine function with respect to the angle is greater for small angles. Therefore, to obtain maximum reading accuracy, the sine of $\theta/2$ is used for phase angles from 0 to 90 degrees. The cosine of $\theta/2$ position is used for angles between 90 and 180 degrees where the rate of change of the cosine function is greatest.

The phasemeter is used in conjunction with an audio oscillator as shown in Fig. 3. A 3-way calibration switch is used with the a-c voltmeter to allow the calibration of the tube outputs. The cathode resistor of V_2 is a potentiometer for adjusting the voltage to one volt. The cathode and plate output voltages of V_1 are calibrated by means of the audio oscillator attenuator control. This procedure eliminates the necessity of using potentiom-

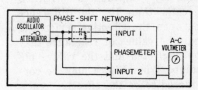

FIG. 3—In practice, the phasemeter is connected as shown here

eters in place of the cathode and plate resistors.

Performance

The phasemeter was first tested for inherent phase shift over the frequency range. The two inputs were connected together to an audio oscillator, and readings of sine $\theta/2$ versus frequency were taken. Under ideal conditions, the voltmeter reading will be zero, indicating zero phase shift, but a residual voltage caused by power supply ripple will normally be measured. This voltage amounted to 0.008 volts over the band, and, if considered a phase shift, equals approximately 1 degree. This is the smallest angle that can be measured.

The phasemeter was tested for accuracy by comparing measured phase shifts against calculated phase shifts of a R-C circuit. Values of capacitance and resistance obtained from an impedance bridge were used in the computations. The voltage across the resistance with reference to that across the series combination was first taken across the band. The voltage across the capacitor was then measured using the same reference. The error in the measured angles averaged 0.5 degrees.

Great differences in input voltages should be avoided. For greatest accuracy, both inputs should be approximately 1.7 volts corresponding to an output of one volt. The accuracy will then be within 1 degree from 1 to 180 degrees. If the input to V_2 is between 5 and 10 volts, then the 1-degree accuracy is maintained only from approximately 10 to 180 degrees. Exces-

sive distortion creates harmonic voltages which predominate for small angles, and leads to an increasingly large error as the phase angle approaches 1 degree. Computation of the error due to the power supply ripple revealed it to be negligible for angles greater than 1 degree.

The writer wishes to express his appreciation to Harry L. Sandberg for his analyses and encouragement. The writer is also indebted to Clem Arnold for his suggestions and cooperation.

REFERENCES

(1) Edwin F. Florman, Andrew Tait, An Electronic Phasemeter, *Proc. IRE*, 37, p 207, Feb. 1949.
(2) Edward L. Ginzton, Electronic Phase-Angle Meter, ELECTRONICS, 15, p 60, May 1942.

Q-Meter Impedance Charts

Three nomographs speed utilization of data obtained with standard Q meter when numerous measurements have to be made. Effective series R, effective parallel R and effective parallel and series reactances of an impedance are given directly

By ROBERT MIEDKE

THE accompanying nomographs are designed to give the effective parallel resistance R_p, the effective series resistance R_s and the effective parallel and series reactances X_p and X_s of an impedance Z when parallel connection to a standard Q meter is used, as shown in Fig. 1.

Limitations of the nomographs are the same as for standard Q-meter equations: R_p is accurate for any impedance; R_s is accurate for impedances with Q greater than 10; the difference between the effective series and parallel values of reactance may be neglected and the values obtained from Fig. 4 may be considered to be the effective reactance when the Q of the imped-

ance being measured is greater than 10. For more accurate values of R_s the unknown impedance should be connected in series with the L of the Q meter.

Instructions for Use

To get R_s, use Fig. 2 after computing values of $Q_1 - Q_2$,

Q_1Q_2 and $(C_2 - C_1)^2$. Join pairs of values as indicated by dashed lines *1* and *2* to get turning points on scales A and B, join these points as per dashed line *3* to get a turning point on scale C, then join the point on C with the value of f as per dashed line *4* to get R_s.

To get R_p, use Fig. 3 in essen-

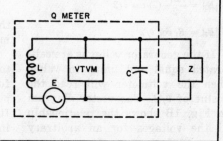

FIG. 1—To obtain required data, impedance being studied is connected in parallel with C of Q meter as shown

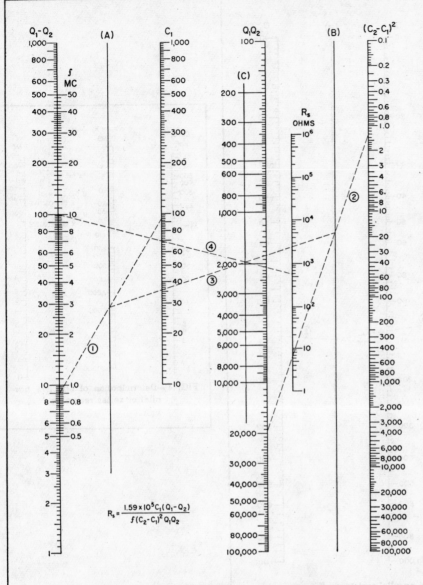

FIG. 2—Nomograph for determining effective series resistance R_s from measurements made with Q meter, using parallel connections

$$R_s = \frac{1.59 \times 10^5 C_1 (Q_1 - Q_2)}{f(C_2 - C_1)^2 Q_1 Q_2}$$

$C_2 - C_1 = 1.1$ and $(C_2 - C_1)^2 = 1.21$.

To find the effective series resistance with Fig. 2, draw a line from 9 on the $Q_1 - Q_2$ scale to 92.6 on the C_1 scale. Mark the intersection of this line with line A. Draw a line from 19,720 on the Q_1Q_2 scale to 1.21 on the $(C_2 - C_1)^2$ scale. Mark the intersection of this line with line B. Connect the points marked on lines A and B and mark the intersection with line C. Connect the point on line C with 10 mc on the frequency scale and read R_s (560 ohms) at the intersection of this line and the R_s scale.

Using the above data and Fig. 3, draw a line from 9 on the $Q_1 - Q_2$ scale to 92.6 on the C_1 scale. Mark where this line crosses vertical line A. Next, draw a line from 145 on the Q_1 scale to 136 on the Q_2 scale. Mark the intersection of this line with vertical line B. Connect the points marked on lines A and B and mark the intersection of this line with vertical line C. Draw a line from the point marked on C to 10 mc on the frequency scale and read the effective parallel resistance (370,000 ohms) where this line intersects the R_p scale. Since this value is much larger than the average tank circuit impedance, it will have little effect.

To find X_s on Fig. 4, connect 1.1 on the $C_2 - C_1$ scale with 10 mc on the frequency scale and read the effective parallel reactance (14,200 ohms) on the X_s scale. Since C_1 is greater than C_2 the reactance is capacitive. This then represents a capacitance of approximately 1 $\mu\mu$f at 10 mc, which will detune the circuit very little.

tially the same way, as indicated by the numbered dashed lines.

To get X_s or X_p, use Fig. 4 in the conventional manner.

Example of Use

Suppose an r-f choke is to be used in the shunt-fed plate circuit of a tube. It is desirable to know the effective parallel resistance R_p and reactance X_p that this choke will shunt across the plate circuit.

Set up the Q meter on the frequency at which measurements are to be made. Record the Q and capacitance as Q_1 and C_1 respectively. Connect the choke between the capacitor terminals on the Q meter, readjust C for resonance, and record Q_2 and C_2. Typical data obtained might be: $f = 10$ mc; $Q_1 = 145$; $C_1 = 92.6$ $\mu\mu$f; $Q_2 = 136$; $C_2 = 91.5$ $\mu\mu$f. Then $Q_1 - Q_2 = 9$, $Q_1Q_2 = 19,720$,

Continued

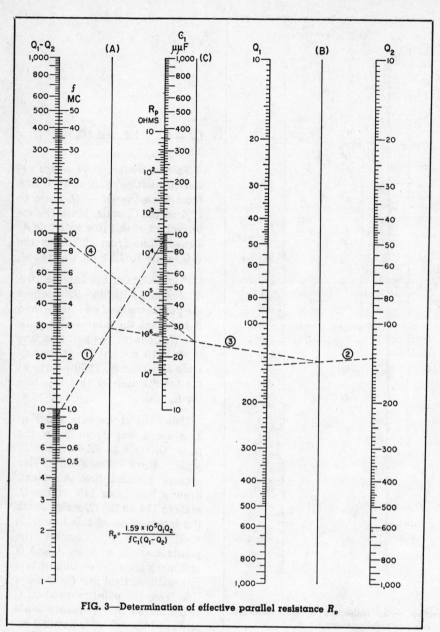

FIG. 3—Determination of effective parallel resistance R_p

$$R_p = \frac{1.59 \times 10^5 Q_1 Q_2}{f C_1 (Q_1 - Q_2)}$$

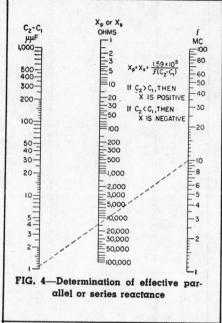

$$X_p = X_s = \frac{1.59 \times 10^5}{f(C_2 - C_1)}$$

If $C_2 > C_1$, THEN X IS POSITIVE

If $C_2 < C_1$, THEN X IS NEGATIVE

FIG. 4—Determination of effective parallel or series reactance

High-Resistance Measurement

By W. G. SHEPARD

ACCURATE measurement of resistance below about one megohm is usually made by means of a Wheatstone bridge using a galvanometer for the null indicator. Above this value the resistance of a galvanometer is too low to properly match the high-resistance arms of the bridge and insufficient indication results. A vacuum-tube amplifier connected to the output of the bridge, however, offers a much higher impedance and is quite effective since the voltage output of a high-resistance bridge is comparatively high.

Figure 1 shows a bridge and amplifier for the purpose. The bridge consists of precision ratio arms, a variable standard, which may be a laboratory-type resistance decade, and the unknown. Since the ratio is 100 to 1, a 1-megohm decade may be used for measurements up to 100 megohms. The accuracy of laboratory decades is usually 0.1 percent or greater, and the ratio arms, if not already this accurate, may be adjusted by putting a 0.1-percent resistor across the unknown terminals of the bridge and a 0.1-percent resistor of 1/100 the value across the decade terminals and then correcting the ratio arms until the bridge balances. The meter-amplifier circuit indicates to much closer than 0.1 percent except when measuring extremely high resistances, so the overall accuracy is perhaps 0.2 to 0.3 percent.

Circuit

The amplifier is a conventional vtvm type in which two triodes are balanced against each other to cancel drift. Any drift that remains may cause a slight shift in the zero position of the meter, but, by using a momentary switch which must be pressed to make the

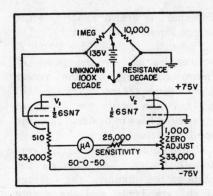

FIG. 1—Circuit of high-resistance bridge and amplifier for convenient measurements up to 100 megohms

measurement, the circuit is automatically placed in the zeroing position before and after every measurement and any shift in zero is immediately apparent. Since a sensitive meter is used, no voltage amplification is necessary.

Grid current flowing through the bridge causes a potential to appear at the grid of V_1, but since the circuit is arranged with the same resistance in the grid circuit in both the zeroing and measuring positions, no error is introduced. It is advisable, however, to keep the grid current at a minimum by applying proper voltages to the tubes.

Because of the high resistances involved, some points in the bridge circuit not connected to the chassis must be carefully insulated from it and from each other, as a slight leakage may cause serious errors in measurement. Although the instrument has been described as a high-resistance measuring device, it can also be used equally well for any resistance down to about 100 ohms simply by reversing the position of the decade and the unknown resistance in the bridge circuit.

Automatic A-C Bridges

Design of bridge and detector circuits used in production lines for automatic measurement of inductance, capacitance, and effective resistance. To cut down computations required, a graphical method of determining phase and amplitude of bridge unbalance voltage is included

By J. F. GRAHAM

PRODUCTION EQUIPMENT performing continuity, insulation breakdown, d-c resistance and simple a-c impedance tests is readily made automatic. But in the measurement of inductance, capacitance and effective resistance, manually operated a-c bridges are still widely employed in spite of costly operator time.

Partly or fully automatic bridges have been developed which perform such tests with accuracy comparable to that of manual bridges.

In the design of any measuring device there are two general approaches. In one method, a quantity is measured accurately and figures are presented to the operator.

An example is a bridge with a calibrated indicator. In the second method, no effort is made to determine actual magnitude. It is simply determined as being less than a set upper limit, and greater than a set lower limit, or within limits.

Most industrial requirements are stated in the form of limits. (For

example, inductance of a particular coil must not exceed 0.51 henry and must not be less than 0.50 henry). This would seem to make the limit-type of measurement the solution to most problems of industrial testing. However, the necessity of measuring reactance or effective resistance introduces certain limita-

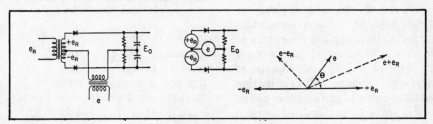

FIG. 1—Simple phase discriminator and vector relationship of voltages involved

tions. If the inductance of a coil is to be measured on a limit bridge with one-percent accuracy, then the effective resistance of the coil must lie within a certain range. Usually, the wider this range can be made the more dependable the test will be. Proper attention to the design of the limit-bridge-plus-detector system can materially extend this range.

Phase Discriminator

Detectors for automatic a-c bridges almost universally depend on the principle of phase discrimination. The circuit of Fig. 1 shows a simple phase discriminator. A d-c output voltage E_o is obtained which is a measure of the phase difference between e and e_R. The voltages supplied to the rectifiers are $e + e_R$ and $e - e_R$. The rectified voltages across the load resistances are proportional to the amplitudes of these two voltages. The d-c difference is E_o.

It can be shown from the vector diagram that

$$E_O = K \cdot e_R (e \cos \theta) \qquad (1)$$

where θ is the phase angle between e and e_R. Thus if e_R is constant, E_o is directly dependent only on the component of e in the direction of e_R. In practice, this relationship is somewhat modified by rectifier characteristics and other factors.

The conditions for proper operation of the phase discriminator must usually be set up by shifting the phase of one of the input voltages. Figure 2 shows a simple phase shifter. This circuit has the virtue of allowing easy shifting of phase up to 180 degrees without changing signal amplitude. It is, however, frequency sensitive.

Typical System

Figure 3 shows a typical arrangement of various elementary circuits. Output E_o is a measure of bridge unbalance and can be made to depend chiefly on signals of preferred phase, discriminating against those of unfavorable phase.

Figure 4 is an idealized version of a bridge output-voltage chart.

The chart is drawn relative to the bridge input voltage $E = A'C'$. Let the potential of the bridge corner B be represented by the point B' (more correctly, by the vector $A'B'$). Since the ratio arms, which are not necessarily resistive, are considered here to be fixed, then the point B' is fixed.

The potential of the bridge corner D, however, depends on the value of the unknown, the settings of the standards, and the supply frequency. Let the standard settings and the frequency be held constant. Then the potential of point D can be located by means of the grid of labelled lines. In this example, resistance R of the test is allowed to vary from 100 to 700 ohms. Inductance L of the test is allowed to vary from 0.1 to 0.7 henry. Unbalance voltage e is the

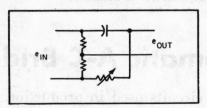

FIG. 2—Capacitor and resistor form simple phase shifter

difference between the potentials of corners B and D. In this case, balance is achieved when $R = 400$ ohms and $L = 0.4$ henry. Vector e,

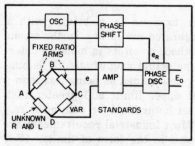

FIG. 3—Arrangement of basic elements for obtaining data of Fig. 4

drawn on the chart, is the result of R becoming 300 ohms and L becoming 0.1 henry.

Assume a desire to measure R with minimum dependence on L. A voltage is taken from supply E and revolved through an angle ψ to get

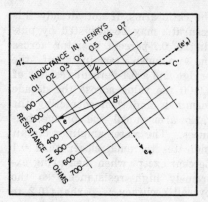

FIG. 4—Ideal bridge output voltage

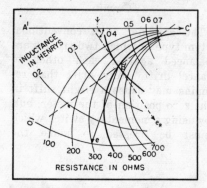

FIG. 5—Grid-type of bridge-voltage chart, with arcs replacing straight lines

e_R. Then by Eq. 1, voltages of this phase will have maximum effect on E_o, and those at 90 degrees will have zero effect.

Furthermore, the only component of e that registers on E_o is the component $B'N$. Now, $B'N$ is of exactly the same magnitude as the unbalance voltage which would result from the unbalance of the resistance alone. Thus variations of inductance have zero effect on the output voltage E_o, as required. A positive E_o means that R is greater than 400 ohms; a negative E_o means that R is less than 400 ohms. A voltmeter reading E_o could be calibrated linearly in ohms resistance unbalance.

A separate discriminator and phase shifter could be used in the same way to measure inductance (reference voltage e'_R).

Such a system would lend itself ideally to an automatic limit test set, say rejecting all product with resistance above 400 ohms, and/or inductance below 0.4 henry. Unfortunately, the rectangular character of the voltage chart of Fig. 4 can seldom be approximated for practical bridges.

Behavior of Typical Bridges

Practical bridge voltage charts appear here in two forms, the grid type of Fig. 5, and the calibrated-arc type of Fig. 6. Figure 5 is read in the same manner as the chart of Fig. 4, with arcs replacing the straight lines.

Figure 6 is read in the following manner: each end of the unbalance-voltage vector e is located by a point on one of the calibrated arcs. The example shown is for $L = 0.2$ henry, $R = 600$ ohms.

For measurement of R, with a minimum of error caused by variations of L, let e_R be the same phase as the line tangent to the balance-arc $L = 0.4$ as drawn in Fig. 5. The unbalance voltage e is shown for the same case as in Fig. 4, $L = 0.1$ henry and $R = 300$ ohms. But this time the component of e in phase with e_R is positive in direction. Hence E_o is positive, erroneously indicating that R is greater than 400 ohms.

The correct negative polarity is not assumed by E_o until the inductance is increased to about 0.3 henry. Voltage E_o, which should be an accurate index of the constant resistance unbalance, varies widely as the inductance changes, and it even assumes the wrong polarity for large deviations of inductance.

Assume the precision of the test must be ±1 percent. Product having a resistance of 404 ohms would be accepted were L to increase slightly from 0.4 henry; or resistances of 396 ohms would be rejected were L to decrease slightly from 0.4 henry. Inductive unbalance here can result in two undesirable actions: rejection of good product and acceptance of defects.

An alternative setting of e_R suggests itself: at a phase angle such that e_R is normal to the balance-arc $R = 400$ ohms. In such a case, inductive unbalance could not lead to the acceptance of faulty product. But it could lead to rejection for resistance under 400 ohms, an equally unsatisfactory condition.

A judicious choice of the phase of e_R is desirable. The main factors influencing this choice are the precision demanded in measurement of R, the expected deviation of L in normal production runs, and the relation of one variable to the other. For instance, other things being equal, R could reasonably be expected to be larger when L is larger.

A helpful step would be redesign of the bridge to have more favorable characteristics. In this example, the R = constant arcs should be made flat enough that the phase angle of e_R is not critical. However, this special bridge design might lead to unfavorable characteristics in the measurement of L. Failing an acceptable compromise, the easiest solution is to switch the product

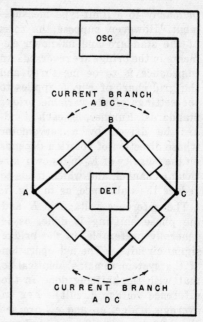

FIG. 8—Current branches set up by high-impedance detector

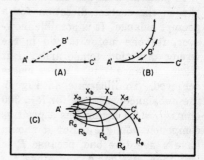

FIG. 9—Charts of corner potentials

into another bridge designed specifically for the measurement of L.

Self-Balancing Considerations

The preceding discussion applies

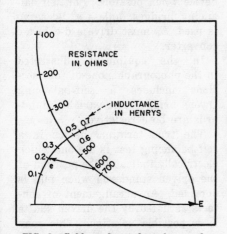

FIG. 6—Calibrated-arc chart for another bridge circuit

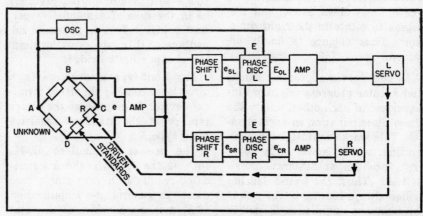

FIG. 7—Self-balancing bridge arrangement in which servomotors drive the variable standards

primarily to a limit-type measurement. However, suppose the roles of the standard and unknown elements in the bridge are reversed. An impedance is to be measured and the grid chart of Fig. 5 applies to the settings of the variable bridge standards. Further, let each standard be driven by a servomotor whose direction of rotation depends on the polarity of E_o in its own particular channel, and which tends to reduce the unbalance, as in Fig. 7.

The reference voltage is E and the phase shifting is done, as is generally preferable, in the bridge signal circuits. (The net operation of the system remains identical to that with the shifting done in the reference voltage circuit). For an average bridge, e_{SL} and e_{SR} are set about 90 degrees different in phase.

In general, both servomotors will run in the correct direction for a prompt balance. It is possible, however, for one motor to run in the wrong direction temporarily. But final balance is nevertheless achieved. To illustrate, in Fig. 5, the unbalance voltage e for $R = 300$ ohms, $L = 0.1$ henry, has a positive component along e_R. But it should have a negative one, because R is less than 400 ohms, and since the servo in Fig. 7 is connected to decrease resistance for positive E_o. The variable resistance standard would seemingly be driven to its lower limit and stay there. But meanwhile, the L servo has steadily been reducing the inductance unbalance. As this happens, the R servo slows down, stops, and then begins to rotate in the right direction. Thus balance is finally obtained.

As both servos approach balance, they become progressively more independent of each other, due to the phase discrimination in each channel. This works against interactive hunting, which, however, is not a great problem at moderate sensitivities. Thus the self-balancing bridge always reaches a true null if the unknown impedance is within the range of the bridge. The effect of one test component on the accur-

CIRCUIT	E_1 LOCUS	CENTER COORDINATES	
		x_c	y_c
(A) R_v R_o jx_o		$\frac{1}{2}$	$\frac{R_o}{2X_o}$
(B) R_o R_v jx_o		0	$\frac{-R_o}{2X_o}$
(C) R_o jx_v jx_o		$\frac{1}{2}$	0
(D) jx_v R_o jx_o		$\frac{1}{2}$	$\frac{-x_o}{2R_o}$
(E) jx_o jx_v R_o		0	$\frac{x_o}{2R_o}$
(F) jx_o R_v R_o		$\frac{1}{2}$	0
(G) jb_1 g_v jb_2 g_2		$\frac{1}{2}\frac{b_2}{b_1+b_2}$	$\frac{1}{2}\frac{-g_2}{b_1+b_2}$
(H) jb_v g_1 jb_2 g_2		$\frac{1}{2}\frac{g_2}{g_1+g_2}$	$\frac{1}{2}\frac{b_2}{g_1+g_2}$

Applied voltage = (1+j0) volts   v = variable elements
All loci pass through point (0,0)   o = fixed elements

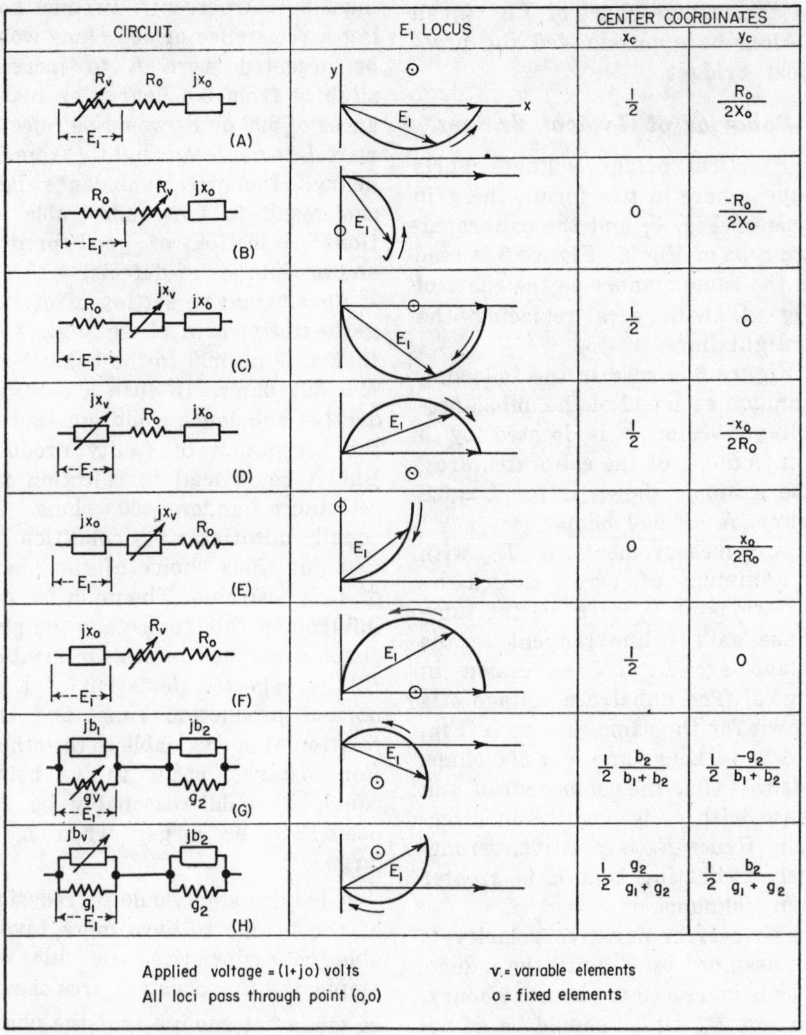

FIG. 10—In cases (B) and (C) if E_1 is across R_a, where $R_o = R_a + R_b$, multiply both center coordinates by R_a/R_o.

If E_1 is across X_a in (E) and (F), where $X_o = X_a + X_b$, multiply both center coordinates by X_a/X_o.

In (G) and (H) b is susceptance and g is conductance

acy of measurement of the other component is eliminated, precisely as in the case of a manually operated bridge. This is the main advantage of this type over the simpler, cheaper limit bridge.

For limit-type measurements, a directional relay is the usual terminal device. It may be of the meter type or of the standard sensitive relay type.

The use of germanium diodes such as the 1N35 in the discriminator results in a very stable zero point. In general, d-c amplification of E_o means a sacrifice of this stability, so that E_o should be impressed directly on the terminal

device when possible. For self-balancing bridges, unless a d-c servo is used, E_o must drive a d-c to a-c converter.

In the equipment illustrated in the photographs, one of four sections includes a self-balancing Owens bridge. The variable standards are both resistive.

The true terminal device in a self-balancing test is the one which electrically indicates the position of the driven standards when null is obtained. An arrangement of contacts actuated by the driven shafts is a possible solution. This may mean a critical mechanical setup, however.

In the equipment illustrated, the problem has been met on an electrical basis. Achievement of balance is signified by the operation of a relay which senses the absence of unbalance voltage via an auxiliary

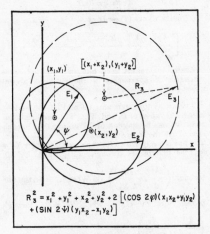

$$R_3^2 = x_1^2 + y_1^2 + x_2^2 + y_2^2 + 2\left[(\cos 2\varphi)(x_1 x_2 + y_1 y_2) + (\sin 2\psi)(y_1 x_2 - x_1 y_2)\right]$$

FIG. 11—Addition of the two voltage vectors to provide E_3

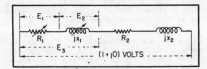

FIG. 12—Circuit employed in text Example 1

circuit; this relay initiates a switching system which transfers each Helipot into a simple d-c limit bridge. The d-c resistance indications then actuate the proper subsequent accept-reject circuits. The d-c bridges themselves are accurate to 0.1 percent and are easily adjustable.

The overall action of the test is analogous to the use of calipers to transfer a certain length from an awkward to a convenient location for measurement. Here, inductance and effective resistance are translated into d-c resistance, and then transferred to convenient measuring circuits as separate items. The same principle can be used, no matter what the driven variable standard is, by mounting a pilot rheostat on the driven shaft.

Unbalance Voltages

Numerical computation of bridge

unbalance voltages is notoriously tedious. Since the voltage to be determined is the difference between two much larger potentials (the potentials of the corners across which the detector is connected), any error in the calculation of corner potentials represents a much larger error in unbalance voltage. Thus a series of slide-rule calculations is apt to be significantly in

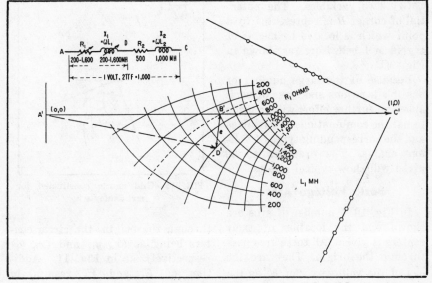

FIG. 13—Grid chart provides E_3 for any value of R_1 and L_1

error. Also, an attempt to correlate such a series of results usually leads to some form of graphical representation. For these reasons, a direct graphical approach is generally simplest and most flexible. A vectorial method especially applicable to bridge problems will be presented here. Better than slide accuracy is readily obtainable on letter size paper.

Accurate determination is best obtained by direct experiment or detailed algebraic analysis. For this reason we will neglect small residuals. In practical cases, a vacuum-tube detector is used. The resultant high detector impedance permits a valuable simplification in bridge calculations: the bridge can be considered to consist of two entirely separate current branches as shown in Fig. 8.

We are interested in the relative potentials of two points, one in each

current branch. These points are the two bridge corners across which the detector is connected. The other two corners are common to both current branches. Let one be assigned zero potential, and the other 1.0 volt. The frequency will not be specified, since it enters directly into the expressions for reactance. The majority of bridges do not have intentional coupling between current branches, therefore this complicating case will not be treated here.

Unbalance-Voltage Charts

Considering one current branch

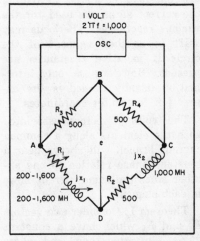

FIG. 14—Chart of Fig. 13 can be applied to this bridge circuit

only, we may represent the potential of the mid-way corner as follows:

(1) No variables. The potential of corner B is represented by a point on the plane as in Fig. 9A (more precisely, by vector $A'B'$).

(2) One variable. The potential is represented by a point which travels along a calibrated arc as in Fig. 9B. The calibration marks correspond to the value of the variable.

(3) Two variables. The potential of corner B is represented by a point which is located by means of a grid of labelled arcs as shown in Fig. 9C.

Because of the large number of possible locations and types of variables, no further effort will be made to list the combinations of variables and the corresponding types of voltage charts. The examples to be given will show typical results.

Basic Voltage Arcs

In Fig. 10, a number of arcs are shown and the location of their centers is given. All these arcs pass through the origin. They are the loci of the voltage vector E_1 as the variable element in the corresponding circuit varies without limit. The curved arrow shows which way the vector head travels as the variable element increases in a positive direction.

The arcs drawn represent the loci when all circuit reactances are positive. The coordinates for the arc-centers are correct providing the correct signs are used for the various reactances. The locus may shift to another segment of the circle if negative reactances are present. However, the only information usually needed is the expression for center coordinates.

The voltage vectors associated with the elements along a common current branch will always bear a constant phase relation to one another since the same current flows in each element.

Theorem I: Consider two vectors E_1 and E_2 which have a constant angle ψ between them, and whose ends are defined by circles passing

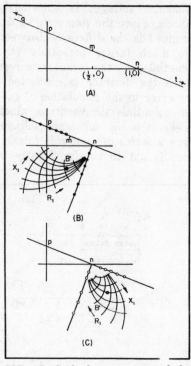

FIG. 15—Grid charts constructed for text Example 2

through the origin, the circle centers being at (x_1, y_1) and (x_2, y_2) respectively, as in Fig. 11. Addition of E_1 and E_2 results in a vector E_3 which also follows a circular locus. The center of the E_3 locus is at $[(x_1 + x_2), (y_1 + y_2)]$. Further, the radius R_3 is given by the expression shown.

Two important cases are:

(a) When $\psi = 0$,
$$R_3{}^2 = (x_1 + x_2)^2 + (y_1 + y_2)^2$$

(b) When $\psi = 90°$,
$$R_3{}^2 = (x_1 - x_2)^2 + (y_1 - y_2)^2$$

The radius is seldom computed, since it usually can be determined by inspection.

EXAMPLE 1. Required, Fig. 12: find E_3 as R_1 and X_1 vary. This will be done for two conditions: (a) R_1 free to vary, X_1 takes temporary values X_1':

Center E_1 arc (Fig. 10A) at $\left[\dfrac{1}{2},\right.$

$\left.\dfrac{1}{2}\dfrac{R^2}{X_1' + X_2}\right]$

Center E_2 arc (Fig. 10F) at
$$\left[\frac{1}{2}\frac{X_1'}{X_1' + X_2}, 0\right]$$

Center E_3 arc (Theor I) at

$$\left[\frac{1}{2} + \frac{1}{2}\frac{X_1'}{X_1' + X_2}, \frac{1}{2}\frac{R_2}{X_1' + X_2}\right]$$

The radius need not be computed, since by inspection, whenever R_1 approaches ∞ the E_3 locus approaches (1, 0).

(b) X_1 free to vary, R_1 takes temporary values R_1'

Center E_1 arc (Fig. 10C) at

$$\left[\frac{1}{2}\frac{R_1'}{R_1' + R_2}, 0\right]$$

Center E_2 arc (Fig. 10D) at

$$\left[\frac{1}{2}, -\frac{1}{2}\frac{X_2}{R_1' + R_2}\right]$$

Center E_3 arc (Theor I) at

$$\left[\frac{1}{2} + \frac{1}{2}\frac{R_1'}{R_1' + R_2}, -\frac{1}{2}\frac{X_2}{R_1' + R_2}\right]$$

Again, the radius need not be computed, since whenever X approaches ∞ the E_3 locus approaches (1,0).

The arc centers can now be plotted for various numerical values of R_1 and X_1. The graphical construction can be speeded up by noting that in each case above the E_3 arc-centers fall on a straight line. The line is easily drawn for each case. (a) When $X_1' = \infty$, the line passes through (1,0); when $X_1' = 0$, through $\left(\dfrac{1}{2}, \dfrac{R_2}{2 X_2}\right)$. (b) When $R_1' = \infty$, the line passes through (1,0); when $R_1' = 0$, through $\left(\dfrac{1}{2}, \dfrac{-X_2}{2R_2}\right)$

Only the abcissa of each arc-center need be computed, since the center must lie on the associated line. Further, each arc may be quickly drawn, since each is known to pass through (1,0).

Fig. 13 shows a plot of E_3, the elements having been given numerical values. The grid allows E_3 to be found for any R_1 and L_1.

An immediate conclusion is that the chart also applies to the bridge of Fig. 14. Output voltage e is the difference in potential between corners D and B. The grid gives the potential of D, and that of B is a fixed point at $\left(\dfrac{1}{2}, 0\right)$ for the element shown. Any ABC branch could be accommodated, whether the potential of B were defined by a fixed point, a calibrated arc, or another grid.

EXAMPLE 2. It is of interest to let X_1 of Fig. 12 become negative (substitute a capacitor for coil X_1). The line tmq of Fig. 15A contains all the centers for condition (a) of Example 1, plus those appearing for X_1 negative. As X_1 decreases from 0 to $-\dfrac{1}{2}X_2$, the center travels from m to p. (See the expression for the arc-center coordinates). As X_1 closely approaches $-X_2$, the center retreats to q at an infinite distance; the circuit approaches resonance.

As X_1 takes up values more negative than $-X_2$, drawing away from resonance, the center appears along tn. Finally, as X_1 approaches $-\infty$, the center again approaches (1,0).

The arcs being swung off from these centers must still pass through (1,0) as before. This results in the grids of Fig. 15B, where X_1 is between 0 and $-X_2$ ohms; or of Fig. 15C, where X_1 is between $-X_2$ ohms and $-\infty$.

For the case of Fig. 15B, a convenient potential B' is needed. This is readily obtained by putting a capacitor in arm AB and a resistance in arm BC. The completed bridge circuit becomes the standard Owens bridge of Fig. 16.

In Fig. 15C, it is more difficult to obtain a suitable balancing potential B' since it must be larger than the supply voltage feeding the other current branch ADC. However, it can be obtained in a number of ways, and some practical advantage may accrue from the fact that X_1 represents a relatively small capacitance. If DC is the test arm, and X_1 and R_1

are variable standards, a variable air capacitor will suffice for X_1 at fairly low frequencies.

EXAMPLE 3. The Owens inductance bridge is often operated in a different mode from that mentioned in Example 2.

By writing out the standard balance equations for

Fig. 16, it appears that $\dfrac{X_1}{R_2} = \dfrac{X_3}{R_4} = \text{constant}$;

and $\dfrac{R_1}{X_2} = \dfrac{X_3}{R_4} = \text{constant}$, so that R_2 is balanced

by X_1 and X_2 is balanced by R_1. Rather than make X_1 a variable, R_2 is held constant. This is done by adding resistance from a calibrated variable to the effective resistance of the test so as to make up the correct balance resistance. The resistance of the test can be deduced from the setting of the variable. Thus both inductance and effective resistance of the test appear in terms of a resistance setting.

Required: draw a voltage chart for the bridge of Fig. 16 as R_1 and R_2 vary over their ranges.

(a) R_1 free to vary, R_2 takes temporary values R_2'.
Center E_1 arc (Fig. 10F) at

$$\left[\frac{1}{2}\left(\frac{-177}{953} \right), 0 \right] = \left(-0.093, 0 \right)$$

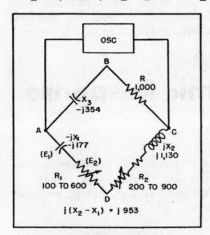

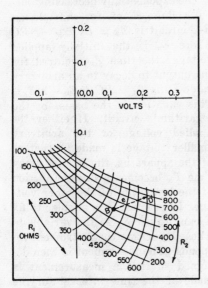

FIG. 16—Circuit of Owens bridge

FIG. 17—Grid chart constructed for Owens bridge in text Example 3

Center E_2 arc (Fig. 10A) at

$$\left[\frac{1}{2}, \frac{R_2'}{2(953)} \right] = \left[0.5, \frac{R_2'}{1,906} \right]$$

Center E_{AD} arc at $\left[0.407, \dfrac{R_2'}{1,906} \right]$

When R_1 approaches ∞, E_2 approaches $(1,0)$, so all arcs pass through $(1,0)$.
(b) R_2 free to vary, R_1 takes temporary values R_1'.
Center E_1 arc (Fig. 10F) at

$$\left[\frac{1}{2}\left(\frac{-177}{953} \right), 0 \right] = \left(-0.093, 0 \right)$$

Center E_2 arc (Fig. 10B) at

$$\left[0, \frac{-R_1'}{2(953)} \right] = \left(0, \frac{-R_1'}{1,906} \right)$$

Center E_{AD} arc at $\left[-0.093, \dfrac{-R_1'}{1,906} \right].$

When R_2 approaches ∞, E_1 approaches $(0,0)$, so all arcs pass through $(0,0)$.
Figure 17 is a grid drawn for the bridge with the numerical values as shown. Point B' is located for the ratio arms specified.

EXAMPLE 4. Fig. 18 is the circuit of a conventional capacitance comparison bridge. Let C_1 and g_1 be the capacitance and conductance of arm AD and let them be free to vary. Fixed values C_2 and g_2 are in arm DC. To draw an output voltage chart:
(a) g_1 free to vary, C_1 takes temporary values C_1'.
Center of E_{AD} arc (Fig. 10G) at

$$\left(\frac{1}{2} \frac{\omega C_2}{\omega C_1' + \omega C_2}, \frac{1}{2} \frac{-g_2}{\omega C_1' + \omega C_2} \right)$$

All arcs pass through $(0,0)$ per Fig. 10G.
The line containing the arc-centers is easily drawn in: when C_1' approaches ∞, line passes through $(0,0)$; when $C_1' = 0$, through

$$\left(\frac{1}{2}, \frac{-g_2}{2 \omega C_2} \right)$$

(b) C_1 free to vary, g_1 takes temporary values g_1'.
Center of E_{AD} arc (Fig. 10H) at

$$\left(\frac{1}{2} \frac{g_2}{g_1' + g_2}, \frac{1}{2} \frac{\omega C_2}{g_1' + g_2} \right)$$

All arcs pass through $(0,0)$ per Fig. 10H.
To draw the line containing the arc-centers: when g_1' approaches ∞, line passes through

$$(0,0); \text{ when } g_1' = 0, \text{ through } \left(\frac{1}{2}, \frac{\omega C_2}{2 g_2} \right)$$

Figure 19 is a grid drawn for this bridge with the elements having values as shown. It is a matter of choice whether the grid is regarded as applying to the excursions of the test impedance, a given comparison standard being used, or the excursions of variable standards, the test impedance being fixed.

EXAMPLE 5. Figure 20A is the circuit of a Maxwell inductance bridge. The test item is in the D-C arm. A common mode of operation is to vary C_1 for reactive balance, and to add a calibrated resistance to that of the test item such that the total resistance in the D-C arm is correct for balance.
Required: draw an unbalance-voltage chart for this bridge, the test item having specified characteristics while C_1 and R_2 vary throughout their ranges.
There is only one variable per current path so this will lead to a calibrated-arc type chart. A calibrated arc is merely a rudimentary grid in which one family of arcs is reduced to a single arc, and the other is reduced to a set of calibration marks. The simplest way to draw and calibrate an arc is to proceed as if a grid were being drawn.
ABC branch:
(a) C_1 varies, g_1 constant. (Main arc)

Center E_{AB} arc (Fig. 10H) at $\left(\dfrac{1}{2} \dfrac{g_2}{g_1 + g_2}, 0 \right)$

(b) Although g_1 is not a variable, let it be free to vary, that is, not defined. C_1 takes values C_1'. (Calibration arcs)

Center E_{AB} arcs (Fig. 10G) at $\left(0, \dfrac{1}{2} \dfrac{-g_2}{\omega C_1'} \right)$

ADC branch:
(a) R_2 varies, X_2 constant. (Main arc)

Center E_{AD} arc (Fig. 10B) at $\left(0, \dfrac{1}{2} \dfrac{-R_1}{\omega L_2} \right)$

(b) As above, let X_2 be free to vary, R_2 takes values R_2' (calibration arcs).

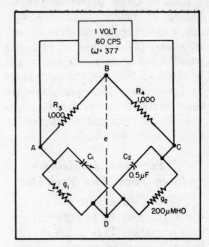

FIG. 18—Circuit of capacitance-comparison bridge

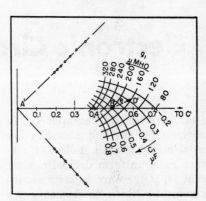

FIG. 19—Grid chart constructed for capacitance bridge of text Example 4

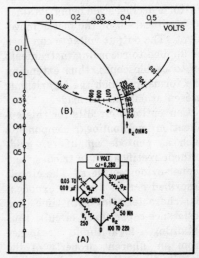

FIG. 20—Circuit of Maxwell inductance bridge, and unbalance-voltage chart

Center E_{AD} arcs (Fig. 10C) at

$$\left(\frac{1}{2}\frac{R_1}{R_1 + R_2'}, 0\right)$$

Figure 20B is a chart drawn for the numerical values shown.

Each example presented the behavior of bridge unbalance voltage e as bridge parameters varied. However, the number of variables was limited to two. A chart might be required for, say, the inductance bridge of Fig. 14, when there are four variables present, two variables in the item under test plus the two variable standards.

For Cases Involving More Than Two Variables

The test item and the variable standards may be in different current branches. This is the current-bridge connection, so-called because at balance the current through the test is readily computed when the total supply current is known. A grid can be drawn for each current path, and e is thus determined, each end of the vector being located by one of the grids. Thus up to four variables per bridge can be accommodated providing that there are no more than two per current branch.

The test item and the variable standards may be in the same current branch. This is the voltage bridge connection, so-called because at balance the voltage across the test is readily computed when the supply voltage is known. (While a balanced bridge remains balanced for either supply connection, the unbalance voltages in general do not correspond.) Here, the presence of four interacting variables precludes two-dimensional graphical representation; we must resort to the determination of voltages for particular conditions of interest.

In such a case, graphical determination of voltages, one by one, presents about the same amount of labor as straight algebraic methods. However, if entirely complete data is not essential, much pertinent information on voltage trends can be obtained by drawing several grids, selecting values of interest for two of the variables and letting the other two vary freely. If a large number of points were computed algebraically and then correlated graphically, we would finally arrive at just such a set of grids.

Acknowledgment

The author wishes to thank R. M. Lester for his valuable criticism during preparation of this paper.

Electronic Circuit has Logarithmic Response

By A. W. NOLLE

INSTRUMENTS for measurements in communications and acoustics are most useful if their indicating meters have uniform decibel scales; that is, if they are logarithmic instruments. Such instruments are more versatile if the voltages that they develop are logarithmically related to their inputs, instead of the uniform decibel scale being obtained by modification of the meter movement. The output voltages can then be applied to recording instruments or to oscilloscopes, thus extending the forms in which the logarithmic presentations can be made.

Conventional circuits for this application use nonlinear components such as pentode amplifiers,[1] grid-cathode rectification in triodes,[2] and copper-oxide rectifiers.[3] The circuit described herein uses the exponential characteristics with time of a resistance-capacitance circuit, thus obtaining logarithmic response from an inherent property of the circuit rather than from an approximate characteristic. The exponent-

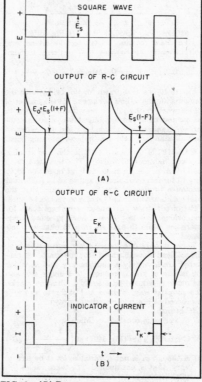

FIG. 1—(A) Response to a repetitive square wave, and (B) sampling action

ial response to square-wave exicitation of R-C and R-L-C circuits is familiar and need not be reviewed here.

Basis of Operation

The exponentially decreasing output voltage E_R of, for example, an R-C circuit is $E_R = E_o \exp -t/RC$ where E_o is the initially applied voltage. the time T_K required for the output to decay to an arbitrary value E_K is $T_K = RC(\ln E_o - \ln E_K)$. This equation is the basis for the logarithmic circuit. If either the applied voltage or the arbitrary smaller voltage is made a constant of the apparatus, the partial decay time T_K becomes a linear function of the logarithm of the other voltage. In practice it is simpler to fix E_K and to use E_o as the variable to whose logarithm the instrument responds. The instrument is then designed so that a measurement is made of the time interval for the voltage under test to decay to a standard value. This one measurement is sufficient to give the logarithm of the amplitude of the voltage.

Practical Circuit Design

Because most voltages that are to be measured vary with time and because continuous indications are usually desired, it is necessary to repeat the process continuously. When this is done, a succession of time measurements is delivered to the final indicating device in such electrical form that an averaged indication of its logarithmic level is always presented.

The repetitive action can be produced simply by applying a square wave whose amplitude is proportional to that of the input signal to an R-C or R-L circuit. The output from an R-C circuit is shown in Fig. 1A in relation to an applied square wave of amplitude E_s. Because the capacitor does not charge completely each half cycle, the peak output voltage is $E_o = E_s(1 + F)$ where $F = \tanh(T/4RC)$, T being the period of the applied square wave. At the end of each half cycle the voltage has decayed to $E_s(1 - F)$. In practice the logarithmic response circuit must be designed so that F is nearly equal to unity if differences of the order of 20 db are to be registered. Thus the peak output voltage of the R-C circuit is essentially equal to the peak-to-peak amplitude of the square wave.

The time required for the output voltage of the R-C circuit to decay to the fixed value E_K is T_K. Measurement of T_K will give the correct indication of the logarithmic amplitude of the square wave provided that the peak voltage $E_s(1 + F)$ is (1) greater than the reference voltage E_K but (2) small enough that the interval T_K is less than half a cycle.

Figure 1B shows a method for obtaining a signal indicative of T_K. An indicator circuit is so arranged that current of constant amplitude flows through an indicating instrument, such as a d-c meter, as long as the output of the R-C circuit is greater than E_K. The output of the

indicator circuit is thus a pulse train modulated in width in proportion to the logarithm of the amplitude of the initial square wave. The average value of this pulse train produces the proper steady deflection of the indicating instrument. If the calibration of the instrument is to remain fixed, it is essential that the period of the square wave be constant.

There are several other practical considerations: The square-wave generator feeding the R-C circuit must have a constant internal resistance. Full-wave operation can be obtained if the indicating circuit operates on both halves of the square wave, responding to E_K, then to $-E_K$. The meter deflection per db can readily be controlled by varying the resistance of the R-C circuit. The absolute level of the meter scale can be controlled by the amplification of the input signal and by the magnitude of the bucking current through the meter, which should be large enough that, in the absence of signal input, the indicating element will be off scale so as to avoid ambiguity.

A Specific Circuit

Figure 2 shows the diagram of a specific circuit which has a logarithmic range of more than 20 db. This circuit is designed for measuring alternating voltages and therefore is provided with an a-c amplifier stage and a balanced voltage-doubler rectifier. This rectifier converts the signal into direct voltages at A and B that are positive and negative respectively by equal amounts as compared to the average potential at D.

A limiting amplifier, excited by the high voltage from the power transformer, develops a square wave at D whose peak-to-peak amplitude closely equals the voltage difference between A and B because of the action of the limiting diodes. A variable bias current is obtained from G to assure that both the rectifying and the limiting diodes operate only within their linear regions. This bias is desirable to avoid operation of the diodes in their low-

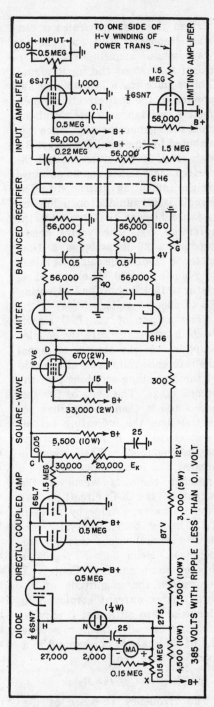

FIG. 2—Circuit diagram of instrument having full-scale response of 20 db

current regions where there is considerable variation of plate resistance, thus improving the linearity of the circuit at low levels. The rectifier-limiter circuit is adjusted so that changes of input level produce very little variation of direct voltage level at D.

The portion of the circuit described thus far generates a constant-frequency (60 cps) square wave whose amplitude is proportional to that of the input signal. This square wave is amplified and applied to the R-C circuit. The effective resistance of this circuit includes the generator impedance contributed by the amplifier stage. Resistance R is adjustable so that the desired scale factor can be obtained on the indicating instrument. The circuit is terminated on a low-impedance bleeder that provides the reference E_K. The values shown produce a 20-db scale on a 1-ma meter; a 30-db scale can be obtained by reducing the 30,000-ohm fixed resistor to 15,000 ohms and adjusting E_K to about 5 volts.

The output of the R-C circuit feeds a two-stage directly coupled amplifier. In the absence of signal the reference voltage E_K at the grid of the first stage acts to cut off the second stage. The plate of the second stage is then at a higher potential than the indicating instrument circuit at H and no current passes the diode. When signal is present, the second stage of the d-c amplifier conducts whenever the output of the R-C circuit is less than its average value by at least E_K. During these intervals, constant current passes through the meter M. Neon bulb N regulates this constant current. Control X determines the magnitude of reverse meter current employed to place the zero off scale; it may be used as a fine adjustment to set the end of the scale to correspond to a specified input voltage.

Response of the Meter

The frequency response of the instrument and its absolute sensitivity within gross limits are determined by the input amplifier, which is conventional. The full-scale indication of the instrument as shown in the circuit diagram corresponds to an input of about 3 rms volts.

With the instrument adjusted for a 30-db scale, it is accurate within 0.1 db over the top 20 db. If the linearity control is properly adjusted, this accuracy can be extended over the full-scale range. Thus, while it is possible to secure substantially ideal performance over a 30-db range, this result is only obtained by careful correction of the rectifier and limiter diodes. Therefore the circuit is shown for a 20-db scale for which critical adjustments are unnecessary. The sensitivity of the instrument to line voltage changes is 0.07 db per volt, which represents a uniform scale drift.

Design Limitations

The serious source of error is the rectifier-limiter circuit. The portion of the meter following the rectifier-limiter circuit of Fig. 2 is accurate within ±0.2 db over a 30-db range.

If it were required to redesign the meter for a 30-db range, an input stage having a larger output capability than the 6SJ7 would be necessary so that the rectifiers and limiters could be operated farther into their linear ranges. If this were done, the square wave would have to be attenuated before going to the grid of the 6V6 power stage.

The maximum useful range of the logarithmic circuit, which begins after the limiter diodes, is determined by the finite on-off sensitivity of the d-c amplifier. This sensitivity is of the order of 0.1 volt, and must be small compared to E_K in order that sharply defined pulses be produced. Thus there is a lower limit to E_K of about 3 volts. If the working range of the circuit is to be as much as 40 db, the peak-to-peak undistorted output of the square-wave amplifier must be greater than 3 volts by the 40 db plus a safety margin of about 3 db, or 400 volts peak-to-peak. Because of this requirement, a reasonably portable instrument is limited to about 30 db full scale.

The R-C filters between the rectifiers and the limiters are important to prevent slow periodic variations of the instrument indication at certain input frequencies. When the input frequency is nearly a multiple of the 60-cps square wave, ripple in the rectifier output is sampled in stroboscopic fashion in the limiting process. Thus a 10-percent ripple component in the rectifier output could produce a cyclic 1-db variation in the instrument indication.

These R-C filters are the chief factors in limiting the speed of response of the instrument; the values for them shown in Fig. 2 are commensurate with the mechanical performance of usual milliammeters. If more rapid response were desired for operation of a high-speed recorder or for presentation of the results on an oscilloscope, it would be necessary to redesign the instrument for operation at a higher square-wave frequency. This change, although increasing the circuit complexity, would produce a faster response by providing more rapid sampling and by permitting reduction of the time constants of the R-C filters.

Acknowledgements

The author is pleased to acknowledge the cooperation of the Ordnance Research Laboratory of the Pennsylvania State College, with whose facilities a preliminary test of the principle of the logarithmic circuit described above was made, and of the Electrodyne Company of Boston, to whom development rights have been assigned.

REFERENCES

(1) S. Ballantine, ELECTRONICS, p 472, 1931, and *Jour. Acous. Soc. Am*, p 10, 5, 1933; also F. V. Hunt, *RSI*, p 672, 4, 1933; W. Holle and E. Lubcke, *Hochfrequenztechn. u. Elektroakustik*, p 41, 48, 1936; M. Nuovo, *Ricerca Scientifica*, p 522, 2, 1937.
(2) M. Lambrey, *Comptes Rendus*, p 1023, 201, 1934, and also M. Nuovo, *Alta Frequenza*, p 206, 8, 1939.
(3) H. G. Thilo, *Zeits. f. Techn. Physik.*, p 558, 17, No. 12, 1936.

High-Frequency Crystal Voltmeter

By B. F. TYSON

A CRYSTAL voltmeter is useful in measuring the gain and response characteristics of the r-f and i-f circuits in f-m and television receivers. Such an instrument is physically small, and when built in probe form can be easily connected to the point of measurement. Inherently, it has high sensitivity and when used with a 10-microampere meter will indicate r-f voltages as low as 0.05 volt.

The voltmeter described here uses a type 1N28 crystal rectifier connected as shown in the circuit diagram of Fig. 1. Other crystals such as types 1N21 or 1N25 can also be used. On the input side, load resistor R_1 and a ceramic d-c blocking capacitor C_1 are built into the probe. On the output side, the r-f components of the rectified current are bypassed to ground through a button mica capacitor C_2 and the direct current to the microammeter is filtered by resistor R_2 and a button mica capacitor C_3.

The physical arrangement of the various parts is shown in the cross-section assembly view of Fig. 2. The smaller diameter half of the probe has the ground and high potential input tabs and contains the blocking capacitor and load resistor. The shielded microammeter lead is brought out of the other half which houses the button-type bypass and filter capacitors and the filter resistor. Note that the large end of cylinder B is made to slide fit into cylinder A and a clip from an octal socket is soldered to the end of the 100-$\mu\mu$f Ceramicon capacitor to receive the contact of the crystal. The larger, probe end of the crystal is held firmly by a finger contactor. Thus, the entire probe is separable near its center for easy insertion of the crystal cartridge.

Fig. 3 is a typical calibration curve of the crystal voltmeter using a 1N28 crystal. Measured characteristics of several 1N28 crystals

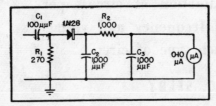

FIG. 1—Circuit diagram of crystal voltmeter

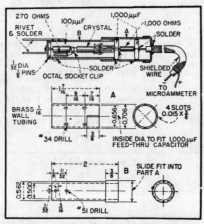

FIG. 2—Crystal probe assembly consists of two cylinders machined so the end of one slides inside the other for rapid replacement of crystal cartridge

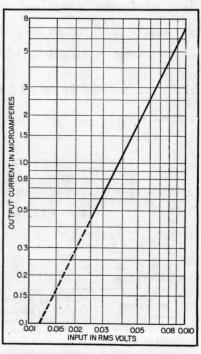

FIG. 3—Typical calibration curve of the crystal voltmeter using a 1N28 crystal

indicate that their sensitivities are in the order of 700 to 1,200 micro-amperes per volt squared and that they have square-low input-output characteristics only for inputs up to approximately 0.1 volt. The compact construction of the probe, minimizes lead inductances and stray capacitances, and the low value of load resistance, 270 ohms, serve to maintain an input-output characteristic substantially independent of frequency from 50 mc to at least 250 mc. At frequencies below 50 mc, the response falls off gradually.

The crystal voltmeter has been checked for susceptibility to burn-out. Peak surges of 500 volts d-c or 130 volts, 60-cycle a-c have shown no effect on the calibration. Likewise, it has been determined that the crystal can withstand r-f voltages to produce approximately 1 ma of direct current, without effect on

calibration. Higher r-f voltages, or mechanical shocks may, of course, cause a change in calibration or permanent damage.

The crystal voltmeter is intended for observation of r-f voltage across low impedances such as the output terminals of a signal generator or a low-resistance plate load of an amplifier tube. Care should be exercised in connecting the probe for high radio-frequency measurements to avoid excessive lead length and the addition of stray capacitance. When making measurements at low frequencies, say below 50 mc, it should be remembered that the 100-$\mu\mu$f d-c blocking capacitor has appreciable series reactance. It will be observed that the action of the microameter needle is somewhat sluggish due to damping by the crystal resistance. A short time should therefore be allowed for the needle to come to rest before reading the meter.

VTVM Circuits

Survey of basic vacuum-tube voltmeter circuits, including pertinent equations, evaluation of circuit performance and accuracy, and frequency and voltage range limitations of each type of circuit

By MYRON C. SELBY

THE ACCOMPANYING TABLE lists the major functional characteristics of eight fundamentally different detecting circuit elements of vacuum-tube voltmeters.

The major performance desiderata of a vacuum-tube voltmeter for frequencies up to several hundred

Circuit	Principle of Operation	Basic Formulas	Input Impedance
DIODE DETECTION (A) (B) HIGH-RESISTANCE VOLTMETER OR AMPLIFIER	C charges to E_{PEAK}. R acts to discharge C. In (B), R' and C' act as a filter to keep r-f out of d-c measuring circuit	For linear diode characteristics, $V_{d-c} = KE_{PEAK}$. $R_{EQ} = \dfrac{R}{2\,I_P R/E_{PEAK}} = \dfrac{R}{2\eta}$ η = rectification efficiency = unity (approx.) as R and E increase. For square-law diode, η is function of E	Equivalent of 1 to 25 megohms shunted with 3 to 10 $\mu\mu f$; 10^5 ohms at 300 mc is possible. In general, is function of R and E. At one value of R, input impedance is practically independent of E
DIODE RECTIFICATION INPUT R_L	$R_P = 0$ by assumption $I_{P0} = 0$ by assumption $R_L I_{AV}$ = average voltage of the positive half-cycle	For a sinusoidal input $I_P = \dfrac{E_{MAX}}{\pi R_L}$	$2R_L$
PLATE DETECTION FULL-WAVE, SQUARE LAW	Approximate parabolic lower curved portion of I_P-E_C characteristic is used. Average plate current is higher than the quiescent plate current. Biased for $i_P > 0$ throughout the cycle. R_L is usually omitted	$\Delta I_P \cong K(E_1^2 + E_2^2 + E_3^2 + \ldots)$ to a first approximation. $\Delta I_P = \dfrac{1}{4\mu_0 g_{m0}(r_P + R_L)} \times$ $\left(\dfrac{\delta g_m}{\delta E_G}\right)(E_1^2 + E_2^2 + E_3^2 + \ldots)$	Approximately 10^7 ohms at frequencies up to few mc shunted by $(C_{GP} + C_{GC})$. May drop to 10^4 or 10^3 at 300 mc depending on tube. $R_G = \dfrac{1}{Kg_m f^2 \tau^2}$ τ = electron transit time
PLATE DETECTION HALF-WAVE, SQUARE LAW	Same as above except that tube is biased to cutoff. For large R_L and $C = 0$, i_P is nearly proportional to e_G during positive half-cycles	For relatively large values of R_L and E, $I_P \cong KE_{AV}$. For small r-f voltages and low values of R_L, $I_P \cong K(E_1^2 + E_2^2 + E_3^2 + \ldots)$	Same as above
PLATE DETECTION PEAK	Tube is biased appreciably beyond cutoff	$I_P \cong KE_{PEAK}$	At negligible transit-time effect $R_G \cong K/f$ $C_G = (C_{GP} + C_{GC})$
GRID DETECTION	Operates on lower curved portion of grid-current grid-voltage curve and straight or curved portions of I_P-E_G characteristic. $X_C << R$	$\Delta I_P = g_m R\Delta I_G$ over linear portion of I_P-E_G characteristic	Relatively low
SLIDE BACK V_0, V_1	D-C bias adjusted to obtain same plate current with and without r-f input. $I_P = I_{P0}$ = few μa	Peak of positive half-cycle = E_{MAX} = $K(V_1 - V_0)$. K approaches unity as E increases and as sharpness of cutoff increases. May be as low as 0.2 depending on tube characteristics and E. V_0 = d-c voltage at $E = 0$. V_1 = d-c voltages at other values of E	$\dfrac{1}{\omega(C_{GP} + C_{GC})}$ Input resistance is approaching leakage resistance across input terminals
INVERTED TRIODE V_P I_G	I_G is reduced when r-f voltage is applied at input. V_P is negative	$E_{PEAK} \cong V_P$ required to produce same I_G. Amplification factor $\cong \dfrac{1}{\mu}$	Resistance is of order of 1,000 megohms shunted by $C_{CP} + C_{PG}$

megacycles are: (1) low-input capacitance; (2) high-input resistance; (3) short internal leads to terminals; (4) high series-resonance frequency of input-lead inductance and capacitance; (5) freedom from transit-time error; (6) maximum voltage range with minimum auxiliary equipment such as amplifiers and voltage dividers; (7) peak voltage calibration for nonsinusoidal waves and rms for sinusoidal waves; (8) linear scale or large number of overlapping scales for square-law indications; (9) negligible zero drift and steady indication; (10) calibration corrections must not be affected by ordinary line-voltage variations, aging and temperature and humidity changes, must remain reasonably constant and must not be affected by tube replacements; (11) v-t voltmeters must not generate disturbing voltages.

Associated circuits, such as amplifiers, current-balancing circuits and voltage dividers, are equally important in determining sensitivity, linearity, and range of the vtvm.

The table and text are excerpts from NBS circular 481, *High-Frequency Measurements*, by Myron C. Selby, published by the Department of Commerce and available from the Superintendent of Documents, U. S. Government Printing Office.

Output and Waveform Effect	Voltage Range	Frequency Range and Error	Calibration Stability	Remarks
Source impedance must be negligible at all harmonics, and level of harmonics must be low, otherwise error may be as large as percentage harmonics present. Output $= E_{\text{PEAK}}$	The upper limit depends on tube rating. With a sensitive d-c voltmeter or a d-c amplifier, the lower limit is a fraction of a volt	Upper limit is affected by series resonance of input L and C, anode to cathode r-f voltages and transit-time error. Range is function of voltage applied. Correction curves may be used to extend range	Good. Depends on constancy of filament voltage and emission. May require yearly calibration	This circuit followed by a self-biasing d-c amplifier seems most suitable for the widest frequency range. To eliminate low-frequency discrimination, the RC constant should be at least 100 at lowest frequency. Input series resonance increases apparent input voltage at fundamental and emphasizes harmonics more than fundamental
No error caused by reversing input, even with unsymmetrical waveform. Output $= E_{\text{AV}}$	Fraction of volt to few hundred volts, depending on R_L and tube rating	Should be calibrated at operating frequency above 1 mc. Probable range up to several mc	Same	R_L may vary from 0 to 1 megohm. For $R_L > 100,000$, error caused by slight curvature of static tube characteristic is negligible
ΔI_P depends somewhat on waveform. Theoretically there is no turnover. Phase of harmonic has no effect. Output $= (E_1^2 + E_2^2 + E_3^2 + \ldots)$	Fraction of volt to top limit within square-law range of tube (a few volts for commercial tubes)	With commercial tubes, low-frequency calibration will hold within 5 or 10 percent to 20 or 30 mc. At higher frequencies calibration at each frequency is necessary	Poor, as a result of tube aging and variations in d-c voltages	Noise output can be corrected for by subtracting it from total output. That is, $\Delta I_x = \Delta I_{\text{TOTAL}} - \Delta I_{\text{NOISE}}$
Subject to turnover and phase of harmonics. For output, see remarks	Fraction of volt to value of E causing grid current to flow	Same	Same	Output $= E_{\text{AV}}$ if plate current characteristic is linear. $= E_{\text{rms}}$ if plate current characteristic is parabolic
Subject to turnover and phase of harmonics (see remarks)	From $E_{\text{MAX}} \cong V_G$ to values causing flow of grid currents	Same	Same	Not recommended. Error might be appreciable
Error may be appreciable (see remarks)	Fraction of volt to few volts with receiving type tubes	Approximately to 10 mc	Very poor	When plate rectification takes place in addition to grid rectification, ΔI_P may equal zero at certain level of E. Output $= E_{\text{rms}}$ or E_{PEAK} depending on input and operating voltages
Subject to turnover. Output $= E_{\text{PEAK}}$ of positive half-cycle	Fraction of volt to few hundred volts. Calibration is indispensable especially below about 10 v. Calibration should be made for given I_P	Approximately to 10 or 20 mc, depending on input capacitance	Good. Practically independent of aging and operating voltage variations	Sharp cutoff is obtained with pentodes connected as triodes, with screen grid used as control element
Subject to turnover. Output $= E_{\text{PEAK}}$	Large voltages, depending on tube design	Possibly to 10 mc (see remarks)	Probably good. No experimental data available	Theoretically frequency range is limited by input capacitance. No experimental data available

Carrier-Frequency Voltmeter

Strength of signals received over power lines, telephone lines and cables in the range between 20 and 500 kc is directly indicated in db, using a fixed-gain double-superheterodyne receiver. A built-in calibration oscillator is provided

By PAUL BYRNE

THE carrier-frequency voltmeter to be described was developed primarily for making measurements on power lines, telephone lines and cables in the region between 20 and 500 kc. The specifications to which the instrument performs are based on the requirements of the Pacific Gas and Electric Company. Special features were suggested by engineers of the Bell Telephone System.

The instrument is essentially a fixed-gain double-superheterodyne radio receiver covering the required frequency range. The d-c output of the final detector operates a microammeter calibrated in db. A variable attenuator, connected between the input terminals and the first grid, provides a wide range of measurable voltages. An injection oscillator, in effect a signal generator, is included to facilitate calibration.

Circuit Details

Referring to the block diagram of Fig. 1 and the complete schematic of Fig. 2, the input filter is of the bandpass variety. The attenuator consists of a wire-wound section and a carbon-resistor section, and operates in 10-db steps.

The variable-frequency oscillator beats with incoming signals in the carrier-frequency range and produces a 1,500-kc signal at the input of an adjustable-gain i-f amplifier.

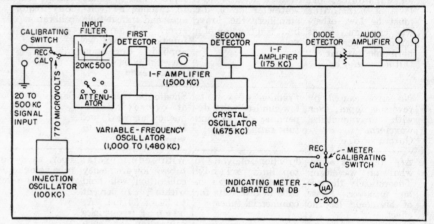

FIG. 1—Functional block diagram

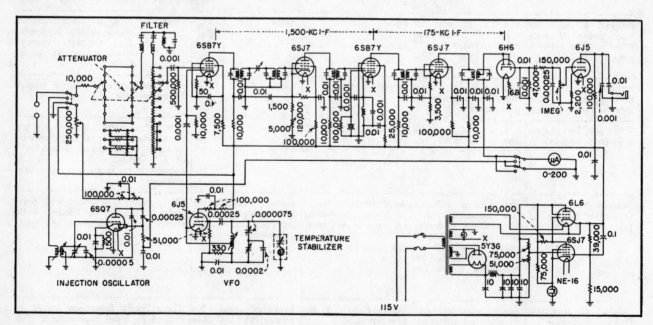

FIG. 2—Complete circuit diagram of the instrument

Temperature stabilization of the vfo is accomplished by means of a variable capacitor consisting of two fixed plates about $\frac{1}{4}$ inch by $1\frac{1}{2}$ inches in size and an intermediate movable plate operated by a $2\frac{1}{2}$-turn spiral of thermostatic bimetal. The output of the 1,500-kc amplifier combines in a second detector with that of a 1,675-kc crystal oscillator to produce a 175-kc signal which is fed to a fixed-gain i-f amplifier. Output of the 175-kc amplifier goes to a third detector. The audio output of this detector drives an a-f amplifier operating a headset used

for monitoring. The d-c output of the third detector operates the indicating meter, which is a 0-200 microammeter.

The injection oscillator delivers 0.77 volt (0 db) to the input circuit of the instrument, operating at 100 kc. A switch permits the output of the injection-oscillator monitoring diode to be read on the indicating meter for calibration purposes. Adequate signal input is provided so frequency calibration of harmonic points above 100 kc on the dial can be checked from the injection oscillator.

Performance Characteristics

The carrier-frequency voltmeter will handle from 77 microvolts to 77 volts at the input, or 80 db below to 40 db above zero level (1 milliwatt into 600 ohms). Selectivity characteristics are approximately 6 db down at 1 kc off resonance, 18 db down at 3 kc off resonance and 40 db down at 7 kc off resonance.

Input impedance is 10,000 ohms in the rejection band, and approximately 20,000 ohms in the pass band.

A-C Voltmeter for Built-In Instrumentation

By LAWRENCE FLEMING

FULL-SCALE sensitivity of 10 millivolts is provided by the electronic voltmeter whose circuit is shown in Fig. 1 and 2.

Designed for built-in instrumentation, the voltmeter is stable, linear and maintains an accuracy of three percent. Covering a range to 50 kc with a full scale sensitivity of 10 mv, it is suitable for a-f measurements made in connection with amplifiers, filters and equalizers.

Figure 1 shows the basic circuit designed by Howard L. Daniels, of Engineering and Research Associates, Minneapolis, Minn. It differs from most a-c voltmeters in the proportioning of the circuit constants. The first stage, V_1 is a voltage amplifier designed to give maximum voltage gain in the required bandwidth. The second stage, V_2, is a current amplifier. Its load resistance is determined by the following considerations: it must be higher than the resistance of the rectifier and meter combination; it must be high enough to limit the overload current through the indicating instrument and low enough to permit a reasonable value of transconductance to be developed in the current amplifier.

A full-wave bridge rectifier may

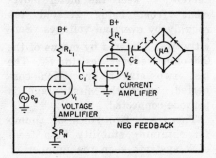

FIG. 1—Basic voltmeter circuit employs full-wave bridge

be employed in conjunction with a microammeter as shown; or a half-bridge may be used as in Fig. 2. The latter arrangement halves the sensitivity. Germanium diodes are used. The low-frequency limit of the instrument is determined by the ratio of C_2 to the plate resistance of V_2.

Since the actual load impedance of V_2 is low, this stage is inherently a wide-band device, and the high-frequency response of the circuit is that of the first stage. Because of this disparity in high-frequency response of the two stages, there is a wide margin of safety against high-frequency oscillation when feedback is applied. The low-frequency response is on a par with that of a conventional two-stage amplifier.

Average-Reading

The deflection of the indicating d-c meter is proportional to the full-wave average value of the a-c voltage applied to the input, since the signal can produce no change in the average charge on C_2.

In Fig. 1, the full-scale range of the circuit is measured by the ratio of meter current to input voltage:

$$\frac{I}{e_i} = \frac{A_1 g_{m2}}{1 + R_n A_1 g_{m2}}$$

where I = current in meter circuit, e_i = input voltage to grid of V_1 A_1 = voltage gain of V_1, g_{m2} = transcon-

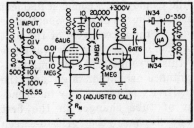

FIG. 2—Practical millivoltmeter circuit maintains 3-percent accuracy from 10 cps to 50 kc

ductance of tube V_2, and R_n = feedback resistance common to input and output circuits. For the case of no feedback, this expression reduces to the product of the gain of the first stage and the transconductance of the second.

Practical Circuit

A practical embodiment of the Daniels principle is shown in Fig. 2; the full-scale sensitivity is 10 millivolts. The frequency range is 10 cps to 50 kc, within 3 percent. Five higher decade ranges are provided. The high-frequency limitation imposed by the first amplifier plate circuit coincides with the limitation imposed by the lack of capacitance compensation in the input step attenuator. Further extension of the high end implies extra complication. In this respect, the performance is narrower than in commercial meters.

The circuit employs 14-db feedback. At 26-db feedback, low-frequency oscillation appears, providing a 12-db margin of safety.

The device is extremely insensitive to tube and line voltage changes, and is not critical as to component placement or lead dress. Filtering and decoupling in the power supply is essential.

Circuits of lower sensitivity may be made using a triode for the first stage, and they are inherently more stable.

Sensitive A-C VTVM

By LAWRENCE FLEMING

OCCASIONS sometimes arise in research work when small voltages must be measured at some point that is isolated, either electrically or physically, from ground. The circuit of Fig. 1 provides a full-scale range of 5 millivolts a-c rms for this purpose, with about 13 db of negative feedback, and has been built to occupy a space of 6 x 6 x 4 inches, including batteries. The instrument was built to measure voltages in the 15 to 40-cycle range, but is accurate within a few percent up to about 20 kilocycles.

Low battery drain and space considerations dictated the use of low B voltage, a rather sensitive d-c indicating instrument, and an A battery common to all stages. To realize the benefits of feedback while employing a common filament battery, the feedback connection is made to the screen grid of the first stage. There are two disadvantages to this arrangement, the input capacitance is rather high and the sensitivity is not entirely independent of tube changes in the first stage because the grid-to-screen path of this stage is outside the feedback loop. In general, however, the linearity and stability of this circuit closely approach that of comparable commercial instruments, and the size and battery drain are much smaller.

The Daniels device of current amplification and current feedback[1]

is employed, with the last stage designed to give the maximum transconductance commensurate with a reasonable value of d-c plate current, to keep the meter movement from being treated too roughly by overload voltages. Sensitivity is adjusted by means of the 290-ohm feedback resistor R_N. The last two stages are triode-connected, while the first stage is pentode-connected.

There are two rules of thumb for obtaining stability in a feedback system: keep the number of reactive components to a minimum, and maintain the widest possible disparity in bandwidth between the different stages. By observing these rules, a margin of about 10 db against oscillation is realized. There are no peaks at the edges of

the pass band. In circuits of this general type, incidentally, the greatest tendency toward oscillation is at low frequencies, rather than high.

A vtvm of this same type has been built that was flat to 700 kc, with a full-scale sensitivity of 100 millivolts. Three 1L4 stages were employed in pentode connection, with 22,000-ohm plate load resistors, and each screen connected directly to the 90-volt B supply.

The circuit shown is particularly tolerant of aging of the batteries. The insertion of a 1,000-ohm resistance in series with the B battery produced a change in calibration of less than 2 percent.

(1) L. Fleming, VTVM For Built-In Applications, ELECTRONICS, p 154, Sept. 1950.

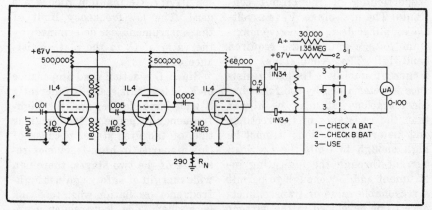

FIG. 1—Vacuum-tube voltmeter for a-c, using only one 67-volt B battery and one 1.5-volt A battery

Vacuum-Capacitor Voltage Dividers

By E. F. KIERNAN

THE VACUUM-TUBE VOLTMETER has been applied extensively to the measurement of potential differences in the research laboratory, in radio servicing and in the field of electronics generally. The popularity of this instrument is due primarily to its high input impedance which allows measurements to be made with a minimum of disturbance to the circuit. High input impedance is achieved by the use of diode vacuum tubes of small interelectrode capacitance and restricted physical dimensions which allow the tubes to be contained in compact probes.

While small physical dimensions facilitate measurements in tight places, they impose limits on the maximum voltage which can be applied. The upper voltage limit gen-

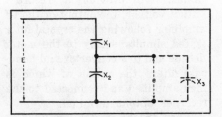

FIG. 1—Vacuum capacitor voltage dividers can be used to extend the range of vacuum-tube voltmeters, and similar indicating devices, without destroying their high-impedance characteristics

erally does not exceed 300 volts rms, and in many instruments is much lower.

The problem of extending the range of a vacuum-tube voltmeter, while at the same time preserving its high-impedance characteristics has not received a great deal of attention. This writer has found that the recent appearance on the market of a variety of compact vacuum capacitors provides components which can be assembled into voltage dividers which will not only extend the a-c ranges of a vacuum-tube voltmeter up into the kilovolts

but will also increase the input impedance as well.

The vacuum capacitor voltage divider may be used in conjunction with a variety of indicators including the electrometer, the cathode-ray oscilloscope, the vacuum-tube voltmeter and the electrostatic voltmeter. In conjunction with an electrostatic voltmeter, it can be used for d-c measurements[1].

Typical Divider

Although dividers may be fabricated by assembling a series of standard transmitting vacuum tubes, using the interelectrode capacitances in various combinations, the vacuum capacitor is much more adaptable. These capacitors may be obtained in values ranging from 1 to 1,000-$\mu\mu$f or more; and in ratings of from 10 to 30,000 volts or higher.

The dividers consist of two sections in series. The voltage division across the divider is proportional to the reactance of the sections. For instance a 5-$\mu\mu$f section in series with a 100-$\mu\mu$f section would divide the applied voltage in the ratio of twenty to one. If 100 volts were applied across the divider there would be a reactive drop of 95.239 volts across the 5-$\mu\mu$f section and a drop of 4.761 volts across the 100-$\mu\mu$f section, neglecting the shunt capacitance of a probe.

In practice, representative probe capacitance will vary between 3- and 9-$\mu\mu$f, depending on the type of diode used. In low-ratio dividers this shunt capacitance connot be neglected.

In Fig. 1, suppose X_1 is the reactance of a 5-$\mu\mu$f capacitor, X_2 is the reactance of a 50-$\mu\mu$f capacitor and X_3 is the shunt capacitance of a probe, say 6-$\mu\mu$f. If the reactance of X_1 is given the value of 1, then the relative reactance of the other

section will be

$$\frac{1}{\frac{C_2 + C_3}{C_1}} = 0.0893$$

The total reactance across the divider, relative to the 5-$\mu\mu$f section, would be $1 + 0.0893$, or 1.0893. The percentage drop across X_2 of any voltage E applied across the divider would be $0.0893/1.0893 \times 100$ or 8.2 percent. In other words, if E equals 100 volts, e would be 8.2 volts.

Since the leakage resistance of vacuum capacitors can be maintained well up in the megohm region, the effective load presented to a source of potential by a vacuum capacitor voltage divider is purely reactive from the low commercial frequencies well up into the megacycles.

The use of these dividers is not restricted to sinusoidal waveforms since pulse voltages may be divided without alteration of the pulse shape.[2] In applications involving very high voltages it is not necessary to locate the indicator adjacent to the divider; standard concentric cables may be used with remote indicators. If it is desirable to adjust the division ratio to some exact value, variable vacuum capacitors make such an adjustment simple.

Although, to the best of this writer's knowledge, there are no commercial vacuum capacitor voltage dividers on the market at the present time, this situation will probably be remedied in the near future. An especially designed unit wherein the two sections, one adjustable in capacitance, are enclosed in one envelope could be made very compact.

REFERENCES

(1) A Meter for High Voltage Measurement, *R. S. I.*, **10**, Oct. 1946.
(2) 100,000 Volt Pulses Measured With Capacitance Voltage Divider, *G. E. Rev.* May 1948.

Direct-Reading R-F Wattmeter

EASE OF OPERATION and excellent accuracy are combined in a direct-reading r-f wattmeter developed by the Naval Research Laboratory for measuring power from 30 to 3,000 microwatts. Instead of the a-c substitution method employed by many types of wattmeters for measurement of r-f power, the new type makes use of a d-c movement meter and precision resistors (thermistors) to achieve an accuracy of 4 percent or better over its power-measurement range.

A thermistor is placed in one arm of a bridge circuit whose other arms are usually 200 ohms each. A given amount of d-c current is passed through the bridge and an adjustable a-c voltage is connected and varied until the bridge is balanced. When r-f power is applied to the thermistor, the d-c current is automatically reduced until the bridge is again balanced. Thus with the bridge balanced, the change in d-c power in the thermistor is equal to the r-f power. A meter circuit is arranged to read this change directly.

Although this instrument was first intended for use in power monitoring work, other uses for it have arisen, such as that of checking signal generator output. The instrument was developed in Radio Division Two of the Naval Research Laboratory.

Bolometer Amplifier for Microwave Measurements

DESIGN AND TESTING of antenna systems and various r-f networks in the microwave regions requires reliable test equipment for determining relative or absolute r-f field strengths. A modulated or pulsed r-f signal is applied to the network and measurements are usually made by using a crystal or bolometer in conjunction with a probe to yield an output voltage $e = kE^x$ where E is the absolute field intensity in the vicinity of the probe, k is a constant which depends upon the probe configurations and units in which e and E are expressed and x is a function which depends upon the crystal or bolometer and generally will differ somewhat from a constant.

Because the output voltage level of the probing devices is low, it is necessary to amplify their outputs before they are metered. The bolometer amplifier, manufactured by Pickard and Burns, Inc., of Needham, Mass., incorporates a tunable variable-bandwidth filter, an eighth power voltage ratio expander, automatic normalization of input signals and an undecaded output voltage for operating automatic recording equipments.

Operating Principle

The instrument functions on a heterodyne system in which the input voltages to both the signal and monitor input channels are converted in balanced modulators to a 50-kc i-f, see block diagram in Fig. 1. The output of the balanced modulator in the monitor channel is amplified and detected to supply bias voltage for the controlled amplifier of the signal channel which provides the automatic normalization of voltages in the signal channel.

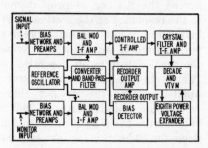

FIG. 1—Block diagram of the Pickard and Burns bolometer amplifier

Ouput of the balanced modulator in the signal channel is amplified in the controlled amplifier and then fed to the crystal filter and i-f amplifier. The output from the i-f amplifier is connected to the meter decade. Following the decade is the meter amplifier and logarithmic voltmeter.

By switching the input of the expander circuit into the output of the decade and the output of the expander into the input of the voltmeter amplifier, eighth power voltage ratio expansion may be obtained. To provide a recorder output voltage, the output of the i-f amplifier following the crystal filter is fed simultaneously to the meter decade and to a converter and bandpass filters, the output of which is then amplified and connected to the recorder output terminal.

When the bolometer amplifier is functioning with linear amplification, the decade output is amplified in the meter amplifier. The output voltage is rectified and metered on the output meter which is calibrated in a-c volts. On expand operation, the output of the decade is multiplied in the eighth power voltage ratio expander circuit to a 400-kc voltage which is then amplified in the meter amplifier, rectified and metered on the output meter.

Instrument Description

Nominal frequency range of the instrument is 400 to 5,000 cycles with the frequency dial calibrated directly in cycles. Bandwidths are selected by a switch and are 6, 12, 22, 50, 100 and 300 cycles. Input impedance is between 250 and 350 ohms for all frequencies between 400 and 5,000 cycles.

The indicating voltmeter has a logarithmic scale and is calibrated in both volts and decibels. The decade used in conjunction with the

meter is calibrated in volts full scale and is adjusted in 20-db steps from 0.01 volt full scale to 100 volts full scale.

Output voltage for recording purposes is 80 db undecaded. This out-

put is at the input frequency and is at an impedance level of approximately 50,000 ohms. Loading up to 0.01 watt maximum is permissible without causing nonlinear amplification in the output.

Load Match Test

By HEINZ E. KALLMANN

IT IS SOMETIMES DESIRABLE to check the impedance matching of a load when there is no proper test equipment on hand. If the load under test happens to be itself an indicator of current, such as a meter or a receiver (without avc), then the following simple test may be made. All the extra pieces of equipment needed are three resistors, each equal to the desired matching impedance. The indicator-load should be sensitive enough to give ample indication when fed from its source, at about one half of the regular load current.

The test consists of making up a bridge circuit, which is somewhat unconventional in that it uses the unknown impedance as an indicator in one of its arms, and that there is a switch in the null-arm where the meter would usually be. As shown in Fig. 1, the impedances in three arms of the bridge are made equal to R, the proper matching impedance of the load under test. But the load may have an impedance $R_L = R + \rho$, where the amount of the matching error, ρ, is positive if R_L is too high, and negative if R_L is too low. The generator, with source impedance R_i, need not be matched and the degree of its mismatch, $\alpha = R_i/R$, need not be known.

If ρ is zero, the load is matched and the bridge is in balance. Then one half of the generator current flows through each bridge arm and no current will flow through the switch S if it is closed. Therefore, turning this argument around, if opening and closing the switch S does not cause any change in the

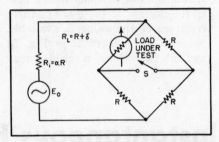

FIG. 1—Simple test setup for determining match between voltage source and load

currents through the bridge arms (through R_L), then the bridge must be in balance and $R_L = R$.

If, however, R_L is not properly matched, then closing of switch S will permit flow of current through the null arm and the currents flowing through the other bridge arms will be altered accordingly.

To determine the error ρ it is enough to observe the change of the current through the load impedance R_L, from the value i_L when the

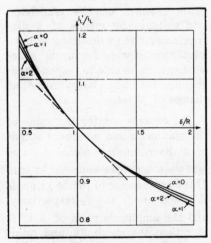

FIG. 2—Curves showing usefulness of match-test bridge circuit

switch $\tilde{S}$ is open to i_L' when S is closed. The ratio of these two current values can be computed from the parameters of Fig. 1 and is found to be:

$$\frac{i_L'}{i_L} = 1 - \frac{1}{\frac{4R}{\rho} + \frac{2\alpha + 3}{\alpha + 1}}$$

This ratio is equal to unity for $\rho = O$; no change in current.

In general, the ratio depends somewhat on the mismatch of the

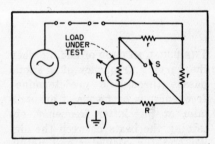

FIG. 3—Alternate test setup for use where three resistors of value R are not readily available

source impedance R_i; its values are plotted in Fig. 2 for R_L ranging from $0.5R$ to $2R$; the three curves shown are computed for different source impedances, one curve assuming that the source is matched, $\alpha = 1$, one curve for negligible source impedance, $\alpha = O$, and one curve, $\alpha = 2$, assuming a source impedance of $2R$. It can be seen that the effect of the source impedance on the bridge measurement is negligible for all practical purposes.

The only detail of the diagram that matters in practice is the tangent of the curves near $\rho = O$, shown as a broken line. It indicates which way and how much the load current changes with closing of the switch S. The load current decreases with closing of S when ρ is positive, or when the load impedance is too high, and vice versa. For small error ρ, the load current decreases by about 1 percent for each 4-percent error in matching impedance.

The smallest detectable change in load current thus sets a generally modest limit to the precision of the test. But within this limit, the load impedance may be checked and adjusted without need of any meter calibration or knowledge of

its curvature. The test is equally applicable to d-c, audio, and high radio frequencies, for balanced and unbalanced systems; and it permits leaving one source and one load terminal grounded where that is necessary.

To make the test, open one of the load connections and insert the combination of three small resistors as shown in Fig. 3. Two of their leads may be bent to form the switch S, to be prodded with a pencil for closing. If there are no three resistors of the value R available, one will do, marked R in Fig. 3; and the two others, marked r, may

be of somewhat different value though equal to each other.

In certain r-f adjustments, it is an advantage that the source and feeder remain loaded with their proper load impedance R. With all four resistors equal to R, the bridge, with open or closed switch, presents to the source the impedance R; and even if R_L is not equal to R, the impedance presented by the whole bridge is much more nearly correct. The impedance presented by the bridge to the load R_L depends on R_i and on whether the switch S is open or closed: for $R_i = R$, it is $0.6R$ in the former case and $1.66R$ in the latter.

Accurate Instantaneous Frequency Comparison

By RAYMOND M. WILMOTTE

THE USUAL METHOD of finding when the varying frequency of a signal passes through a predetermined frequency, is by means of an oscillator at this latter frequency, obtaining the beats between the signal and the oscillator and noting when the beat frequency passes through zero. That process is in general simple and satisfactory except in the case when the frequency of the signal varies rapidly. When there is a very rapid change, the beat frequency may not remain long enough at a low value for a circuit to be able to recognize it as a low frequency. The key characteristic in such a case is not that the beat frequency is zero at a particular instant, but that it changes sign. Unfortunately most circuits are unable to detect the difference between a positive and a negative beat frequency.

This problem came up in connection with special work on certain f-m systems and was disclosed some time ago to the Patent Office.

A simple circuit to distinguish between positive and negative beat frequencies makes use of the theory of the operation of limiters. It is known that when two f-m signals of different but nearly equal amplitude are passed through a limiter, the resulting output contains short periods during which the rate of change of phase is very large. These phase changes can be translated into voltages by means of a discriminator circuit designed to have a sufficiently wide frequency characteristic to be able to respond adequately to these large rates of change of phase.

The expressions for the value of the maximum and minimum output of a discriminator caused by two signals are simple and well known. If the frequencies of the two signals A and B are f_A and f_B respectively, and the amplitude ratio of A to B is r then the maximum and minimum responses of the discriminator are respectively proportional to

$$f_A + q\left(\frac{r}{1+r}\right) \quad (1)$$

and

$$f_A - q\left(\frac{r}{1-r}\right) \quad (2)$$

where

$$q = f_A - f_B \text{ and } r > 1$$

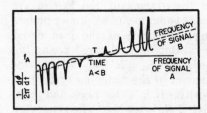

FIG. 1—Curve shows rate of change of phase of resultant as frequency B passes through frequency A

It is to be noted that when q is positive f_A is less than expression 1 and greater than expression 2, while when q is negative the reverse is true. It is also to be noted that in either case when r is nearly equal to unity, the maximum given by expression 2 differs very much more from the mean value f_A than the maximum given by expression 1.

The application of these results to the simple case of signal A of steady frequency and another signal B of frequency varying linearly is shown in Fig. 1. The horizontal line corresponds to f_A, the inclined dashed line, to f_B. At time T the two frequencies are equal. The line with spikes corresponds to the rate of change of phase of the resultant when the two signals A and B have passed through a limiter.

It is seen that as the beat frequency increases in numerical value, the spikes increase in size and occur more frequently. At time T when the beat frequency is zero the spikes disappear. Before time T the spikes are negative while after time T they are positive. That is so if the intensity of A is less than B. If A were greater than B the reverse would be the case. The important point for the present purpose is that the direction of the spikes changes as the beat frequency passes through zero. The direction of the spikes indicates therefore whether the beats are positive or negative, that is whether the frequency of A is greater or less than that of B.

The spiked line is readily turned into a voltage of the same wave form by means of a discriminator

or the equivalent. By finding from this wave form whether the positive peaks are greater or smaller than the negative peaks it is therefore possible to ascertain the polarity of the beat frequency provided the ratio r remains either greater or less than unity.

Circuit

A circuit for this purpose is shown in block diagram in Fig. 2.

The signal B is amplified, then limited and passed through a filter. The purpose of this limiter and filter is to obtain a signal of predetermined amplitude. An oscillator set at the desired frequency is added to this signal, its amplitude being either slightly greater or

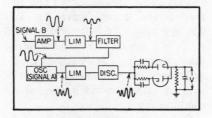

FIG. 2—Block diagram of equipment for determining exact instant when one variable frequency is of same value as another

slightly less than the signal B at that point of the circuit. It is important that the ratio of the signal

intensities remains substantially the same and does not pass through unity. The two signals A and B are passed through a limiter and discriminator which produces the spiked wave form shown in Fig. 1.

This output is then analyzed by means of two diodes to establish whether the positive maximum is greater or less than the negative maximum. The polarity of the voltage V provides the required indication. When V is zero the frequencies of A and B are equal. Thus the time T is obtained.

A corollary to this system can be developed into a means for finding accurately when the amplitude of a signal equals that of another. If the frequency of signal A is greater than that of signal B, the spikes will be negative when the amplitude of signal A is greater than that of signal B, and vice versa. The method consists, therefore, of making the frequency of signal A always either consistently greater or consistently less than that of B and finding whether the spikes are positive or negative by a circuit similar to that described. The point at which the spikes change sign is very sharp and indicates the point of equal amplitude of the two signals.

Carrier-Shift Check Meter

By J. W. WHITEHEAD

DURING the second World War a requirement arose for a simple and convenient means of checking the setting up of a transmitter working on a carrier-shift teleprinter circuit. Continuous indication of shift was not required. The method adopted is to set a stable oscillator to the transmitter *space* frequency. The beat frequency obtained between this oscillator and the transmitter when on its *mark* frequency is then equal to the carrier shift, and by comparing the note thus

produced with that generated by a stable audio frequency oscillator set to the required frequency, an indication of the error in the transmitter shift tuning is obtained and can be corrected.

The circuit layout is shown schematically in Fig. 1. It contains three main items—a stable r-f oscillator, a stable a-f oscillator, and the comparison unit or mixer.

A useful, but not essential, source of r-f is an oscillating wavemeter which is provided with a

crystal check, such as the U. S. Army frequency meter type BC-221. By using this meter as a basis of the scheme, it is possible to provide, at the same time, a convenient check on the transmitter carrier frequency.

For the a-f generator, a cathode-tap oscillator was found to be a convenient form, using as a resonant circuit a fixed capacitor and one winding of a transformer. Output is taken from a second winding on the transformer and fed to the mixer unit. An attempt made to carry out the final adjustment by means of d-c through a third winding was unsuccessful, and units are individually tuned by strapping further capacitors across the tuned winding.

The output from the audio oscil-

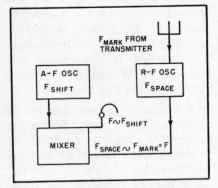

FIG. 1—Essential stages of a system for checking carrier shift

lator is taken to the grid-filament circuit of the mixer tube, the cathode circuit of which is fed with the audio output from the oscillating frequency meter. This latter tone is generated by heterodyne action within the meter between the *space* frequency produced by the meter and the carrier shift transmitter on its *mark* frequency. The audio signal resulting in the plate circuit of the mixer is applied to phones, and the beats heard allow accurate setting of the transmitter *mark* frequency.

Mixer

For simplicity of construction it was considered desirable to use one tube for the two necessary circuits,

and the double triode 6C8G was selected. Each section of this tube has its separate cathode, a fact which allows virtually complete isolation of the two circuits, thus making for enhanced frequency stability of the oscillator.

Referring to Fig. 2, the winding of transformer between terminal 4 and earth is tuned by means of fixed capacitors at C_1, strapped across it to produce the desired frequency. The precise values of these capacitors varies from unit to unit, and each must therefore be individually tuned. The scope of the instrument may be increased by providing switch S_2 to bring in further capacitors C_2 in parallel with the first bank to secure a second audio frequency. (The two frequencies in use were 850 and 720 cps respectively). Terminal 3 on T_1 is a tap on the tuned winding taken directly to the cathode of V_1, and terminal 4 connects with the grid of this tube via a parallel r-c combination.

Output from the a-f oscillator is taken from T_1 and applied to the other section of the 6C8G, V_2. The audio output from the frequency meter is applied across the cathode resistor via the capacitance. Across the plate load, therefore, appears the beat note resulting from the superposition of the two audio frequencies, and it is reproduced in the phones which are plugged in at J_1.

It was found convenient to tune the frequency meter to zero beat on *space* without switching off the a-f oscillator, and for this purpose a second jack J_2 is provided. This

jack is connected across the audio input from the frequency meter, and has an additional contact which is arranged to short the grid of the audio oscillator to ground when the jack is in use, thus stopping that tube from oscillating and avoiding the complication of having a continuous additional note in the phones while tuning to zero beat.

It may be possible for an inexperienced operator to obtain an apparent tuning point when the two tones are harmonically related. A three-position nonlocking key is therefore provided to enable the two tones to be heard independently, thus ensuring that they are of exactly the same frequency.

The original prototype was calibrated against a standard tone generator to an accuracy of ± 1 cycle, and this was used as a standard against which further models were checked. During a long period of use the stability of all the models has been good and the results have been eminently satisfactory.

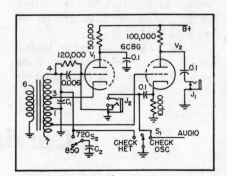

FIG. 2—Audio oscillator and mixer circuit. The center position of switch S_1 is the normal position

Direct Frequency Measurement

By L. M. BERMAN

SUCCESSIVE DEMULTIPLICATION of the frequency to be measured provides a direct method of measurement. The frequency f_x can be considered to be $k10^n + f_r$ where k and n are integers and f_r is the residual fre-

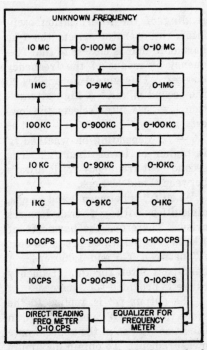

UNKNOWN FREQUENCY

10 MC	0-100 MC	0-10 MC
1 MC	0-9 MC	0-1MC
100 KC	0-900 KC	0-100 KC
10 KC	0-90 KC	0-10 KC
1 KC	0-9 KC	0-1 KC
100 CPS	0-900 CPS	0-100 CPS
10 CPS	0-90 CPS	0-10 CPS
DIRECT READING FREQ METER 0-10 CPS	EQUALIZER FOR FREQUENCY METER	

To the left is a chain of decade standard frequency generators. In the center are harmonic generators, each driven from its decade frequency. These generators feed mixer circuits that are simultaneously fed by the unknown frequency. To the right are low-pass filters passing only components of the unknown frequency lower than the decade being measured. In this manner each digit of the frequency can be determined

quency lower than 10^n. To measure the unknown frequency, it is heterodyned with a standard frequency to produce a beat that will pass through a low-pass filter whose cutoff frequency is 10^n. The required standard beating frequency for this condition is $k10^n$; thus, knowing the standard frequency in use when the low-pass filter is passing a signal, one finds k, the first digit of the frequency being measured.

Residual frequency passed through the filter becomes a new unknown frequency that can be determined in like manner. Cutoff frequency of the second filter is 10^{n-1} and the standard beating frequency is $k_1 10^{n-1}$. Measurement consists of finding the required k_1 to obtain a signal through the filter; this k_1 is the second digit of the frequency. Number of successive demultiplications depends on the accuracy to which frequency is to be measured; a direct-reading frequency meter indicates the final residual frequency.

Arrangement of Equipment

The accompanying figure shows a frequency meter employing the principle of demultiplication. A chain of relaxation oscillators and harmonic generators in the left hand column provides the standard frequencies for successive demultiplications. The 100-kc stage is synchronized by a crystal-controlled 100-kc oscillator (not shown). An oscilloscope on each relaxation oscillator (100, 10, and 1 kc) indicates proper synchronization. The harmonic generators are class-C amplifiers. Each decade frequency generator feeds a harmonic generator so that the first nine harmonics of that decade are available by switching. A vacuum-tube voltmeter shows the level of the selected harmonic. A 6L7 is used as mixer. A second vtvm indicates if a signal is passing the filter.

In operation the unknown frequency is applied to the first mixer. If it is lower than the cutoff of the first filter, the signal indicating vtvm will deviate; if not, then the proper beating frequency is selected from the harmonics of the highest decade oscillator. The process is followed through successive demultiplications; the residual frequency being indicated on the direct-reading frequency meter. As a check on the operation of the equipment, higher instead of lower harmonics can be used to produce the required beat-frequencies to pass the filters, and the unknown frequency found by subtraction.

To provide isolation from power-line frequency, the actual filters are band-pass. The 10 mc, 100, 10, and 1 kc filters pass from 600 cps to a frequency 600 cps above their normal ones; the 100-cps filter passes from 120 to 220 cps; and the 10-cps filter passes from 10 to 20 cps. The 100-cps standard frequency has been increased to 500 cps, and the 10-cps one to 110 cps. Thus harmonics of these last two beating frequencies are actually high. The direct-reading frequency meter indicating instrument scale has been increased by 610 cps so that the final frequency reading is correct without modification.

Reliable operation of the instrument depends on the mixers functioning on the proper portions of their characteristics, necessitating an input of ten millivolts below 10 mc and 0.8 volts above 10 mc. That there is sufficient voltage can be seen from the vitvm. The frequency measured by the demultiplier is, except for that portion read on the direct-reading instrument, independent of operator's judgment in reading an indicating instrument. Furthermore, no forehand knowledge of the order of magnitude of the unknown frequency is required.

Production-Line Frequency Measurements

Simplified equipment allows relatively inexperienced personnel to make extremely accurate measurements of frequencies up to 10 mc. Entire system is standardized against WWV by simple adjustments while frequency measurement is being made

By GEORGE J. KENT

MOST MODERN frequency-measuring devices depend, to a great extent, on the skill and experience of the operator. In cases where qualified operating personnel is readily available, these systems are satisfactory, but in most instances, skilled labor is at a premium.

The equipment described here and illustrated in the photographs permits accurate frequency measurements to be made by relatively inexperienced operators. After about twenty hours training and practice, an operator can make rapid measurements at 100 kc to 10 mc within 1 or 2 cps.

Method of Measurement

Frequencies are measured by a system of bracketing. The first digit (usually 2 to 10 mc) is determined by the calibration of a communications receiver. The second digit is determined by bracketing the unknown signal between known harmonics of a 100-kc harmonic generator whose fiftieth harmonic is constantly kept at zero beat with WWV. Subsequent digits are obtained by a combination of brackets and finally the last two significant figures are taken from a calibrated audio oscillator using a scope and Lissajous figures.

A block diagram of the equipment involved is shown in Fig. 1.

The frequency standard consists of a 100-kc oscillator and a series of three 10-to-1 frequency dividers. The beat between the 5-mc signal of WWV and the fiftieth harmonic of the 100-kc oscillator is heard

constantly by the operator from a loudspeaker connected to the receiver. In this way, the 10-kc, 1-kc and 100-cps subharmonics and the 100-kc fundamental are all kept standardized during the measurement procedure. When the standard is so adjusted, the receiver is tuned to the unknown frequency f_x radiated by the apparatus under test. The first digit of f_x is read from the receiver tuning dial and the second digit approximated from the tuning dial setting. Then, the unknown signal is bracketed between two harmonics of the 100-kc oscillator, thereby verifying the second digit. The next digit of the unknown frequency is then found by bracketing between harmonics of the 10-kc standard, which are readily identified also by tuning the receiver to each harmonic in turn. The 10-kc harmonic f_h' that is closest to the unknown frequency is recorded.

The unknown, and all of the 10-kc harmonics, are then injected into the first mixer. Out of the numerous beats, a low-pass filter selects the lowest, $f_b' = f_h' - f_x$ or $f_x - f_h'$ depending on whether f_h' is higher or lower than f_x. Beat frequency f_b', always between 0 and 5,000 cps, is applied to the Y terminals of an oscilloscope through SW_1 set at 1. A calibrated audio interpolation oscillator is connected to the X terminals of the oscilloscope, and by means of Lissajous figures, an approximate measurement is made.

Beat note f_b' is then applied to the second mixer. Knowing the approximate value of f_b' from the

reading of the interpolation oscillator, the operator selects the 1-kc harmonic that is closest to that frequency by means of the frequency booster. This signal he applies to the second mixer. A high-attenuation low-pass filter selects the lowest beat $f_b'' = f_h'' - f_b'$ or $f_b' - f_h''$ depending on whether f_b' is higher or lower than f_h''. The second beat frequency f_b'' is always between 0 and 500 cps.

When f_b'' is between 0 and 25 cps, difficulties with a-f transformers arise. Therefore the harmonic of 1 kc is selected which produces beat f_b'' between 975 and 1,000 cps. A band-pass filter for this frequency range is provided for such cases.

The output f_b'' is applied to the scope through SW_1 and measured in the same way as in the approximate measurement. To obtain maximum accuracy at this point, the frequency standard is now kept at exact zero beat with WWV, as indicated aurally over a loudspeaker. In this way, the last two digits are found, and the fine measurement step is completed.

Description of Equipment

The frequency standard used is basically accurate within ± 0.001 percent. The frequencies of all outputs of this standard are adjusted simultaneously by means of a vernier-operated trimmer, thereby providing a momentary accuracy of better than 1 part in 10 million.

The 100-kc and 1-kc harmonic generators are of the germanium diode type. The separate 100 and 10-kc harmonic generator employs a 6SJ7 and provides sufficient harmonic output that the 2,000th harmonic can be identified in the receiver. Harmonics up to the 1,000th have been used for measurements.

The first mixer employs a pentagrid converter type 6SA7. The three filters discriminate against unwanted beats produced by adjacent harmonics of 10 kc and 1 kc. Figure 2 shows the characteristics of the two low-pass filters. The sum of the wanted and main unwanted beats is always 10 kc or 1 kc. The curves show the desired beat f_b' or f_b'' plotted on the abscissa against the attenuation of the unwanted frequency. Other unwanted beats are either more attenuated or too weak to interfere with operation.

The second mixer is shown in Fig. 3. The important advantage of the push-pull germanium diode balanced-bridge arrangement is that only odd mixing modulation product frequencies appear in its output. Also, both f_b' and f_h'' disappear from the output of the mixer.

The receiver used has a main dial that is accurately calibrated in 100-kc steps. Vernier and bandspread dials facilitate the measurements.

A crystal-controlled variable-selectivity circuit provides a very narrow pass band. This feature is important, since in some measurements the receiver is used both as a mixer and filter. The S meter allows the operator to count and identify the harmonics as well as to estimate the relative strengths of the measured signal and harmonics.

The audio-frequency interpolation oscillator covers a band of frequencies from 6 to 6,000 cps. Its dial is broad enough to permit evaluation of about 2 cps on the most congested range below 500 cps. The oscilloscope is conventional.

Applications

The equipment described is used mainly for measurement and calibration of fundamental frequencies of crystals in frequency monitors and oscillator circuits. It is also used for adjusting crystals and for calibrating and measuring frequency drift of signal generators and audio oscillators.

The percent accuracy of measurements depends on the measured frequency. Since at the instant of measurement the 10-kc and 1-kc harmonics are standardized against WWV, the main source of inaccuracy lies in the interpolation oscil-

lator. As has already been mentioned, the inherent accuracy of this apparatus is better than 1 percent. However, by means of a switch, the interpolation oscillator can quickly be checked by comparing it with the outputs of the 1-kc

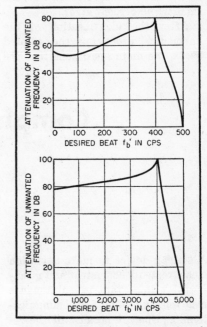

FIG. 2—Curves show characteristics of 0 to 500 and 0 to 5,000 low-pass filters

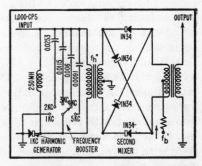

FIG. 3—Frequency booster circuit picks out desired harmonic of 1-kc harmonic generator. Push-pull crystal mixer produces only odd mixing modulation products

and 100-cps standards. When utmost accuracy is needed, this calibration may be performed immediately after the reading is made using Lissajous patterns.

It has been established in practice that maximum error made when measurements are performed

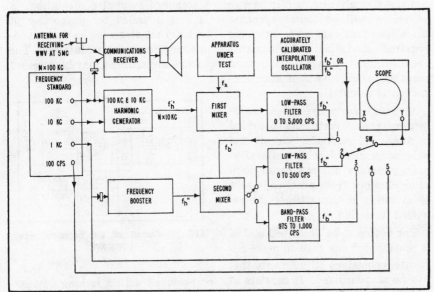

FIG. 1—Equipment is standardized by beating fiftieth harmonic of 100-kc oscillator with 5-mc signal from WWV. Interpolation oscillator calibration may be checked against 1,000 and 100 cps subharmonics of 100-kc oscillator

is about ± 2 cps. This happens only when f_b'' is close to and below 500 cps. In most other cases the error is about ± 1 cps. Thus when referred to the frequencies usually measured, namely from 2.5 to 10 mc, the average error is from 4 to 1 part in ten million. The higher the measured frequency, the smaller the percent error.

After the identification of the harmonics producing the wanted beats, the main operations that the operator has to perform are: to zero beat from the speaker, to stop simultaneously the elliptical pattern on the oscilloscope screen and immediately after that to read the dial of the interpolation oscillator. Then, he simply fills in the readings on a form and performs two simple additions or subtractions.

Actual in-use experience with the equipment for the past two years indicates that results of measurements of the same frequency, independently obtained by different operators, do not differ by more than 1.5 cps.

The author wishes to thank Brynjulf Berger whose suggestions and cooperation contributed greatly to the success of this project, and Joseph Bagdon for his constructive criticism. He also wishes to express his appreciation to Ernest Reuther for his assistance in construction and adjustment of this equipment.

Complex Tone Generator for

Deviation Tests

By FRANK A. BRAMLEY

A SIMPLE device to make deviation measurements consistent and meaningful is important to maintenance men working on all f-m communications equipment because of the recent FCC ruling that measurements must be made on such equipment at regular intervals for both frequency and modulation deviation.

Manufacturers have put new equipment on the market to make deviation measurements due to modulation very simple, but this solves only half the problem. If tone is used in making deviation tests the measurements are quite consistent, but with voice it is difficult to get the same results twice even with the same voice used to make all tests.

Preliminary tests with new type deviation meters prove that there are wide differences in the amount of deviation caused by various operators' voices even when compression or modulation limiters are used.

Older sets are usually not provided with any adjustments whatever and parts must be replaced in order to standardize the circuit. New sets with compression and lim-

iter circuits provide some adjustment, but these circuits do not operate the same on tone as they do with voice. The amount of compression produced with tone differs just as deviation produced by tone differs from that produced by voice.

If average settings on a given piece of equipment are used, and the equipment has no limiter or compression circuits, a fair sample of voices will be found to cause deviations that vary up to twice the required deviation. Adjustments are difficult to arrive at in such cases and some means of standardization is essential.

In many early type f-m transmitters the adjustments provided to tune the oscillator circuit not only cause considerable center frequency change but can cause deviation changes from practically zero to as much as three times the required deviation.

The device to be described makes it possible for one man to make accurate, consistent adjustments that can be standardized. It consists of a two-tube battery-operated complex tone generator arranged to start automatically when a micro-

phone is inserted in a special holder, see Fig. 1.

Insertion of the microphone depresses a snap-action switch in the filament circuit of the instant-heating tubes. A headphone unit placed just below the holder supplies the microphone with a complex tone. A volume control is provided to adjust the output to a level that will cause a standard amount of deviation. A jack is installed for connection of an external db meter so that standard output can be maintained. The volume adjustment may be recessed

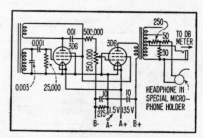

FIG. 1—Circuit of the complex tone generator

or provided with a locking device.

The oscillator-amplifier circuit used is not as simple as it might be but is stable and reasonably simple to build. It consists of a tickler-type feed-back oscillator and is adjusted by means of the grid-circuit constants to generate a complex tone having components over a wide band of frequencies. In this way the human voice is simulated to some degree and a more realistic measurement is provided.

The amplifier stage is necessary to isolate the transducer and volume-control circuits from the oscillator. Simpler circuits cause the tone to change when the volume is adjusted; the resistance - coupled amplifier eliminates this tendency.

The device shown was built to be used with Western Electric type-F3 handsets or the equivalent, but the circuit may be easily adapted to most other types of microphones.

It is important to place the microphone in a stable position over the reproducer. This can be further insured by mounting a leaf-actu-ated switch so that the tubes will not be lighted unless the microphone is properly placed.

The reproducer is mounted inside the metal case just under the microphone holder and a hole is cut in the box to release the sound.

A gimmick may be fastened to the box by means of a short chain to hold the pushbutton down.

The oscillator transformer may be any low or medium-grade transformer having a turns ratio of two or three to one. Low-grade units usually oscillate better. It is not possible to specify the exact size of the other grid circuit components because they will be dependent on the transformer used.

The output transformer matches the output pentode to a pad in the 500-ohm range so that standard db meters can be used without a correction factor. The pad reduces the level and matches the 50-ohm earpiece.

Standard portable batteries fit within the case and since the device operates only when the microphone is inserted in the holder, battery life is long.

In deciding upon grid-circuit values, it may be helpful to view the waveform on an oscilloscope while listening to the reproducer. A pleasing tone of apparent medium frequency seems desirable, one that looks quite complex but does not have any one predominating component. Strong high frequency or supersonic components are undesirable and very low frequencies are unnecessary.

By comparing the deviation produced by this device with a number of average voices that produce satisfactory deviation, a standard setting can be reached. If compression and limiting are employed the result should be a satisfactory and uniform deviation for all units.

Signal Strength Analyzer

System of thyratrons and mechanical counters automatically totals amount of time that any changing d-c voltage exceeds each of twelve chosen values. Provides greater accuracy at fraction of cost and complication of other methods

By RALPH W. GEORGE

CERTAIN RADIO PROPAGATION studies require continuous records of the percent of time a signal is above, or below, selected values over a range of variation. For example, in measuring television signal strength, it is important to know what percentage of time a usable signal can be received in a certain location.

One method for determining this voltage-time information involves the time-consuming process of going over signal strength recorder charts and adding up the time intervals during which the signal exceeds each level step. The automatic method described here accomplishes the same purpose with improved accuracy and with considerable economy, as compared to other methods. Other applications for the basic principle involved can probably be made to advantage.

The equipment gives a direct reading of the total time that a fluctuating voltage exceeds each of twelve selected values. The total time for each signal level may be read at any desired time interval.

The analyzer is designed for long-term operation. Calibration drift is inherently small. The equipment consists of two units, a control unit and a minute counter unit, the latter showing the total time in tenths of a minute on a separate counter for each voltage level. The counter-operating input voltage is determined by the bias on a miniature type thyratron with associated relay in the control unit. A separate permanent-magnet type synchronous motor, chosen for its fast starting and stopping characteristics, drives each counter.

In laboratory tests, average time measurement errors per on-off cycle have been measured as low as 0.01 second using square-wave keying on one circuit. Under more normal operating conditions, as with an input voltage changing at the rate of about 0.5 volt per second, the error may be as large as 0.1 second per on-off cycle. Test runs were made over various periods of time, from 40 minutes to 24 hours using one on-off cycle per minute.

Input impedance of the control unit is on the order of 1 to 2 megohms, working against ground. When all the thyratrons are cut off, corresponding to maximum input, the input impedance is determined by the overall impedance of the wiring and components to ground. The minimum range of input voltage depends on the use. For signal propagation studies it appears to be on the order of 0 to −15 volts. A larger voltage range will, in general, reduce errors in measurement. Source impedance of the input should be as low as possible and preferably should not exceed 50,000 ohms.

Principle of Operation

The basic functions will be described with reference to the simplified diagram shown in Fig. 1. Thyratron V_1 is the first tube to be cut off as the input voltage is raised above zero. A fixed negative bias of something less than 2 volts is obtained from the bias supply and adjusted by means of potentiometer R_1 so that an input voltage of the desired value (assumed to be less than 1 volt) will cut off V_1.

This de-energizes RE_1 which does the following: (1) turns on the synchronous motor driving counter No. 1, (2) turns on the neon light No. 1 to give a visual indication of operation, and (3) connects the input circuit to the grid of V_2. Tube V_2 has a higher positive bias than V_1, hence requires a higher input voltage to cut it off. This operating sequence is carried through 12 stages.

The bias system shown permits an independent and wide range of choice of the input voltage required for operation of each stage. The orderly sequence of operation must be preserved. The fixed bias divider may be eliminated by the use of suitable taps on the bias battery.

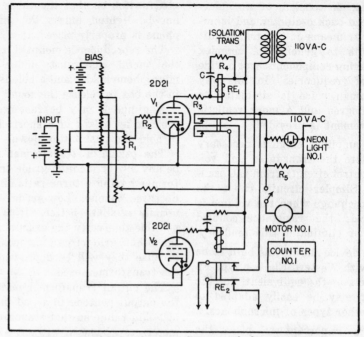

FIG. 1—Simplified schematic diagram of thyratron circuit. Fairly-sensitive, fast-operating standard telephone relays having coil resistances from 2,500 to 14,000 ohms have been used successfully

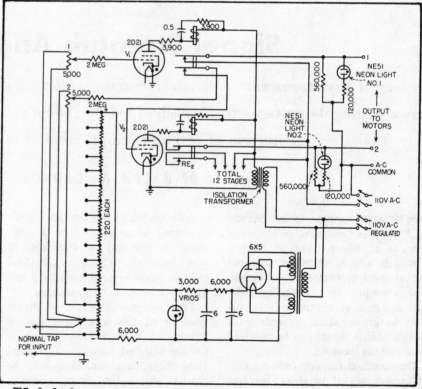

FIG. 2—In the actual equipment, the battery bias supply of Fig. 1 is replaced by an a-c supply as shown

Only one thyratron in the conducting condition, which is the only condition in which appreciable grid current can flow, is connected to the input circuit at any time. This fact, and grid resistor R_2, keep the maximum grid current flowing in the input circuit down to less than one microampere for normal bias adjustments of a few volts difference between adjacent stages. The conducting condition is maintained by leaving the grids floating when the tubes are not connected to the input circuit. Plate resistor R_3 limits the peak plate current to a conservative value. Resistors R_2 and R_3 are also important in suppressing spurious r-f radiation.

The smoothing filter R_4 and C, and the series resistor R_3, are adjusted to give a minimum differential in grid voltage for on-off operation of the relay.

Stray a-c coupling in the wiring is likely to be sufficient to light the neon light when the counter motor is disconnected and the relay contacts are open. Resistor R_5 serves to reduce this voltage, by virtue of the relatively high impedance of the source, to a value insufficient to break down the neon.

The circuit in Fig. 1 can be modified to operate with substantially the same characteristics for a zero to positive input voltage. In this case, the motor-control contacts should be closed when the relay is energized and the grid to the preceding stage should be opened. With zero input voltage, the grids would all be connected to the input and biased beyond cutoff.

A d-c amplifier can be used on the input in those applications where the added instability factor of the d-c amplifier can or must be tolerated.

Performance

The usefulness of the system is determined by (1) its stability with time, (2) the difference in input voltage required to open and close the relay contacts, and (3) the error in time measurement of grid controlled intervals.

The average time measurement error of the present equipment has been found to be less than 1/50 second per time interval, or on-off cycle, for time intervals of a few seconds or more. The fast starting and stopping characteristics of the synchronous motor used account for the small error. This motor has a low-inertia rotor, revolving at 100 rpm, which is damped by a permanent magnet in the field. The above time measurement error will not be detected except with square-wave input.

For maximum long-term stability of this system, the plate supply should be regulated. The 2D21 is relatively insensitive to ±10 percent change from normal heater voltage. The tube is operated at conservative values of plate current and should have a long life. The grid operating voltage of the 2D21 is satisfactorily constant over a wide range of ambient temperature. A set of 12 tubes in normal operating service has given satisfactory and trouble-free service during the past year. The bias supply and all resistors must be kept as constant as possible under all conditions.

Sources of Error

The inherent errors in this measuring system can be made relatively small, as will be illustrated in the following example. Assume a calibration error of ±0.1 volt including operating differential and drift, and a desired maximum error of 0.5 db in a signal recording application. This implies that a change in receiver input of 0.5 db must result in a change of not less than 0.2 volt in the receiver output.

To cover a wide range of signal fading, the receiver output should be a logarithmic function of the input, in which case the output change will be 0.4 volt per db change of input. If the system is calibrated in 6-db steps, starting at 6 db above $1\mu v$ per meter for instance, the 12 steps in the analyzer will accommodate a range of 72 db and require a maximum input voltage of 28.8 volts. In such practice, it is desired to operate the lowest-level stage as low as possible if very deep fading is to be encountered.

The calibration error assumed in the above example is conservative and may be much lower under favorable conditions. During a 7-day test the input voltage required to operate the relay, including the operating differential, was constant to within ±0.06 volt. The line voltage was not regulated and varied between 107.5 volts and 110 volts.

Less than 5 percent of over 100 type 2D21 tubes tested were found to have an appreciable change in operating grid voltage depending on the time the tube was previously in the conducting or nonconducting condition. A half-minute in each condition before checking the on-off operating grid voltage has been sufficient to show this fault.

Hum pickup in the grid circuit of the 2D21 thyratron must be kept at

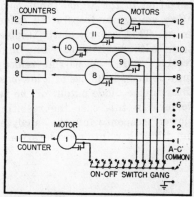

FIG. 3—Separate on-off motor switches are used to eliminate common a-c coupling through motors which would cause all neon lights to light when any motor control relay is closed

a minimum for optimum operation. This requires some care in the arrangement of the input circuit and wiring The relay should also be so arranged that a separate stack of contacts is used exclusively for switching the grid into the input circuit.

Control Unit

The circuit diagram of the control unit, Fig. 2, is essentially an expansion of Fig. 1 to include the necessary switches, power transformers and an a-c operated bias supply to replace the bias battery used in the simplified version.

A floating, a-c operated, regulated bias supply is used. This supply introduces some hum in the input circuit. The source of this hum is of fairly high impedance and therefore has more serious effects when a high-impedance signal input source is used.

In some cases the hum has been reduced by introducing a compensating voltage to ground from one of the transformer windings not connected to the bias circuit. The electrostatic shield was found to be useless in these transformers. The choice of the a-c plug polarity influences the hum and therefore has an effect on the relay operation and operating differential. An average operating differential not exceeding 0.1 volt was obtained with a 50,000-ohm input signal source.

Tube noise in a signal recording application may give an annoying variation in the signal input operating voltage and operating differential. This is particularly troublesome with weak signals and high receiver gain. A partial remedy may be had in the use of a low-pass filter in the diode output of the receiver. In this case the resulting slower response of the analyzer must be taken into consideration.

Counter Unit

The counter unit is usually turned off when making calibration adjustments on the control unit. Each motor in the counter unit (Fig. 3) must be disconnected separately to eliminate a common a-c coupling through the motors, which would cause all neon lights to be lighted when any motor-control relay contact is closed.

With five wheels, each counter will register a total of 9,999.9 minutes, or about 166 hours. Zero can be reset manually if desired.

Each counter is driven by its respective motor through a gear system giving a speed reduction of 100 to 1, so the right-hand counter wheel rotates at 1 rpm and reads direct to 1/10 minute. The numbers on the counter wheels are about $\frac{1}{4}$ inch high. The loads on the motors are so light that they are capable of starting and running backwards if there is a slight chatter in the closing of the relay con-

tacts. This was avoided by means of a simple ratchet stop engaging 4 teeth cut in the hub of the worm mounted on the motor shaft. Thus, if started in reverse, the motor is stopped in not more than $\frac{1}{4}$ revolution at which point it starts in the forward direction. The maximum resulting error, which will occur rarely, will be about $\frac{1}{2}$ revolution or 0.3-second time lost.

The compact arrangement of the counter unit permits as many as 3 counter units, and a panel containing reference time clocks, to be set side by side so that a photographic record of three measuring systems can be made with one camera. Signal-strength recording systems in use at present employ a 16-mm movie camera with an exposure rate of 1 frame every hour. A synchronous, motor-driven timer turns on flood lights a few seconds before operating the camera shutter. A 7-day clock and a 60-cycle line-controlled clock are used so that errors due to power failures will be apparent.

Accurate Time for Broadcast Studios

Inexpensive synchronous clocks keep time within 0.1 sec when driven through an audio amplifier at exactly 60-cps from a tuning-fork controlled multivibrator. They can be set when the multivibrator runs free at 55 or 70 cps

By JAMES H. GREENWOOD

ACCURATE time is necessary in every broadcast studio to comply with FCC program-log requirements as well as for coordination of local and network programming. For these purposes, an accuracy of $\pm$ 1 second is adequate.

Anyone who has investigated the various means for telling time has found an almost endless variety. The exactness that may be

obtained is limited only by the complexity and cost that can be tolerated. Every application has its own special requirements. The system to be described was designed to meet the needs of a radio broadcasting station in which various sizes and models of clocks were required for the different studios, control room, announce booths and recording room.

Many radio stations subscribe to a commercial time service that provides a special clock or clocks, which are corrected by a timing impulse sent out each hour. The system to be described comprises a 60-cps multivibrator controlled by a 240-cps tuning fork. Any reasonable number of inexpensive self-starting synchronous clocks can be operated from the 50-watt audio amplifier driven by the time standard. Means are provided for speeding up or slowing down the standard. The system can be checked to an accuracy of 0.1 second at any five-minute interval using the standard-time broadcasts of WWV.

Ten clocks are in use at present, although this is not the limit of the equipment. The larger clocks require about 4 volt-amperes, but less than 3 watts. Each clock has been adjusted for maximum power factor by connecting a capacitor across the motor winding, the capacitor being mounted within the clock case. The adjustment is not critical and only two values of capacitors are used, 0.5 μf for one type of clock and 0.75 μf for another. Overcorrection of some clocks is offset by undercorrection in others.

P-F Correction

Power-factor correction could also be accomplished for the system as a whole with all clocks connected. This alternative is less satisfactory because correction is not automatic with the addition or subtraction of clock units. Removal of the entire clock load from a tuned-output amplifier might result in damage to the output transformer.

Adjusting the clock's power factor to unity is the same as tuning the clock to resonance. The method is simple as shown in Fig. 1. Various capacitances are tried for each type of clock used and the voltage across the resistor recorded for each value. When the parameters for a type are plotted as shown in Fig. 1B and joined by a smooth curve, the capacitance resulting in minimum voltage provides maximum power factor.

All of the available clocks were found to have backlash in the gears between the second and minute hands so that they would not track together. If adjusted to agree at 15 minutes before the hour, the minute hand would lead the second hand at 15 minutes past the hour, sometimes by ¾ minute, which would then be read as a full minute.

Drags have been installed on all

clocks so that the minute hand is being pushed at all positions. The design of the drag differs for different sizes and styles of clocks, but usually consists of a thin phosphor-bronze spring pressing against the intermediate gear that transfers

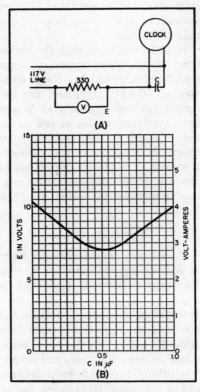

FIG. 1—Circuit (A) for determining clock power factor. Various capacitors are tried and the results plotted at (B). Correct compensation is secured with capacitance giving minimum volt-amperes

motion from the minute to the hour hand. It is readily accessible and a drag at this point takes up play in all the gear train ahead of it.

Counterbalances were also installed on the minute hands of the larger clocks to reduce the amount of friction required in the drag. Clocks so modified can be used indiscriminately on either 60-cycle power lines or from the time standard.

Setting the Clocks

The time standard is a type 2001–1 fork unit followed by a multivibrator that can be locked

in at 60 cycles, at which the output is tuned. The entire assembly was purchased as a package from American Time Products, Inc. It is followed by a commercial audio amplifier designed to operate on about 1 milliwatt input power at high impedance. Additional amplifiers can be bridged across the same 60-cycle source if needed to operate another set of clocks. Although the nominal output power is 50 watts, only about 40 watts is available at the operating frequency.

Necessary flexibility in a clock system requires that there be a means of advancing or retarding the movement in order to set it. Although there are a number of systems possible, such as selsyns operating from a three-phase power line, there is always the danger of correcting so rapidly that the instantaneous frequency of the supply falls beyond the capacity of the clock to follow synchronously. Besides, life of a clock run at high speed (such as 120 cps) is seriously reduced. Slowing the system by simply shutting off power is not feasible because some clocks coast more than others.

A good solution is modification of the multivibrator to permit operation slightly above and below 60 cps, as shown in the circuit of Fig. 2. When switch S_1 is in the center position, normal operation occurs at 60 cps. In the upper position the clocks run fast and in the lower they run slow. Because the multivibrator output is tuned for 60 cps, operation at a higher frequency results in reduced output. Accordingly, resistor R_2 is automatically switched in to reduce the 60-cps output but is disconnected during operation at higher or lower frequencies.

Contacts on the upper portion of the switch, S_{14}, in the cathode circuit of the 12AU7 tube, should be of the shorting type (make-before-break) so that there will be no interruption of the multivibrator as the switch is operated. The switch should disconnect the tuning-fork drive before it has changed the speed of operation of the multivibrator to either fast or slow speed. This action eliminates beat notes between the tuning fork and the detuned multivibrator and also assists in maintaining uniform output voltage. A switch having suitable characteristics can be assembled from one switch deck with nonshorting contacts (disconnecting the input) and one switch deck with shorting contacts (controlling the speed of the multivibrator).

Frequency Limits

The resistor and capacitor values shown in Fig. 2 result in setting frequencies of about 70 and 55 cps. Frequencies of 66 cps and 54 cps would be somewhat preferable since the change in each case would then be 1 second in 10, simplifying the daily setting against WWV signals.

The variable 3,000-ohm resistor R_1 in the multivibrator cathode circuit should be initially adjusted to the center of the range over which the tuning fork maintains control. An oscilloscope is handy at this time. One pair of plates is connected to the amplifier output and the other pair to the 60-cps power

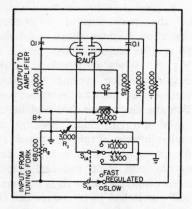

FIG. 2—Multivibrator circuit ordinarily tuned to 60 cps and driven by tuning-fork. In free-running positions of switch S_1 it can be used to speed up or slow down clock system for setting

line. If the clock-amplifier and the power-line frequencies are the same, the pattern on the scope will be stationary. When the multivibrator is detuned so far that the fork loses control, the pattern will rotate several times a second. The

condition becomes immediately apparent with an oscilloscope, whereas several minutes would have to elapse before a change in the speed of the clock system could be detected. The exact speed of the fast and slow positions can be determined in the same manner if a calibrated audio oscillator is used instead of the power line on one pair of plates.

It will be noticed that the waveform of the time standard is not perfectly sinusoidal. Few commercial 50-watt amplifiers are designed for full undistorted power output at frequencies as low as 60 cps. Usually most of the distortion occurs in the output transformer. However, it is almost impossible to produce sufficient overload distortion to disturb the operation of the clocks.

Auxiliary Power

It was not considered necessary to provide a spare amplifier or tuning fork. Instead, provision is made to switch the clock system automatically onto commercial power if the regulated supply falls below 90 volts. At the same time, power is removed from the amplifier, tuning fork and multivibrator and a warning light goes on at

master control. As shown in Fig. 3, power is available from two separate trunks. Commercial power for the emergency operation of the clocks is obtained from the trunk other than that used for the amplifier. A plug-and-socket system allows rearrangement of power inputs.

The undervoltage relay used to transfer the clocks from one system to the other is a standard 5-pole double-throw type designed for 115 volts 60 cps. A resistor R_1 can be added to cause the relay to drop out with 90 volts across the coil and resistor in series. In the unoperated position of the relay, this resistor is shorted out in order that the voltage at which the relay characteristically closes will not be essentially altered by this addition. The contacts should be adjusted so that as the voltage across the relay is reduced contacts 2 and 3 open before contacts 10 and 11 close. This arrangement will prevent any tendency towards chattering in normal operation. Since the relay is connected across the amplifier output, its power factor should be compensated as was that of the clocks.

Maintenance practice demands that the amplifier system be checked periodically. This is accomplished

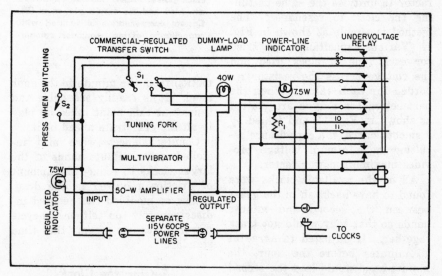

FIG. 3—Automatic switching circuits to transfer clock system from regulated 60-cps source to commercial power. Amplifier and associated circuits can be checked without interfering with clocks. Two power mains insure continuity of service

by means of the dpdt switch S_1 in the COMMERCIAL SOURCE position. It applies power to the amplifier without disconnecting the clocks from the commercial system. A 40-watt lamp load is connected to the output of the amplifier at the same time.

After the amplifier has been adjusted for normal output, pushbutton S_2 (Fig. 3) is held down, maintaining an uninterrupted supply of power to the amplifier while the dpdt switch S_1 is returned to the REGULATED SOURCE position.

To facilitate maintenance, a plate-current metering system is used, with appropriate resistors connected in the plate or cathode circuit of each tube. A rotary triple-pole switch connects a 1-milliampere meter across the resistors in sequence. For a-c measurements on the output voltage from the amplifier and that of the power lines, a copper-oxide rectifier is switched into the circuit. The meter and selector switch are illustrated.

Clock Outlets

Special outlets are installed in the clock wiring system so that it is impossible to plug in other devices. The outlets are Hubbell 6822 or equivalent two-wire polarized. Alternatively, a standard double-T slot, single, plastic receptacle can be modified by cementing Bakelite plugs in the arms of one of the T's. Each clock is equipped with a 6918 polarized plug cap. This cap can be used in any receptacle having double-T slots, allowing the clocks to be tested on commercial power.

Standardizing the System

In order to compare the system with the standard time signals from WWV the special clock (illustrated) was assembled. It comprises a B3 Telechron motor operating at 1 rps, mounted with a suitable face plate, cover glass and indicating hand. The dial is divided into ten portions as shown. The hour, minute and second are determined from a standard clock, while tenths of a second are clearly indicated by the position of the hand at the start of the tick from standard-frequency station WWV.

MICROWAVES

UHF Communications System

Crystal-controlled microwave transmitter and companion double-superheterodyne receiver operating in 940-960 mc band provide seven voice channels for communication, telemetering and remote control, with maximum bad-weather reliability for public utility systems

By FRANK B. GUNTER

EXPANSION of the facilities of industrial organizations such as power companies, railroads and pipe lines has created an increasing demand for point-to-point communication facilities for voice communications, supervisory control, telemetering, load control, protective relaying and allied functions. However, the crowding of the lower-frequency spectrum and the susceptibility of wire lines to outage in sleet storms and other bad weather make it desirable to perform many of these functions by using uhf radio equipment.

An analysis of possible customer applications indicated that most customer needs could be met with seven voice channels and that a large number could be met with as low as four voice channels. Based on this investigation, it was decided to develop microwave equipment operating in the 940–960 mc band, having a signal bandwidth of 30 kc, and to develop audio multiplexing equipment which could transmit seven voice channels in the 30-kc band. In applying the voice channels, several tones can be used in each channel to permit several functions to be carried out simultaneously.

A block diagram of the uhf transmitter and receiver is given in Fig. 1. The 6-mc phase-modulated crystal oscillator is followed by four tripler stages and a doubler output stage to get to the desired output frequency. The receiver is a double superheterodyne type with crystal-controlled oscillator and a tunable-cavity preselector at the input.

UHF Transmitter

A phase modulator was chosen for the transmitter because of circuit simplicity and because it permitted direct crystal oscillator control of frequency. A reactance tube may be used for phase modulation, but it has a disadvantage. The output circuit of such a reactance tube will ordinarily have inductive and capacitive components of admittance which are individually large compared to the conductive component. To minimize harmonic distortion, however, the variable reactive admittance introduced by modulation must at maximum modulation be small compared with the conductive component and therefore very small compared with the individual reactive component of the circuit admittance. Thus a very accurate tuning adjustment of the tank circuit is required to maintain the entire output circuit, including the reactance tube, normally conductive.

Variable Conductance

The phase modulator used is a variable-conductance type in which the reactive components of the output circuit admittance do not directly enter into the phase deviation. This results in a phase modu-

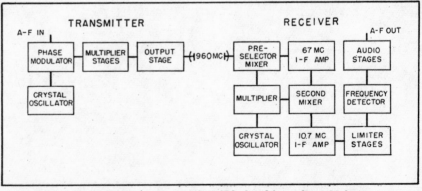

FIG. 1—Complete uhf system providing 30-kc band for audio multiplexing

lator which is not highly critical in adjustment for very low percentages of harmonic distortion. This phase modulator is inherently regenerative since its function is to provide a variable negative conductance, but circuit constants were selected which eliminated the possibility of oscillation.

The variable-conductance phase modulator is represented in the simplified diagrams of Fig. 2. Modulator tube V_1 varies the conductance of the load offered to the crystal oscillator tube by tank circuit C_1–T_1. The equivalent circuit in Fig. 2B shows that the modulator presents an admittance to terminals 1 and 2 that contains a negative conductance vector whose magnitude is proportioned to the transconductance G_m

If we combine these equations and, by proper design, make $1/\omega C'$ very much greater than $R + j\omega L'$, we obtain

$$Y = \frac{I_1 + I_P}{E} = \frac{1}{R_P} - G_m \,\omega^2\, L'\, C' + j\,(\omega C' + G_m R\omega C') \qquad (4)$$

Since $G_m R$ is very much less than 1 and $\omega C'$ is very much greater than $G_m R \omega C'$, there remains

$$Y = \frac{1}{R_P} - G_m \,\omega^2\, L'\, C' + j\,\omega\, C' \qquad (5)$$

We can now replace Fig. 2A with Fig. 2D, with G_a representing the equivalent parallel conductance of T_1 including secondary loading. Here $-j/\omega L$ is the inductive susceptance of the transformer, $j\omega C$ is the capacitive susceptance of all capacitances involved, $1/R_P$ is the

ceptance B which varies by the angle θ as G_m is varied by modulation. If θ is kept small enough so it is approximately equal to $\tan \theta$, then the phase of the oscillator current varies linearly with modulation.

The low-power multiplier (tripler) stages of the transmitter consist of push-pull triode tubes. Push-pull operation was chosen to eliminate even-order harmonics. A small amount of regenerative feedback (well below that required for oscillation) in each stage improves efficiency. Tuning components are selected so that the multiplier stages cannot be tuned to the wrong harmonic.

Mechanical and electrical features of the driver and output stages both using Lighthouse-type planar-element triodes, are shown in Fig. 3. The input (cathode) circuit of the driver stage extends outside the plumbing assembly and is adjustable in inductance by positioning of the crossbar which connects between the cathode posts of V_1 and V_2. The heater and cathode d-c leads are contained inside the plumbing assembly and leave it at the r-f ground potential. The 480-mc output circuit of V_1 is a cavity tuned by C_2. An adjustable regenerative feedback control C_1 is provided to improve efficiency.

The 480-mc output of V_1 couples to the cathode input circuit of doubler amplifier V_2 through an orifice connecting the two cavities. This cathode input circuit is fixed tuned and is designed to be resonant below normal operating frequency. The V_2 output circuit is tuned by C_4 and also has a regenerative feedback control C_3 to improve efficiency. Output (940–960 mc) from this cavity is taken from loop L_1, which is normally connected to the transmitting antenna through coaxial cable. An additional loop, L_2, is provided for monitoring.

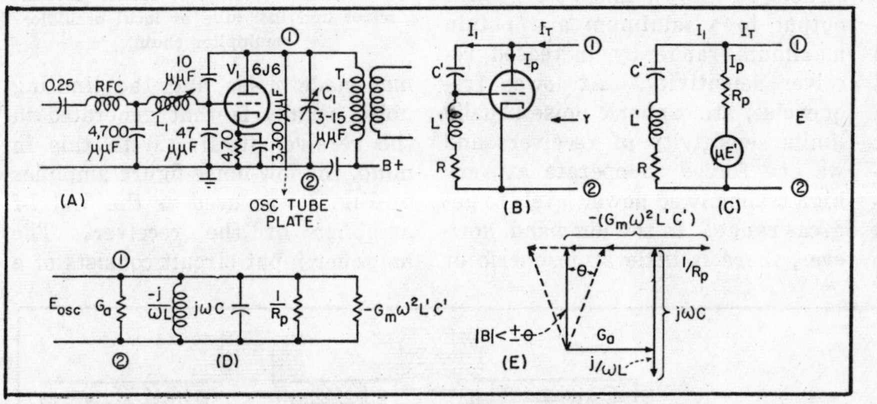

FIG. 2—Phase modulator, with equivalent circuits and admittance vector diagram

of V_1. This admittance vector is then combined vectorially with the admittance of the load circuit to produce a susceptance vector whose angle is a function of the G_m of the modulating tube. If the operating point of the phase modulator tube is selected so that G_m is a linear function of modulation, then the phase of the current in the load circuit is a linear function of modulation.

Figure 2C is equivalent to Fig. 2B with E' representing the modulating voltage. The following equations can be set up:

$$I_1 = \frac{E}{R + j\,(\omega L' - 1/\omega C')} \qquad (1)$$

$$I_P = G_m E' + \frac{E}{R_P} \qquad (2)$$

$$E' = \frac{E\,(R + j\,\omega L')}{R + j\,(\omega L' - 1/\omega C')} \qquad (3)$$

positive conductance of the modulator tubes, and $-G_m\,\omega^2\,L'\,C'$ is the negative conductance of the modulator circuit.

The vector diagram of Fig. 2E shows the addition of all of these admittances, giving a resultant sus-

Table I—System Characteristics

Tuning range—*940–960 mc*
Transmitter output—*5 watts*
Transmitter spurious output— *–60 db*
Frequency stability—*better than 0.005%*
Receiver sensitivity—*10 microvolts input for 20 db noise quieting*
Rejection of modulated signal 1 mc from center frequency of receiver—*80 db*
Receiver spurious response— *–70 db*
System noise and distortion—*less than 1%*
System intermodulation—*less than 1%*
Maximum channel attenuation permissible —*125 db*

UHF Receiver

At the input of the receiver is a double-tuned cavity-type preselector. This unit, together with the last tube in the local oscillator multiplier chain and the detector crystal, is shown in Fig. 4. The inductances and capacitances indicated symbolically here actually consist of posts and diaphragms extending into and across the walls of a rectangular cavity. Thus, L_2 and C_2 represent one tuned circuit which is coupled by diaphragm M_2 to another tuned circuit represented by L_3 and C_3. These two tuned coupled circuits provide the selectivity desirable for discrimination against strong off-frequency signals from radar sets and other high-powered equipment which might shock-excite the cavity and damage the detector crystal.

Radio-frequency input to the cavity is obtained by means of a post represented by L_1, which is coupled to the two tuned circuits by another post represented by M_1. The plate tank circuit of local oscillator multiplier tube V_1 comprises a post and tuning screw represented by L_5 and C_5. The incoming r-f signal from the double-tuned preselector circuit and the output from the local oscillator are coupled to the detector circuit by another post represented by L_4. To give further protection to

the crystal detector against the possibility of excitation of the cavity by higher-frequency signals which might cause the cavity to resonate under some other mode, a low-pass filter consisting of L_6, C_1 and C_4 is inserted between the cavity output post and the crystal detector.

To facilitate tuning the preselector, a loading resistor can be placed in each tuned circuit of the cavity to load it so that the other section can be tuned independently. The cathode cavity of V_1, which acts as a tripler stage, is excited at about 340 mc from the local oscillator multiplier chain. The output of the crystal detector is at 67 mc.

Generally speaking, the larger the power output from a uhf tube, the shorter its life. This makes it desirable to limit transmitter power output to a minimum and obtain maximum range by increased receiver sensitivity. At lower frequencies, atmospheric noise usually limits sensitivity of receivers and we are forced to operate at very high transmitted power levels to get great range. In the uhf band, however, there is little atmospheric or

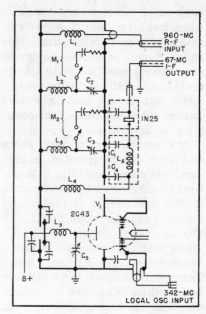

FIG. 4—Receiver preselector, crystal mixer and last tube of local oscillator multiplier chain

man-made noise and the limiting noise usually is that generated in the receiver itself. With this in mind, the low-noise-figure amplifier of Fig. 5 was used as the first i-f amplifier of the receiver. The amplifier input circuit consists of a

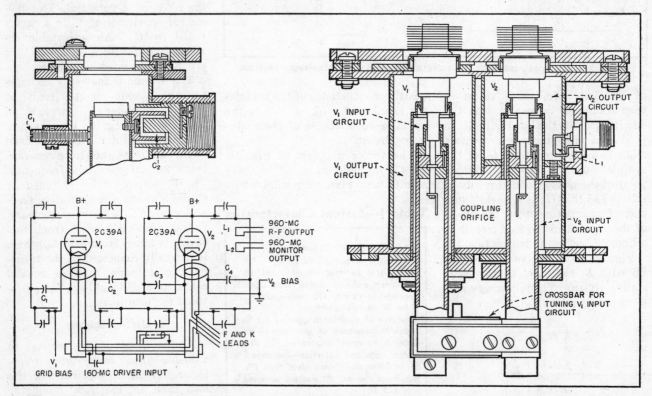

FIG. 3—Mechanical and electrical details of plumbing used with Lighthouse tubes for driver and output stages of transmitter

triode-connected 6AK5 which drives a grounded-grid 6J6 stage. This combination has the gain and stability of a pentode and the low input impedance of a triode, giving a very low noise figure.

The amplifier tank circuits are tuned by adjustable brass slugs. The coils are shunted by capacitors to minimize variations in tuning with variations in tube characteristics. These circuits are damped by 6,800-ohm resistors in the grid circuits of succeeding stages to obtain desired band-pass characteristics.

The overall gain at 67 mc from the crystal to the second mixer grid is about 90 db. Remote-cutoff tubes are used and avc voltage is applied to prevent nonlinear operation of the receiver, giving adjacent-channel performance comparable with the overall selectivity.

The second mixer is a type 6J6 dual-triode, with the output signal from the 67-mc i-f stages fed to one grid and a local oscillator signal fed to the other grid. A common cathode inductance mixes the two signals to give a 10.7-mc output which is fed to the second i-f amplifier.

The 10.7-mc i-f amplifier assembly is largely conventional in design, using three 6AU6 amplifier stages operated with fixed bias. The gain per stage is about 25 db. The i-f transformers for these stages are slightly under-coupled and loaded to give the desired pass band.

The avc voltage for the 67-mc i-f amplifier is obtained from a dynamic limiter circuit, which is effectively a voltage doubler operating across the output of the last 10.7-mc

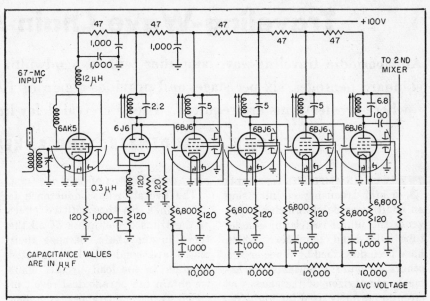

FIG. 5—Details of 67-mc i-f amplifier, which feeds into second mixer stage to produce 10.7-mc second i-f value for further amplification

i-f transformer. The avc voltage is delayed by the connection of a 1-megohm resistor to +150 volts. The avc bus is prevented from going positive by half of a 6AL5 dual-diode connected to it.

Additional limiting at 10.7 mc is obtained in a grid bias limiter using a 6AU6 tube. This limiter is operated with a short time constant in its input grid circuit to enable it to handle high-frequency amplitude modulation produced by adjacent-channel signals.

The frequency discriminator is of the ratio-detector type. The transformer is tuned by a variable air dielectric capacitor in the primary and a powdered iron slug in the secondary. The fixed secondary capacitor is of the zero-temperature-coefficient type to minimize effects of changing temperature. A

bifilar winding is used for the secondary to maintain good balance.

The audio-frequency amplifier consists of three stages— a pentode voltage amplifier, a pentode phase inverter, and push-pull pentode output tubes with cathode circuits provided with a means of balancing anode currents for minimum harmonic distortion. The amplifier is designed to give outputs up to +16 dbm with low distortion at frequencies up to 30,000 cycles.

After extensive laboratory tests, preproduction models of this equipment were installed on the property of the Pennsylvania Electric Corp. near Johnstown, Pennsylvania, and put in operation in February 1949. These sets have been operating on a 24-hour-a-day basis to supply voice communications, telemetering, supervisory control and protective relaying.

Traveling-Wave Chain Amplifier

An aperiodic traveling-wave amplifier with a bandwidth from 10 kc to 200 mc uses standard pentodes, six per stage, and provides a gain of 10 db. Stages may be cascaded where greater gains are required. Uses Percival delay-line coupling, or distribution

By H. G. RUDENBERG AND F. KENNEDY

THE CHAIN AMPLIFIER represents a high-frequency circuit using an additive principle which circumvents the limits restricting single-tube wide-band amplifiers which have been described by Wheeler and others. Figure 1 presents a schematic comparison of the classes of circuits normally used for high-frequency amplifiers, and the further development into a full chain. For purposes of comparison, only the interstage coupling networks are shown. Figure 2 shows the experimental circuit and response of an early form of such an amplifier.

The circuit utilizes a chain of vacuum tubes, the grids of which are connected to the various nodes of one delay line and the plates of the tubes to the corresponding nodes of a second line of similar time delay. These lines can be lumped-constant low-pass filters, having series inductances separating the shunt capacitances which include those of the tube electrodes and wiring. Traveling waves impressed on the grid line at one end of the chain emerge at the opposite end of the chain on the plate line, amplified by the tubes which essentially operate in parallel. Stages are cascaded by connecting to the plate line of the first chain the matched grid line of another amplifier chain through appropriate coupling networks.

Primarily the improved performance of the Percival circuit is due to the separation of the interelectrode capacitances of adjacent tubes. Thus, the impedances and limiting frequencies of the delay lines are a function of the electrode and

* Now with the Raytheon Manufacturing Co. at Waltham, Mass.

stray capacitances of only one tube.

The overall transconductance is determined by the additive effect of the transconductances of all the tubes in the chain, because their plates are conductively connected together in the load circuit. Thus we obtain the paradoxical result of added transconductances and separated tube capacitances.

Traveling-Wave Tube Comparison

The traveling-wave or helix tube of Kompfner and its later development by Pierce, Field and others is much more recent than the chain circuit. Its operating principles are quite different from those of the pentodes used in the chain amplifiers, being more analogous to the operation of a klystron. Basically, the traveling-wave tube is characterized by a completely distributed helix coaxial with an electron beam. Electromagnetic waves traveling on the helix from the cathode end toward the collector (Fig. 3) continuously interact with the electron beam and travel down the tube with approximately the same velocity as the electrons.

In the simpler forms of these tubes the amplified wave is taken off from the output end of the helix. This contrasts markedly with the chain amplifier which consists of a number of pentodes linking two lumped-constant delay lines. Here the electrons flow from the grid line to the plate line within each tube. They only flow down the plate line after leaving the tubes.

These differences of operation result in considerable differences of characteristic. The standard tubes of the Percival chain circuit are used with a conventional power

supply of several hundred volts. The Kompfner helix-type traveling-wave tube is commonly operated at several thousand volts.

The fact that several wave lengths of a high-frequency wave on the helix are necessary to ensure proper space charge bunching and wave amplification means that such a tube will operate at high frequencies, usually several hundred or thousand megacycles. In fact, no longitudinal-velocity-modulated tube will operate at very low frequencies. Furthermore, the conductively common input and output circuit of the helix tube would only lead to regeneration at low frequencies. In addition, the requirement of a definite constant electron beam velocity makes the tube quite critical in regard to beam voltage.

On the other hand, the chain amplifier circuit, with proper coupling networks, can perform at low frequencies and, in principal, at d-c. The plate and grid circuits, although delay lines, are physically separate from each other and should have no coupling other than that provided by the electron streams of the many tubes. Thus, although the upper frequency limit of the chain, as limited by most pentodes, is near 300 megacycles, this bandwidth represents many decades of the spectrum. On the other hand, a bandwidth of 1,000 megacycles at 3,000 megacycles, a representative traveling-wave tube operating point, is not even one octave of relative bandwidth.

In order to calculate the performance of a chain amplifier we must first examine its operation in more detail. The plate current of each tube divides, one half traveling

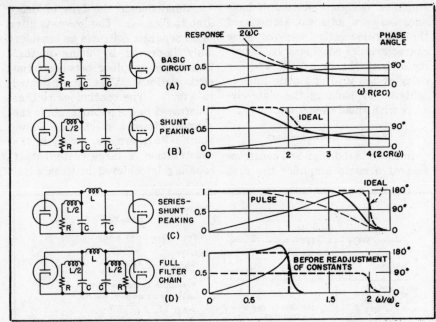

FIG. 1—Schematic comparison of several circuits normally used for high-frequency amplifiers and the further development into a full chain amplifier

forward and the other half backward along the anode line to its termination or load. Consequently, at the output end of the plate line, Fig. 4, the currents traveling forward from all the anodes will add, provided that their phases are synchronous. This condition is achieved with lines having equal delays.

The parallel operation of the tubes is most easily visualized by noting that the contributions to the output from all tubes have traveled, either on the grid or on the plate line, through the same number of delay-line sections. The currents traveling backward on the plate line are, except at the lowest and highest frequencies, out of phase with each other and nearly cancel. They are absorbed by the plate resistor which should be chosen to prevent reflections. This also applies to the grid terminating resistor.

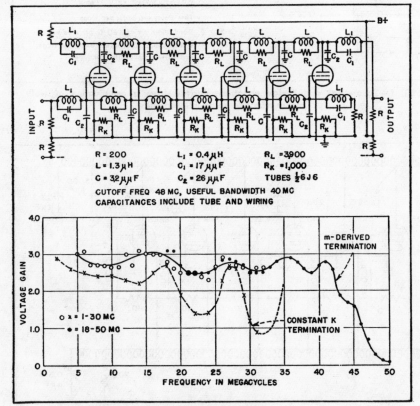

FIG. 2—Experimental full chain circuit used to check design equations. One half of a push-pull amplifier circuit is shown. The graph shows the gain of the delay-line-coupled traveling-wave amplifier. The improvement obtained through the use of m-derived terminating sections over a constant-coupling termination is obvious

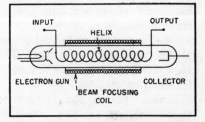

FIG. 3—The chain amplifier, which is not to be confused with the traveling-wave tube

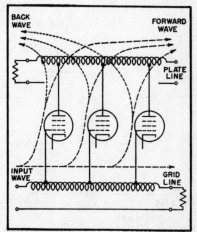

FIG. 4—The plate current of each tube of a chain amplifier divides, one half traveling forward, and adding with that of other tubes, and the other half traveling backwards and canceling with backward currents from other tubes

Operation and Design

Figure 5 lists the theoretical and design equations which can be derived from a combination of well-known tube and delay-line formulas. For a simple line all the standard delay-line design equations are applicable. Two important design factors should be considered. The first is optimum gain per chain. Cascading of stages with gains less than unity is useless. However, in stages with large gains additive connections of tubes increase the gain more slowly than multiplicative connections.

The optimum balance occurs when enough tubes are added to a chain to achieve a gain of $E = 2.718$ (8.7 db) and then such chains are cascaded. Such a design is most economical of tubes. As a gain of E is nearly 10 db, this value was used in the design of a commercial amplifier circuit (Fig. 6).

Secondly, the adverse effects on the frequency response of both the back wave of the amplifier and the standing waves on the lines must be avoided by matching the delay lines to their terminating resistors. This required the use of m-derived terminating sections.

Linear phase and impedance characteristics are two other important considerations in chain amplifier design. Mutual inductance between adjacent sections of the delay-line coils improves these characteristics considerably. Equality of both the impedance and the delay of the grid and plate lines is achieved by padding the plate circuits with small capacitors.

Practical Considerations

In the actual design and construction of a chain amplifier the first consideration is the type of delay line to be used. The low-pass filter with separate coils can be considerably improved by using mutual-inductance coupling between adjacent sections. This is illustrated in Fig. 7. The continuous coil, as illustrated in the photograph, is the simplest from a mechanical viewpoint. Furthermore, owing to the construction, a large coefficient of coupling is achieved between adja-

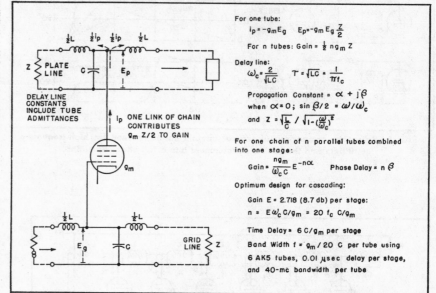

FIG. 5—Theoretical and design equations derived from a combination of well-known tube and delay-line formulas

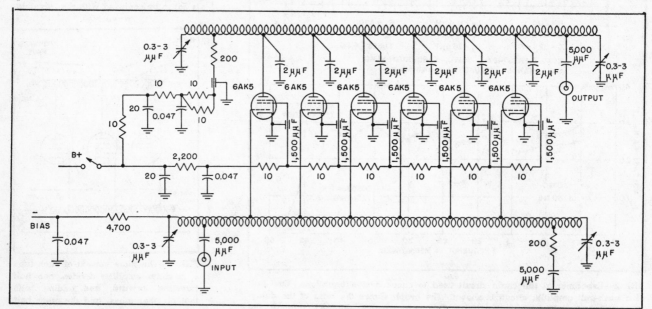

FIG. 6—The gain of the amplifier whose circuit is shown above is about 10 db to 200 mc

cent sections of the line. This has the beneficial effect of a more linear phase response.

A more elaborate configuration is the bridged-tee or all-pass line. This combination of mutual-inductance coupled coils and bridging capacitors has the advantages of constant impedance and good delay response. These are characteristic of the lattice-type filter from which this configuration is derived.

As mentioned previously, the delay lines are critical as to terminating impedances. The impedance of a low-pass filter or a continuous-coil type of line changes with frequency, and so matching sections are required to match the load resistors. A mismatch results in standing waves, the amplitudes of which are proportional to the products of the reflection coefficients from the two ends of the mismatched lines. In the case of the lines shown in Fig. 2 and 6, matching half-sections have been used for terminations. The variable capacitors at the ends of the section provide some adjustment for stray capacitance, as well as for the connecting capacitance at the input and output coaxial cable connectors.

Equality of impedance of the two lines may be achieved by adding a small capacitance at each section of the plate delay line. This also has the effect of equalizing the delay in the plate and grid lines although it produces a slight reduction of voltage gain. The equality of line impedances also facilitates the matching of the plate line to the

grid line of a following chain or stage when two are cascaded.

Some low-pass compensation is desirable if an extended low-frequency response is required. This can be achieved by placing a compensating capacitor in series with the resistor terminating the grid line. With careful choice of components the amplifier shown in Fig. 6 can have a cutoff as low as 10 kc.

Of considerable importance in the practical construction of all very-wide-band amplifiers is the shielding between adjacent components of the grid and plate circuits. Similarly, it is important that there is no coupling between stages due to common ground currents.

High-Frequency Limitation

The ultimate high-frequency limit of the chain amplifier is set by the large grid input admittance of most tubes at high frequencies. At 200 megacycles the input conductance of a 6AK5 pentode is in the neighborhood of 2,000 ohms. Thus, a chain of such tubes introduces considerable damping into the grid delay line at the highest frequencies. Some reduction of grid loading is possible by controlling the screen lead inductances. For further extension of the frequency range, tubes should be used in which the cathode inductance does not cause such large grid loading.

Acknowledgment

Considerable work has recently been performed at many laboratories on the chain amplifiers. We

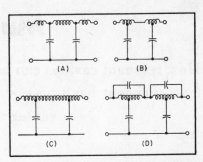

FIG. 7—Steps in the development of the best type of delay line to use in a chain amplifier

wish to acknowledge the continued interest of E. L. Chaffee who directed the work while one of the authors held an NRC-RCA Fellowship in Electronics at Harvard University. The basic experiments at Harvard University were assisted by ONR contract N5ori-76 T.O.I. Further development was performed at Spencer-Kennedy Laboratories, Inc.

BIBLIOGRAPHY

W. S. Percival, British Patent 460,562 (1935-37).
H. A. Wheeler, Wide-Band Amplifiers for Television, *Proc. IRE*, **27**, p 437, 1939.
Television Antennas for Apartments, ELECTRONICS, p 100, May 1947.
H. G. Rudenberg, Some Characteristics of a Delay-Line Coupled Wide-Band Pulse Amplifier, (Abstract), *Phys. Rev.* **73**, p 543, 1948.
H. G. Rudenberg, Progress Reports, Cruft Laboratory, Harvard University, Contract N5ori-76 T.O.I.
E. L. Ginzton, W. R. Hewlett, J. H. Jasberg and J. B. Noe, Distributed Amplification *Proc. IRE*, **36**, p 956, 1948.
H. E. Kallmann, Television Antenna and R. F. Distribution Systems for Apartment Houses, *Proc. IRE*, **36**, p 1153, 1948.
J. B. Trevor, Artificial Delay-Line Design, ELECTRONICS, p 135, June 1945.
Editorial, ELECTRONICS, p 67, Dec. 1948.

Multiplexing Klystrons

How resonant cavities can be employed to give good isolation between channels, no signal loss, sufficient band pass, simple tuning and no interference in receiver circuit. Disadvantages of other possible methods are discussed

By WILLIAM L. FIRESTONE

SINCE THE CONCLUSION of World War II, progress has been made on multiplexing and duplexing equipments in connection with utilizing the microwave spectrum for communications. The information presented in this paper was obtained as a result of experimental work to determine the best method of combining simultaneously several modulated r-f signals in a single microwave transmission line for communication purposes.

Several possible methods of combining with a frequency-sharing principle are as follows: use of the hybrid T, directional couplers, line stretchers, tunable stubs, multiple-feed antennas, band-pass or band-reject cavities and various special devices for setting up and controlling standing waves.

Use of hybrid T and directional couplers was disregarded because the incident energy splits up into two parts and normally results in an undesirable 3-db loss per coupler or T unless auxiliary equipment is used to recombine the divided energy in the proper phase.

The first attempt at double combining was to use a line stretcher. Figure 1A shows a simple schematic diagram of the laboratory setup. Varying the length of the line stretcher has an effect on both the power output and the crosstalk between channels. Since tuning both klystrons for maximum power output results in a minimum of crosstalk, this is the proper condition to achieve.

The overall results indicate a crosstalk ratio of 47.5 db which represents a higher degree of crosstalk than can be tolerated. Also, there was evidence of klystron fre-

quency pulling so the method was disregarded.

Figure 1B shows a triple combiner using line stretchers. When attempting to combine three or more generators by this method, each generator with its line stretcher must cause a high impedance to appear at the T junction to the other signals. Therefore, a match can no longer be obtained by adjusting the line stretcher over a small range because the line stretcher must be long enough to accumulate enough wavelengths to reject two or more frequencies. Because the combiners had to be so large in size and were extremely difficult to tune, they were finally disregarded.

Stub Tuners

The next series of tests was performed with stubs using a special double combiner built for the purpose, see Fig. 2A. Here each stub must reject one frequency and pass one frequency for proper operation. Lengths of the stubs are

$$L_3 = (2n_1 - 1)\lambda_{ga}/4 = 2m_1\lambda_{gb}/4$$
$$L_2 = (2n_2 - 2)\lambda_{gb}/4 = 2m_2\lambda_{ga}/4$$

Each of these equations has two unknowns and a simple solution for n and m could be found graphically or by trial and error. For a three-stub tuner, each stub must reject two and pass one frequency and the solution for L becomes increasingly difficult.

It was found best to tune the klystron plunger for maximum output from the klystron and leave it there while the stubs were adjusted and the other dimensions changed as desired.

If the distance between the generators and the T junction is varied, tuning of the stub is affected. However, for certain spacings of the klystrons to the T junction, the stubs had practically no effect and preliminary indications were that the generators were operating properly.

The real reason for disregarding stub tuning is that an excessive number of stubs is required for even a reasonable number of channels. The formula relating the number of channels to the number of stubs required is

$$(n - 1)\, n = k$$

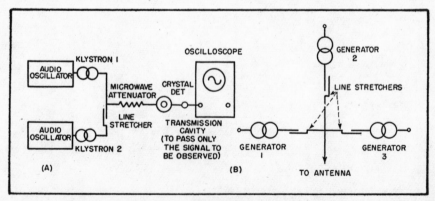

FIG. 1—Double combiner using one line stretcher (A) and triple combiner using line stretchers (B)

where n is the number of channels and k is the number of stubs required. Thus, for six channels, 30 stubs are required.

After stubs were eliminated from consideration, line stretchers were reconsidered except that now the conventional types of line stretchers were replaced with waveguide spacers.

A waveguide spacer is a flat piece of metal of any given thickness whose outer dimensions permit it to be screwed between waveguide flanges and whose inner dimensions are the same as the waveguide. In effect it is a small transformer at short wavelengths.

Advantages of using spacers are that they can always be constructed short in length and their mechanical and electrical length is easily measured. Disadvantages are that they cannot be adjusted as easily and continuously as most conventional-type line stretchers which means that many spacers of different lengths should be kept on hand at all times if they are to be used.

Fixed-Tuned Combiners

Using the waveguide spacers and conventional starting sections (pieces of waveguide that hold the generator and start the energy down the waveguide), several fixed-tuned combiners were developed. The final version of the double combiner is shown in Fig. 2B. The lower frequency channel, in this case 8,300 mc, is the channel that always has the largest amount of crosstalk.

The crosstalk on both klystrons can be better than 60 db down if the klystrons are spaced 200 mc apart. If they are spaced closer than 200 mc, then a loss in power between two and three db will also decrease the crosstalk to the indicated value.

A triple combiner was developed next using the same principles. It worked satisfactorily and all crosstalk readings were better than 68 db below the signal level. It must be kept in mind, however, that the double and triple combiners described depend on a frequency separation of 200 mc to keep the crosstalk down to 68 db.

It is still not known what kind of impedance the complete combiner would present to an incoming signal when this combiner is used as part of a duplexer. If the incoming signal were close in frequency to one or all of the transmitter frequencies, it is likely that the weak received signal would be lost in the transmitter plumbing.

Multiple-feed antennas, one antenna for transmitted signals and one for received signals, were disregarded because the coupling between the two antennas would be excessive. Undesired transmitted signals would get into the receiver circuit at an excessively high signal level and cause crosstalk.

Many experiments were run using every kind of cavity from a cylindrical tunable resonant cavity of high Q to rectangular semitunable resonant cavities of low Q. At all times, the spacing of the klystron to the cavity was kept in mind and the waveguide spacing between channels properly adjusted. Many different klystrons had to be used in any given setup to prove that any arbitrary klystron would work properly in any position or have sufficient power output and f-m modulation capabilities without excessive frequency pulling.

Resonant Cavities

Band-pass and band-reject cavities[1,2,3] are in reality filters. They are called cavities because at microwave frequencies the filters take the form of partially enclosed sections of hollow waveguide.

The ideal rejection filter would reflect perfectly within a certain band and pass perfectly outside of this band. Series-resonant circuits placed at quarter-wave intervals along the waveguide, properly distributed in impedance and all tuned close to the center frequency of the channel to be rejected, accomplish this end.

The ideal band-pass filter would pass perfectly within a certain band and reject perfectly outside of this band.[1,4] This can be done by using two resonant irises separated approximately by a half wavelength. The irises form a resonant cavity and are coupled to the next pair of resonant irises by a quarter wavelength.

Any number of pairs of irises

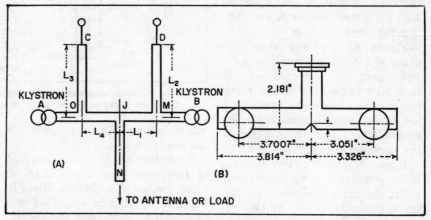

FIG. 2—Combiner using tunable stubs for two channels (A) and fixed-tuned double combiner with notched T (B)

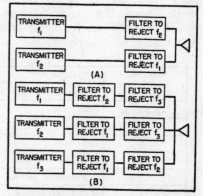

FIG. 3—Block diagrams of combiners using band-reject filters; (A) two channels, (B) three channels

could be cascaded to give the proper band-pass characteristics although the higher the Q of the individual cavities, and the greater the number of them, the greater would be the insertion loss. This is true because as the Q is increased in waveguide cavities, the coupling is automatically decreased, thereby increasing the insertion loss. Also, insertion losses are additive for series cavities.

Figure 3A shows a block diagram of a combiner using band-reject filters for two channels. If each filter has a high enough rejection to the unwanted signal and a low enough insertion loss to its own transmitter signal, the solution of the combiner is easily obtained.

Figure 3B shows a block diagram of a combiner using band-reject filters for three channels. Six filters are now required. If the frequencies are spaced in some fortuitous manner, it may be possible to reject several frequencies with a single rejection cavity having the proper rejection range.

Assuming no special simplifications are made in respect to frequency allocation and that each cavity is designed to do a single job as indicated, the number of rejection-type cavities or filters required is indicated in Table I.

The table shows that the number of cavities required to combine several channels becomes excessive. The number of stubs required is the same as the number of filters required for a given number of channels, which is to be expected since each stub and each rejection cavity have the same purpose, namely to pass one frequency and reject another. Their manner of

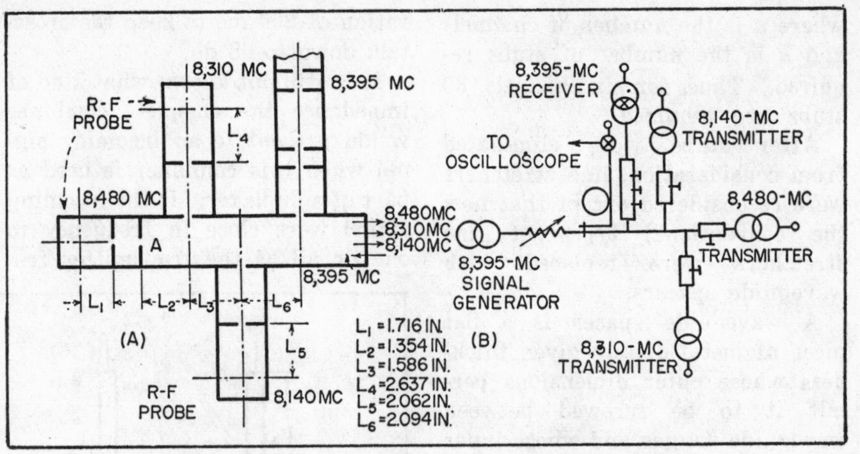

FIG. 4—Physical arrangement of cavities in a multiplexing system using three transmitters and one receiver (A) and schematic diagram of this system (B)

accomplishing this purpose is different.

From Fig. 3B, it can be seen that if frequency f_1 is lower than all other frequencies, the two filters in its channel could be combined into one low-pass filter and thereby reject f_2 and f_3. Similarly, if f_3 were higher in frequency than all other frequencies, then it would be possible to replace the two filters in the f_3 channel by one high-pass filter and thereby reject f_1 and f_2. It is important to note that using this procedure would simplify the number of filters only in the highest and lowest frequency channels and could not reduce the number of filters in all other channels.

The final system that was worked out as being the best for multiplexing with a high degree of isolation between channels and without excessive signal loss is very similar to that proposed by A. J. Fox except that all of the details and dimensions of a practical system have been determined.

Final System

In the final version of the system, three transmitters and three receiver channels were all connected to the main line. Figure 4A shows the physical arrangement of cavities in a less complex system utilizing three transmitters and only one receiver. Figure 4B is a schematic diagram of the simpler system.

The receiver channels consist of three cavities $\lambda_g/4$ coupled. Each section has a Q of 150. This combination results in a band-pass characteristic which is sufficiently wide and also permits the received signal to go through with less than two db of loss. It also sufficiently attenuates the transmitter signals so as to permit no interference effects in the receiver circuit.

The transmitter channels have single waveguide cavities with a Q of 100. This value of Q is sufficient to keep other signals out to such an extent that the cross modulation is 68 db below the signal level in the given channel. The cavities cause only one-db loss of transmitter power.

Each transmitter and receiver channel, except the end transmitter, is spaced electrically an odd number of quarter wavelengths (at its own wavelength) from the end transmitter channel which acts as a stub for all other channels.

The 8,310-mc transmitter is spaced electrically from the 8,480-mc cavity by $3\lambda_{g1}/4$, where λ_{g1} is the wavelength at 8,310 mc, see Fig.

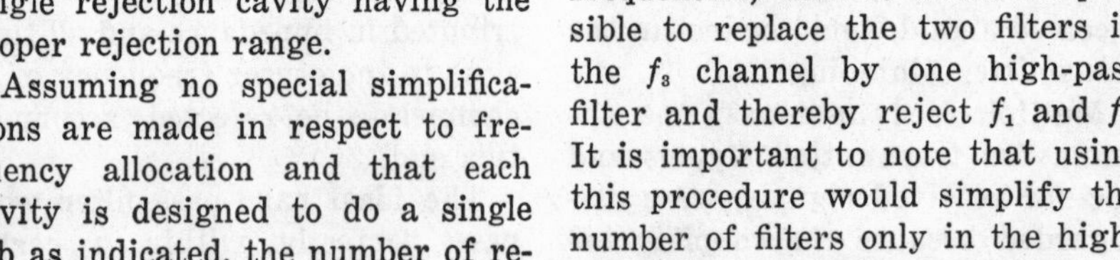

⏦	ATTENUATOR, FIXED	↓	SLOTTED LINE
⏦	ATTENUATOR, VARIABLE	○	CAVITY, CYLINDRICAL
⏦	SAND LOAD	▭	CAVITY, WAVEGUIDE
	DIRECTIONAL COUPLER	◁	HORN ANTENNA
⊙⊙	KLYSTRON	⊙	CONVERTER
⊗	CRYSTAL MIXER, FIXED	◗	CAVITY BUILT ON GUIDE
⊗	CRYSTAL MIXER, VARIABLE	—	LINE STRETCHER
⏛	STUB TUNER, DOUBLE	I_S I_P	TEE, SERIES(S)PARALLEL(P)

Symbol designations used throughout all illustrations

4A. This spacing is shown on the diagram as L_2. By comparing L_2 to λ_{g1}, it can be seen that L_2 is in reality 0.6 wavelength but 270 electrical degrees. The mechanical dimensioning is not identical with the electrical dimension because the 8,480-mc cavity presents some reactance at 8,310 mc at point A in Fig. 4A.

Considering that the Q of the cavities is only 100 and that the 8,480-mc klystron presents a certain impedance, it would not be expected that the klystron would present zero reactance at point A, the necessary condition for spacing each channel an odd number of wavelengths from the end channel.

The 8,140-mc channel is spaced $5\lambda_{g2}/4$ electrical wavelengths from the end channel and the 8,395-mc channel is spaced $9\lambda_{g3}/4$ electrical wavelengths from the end channel. The $\frac{1}{4}$, $\frac{3}{4}$ and 7/4 wavelength points were not used because of physical limitations.

Reflections from the transmitter

Table I—Number of Channels Versus Number of Filters

Number of Channels To Be Combined	Number of Filters Required
2	2
3	6
4	12
5	20

cavities were of such a nature as to cause a minimum of frequency pulling of the transmitter klystrons.

The system using three transmitters and three receivers per main waveguide line has been used successfully for many months in a complete microwave link. One of the advantages of the system is its simplicity of tuning. Once it is properly built and aligned there is nothing further to adjust except the klystron frequency.

Since different systems of multiplexing were tested in developmental work over a period of years, many different kinds of laboratory setups were required. A typical

laboratory setup for a triple combiner is shown in Fig. 5.

If a simpler version of combining were desired, such as a combiner with only one transmitter and one receiver, it would be possible to eliminate the band-pass cavity associated with the transmitter by proper spacing of all elements. This simplified system is now in actual field use.

Contemporary Work

Engineers of one research laboratory propose a band-pass filter to limit transmitter output spectrum. Use of the band-pass filter also makes the problem of antenna duplexing somewhat simpler.

Antenna duplexing using band-rejection filters only has been proposed but the number of rejection filters needed to protect the receiver mixer crystal completely from burnout and to prevent saturation of the receiver first grid may be impractical. Use of a band-pass filter in the transmitter output circuit together with the previously suggested band-rejection filter in the receiver line would give the required isolation with a minimum of filter elements. This plan makes possible antenna duplexing, smaller frequency separation between transmitter and receiver and limited transmitter spectrum output. Figure 6 shows a block diagram of such an arrangement.

There are different requirements for the multiplexer just described and the combiner or multiplexer developed here. First, in the above system there is no need to combine several transmitters at once because position-modulated pulses are used to send several pieces of information over the same channel. The combiner developed here uses frequency-modulated c-w oscillators and, normally, several channels would be required for carrying different types of signals.

Second, band-pass filters are used only to conserve the use of the r-f spectrum whereas band-pass filters have been suggested herein not only

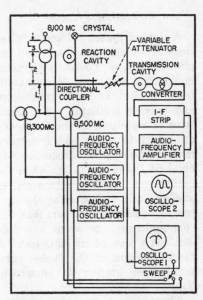

FIG. 5—Setup for a triple combiner

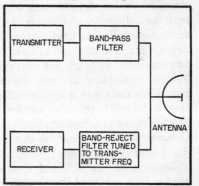

FIG. 6—Relay using resonant cavities

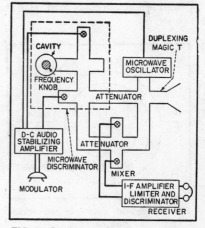

FIG. 7—Duplex system for microwaves

for that purpose but also in order to isolate each channel from the next. Last, from previous discussion the conclusion reached would be to use a multiplexer consisting completely of tuned resonant band-pass cavities.

Duplex System

A duplex system of communications for microwaves, built and explained by R. V. Pound, is a system in which a single microwave oscillator is used as both transmitter and beating oscillator.[5] The oscillator is stabilized at the frequency of a high-Q cavity and frequency modulated about this frequency. If one-half the power is lost when the oscillator is used as a transmitter and one-half is lost when the system is used as a receiver, then for communication between any two stations a total of six db is lost. A block diagram of the duplex communication station is shown in Fig. 7.

There are several factors that simplify the building of such a system, including the following: only voice modulation is used instead of video, only one channel is used at any one time so there are no problems of combining or crosstalk between channels and a total modulation bandwidth of only ten kc is used. There is a loss of six db per channel which is excessive for the development discussed.

Because of the different type of modulation used and the bandwidth required, the system described by Pound is not too concerned with the

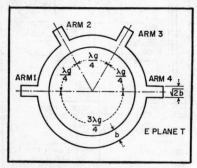

FIG. 8—Hybrid circuit or waveguide ring network

f-m linearity of the modulated oscillator. This factor can not be ignored in a more complicated system. Much a-m and f-m distortion can be tolerated in a system requiring only intelligible voice to be transmitted.

Nonreflecting Branching Filter

A nonreflecting branching filter for microwaves has been designed by W. D. Lewis and L. C. Tillotson.[5,6] The circuit consists of two hybrid junctions, two identical channel reflection filters tuned to the dropped channel and two quarter-wavelength sections of line. The hybrid circuit is shown in Fig. 8.

The circuit in Fig. 9 as shown

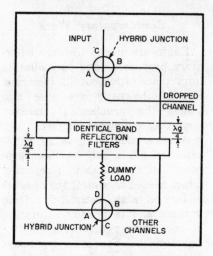

FIG. 9—Constant-impedance channel-dropping filter

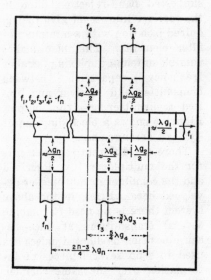

FIG. 10—Multiple separator using resonant cavities

could be called a separator insofar as it separates many signals from each other. If at each point of extraction of a signal the procedure was reversed and a signal was in-

serted, the result would be a combiner which should function without excessive losses.

Discrimination against other channels and image responses was measured at 20 db or more. To improve crosstalk discrimination it would be necessary to place auxiliary filters in the branch arms which would increase the insertion loss slightly.

Measured insertion loss of the system varied from 0.5 to 1.0 db. This insertion loss was measured between the input line and various output lines with the lowest insertion loss occurring in the lowest frequency channel.

The requirement for crosstalk developed in the system by the author is 68 db or more, making the amount of selectivity of the system just described inadequate.

Multiple Separation

A multiple separator has been considered in which channel filters are connected across a transmission line or waveguide in such a way that power in each signal is diverted to appropriate branches with negligible loss.[7] A diagram of a multiple separator developed by A. J. Fox is shown in Fig. 10.

Several important facts are missing from the discussion of this system, namely; the center frequency and frequency separation between channels, the amount of crosstalk between channels, the insertion loss and frequency band pass of the waveguide cavities and the nature of the spacing between the mixers and the cavities. The author has used the cavities only as a separator and does not indicate their possibility for use as a combiner or in a duplexer.

Several microwave relay systems have been discussed by various authors but in most instances only one r-f carrier was used and, consequently, the problems of combining, separating or of crosstalk between channels do not occur.[8,9]

REFERENCES

(1) R. M. Fano and A. W. Lawson, Jr., Microwave Filters Using Quarter Wave Couplings, *Proc. IRE*, 35, Nov. 1947.

(2) W. L. Pritchard, Quarter Wave Coupled Wave Guide Filters, *Jour. App. Phys.*, 18, p 862, Oct. 1947.

(3) W. D. Lewis and L. C. Tillotson, A Non-reflecting Branching Filter for Microwaves, *BSTJ*, 1, p 83, 1948.

(4) C. G. Montgomery, "Technique of Microwave Measurements," Radiation Laboratory Series, McGraw-Hill, p 522, 1947

(5) R. V. Pound, A Duplex System of Communications for Microwaves, *Proc. IRE*, 36, p 840, July 1948.

(6) H. T. Friis, Microwave Repeater Research, *BSTJ*, 4, p 183, 1948.

(7) G. L. Ragan, "Microwave Transmission Circuits, Radiation Laboratory Series, McGraw-Hill, p 708, 1948.

(8) R. E. Lacy, Two Multichannel Microwave Equipments for the U. S. Army Communication Network, *Proc. IRE*, 35, p 65, Jan. 1947.

(9) L. E. Thompson, Microwave Relay System, *Proc. IRE*, 34, Nov. 1946.

BIBLIOGRAPHY

Members of the MIT Staff, "Principles of Radar", Sec. Ed., 8-85, 1946.

F. E. Terman, "Radio Engineers Handbook", McGraw-Hill, First Ed., p 565, 1943.

R. I. Sarbacher and W. A. Edson, "Hyper and Ultra High Frequency Engineering", 1947.

Studio-Transmitter Link

EQUIPMENT installed as tne studio-to-transmitter link for f-m station WFMI, Portsmouth, N. H., operates on 940.5 megacycles, perhaps the first permanent stl on that frequency. Because Portsmouth is only 50 feet above sea level, the broadcast transmitter is located on Saddleback Mountain, 1,180 feet high and 21 miles distant.

Studio-transmitter link equipment was designed to meet FCC requirements for f-m stations relaying their programs from the studio to transmitter in instances where, for one reason or another, wire lines are not feasible.

The basic exciter unit used in Harvey Radio Laboratories f-m broadcast transmitters has been slightly modified by the manufacturer. This unit utilizes the Phasitron system as shown in the block diagram of Fig. 1. For the stl, the

normal crystal frequency of 200 kc is changed to 400 kc since the frequency stability tolerance can still be easily met and one stage of frequency multiplication is eliminated.

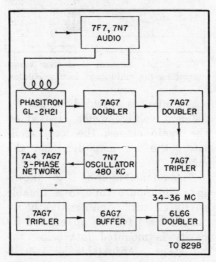

FIG. 1—Stages of the exciter unit for f-m stl transmitter

The series of doubler and tripler stages produces an output from this exciter unit at 34 to 36 mc. Conventional circuitry is used with complete metering of all circuits.

The circuit of the power tripler panel is shown in Fig. 2. This contains an 829B operating class C tripling from 34-36 mc to 102-109 mc, which drives a pair of 2C43 lighthouse triodes in push-pull tripling from 102-109 mc to 306-327 mc. The 829B stage is a conventional lumped-constant circuit. The input circuit of the second tripler is also a lumped-constant circuit but the plate circuit is tuned by parallel lines.

The input circuit of the third tripler, also a pair of 2C43 tubes, is a parallel line circuit and the plate circuit utilizes precision cavities tuned to final frequency.

The final amplifier is a grounded-

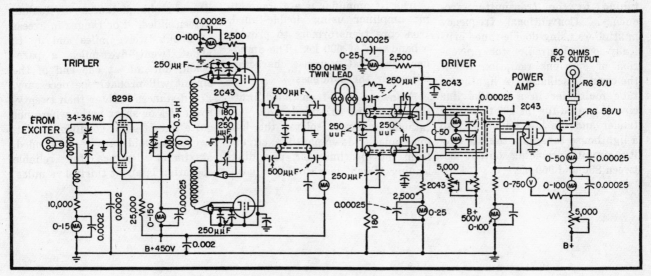

FIG. 2—Tripler stages are driven by the exciter at 35 mc and provide output on 950 mc

grid 2C43 lighthouse tube in a tunable cavity circuit, having an output of 5 watts. The filament transformer which supplies all lighthouse tubes is controlled by a Variac and monitored by a voltmeter.

Measurements in the laboratory and in the field show that the transmitter meets the requirements laid down. The tuning range is 920 to 980 mc; frequency stability is better than the requirement —being 0.001 percent; frequency deviation is ±200 kc; f-m hum and noise level is better than 70 db below 100 percent modulation; a-m hum and noise level are more than 50 db down; the frequency response of the audio system matches the standard 75-microsecond preemphasis curve to within 1 db from 50 cps to 15 kc; a-f distortion is less than 0.5 percent between 100 cps and 7.5 kc and less than 1 percent from 50 cps to 100 cps and from 7.5 kc to 15 kc.

A block diagram of the receiver is shown in Fig. 3. The i-f is 30 mc, requiring local oscillator power at 890–950 mc for reception of 920–980 mc. This frequency is obtained by the series of triplers shown.

The oscillator is crystal-controlled, using a temperature-controlled crystal in the vicinity of 3.8 mc. This circuit is provided with a vernier control to allow precise tuning to the transmitter frequency. Conventional frequency multipliers using double-tuned critically-coupled circuits for prevention of spurious radiation follow the crystal oscillator. A lighthouse tube multiplier in a parallel line circuit is used for the 100 to 300-mc tripler and the last tripler is also a lighthouse tube, in a tunable cavity circuit, providing output between 890 and 950 mc.

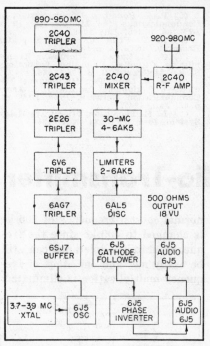

FIG. 3—Block diagram of receiver stages including the multi-stage local oscillator

A control is provided for the d-c filament voltage which is used on the audio stages, the local oscillator, the r-f amplifier, and the mixer.

The r-f amplifier is a grounded-grid lighthouse tube in a tunable cavity circuit. Another lighthouse tube is used for the mixer, and its cavity is mounted just below the r-f stage. Adjustable local oscillator injection is provided into the mixer cavity.

The i-f amplifier is a 4-stage 30-mc amplifier using double-tuned, iron core transformers to provide a bandwith of 600 kc. The amplifier has a flat response characteristic over the bandpass.

Following the i-f, cascaded limiters feed the discriminator. A cathode follower isolates the low impedance de-emphasis circuit from the discriminator, providing loading which does not vary with frequency. A vtvm measures discriminator output, to provide a reading of kilocycles off resonance.

The audio system, shown at the upper right in Fig. 3, consists of a phase inverter followed by two push-pull stages. Triodes are used throughout for minimum distortion. A precision gain control having 45 steps of 1 db each is used to control the output. Maximum output is +18 vu and is monitored by a vu meter. Balanced 500/600-ohm output is provided. Audio frequency distortion is less than 0.5 percent from 50 cps to 15 kc.

Measurements in the laboratory and in the field show that the receiver is quieted by an RMA quieting signal of 3 microvolts, that its noise figure is 10 db and that the hum and noise level is more than 70 db down. Because of the high frequency stability of the receiver, it is possible to use it as a partial frequency monitor.

Either of two types of antennas are used with the stl. The corner-reflector type has a gain of 12 db and its directivity characteristics are such that at all azimuth angles greater than 30 degrees from the direction of maximum directivity, the power is down 15 db. The paraboloid antenna uses a 72-inch reflector which provides a gain of 23 db.

The standard corner reflector antennas are intended for use at line-of-sight distances of ten to fifteen miles. For ranges in excess of about twelve miles and up to about twenty-five miles, a paraboloid antenna at one end of the circuit will probably be necessary. For distances greater than twenty-five miles or short paths where not quite line-of-sight conditions exist, two paraboloids are recommended. Maximum distance for reliable operation is about thirty-five miles.

Corrugated-Waveguide Band-Pass Filters

High-pass properties of a waveguide are combined with low-pass properties of a corrugated surface in a filter designed to give a rapid transition between pass and attenuation bands. Single corrugated element does work of several elements in conventional designs

By J. C. GREENE

RAPID TRANSITION between pass and attenuation bands and a wide frequency range free of spurious responses are desirable properties of a band-pass filter. Such a filter can be realized readily by combining the high-pass properties of a waveguide with the low-pass property of a corrugated surface.

In a particular application a filter was designed which had a pass-band between 2,080 mc and 2,800 mc and 70-db attenuation, relative to the pass-band response, at 2,900 mc. There were no responses which were not attenuated by at least 60 db from 2,900 mc to above 10,000 mc.

Because of the high-pass characteristic of a waveguide, a band-pass filter can be formed readily by incorporating a low-pass structure into the waveguide. One such low-pass structure is the corrugated surface for which approximate field solutions have been given in the literature[1-6].

The design considered in this paper for utilizing the corrugated surface structure is shown in Fig. 1, where one broad face of the waveguide is replaced by a tapered corrugated surface. Approximate solutions for the attenuation and phase characteristics of the filter in Fig. 1 are obtained by combining design relations[5] with a loaded-line equivalent circuit representation[1].

An idealized pass-band shape is illustrated in Fig. 2. The low-frequency cutoff f_c is provided by the normal cutoff of the waveguide, while the high-frequency cutoff $f\infty$, at which there is infinite attenuation, is provided by a resonance of the slots in region C of the corrugated surface.

The slots in region B of the corrugated surface serve a two-

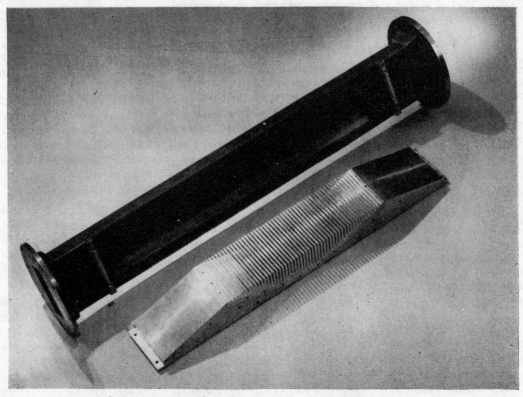

Section of waveguide and corrugated surface which fits into it

fold purpose. They provide additional resonant elements in the upper rejection band ($f > f\infty$) to prevent repetitive pass bands. In addition they serve as a smooth taper which transforms the characteristic impedance of region C into the characteristic impedance of the waveguide through the taper in region A.

Filter Characteristics

The loaded transmission-line representation of one slot in the corrugated surface is shown in Fig. 3. The characteristic equation of the frequency spectrum relating the phase shift ϕ across one element of the loaded line (including both the slot and the transmission line of length l' to the phase shift θ along l' between two adjacent slots is

$$\cos\varphi = \cos\theta - (Z/2Z_0)\sin\theta\tan(p\theta) \quad (1)$$

where $\varphi = 2\pi l'/\lambda_s$
$\theta = 2\pi l'/\lambda_g$
$p = (b-b')/2l'$
Z = characteristic impedance of the slot
Z_0 = characteristic impedance of the unloaded line
λ_g = guide wavelength in the unloaded line
λ = free-space wavelength
λ_s = guide wavelength in the loaded line

λ_g is related to λ by the expression

$$\lambda_g = \lambda/\sqrt{1-(\lambda/2a)^2} \quad (2)$$

where a is the broad dimension of the waveguide.

Putting $\phi = \beta - j\alpha$ and neglecting resistive losses one obtains for the pass band ($\alpha = 0$)

$$\cos(\beta + 2n\pi) = \cos\theta - (Z/2Z_0)\sin\theta\tan(p\theta) \quad (3)$$

where $n = 0, \pm 1, \pm 2$, etc and in the cutoff band ($\beta = 0$ or π)

$$\pm\cosh\alpha = \cos\theta - (Z/2Z_0)\sin\theta\tan(p\theta) \quad (4)$$

where α = attenuation in nepers per section of loaded line, ($\beta + 2n\pi$) = phaseshift per section of loaded line.

The values of $n \neq 0$ in Eq. 3 represent space harmonics of the fundamental ($n = 0$) component of the wave. The positive values of n represent transmitted waves, the negative values reflected waves. All of these components

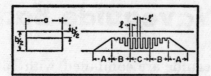

FIG. 1—Mechanical drawing of tapered corrugated surface which replaces one face of the waveguide

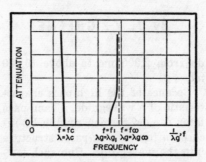

FIG. 2—Idealized pass-band shape. High-frequency attenuation at $f = \infty$ is provided by resonance of the slots in region C of corrugated surface (see Fig. 1)

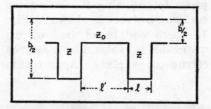

FIG. 3—Loaded transmission line representation of one slot in the corrugated surface

are necessary to fully describe the propagated wave.

To simplify the analysis, the space harmonic components are neglected. This is a valid assumption in the pass band, since the amplitudes of the space harmonics are greatly reduced in the pass band[6]. The assumption becomes less valid as the frequency approaches that at which the slots become resonant.

Design relationships among the dimensions of a slot are[5]

$$b'/2 < l' < (\lambda_{g1})^2/10 \quad (5)$$
$$b'/b < 0.1 \quad (6)$$

where λ_{g1} is the guide wavelength in the unloaded section at the upper cutoff frequency, f_1. It can be demonstrated that the pass-band resistive losses due to a finite conductivity in the conducting surfaces vary inversely with

the quantity b'/b. This value was chosen to be as large as possible, namely 0.1. It may be seen from Eq. 4 that an infinite attenuation occurs when $p\theta = \pi/2$. The frequency at which this infinite attenuation occurs is $f\infty$. However,

$$\theta = 2\pi l'/\lambda_g = \frac{2\pi}{\lambda_g}\frac{(b-b')}{2p}$$

Hence at the infinite attenuation frequency ($\lambda_g = \lambda_g\infty$)

$$p\theta\infty = \pi/2 = \frac{2\pi}{\lambda_g\infty}\frac{(b-b')}{2}$$

or

$$\frac{(b-b')}{2\lambda_g\infty} = 1/4 \quad (7)$$

Eq. 7 means that at the infinite attenuation frequency, the slot depth, $(b-b')/2$, equals one quarter of a guide wavelength.

The values of l and l' are not critical and are generally chosen to keep the over-all length of the filter as short as possible. Typical values are $l' = 2l = 0.1\lambda_{cg}\infty$. The value of the ratio Z/Z_0 is taken to be $2l/b'$, the ratio of the slot height to the line height.

Theoretical curves relating ϕ and α in db to θ are shown in Fig. 4. The curves have been calculated for $p = 2$ and $Z/Z_0 = 2$. At the point of infinite attenuation, $\theta = 45$ deg, while at the upper cutoff point $\theta = 36$ deg. Hence the ratio of the cutoff wavelength, λ_{g1}, to the infinite attenuation wavelength, $\lambda_g\infty$ is $\lambda_{g1}/\lambda_g\infty = 45$ deg/36 deg = 1.25. The slot requires the cutoff wavelength to be decreased by 25 percent before its attenuation becomes infinite.

Referring to Fig. 4, representing the characteristics of the slots in region C of the filter, it can be seen that repetitive pass bands will occur. The first repetitive pass band occurs when $\lambda_g = \lambda_{g1}/2$. To avoid this pass band as well as higher ones, it is necessary to include slots in region B of the filter which will resonate in the vicinity of the higher passbands. In general, this condition is fulfilled merely by having a reasonable length of taper.

Design Procedure

The filter can be easily incorporated as an inserted section in a waveguide, with waveguide input and output. It can also be incorporated into a coaxial line through the use of waveguide to coaxial transformers. The transforming sections form the input and output of the filter.

The low-frequency cutoff determines the wide dimension of the waveguide, a, and is simply related to it by

$$\lambda_c = 2a$$

Generally, both the upper cutoff frequency f_1 and a minimum attenuation at a point between f_1 and $f\infty$ are specified. Once these are known, the slot depth and number of slots in region C can be determined. First λ_{g1} is calculated from the high-frequency cutoff f_1 by Eq. 2. Because $\lambda_{g1}/\lambda_g\infty = 1.25$, $\lambda_g\infty$ may be readily found. The slot depth is then made equal to $\lambda_g\infty/4$.

The number of slots required is the desired attenuation in db at some frequency between f_1 and $f\infty$ divided by the attenuation of one slot at that frequency as determined from Fig. 4.

The lengths of the tapered sections in regions A and B should be about equal and as long as possible for the best match. A theoretical curve relating the vswr introduced by a taper as a function of its length has been given by Frank[7]. From this curve and a consideration of the variation in guide wavelength in the pass band, a value giving small mismatch reflections over the entire pass band is found to be 1.5 λ_c or $3a$.

Experimental Results

An experimental curve for the filter based on the previous design considerations is given in Fig. 5. The corrugated surface was designed to be inserted in standard 1.5 by 3-in. waveguide having a cutoff frequency of 2,080 mc. The desired upper cutoff frequency was 2,800 mc ($\lambda_{g1} = 16.0$ cm.) This gives the infinite attenuation frequency as 3,200 mc ($\lambda_g\infty = 12.8$ cm). It was also desired to have

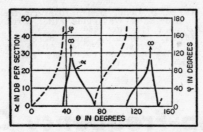

FIG. 4—Theoretical curves relating attenuation in db per section and phase shift across one slot for transmission line of length l' (see Fig. 1) to the phase shift along the distance between two slots

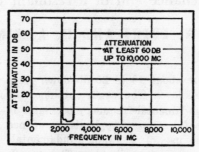

FIG. 5—Attenuation curve for actual filter constructed

at least 70 db of attenuation at 2,900 mc ($\lambda_g = 15.0$ cm).

Because λ_{g1} corresponds to $\theta = 36$ deg on the curve of Fig. 4, at $\lambda_g = 15.0$) cm, $\theta = 38.4$ deg. From Fig. 4, the attenuation in db per slot at $\theta = 38.4$ deg is 9 db. Hence eight slots in region C should be sufficient to give the desired attenuation. Actually ten slots were used because the attenuation of a slot will be slightly less than shown in Fig. 4 due to resistive losses in the slot. The pass-band loss, averaging approximately 2.5 db, is a combination of resistive loss in the slots and mismatch loss in the tapers.

Higher Order Modes

In the above analysis it was assumed that only the dominant mode $TE_{1,0}$ is propagated. For the usual waveguide dimensions (broad face twice as wide as the narrow face) higher-order modes may be propagated at frequencies greater than twice the normal cutoff frequency. If these higher-order modes are propagated, spurious responses

may appear in the rejection band.

Because of the symmetry of the filter, only $TE_{1,m}$ ($n = 0,1,2, \ldots$) and $TM_{1,m}$ ($n = 1,2,3, \ldots$) modes can be excited within the filter itself[4]. The first of these modes, the $TE_{1,2}$ and the $TM_{1,2}$ will not be propagated for frequencies less than four times the normal cutoff frequency. In general this is far enough into the rejection band to be of little consequence.

Should higher-order modes, such as the $TE_{2,0}$, $TE_{3,0}$ be set up in the input section leading to the filter, they will pass through the filter and produce narrow spurious pass bands for frequencies in the vicinity of twice the normal cutoff frequency, three times this frequency, and so on.

At the cutoff frequency for the higher modes, the guide wavelength for these modes is infinite and rapidly decreases as the frequency is increased. Until the wavelength decreases to a value such that the slots in region C become resonant, no attenuation is offered to the modes.

The higher modes can often be eliminated by careful design of the input circuit to eliminate asymmetrical structures tending to excite the higher-order modes. They may also be eliminated in the output section when of a special type, such as ridged waveguide output. In this case, the ridged section is designed so that it passes the dominant mode, but is cut off for the higher-order modes in the vicinity of the spurious response pass bands. Compensating sections of different widths, a, can be included in the filter proper so that they are below cutoff for the higher-order modes over the frequency range of the spurious responses[8].

REFERENCES

(1) A. W. Lines, G. R. Nicoll and A. M. Woodward, Some Properties of Corrugated Waveguides, Telecommunications Research Establishment Report No. T2114; reprinted in *Proc. IEE*, **97**, Part III, No. 48, July 1950.
(2) C. C. Cutler, Electromagnetic Waves Guided by Corrugated Conducting Surfaces, Bell Telephone Laboratories Report No. MM44-160-218.

(3) H. H. Goldstein, The Theory of Corrugated Transmission Lines and Waveguides, Rad. Lab. Report No. 494, April 1944.

(4) S. B. Cohn, Analysis of a Wide-Band Waveguide Filter, *Proc. IRE*, 37, p 651, June 1949.

(5) S. B. Cohn, Design Relations for the Wide-Band Waveguide Filter, *Proc. IRE*, 38, p 799, July 1950.

(6) W. Rotman, A Study of Single-Surface Corrugated Guides, Air Force Cambridge Research Laboratory Report No. E5055, Feb. 1950.

(7) N. H. Frank, Dielectric Structures in Waveguides, "Rad. Lab. Handbook," p 30, Feb. 1943.

(8) Radio Research Laboratory Staff, "Very-High-Frequency Techniques," McGraw-Hill Book Co., New York, Section 27-28, 1947.

UHF Sweep-Frequency Oscillator

Measurements and tests in the uhf television band are facilitated by the equipment described. Maximum sweep of 30 mc from 470 to 890 mc, at a rate synchronized with the power line, is provided by a motor-driven capacitor plate rotated at the high-impedance end of a resonant cavity

By J. E. EBERT AND H. A. FINKE

IN DEVELOPING a sweep oscillator for the new uhf television band, a choice exists in attempting to frequency-modulate a fundamental oscillator directly or to resort to a mixing method involving either the frequency addition of two lower-frequency oscillators or subtraction of two higher-frequency oscillators.

An output of the order of several volts across 50 ohms is available using a 6F4 triode as a fundamental oscillator, whereas any simple mixing method using two oscillator tubes will result in a maximum out-

put about 10 to 20 db down from this level. The larger output of the fundamental-frequency oscillator is useful in many applications. Since the use of a swept fundamental-frequency oscillator offers much greater ease and simplicity of operation and greater freedom from harmonic output, this type of oscillator is more desirable provided the problem of obtaining satisfactory frequency sweeping does not become too complex.

The sweep oscillator to be described covers a range from 470 to

890 mc with a maximum sweep of at least 30 mc at a rate synchronized with the power line. At least 2 volts across 50 ohms is available at any frequency within the specified band, and this voltage can be continuously attenuated by a front panel control to a value of 90 decibels below the maximum output.

At any fixed setting of the attenuator, the output does not vary by more than 1.5 db from the average output at that setting over the entire specified frequency band. Leak-

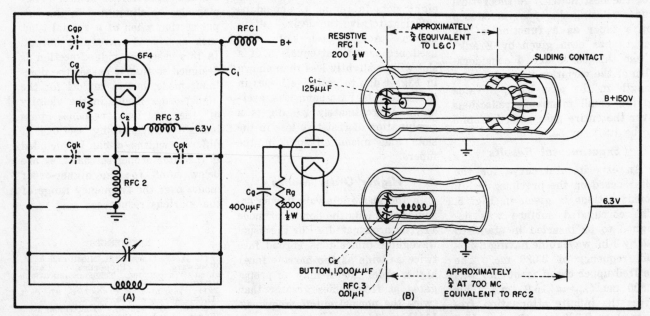

FIG. 1—Basic oscillator circuit and coaxial-line equivalent

age from the oscillator has been minimized by use of completely enclosed coaxial line circuits.

The modified Colpitts oscillator circuit shown in Fig. 1A was selected as best suited for the purpose in this television application.

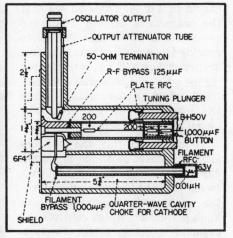

Fig. 2—Physical construction of coaxial-line oscillator

Resonance is obtained between the plate and grid of the 6F4 acorn triode while the plate-to-cathode and grid-to-cathode interelectrode capacitances form a well-proportioned capacitive voltage-dividing network to complete the Colpitts arrangement. Both the cathode and filament circuits are choked to minimize their shunting effect across the grid-to-cathode interelectrode capacitance.

Since adequate shielding is of great importance, the oscillator was constructed in a self-shielding coaxial line. A coaxial line equivalent of the basic oscillator circuit is shown schematically in Fig. 1B.

A cutaway view showing the mechanical construction of the coaxial line oscillator is shown in Fig. 2.

The main body of the oscillator is made from a single bronze casting. The glass body of the oscillator tube is recessed in an indentation in the center conductor to provide a low-impedance connecting line between the resonant circuit and the tube elements. This low-impedance connecting line is necessary to obtain a satisfactory tuning rate at the high-frequency end of the band.

The coaxial-line section used to choke the filament is chosen in length to offer maximum impedance at the center-band frequency. Sufficiently high impedance is obtained at the band edges to give good performance.

Output power is capacitively coupled from the oscillator tank circuit through a coaxial line connected close to the high-voltage point of the resonator as shown in Fig. 2. The harmonic content at this point is small. The output line is terminated in a 50-ohm resistor to provide a reasonably well matched output impedance.

The output is attenuated by withdrawing the pickup line from the axis of the resonant cavity. As the center conductor of the output line is withdrawn the coupling is obtained through the intervening section of tubing which acts as a circular waveguide operated below its cutoff frequency.

The rate of attenuation through a waveguide used under these conditions is almost linear and constant over a wide range of frequencies which makes it possible to have a calibrated attenuator control. Typical power output characteristics for the oscillator are shown in Fig. 3.

Mechanism for Sweeping

Frequency sweeping is accomplished by varying the capacitance between the high-impedance end of the cavity and ground. There are a number of ways of varying this capacitance but the two most straightforward approaches consist of either vibrating a metallic strip in reed-like fashion against the end of the cavity or employing a motor drive to vary the capacitance by rotating a specially shaped capacitor plate. In either case, the motions have to be synchronized with some convenient standard such as the 60-cycle line so that a sta-

Closeup of specially shaped capacitor and its motor drive system

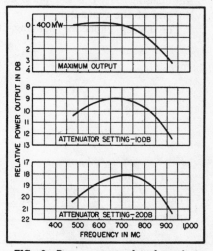

FIG. 3—Power output plotted against frequency for several attenuator settings

tionary picture can be obtained on a viewing oscilloscope.

The vibrating capacitor presents certain problems that involve difficult electronic or electromechanical solutions. A driven reed has a motion that includes harmonic components of the driving frequency. A reed driven by a sine-wave power source should be viewed on an oscilloscope with a sine-wave sweep to preserve the frequency linearity of the base line. A sine sweep, however, requires perfect synchronism so that the return trace may exactly coincide with the forward trace. The presence of mechanical harmonics prevents this.

This problem can be circumvented by electronic means. The reed could be driven with a sawtooth wave form and the return portion of the sine sweep could be blanked, but a solution for the second or rotating approach is simple and direct.

One photograph shows the mechanical arrangement used for the rotational method of sweeping the frequency. A synchronous motor is used to rotate a specially shaped capacitor plate which is sprayed on the face of a plastic disc. The ideal shape of the capacitor plate when a sawtooth sweep is used on the oscilloscope is one that will allow the frequency of the oscillator to vary linearly with angular rotation of the driving motor. The magnitude of the sweep is varied by changing the spacing between the plate and the end of the resonator.

The sweep capacitor spacing is controlled by the angular rotation

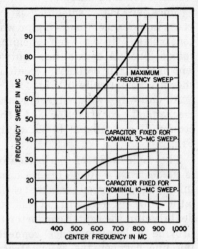

FIG. 4—Frequency sweep versus frequency for several capacitor settings

of an eccentrically mounted circular cam. The cam follower is spring loaded and the front panel control is coupled to the cam through a conventional gear train having a 4 to 1 rotational ratio. This ratio is desirable since the entire cam throw occurs in only 180 degrees of rotation.

The synchronous motor used has the property of locking in on any one of four points on the cycle of the input 60-cycle power source. Phasing between the similarly locked internal sawtooth sweep on the viewing oscilloscope and the rotating motor can be roughly adjusted to any one of the four motor positions by momentarily breaking the motor circuit and allowing the motor armature to slip one position.

Fine adjustment in phase is made with controls on the oscilloscope.

Dial Details

A curve of the sweep characteristics of the complete oscillator is shown in Fig. 4. This shows that the magnitude of the frequency sweep for a given capacitor plate spacing is not constant over the frequency range. This is corrected through the use of a dial arrangement which automatically shows the magnitude of the frequency sweep as the frequency is varied.

To accomplish this, the dial consists of a chart on which is plotted curves for constant frequency sweep with the tuning plunger position as the ordinate and the angular knob movement, which controls the capacitor spacing, as the abscissa. This chart is viewed through a slot in the panel and is arranged to move past this slot as the oscillator frequency is varied.

A pointer travelling along the slot is mechanically connected to the sweep capacitor. The chart is drawn so that the end of this pointer indicates directly the magnitude of the frequency sweep at any oscillator frequency and at any capacitor plate setting.

Two simple cord and pulley systems are used to drive the pointer and chart in the frequency sweep indicating system. The pointer is connected to the sweep magnitude control and the chart position is coupled to the tuning plunger position.

Kilomegacycle Buzzer Test Oscillator

Pulses of broad-band energy are injected into a tunable cavity at 800 cps. Output at any desired frequency between 3 and 11 kmc can be selected. A piston attenuator permits variable output up to 200 microvolts into a 50-ohm load. Development technique is traced from a model twenty-five times desired scale

By G. L. DAVIES, C. B. PEAR, JR. AND P. E. P. WHITE

ALTHOUGH activity in the kilomegacycle region has increased greatly in recent years, signal sources are still largely restricted to narrow-band tuning. This is an annoyance when testing fixed-frequency detecting devices, and a real handicap in testing wide-range receivers.

One of the latest instruments to help solve this problem is a simple, compact test oscillator covering 3,000 to 11,000 mc in one continuous tuning range. No tubes are used. A battery-driven buzzer operating on the doorbell principle provides audio-modulated signals everywhere in the band, and a plunger-tuned cavity selects the desired frequency. A piston-type attenuator controls the output level.

Scaled-Up Model

The lack of wide-range signal-generating equipment was in itself a difficulty during the oscillator's development. Problems in tuning-cavity design showed the desirability of experimental work, but no satisfactory signal source was available. An interesting application of the model technique in reverse solved the difficulty by providing a cavity in which every dimension was twenty-five times the corresponding dimension of the cavity in the final unit. Thus, frequencies were scaled down into the scope of readily available test equipment.

The simplicity of the buzzer test oscillator is evident from the schematic diagram in Fig. 1. A buzzer, energized by the 3-volt battery through the r-f filter produces

short, sharp pulses of current, which are coupled into the cavity through the input coupling loop. The cavity is sharply resonant at a single frequency determined by the position of the tuning plunger. It selects a component from the broad spectrum of frequencies comprising the buzzer output. This signal is coupled to the loop on the variable-attenuator piston that controls the output amplitude. The output signal is in the form of short pulses of r-f energy recurring at the rate of 800 per second. Maximum output

voltage is at least 200 microvolts into a 50-ohm load.

The original unit employed an open-ended cylindrical cavity, which was poor from the shielding standpoint. The tuning dial calibration was considerably cramped at one end of the scale, and the available output signal varied appreciably over the frequency range. The desire to improve these characteristics led to the use of the scale model.

The Ashcan

In this development, an ex-

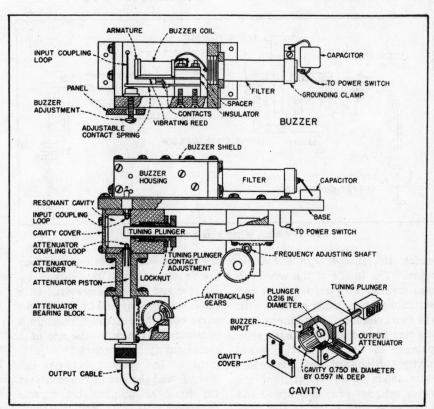

Mechanical layout of the oscillator, with detail of cavity at lower right. The buzzer generator is coupled to the cavity through a loop

panded model was used rather than the smaller scale customarily employed in antenna experiments. All measurements were made in the region of 120 to 440 mc, where suitable equipment was readily available and the frequency data multiplied by an appropriate factor. The idea for the use of this method was derived from experiments performed by Barrow and Mieher[1] at MIT.

Since the actual cavity in the unit was approximately ¾ inch in diameter by one inch long, a model twenty-five times this size was considered reasonable. Accordingly, a local tinsmith was commissioned to make a large cylinder 18¾ inches in diameter and 25 inches long, and a smaller cylinder, to simulate the tuning plunger, six inches in diameter and 36 inches long. The material used was 22-gage galvanized steel, and the appearance of the assembly made its title certain: the Ashcan.

It was fitted with a plywood cap over the large cylinder, through

The coupling loops were positioned 90 degrees apart around the circumference of the cylinder, as this was the position desired in the final uhf cavity. One of these loops was used to feed energy into the cavity from an oscillator covering the desired frequency range, and the other loop was used for output coupling. A type 1N21B crystal and microammeter served as a detector. Frequency measurements were made by means of a General Radio type 720-A heterodyne frequency meter.

Despite the crude construction and use of sheet steel for the inner and outer cylinders, the Q of the cavity was in the vicinity of 1,000, permitting precise settings to be made. Lines drawn on the portion of the inner cylinder extending above the wooden cap permitted reading of length of plunger inside the cavity.

The first tests made with an open-ended cavity showed the same tuning curve as the original buzzer test oscillator cavity unit, as well as

at the high-frequency end of the tuning range.

It appeared that closing the open end of the cavity would, in our case, achieve the results desired. This effect was tried and found to improve Q throughout the operating range and to provide a much flatter

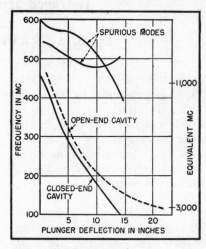

FIG. 2—Calibration of the scale model, showing improvement resulting when end was closed. Spurious modes are outside operating range

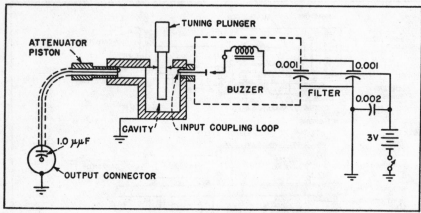

FIG. 1—Circuit of the buzzer test oscillator

which the smaller cylinder could move. The inside of the wood cap was covered with copper sheet and suitable fingers made contact with the two cylinders. The inner cylinder was capped to simulate the solid plunger to be used in the actual cavity. Standard uhf connectors were mounted in the wall of the outer cylinder near the capped end to serve as connections to the small coupling loops mounted on the inner ends of these connectors.

the rather wide variation of output previously noted. Data given by Barrow and Mieher suggested that the low-frequency end of the tuning curve could be controlled through a considerable range by the use of a closed cavity. Appropriate adjustment of the spacing between the plunger and the end of the cavity at the limit of plunger travel was necessary. It was also reported that the cavity oscillations were very weak in an open-ended cavity

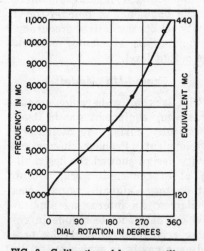

FIG. 3—Calibration of buzzer oscillator. Small circles are values predicted from large-scale model for which an equivalent frequency scale is shown

tuning curve, as shown on Fig. 2. However, resonances at higher modes became apparent. This condition was undesirable since it meant that more than one resonance frequency could exist for a given setting of the tuning plunger. The unwanted modes were identified[2] as the $TE_{1,1,1}$ and the $TE_{0,1,1}$ types.

Mode Suppressors

In the large-scale sheet-metal Ashcan it was a simple matter to introduce a set of mode-suppressing slits[3] that eliminated the $TE_{1,1,1}$ mode of oscillation. However, since the $TE_{1,1,1}$ is appreciably higher in frequency than the desired $TM_{0,1,0}$ and unlike the latter is a function of cavity length, it was decided to make the cavity shorter. This change raised both the undesired modes out of the chosen frequency range of the oscillator. The mode suppressing slits became unnecessary. The final position of the $TE_{1,1,1}$ and $TE_{0,1,1}$ modes is indicated at the top of Fig. 2.

It should be noted that the desired resonance curve represents a transition from the $TM_{0,1,0}$ mode (when the tuning plunger is entirely backed out of the cavity) towards the $TM_{0,0,P}$ mode[1], which would occur when the plunger almost touched the opposite end wall. However, the resonant frequency would then be much below that required for this application and motion of the plunger is stopped while operation is still a combination of the two modes mentioned above.

Experimental work at the Ashcan's convenient frequency range and physical size having been concluded, the resulting design was scaled back to 3,000-to-11,000-mc dimensions. The closed-end cavity now employed presents much less of a shielding problem than the original open-end unit. Provision was made for batteries, buzzer, and a piston-type attenuator with 100-db range.

The action by which the buzzer excites the cavity seems to be a high-frequency oscillation causing a pulse of perhaps five amperes maximum amplitude in the contacts at their break, when the voltage across the coil rises sharply to a value over 200 volts. It is necessary that each pulse be clean, and that the repetition rate be high enough to furnish an easily distinguished audio note for the operator's convenience while not being so high that the average battery current is excessive.

Selection of Buzzer

Several commercial buzzers were tried. Inherent unsuitability for this application ruled out some units—for example, a standard power-pack vibrator was found to have excessive bounce at contact make, causing one or more break pulses at this time. Other buzzers drew more battery current than operating economy could permit, had an unstable repetition rate or operated at a frequency outside the desired range. The buzzer finally employed was conventional, but it was carefully designed and constructed to avoid the above faults. The operating value of 800 cps was chosen as a modulation value permitting low battery current and yet capable of being distinguished through receiver noise.

In use, the buzzer test oscillator has been found to perform almost exactly as the large scale model had predicted, as shown by the calibration curve of Fig. 3. Available test equipment has not permitted a full search of the upper frequency region to make sure that the undesired modes of oscillation are in the

same relative position that model tests had shown. At each frequency where tests have been made, the agreement with the model's results has been excellent.

The unit is compact and rugged, weighing less than 11 pounds complete. The current drain on the self-contained batteries is between 30 and 150 ma, depending on buzzer adjustment. When operated at normal temperatures the battery life for continuous operation should be in excess of 300 hours, or considerably more for intermittent operation. The oscillator thus provides a completely self-contained, relatively trouble-free, portable source of uhf signals. No heating-up time is required, the unit being ready for operation as soon as the battery switch is thrown.

The first example of a test oscillator of this sort was made at the Radio Research Laboratory[4] at Harvard during the war. A second model was later made by the Naval Research Laboratory, Bellevue, D. C., and the design development described here was supported by the Bureau of Aeronautics of the Department of the Navy.

REFERENCES

(1) W. L. Barrow and W. W. Mieher, Natural Oscillations of Electrical Cavity Resonators, *Proc. IRE*, 28, No. 4, p 184, April 1940.

(2) I. G. Wilson, C. W. Schramm, and J. P. Kinzer, High Q Resonant Cavities for Microwave Testing, *B. S. T. J.*, 25, No. 3, p 408, July 1946.

(3) J. P. Kinzer and I. G. Wilson, End Plate and Side Wall Currents in Circular Cylinder Cavity Resonator, *B. S. T. J.*, 26, No. 1, p 31, Jan. 1947.

(4) Buzzer Signal Generator for 3,000 MC, ELECTRONICS, p 140, Oct. 1946.

Microwave Generator with Crystal Control

Portable 3,100-mc signal generator with pulsed or c-w output is useful for field testing of radar and beacon receivers. Substituting crystals in two channels gives up to 600-mc frequency range without changing other circuit components

By W. F. MARSHALL

THE need often arises for a portable microwave signal source suitable for field testing of radar and beacon receivers. Among the prime requisites of such a generator are minimum size and weight and accurate frequency calibration.

Laboratory oscillators employing klystrons or lighthouse tubes require some kind of frequency-indicating device for accurate determination of output frequency. Since inclusion of such equipment in a portable set is not practical, it is desirable to use accurate crystal control of output frequency.

The signal generator to be described is an adaptation of the method of frequency generation employed by the Bureau of Standards and the MIT Radiation Laboratory[1] to a portable instrument suitable for field test work. The unit can be adapted for use with any system where microwave power requirements are modest, with little increase in over-all dimensions and no appreciable loss in portability.

The generator consists of a three-tube r-f section, a three-tube modulator section and a three-tube power supply. The r-f unit consists of a dual triode crystal oscillator operating near 50 mc, followed by two stages of frequency multiplication. The resulting signal is applied to a silicon crystal multiplier mounted in a standard S-band crystal mixer.

Output from the mixer provides an S-band signal of accurately known frequency. For receiver testing, which is the primary use of the present unit, a pulsed signal is normally desired and provision is made for internal generation of a modulating pulse.

For convenience in oscilloscopic

testing of receivers, a suitable sync source is provided with a variable delay between the output sync pulse and the modulator pulse. For maximum utility, provision is made for use of an external trigger for synchronization with other system components.

The cathode-coupled series-mode oscillator has been found ideally suited to operation of crystals at harmonics of their fundamental mode. This oscillator originally proposed by Butler[2] and further developed by Goldberg and Crosby[3] consists of a grounded-grid amplifier driving a cathode follower. Output of the cathode follower is in the proper phase to supply positive feedback to the grounded-grid stage. By using a quartz crystal as the cathode-coupling impedance, the feedback will be of the proper phase and maximum magnitude at the series-resonant frequency of the crystal. At all other frequencies the loop gain and phase-shift conditions will forbid oscillation.

Frequency Stability

This type oscillator is greatly immune to changes in tube characteristics, operating voltages and stray circuit impedances. Both the input and output impedances of the amplifier are low, less than 200 ohms, a criterion which analysis will show to enhance frequency stability. Operation of the crystal at its series or low-impedance mode will minimize the effect of variation in circuit constants.

A recent proposal by H. Cressman of Bendix Radio places the crystal in the grid circuit of the grounded-grid amplifier, thus achieving a grounded-grid condi-

tion only at the series resonant frequency of the crystal. At other frequencies the degeneration provided by the high-impedance grid circuit forbids oscillation. Cathode-coupled feedback is provided by a capacitor with the over-all operation essentially the same as previously described.

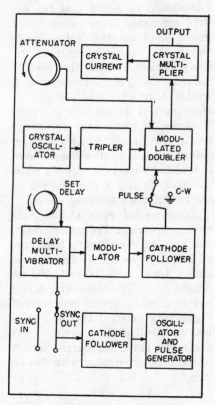

Block diagram of S-band generator

Some simplification in circuitry is provided by the Cressman oscillator in multiple-channel operation, in that one crystal terminal may be grounded and switching accomplished at the other terminal. Such an oscillator will run only at the fundamental and odd harmonics.

The oscillator employed by the author is essentially that of Cressman and is shown schematically in Fig. 1. A dual triode is employed as the oscillator. The plate tank of the grounded-grid stage is a slug-tuned, seven-turn coil on a 0.5-in. Bakelite form resonated by stray capacitance. The high L to C ratio plus the lossy iron core results in a broad-band plate impedance capable of providing adequate gain to sustain oscillation over the desired band of 50 to 51.666 mc. The broad-band amplification also increases the over-all stability of the oscillator since loop phase shift will only vary slowly with frequency.

Amplitude limiting is provided by grid-leak bias on the cathode-follower stage. The crystal circuit uses an ordinary toggle switch for channel selection. A 33,000-ohm resistor shunting the crystal provides a d-c return for the grid and is large enough to prevent oscillation in the absence of a crystal.

Output may be taken from the oscillator at several points, including the plate of V_{1A}, the cathode of V_{1B} or the plate of V_{1B}. In the last case the plate load may be a band-pass circuit tuned to a still higher harmonic of the crystal frequency, thus permitting the generation of crystal-controlled signals at frequencies upward of 200 mc in a single stage.

Resistor Load

Output necessarily falls off rapidly with increased multiplication and a resistor load provides output at the 50-mc level. The resistor is small enough to have a negligible effect on the output impedance of the cathode follower or upon the magnitude of the feedback voltage and large enough to provide some gain for driving the following stage.

Only discreet selected frequencies are available from such an oscillator but, in cases where operating frequencies are definitely specified, crystals may be selected accordingly. No limitation to two channels of operation is imposed. Turret selection of crystals for ten or more channels is entirely feasible. The range of frequency coverage is limited by the tuning range of the plate coils in the oscillator and multiplier stages. Coverage at S-band of 600 mc is practical with the present circuit.

The oscillator output is R-C coupled to a conventional tripler stage, a 6AK5 operated approximately class C, as shown in Fig. 2. The plate load of the tripler is a two-turn slug-tuned coil resonated by stray capacitance and sufficiently broad-band to cover the range of 150 to 155 mc without requiring retuning. Bias for this stage as well as the following stage is obtained from a bleeder across a regulated negative power supply.

Output of the tripler is R-C coupled to the grid of a doubler stage which serves as a modulated output amplifier, shown in Fig. 2 and 3. The output tube is a 6AS6 pentode, chosen for its sharp-cutoff suppressor-grid characteristics as well as its excellent uhf capabilities. For c-w operation the suppressor is returned to the cathode

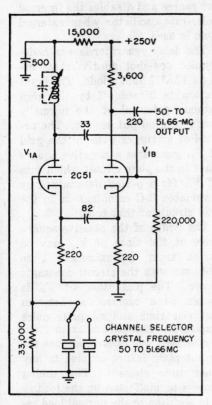

FIG. 1—Cathode-coupled oscillator

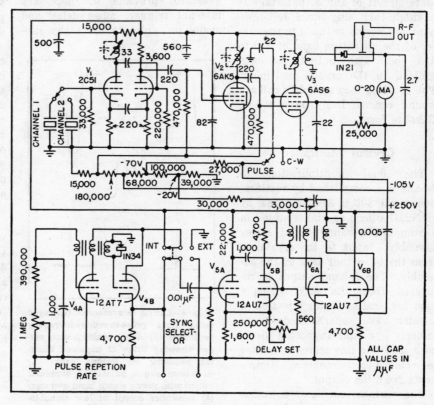

FIG. 2—Schematic diagram of S-band signal generator

and the tube operates as a conventional doubler. For pulsed operation, the suppressor is returned through a resistor to a bias well below cut off.

A positive pulse supplied to the suppressor permits the tube to conduct for the duration of the pulse. The requirements imposed upon the modulating pulse are less severe than would be the case for plate modulation, particularly if sufficient pulse amplitude is available to drive the suppressor well above ground.

Control of the output signal strength is made possible by a potentiometer in the screen-grid circuit of the 6AS6. The drive supplied to the crystal is thus set by the level of the screen voltage, and smooth control of the output voltage at S-band is available over a range of at least 70 db with an ordinary wire-wound potentiometer.

Use of a wave-guide-below-cutoff attenuator in the output line was termed unnecessary since no means of measuring power input to the attenuator is provided. The plate circuit of the output stage is a single-turn slug-tuned self-resonant coil normally tuned to the center of the operating band of 300 to 310 mc. The output is loop-coupled to the crystal multiplier. The coupling loop and plate coil are wound concentrically on a 0.5-in. Bakelite form.

Crystal Multiplier

The final multiplication to S-band is accomplished by rectification of the 300 to 310-mc signal by a 1N21C silicon crystal mounted in a standard S-band coaxial mixer assembly. Input to the crystal is from the i-f output jack of the assembly. The S-band output is recovered from the jack normally used for local oscillator injection in a microwave superheterodyne receiver. The stub-supported oscillator injection line serves as a filter to remove low-frequency components from the output.

The variable oscillator injection probe provides a means of setting

the maximum S-band output obtainable. Lesser outputs are obtained by controlling the screen voltage of the output stage. The remaining connection to the mixer assembly provides a d-c path for the crystal through a milliammeter

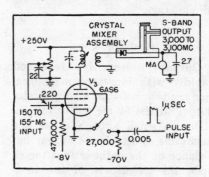

FIG. 3—Pulse-modulated r-f doubler and output stage

to ground. Crystal current may be monitored in the c-w position to give a rough approximation of power output based on a previous calibration.

Modulator

The modulator section of the generator provides the necessary internal trigger, pulse delay and modulator pulse to drive the sup-

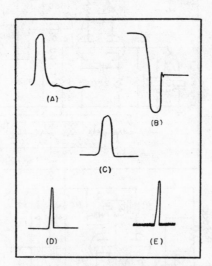

FIG. 4—Circuit waveforms: (A) sync pulse from pulse-repetition-frequency oscillator; (B) delay multivibrator output, showing firing of triggered blocking oscillator on trailing edge; (C) modulator output pulse; (D) generator output with strong signal input and agc; (E) generator output at low signal-to-noise ratio, with no agc

pressor of the r-f output stage. Internal sync is provided by a conventional free-running blocking oscillator using one section of a 12AT7 dual triode, V_4, in conjunction with a pulse transformer.

Pulse repetition rate is variable from 200 to 800 pps by means of a potentiometer in the grid-return lead of the oscillator. Two windings of the pulse transformer are used for a 1-to-1 plate-to-grid feedback loop. A third winding is used to drive the second section of the 12AT7 as a cathode follower.

The cathode follower output is a positive pulse of approximately 100 volts amplitude and 0.75-μsec duration. The negative overshoot would terminate the period of the delay multivibrator prematurely and is accordingly clipped by a 1N34 diode, as in Fig. 4. The pulse is fed to a panel jack as a sync pulse for auxiliary equipment and also to the grid of a delay multivibrator, V_5. A second panel jack provides for use of an external input trigger where such operation is more desirable. A switch selects the trigger source and disables the internal pulse-rate oscillator when external sync is used.

The delay generator is a cathode-coupled one-shot multivibrator using a 12AU7 dual triode. The input section is biased off by the high cathode potential of the normally conducting output section. The arrival of a trigger pulse at the grid of V_{5A} generates a negative square wave in the plate circuit which cuts off V_{5B} for a period determined by a variable R-C combination in the grid circuit of that tube.

The width of the positive square wave at the plate of V_{5B} may be varied from approximately 1 to 300 μsec with the circuit constants shown. The plate load of V_{5B} is chosen as a compromise between fast rise time and adequate pulse amplitude. The particular multivibrator used was chosen because the output plate is not coupled to any other tube element. The timing process is unaffected by the load.

In addition to the normal load resistor, the plate circuit of V_{5B} contains the plate winding of the modulator blocking oscillator. The positive-output square wave is differentiated by the combination of the plate load resistor and the transformer inductance. The trailing edge of the square wave thus provides a sharp negative trigger in the plate circuit of V_{6A}, a 12AU7 connected as a biased oscillator. A 1-to-1 coupling to the grid of V_{6A} with appropriate phase reversal initiates a cycle of oscillation and produces a 1-μsec pulse of 100 volts amplitude, as in Fig. 4.

A fixed bias of −20 volts prevents a free-running condition in the modulator. The output pulse is coupled through an isolating cathode follower to the pulse—c-w selector switch for use in modulating the suppressor of V_3.

The blocking oscillator described will generate pulses with a maximum duration of about 3 μsec, limited by the low-frequency response of the pulse transformer. Variation of the pulse width by a panel control is impractical. However, the present unit was designed with a specific microwave system in mind for which a fixed pulse width is desirable.

Test Results

Tests have been conducted with the completed generator on an S-band receiver with very satisfactory results. The output signal necessarily contains a large number of frequencies, chiefly harmonics of the 300 to 310-mc output and a number of beat frequencies at intervals of 50 mc. Some type of preselection is desirable in order to utilize a specific output harmonic. For use with equipment not having preselection, an external transmission cavity tunable over the operating range of the signal generator may be required.

Output voltages of 12 mv into a 50-ohm receiver have been obtained with 15 ma of rectified crystal current referred to a c-w basis. To date no crystal failures have occurred despite the rather large peak currents being passed. Operation over a 100-mc S-band is possible by selection of the proper crystal. No retuning of the three band-pass plate loads is necessary.

A panel meter for monitoring crystal-multiplier current is provided and serves as a tuning indicator when the generator is operated in a c-w condition. Crystal current also provides a rough indication of the output power available.

Frequency checks indicate an accuracy of at least 0.002 percent in the S-band output. The pulse repetition rate, though not usually critical, has very acceptable stability. A change of ± 10 volts in supply voltage produces a 1-pps change in the 800-pps rate. The delay between sync pulse and the modulator output pulse does not re-

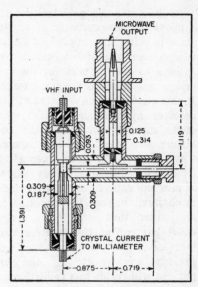

Cross-section of crystal mixer assembly

quire any great stability. However, only ± 1 μsec variation is produced by ± 10 volts variation in plate supply.

The author wishes to express his appreciation for the assistance and advice of James F. Gordon in the development of this instrument and to C. C. Bath and G. W. Clevenger for suggestions as to circuit arrangements.

REFERENCES

(1) C. A. Montgomery, "Technique of Microwave Measurements", MIT Radiation Lab Series, McGraw-Hill Book Co., 1947.
(2) F. Butler, Cathode Coupled Oscillator, *Wireless Engineer*, p 521, Nov. 1944.
(3) H. Goldberg and E. Crosby, Series Mode Crystal Oscillator Circuit, *Proc. of NEC*, 1947.

Compact Microwave Signal Generator

By WILLIAM EISNER

THE KLYSTRON SIGNAL GENERATOR to be described provides a handy source of microwave energy for use in studying uhf phenomena, as a demonstration unit to illustrate microwave beacon systems, or as a piece of test equipment for making sensitivity and signal-to-noise measurements on microwave receivers. The unit employs a 2K25 klystron operating at approximately 10,000 mc, and either modulated or continuous-wave output is available.

The unit consists of three main sections: the rather unique circuits used for modulating the klystron output, the scope and its associated circuits to give a visual indication of the modulating pulses, and the power supply section.

The klystron signal generator utilizes a system of modulation which was developed by Robert Rudin, formerly associated with the Leru Laboratories. The system is based on the intermittent generation of a carrier of constant amplitude with the ratio of on to off periods being varied.

To illustrate this principle, let us suppose that the emission of an r-f wave is being interrupted at a certain rate and that the on periods are as long as the off periods; the envelope will then be a square wave. If this signal is then detected at the receiver by a diode rectifier, the diode current will follow the envelope and the resulting square wave, if averaged over a period of time, will assume a steady value. If now the ratio of on to off periods is changed so that the emission is on longer than off, the average diode current at the receiver will increase. Lengthening the off periods and shortening the on periods will result in a reduction of diode current.

It is convenient to keep the repetition rate (25,000 pps) of the pulses constant and vary the length of the on periods. Also instead of completely cutting off the emission of the carrier wave during the off periods, its amplitude can be reduced to a constant predetermined fraction of the amplitude during the on periods. It is seen that the relative variations of diode current depend only on the ratio of on to off periods and are independent of the actual amplitude. It is therefore possible to pass the received signals thru amplitude-limiting devices before detecting them and in this way practically eliminate the influences of variations in transmission.

To accomplish the cutting on and off of the 2K25 klystron output in a practical way, the circuit of Fig. 1 is used. A sawtooth voltage is applied to V_1. The cathode of V_1 is biased by the voltage output of the cathode-follower triode V_3 which in turn is modulated by the a-f input. The steady cathode bias of V_1 is determined by R_5 which also determines the grid bias of V_3. The drop in the cathode resistor R_2 determines the bias of V_1 and determines the ratio of on to off of V_1. The plate current of V_1 is carried thru R_3 and the voltage drop of the plate current thru R_3 is applied to the control grid of V_2. The length of the plate current pulses in V_2 are the on and off periods desired (see Fig. 2). These pulses are amplified and used to turn the Klystron plate voltage on and off.

The front panel controls provide a means for varying the klystron

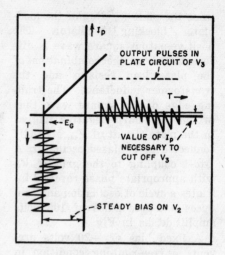

FIG. 2—Curve of E_G vs I_P showing how length of output pulses is changed by modulator shown in Fig. 1

repeller voltage and thereby vary the r-f frequency within narrow limits. The klystron can also be operated continuous wave. If the klystron is to be evenly pulsed (no modulation), the centering control is used to vary the length of the pulse, and this modulating pulse can be seen on the scope. The meter on the front panel gives the average klystron cathode current.

The output of the microwave generator may be radiated by the antenna system, shown in the photograph, which is mounted on a swivel arrangement so that the r-f can be radiated in any desired direction. Or the parabolic reflector and end piece may be removed and a 3-cm waveguide clamped in place and used to pipe the microwave signal to the desired location.

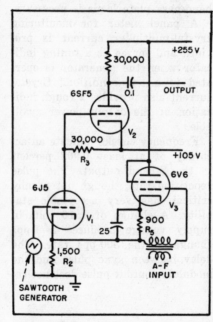

FIG. 1—Circuit diagram of unique modulator used in microwave signal generator

Self-Regulating Field Excitation for Magnetrons

By H. C. EARLY AND H. W. WELCH

STABLE MAGNETRON OPERATION can be obtained by utilizing the anode current as excitation for the magnetic field, instead of using a permanent magnet or a separately excited electromagnet. The volt-ampere characteristic of the magnetron can be made to correspond to a constant power curve over a significant part of the operating range, or to optimum modulating conditions.

Series Magnet Connection

Using a series connection of field and anode circuit, adjustment of anode voltage is less critical and the tuning range for fixed voltage is greater than for constant magnet excitation. In experimental circuits it is possible to put the tube into oscillation at low power, observing tube operation before applying full power. The oscillating state of a magnetron with series excitation rises uniformly with applied power instead of suddenly for fixed excitation, as shown in Fig. 1. Parasitic oscillation at low anode voltages or oscillation at abnormal modes is avoided. In addition, the high inductance of the magnet winding can be used in the anode power supply filter, and the output power can be controlled by a single Variac in the input power line.

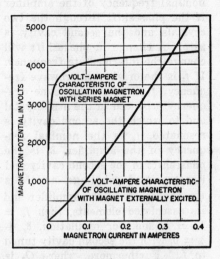

FIG. 1—Comparison of oscillating magnetron characteristics. (Labels should be reversed)

Design of the field magnet is restricted. Minimum anode current and maximum flux required

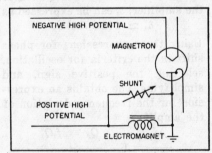

FIG. 2—Magnetron with series field excitation of its magnet

by the tube determine the amount

of iron, thermal capacity, and number of turns of the magnet. If the magnet saturates, self-regulating properties of the circuit are lost.

The circuit can be connected as shown in Fig. 2. The magnet winding can be used in the power supply filter provided the plate transformer has low capacitance to ground. The anode block of the magnetron is at ground potential for convenience in providing water cooling. The shunt provides adjustment of the field to match the characteristic of the particular tube, or to control the output power.

Although a separate field excitation supply is unnecessary, the anode supply must provide the voltage drop through the magnet winding. A spark gap or Thyrite resistor across the magnet winding should be provided for protection of its insulation against voltage surges. The series magnet reduces effects of changing line voltage and power supply ripple. A combination of series and shunt field windings can be used to obtain a variety of characteristics. Thyrite resistors can be used for field shunts to further alter the overall magnetron operation. (Work reported herein was done at RRL under contract with OSRD, NDRC, Div. 15.)

Stabilizing Frequency of Reflex Oscillators

By GEORGE G. BRUCK

MICROWAVE GENERATORS can be stabilized in frequency in several ways. The method to be described is advantageous in that it is all electronic, uses fewer circuit components than some methods, and incorporates several simplifications

of the plumbing. Used with a 10-kmc oscillator, this circuit maintains the frequency within one part in 10^8.

Duplex Heterodyne

The operating principle can be

followed through the block diagram. Microwave energy from the oscillator enters the main waveguide G by way of the probe P and flows in the indicated direction. The energy is tapped through the first iris I, which admits a small amount of energy to the upper cavity C_1. This cavity has low Q (of the order of 1,000) and serves chiefly to isolate the subsequent portions of the circuit from the main guide.

A fraction of this energy is admitted to the first crystal X_1 (such as a 1N/23B) where it mixes with energy from the intermediate-frequency amplifier output (approximately 30 mc). The resulting sum (or difference) frequency is transferred into the second cavity C_2 through the third iris I_3. This cavity has a high Q and is used as the

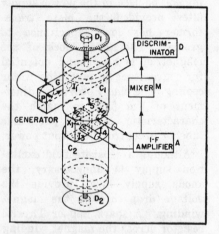

Microwave plumbing is shown pictorially in block diagram of stabilizer

frequency reference. The energy in the second cavity is coupled through the forth iris I_4 to the second crystal X_2 where it is mixed with energy from the first cavity coming through the fifth iris I_5. The result is the intermediate frequency, which is returned to the i-f amplifier input to produce oscillation through the system at or near the intermediate frequency.

Oscillation occurs only if the microwave generator delivers sufficient power to the mixer crystals, which condition is dependent upon the coupling of the irises. Because the crystals require voltages of a given magnitude for best operation as mixers, the irises have optimum size, but are not critical. The choice of cavity and coupling in the upper section should be such as to sufficiently attenuate the uhf generated in the first crystal, so that

feedback through any channel but the high Q cavity is avoided. Using the highest possible i-f will make attenuation of this uhf easier.

Criteria for Oscillation

The system will oscillate at the nominal frequency of the amplifier if the phaseshift through the two crystals and the second cavity is zero. A change in phaseshift will change the intermediate frequency. If f_1 is the original microwave frequency, f_2 is the heterodyne frequency produced in the first crystal and to which the second cavity is resonated, f_3 is the nominal frequency of the amplifier, δ_2 is the phaseshift in the second cavity and its associated couplings, and δ_3 is the phaseshift in the amplifier and its associated elements, then $f_2 = f_1 \pm f_3$ and, for oscillation, $\delta_2 + \delta_3 = 0$, with the second cavity tuned to f_2. Furthermore, where Q_2 is the loaded Q of the second cavity, δ_2 near resonance is

$$\delta_2 \approx 2(\Delta\omega_2/\omega_2) Q_2$$

where $\Delta\omega_2$ is the deviation from resonance. By introducing Q_3, defined as the equivalent over-all Q of the amplifier, δ_3 can be expressed as

$$\delta_3 \approx 2(\Delta\omega_3/\omega_3) Q_3$$

Using these expressions for phase shift in the criteria for oscillation, selecting the positive sign, and simplifying, one obtains an expression for the frequency deviation of the amplifier

$$\frac{\Delta f_1}{\Delta f_3} = 1 - \frac{Q_3}{Q_2} + \frac{f_1 Q_3}{f_3 Q_2}$$

If the negative sign is taken, all terms of the righthand side of the equation are negative. There are two other possible combinations of signs, but they represent unstable conditions.

For the relationship between frequency deviation of the amplifier and the microwave oscillator to be independent of the circuit elements, Q_3 must be small; that is, the phase changes very little with frequency near resonance; Q_3 can be made zero over an appreciable bandwidth, which, although not indispensable, is desirable. Almost any 30-mc

radar i-f strip can be adapted for the purpose, giving an i-f deviation approximately half the microwave deviation, which is favorable for proper stabilization. Because grid current in the amplifier will cause noticable detuning, such nonlinear elements as Thermistors or Thyrites should be introduced to limit the amplitude of oscillations so that detuning is unnoticeable.

Oscillator Control

Recovery of information from the i-f strip is straightforward. Any discriminator, separated by a buffer stage, supplies sufficient output to control a reflex oscillator. The oscillator control completes a negative feedback loop from generator through guide to first cavity through the mixers and second cavity to the oscillating i-f amplifier, hence through the discriminator back to the generator. Phaseshifts throughout this loop must not introduce f-m oscillations in the overall system.

Frequency modulation can be introduced by injecting the audio-frequency signal through an additional mixer between the i-f amplifier and the discriminator. The i-f output (30 mc) is mixed with a frequency-modulated auxiliary oscillator (10 mc); the resulting difference frequency (20 mc) drives the discriminator. Drift in the auxiliary oscillator will, of course, affect the microwave oscillator, the microwave deviation being about twice that of the auxiliary oscillator.

The complete circuit is easy to adjust and operate. The microwave components are not critical, can be assembled in advance, and need no adjustments. The two cavities can be coupled mechanically for tuning. The second or reference cavity must have an effective Q higher than 10,000 and high thermal stability; it is preferably constructed from such low expansion alloys as Invar. The coupling irises should be small. The amplitude control of the i-f amplifier must keep the d-c in the two mixer crystals constant. In testing the circuit, two oscillators were easily kept within 100 cps of each other.

The circuit was developed while the author was with Raytheon Mfg. Co.,

Waltham, Mass, and the inventions are assigned to that organization.

Wide-Range Resonators for VHF and UHF

By G. F. MONTGOMERY AND P. G. SULZER

THE RESONATORS discussed in this note have been used successfully as oscillator tank circuits between 50 and 550 megacycles. Their large tuning range suggests that they may be useful in uhf television receivers or in laboratory oscillators. Work on the resonators was inspired by Aske's description[1] of a single-ended variable capacitance-inductance tuned circuit. Two experimental balanced types, drawings of which are shown in Fig. 1, were machined from brass tubing. Tuning is effected by moving a cylindrical conducting slug axially through the resonator. Terminals of the resonators are located at points x. There is a superficial resemblance to the coaxial butterfly circuits described by Karplus[2], but the resonators are essentially lumped-constant devices rather than transmission line sections.

The resonator of Fig. 1A consists of a single-loop inductance connected to capacitors made up of two short half-cylinders and the tuning slug. The minimum frequency is produced when the slug is entirely contained by the half-cylinders, since then both the capacitance and the inductance are at a maximum. Conversely, the maximum frequency is produced when slug is contained by the loop. The resonator shown in Fig. 1B is similar in that half-cylinders are employed for capacitors; however, the inductors consist of two parallel strips, as shown. The tuning mechanism is essentially the same as for the first resonator.

Optimum ratios of the resonator dimensions for maximum tuning range are probably best determined by experiment. But if it is assumed that the tuning slug shall always remain inside the resonator, then

it appears that maximum variation in the capacitive and inductive parts of the resonator will be obtained for $b = c + d$ in **Fig. 1 A** and for $b = d$ in **Fig. 1B**.

In Fig. 1A, assume that the dimensions are fixed at

$$a = b = 2c = 2d$$

and that the slug length is b. Then the maximum capacitance with air

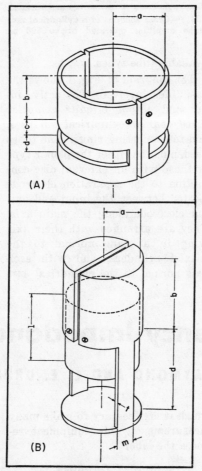

(A)

(B)

FIG. 1—Experimental vhf-uhf resonators, having frequency ranges from 50 to approximately 550 mc

dielectric will be, approximately,

$$C = \frac{0.225 \, \pi \, a^2}{2 \, r} \; \mu\mu f,$$

where r is the radial clearance be-

tween slug and resonator, the dimensions being in inches. The corresponding maximum inductance, assuming a thin conductor and neglecting skin effect, will be, approximately,

$$L = 0.071 \, a \; \mu h$$

and the minimum resonant frequency will be

$$f \approx 1,000 \sqrt{\frac{r}{a^3}} \; mc$$

If r/a is a constant k, then

$$f \approx 1,000 \frac{\sqrt{k}}{a} \; mc$$

where a is in inches.

In Fig. 1B, assume that

$$b = d = l = 2a = 5m = 24t$$

Then the maximum capacitance will be, approximately,

$$C = 0.112 \left(\frac{\pi \, ab}{r} + \frac{\pi \, a^2}{2r} \right)$$

$$= \frac{0.28 \, \pi \, a^2}{r} \; \mu\mu f$$

where r is both the radial clearance and the axial clearance between the slug and the inside end of the resonator.

The corresponding maximum inductance will be, approximately,

$$L = 0.04 \, a \; \mu h,$$

and the minimum resonant frequency will be

$$f \approx 850 \sqrt{\frac{r}{a^3}} \; mc$$

If r/a is a constant k, then

$$f \approx 850 \frac{\sqrt{k}}{a} \; mc$$

where a is in inches.

REFERENCES

(1) Vernon H. Aske, Front End Design for a 400-Mc Receiver, *Tele-Tech* 9, p 46, Sept. 1950.
(2) Eduard Karplus, Wide-Range Tuned Circuits and Oscillators for High Frequencies, *Proc. IRE* 33, p 426, July 1945.

Power Tubes in Parallel at UHF

By J. R. DAY

CURRENT INTEREST in television and other communications methods at uhf centers about the problem of obtaining appreciable power output from conventional equipment. The aural transmitter furnished for an experimental television system operating in the frequency range from 500 to 550 mc employs six type 2C39 tubes, air-cooled, with a power output of 100 watts. In addition, the output stage acts as a tripler.

The arrangement illustrated is the simplest and most straightforward way found to parallel uhf tubes for increasing power capabilities. Possible means were limited by the requirements that n times the power of 1 tube be secured with n tubes, and that the arrangement have substantially the same upper frequency limit as an optimum design for a single tube. These two requirements are related in that in undesirable designs failure to secure n times the power with n tubes usually is due to a progressive lowering of the upper frequency limit as n increases. The present circuit meets these requirements for all practical values of n, and is amenable to use with currently

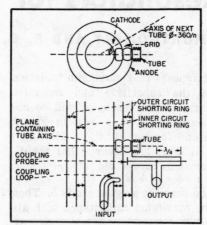

FIG. 1—Cross sections of a cylindrical multitube amplifier operated above 500 mc

available tube types.

The diagram of Fig. 1 shows the basic idea involved. The active input and output circuits comprise three coaxial cylindrical surfaces, and four shorting rings. The tubes used, must be either the planar type or those with an external disc connection to the separation electrode located between the input and output electrode along the main axis. They are arranged with their axis lying in a plane normal to the coaxial cylinders, and with each axis normal to the cylindrical sur-

faces. The plane of the tubes is normally about half way between the shorting rings so that in effect they are at or near the voltage loop of a resonant half-wave coaxial circuit. The tube capacitances shorten the circuit, but no more for n tubes than for one with the same distributed parameters for the circuit involved. The tubes are oriented, to facilitate insertion, so that the smallest electrode connection is inward. Thus with 2C43's the outer circuit would be the grid-cathode, while with 2C39's it would be the plate-grid circuit.

The possibility that this type of circuit could support extraneous modes was examined. Neither paper work nor experiment disclosed any unusually favorable conditions for such modes. Of the second order possibilities the most likely seemed to be the one wherein the electric field is normal to the cylindrical surfaces and varies in intensity along a path in a plane normal to the axis of the cylinders. Such a mode could always be suppressed by means of a slot parallel to the cylinder axis. Removal of tubes did not cause excitation of spurious modes.

High-Frequency Impedance Plotter

By R. C. RAYMOND AND C. E. DRUMHELLER

A HIGH-FREQUENCY impedance-measuring system consisting of a circular slotted line that is scanned rapidly by a probe, an oscilloscope and a mechanical computer has been developed. It is fairly accurate for standing wave ratios less than 4 to 1 and covers a range from 140 to 1,200 mc. For rapid surveys in which accuracy is not important at large standing wave ratios but in

which it is necessary to make many measurements, this equipment reduces the labor.

Basis of Operation

To reduce the measurements to the magnitude and phase angle of the impedance being studied, the standing wave is presented on an oscilloscope and then transferred to a circular impedance chart by the

cord-and-linkage computer of Fig. 1. The trace on the oscilloscope is obtained as shown in Fig. 2, showing second portion of the computer.

An oscillator feeds a circular slotted line through an impedance matcher. The slotted line is a section of a coaxial line formed in a circle of 11-inch mean diameter, made by turning grooves in two brass discs. The center conductor of copper wire is supported in a polystyrene ring milled to accept it and with a slot for the probe. At one end the line smoothly joins a straight section terminating in a coaxial fitting. The other end of the line is brought through the back cover. Because the line is proportioned to have the same characteristic impedance and diameter as the cable with which it is used, tapers are unnecessary.

This circular construction of the slotted line enables the probe to be moved continuously around it. The varying r-f current thus picked up is fed through a detector to a balanced amplifier that is flat from 30 cps (the frequency with which the probe travels around the line) to about 100 cps to a 12-inch cathode-ray tube, which gives a useful swr plot 6 by 8 inches. The vertical amplifier must have sufficient sensitivity to produce full-scale deflection with inputs of the order of 100 microvolts. The linear sweep circuit is synchronized with the rotating probe. The trace on the crt is then the squared swr as a function of position along the line. This is the same information that would be obtained on a manually-operated slotted line, and the load impedance could be obtained from it by the same computations. However, it is simpler to use a mechanical computer.

Phase Angle and Magnitude

There are two computations necessary. These are performed by two motions for plotting a point on the impedance chart: (1) a rotation of the chart corresponding to a measured line distance in half wavelengths and (2) a radial motion corresponding to a standing wave ratio. The first computation is accomplished by the mechanism of Fig. 1, the second by that of Fig. 2.

The standing-wave pattern on the oscilloscope is adjusted to a reference frame using the centering and gain controls. When the detector probe passes through the short space in the circular line between the input and output connectors,

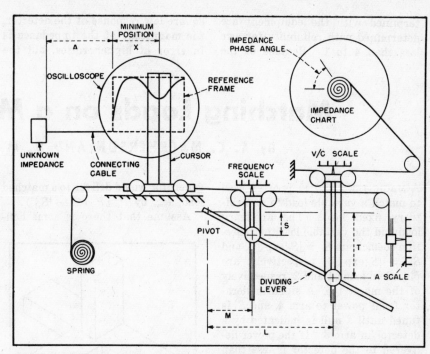

FIG. 1—Mechanical computer transfers position of minimum of standing wave ratio pattern traced on c-r tube to phase angle of unknown impedance on Smith chart

there is no signal, thus a zero reference is established as shown in the lower left-hand corner of the oscilloscope (Fig. 1) to which the reference frame is positioned. To determine the angle of rotation of the impedance chart, the distance from the unknown impedance to the cur-

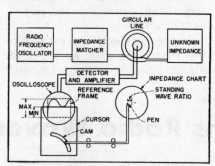

FIG. 2—Standing wave ratio, obtained from circular slotted line, is displayed on oscilloscope, then transferred to impedance chart to give value of unknown impedance

rent-minimum shown on the oscilloscope must be found. If a connecting cable is used between the unknown impedance and the slotted line, its electrical length must be considered. This is done by the *A* scale, which is calibrated at the oscilloscope in terms of equivalent length of the cable. The elements of the dividing lever are then set to

the proper positions on their scales, one for operating frequency, the other for the relative velocity on the wave in the slotted line. The lever is then moved so that the vertical cursor intersects the swr pattern at its minimum. With the computer built to the proper dimensions for the particular paramaters used in the setup (velocity of propagation in the slotted line, circumference of chart driving drum and so forth), the chart is rotated to show the proper phase angle.

The magnitude of the unknown impedance is determined by the standing wave ratio. The trace on the oscilloscope is adjusted, using the gain control, so that it touches the top and bottom of the reference frame, as shown in Fig. 2. The horizontal cursor is then aligned with the minimum. This position is transferred, through a cam that is made by plotting the square law characteristic of the detector, to the impedance chart.

With this equipment the characteristics of wideband systems can be determined quickly and the effects of adjustments on them readily observed. Both the phase angle and impedance magnitude determined with the equipment are determined with reliability for swr less than 4 to 1. Because of the square law response of the detector, the magnitude of the impedance is in error at higher ratios, but the phase angle is still in good agreement with other measurements.

Matching Loads on a Magic Tee

By A. C. MACPHERSON AND D. M. KERNS

A MAGIC TEE (Fig. 1) is often used to match a variable load to an arbitrary fixed load. The arbitrary load and the variable load, of reflection coefficients $S_1 = |S_1|\exp j\theta_1$, and $S_2 = |S_2|\exp j\theta_2$ respectively, are placed on arms 1 and 2, respectively of the magic tee. A signal generator feeds power to arm 4, and S_2 is tuned until a null is indicated by a detector in arm 3. If the power delivered to the detector is less than the minimum power the detector can indicate, the null is only apparent and will be observed for a range of values of S_2 in the neighborhood of S_1. There follows a method of evaluating the limits of this range.

Assume that the generator and the detector are reflectionless. Then it can be shown that for a symmetrical lossless magic tee $4P_3/P_4 = [\ |S_1|^2 + |S_2|^2 - 2|S_1|\ |S_2|\cos(\theta_1 - \theta_2)\ ]$, where P_3 is the power delivered to the detector in arm 3 and P_4 is the power fed into arm 4. Power P_4 is related to the power that the

generator would deliver to a matched load, P_m, by $P_4 \cong P_m(1 - |S_1|^2)$.

Assume that there is some definite value of P_3 which is the minimum power that the detector can indicate.

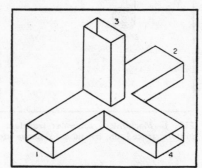

FIG. 1—Magic-tee network used to match variable load to an arbitrary fixed load

Since the above expression has the form of the law of cosines, a very simple geometric solution presents itself.

On the complex plane, draw S_1 to any convenient scale as shown in Fig. 2. Using the same scale, with

the terminus of S_1 as a center, draw a circle of radius $2\sqrt{P_3/P_4}$. Then the locus of the terminus of S_2 will be on or in this circle. (The figure is drawn for the following values: $P_3 = 10^{-6}$ watts; $P_4 = 10^{-2}$ watts; $S_1 = 0.1\exp(j\pi/4)$). It is clear from the drawing that in general the largest possible difference between $|S_1|$ and $|S_2|$ is $2\sqrt{P_3/P_4}$, and the largest possible difference between θ_1 and θ_2 is given by $\sin(\theta_1 - \theta_2) = 2\sqrt{P_3/P_4}/|S_1|$.

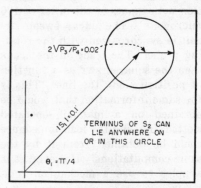

FIG. 2—Geometric solution of magic-tee load-matching problem

Citizens Radio Wavemeter

Two coaxial-type wavemeters are described in detail for guidance of experimenters developing equipment for the band from 460 to 470 mc. Accuracy may be made adequate for use with class B gear or, by greater construction precision, with class A transmitters

By WILLIAM B. LURIE

THE GRADUAL PUSH toward more widespread use of the frequencies above 300 megacycles by the general public, and by non-commercial and non-research organizations such as radio amateurs and owners of Citizens Radio Service equipment, has created a need for some means of checking transmitted frequency in this range.

Perhaps the simplest method is by means of a Lecher line, but this is subject to the limitations of maximum accuracy obtainable, susceptibility to external influence, maximum sensitivity, and fineness of tuning. For example, the AN/APT-5 radar jammer (recently available as surplus equipment) was furnished with a simple parallel-line wavemeter, calibrated directly in centimeters. By careful adjustment, this wavemeter should indicate the half-wavelength being monitored to ±0.2 cm, yielding a limiting accuracy at 50 cm (600 mc) of ±0.4 cm, or ±0.8 percent. The pilot-light indicator on this wavemeter requires only about 50 milliwatts for a reasonable indication. This type of device, however, can be thrown far off calibration by proximity effects and poor contacts on the slider. In fact, one commercial manufacturer of a similar instrument rates it at 2-percent accuracy.

Cavity frequency meters (more correctly, wavelength meters) should be inherently free from external influences, being entirely shielded. They may be made and calibrated as accurately as machine tools and temperature effects will allow and may be made as fine in tuning as machined screw threads can be fashioned.

Basic Design

Consider first a section of air-dielectric coaxial line, as shown in Fig. 1. For the physical constants shown, this section will have a characteristic impedance Z_o equal to 138 $\log_{10} (b/a)$. If this line is completely shorted at one end, and power is coupled in at that end, the cavity so formed will have a reactance X at any frequency f given by the relationship

$$X = Z_o \tan (2\pi l/\lambda) = Z_o \tan (2\pi fl/c)$$

If, now, a capacitance C is added across the open end from the center to the outer conductor, such that $X_c = -1/2\pi fC = -Z_o \tan (2\pi fl/c)$, the line will be tuned to resonance. If the capacitor is made variable, the whole instrument, when calibrated, comprises a wavemeter.

To improve the shielding, the open end of the line is usually closed by adding an end plate or disk, after which the simple calculation for unloaded resonant wavelength must be considered approximate, since the radial electric field near the end of the center conductor is distorted by the end disk. Further, the capacitance between the end disk and the center rod itself becomes a pertinent part of the loading or tuning capacitance. If the center rod is made larger in diameter, and its separation from the end disk made variable, this variable capacitance may be made to alter the resonant frequency of the unit, which now may be considered to be a loaded coaxial TE_M-mode cavity, with variable capacitance loading.

The amount of loading capacitance may be calculated as described above, from the equation

$$\left| \frac{1}{2\pi fC} \right| = \left| Z_o \tan (2\pi fl/c) \right|,$$

$$C = \frac{1}{2\pi fZ_o \tan (2\pi fl/c)}$$

Assuming that all of this capacitance will be provided between the center rod and the end disk, the approximate equation $C = 0.2235 A/d$ for parallel-plate capacitors may be applied, giving

d = $0.2235 \; A \; \times \; 2\pi fZ_o$ tan $2\pi fl/c = 0.447\pi AfZ_o$ tan $2\pi fl/c$ where A is area of one plate in square inches and d is plate separation in inches.

Thus, all of the factors necessary for design of a simple cavity wavemeter may be calculated, with the exception of the effect of distortion of the field near the end plate. The coupling loop, for example, must not be too large, or the variable reactance of the cavity, while tuning, will be strongly reflected into the circuit being calibrated. This may cause detuning of the oscillator, or pulling, or cavity heating on a high-powered circuit.

A large loop will project out of the high-current high-magnetic-field end of the cavity, into the region where the radial electric field should be appreciable. Since a conductor cannot tolerate an electric field gradient along its length, the field must be distorted, and so one more error in the basic cavity calculation is introduced.

If the loop is too small, on the other hand, then it will not be able to cut enough lines of flux in the cavity to couple the cavity into the external circuit. This will result in too low an apparent Q, evidencing itself in extremely broad tuning, and a consequently inaccurate indication of resonance. A compromise must be effected on the undercoupled side, to prevent overcoupling, pulling, and a large error in the prediction of the range of operation.

Practical Design

In the 460-470 megacycle region, a quarter-wavelength is about 6.5 inches, and so an inside cavity length of about four inches was tried in the first experimental model. The length must be shorter than a quarter-wavelength so that it may be tuned to resonance by the addition of the loading capacitance.

For the cylinder, stock brass tubing 2¾-inch O.D., 2-9/16-inch I. D. was used. The center rod was a piece of 1¼-inch brass rod, with the end facing the plunger tapered to one inch. The characteristic impedance was calculated to be about 43 ohms. End pieces were machined from 3½-inch diameter brass rod, and the variable capacitance was provided by threading a 1¼-inch diameter rod into one end piece, at 48 threads per inch.

Power was coupled into the cavity by a coupling loop placed in a radial plane at the low-voltage-high-current end of the cavity. In addition, a fixed capacitance of about 3 micromicrofarads (Erie type NPOK) was soldered across as shown in Fig. 2.

Calibration was accomplished by loosely coupling the cavity as a shunt on the line from an oscillator to an antenna, and monitoring the radiated power with a broad-tuned radiated power meter and a Lavoie microwave frequency meter. A section of RG-21/U cable was used as an attenuator after the oscillator, to minimize pulling effect on the unstabilized BC-645 oscillator. The arrangement is shown in Fig. 3.

The cavity impedance was actually reflected, through the r-f transformer action of the coupling loop, back to the main line where it appeared as a shunt reactance. Standard r-f cable (RG-8/U) was used throughout, except for the section of high-attenuation cable mentioned. Standard type N fittings (UG-21/U, UG-58/U, UG-29/U and UG-107/U) were used.

No difficulty was experienced in determining the position corresponding to cavity resonance; a distinct dip in radiated power was observed. Care must be taken to avoid spurious responses, if other frequencies are present in addition to the fundamental. The curve of Fig. 4 shows the calibration of this first model. The tuning sensitivity near 465 mc is about 90 degrees plunger rotation for one megacycle, or about four megacycles per turn.

Second Model

On the basis of this rough model, a second cavity was built, as shown in Fig 5. Stock brass tubing of 1.75-inch O.D., 0.083-inch wall thickness was used as the cylinder. The center rod was machined down to 0.415-inch diameter, from 0.875-inch brass rod, leaving a ¼-inch portion at full diameter as a fixed capacitance plate.

All pieces were silver plated before assembly. After plating, the characteristic impedance was expected to be near 80 ohms, 77 ohms being the figure generally quoted as the impedance for optimum Q.

End pieces were machined from 2-inch O.D. brass disks ⅜-inch thick; the variable capacitance was provided by threading a ⅞-inch dia-

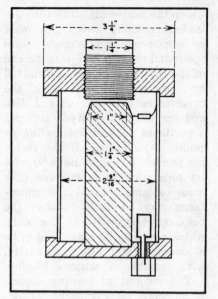

FIG. 2—Mechanical drawing of first model of cavity wavemeter

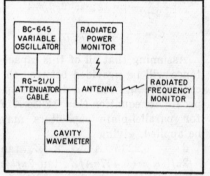

FIG. 3—Block diagram of setup for calibration and schematic circuit of cables to wavemeter

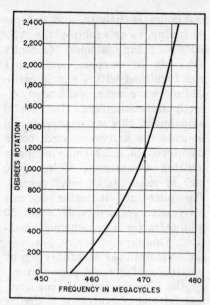

FIG. 4—Calibration curve of first model constructed

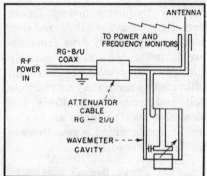

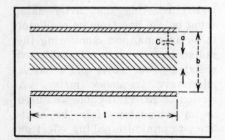

FIG. 1—Basic concept of coaxial line used to develop wavemeter

meter rod into one end piece, at 64 threads per inch.

Calibration was again accomplished by recording resonant frequency versus angular rotation of this plunger, instead of longitudinal displacement. A scribe mark was placed on the external portion of the plunger and the outer face of the end disk was marked off every 30 degrees, thereby providing a dial on which to read plunger rotation and, therefore, displacement.

Calculations from the formulas are as follows: $l = 5$ inches $= 12.7$ cm; $A = 0.6$ square inches, $Z_o = 80$ ohms. Then $1/C = 502\ f \tan 2.66 \times 10^{-3} f$.

In the region of 460–470 megacycles, a change of 10 mc should require a shift of 0.0096 inch, while

one turn of the plunger at 64 threads per inch advances it 0.0156 inch. One turn, then, should be about 16 megacycles, at a center frequency of 465 mc, or about 13 mc at 475, 11 at 485, or 9.4 at 495 megacycles. Actual tuning as measured on the first cavity of these dimensions was 9 mc per turn at 465 megacycles, indicating that the effective capacitive effect of the field distortion at the high-voltage end was about 0.45 $\mu\mu f$, sufficient to shift the resonant frequency 30 megacycles.

Accuracy

Since the tuning sensitivity was 9 mc per turn, or per 360 degrees, the accuracy of scale reading should be better than ±5 degrees, or

±0.13 mc, or ±0.028 percent. Even allowing for ±10 degrees backlash in threads, ±.08 percent at any one temperature should be assured.

The question of temperature, however, is of major concern. Making all parts of brass, an expansion coefficient of about 18 parts per million per degree Centigrade may be expected (1.000018). Since the fundamental resonant wavelength is proportional to the physical length of the cavity (unloaded), the resonant frequency will lower 0.0018 percent per degree rise in temperature.

In the 5-inch long 460–470 mc cavity, the unloaded resonant frequency is 590 mc, and will therefore shift $590 \times 18 \times 10^{-6}$, or 10.62 kc per degree C. However, the spacing between the center rod and the plunger will increase in proportion, 0.0018 percent of 0.1292 inch, or 2.32×10^{-6} inch per degree C.

A tuning sensitivity of 9 mc per 15.6×10^{-3} inch has been observed, corresponding to 1.33 kc for 2.32×10^{-6}, giving an overall frequency shift of 9.29 kc per degree C. Over a range of 50 to 90 F, or about ± 10 C, a frequency uncertainty of ±0.093 mc, or ±0.02 percent is introduced, bringing the total to near 0.1 percent.

Using low-expansion coefficient material, a saving of only 0.002 percent per degree C may be realized, while backlash effects in worn or poorly machined threads can produce forty times this effect. Even so, an amateur machinist should be able to manufacture a cavity wavemeter which, after calibration, should meet the class B FCC tolerance of ±0.4 percent for Citizens Radio Service equipment.

Increased Sensitivity

An interesting design improvement is the substitution of a fixed capacitor for a portion of the loading capacitance. It has been calculated that 1.406 μμf is required at 470 mc, of which 0.45 μμf is supplied in stray and fringing capacitance, leaving 0.956 to work with. If 0.5 μμf of fixed capacitance is added in the form of a small ceramic capacitor, such as an Erie Ceramicon, type N330K, soldered directly across from the flared end of the center rod to the brass cylinder near the end plate containing the tuning screw (see Fig. 2), then distances d_1 in Table I are applicable, instead of d. These have been calculated assuming 0.45 + 0.5 or 0.95 μμf of fixed capacitance, plus 0.456 μμf of variable capacitance at 470 megacycles.

The tuning sensitivity near 465 mc has now been changed from 9 mc per turn (0.0156 inch) to about 2 mc per turn, and the error caused by ±15 degree plunger uncertainty has been reduced to ±87 kc, or ±0.0187 percent. Furthermore, use of a negative temperature coefficient capacitor of 0.5 μμf will provide some correction for thermal expansion of the cavity. The change of a 0.5 μμf N330K capacitor in one

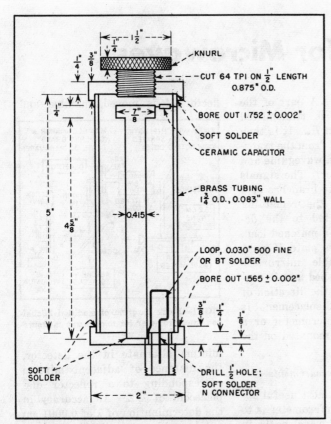

FIG. 5—Complete mechanical details of final wavemeter. All parts were silver plated before final assembly

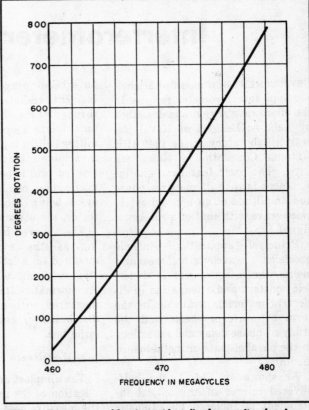

FIG. 6—Frequency calibration with a fixed capacitor forming a portion of the loading capacitance

degree C is 165×10^{-6} $\mu\mu$f; the sensitivity to a capacitance shift is 10 mc per 0.156 $\mu\mu$f, or 10.57 kc for 165×10^{-6} $\mu\mu$f, very closely balancing the 9 to 10 kc calculated.

Another attempt at temperature compensation may be made by making certain portions of the cavity of material of thermal expansion coefficient different from that of brass. The center rod, for example, may be made in two pieces, one of brass, (of expansion coefficient about 18×10^{-6} per degree C), and one of steel (of expansion coefficient about 12×10^{-6} per deg. C.

Theoretically, by careful adjustment of the length of the steel section, the natural overall negative temperature coefficient of frequency may be exactly balanced, but actually this is not practicable. Furthermore, the effects of soldering, whether low-temperature or high-temperature, are such as to make the exact expansion coefficients unpredictable. Also, the mathematics of the capacitance-

loading calculation shows that such a correction would only be effective over a narrow temperature range. In practice, it is wise to calibrate a cavity wavemeter at several temperatures.

Alternative Design

The last variable source of error may be eliminated by using a high-grade micrometer movement for the plunger, careful machining of the threads, or the use of two threaded pieces as a differential thread for the plunger movement, making one 26 and one 28 threads per inch, and making one left-handed and one

right-handed. In large threads of this type, a tighter fit is allowable, and turning one turn on each will provide a net plunger movement, axially, of 0.03846 minus 0.03571 or 0.00275 inch, as compared with 0.01563 inch per turn on 64 turns per inch. This complicates calibration somewhat, but the improvement of accuracy by a factor of five would be highly desirable, and would bring the percentage error below 0.01 percent, suitable for use with class A Citizens Band equipment, required to be within ± 0.02 percent.

Table I—Calculated Values

f in mc	$\tan 2.66 \times 10^{-3}$ f	$502 f$ ($\times 10^{12}$)	$1/C$ ($\times 10^{12}$)	C in $\mu\mu$f	d in inches	d^1
450	2.55	0.2259	0.576	1.735	0.0771	0.171
460	2.77	0.2309	0.640	1.563	0.0858	0.219
470	3.105	0.2359	0.711	1.406	0.0954	0.294
480	3.312	0.2410	0.798	1.254	0.107	0.441
490	3.664	0.2460	0.901	1.110	0.1209	0.839
500	4.087	0.2510	1.026	0.975	0.1375	.....

Interferometer for Microwaves

DEVELOPMENT of a modified Michelson type interferometer for use in the microwave region was described by Bela A. Lengyel of Naval Research Laboratory at the 1949 IRE National Convention in New York City. The basic feature of the instrument is that it compares phase and amplitude of an approximately plane wave with that of a reference signal.

Principal applications include precision wavelength measurements, the measurement of dielectric constant and attenuation in dielectric materials available in the form of uniform sheets and the study of phase delay and reflections in the parallel-plate or metal-loaded media.

As shown in Fig. 1, the half-silvered mirror of the optical instrument is replaced by a plastic sheet O on which conducting dots

have been sprayed. A part of the incident radiation is transmitted through O into horn H_2. It is then united with a signal from the transmitter led through a waveguide and a variable attenuator. The signals are fed into opposite branches of a magic tee, one of the remaining arms being connected to the detector, the other to a matched load.

The silvered brass plate M serving as the movable mirror is mounted on a lathe bed and is constrained to move in the direction of its normal. Its displacement is measured with a micrometer or a dial indicator gage mounted on the lathe bed.

Wavelength Measurements

The simplest and most useful application of the interferometer is to the measurement of wavelengths in the 3-cm band and shorter. As re-

flector M is moved, maxima and

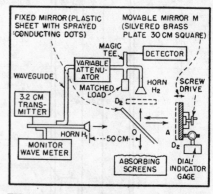

FIG. 1—Block diagram of modified Michelson interferometer for microwave measurements

minima alternate in the detector, the distance of adjacent minima corresponding to a reflector displacement of $\lambda/2$. An accuracy in the determination of λ of 0.0001 cm can be achieved easily in the 3-cm band.

Dielectric Constant Measurements

The interferometer is well suited to the rapid determination of the dielectric constant (specific inductive capacity) of materials available in large, reasonably uniform sheets that are only moderately reflecting and absorbing.

The amplitudes in the two branches of the interferometer are first equalized by adjustment of the attenuator for the highest standing wave ratio, then the position of M for a minimum signal in the receiver is obtained. Next the dielectric sheet is introduced at D_1 and the displacement of M (toward O) required to restore a minimum is noted. This displacement is a measure of the phase delay caused by the introduction of the dielectric sheet in the path of the rays, and can be used for computation of the dielectric constant k. As in optics, it is advantageous to use $n = k^{0.5}$. Let the shift of the minimum position be $\Delta/2$. This means a shortening of the path by Δ. When the multiple reflections within the sample are neglected, the change in path length caused by the introduction at normal incidence of a sheet of thickness d and index of refraction n is $(n-1)\,d$, hence $n = 1 + \Delta/d$.

When $n > 1.5$, the multiple reflections between the two faces of the sheet are no longer inconsequential and the value of n will be in error unless the sheet happens to have a thickness which is an integral multiple of the quarter wavelength in the sheet.

Highly Reflecting Materials

When the material to be measured is highly reflecting it is practical to employ the interferometer as the free space analog of the von Hippel shorted-line instrument. The dielectric sheet is then placed at D_2. Again the shift of the position for minimum is observed. In this manner it is possible to calculate the distance of the first minimum of the electric field from the face of the dielectric sheet. Von Hippel's method requires this distance x_o and m, the amplitude standing wave ratio, for the calculation of the complex propagation constant in the sheet. On the interferometer m is determined by moving the sample sheet and the metal mirror and keeping the detector fixed.

While a power standing wave ratio of 10^6 is easily obtained in an empty guide or coaxial line, such is not the case for the interferometer. This fact limits the application of von Hippel's general method to the case of highly absorbent sheets.

Finally, the interferometer is a useful instrument for measurements of parallel plate media of nominal dielectric constant less than one, and of loaded or synthetic dielectric materials intended for microwave lenses. These media cannot be placed in a guide; all measurements must be performed in free space.

Limitations of Instrument

The limitations of the microwave interferometer are inherent in the transmitting and receiving antennas, which are not reflectionless and which do not produce a narrow beam such as is commonly available in optics. Diffraction and scattering become the factors that limit the performance of the instrument. Another limiting factor is the presence of unwanted reflections.

OSCILLATORS

Overtone Crystal Oscillator Design

Quartz crystals can be made to operate directly on odd overtones up to 150 mc, with high power output and better stability than crystal would normally have at its fundamental. Technique involves shunting crystal with proper value of inductance and tuning plate tank for the desired overtone frequency

By GEORGE H. LISTER

THE INCREASING use of frequencies above 30 mc for limited-range communication and control purposes means that closely spaced channels are needed to provide for the many services that would like to use these frequencies. This close spacing, at least at the present state of the art, requires crystal control to provide the required carrier frequency stability.

Crystals can be ground to operate on fundamental frequencies as high as 30 mc. The Bureau of Standards has, in fact, processed crystals to 100 mc, but their commercial manufacture is probable only at some much later date. Making crystals physically thinner presents so many problems that some other means was sought for producing high frequencies directly from low-frequency crystals.

The goal was to find a circuit operating technique that in effect would slice a crystal electrically into the desired thinner plates, so that thick crystals could be made to vibrate with adequate power output at values much higher than their fundamental frequency. The development to be described achieves this goal by utilizing in a unique way the presence of overtone activity in certain types of quartz crystals. Overtone activity, to be described, should not be con-

fused with operation as a frequency multiplier, wherein the plate tank is tuned to a harmonic of the fundamental.

Nature of Overtones

Many crystals, particularly BT and AT cuts, exhibit strong overtone activity wherein the crystal appears to consist of layers of active material operating in shear modes, with opposite outside faces going in opposite directions as shown in exaggerated form in Fig. 1. For the third overtone the crystal acts as if it had three equal layers; for the fifth, five layers; for the nth overtone, n layers, where n is always an odd number. The thickness of each vibrating layer is approximately $1/n$th the thickness of the crystal at its fundamental.

Overtone crystals (improperly called harmonic crystals) have been on the market for some time, but most of these utilize the third overtone (generally around 30 mc) because higher-order overtones could not be developed by conventional circuitry. Investigation showed, however, that almost all carefully processed AT or BT-cut crystals exhibit activity on higher overtones such as the 5th, 7th, 9th, 11th and 13th. Many crystals even show activity at the 23rd overtone and a few have actually indicated activity on the 29th overtone, which for a 10-mc crystal would be around 290 mc.

The overtone frequency of a crystal is not an exact multiple, or harmonic, of the fundamental. Harmonics can only be obtained electrically, whereas crystal over-

---

ADVANTAGES OF OVERTONE CRYSTAL OSCILLATORS

Direct crystal control up to 150 mc with 10-mc or lower-frequency crystals

Overtone frequency is only frequency present in circuit, hence no spurious radiation

Direct frequency modulation is possible and practical, including carrier-frequency shift by d-c for keying or telemetering

Temperature-frequency stability better than crystal itself

Excellent voltage-frequency stability even up to 70 volts plate voltage change

Vibration and severe jarring do not affect frequency

Higher efficiency and much smaller vhf and uhf equipments, reducing battery drain and weight of mobile units

---

tones are the result of pure mechanical vibration. The frequencies of overtones approach corresponding harmonic values but are either higher or lower by an unpredictable amount. For this reason, overtone crystals are ground to the desired overtone frequency and marked with that value, the fundamental being ignored.

An analogy is the string of a piano, which vibrates over its entire length to produce the fundamental note and over shorter lengths to produce overtones. The frequencies of these musical overtones are close to corresponding harmonic values but not equal to them, as any musician will testify.

It should also be pointed out that a crystal will vibrate at only one overtone at a time. The overtone at which it vibrates depends on the resonant frequency of the circuit of which the crystal is a part.

Overtone crystals are ordered to an exact frequency, which is the frequency at which the electrical reactances of the crystal are equal

- Example of 460-mc mobile unit delivers 22 watts frequency-modulated output at 468.72 mc with ±10-kc carrier stability. Total current drain from 6-volt battery is 10 amp for receiver and 31 amp for transmitter. Total weight is 43 lb

- Transmitter crystal with fundamental of approximately 8.68 mc operates directly on 78.12 mc, which is 9th overtone. Reactance modulator for oscillator is driven by single a-f stage. Following crystal is low-power neutralized 6C4 isolating amplifier and 832A tripler stage with long-line plate tank coupled by balun to 4-150A final stage operating as doubler in cavity with 550 volts at 90 mc. Deviation is ±25 kc, with automatic deviation control. Audio fidelity is within 2 db from 60 to 10,000 cps

- Overtone crystal oscillator in receiver operates at 76.46 mc and is followed by 6AK5 six-times multiplier to get ample injection voltage for mixer. Grounded-grid amplifier stage precedes mixer; following it are three 10-mc i-f stages, limiter, discriminator, squelch circuit and final audio stage delivering 0.8 watt output. Sensitivity is better than 1 microvolt for complete limiting

and opposite and thus cancel. This frequency value is the true overtone value of the crystal alone, without holder or circuit. The circuits referred to operate at frequencies slightly removed from this series resonance value.

Oscillator Circuit Analysis

A study of existing circuits was made to determine why crystals exhibiting higher-order overtone possibilities would not perform on these overtones in conventional circuits. The conventional crystal oscillator circuit of Fig. 2 contains all of the important elements affecting the operation of a crystal. Typical equivalent values for a 10-mc crystal having a Q of 160,000 are $L = 0.02533$ h, $C = 0.01$ μf and $R = 10$ ohms. A typical value for C_T, the sum of C_1, C_2, C_3 and C_4, is 35 $\mu\mu f$.

The curves in Fig. 3 correspond to conventional operation of a quartz crystal at its fundamental frequency. The reactances of L and C vary with frequency in the manner shown in Fig. 3A, giving the curve of X_T as the algebraic sum of the reactances of the crystal.

The susceptance of crystal reactance X_T is shown in Fig. 3B. When added to the susceptance of the shunt capacitance C_T existing across the crystal terminals, curve Y_T is obtained. The reactance curve of this total crystal circuit susceptance is given in Fig. 3C. This curve indicates that a crystal used in a conventional circuit will

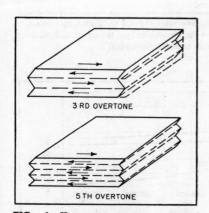

FIG. 1—How an overtone crystal works. The crystal acts as if electrically sliced into odd number of layers

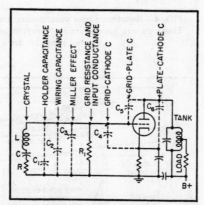

FIG. 2—Conventional crystal oscillator circuit, drawn to emphasize the important elements affecting crystal operation

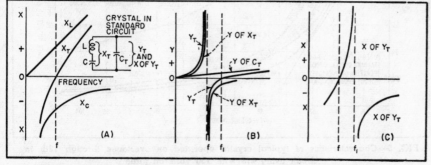

FIG. 3—Reactance and susceptance curves for standard crystal circuit

operate as a parallel resonant circuit at an antiresonant frequency f_1. At this frequency the total susceptance Y_T in Fig. 3B is practically zero and the total reactance approaches infinity. This value f_1 is the fundamental frequency value stamped on the crystal holder, and represents the crystal in its usual circuit, not the crystal alone.

The fundamental crystal oscillator frequency f_1 is only slightly higher than the resonant frequency f of the crystal itself without holder or circuit. Due to the large ratio between C_T and C, slight changes in C_T have but a small effect on the oscillator frequency f_1, hence the conventional oscillator circuit has good frequency stability.

Now suppose that we add capacitance across the crystal. This causes the curve for Y of C_T in Fig. 3B to rise higher, so that Y_T crosses the X axis at a lower frequency and thereby makes f_1 approach f. Adding to C_T thus lowers the fundamental frequency of the crystal oscillator circuit slightly. This characteristic is widely used by engineers of radio and television stations for adjusting their carriers exactly to the assigned frequency. However, adding to C_T causes the impedance of the tuned grid circuit (comprising the crystal and circuit capacitance) to decrease. The result is lowered output, and added capacitance thus produces only a small frequency change while at the same time reducing output considerably in a conventional crystal circuit.

This brief review of crystal oscillator theory sets the stage for an explanation of how a crystal can be made to operate directly on an overtone in essentially this same circuit.

Overtone Operation

If a 10-mc crystal is used in the circuit of Fig. 2 as before but the plate circuit is tuned to approximately 30 mc, the value of C_T remains about the same as before, but the equivalent C of the crystal becomes approximately one-third

of what it was at the fundamental. The equivalent L of the crystal is likewise reduced to approximately one-third. The ratio of C_T to C now is approximately three times that of the circuit at the fundamental, just as if we added capacitance to C_T at the fundamental.

Referring back to the values of the example, tuning the plate to approximately 30 mc so the crystal operates on its third overtone has the effect of adding capacitance of about 3×35 $\mu\mu$f across the crystal at the fundamental. The result is that the 10-mc crystal operates on its third overtone just as though it were a 30-mc crystal, except that now we have a low-impedance grid circuit and greatly reduced output.

When the plate circuit is tuned to the 5th overtone (about 50 mc in this example), the value of C_T again remains essentially the same as at the fundamental but C drops to about one-fifth of what it was at the fundamental. As a result the ratio of C_T to C goes up still more, the grid circuit impedance gets still lower, and power output drops practically to zero. Above the fifth overtone, the circuit will not oscillate at all.

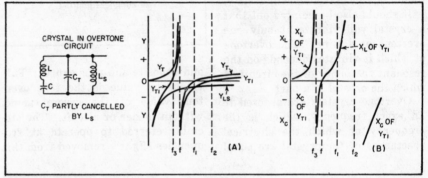

FIG. 4—Reactance and susceptance curves for overtone crystal oscillator operation. These curves are drawn for a crystal operating as an equivalent inductance. Similar curves may be drawn for the capacitive crystal

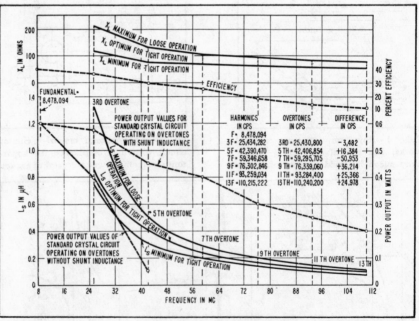

FIG. 5—Characteristics of typical crystal operated on overtones through 13th in circuit using 6J6 with 150 volts on plate

Overtone Circuit Requirement

An oscillator circuit that will permit crystals to operate on high-order overtones must have a high grid-circuit impedance. One way of achieving this impedance is to utilize the ability of a piezoelectric crystal to appear as a capacitive impedance when energized at a frequency below the series resonant frequency of the crystal L and C.

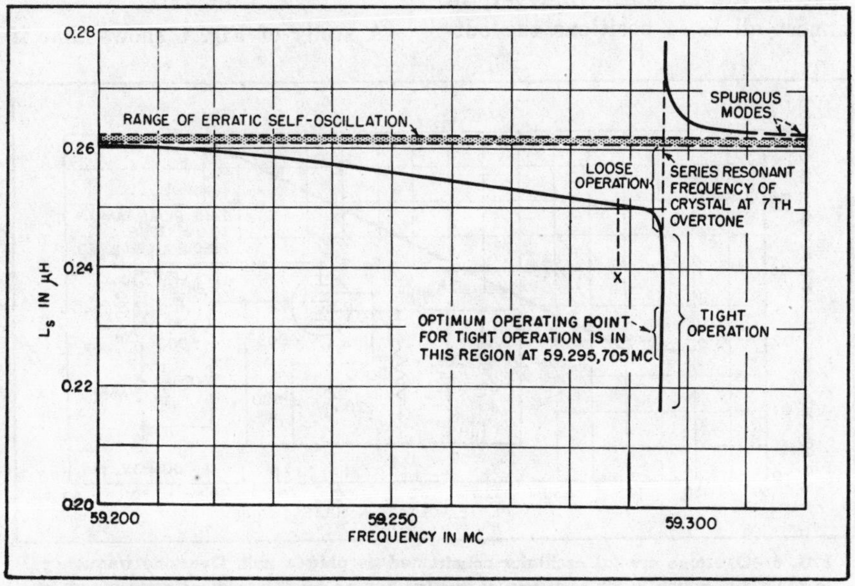

FIG. 6—Frequency characteristic at 7th overtone (59.295,705 mc) of quartz crystal having natural frequency of 8.478,094 mc, operating in 6J6 circuit

The crystal can then combine with an input circuit that is inductive to form an antiresonant grid circuit having high impedance as desired.

To make the input circuit appear inductive, the normal circuit capacitance C_T is shunted with an inductance of such value that the combination of the two appears as a high-value inductance at the operating frequency of the crystal.

The curves in Fig. 4 show how addition of shunt inductance L_S affects the susceptance and reactance of the crystal oscillator circuit of Fig. 3. The total susceptance Y_T of the grid circuit is added to susceptance Y_{LS} of the new shunt inductive reactance to get curves Y_{T1} for the combination. The resulting reciprocal curves (X_L of Y_{T1}) in Fig. 4B are the reactances of the combined input circuit without taking into account the values of resistance in the circuit. The curves indicate that two antiresonant frequencies are possible, f_2 being above and f_3 being below the series resonant frequency f of the crystal at the overtone selected. Actually, only f_3 is obtained in practice, because at that frequency the grid circuit has maximum impedance. The curves are intended to show only a method of obtaining a high grid circuit impedance (X_L of Y_{T1}) at operating frequency f_3, hence are not drawn to scale.

An overtone crystal is operated in the capacitive condition rather than in the inductive condition as is usual practice at low frequencies, for one important reason. AT or BT-cut crystals when flat or convex, as are most crystals, have spurious modes or activity points above the natural frequency of the crystal. This often results in erratic operation when the circuit is operated at crystal overtones in the inductive crystal condition. By deliberately choosing the capacitive crystal condition, operation is below the natural frequency of the crystal (or below the corresponding value for overtones) and spurious-mode operation is almost impossible.

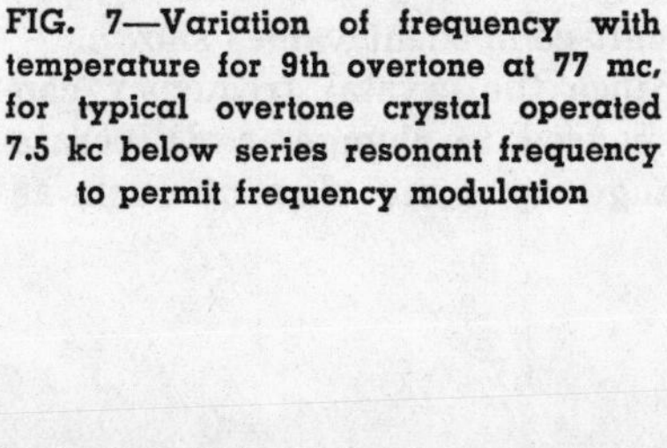

FIG. 7—Variation of frequency with temperature for 9th overtone at 77 mc, for typical overtone crystal operated 7.5 kc below series resonant frequency to permit frequency modulation

Overtone Oscillator Data

The curves in Fig. 5 show the characteristics of an overtone crystal calibrated, ground and finished to operate on its 9th overtone at 76.339,060 mc. The exact frequencies of this crystal operating at its many other overtones are tabulated, along with the differences between these overtones and the multiples or harmonics of the 8.478,094-mc fundamental crystal frequency.

The amount of inductive reactance needed to provide operation at the many overtones of this crystal when in the capacitive condition is also shown, along with the power output and efficiency of a test oscillator at each overtone. The plate tank circuit in all cases was inductively coupled to a Bird Termaline wattmeter for power measurement. Wherever possible the plate power input to the test oscillator was kept constant at the different overtones.

The results shown in Fig. 5 indicate that an overtone crystal can meet all of the requirements of a crystal oscillator of the power type up to the 11th mode. Such a crystal is satisfactory up to the 15th mode for a receiver local oscillator since such an oscillator has lower power requirements.

The overtone values of a crystal are not always fixed. Those given are for optimum operating conditions, but can easily be shifted to slightly higher values or considerably lower values by changing the value of shunt inductance L_S with a slug or other means. A study of the frequency characteristics at one overtone, the 7th, is shown in Fig. 6. The nominal or optimum overtone value is approximately in the middle of the vertical portion of the curve, corresponding to about 0.23 μh for L_s. Decreasing L_s from this value lowers the output but increases the frequency only a little.

Increasing L_s has a similarly negligible effect on frequency up to the knee of the curve, but further increases in L_s then make the overtone frequency decrease appreciably. The relation is quite linear, hence frequency modulation becomes a simple matter.

It should be pointed out that L_s can be a fixed inductance smaller than needed, shunted by a trimmer capacitor that is used for adjusting the operating frequency near the selected overtone.

Frequency Modulation

To produce frequency modulation, L_s is set to a value in the linear range such as at X, and a reactance tube or other variable reactance is connected across L_s to sweep its inductive reactance above and below the value for point X. Crystal frequency follows the variations in the reactance, giving the desired frequency modulation. Point X is here about 7.5 kc below the nominal overtone value, but the frequency excursion would be limited to about ±5 kc in order to stay off the knee of the curve. In a uhf or vhf f-m transmitter, multiplier stages following the overtone oscillator would multiply this 5-kc deviation of the oscillator. Point X is still a stable crystal frequency but one that can be caused to change because the magnitude of change needed is not too great.

Greater frequency deviations could be obtained by moving point X further away from the knee of the curve, but circuit stability is then sacrificed. For this reason, overtone oscillators in f-m transmitters use relatively small crystal frequency swings and rely on frequency multipliers to provide the required deviation at the final carrier value.

A "tight" overtone crystal oscillator is defined as one that is operating over the nearly vertical portion of the curve of Fig. 6. Operation at other points on the curve is described as "loose," permitting adjustment of the output frequency or frequency modulation.

Stability

In the tight positions the temperature-vs-frequency stability of the overall circuit essentially is that of the crystal. However, in almost all loose positions the output frequency can be corrected by proper choice of temperature coefficients for components to result in an overall temperature-vs-frequency stability that is considerably better than that of the crystal itself. This is illustrated in Fig. 7; the entire curve is below the coefficient of the crystal itself, which is approximately 1.0 part per million per degree C.

Voltage stability of a typical overtone crystal oscillator operating at the 9th overtone at 77 mc is illustrated in Fig. 8. Even for the total 70-volt plate-voltage change represented by the entire curve, voltage stability is excellent with circuit component values shown.

Since the crystal frequency can be caused to change, a deliberate change by some element such as the plate bypass capacitor can, if that element is of the proper coefficient and size, correct the entire circuit for effects of temperature variations. Overtone crystal circuits have been produced which will maintain the frequency to better than one part per million over a temperature range of 0 to 185 F, which is many times better than the crystal itself in normal circuitry.

F-M Version

A study of Fig. 6 shows that if the circuit is frequency-modulated, large excursions of the variable reactance can cause the crystal to stop oscillating at either extreme of the change. If L_s is reduced below a certain critical value (about 0.215 μh in this case), the circuit stops oscillating. If L_s is increased above another critical value, the circuit goes into erratic self-oscillation. With further increases in L_s, the circuit will change over to a type of oscillation in which the crystal appears as an equivalent inductance, represented by the curve at the upper right. With still further increases, above about 0.27 μh, the circuit ceases oscillation.

A form of automatic deviation control becomes necessary to maintain assigned channel bandwidth

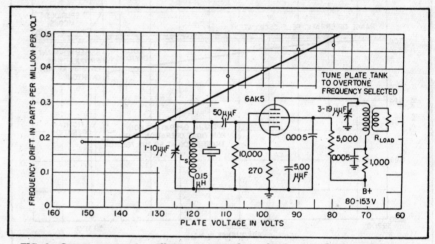

FIG. 8—Overtone crystal oscillator constructed as plug-in unit. Overtone frequency is 77.00 mc, which is 9th overtone of crystal having fundamental of approximately 8.55 mc. Power input is 1.8 watts and power output 0.3 watt for 150-volt plate supply. Curve shows stability of output frequency over 70-volt variation of plate voltage provided by external power supply

and to make impossible the stopping of the oscillator with excessive amplitudes of the modulating voltage. Figure 9A shows a typical reactance modulator used with an overtone crystal oscillator, while Fig. 9B shows the resultant injected capacitance C_I of the modulator circuit. Slight modifications in the circuit result in the C_I/E_g curve shown in Fig. 9C. By operating such a revised circuit at point X with no modulating voltage applied, and coupling that modulator through fixed-capacitor C of a value substantially equal to C_I at point X, the resultant C_I at the crystal appears as in Fig. 9D. The value of C_I then can vary between two limits, one of which is zero and the other the value of C. Such a simple automatic deviation control circuit holds the frequency excursion to definite limits. Even the failure of the modulator tube can only cause frequency changes that are within the channel assigned.

Crystal Heating

At the frequencies under consideration (70 to 110 mc, corresponding to the 7th, 9th or 11th overtone of a 10-mc crystal), the usual grid-to-plate capacitance of small triodes such as the 6C4 and 6J6 provides feedback that can be excessive. The rapid change in frequency which often occurs in the first few seconds after starting a crystal oscillator usually is the result of heating of the crystal due to excessive feedback and resultant high r-f voltage across the crystal electrodes.

In all antiresonant circuits the crystal is a capacitance with the quartz as a dielectric. Excessive r-f voltage across this capacitance will cause undue heating of the crystal which the holder cannot dissipate. The feedback should therefore be controlled to a point where only enough excitation is provided to permit satisfactory output from the circuit.

The use of a pentode or similar tube with properly adjusted feedback results in highly stable circuits with little crystal heating.

Feedback adjustment is experimentally determined and subsequent production of oscillators for any given overtone of operation simply provides a fixed spacing and form factors of grid and plate coils.

Since an overtone crystal operates directly on its overtone value, with no output at the fundamental, sideband problems are practically nonexistent. For example, if a crystal is operated on its 9th overtone at 90 mc and fed to a doubler and tripler to get 540 mc, the lowest undesired component that can produce sidebands at 540 mc is 90 mc. This is too far off from the carrier to be of any consequence in properly designed circuits.

With conventional frequency multiplication to 540 mc from a 10-mc fundamental, sidebands removed from the carrier frequency by a value equal to the fundamental or double or triple the fundamental value are present in the output of the final stage. Frequency multiplication from a fundamental in both transmitters and receivers is thus a serious deterrent to close spacing of uhf channels.

Conclusions

Equipment using circuits meeting all of the requirements for both transmitting oscillators and local oscillators of receivers has been in operation over 18 months. Performance during that time has been entirely satisfactory for mobile and fixed station uses. Fixed stations in extremely unfavorable locations, such as on oil drilling rigs, have proven the circuits to be stable, efficient and adequate for all purposes investigated. The circuits operate at conservative values of plate voltage, plate current and plate dissipation, so that long and stable tube life can be expected.

The audio quality resulting from the frequency-modulated oscillators is exceptionally good and approaches that obtained by f-m broadcasters. It is dependent only on the small speech amplifier used ahead of the modulator and the point on the curve chosen to operate the crystal. Actually, the crystal may be modulated with d-c applied to the modulator grid, which causes instantaneous frequency shift in a direction depending on the polarity of the modulating voltage. The amount of the shift is determined by the limiting values in the circuit and the amplitude of the modulating voltage.

For cooperation in developing and testing the crystal overtone oscillators described here and for work leading to patent applications,

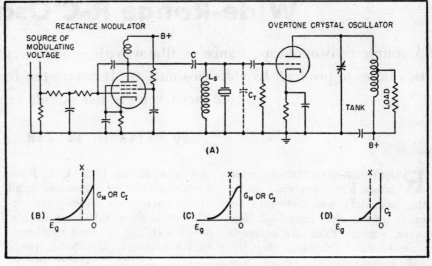

FIG. 9—Frequency-modulated crystal oscillator using overtone crystal, and curves showing injected capacitance provided by reactance modulator under various conditions

the author expresses appreciation to A. R. Panetta, now with Boston University, and to R. C. Blauvelt and R. N. Lister, chief engineer and plant superintendent, respectively, of Electronic Research & Mfg. Corp.

BIBLIOGRAPHY

William A. Edson, High Frequency Crystal-Controlled Oscillator Circuits, Progress Report No. 2, 1948, Signal Corps Project 142B at Georgia Institute of Technology, Atlanta, Ga.

W. P. Mason and I. E. Fair, A New Direct Crystal-Controlled Oscillator for Ultra-Short-Wave Frequencies, *Proc. IRE*, 30. p 464, 1942.

H. Goldberg and E. L. Crosby, Series Mode Crystal Circuits, *Tele-Tech*, p 24, May 1948.

B. E. Hill Jr. and S. L. Kenyon, Investigation of Oscillator Circuits for Use With CR-9/U Over-Mode Crystal Units, Naval Research Laboratory Report No. R-3158.

F. Butler, Series Resonant Crystal Oscillators, *Wireless Engineer*, June 1946.

J. K. Clapp, A Crystal Mode Indicator, *The General Radio Experimenter*, p 1, Feb. 1949.

F. E. Terman, "Radio Engineers' Handbook," McGraw-Hill, 1943, p 493; Fig. 12 shows positioning of spurious modes of quartz crystals.

Wide-Range R-C Oscillator

A simple resistance-capacitance oscillator with good waveform and constant output uses two tubes to produce 15 volts rms output. It covers the frequency range from 20 cycles to 2 megacycles in five decade ranges

By PETER G. SULZER

RESISTANCE-CAPACITANCE oscillators have seen wide use in the laboratory and elsewhere because of several important features, among which are compactness, excellent frequency stability, and a wide tuning range. Unfortunately their application has been restricted to audio and ultrasonic measurements with a top frequency of approximately 200 kilocycles. It is the purpose of this paper to describe a new but simple circuit that functions over the range from 20 cycles to 2 megacycles with good waveform and constant output.

In developing the new oscillator, the limitations of previous types were considered. The first[1], Fig. 1A, consists of an amplifier with two feedback paths; regeneration occurs at all frequencies, while the degenerative loop contains a parallel-T null network. Thus oscillation takes place at the null frequency. The principal disadvantages are that three circuit elements must be varied to change frequency, and that a two-stage amplifier is required to provide proper phasing. Phase shifts become important at the extremes of the frequency range, affecting frequency calibration.

A second oscillator,[2] Fig. 1B, is somewhat similar to the first. However, degeneration is provided at all frequencies, while regeneration occurs through a half-Wien bridge, which exhibits a broad maximum in its response. Oscillation tends to occur at the frequency of the maximum, but the Q of the Wien circuit—about 0.3— is so low that phase shifts in the amplifier will affect the frequency calibration.

The phase-shift oscillator,[3,4,5] one form of which is shown in Fig. 1C, contains a 180-degree network in a single feedback loop. Although it is the simplest of the oscillators described, functioning with a single tube, a minimum of three circuit elements must be varied to change frequency. Furthermore, it is found that an additional tube is required to provide suitable amplitude regulation, and that high-frequency operation is limited by the low impedance of the phase-shift network at the high frequencies.

Circuit Development

In an attempt to improve the oscillator of Fig. 1A, the bridged-T network[6] of Fig. 2A was investigated. This simple network, which has been used for the measurement of high resistances at radio frequencies, has but four circuit elements, as compared with six for the parallel-T. Although a true null is not produced, a fairly-sharp minimum, accompanied by zero phase shift, occurs at $\omega_0 = 1/[C(R_1R_2)^{\frac{1}{2}}]$. It is seen from Fig. 2B, that the selectivity is improved by increasing the ratio R_1/R_2. It can be shown that, for large values of R_1/R_2, the equivalent Q of the network approaches $\frac{1}{2}(R_1/R_2)^{\frac{1}{2}}$. Thus phase characteristics superior to those of the network of Fig. 1B are

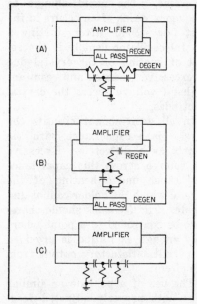

FIG. 1—Block diagrams illustrating types of R-C oscillators

easily obtained, with consequent reduction in the effects of amplifier phase shift when employed in an oscillator.

A very useful feature of the bridged-T is that a trimmer capacitor (shown dotted) placed across the vertical arm will permit minor adjustment of ω_0 where the capacitances C are small. Therefore, if capacitive tuning is used it is possible to adjust the upper end of a frequency range nearly independently of the lower end. This is helpful when the circuit is employed in an oscillator where a single dial calibration must suffice for two or more decade ranges.

Figure 2C is a simplified schematic diagram of the new oscillator, which consists of an amplifier, V_1, driving a cathode-follower, V_2. Regeneration is provided at all frequencies by cathode-to-cathode feedback through a lamp as a series resistor, while the degenerative loop contains the bridged-T network. Oscillation tends to take place at ω_0, the frequency of minimum degeneration, while amplitude stabilization is provided by the positive-resistance-current characteristic of the lamp. The combination of amplifier plus cathode follower is ideal for this application because it provides wide-band operation with small phase shift and low output impedance.

Figure 3 is the schematic diagram of the compact oscillator illustrated. The frequency range, 20 cycles to 2 megacycles, is covered with a small dual variable capacitor, C_1C_2, of the type used in broadcast receivers. A frequency ratio of 10 to 1 is covered in each range, while ranges are changed by switching resistors R_1 and R_2. The output is 15 volts rms from the cathode of V_2, remaining constant within one decibel at all frequencies. Although the distortion was not measured, it is believed to be

very low, since oscillation will stabilize at an amplitude approximately one-third of that at which clipping occurs.

Certain circuit details are of considerable importance in obtaining

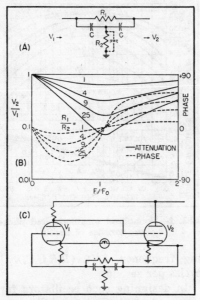

FIG. 2—Bridged-T network (A), its characteristics (B), and simplified schematic of the new oscillator

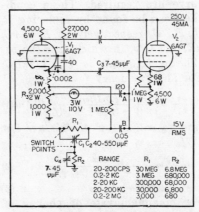

FIG. 3—Complete circuit of the wide-range oscillator showing component values and characteristics for all ranges

proper operation of the oscillator. In making the initial adjustments the points marked A and B were opened to permit the voltage gain

from the grid of V_1 to the cathode of V_2 to be checked. Positive feedback peaking[7] is provided by C_3, which was adjusted for constant gain through two megacycles. In this manner, good phase response is obtained. The points A and B were then closed, and R_3, which controls positive feedback, was set for constant output with low distortion on all ranges. The low-frequency end of each range was set by trimming R_1, assuming that R_2 had the indicated value. It was found that the two low-frequency ranges covered the dial properly; however, it was necessary to employ C_4 to align the upper end of each of the high-frequency ranges. Additional switching was not involved because it was possible to leave a separate trimmer capacitor C_4 connected across each of the resistors R_2.

It should be noted that it is essential that the oscillator be well shielded to prevent synchronization with the line frequency and submultiples thereof. The unit described is built into a cabinet that also contains a power supply and output amplifier.

REFERENCES

(1) Britton Chance, "Waveforms", McGraw-Hill Book Co., New York, p120.
(2) F. E. Terman, R. R. Buss, W. R. Hewlett, and F. C. Cahill, Some Applications of Negative Feedback with Particular Reference to Laboratory Equipment, *Proc. IRE*, 27, Oct. 1939.
(3) E. L. Ginzton and L. M. Hollingsworth, Phase-Shift Oscillators, *Proc. IRE*, 29, Feb. 1941.
(4) R. W. Johnson, Extending the Frequency Range of the Phase-Shift Oscillator, *Proc. IRE*, 33, Sept. 1945.
(5) P. G. Sulzer, The Tapered Phase-Shift Oscillator, *Proc. IRE*, 36, Oct. 1948.
(6) P. M. Honnell, Bridged-T Measurement of High Resistances at Radio Frequencies, *Proc. IRE*, 28, Feb. 1940.
(7) P. G. Sulzer, Circuit Techniques for Miniaturization, ELECTRONICS, Aug. 1949.

Optimum Conditions for an R-C Oscillator

By H. A. WHALE

RESISTANCE-CAPACITANCE NETWORKS of the type shown in Fig. 1 occur in many electronic circuits. The network is used in feedback oscillators of the Wein bridge type, in which case the components can be proportioned in accordance with relations presented in this discussion to provide optimum frequency stability. Although these relations are derived for the particular bridge oscillator under examination, they are also valid for a resistance-capacitance amplifier made frequency selective by choice of coupling or where feedback is used to give an amplifier having rejection for a narrow band of frequencies.

Wein Bridge Oscillator

In the common R-C cathode-coupled oscillator of the Wein bridge type[1], the components of the feedback network are proportioned so that R_1C_1 equals R_2C_2, under which condition the ratio of output voltage E_2 to input voltage E_1 varies with frequency in the manner

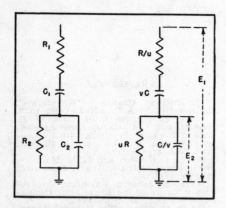

FIG. 1—Circuit under consideration is common to many applications

shown in Fig. 2 by curve for $U^2 = 1$ [2,3]. The frequency selectivity of this particular type of oscillator is due to the comparatively rapid change with frequency of the phase between the input and output voltages in the vicinity of the oscillat-

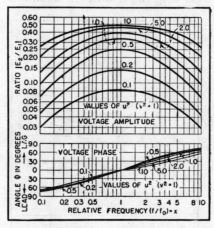

FIG. 2—Normalized amplitude and phase characteristics of circuit

ing frequency, $1/[2\pi(R_1R_2C_1C_2)^{1/2}]$ cycles per second.

In designing such oscillators for the greatest frequency stability, the conditions for the most rapid change of phase with frequency and for the most sharply peaked $|E_2/E_1|$ curve are required. These conditions can be found by replacing R_1 C_1, R_2, C_2 respectively by R/u, vC, uR, and C/v, in which case the oscillating frequency is $f_o = 1/2\pi RC$. For any frequency f

$$\frac{E_2}{E_1} = \frac{y(f/f_0)^2 + j(f/f_0)[1 - (f/f_0)^2]}{[1 - (f/f_0)^2]^2 + y^2(f/f_0)^2} uv \quad (1)$$

where $y = (u^2 + v^2 + u^2v^2)/uv$. Let $(f/f_0) = x$, then

$$\left|\frac{E_2}{E_1}\right| = \frac{uvx}{[(1 - x^2)^2 + (xy)^2]^{1/2}} \quad (2)$$

$$\phi = \tan^{-1}(1 - x^2)^2/xy \quad (3)$$

For maximum rate of change of phase with frequency, differentiate ϕ with respect to x. Inasmuch as interest is in values near $\phi = 0$ at which $x = 1$

$$\phi = (1 - x^2)^2/xy \quad (4)$$

therefore

$$\frac{d\phi}{dx} = -(x^{-2} + 1)/y \quad (5)$$

$$\approx -2/y \quad (\text{near } x = 1) \quad (6)$$

Because x is nearly unity near the oscillating frequency

$$\left|\frac{E_2}{E_1}\right| = \frac{uv[1 - (1 - x^2)^2/2(xy)^2]}{y} \quad (6)$$

The magnitude of the term $(1 -$

$x^2)^2/2(xy)^2$ determines the sharpness of the resonance peaks, for the smaller is y the more rapid the change with x. Thus, as would be expected, the rate of change of phase and the sharpness of the resonance peak both depend on the same parameter y.

The problem is to determine the values of u and v for which y is a minimum. To do so, let $v^2 = 1$, in which case $C_1 = C_2$, and then $y = (2u^2 + 1)/u$. This relation is a minimum when $u^2 = 0.5$. Various calculated amplitude, and phase curves for $v^2 = 1$ and different value of u^2 are shown in Fig. 2 with the value of u^2 indicated for each curve.

For any general value of v^2 there is an optimum value of u^2 and vice-versa. The general expressions are obtained.

$$\frac{dy}{du} = \left(\frac{d}{du}\right)\frac{u^2 + v^2 + u^2v^2}{uv} \quad (7)$$

$$= -(v/u^2) + (1/v) + v \quad (8)$$

which equals zero when

$$u^2 = v^2/(1 + v^2) \quad (9)$$

Similarly, for a given value of u^2 the optimum value of v^2 is

$$v^2 = u^2/(1 + u^2) \quad (10)$$

Carrying the logic further, put Eq. 9 into the expression for y, then

$$y^2 = 4(1 + v^2) \quad (11)$$

which has its minimum when $v^2 = 0$, and then $u^2 = 0$. Thus the criteria for the sharpest resonance curves and the most rapid change of phase near the resonant frequency are that u and v are as small as possible consistent with maintaining either Eq. 9 or 10. When u and v are both small, they are nearly equal.

Figure 3 presents curves for various values of (u^2, v^2). These curves include the cases for u^2 and v^2 both vanishingly small; that is, the theoretically best conditions that can be obtained. Also included in Fig. 3 are some experimental points obtained with the indicated values.

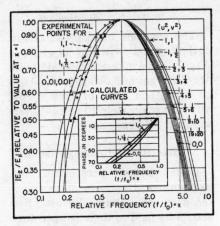

FIG. 3—Experimental points fall close to the calculated resonance curves

For the conventional case at $x = 1$

$$u^2 = v^2 = 1; \quad d\phi/dx = -2/3$$

while for the optimum case at $x = 1$

$$u^2 = v^2 \rightarrow 0; \quad d\phi/dx = -1$$

Practical Considerations

The foregoing analysis indicates that for maximum stability the ratios C_2/C_1 and R_1/R_2 should be as large as possible consistent with a given (frequency) relationship between them. In oscillators employing this type of feedback circuit; condition for oscillation is

$$1 + R_1/R_2 + C_2/C_1 < A \qquad (12)$$

where A is the gain in the auxiliary amplifying circuit. Using the fore-

going notation, this condition can be expressed as

$$1 + 1/u + 1/v < A \qquad (13)$$

Thus the minimum values of u and v that can be employed are determined by the gain that is available from the amplifier.

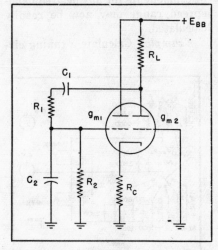

FIG. 4—Typical oscillator circuit to which design can be applied

For example, in the cathode-coupled oscillator[4] shown in Fig. 4, the condition for oscillation is

$$E_2 > A E_1 \qquad (14)$$

or

$$\frac{uv}{y} > A = g_{m1} g_{m2} R_C R_L \qquad (15)$$

which means that

$$1 + 1/u + 1/n < g_{m1} g_{m2} R_C R_L \qquad (16)$$

where g_{m1} and g_{m2} are the mutual conductances of the two triode sections under the operating conditions.

If the oscillator is to cover a range of frequencies, the ratio C_2/C_1 must remain constant over the band. This consistancy can be accomplished by using a ganged tuning capacitor with, for example, C_2 consisting of three sets of plates in parallel and C_1 the other set. Then $v^2 = 0.33$. Thus for optimum stability with this value of v^2, $u^2 = 0.25$. The condition for oscillation becomes

$$g_{m1} g_{m2} R_C R_L > 8 \qquad (17)$$

For usual triodes, R_C is approximately 500 ohms, and g_m is approximately 2,000 microhms, therefore R_L should be greater than 4,000 ohms.

REFERENCES

(1) H. H. Scott, A New Type of Selective Circuit and Some Applications, *Proc. I. R. E.*, p 226 Feb. 1938.
(2) F. E. Terman, R. P. Buss, W. R. Hewlett, and F. C. Cahill, Some Applications of Negative Feedback with Particular Reference to Laboratory Equipment, *Proc. I. R. E.*, p 649 Oct. 1939.
(3) F. E. Terman, "Radio Engineers' Handbook", McGraw-Hill Book Co., New York, p 505 1943.
(4) Keats A. Pullen, The Cathode Coupled Amplifier, *Proc. I. R. E.*, p 402 June 1946.

Bandspreading Resistance-Tuned Oscillators

By SEYMOUR BARKOFF

ONE COMMON characteristic of most audio signal generators is the crowding of the calibration markings on the frequency dial toward the upper end of the audio frequency spectrum. Such crowding usually causes difficulty in interpolating frequency readings accurately between dial markings. Occasionally, the need arises for greater accuracy and precision in frequency readings.

It is the purpose of this article to describe a simple means of add-

ing bandspread to a particular laboratory oscillator. Sufficient design information will be included to make the method applicable to other oscillators of the same general type, and for any desired frequency ranges.

Theory

The audio oscillator selected for the job was the Hewlett-Packard Model 200B, which consists of a two-tube audio oscillator and a two-tube feedback amplifier. Only the

oscillator circuit is dealt with here, since the amplifier circuits are unaffected by the bandspread revision.

The basic circuit of the two-tube oscillator is shown in Fig. 1. The circuit resembles that of a multivibrator, except for the method of feeding grid and cathode of the 6J7 stage. Oscillations take place at a frequency at which the 6J7 grid voltage is in phase with the 6F6 plate voltage. The Wien bridge network, $R_1 C_1 R_2 C_2$, determines the frequency at which these two voltages are in phase. The frequency is made smoothly variable through the use of a standard type of ganged variable air capacitor for C_1 and C_2. Each of these consists of two sections of a four-gang capacitor, with a maximum capacitance of 525 $\mu\mu$f per section.

Trimmers are used across C_1 and C_2 for the purpose of calibration and maintenance of a constant amplitude of oscillation.

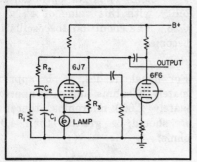

FIG. 1—Basic circuit of a well-known resistance-tuned oscillator to which bandspreading will be added

In modifying the oscillator, the most desirable method is to remove the original bandswitch, together with the tuning resistors assembled on it, and substitute another switch having the desired number of positions and circuits. The original resistors, or preferably new ones, are then assembled onto the switch together with the extra components for the bandspread ranges. Additional tuning scales may then be placed on the frequency dial, or a new dial substituted.

Bandspread Computations

In the original tuning circuit of the oscillator, all of the tuning component values are specified in the manufacturer's instruction book except the ΔC of the tuning capaci-

tor, and the minimum capacitance, $C_{\min}$, across C_1 and C_2 each when the tuning capacitor is set to the high-frequency end of the dial. The values of ΔC and $C_{\min}$ are obtainable by simple calculation: $C_{\min} = 86$ $\mu\mu$f and $\Delta C = 1{,}019$ $\mu\mu$f. Values of components for any desired bandspread range may now be readily calculated.

Example: Calculate a tuning cir-

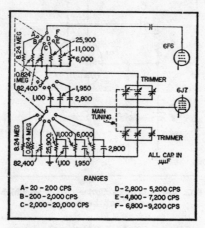

FIG. 2—Complete bandspread circuit covering 3 to 5, 5 to 7 and 7 to 9-kc ranges in addition to original bands

cuit to produce a range of 3,000 to 5,000 cycles for a complete rotation of the tuning capacitor.

$$\frac{f_{\max}}{f_{\min}} = \frac{C_{\min}^1 + \Delta C}{C_{\min}^1}$$
$$C_{\min}^1 = 1{,}529 \ \mu\mu\text{f}$$

The tuning circuit already contains a $C_{\min}$ of 86 $\mu\mu$f. Therefore, a fixed capacitor of $1{,}529 - 86 = 1{,}443$ $\mu\mu$f must be added across each two sections of the tuning capacitor.

The tuning resistors are selected to give a frequency of 5,000 cycles with the tuning capacitance at minimum, which is 1,529 $\mu\mu$f.

$$R = \frac{1}{2\pi f C} = 20{,}900 \text{ ohms}$$

The complete bandspread circuit including the switching is given in Fig. 2. The values indicated obtain three ranges of 3,000 to 5,000, 5,000 to 7,000, and 7,000 to 9,000 cycles, with approximately 10 percent overlapping of ranges.

Selection of Components

Resistors and capacitors for bandspread circuits must be selected with care. Particular attention should be paid to their temperature coefficients, for frequency drift due to warmup shows up much more readily on a bandspread than on a compressed scale. For example, a drift of 1 percent at 5,000 cycles will nullify the accuracy of a dial which may have initially been calibrated to an accuracy of 20 cycles.

It has been found most desirable to use wirewound resistors and silver mica capacitors as the tuning elements for the bandspread circuits. The resistors should be wound non-inductively, and of a wire with the lowest possible temperature coefficient. The writer has used resistors made with 331 Alloy, also known by the trade names of Karma and Evenohm. This wire has about the same temperature coefficient as manganin (0.00002 per C) but holds it over a wider temperature range than manganin. The silver mica capacitors should likewise have a zero temperature coefficient.

It has been found that at the upper end of the third bandspread range—9,000 cycles—that the drift over a two-hour period from a cold start is less than 20 cycles, or about 0.2 percent. This should prove satisfactory for most applications.

Transistor Oscillator

Audio oscillator built around crystal triode, used to frequency modulate rocket telemetering system, has numerous advantages over vacuum-tube equivalent. Transistor characteristics are reviewed, and design data for similar circuits in other applications are presented

By FRANK W. LEHAN

THERE EXIST TODAY many systems for the telemetering of information from rockets or other flight-test vehicles by means of a radio link. One of the more popular systems is known as the f-m/f-m system.[1,2] This system uses the frequencies of a number of audio tones to convey the data to the ground on a frequency-modulated radio carrier.

One frequently-used method of converting a telemetered quantity into an audio frequency is the variable-inductance gage. With this technique an air gap in the magnetic circuit of the gage is made dependent upon the measured quantity. The gage is then used as an inductance in the tuned circuit of an audio oscillator, thereby controlling its frequency.

Many audio oscillator circuits have been used. The oscillators are

flown in rockets and they must operate under field conditions; hence certain design criteria are imposed upon them. Necessary characteristics of the audio oscillators include small size, light weight, low power consumption, simplicity, ruggedness, and frequency stability with changes of supply voltages or external conditions.

The Bell Telephone Laboratories transistor,[3] used in an extremely simple oscillator circuit, shows promise of providing a useful solution to the telemetering audio-oscillator problem.

The Transistor

A transistor was procured through the efforts of the Army Ordnance Department and the Signal Corps. The audio-frequency behavior of the transistor is described by the experimentally obtained

characteristic curves illustrated in Fig. 1 if its input and output voltages and currents are as designated in Fig. 2A.

For small increments of voltage and current (small signal operation), the incremental operation of the transistor may be expressed by any of a number of equation pairs. The following pair is convenient for this analysis:

$$E_E = R_E\,I_E + R_{CE}\,I_C \qquad (1)$$
$$E_C = R_{EC}\,I_E + R_C\,I_C \qquad (2)$$

The values of R_E, R_{CE}, R_{EC}, and R_C in Eq. 1 and 2 for a given region of operation may be determined from the characteristic curves or from more direct measurements, using methods similar to those used in determining the values of μ, R_P, and G_m for a vacuum tube. R_E, R_C, R_{CE}, and R_{EC} may be written as follows:

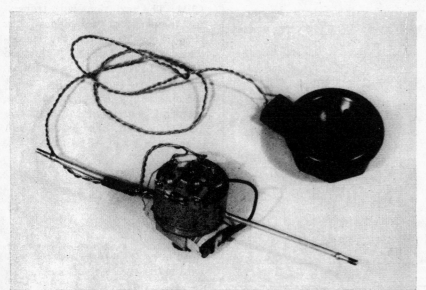

An experimental transistor oscillator with a telemetering pressure gage attached. The battery, strapped below the gage, will run the unit for several days. Experimental performance curves are shown in Fig. 3

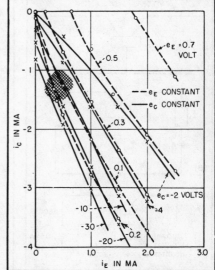

FIG. 1—Experimentally-determined characteristic curves of the transistor used. The desired operating region is shaded

$$R_E = \frac{\delta e_E}{\delta i_E}, \; i_C \text{ constant} \quad (3)$$

$$R_C = -\frac{\delta e_C}{\delta i_C}, \; i_E \text{ constant} \quad (4)$$

$$R_{CE} = \frac{\delta e_E}{\delta i_C}, \; i_E \text{ constant} \quad (5)$$

$$R_{EC} = \frac{\delta e_C}{\delta i_E}, \; i_C \text{ constant} \quad (6)$$

Typical values of R_E, R_C, R_{EC}, and R_{CE}, found by using Eq. 3 through 6 and the characteristic curves, in the normal operating range of a transistor are, $R_E = 1,400$, $R_C = 33,000$, $R_{CE} = 700$ and $R_{EC} = 77,000$ ohms.

The Oscillator

Consider the transistor connected in the circuit shown in Fig. 2B. The batteries B_1 and B_2 are of such voltage that they cause the transistor to operate in the desired region of Fig. 1.

The two incremental mesh equations for the circuit of Fig. 2B are easily written by inspection as follows:

$$(Z_1 + R_E + Z_B) I_E + (R_{CE} + Z_B) I_C = 0 \quad (7)$$

$$(R_{EC} + Z_B) I_E + (Z_2 + R_C + Z_B) I_C = 0 \quad (8)$$

In order that Eq. 7 and 8 have a solution, other than the trivial one of $I_E = I_C = 0$, the determinant of the equations must equal zero.[4] Thus

$$\begin{vmatrix} Z_1 + R_E + Z_B & R_{CE} + Z_B \\ R_{EC} + Z_B & Z_2 + R_C + Z_B \end{vmatrix} = 0 \quad (9)$$

Hence

$$(Z_1 + R_E + Z_B)(Z_2 + R_C + Z_B) = (R_{EC} + Z_B)(R_{CE} + Z_B) \quad (10)$$

$$Z_B = \frac{(Z_1 + R_E)(Z_a + R_C) - R_{EC} R_{CE}}{R_{EC} + R_{CE} - (Z_1 + R_E) - (Z_a + R_C)} \quad (11)$$

If stable oscillations are to occur, Eq. 11 must be satisfied at the desired real frequency ω_0 and at no other point in the complex frequency plane.

The circuit of Fig. 2C is one of several circuits suggested by Eq. 11 which, when tried, gave stable oscillation. It appeared to provide the most satisfactory operation. The circuit oscillates at the parallel resonant frequency of the tuned circuit, the frequency at which the circuit appears as a pure resistance of magnitude approximately given by $Q\omega L$.

The sizes of R_1 and R_2 are not critical over a wide range since the transistor limits (in a manner similar to vacuum tubes) the oscillation amplitude by means of nonlinearities, which adjust the values of R_E, R_C, R_{EC} and R_{CE}. Values of 2,500 and 5,000 ohms for R_1 and R_2, respectively, have proved satisfactory.

Caution should be observed in making R_1 and R_2 too small or in letting the d-c resistance of the parallel resonant circuit become too great; otherwise the transistor will become d-c unstable and be damaged by the excessive currents. By means of Eq. 11, d-c instability may be investigated.

When the values given for R_1 and R_2 are substituted in Eq. 11, a value of 2,600 ohms is obtained for Z_B. This value of Z_B, or greater, is readily achieved by a parallel resonant circuit which has reasonable values of Q and L/C. (The variable inductance used in the experimental oscillator had a Q of approximately 9 at the oscillation frequency.) The d-c resistance of the circuit may be easily made much smaller than 2,600 ohms so that d-c stability is assured.

An experimental transistor oscillator with a telemetering pressure gage is shown in the photograph. The battery shown will run the unit for a number of days.

Experimental values of frequency and output voltage for the circuit of Fig. 2C are shown plotted in Fig. 3 for variations in supply voltage (3A) and transistor temperature (3B). The variations with transistor temperature are undesirable, but it is considered that the temperature of the unit during flight time may be held reasonably constant. Temperature compensation is at present being investigated. The harmonic content of the output is under 5 percent. The battery drain is of the order of 0.5 to 1 ma.

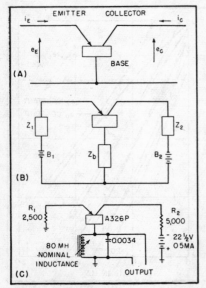

FIG. 2—Actual circuit diagram of transistor oscillator is shown in C. Basic circuits are shown in A and B

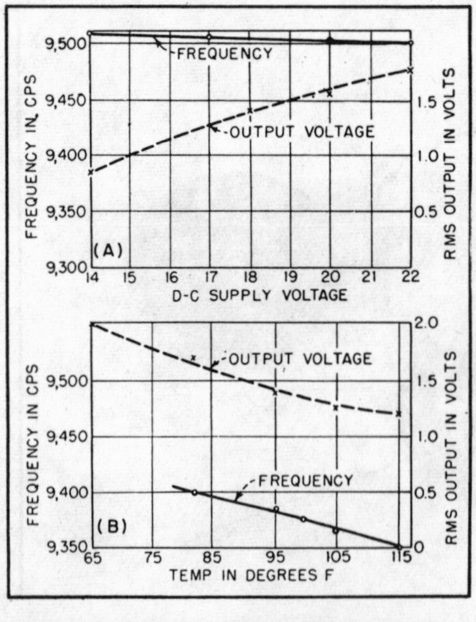

FIG. 3—Frequency and audio-output-voltage curves for experimental transistor oscillator shown in the photograph

REFERENCES

(1) G. H. Melton, Multichannel Radio Telemetering for Rockets, ELECTRONICS, p 106, Dec. 1948.
(2) J. C. Coe, Telemetering Guided-Missile Performance, Proc. IRE, p 1,404, Nov. 1948.
(3) The Transistor—a Crystal Triode, ELECTRONICS, p 68, Sept. 1948.
(4) E. A. Guillemin, "Communications Networks," 1, p 174, John Wiley and Sons, 1931.

Square-Wave Generator Using Gated-Beam Tube

Output from 50 to 500,000 pulses per second is provided in five steps for checking frequency response, phase shift or transient response. Simple circuit includes a symmetrical multivibrator, gated-beam tube, wide-band amplifier and cathode-follower output

By LOUIS E. GARNER, JR.

MOST SQUARE-WAVE generators are fairly expensive because they employ several cascaded amplifier stages to provide adequate clipping action. With only five tubes used in the complete instrument, a square-wave generator using a 6BN6 gated-beam tube as a clipper[1] delivers a signal with good waveform, fast rise time and wide frequency range. The schematic diagram of such an instrument is shown in Fig. 1.

Circuit Description

Referring to the schematic diagram of Fig. 1, a 12AU7 twin-triode, V_1, is used as a plate-coupled symmetrical multivibrator. Five separate frequencies of operation are provided with each frequency obtained by changing the grid-plate R-C circuits by means of switch S_1. The grid resistors are dual potentiometers which can be adjusted to supply exact frequencies on each switch position regardless of coupling-capacitor tolerances.

The nonsinusoidal signal appearing across plate load R_2 is applied through C_{11} to the gated-beam clipper V_2. Both plate and screen voltages on this tube must be kept low for good clipping.

A square-wave signal appears across plate load R_{20} and is applied through C_{14} to the wide-band voltage amplifier V_3. The amplified square-wave signal is then applied through C_{15} to the cathode-follower output stage V_4 which permits a low-impedance output.

Direct voltages to operate the instrument are supplied by a conventional full-wave rectifier power supply using a 5Y3GT.

Design Features

Small-value plate-load resistors are used in each amplifier stage to provide wide frequency response and to minimize the effect of distributed capacitance.

To amplify a square-wave signal with minimum waveform distortion, an amplifier should be capable of amplifying frequencies without attenuation to at least the tenth harmonic of the square-wave fundamental frequency. Since the highest frequency square-wave signal supplied by this unit is 500,000 pps, the amplifiers must be reasonably flat to better than 5 megacycles. By

the final square wave will be free of overshoots, ringing and high-frequency phase shift.

At low frequencies, other problems are encountered. Since a low-frequency square wave may be considered as a switched d-c signal, the amplifier circuits must be capable of holding a steady level during a period equal to one-half a cycle of the lowest-frequency square wave to be obtained. Towards this end, large R-C time constants are used in coupling between stages and large-capacitance electrolytics are used in filtering and by-pass circuits.

Several requirements dictated the design of the output circuit. In

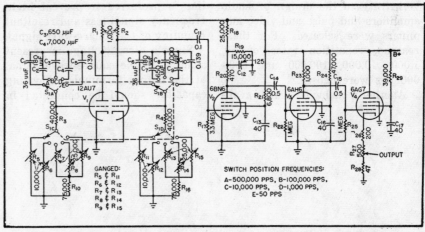

FIG. 1—Circuit diagram for square-wave generator. The clipper stage employs a 6BN6 gated-beam tube

using small plate-load resistors and care in wiring it has been possible to accomplish this without having to use peaking coils or other means to boost the high-frequency response. This is desirable so that

common with all wide-band devices, the output impedance had to be low. At the same time, it was desired to provide control over the output level at minimum cost and without distortion of signal waveform at different levels.

A cathode-follower output circuit was selected and a low-resistance potentiometer, R_{27}, used to control the output level. Even with these precautions, the waveform suffered near the ends of rotation of the control. This was due to the frequency consciousness of a potentiometer type of control. To minimize this effect, fixed resistances, R_{26} and R_{28}, were added to prevent adjusting the control to extreme limits.

In the final circuit, it is possible to adjust the output level over the desired range without waveform distortion from 50 to 500,000 pulses per second.

Choice of Frequencies

Since a square-wave signal is satisfactory for checking an amplifier to at least the tenth harmonic of its fundamental repetition rate, it is not necessary to provide continuous frequency coverage in a square-wave generator. Four or five frequencies, if carefully chosen, are satisfactory for all normal work.

Frequencies permitting the final instrument to be applied with equal versatility to the design of audio amplifiers and pulse and video amplifiers were selected. For these reasons, repetition rates of 50, 1,000, 10,000, 100,000 and 500,-000 pps were chosen.

Another model will be made available for wide-band, high-fidelity audio-amplifier work. It will supply signals at 50, 500, 5,000, 10,000 and 20,000 pps.

Output-signal level may be adjusted by means of R_{27} from approximately 0.8 to 8 volts peak-to-peak. This permits checking not only complete amplifier circuits but also individual stages and attenuator circuits. Output impedance varies from about 50 ohms to approximately 550 ohms, depending on the attenuator setting.

Rise time is good, and for the 500-kc signal is better than 0.07 microsecond.

Applications

The final instrument may be used for checking amplifiers, peaking or ringing networks, attenuator circuits, phase-shift circuits and pulsing circuits or devices.

For pulse formation, a conventional differentiating circuit may be used in conjunction with the square-wave generator.

When the instrument is used, normal precautions should be followed. Unless necessary to minimize hum pickup, a shielded output cable should not be used. An open line is preferred to prevent high-frequency signal loss and resultant rounding of the square-wave signal.

Since a direct voltage is present along with the square-wave signal at the output terminal, a blocking capacitor should be connected in series with the hot lead if d-c cannot be tolerated in the circuit to which the generator is connected. The size of this capacitor will be determined by the input impedance of the circuit to be tested and, for this reason, a capacitor was not incorporated as part of the instrument. The capacitor used should be selected to provide an R-C time constant, with the input impedance of the circuit to be tested, at least 25 times greater than the time of one cycle of the lowest-frequency square-wave to be used.

In all cases, connections to and from the circuit tested should be kept as short as practicable. Long leads may introduce sufficient inductance in some amplifier circuits so that resonance at comparatively low frequencies occurs. This results in overshoots and transient oscillation when signals having a short rise time are used. Such distortion of the square-wave signal may lead to incorrect conclusions concerning the circuit tested.

The author wishes to thank Joseph Kaufman, Director of Education, National Radio Institute, for his encouragement and suggestions during the design of this instrument and Mort Massie for his help in securing special samples necessary for the construction of an experimental model.

REFERENCE
(1) Robert Adler, A Gated Beam Tube, ELECTRONICS, p 82, Feb. 1950.

Frequency Division with Phase-Shift Oscillators

Divisions as high as seven are easily obtained with standard component parts requiring only initial adjustment. Practical circuits described are customarily employed to obtain accurate power frequencies. They find additional use in the lower-frequency stages of frequency standards calibrated at r-f

By CHARLES R. SCHMIDT

THE resistance - capacitance phase-shift oscillator has desirable charactertistics as a frequency divider. When suitably modified, it is possible to obtain relatively large division ratios that are unaffected by tube replacement, component drift due to aging or temperature. The single triode used per division gives it an advantage over conventional multivibrator types. In operating latitude it approaches that of the inductance-capacitance oscillator.[1] It is advantageous in that the transformers are replaced by resistance-capacitance networks as frequency-determining elements, with a consequent reduction in cost and weight.

Dividers operating from both crystal and tuning-fork oscillator standards have been constructed to give dependable 60-cycle output for motor drive applications. Divisions by five, six and seven were used in these designs. Scale-of-ten divisions in a single stage have also been used. They require more care in initial alignment because of the restricted locking range.

The resistance-capacitance phase-shift oscillator is particularly applicable in divider chains where the output frequency is below 10 cycles. In this frequency range, other dividing methods are undependable or require components of large size.

The basic phase-shift oscillator used for frequency division is shown in Fig. 1. The circuit is the standard four-section, series-capacitance shunt-resistance type and was favored over the three-section type because less gain is required for oscillation. It is desirable at higher frequencies where the tube output capacitance decreases the stage gain. Departures from the standard oscillator are found in the use of capacitors C_1 and C_2 and in the operating point of the tube.

Capacitor C_1 couples the control frequency, which is some multiple of the output frequency, into the frequency-determining n e t w o r k. This capacitor serves the additional function of dropping the control voltage to a suitable value for proper operation. The magnitude of C_1 is such that it only slightly affects the frequency of oscillation of either stage.

Output is taken from the plate of the tube through an appropriate coupling capacitor C_2, either to the grid of the following divider stage, or into the output load resistance. Each stage oscillates with an amplitude of about 60 volts at the design-center supply voltage of 300 volts. The operating point of the tube determined by the plate and cathode resistors is such that strong harmonics of the oscillating frequency are produced. The control-frequency voltage combines with the harmonic that is nearest in frequency, causing the frequency of the oscillator to change to an exact control frequency submultiple.

A 100-cycle oscillator can be used as a divider of frequencies of 500, 600 and 700 cycles without modification, because fifth, sixth and seventh harmonics of the fundamental frequency are generated. When locking of the oscillator occurs, the control frequency determines its frequency and the output wave shows a fundamental plus a pronounced harmonic at the control frequency. As the control frequency is varied the phase of this harmonic varies with respect to the fundamental wave. If the control frequency is changed sufficiently the divider will unlock. This effect is noticed in the ouput wave by the harmonic's continually changing phase with respect to the fundamental.

In Fig. 2 the locking range of a 100-cycle divider is shown as a function both of controlling frequency and magnitude of the capacitance C_1. In obtaining this data, the controlling frequency voltage was kept constant at 60 volts and applied to C_1 through a 100,000-ohm resistor to simulate the driving impedance of the preceding divider stage. The locking range is seen to be generally better for control frequencies that

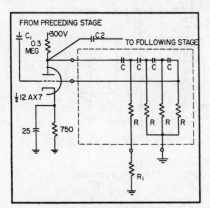

FIG. 1—Basic divider circuit illustrates importance of couplings

are odd multiples of the oscillator frequency than it is for those that are even multiples. When C_1 is small little of the control frequency energy is introduced into the oscillator and hence the locking range for a given division is restricted. When C_1 is made too large so much control frequency is introduced that the divider acts as an amplifier with the control frequency as output.

standard-tolerance components in the phase-shift network that the frequency be adjusted by padding the first resistance in the network (shown as R_1 in the Fig. 1) to a suitable value. In the models constructed, the phase-shift resistors and capacitors of a stage are arranged in separate shield cans, indicated by the dotted lines. In practice, the first 150,000-ohm resistor

tion of from 200 to 400 volts will not cause the divider to unlock. This stability results because the phase-shift oscillator's frequency is only slightly affected by supply voltage. The control voltage required to obtain locking is not critical.

The diagram of Fig. 4 shows a divider designed to give 60-cycle output controlled by an 1,800-cycle tuning-fork frequency standard.

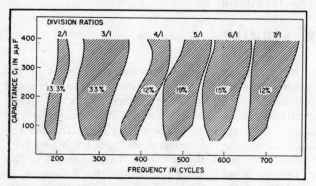

FIG. 2—Shaded areas indicate the locking range as a function of input coupling and frequency. Supply voltage is 300 v, frequency 100 cycles and resistance R is 200,000 ohms

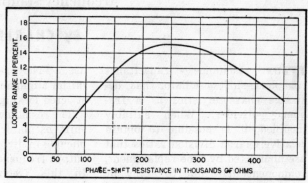

FIG. 3—Locking range in percent as a function of phase-shift resistance in thousands of ohms. The oscillator frequency used is 100 cycles and division ratio is six-to-one

The locking range curves indicate that for the 100-cycle output divider a 250-$\mu\mu$f coupling capacitor from the previous stage will give the widest locking range for divisions by five and six, but a somewhat larger capacitor is required for divisions by seven for optimum operation. The locking range as a function of the phase-shift network resistance is shown in Fig. 3 for a 100-cycle oscillator. This curve was taken for a division by six and is indicative of the results obtained for other divisions.

In designing a divider stage, the required oscillating frequency of the stage is determined, and the standard formula for the frequency of a four-section phase-shift oscillator is used,[2] making the R of the formula 200,000 ohms. In this way the required C is obtained. If the value of C determined in this way is not close to a standard value, a different R above 200,000 ohms can be chosen. Figure 3 shows that the operating range will only be slightly affected by this change of resistance.

It is usually required, when using

is brought out to a terminal. The padding resistor R_1 completes the connection to ground.

Using the optimum values as determined by the foregoing, the operation of the divider is independent of supply voltage variations over a wide range. By setting the center of the locking range at the control frequency a supply-voltage varia-

The first stage divides by six (300-cycle oscillator) and the second stage by five (60-cycle oscillator). For a divider of this type, employing two divisions of a low order, standard-tolerance components of the values shown will produce satisfactory lock-in between the oscillators.

In order to insure stable opera-

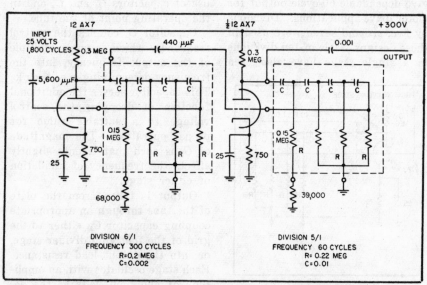

FIG. 4—Synchronous motor-control giving frequency division of 30

tion despite variations in the oscillator frequencies with time, the frequency of each stage should be adjusted for the center of the control range. In practice, when the incoming 1,800-cycle frequency is applied to the vertical plates and the output from the plate of the first stage to the horizontal plates of an oscilloscope, a six-loop Lissajous figure is observed. By replacing R_1 with a resistance box its value can be adjusted so that the divider will unlock for a high value of resistance and also for a low value. A value is then chosen to give the midfrequency between these two drop-out points. By transferring the oscilloscope connections to the next stage, the procedure can be repeated to place the divider in final adjustment.

Range	Percent	Mid-frequency
1,645-1,895	14.1	1,770
1,671-1,947	15.2	1,809
1,669-1,931	14.6	1,800
1,668-1,932	14.6	1,800
1,656-1,932	15.3	1,794
1,694-1,945	13.7	1,819

This divider gave a control range of 15 percent when operated from a 25-volt control-frequency input. The tabulation shows the variation in locking range of the overall divider for six random-choice 12AX7 tubes.

The results indicate that for each tube there is ample latitude for frequency drift of the oscillators

around the 1,800-cycle midfrequency.

A frequency standard with 60-cycle output controlled from a 90.72 kc crystal is shown in Fig. 5. Terminal connections, only, to the phase-shift circuit-blocks are shown. The R-C values, division ratios and oscillating frequencies of the dividers are indicated. There is one notable exception in this design. An inductive plate load is used in place of the usual resistive load in the first divider stage. The fundamental frequency of this oscillation is 12,960 cycles with a 90.72-kilocycle seventh harmonic.

The usual plate-load resistance of 300,000 ohms together with the plate-cathode capacitance of the tube reduces this harmonic to a level where satisfactory locking cannot be obtained. A 100-millihenry powdered-iron-core inductance provides the necessary high plate impedance together with sufficient peaking effect to insure the high-frequency response of the stage. The use of the inductive plate load requires that the operating point be readjusted. It was done by using a resistance-capacitance plate-decoupling filter and eliminating the cathode resistor. The alignment procedure for this divider is the same as for the previous one. In operation the overall locking range was 12 percent which is determined by the 7-to-1 stage.

The voltage limits for satisfactory operation were 200 to 400 volts.

Experience with R-C and L-C oscillators of various types as frequency dividers indicates the following general requirements: a frequency-determining network of appreciable Q; a distortion element that produces harmonics; and the combining of the control frequency with the appropriate harmonic and the injection of the resultant into the oscillating circuit. The Q will determine the locking range; the lower the Q the broader will be that range. Using high-Q oscillating circuits and good distortion elements, stable divisions by as high as 300-to-1 are possible in a single stage.[3]

In the divider described in this article, the phase-shift network provides the low-Q frequency-determining element for a broad locking range. The distortion is produced in the tube itself. Control frequency and oscillator harmonic are combined at the grid of the stage. In this way the phase-shift oscillator meets the requirements in an economical way, using a minimum of tubes and components.

REFERENCES

(1) E. Norrman, The Inductance-Capacitance Oscillator as a Frequency Divider, *Proc. IRE* 34, Oct. 1946.
(2) E. L. Ginzton and L. M. Hollingsworth, Phase-Shift Oscillators, *Proc. IRE*, 29, Feb. 1941.
(3) M. Silver and A. Shadowitz, A High Ratio Multivibrator Divider, Federal Telecommunication Laboratories, Inc., Technical Memorandum No. 261, Feb. 1947.

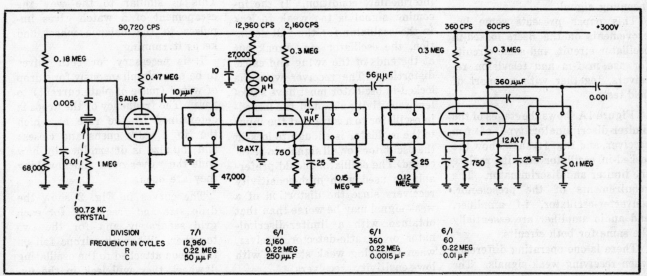

FIG. 5—Divider system using a 90.72-kc crystal gives highly accurate 60-cycle output

Locked-in Oscillator for TV Sound

Electronic selectivity gained with locked-in oscillator provides ability to reject an unwanted signal much greater than can be obtained with tuned circuits alone. Circuits can be used with intercarrier system or 21.25-mc i-f amplifier

By MURLAN S. CORRINGTON

DEVELOPMENT WORK on frequency-modulation receivers has shown that in order to obtain certain desirable performance characteristics it is necessary to convert frequency-modulated broadcast signals, modulated in accordance with present frequency-modulation standards, to signals having reduced swing before they are sent through the discriminator of a receiver and converted to audio-frequency signals. If the first intermediate frequency of a standard f-m receiver is 10,700 ± 75 kc, division by five gives 2,140 ± 15 kc.

The locked-in oscillator provides a simple method for dividing the instantaneous frequency by five. The incoming signal voltage is applied to the first grid of a pentagrid mixer tube, and the third grid and plate are connected in a regular feed-back oscillator circuit. The first grid serves to inject pulses of current into the plate circuit and causes the oscillator to lock in at one-fifth the frequency of the incoming signal.

This paper presents some improvements on the Beers locked-in oscillator circuit, and some circuits for use in f-m and television receivers, together with a report of field tests.

Figure 1A shows the stages of the limiter-discriminator type of f-m receiver, and Fig. 1B shows how the locked-in oscillator circuits replace the limiter and discriminator. The requirements of the preselector, converter-oscillator, i-f amplifier, and audio amplifier are essentially the same for both circuits.

There is one operating difference when receiving weak signals. The limiter-discriminator receiver can receive a signal so weak that it will not operate the limiter and yet give a usable output if there are no large variations in the amplitude of the incoming wave. These variations can be caused by multipath transmission, by common or adjacent-channel interference or by excessive i-f selectivity.

The locked-in oscillator is either locked in or it isn't; there is no intermediate condition. If the incoming signal is too weak to lock in the oscillator for the full deviation, the oscillator may break out at the ends of the swing and cause distortion. The receiver with the locked-in oscillator must have sufficient sensitivity ahead of the locked-in oscillator to assure that the input to the oscillator is enough to lock-in the oscillator for all signals to be received. The oscillator should preferably be used with high-sensitivity receivers since the distortion of a weak signal may be worse than that obtained with a limiter-discriminator or a ratio-detector receiver, when receiving weak stations with low-sensitivity receivers.

Mechanical Analogy

Figure 2 shows a simple mechanical analogy for the locked-in oscillator. The No. 1 and No. 3 grids of a pentagrid tube are represented by valves that open and close, corresponding to the swings of the grid voltages. The No. 1 valve has a variable opening, corresponding to the variation of the input voltage, and the No. 3 valve is tripped once by the flywheel in each cycle. This is similar to the way the escapement of a watch gives impulses to the balance wheel and keeps it running.

It is necessary for both valves to be open simultaneously for a drop of water (pulse of plate current) to pass. The frequency of the drops is determined by the rate at which the No. 1 valve opens and closes; and the size is determined by how wide the valves open and how long they are open.

The curves in Fig. 2 show the drop size and frequency for each grid separately and for the two together. When the drops fall on the spoon attached to the oscillating flywheel, they will lock in the fly-

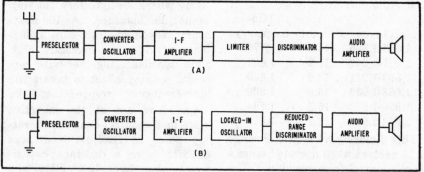

FIG. 1—Stages of receiver employing a locked-in oscillator (B) compared to a conventional receiver (A)

wheel with the falling drops and maintain oscillation as long as the frequency of the drops is near the resonant frequency of the flywheel, or an integral multiple of this frequency.

If the rate of the flow of drops is increased, there will be a phase shift between the two valves, so the resultant drops will not be the same size as before. There may be a big one followed by a little one. If the big drop hits the spoon when it is starting its downward motion, the drop will be in the spoon for a fairly long time and the weight can therefore do considerable work on the wheel and thus will speed up the system, keeping it locked in. Likewise if the big drop hits near the bottom of the swing of the spoon, it can do only a small amount of work and the system will slow down. It is thus evident that the drops can lock in the flywheel over a range of frequencies if the relative phase of the two valves is adjusted properly.

Locking-in Action

The theory of the locking-in process can be explained in the following manner. In the circuit of Fig 3 the oscillator is connected with feedback from the plate tank circuit to the No. 3 grid. This oscillator grid is operated with self bias through grid resistor R_3. Each time the grid voltage swings positive it draws grid current. For an intermediate frequency of 4,500 kc, the grid operates at one-fifth of this frequency or 900 kc.

The amplitude of the oscillation is determined by the curvature of the E_g-I_p characteristic and is usually so great that the grid voltage swings well into the curved parts of the tube characteristic during the cycle. This means that pulses of plate current are produced having component frequencies 2ω, 3ω, 4ω, ... where ω is the natural frequency of the tuned plate circuit L_2C_4. These harmonics are applied to the No. 3 grid through the mutual coupling. Additional harmonics are produced by the grid current pulses.

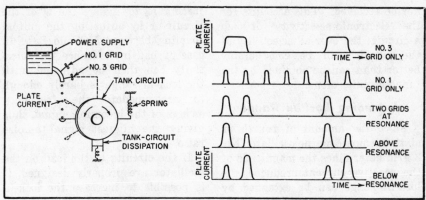

FIG. 2—Mechanical analogy for locked-in oscillator operation

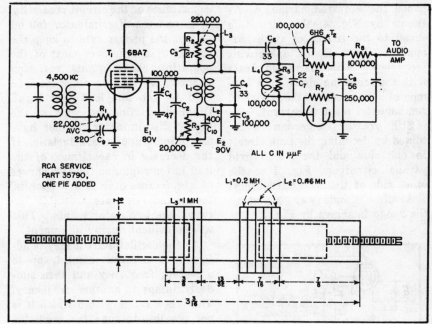

FIG. 3—Circuit and coil construction of oscillator for intercarrier sound

When the incoming signal at 4,500 kc is applied to the tube, the tube operates as a converter and combination frequencies will be produced equal to $\pm 5\,r\omega \pm s\omega$ when r and $s = 0, 1, 2, 3, \ldots$ Since the plate circuit is tuned to 900 kc, the only frequencies which will be amplified are those of frequency ω; the others are bypassed effectively. If $r = 1$, then $s = 4$ or 6 will give frequency ω. Then the fourth and sixth harmonics of the oscillator beat with the incoming signal to produce the frequency ω in the tank circuit.

If the incoming signal is not exactly five times that of the tank circuit, this combination beat fre-

quency current will not be in phase with the fundamental tank circuit current but will be slightly out of phase. The reactive component of this current will cause the oscillator to work like a reactance tube, thus changing the frequency of the tank circuit just enough to lock it in. This is equivalent to the operation illustrated by Figure 2.

The maximum amount of reactive current is produced when all of this beat-frequency current is 90 degrees out of phase with respect to the fundamental tank circuit current. This determines the ends of the lock-in range. If the frequency of the incoming signal is outside this range, the oscillator cannot lock in, and the signal cannot be received. This accounts for the "electronic selectivity" of such a circuit; the over-all selectivity of the circuit will be considerably better than can be obtained by the tuned circuits alone.

Extending Lock-in Range

Since the amount of fourth or sixth harmonic on the oscillator No. 3 grid determines the magnitude of the reactive current produced, the lock-in range can be extended by placing a parallel tuned circuit in series with the No. 3 grid to enhance the required harmonic. As shown by Fig. 4, this circuit is tuned to the fourth or sixth harmonic of the oscillator tank circuit frequency. This harmonic beats with the incoming signal (5th harmonic) to produce the required fundamental reactive current.

Still greater range can be obtained by detuning the tank circuit to one side and the No. 3 grid parallel circuit of Fig. 4 to the other side of the center frequency.

Another simple way to extend the range is shown by Fig. 3. The

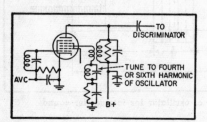

FIG. 4—Tuned circuit in series with No. 3 grid is adjusted to fourth or sixth harmonic of oscillator

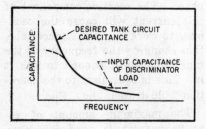

FIG. 5—Frequency change with variation of input capacitance

coupled circuit L_3C_3 is used to broaden out the selectivity curve of L_2C_4 and give increased lock-in range. Continuous variation of selectivity can be obtained by ad-

justing R_2 to change the Q of the circuit or by adjusting the mutual coupling between L_3C_3 and L_2C_4. In case of bad interference the selectivity can then be adjusted until the lock-in range is barely enough to accommodate the frequency swings of the incoming signal, thus giving the highest signal-to-noise ratio.

If the circuits of the load on the oscillator are properly designed, it is possible to increase the lock-in range. The discriminator of Fig. 3 was designed so that the input capacitance of the circuit consisting of C_6 and the discriminator fall off at just the proper rate to keep the oscillator in tune over most of the operating range. This variation is shown by Fig. 5. Care must be used to get this load just right. Other discriminators, such as the Seeley discriminator, do not have the proper input characteristic. If the decrease in capacitance of the load is too rapid, so the two curves of Fig. 5 cross over at three points, the circuit becomes unstable between the two outer points. This will be evident during alignment.

As the oscillator frequency is adjusted, it changes smoothly up to a certain frequency and then suddenly jumps to another frequency. There is a range within which it is not possible to tune the oscillator because of the instability. Usually

this can be corrected by using a smaller coupling capacitor between the oscillator and discriminator, or by adding a small series resistor, or by redesigning the discriminator.

Design of Discriminator

A very simple discriminator is used in this system. In Fig. 3, capacitor C_6 couples the discriminator to the oscillator. The tuned circuit L_4C_7, together with the interelectrode capacitance of the diode (in parallel with R_7), forms the discriminator. At series resonance between L_4 and the interelectrode capacitance of the lower diode, a maximum voltage appears across this diode. At parallel resonance of L_4 and C_7 a maximum of voltage appears across the upper diode. The result is a balanced discriminator, with the bandwidth determined by the difference between the series and parallel resonant frequencies.

Resistor R_6 controls the parallel Q of the circuit and R_7 controls the effective series Q. For best linearity these two values of Q should be approximately equal. But R_7 will therefore not necessarily equal R_6, since one shunts the series capacitor and the other is across the entire circuit.

Adjustment

For the circuit of Fig. 3, the auxiliary coupled circuit L_3C_3 is

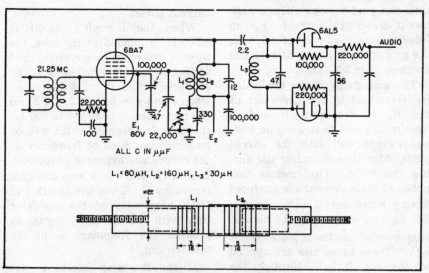

FIG. 6—Locked-in oscillator for 21.25-mc sound channel. Coils L_1 and L_2 are slightly overcoupled and mounted in a separate shield can from L_3

tuned to the same frequency as the oscillator tank circuit (900 kc) and is slightly overcoupled with respect to the circuit, L_2C_4. To adjust the circuit, tune the oscillator tank circuit until the oscillator locks in with an incoming frequency-modulated signal from a signal generator, which feeds into the i-f channel at 4,500 kc.

Remove the modulation, leaving the carrier at 4,500 kc. Adjust the discriminator to zero balance by connecting a d-c voltmeter from either end of R_s to ground and adjusting L_4 until there is no voltage from R_s to ground. Next adjust L_2 until the lock-in range is approximately symmetrical about the center frequency (900 kc). Then adjust L_3 to extend the lock-in range to the desired amount. A slight readjustment of L_2 may be necessary for best results.

For a practical application of the circuit, the constants shown can be used. The oscillator transformer can be made from a standard i-f transformer (RCA service part 35790) by adding one pie, increasing the coupling by moving the coils closer together and reconnecting the pies. The oscillator tank coil L_2 is composed of three pies in series aiding and L_1 is formed of two pies, one on each side of L_2, connected in series aiding. This gives fairly tight coupling without increasing the inductance of L_1 beyond the allowable limits. The cores are inserted into the coils as shown.

If the effective coupling between L_2 and L_3 is gradually increased from some low value by moving L_3 closer to L_2 the lock-in range will increase uniformly until the oscillator begins to give a distorted output in the middle of the lock-in range. Further increase in coupling will cause the oscillator to break out in the middle of the range but not at the ends. This gives a simple means for adjusting the lock-in range.

The same result can be obtained by shunting L_3 with a variable resistance, since a decrease in the Q of L_3 is equivalent to a decrease in

coupling. Loading a transformer with resistors decreases the effective coupling.

In a standard television receiver with a sound i-f of 21.25 megacycles, the locked-in oscillator can be simplified to that shown by Fig. 6. Because of the limited deviation used, no circuits are needed to extend the lock-in range. This circuit requires separate shield cans for the oscillator and the discriminator. If it is preferred to use a single coil assembly and shield can,

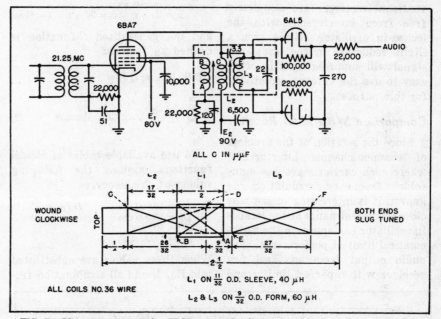

FIG. 7—Alternative circuit for 21.25 mc, with all three coils mounted on one form and installed in one shield can

the circuit shown in Fig. 7 is satisfactory. All three coils are on the same form and can be adjusted with the two iron cores.

Performance During Interference

To test the locked-in oscillator circuit of Fig. 6 under operating conditions, it was installed in an RCA 8T241 television receiver in place of the amplifier and discriminator in the 21.25-mc sound channel. The lock-in range was approximately $\pm$ 25 kc at 0.3-volt input to the No. 1 grid of the 6BA7, $\pm$ 100 kc at 1-volt input and $\pm$ 200 kc at 5 volts input.

The complete locked-in oscillator receiver was tested by connecting two signal generators to the input

antenna terminals, one to represent the desired signal and the other to represent the common-channel interfering signal. The desired signal was at 179.75 mc (channel 7) modulated with a deviation of $\pm$ 22.5 kc and an audio repetition rate of 1,000 cycles per second. The second signal had the same center frequency and deviation but an audio rate of 400 cycles per second.

The curves of Fig. 8 show how the receiver completely suppresses the undesired signal until the two are almost equal. In the first pair of curves the desired signal was 100 microvolts, and the undesired one was gradually increased until it equaled and then captured the desired signal. The amount of 400 and 1,000-cycle audio in the output was measured with a wave analyzer. For the input of 100 microvolts the locked-in oscillator barely had enough signal to work, but as the level increased the capture effect is very pronounced.

The curves show that if the undesired signal is 80 percent of the desired signal, for an input of 10,000 microvolts, the 400-cycle note is down 32 db, while with the standard receiver it is only down 8 db. The final value of the 400-cycle amplitude is slightly higher than that for 1,000 cycles because of the 1-db difference in the 75-microsecond deemphasis curve.

The practical meaning of this test is that if the receiver is capable of suppressing any undesired carrier wave unless it is at least 80 or 90 percent as strong as the desired carrier wave, compared to about 30 percent for a conventional receiver, the area in which such interference can occur is very much reduced. Many areas where intolerable distortion occurs in conventional receivers are completely free from interference with the locked-in oscillator. Since even a slight reduction in the undesired signal will suppress it, it is often easy to use the antenna directivity for this purpose.

Comparison With Ideal Receiver

Since the solution of the problem of common-channel interference, where each carrier wave has sinusoidal frequency modulation, is known, it is interesting to see how close the performance of the locked-in oscillator can approach the mathematical limit of performance. The audio output from an ideal f-m receiver with a perfect limiter and a very wide but linear discriminator is given by the equation

Audio output
$$= D_1 \cos 2\pi \mu_1 t +$$

$$\sum_{r=-\infty}^{\infty} \sum_{s=-\infty}^{\infty} (r\mu_1 - s\mu_2)$$

$$C\left(r, \frac{D_1}{\mu_1}; s, \frac{D_2}{\mu_2}; x, 0\right) \cos (r\alpha - s\beta) \quad (1)$$

where x = ratio of carrier wave amplitudes
D_1 = deviation of first carrier wave
μ_1 = audio repetition rate of first carrier wave
D_2 = deviation of second carrier wave
μ_2 = audio repetition rate of second carrier wave
$\alpha = 2\pi \mu_1 t$, $\beta = 2\pi \mu_2 t$, t = time,

and the generalized C-function is defined as follows:

$$C(k, l; m, n; x, \theta) =$$

$$\sum_{s=1}^{\infty} \frac{(-x)^s}{s} J_k(sl) J_m(sn) \cos s\theta \quad (2)$$

To use available tables of Bessel functions, assume the following values of frequency,

$D_1 = 10,000$ cps	$D_1/\mu_1 = 25$
$D_2 = 10,000$ cps	$D_2/\mu_2 = 10$
$\mu_1 = 400$ cps	
$\mu_2 = 1,000$ cps	

When these values are substituted into Eq. 1, and all combination frequencies equal to ± 400 cps and $\pm 1,000$ cps are sorted out and combined, the results are

400-cycle distortion = 800

$$\sum_{n=-\infty}^{\infty} C(10n+1, 25; 4n, 10: x, 0)$$
cycles per second $\quad (3)$

and the 1,000-cycle distortion = 2,000

$$\sum_{n=-\infty}^{\infty} C(10n, 25; 4n-1, 10: x, 0)$$
cycles per second $\quad (4)$

The C-functions were computed, in accord with Eq. 2, and the series summed in accord with Eq. 3 and 4.

Figure 9 shows the capture effect to be expected in an ideal f-m receiver under the assumed conditions. As the level of the 1,000-cycle interfering carrier wave is raised toward equality with the 400-cycle wave, the amount of the 1,000-cycle component in the audio output rises uniformly from a value approximately 64 db down when the ratio of carrier wave amplitudes is 0.1 to a point approximately 37 db down when the amplitudes are equal. At this point the 1,000-cycle carrier wave suddenly captures the other wave, causing full output at 1,000 cycles, and the 400-cycle component drops approximately 38 db. Beyond this point the amount of 400-cycle interference decreases smoothly.

The curves of Fig. 8 and 9 are not directly comparable because the deviation is different. However, for the higher signal levels the locked-in oscillator comes very close to the mathematical limit of performance. In a laboratory setup, working the signal generators directly into the i-f amplifier, it is possible to come so close to the ideal that a change in level as small as 5 percent will cause one signal to capture the other and almost completely suppress the accompanying distortion.

Extensive field tests have been made to compare such a locked-in oscillator with other conventional receivers such as the limiter-discriminator circuit, the intercarrier-sound system and the ratio detector. In every case the locked-in oscillator

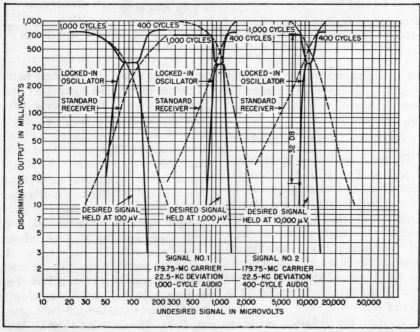

FIG. 8—Comparison of interference rejection of locked-in oscillator and RCA 8T241 receiver

was at least as good as any of the others and whenever the interference was severe it usually was better. At times it gives a signal almost free from noise when the other systems are so distorted they are unintelligible.

Conclusions

It is often desirable to convert frequency-modulated signals having a frequency deviation up to $\pm$ 75 kc to signals of reduced carrier frequency and of reduced frequency deviation before they are sent through the discriminator of a receiver and converted to audio-frequency signals. Division of the instantaneous frequency by five reduces normal maximum frequency swings from $\pm$ 75 kc to $\pm$ 15 kc. Smaller deviations are reduced in proportion. The locked-in oscillator provides a simple and practical means for performing this division.

Since the tube operates as an oscillator with fairly large voltages on the No. 3 grid, the grid voltage swings well into the curved parts of the tube characteristic and generates harmonics in the No. 3 grid circuit. When the division ratio is five to one, the fourth and sixth harmonics of the oscillator beat with the incoming signal to produce a current having a difference frequency, which is just equal to the output frequency. When the incoming signal frequency is exactly five times the normal oscillator frequency, this injected current, which has the same frequency as the oscillator, is in phase with the normal plate current.

When the incoming signal frequency is increased, the injected current lags the normal plate current and cancels part of the leading current through the tank-circuit capacitor, thus effectively lowering the capacitance and raising the frequency of the circuit. This enables the oscillator to remain locked-in. The maximum amount the incoming signal frequency can be increased before the oscillator breaks out occurs when the incoming signal and likewise the injected current lag the

normal plate current by 90 degrees, since this results in maximum quadrature current.

In a similar way, when the incoming signal frequency is less than five times the normal plate circuit frequency, the injected current leads the normal plate current and is thus equivalent to a larger capacitor in the tank circuit. This lowers the oscillator frequency and enables it to remain locked in. The lower end of the lock-in range is reached when the injected current leads the normal plate current by 90 degrees. The circuit thus behaves like a reactance tube since it generates a quadrature component in the plate circuit.

Self Bias

When the tube operates with self bias on the grid, the output voltage from the oscillator is substantially constant for large variations in the signal voltage. It thus eliminates the need for a limiter in f-m receivers since the incoming signal is used only to control the frequency of the locked-in oscillator and not to produce a voltage output.

It is relatively easy to design the external load on the tank circuit so the equivalent input capacitance decreases with increasing frequency.

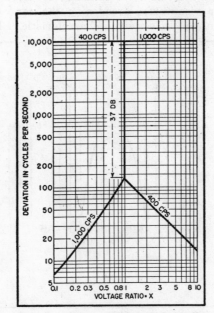

FIG. 9—Capture effect in a theoretically ideal f-m receiver

quency at just the proper rate to keep the oscillator in tune over a wide portion of the lock-in range. This results in improved performance and an extended lock-in range. The L-C ratio of the tank circuit can be adjusted to just match the frequency discriminator for best operation.

When receiving a standard f-m signal, it is important that the oscillator have a lock-in range somewhat greater than the total swing of the transmitter. If it does not, slight mistuning or oscillator drift, or overmodulation at the transmitter, will cause the oscillator to break out at the ends of the frequency swing and this results in disagreeable distortion.

It is possible to obtain an adequate lock-in range in several ways. Proper match of the discriminator to the oscillator is important, and this can be obtained by adjustment of the L-C ratio of the tank circuit, by varying the series coupling capacitor, by adjustment of the Q of the circuit in the discriminator, or by the addition of circuits which selectively control the amplitudes of the harmonics in the oscillator circuit. The last method enables very wide lock-in ranges to be obtained. With conventional tubes, the circuits should be designed to supply at least 0.5 to 1.0 volt on the input grid.

Extensive laboratory and field tests show that the performance of the locked-in oscillator comes very close to the mathematical limit for an ideal receiver. A standard television receiver with such a sound channel can suppress an interfering carrier wave less than eighty percent of the desired wave. This means that in fringe areas where there is considerable interference the locked-in oscillator is capable of reducing the area of interference considerably. If antenna directivity is also used, it will be possible to clear up most cases of interference.

A receiver with the locked-in oscillator must have sufficient sensitivity ahead of the locked-in oscillator to assure that the input to the oscillator is enough to lock-in the oscillator for all signals to be received. This means that the circuit should preferably be used with high-sensitivity receivers since the distortion of a weak signal may be worse than that obtained with a limiter-discriminator or a ratio-detector receiver, when receiving weak stations with low-sensitivity receivers.

BIBLIOGRAPHY

G. L. Beers, A Frequency-Dividing Locked-in Oscillator Frequency-modula-tion Receiver, *Proc. IRE*, 32, No. 12, p 730, Dec. 1944. Also U. S. Patent 2,356,-201, filed Feb. 12, 1942, issued Aug. 22, 1944.

Lord Rayleigh, "The Theory of Sound," Macmillan and Co., Ltd., London, 1, 2nd ed., p 66, 1937.

Hans Seiberth, Mitnahmeerscheinungen in der Akustik, *Hochfreq. und Elek.*, 45, No. 5, p 148, May 1935.

E. V. Appleton, The Automatic Synchronization of Triode Oscillators, *Proc. Camb. Phil. Soc.*, 21, p 231, 1922.

Donald L. Herr, Oscillations in Certain Nonlinear Driven Systems, *Proc. IRE*, 27, p 396, June 1939.

W. Wenke, Die Instabilität linearer und nichtlinearer Schwingungen (Mitnahme-schwingungen), *Hochfreq. und Elek.*, 55, No. 3, p 94, March 1940. Also p 109, Apr. 1940.

Samuel Sabaroff, Theory of Frequency Controlled Oscillators, *Jour. App. Phys.*, 11, No. 8, 538, Aug. 1940. See also S. Sabaroff, Frequency Controlled Oscillators, *Communications*, 19, No. 2, p 7, 1939.

H. Samulon, Über die Synchronisierung von Röhrengeneratoren, *Helvetica Physica Acta*, 14, No. 4, p 281, 1941.

C. W. Carnahan and Henry P. Kalmus, Synchronized Oscillators as F-M Receiver Limiters, ELECTRONICS, 17, p 108, Aug. 1944.

Robert Adler, A Study of Locking Phenomena in Oscillators, *Proc. IRE*, 34, p. 351, June 1946.

D. G. Tucker, Nonlinear Regenerative Circuits, *Wireless Eng.*, 24, No. 285, p 178, June 1947.

U. S. Patent 2,488,584, Murlan S. Corrington, filed Dec. 8, 1943, issued Nov. 22, 1949.

U. S. Patent 2,488,585, Murlan S. Corrington, filed May 29, 1945, issued Nov. 22, 1949.

U. S. Patent 2,440,653, Murlan S. Corrington, filed Nov. 14, 1944, issued April 27, 1948.

Murlan S. Corrington, Frequency Modulation Distortion Caused by Common and Adjacent-channel Interference, *RCA Review*, 7, No. 4, p 522, Dec. 1946.

Stabilized Master Oscillator for Multichannel Communication

Crystal-conserving systems for precise, stable generation of r-f energy are analyzed, with details of commercial 31-tube version using a single 100-kc crystal and motor-controlled afc to provide any desired frequency from 2 to 4.5 mc with 5-ppm accuracy

By E. W. PAPPENFUS

THE STABILITY of the transmitter and receiver in a communication link plays an important part in the channel spacing of the system. This is shown in Fig. 1A, which illustrates a typical communications receiver selectivity characteristic with the receiver tuned to a voice channel at 15 mc and having 2.5-kc sidebands centered in the selectivity curve. Reception is considered satisfactory if receiver selectivity does not drop more than 6 db at the limits of the sidebands. Undue interference from the adjacent channel can be avoided even when this is a strong signal if the attenuation of the adjacent channel is at least 60 db. If we assume a selectivity curve with a 3-to-1 shape factor, the space to the edge of the adjacent channel will be 7.5 kc, giving rise to channels of 14.990, 15.00, and 15.010 mc for the example illustrated.

If we assume an instability of 100 parts per million (0.01 percent) in the transmitter and receiver fre-

quency-generating system, we have the condition shown in Fig. 1B. Here the transmitted frequency is assumed to have drifted higher and the receiver local oscillator lower, or vice versa, broadening the required selectivity characteristic.

Of course, when transmitter and receiver drifts are in opposite directions the effects are reduced and approach the condition of Fig. 1A.

To allow for the maximum deviation of the channel within the selectivity characteristic, a band-

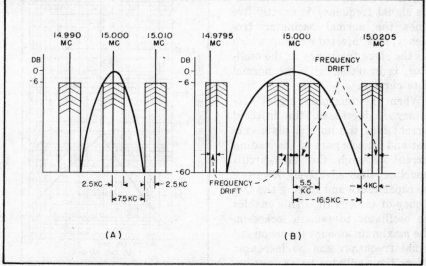

FIG. 1—Example illustrating how transmitter and receiver frequency instability increase the spacing required between communication channels

width of 11 kc is required at the 6-db points of Fig. 1B. With a shape factor of 3 to 1, this results in a skirt selectivity at the 60-db point of 16.5 kc which, when added to the 2.5-kc sideband and the 1.5-kc instability assumed for the adjacent channel, calls for a channel spacing of 20.5 kc or channels centered on 14.9795, 15.0000 and 15.0205 mc. This shows the increased channel spacing and consequent reduction in the number of available channels due to instabilities in transmission and reception.

Oscillator Stability

The crystal oscillator provides a satisfactory answer to the stability problem for many applications. During World War II, however, military forces found that it was

for 1.5 to 1 tuning ratio. Recent developments with temperature control indicate that stabilities in the order of 200 parts per million will be attainable in the near future.

The present state of the crystal oscillator art indicates that within the range 0 to 50 C, a tolerance of 30 parts per million is possible. Use of a crystal oven reduces this to about 3 parts per million. Commercially available laboratory 100-kc standards are available with long-term stabilities of about 0.1 parts per million. About the ultimate in stability is that of the Bureau of Standards radio station WWV, which is 0.02 parts per million.

With a master oscillator, equipment can be adjusted to a multiplicity of frequency channels, while the crystal oscillator is limited to

signals. In the descriptions to follow, the frequency values are chosen for ease of explanation and may not be ideal from the standpoint of spurious output.

As indicated in Fig. 2, a crystal oscillator and tap switch provide stable crystal-controlled frequencies from 10.2 to 12.2 mc spaced every 0.1 mc. The selected signal is fed through an isolation amplifier and bandpass filter to a mixer for combining with the output of another multicrystal oscillator that provides frequencies spaced 0.01 mc in the range of 8.200 to 8.110 mc. The difference frequency as selected in a tuned amplifier yields an output of 2 to 4 mc.

This system is readily adaptable to a direct-reading frequency dial in which megacycles and tenths of

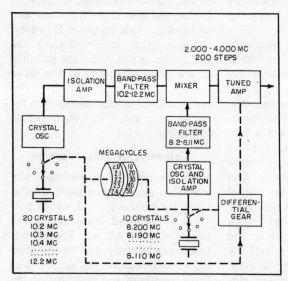

FIG. 2—Synthesis of desired frequency by mixing outputs of two multicrystal oscillators

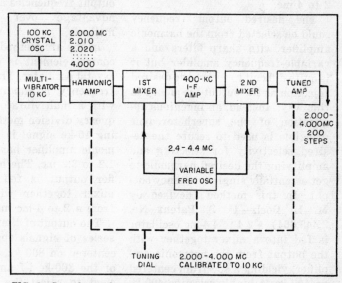

FIG. 3—Superheterodyne method using single crystal, harmonic amplifier and vfo

strategically unwise to be bound to a single channel or even a moderate number of channel frequencies. Accordingly, interest in variable-frequency master oscillators and other multifrequency generating schemes was renewed.

With increased development of temperature-compensating capacitors and stable permeability-tuning cores, it was possible to maintain the temperature and calibration accuracy of a variable-frequency oscillator without temperature control to within 400 parts per million

just a single frequency of operation or a multiple. A system is needed that combines the accuracy of the crystal oscillator with the versatility of the master oscillator. This paper will describe several systems which provide this desired end effect.

Multicrystal System

A method which has been used on the Collins 51R navigation receiver involves synthesis of the desired output frequency through addition of a number of stable input

a megacycle are indicated by a dial connected to the first tap switch, and 10-kc increments are indicated by a dial connected to the second crystal tap switch. At each position of the first tap switch there are available ten different output frequencies depending upon the position of the second tap switch, so the system illustrated provides 200 10-kc steps in the range of 2 to 4 mc. This output can be multiplied as desired to provide transmitter excitation or receiver injection.

The disadvantage of the system

is that it has certain spurious output frequencies and a stability which is less than with direct crystal control because the source crystals are higher in frequency than the available output from the generator.

Superheterodyne System

The foregoing system requires a large number of crystals (30 for 200 output channels). This is a disadvantage which can be avoided through the use of the circuit of Fig. 3. Here a 100-kc crystal oscillator of high stability is subdivided to 10 kc with a multivibrator or regenerative divider. The resulting highly accurate 10-kc signal is then fed into a harmonic amplifier that produces a spectrum of frequencies spaced 10 kc apart in the range of 2 to 4 mc.

The desired output frequency could be selected from the harmonic amplifier with sharp filters and a variable-frequency amplifier but it is quite difficult to secure the desired rejection at the output frequency in this way. Instead, an ingenious application of the superheterodyne principle is used to secure the desired selectivity for selecting and amplifying the desired harmonic to get essentially single-frequency output. In this method (devised by M. L. Doelz—U. S. Patent No. 2,445,664), a 2.4 to 4.4-mc oscillator is fed into a mixer together with the output from the harmonic amplifier, yielding a spectrum centered on 400 kc. A highly selective 400-kc i-f amplifier can be built yielding attenuation of up to 100 db or more for the adjacent undesired channel. Output of the 2.4 to 4.4-mc variable-frequency oscillator is also fed into a second mixer along with the 400-kc i-f output signal. The difference frequency is used here to give the desired output in the range of 2 to 4 mc.

The frequency-indicating dial, which controls the tuned circuits of the variable-frequency oscillator and tuned amplifier, is calibrated from 2 to 4 mc in 200 ten-kc steps. If desired, the harmonic amplifier can be made a bandpass circuit to

eliminate the necessity for tuning. The tuned output amplifier must have several tuned circuits of high selectivity to eliminate the oscillator injection frequency and the sum frequency.

AFC Oscillator System

The system just described has the advantage of providing a multitude of output channels with only a single crystal, but has a disadvantage of requiring a high degree of selectivity to eliminate spurious output which might be radiated by the transmitter and cause undesired responses when used for further injection. Using the master variable-frequency oscillator directly, with a servo-motor automatic frequency control for the oscillator as in Fig. 4, avoids some of these spurious output frequencies and hence offers advantages over the foregoing methods.

In the afc method, the frequency control element is again a 100-kc crystal oscillator. This stable source frequency is subdivided to 10 kc with a multivibrator or other frequency division method. The resulting 10-kc signal is fed into a harmonic amplifier having a range of 1.2 to 3.2 mc. The harmonic amplifier output is fed into the first mixer together with the output from a 2 to 4-mc master oscillator.

The output of the first mixer is a series of signals spaced 10 kc and centered on 800 kc. The selectivity of the 800-kc i-f amplifier is sufficient to reject the undesired signals at 790 and 810 kc.

The output of the 800-kc i-f amplifier is fed into two mixers which also receive a frequency of 800 kc derived from the 100-kc crystal oscillator. One 800-kc injection is shifted 90 degrees in a phase shifter. The resulting audio beat note from the beat detector, when the i-f amplifier is not centered on 800 kc, is also shifted 90 degrees, producing audio-frequency voltages in quadrature that operate a two-phase servo motor after amplification.

The output shaft of the servo motor drives a small trimmer capaci-

tor that adjusts the master oscillator to coincidence with a selected spectrum point. The motor receives beat-frequency voltage of the proper phase to correct the master oscillator to the desired zero beat condition as heterodyned to 800 kc.

The stability of the master variable-frequency oscillator must be such as to insure that it is within 5 kc of the indicated frequency, after which the afc system will select the desired spectrum points and adjust the oscillator so that its frequency is identical with the stable spectrum point within the limitations of the servo system. The a-f amplifiers must respond essentially down to zero frequency to get precise control.

It is not necessary to use a motor-controlled afc to secure correction of the master oscillator. A discriminator and reactance tube can also be used for this purpose. However, the correction motor method has the advantage of moderate stability in the event of failure of the servo system, while failure of the reactance tube-discriminator system results in erratic or uncontrolled operation.

Commercial AFC Version

An example of a commercially available stabilized master oscillator is the Collins 708A-2, which provides a stabilized frequency in the range of 2 to 4.5 mc. The output frequency is controlled by an internal or external 100-kc source. The setup accuracy and stability of the desired output frequency is ± 5 parts per million for variations in temperature from 0 to 50 C and wide ranges of humidity. An autotune arrangement provides automatic tuning so that any one of ten preset output frequencies can be selected at will from a remote selector switch. Sufficient voltage is available at the output terminals to excite the early stages of a transmitter or to serve as local oscillator injection for superheterodyne receivers.

The block diagram in Fig. 5 indicates the operating frequencies of the subunits. The master oscillator operates in the range of 1 to 1.5 mc and is multiplied by 2 or by 3 to yield output in the range of 2.0 to 3.0 mc or 3.0 to 4.5 mc to a final amplifier stage.

The 100-kc standard, using a highly stable temperature-controlled crystal, acts as an external frequency standard if desired. This crystal oscillator also feeds into two cascaded flip-flop or scale-of-two dividers, resulting in output at 25 kc accurately controlled by the 100-kc source. An auxiliary output of 450 kc is available for beat-frequency injection when the stabilized master oscillator is used in conjunction with a communications receiver.

The desired harmonic of 25 kc is selected in a tuned harmonic amplifier in the range of 9.125 to 21.625 mc and is fed into a first mixer together with the 10th or 15th harmonic of the master oscillator in the range 10 to 22.5 mc. The resulting intermediate frequency is in the range of 875 to 900 kc. An output tuning dial simultaneously tunes the harmonic amplifier and the multipliers. The frequency which is fed into the first i-f amplifier is dependent upon the relative position of the master oscillator harmonic in the 25-kc spectrum as related to the output from the harmonic amplifier. Every integral 5-kc point on the master oscillator dial produces frequencies of 875 and 900 kc in the first i-f amplifier. These 5-kc points are considered base or reference points to which the interpolation control reading is added. Master oscillator settings between these 5-kc points result in an i-f value somewhere between 875 and 900 kc.

The first i-f amplifier output is fed into a second mixer, together with the output from an interpolation oscillator subdivided by a factor of eight in three scale-of-two dividers. Since the output of the interpolation divider is high in harmonic content, it must be filtered before it is fed into the second mixer.

The output of the second mixer is at 800 kc for zero error, and the bandwidth of the second i-f ampli-

fier is sufficient to include only the variation in frequency due to error in the system. The output of the second i-f amplifier is divided by eight in a regenerative divider and fed into diode mixers where it is compared with a 100-kc signal derived from the crystal standard. One of the fixed-frequency input signals is shifted 90 degrees before it is fed into the diode mixer so that audio voltages are in quadrature.

Further amplification following the diode mixers provides two-phase

power to an afc motor connected to a trimmer capacitor across the master oscillator tank circuit. When the frequency of the master oscillator is the desired value as indicated by its dial plus the frequency indicated on the interpolation oscillator dial, a zero-beat condition exists between the divided output of the second i-f amplifier and the 100-kc standard. If an error is present in the setting of the master oscillator, or if it has drifted due to a change in ambient tempera-

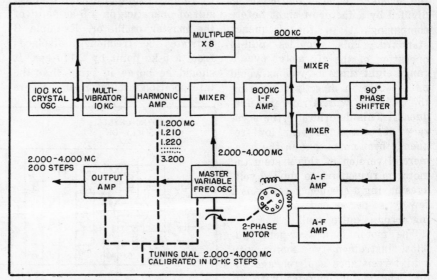

FIG. 4—Superheterodyne system variation using servo-motor afc, with output frequency furnished directly by master variable-frequency oscillator

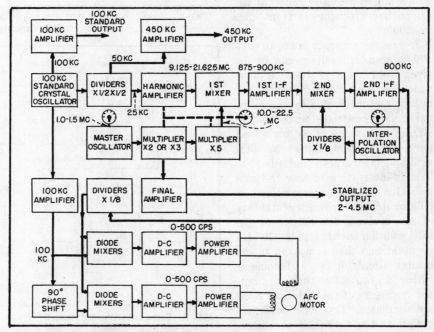

FIG. 5—Commercial version of stabilized master oscillator system of Fig. 4

ture or other service conditions, a two-phase audio beat note is applied to the afc motor, bringing about rotation in such a direction as to reduce this beat note to zero and thus correct the master oscillator frequency to the exact desired value plus or minus the servo, 100-kc standard and interpolation oscillator errors.

Since it is difficult to secure a tuning motor which will follow a wide range of audio beat frequencies, the error-voltage frequency of the master oscillator harmonic is divided by a factor of eight before comparing it to the frequency standard. This provides pull-in operation of the afc motor over a range eight times as wide as would be the case in directly comparing the oscillator with a reference frequency. This deteriorates the accuracy of control at very low-frequency beat notes, but in the commercial version of this system the motor is responsive to applied voltages having a frequency as low as a few cycles per second so the resulting error is quite small.

The motor is a four-pole two-phase instrument-type motor with a high-resistance squirrel-cage rotor. The motor operates with an applied voltage up to 400 to 500 cps, which allows a pull-in range at the comparison frequency of from 3,200 to 4,000 cps.

If greater accuracy is required, a 100-kc standard voltage can be derived from an external source to reduce the error from ±2 parts per million as contributed by the internal crystal-controlled oscillator at 100 kc to a value of as low as 0.1 part per million using the best available laboratory standards.

It is interesting to note the contribution of the interpolation oscillator to the frequency stability of the system. The output of the interpolation oscillator is divided by eight and then compared to the master oscillator at a frequency which is always five times the output frequency of the stabilized master oscillator. Thus the error, in cycles, at the output of the interpolation oscillator is divided by a

factor of 40 as referred to the output frequency of the instrument. Since the tuning ratio of the interpolation oscillator is small, its stability is such that it does not contribute more than one to two parts per million to the output inaccuracy.

Perhaps the best method of indicating the operation of the stabilized master oscillator equipment is to give examples of the frequencies present at the different circuits for several values of output frequency. In Table I, example A shows the result of operation on a 5-kc point of the master oscillator. Example B indicates a frequency displaced from a 5-kc point by 2,170 cps. It should be borne in mind that the interpolation oscillator dial covers

the range 0 to 5 kc. Because of this the base frequency, to which the interpolation dial reading must be added, changes every 5 kc on the main dial. Therefore, to tune to 3.517170 mc. the master oscillator would be set above the 3.515 point and the interpolation dial again would read 2,170 kc.

Example C corresponds to Example B except that here an error of 300 cycles is assumed at the output frequency of the equipment. This example indicates the error voltages present in the various parts of the equipment and shows the beat frequency applied to the tuning motor.

Circuit Details

The 100-kc crystal-controlled os-

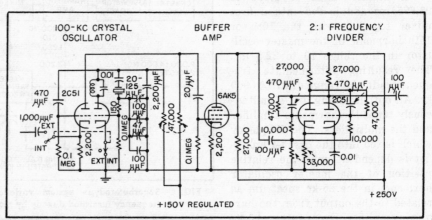

FIG. 6—Crystal oscillator that determines accuracy of output frequency generated by afc-stabilized variable-frequency oscillator

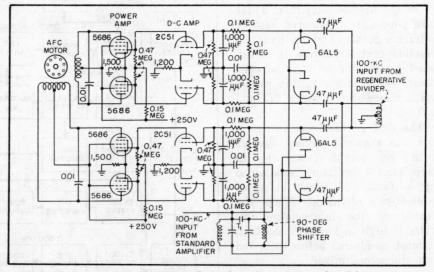

FIG. 7—Servo-motor control circuit. Audio beat frequency produced by error in master variable-frequency oscillator is amplified to drive motor that retunes vfo until beat frequency disappears

cillator used as a frequency standard is shown in Fig. 6. A switch allows the substitution of an external 100-kc source, in which case the left-hand section of the dual triode functions as an r-f amplifier feeding succeeding stages of the equipment. The parallel-tuned *L-C* circuit serves to trap out a spurious mode present in some 100-kc crystals. A 6AK5 triode-connected amplifier serves as an isolating stage between the 100-kc oscillator and the 50-kc divider. The divider has the advantage of fail-safe operation, wherein there is no spurious output if the 100-kc source fails.

The heart of the entire stabilized master oscillator is the hermetically sealed variable-frequency oscillator using a powdered iron core traveling within a solenoid coil, with variable space between turns to secure a linear relationship between frequency and dial rotation. By hermetically sealing the oscillator and rotating the shaft through a pressure-tight seal, it is possible to secure calibration and temperature stability of ± 800 cycles at the fundamental frequency of the oscillator. Temperature compensation is accomplished by using ceramic capacitors with the desired temperature coefficient and by appropriate design of the tank coil. Final production linearity adjustment is realized with an adjustable cam that compensates for manufacturing variations in the coil and core. The interpolation oscillator has the same physical characteristics and differs only in the resonant circuit components.

AFC Motor Control

The motor control circuits are quite interesting. The output of the 800-kc second i-f strip is subdivided in a regenerative divider and then fed into 6AL5 diodes along with the output from the 100-kc amplifier, as shown in Fig. 7. Loosely coupled resonant circuits in T_1 provide a 90-degree phase shift in the 100-kc reference voltage so that push-pull two-phase a-f voltage is fed into the 2C51 d-c amplifiers. These in turn drive 5686 beam tetrode tubes that

serve as power amplifiers feeding the two windings of the afc motor in push-pull. The push-pull arrangement is used to eliminate d-c flux in the motor windings. Only the flux due to the beat-frequency voltage drives the armature. Relay contacts, not shown, connect the motor windings to 60-cycle power for initial tuning of the equipment.

In tuning, a SETUP-OPERATE switch is thrown to the SETUP position, which drives the afc motor and capacitor to a centered position and disables the motor control circuits. The master oscillator dial is then set to frequency as closely as possible. The interpolation oscillator dial is adjusted to indicate the frequency increment to be added to the 5-kc point next below the desired frequency and an output tun-

ing dial is set to the correct position as indicated on a direct-reading dial. A headphone jack across the motor control circuits provides aural indication of the accuracy with which the master oscillator is adjusted. If a fairly low beat note is heard (0 to 400 cps), the adjustment of the master oscillator is sufficiently accurate for afc operation. If not, further adjustment of the master oscillator dial will yield a low beat note suitable for afc control. The switch is then thrown to OPERATE, which restores the motor control circuits. The motor then operates under control of the beat-frequency signal and rapid correction of the master oscillator frequency occurs. Thereafter the frequency of the master oscillator is under continuous surveillance so

Table I—Three Examples of Frequencies Present in Stabilized Master Oscillator System

	100 kc standard	Divider output	Harmonic amp mc	1st mixer kc	1st I-F amp kc	2nd mixer kc	2nd I-F amp kc	Regen dividers kc	Motor frequency cps
A	100 kc	25 kc	16.600 16.625 16.650 etc	900 875 850 etc	875 900	800 825	800	100	0
B	100	25	16.650 16.675 16.700	910.85 885.85 860.85	885.55	800	800	100	0
C	100	25	16.650 16.675 16.700	862.35 887.35 912.35	887.35 $\triangle f = +1,500$ cps	801.5 $\triangle f = +1,500$ cps	801.5	100.1875 $\triangle f = +187.5$ cps	187.5

	Output freq mc	MO dial freq mc	MO freq mc	Multiplier $\times 10$ $\times 15$ mc		Interpol divider kc	Interpol osc freq kc	Interpol dial kc
A	3.500000	3.500	1.166666	17.500000	A	75.00	600	0.000
B	3.512170	3.512	1.170723	17.560850	B	85.85	686.8	2170
C	3.512470 $\triangle f = 300$ cps	3.512	1.170823 $\triangle f = +100$ cps	17.562350 $\triangle f = +1,500$ cps	C	85.85	686.8	2170

that it is constantly corrected for thermal, humidity or voltage effects.

The 31 tubes used in this circuit might appear excessive until it is realized that the accuracy of adjustment and the stability after adjustment of this frequency generator are far in excess of that obtained previously in variable-frequency oscillators. A decided advantage of this method is that failure of the afc circuits does not necessarily destroy the usefulness of the system. Only three tubes are essential for operation as a normal master oscillator-power amplifier with moderate stability.

The writer wishes to express his appreciation to R. T. Cox for suggesting the basic system used in the stabilized master oscillator.

Constant-Amplitude Oscillator

By NORRIS C. HEKIMIAN

FOR many applications it is desirable to have a source of r-f voltage which remains reasonably constant in spite of changes in tube parameters, supply voltage, heater voltage and load impedances. Adjustable-frequency oscillators should be stabilized against changes arising from variations in component parts and circuit reactances.

In the past, several systems have been devised to stabilize oscillators, including a modified avc system and fixed-level clipper circuits. The avc system is ineffective in stabilizing class-C oscillators because of the self-biasing feature of such oscillators.

The fixed-level clipper has a strong harmonic content in the output waveform. This effect can be reduced by adding a second resonant circuit after the clipper, resulting in increased output impedance and attendant circuit-tracking difficulties.

The oscillator to be described does not suffer from the foregoing difficulties to any appreciable extent. It offers the advantage, in application to oscillators which are adjustable over a wide frequency range, of tending to maintain Miller effect capacitance constant by keeping the apparent grid-plate gain of the oscillator reasonably constant. Oscillator frequency calibration drift is minimized by maintaining the tube input and output capacitances practically constant. Clipping of the output waveform is reduced to very low levels. The only clipping that occurs is due to the diode across the output.

The circuit arrangement as shown in Fig. 1, is essentially that of a conventional oscillator followed by

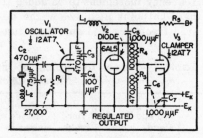

FIG. 1—Clamped oscillator circuit

a diode across the output terminals. The diode-rectified output is applied to a biased control or clamper tube sharing the same plate-dropping resistor with the oscillator.

With the clamper initially biased in the region of plate cut-off, the rectified oscillator output is applied as a positive voltage to the control tube grid. When the oscillator output voltage reaches a sufficiently high level, the clamper draws plate current and reduces the oscillator plate voltage, thus dropping the voltage to a relatively fixed level.

Normally, the bias voltage E_k is adjusted so that the control tube is always slightly conductive at the minimum level of oscillator voltage anticipated so that positive control action is had at all times. Under these conditions, Fig. 2, the best regulating characteristics are obtained with as large a value of R_5 as is practical to obtain the desired output voltages.

Figure 3 shows the controlling effect of E_k upon the output voltage. The bias voltage supply for E_k should be of low impedance to maintain E_k constant. In the test model of the constant-amplitude oscillator, E_k was obtained from batteries with internal resistances of about 5 ohms.

In Fig. 1, C_1 is a frequency-shifting trimmer and L_2 is a crystal-peaking coil employed when using a fifth overtone crystal (30 mc), the particular application for which the constant-amplitude oscillator was developed. Coil L_1 resonates at the crystal frequency with the circuit capacities shown.

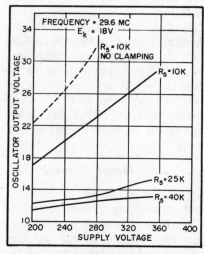

FIG. 2—Oscillator characteristic curves for different values of voltage-dropping resistance

Figures 2 and 3 illustrate the output amplitude stability obtained when the supply voltage, the bias voltage on V_3 and plate-resistor R_5

are varied. Constancy of amplitude versus supply voltage is easily measured and reflects to some extent the increased stabilization against tube parameter changes.

While it is possible to analyze graphically the constant-amplitude oscillator circuit, it is necessary to obtain at least one oscillator characteristic to do so. In most cases it may be advisable to determine circuit values roughly and then adjust the actual oscillator for optimum operation. In practice the output voltage is determined largely by the bias voltage E_k, as shown in Fig. 3, with R_5 adjusted for satisfactory regulation. Care should be taken to allow for sufficient dissipation in R_5. A power-type resistor is generally necessary.

Improved clamping may be ob-

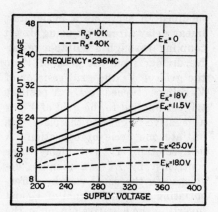

FIG. 3—Oscillator characteristic curves

tained by certain circuit modifications. By employing a voltage-multiplier type of rectifier to drive the clamper tube, a greater ratio of d-c control bias to r-f output voltage is obtained with resulting improved regulation. By using a power amplifier as a clamper instead of a type similar to the oscillator, the greater plate-current capabilities result in more positive control action.

If the clipper diode is fed from the final output of oscillator-buffer circuits with more gain included between the oscillator and the rectifier-control circuit, the sensitivity to small changes in output is increased and increased stability results.

Although the circuit described was designed for use as a fixed-frequency local oscillator in a gain-stable receiver, it is of value in other applications. Some suggested uses are in exciters, signal generators and high-quality communications receivers.

Voltage-Controlled Multivibrator

By JULIAN M. STURTEVANT

REGENERATIVE FEEDBACK, which has been employed previously in improving the linearity of sawtooth generators, may be applied to multivibrators and blocking oscillators to give frequency characteristics showing linear dependence of frequency on the first or second power of an input direct voltage.

The frequency of a free-running multivibrator is determined by the time constants in the grid circuits and the voltages to which the grid resistors are returned. If we represent by E_{1min} the minimum voltage reached by the grid of V_1 (Fig. 1A), by E_{co} the cutoff voltage of V_1, and by E_1 the voltage to which R_1 is returned, then the recovery of the grid of V_1 follows the exponetial curve given by

$$e_1 = E_1 - (E_1 - E_{1min}) e^{-\frac{t}{R_1 C_1}} \quad (1)$$

provided $R_1 >> R_{L1}$, and the off time of this tube is

$$t_1 = R_1 C_1 \ln \frac{E_1 - E_{1min}}{E_1 - E_{1\infty}} \quad (2)$$

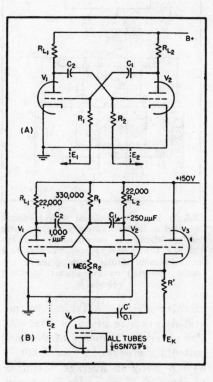

FIG. 1—Schematic diagrams of ordinary (A) multivibrator, and one having a frequency which varies with a direct voltage E_2

Similar expressions hold for V_2. It is evident that the frequency of the multivibrator, given by

$$f = \frac{1}{t_1 + t_2}, \quad (3)$$

can be varied by varying E_1 and E_2.

The logarithmic dependence of f on E_1 and E_2 can be changed to a linear variation by employing regenerative feedback to convert the grid recovery curves to straight lines. This type of feedback has been very successfully employed in the design of accurately linear sawtooth generators.

In the circuit of Fig. 1B, the current which charges C_2 during the recovery of the grid of V_2 is held nearly constant by employing feedback from the cathode follower V_3 to maintain a constant voltage drop across R_2. The analysis of this circuit is very simple if the impedances of the source of E_2, the diode V_4 and the cathode follower are small enough so that the coupling capacitor C' can be charged to the required voltage in a time short compared to the off time of V_2. If this condition is fulfilled, the initial voltage across R_2 will be $E_2 - E_{2min}$. This voltage will be maintained if

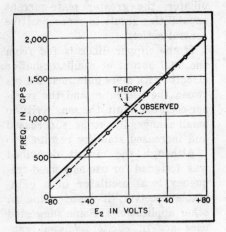

FIG. 2—Curve showing frequency variation of multivibrator of Fig. 1B as a function of voltage E_2

$C' >> C_2$, and the slope of the grid recovery line will then be $(E_2 - E_{2min})/R_2C_2$. Thus the off time of V_2 is given by

$$t_2 = R_2C_2 \frac{E_{2co} - E_{2min}}{E_2 - E_{2min}} \qquad (4)$$

If $R_1C_1 << R_2C_2$, so that the off time of V_1 is negligible compared to that of V_2, the frequency is very nearly

$$f = \frac{1}{R_2C_2} \frac{E_2 - E_{2min}}{E_{2co} - E_{2min}} \qquad (5)$$

Obviously E_K must be less than E_{2min} to have the cathode follower function properly.

The data plotted in Fig. 2 were obtained using the circuit parameters indicated. The off time of V_1 was about 40 microseconds. The solid line is calculated using the characteristics of 6SN7 tubes given in the tube manual; the circles are frequencies measured by using the sawtooth waveform at the cathode of V_3 as sweep voltage for an oscilloscope on the vertical plates of which the output of a Hewlett-Packard audio oscillator was impressed. The frequency-voltage relation is linear within an average deviation of $\pm$ 4 cycles over a 20-fold range of frequency, and agrees well with that predicted by Eq. 5.

The circuit of Fig. 1B can be

modified to serve as a moderately linear delay circuit by using direct coupling through a suitable resistive divider from the plate of V_2 to the grid of V_1, the grid resistor of V_1 being returned to E_K. A positive trigger applied to the grid of V_1, or a negative trigger to the plate, will initiate one cycle of operation. A delayed trigger, with delay time controlled by E_2, can then be developed in the usual way by differentiating the plate signal of V_2 and inverting the negative pip, or by the use of a blocking oscillator.

Regenerative feedback may be applied in a similar manner to a blocking oscillator, although, as might be expected, there is considerably more short time fluctuation, or jitter, than found with the multi-

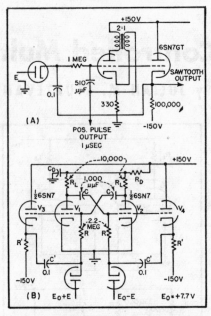

FIG. 3—Blocking oscillator with feedback to provide linear frequency change with voltage change is shown in B. The circuit in A shows how regenerative feedback on both multivibrator grids gives a frequency varying as the square of direct voltage E

vibrator circuit. A typical schematic diagram is given in Fig. 3A. The observed frequency of this circuit fits the equation $f = 2,030 + 34.4 E$ with an average deviation of about $\pm$ 16 cycles for E between -60 and $+80$ volts (frequency between 2 and 4,800 cycles).

A multivibrator whose frequency

is linearly dependent on the square of a direct voltage is obtained by applying regenerative feedback to both grids. If the circuit is completely symmetrical as shown in Fig. 3B, and $E_1 = E_0 + E$, $E_2 = E_0 - E$, the frequency is given by

$$f = \frac{1}{t_1 + t_2} = \frac{(E_0 - E_{min})^2 - E^2}{2RC(E_{co} - E_{min})(E_0 - E_{min})} \qquad (6)$$

The control voltages can be supplied by a differential direct-coupled

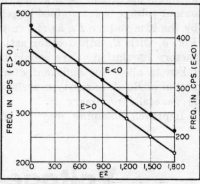

FIG. 4—Frequency of multivibrator shown in Fig. 3B as a function of the square of the voltage E

amplifier having cathode-follower outputs.

The behavior of this circuit is illustrated by the data plotted in Fig. 4. For both $E > 0$ and $E < 0$, the square law relation

$$f = 424 - 0.1153\ E^2 \qquad (7)$$

holds with an average deviation of ± 3 cycles.

Stability of Circuits

The short time stability of the multivibrator circuits is quite good, there being very little observable jitter. However the stability with respect to supply voltages is such as to indicate that well-regulated power supplies should be used. Over the larger part of the frequency ranges in the data reported above, the frequency of either multivibrator circuit changes by less than 3 percent for a 10-percent change in tube heater voltage; however, at the lower frequencies, where the grid voltages pass cutoff with relatively small slope, a frequency change of as much as 10 percent may result from a 10-percent change in heater voltage.

Series Sawtooth Oscillator

By MAJOR CHANG SING

MOST SAWTOOTH oscillators and multivibrators employ tubes connected in cascade. There has been no circuit of relaxation oscillators employing tubes connected in series. This is mainly due to the difficulty that the plate of one tube is not connected to B+ directly.

Figure 1A shows the schematic circuit of a new series sawtooth oscillator and Fig. 1B the different waveforms obtained. When the switch is on, C_1 is charged through V_1. The cathode potential of V_1, which is connected to the plate of V_2 via the resistor R_2, increases exponentially and the plate of V_1 follows with it. As the charge on the capacitor becomes large enough, the discharging tube V_2 starts to conduct and R_2 carries the plate current of V_2 to bias V_1 off. The plate of V_1 rises to B+ and makes V_2 conduct more. In this state (V_1 cut off and V_2 conducting) C_1 discharges through V_2. The waveform on the plate of V_2 is similar to that on the cathode of V_1 except a fall at the beginning of the discharge due to the drop across R_2. When the drop across R_2 is not sufficient to cut off the plate current of V_1, the plate potential of V_1 falls and drives the grid of V_2 to follow it. This decreases the drop of R_2 and V_1 con-

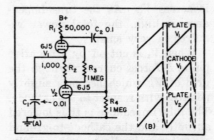

FIG. 1—Basic diagram and voltage waveforms for series sawtooth oscillator

ducts progressively. By the cumulative action V_1 conducts and V_2 is cut off. Then C_1 will charge again and the operation is repeated in the similar manner.

The waveforms produced at the cathode of V_1 and the plate of V_2 the sawtooth-shaped and that on the plate of V_1 is trapezoidal. To improve the linearity of the charging curve a pentode could be used instead of a triode for the charging tube V_1 and a positive grid return for V_2. When the cathode of V_1 rises, its plate (or screen grid) follows it, the voltage working on the constant-current portion of its characteristic curve. The use of the positive grid of V_2 causes the tube conducting at the lower potential so that only the linear portion of the charging curve is utilized. The improved circuit is shown in Fig. 2.

In this circuit C_1 and R_1 are coarse and fine controls of frequency respectively. To improve the linearity R_2 should be small but its minimum value is limited by the plate current of V_2 so that R_2 is

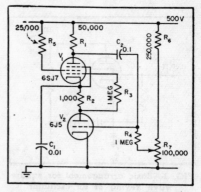

FIG. 2—Improved circuit of series sawtooth oscillator

about 1,000 ohms preferably. Variable R_7 serves as a velocity control. The time constant of C_2 and R_4 should be long enough to avoid the blocking action.

Raising the high voltage is also a method of improving the linearity of the charging curve. In this case the high voltage used is from 280 v to about 500 v. The range of operating frequencies can be varied anywhere from a few cycles per second to 0.5 mc.

Square-Wave Keying of Oscillators

By J. CARL SEDDON

HIGH peak power oscillators of low duty cycle present a difficult modulating problem if the pulse width is wide or extremely variable. A low-power circuit is illustrated which makes possible square-wave grid modulation of oscillators over a wide range of pulse widths and

duty cycle. Only 15 watts average power will control an oscillator capable of giving 7.5 kilowatts peak power output. Pulse widths from 2 to 140,000 microseconds have been used, and this range can easily be extended. The circuit is also useful for obtaining high-voltage video

pulses, either negative or positive.

The pulse transformer is useful in applications where pulse widths are not too great. However, if pulse widths are more than about 100 microseconds, the pulse transformer becomes bulky and pulse shape suffers. This is particularly serious when pulse widths are to be variable and coded in some way, such as two or three closely-spaced pulses of variable widths and spacing. The circuit described in this paper is practically independent of pulse widths and operates with a minimum of power required.

Basic Keyer Circuit

The circuit in Fig. 1 will square-wave key a grid-controlled oscillator, but requires considerable power

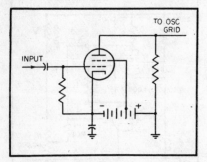

FIG. 1—Basic arrangement for square-wave keying of an oscillator

if the duty cycle is low. If there is no pulse at the grid of this tube, the plate potential will be considerably negative with respect to ground potential, and the oscillator will be kept cut off. When a negative pulse is applied to the tube, the plate will rise rapidly to ground potential. The oscillator will then oscillate. At the end of the pulse, the tube becomes conducting and the plate goes more negative, thus shutting off the oscillator.

Plate potential must be considerably more negative than that required to merely keep the oscillator cut off. As the plate resistor cannot be increased, because of the fact that it acts as the grid resistor for the oscillator, there is considerable power dissipation in the tube and resistor.

Use of Resistance Tube

If the plate resistor is replaced by a vacuum tube, the impedance of the tube can be kept high during nonoperating time and low during operating time. In this way, the bias power required can be reduced by a factor of ten or more. Such a

circuit is shown in Fig. 2.

The current flowing through the two tubes in series causes a voltage drop across R which nearly cuts off V_2. As V_1 is freely conducting, nearly all of the bias supply voltage is across V_2. As the tube impedance is high, the total power required is very small.

When V_1 is cut off by a negative pulse, L forces current through the grid of V_2, which becomes slightly positive with respect to the cathode. The tube impedance is thus lowered abruptly and the cathode-to-ground capacitance is discharged rapidly, bringing the oscillator grid to ground potential. The oscillator starts oscillating, with its grid current flowing through V_2. On completion of the negative pulse, V_1 again becomes conducting. This causes the grid of V_2 to drop to nearly the value of the bias supply voltage, thus cutting off V_2. The cathode of V_2 rapidly goes more negative due to the electron currents flowing in from V_1 and from the oscillator. The oscillator is thus abruptly forced to stop oscillating.

Performance

This circuit has produced 750-volt positive pulses from 15-volt negative pulses, and has required a maximum of only 15 ma. The rise and decay times were less than one microsecond. Using an 807

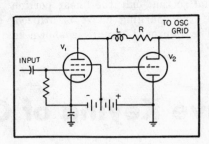

FIG. 2—Economical square-wave keyer circuit using triode as plate resistance

tube in triode connection for V_2, a one-kilowatt average power output transmitter was square-wave keyed with pulse widths varying from 140,000 to 2 microseconds. The repetition frequency of the 2-microsecond pulses was 200 kc.

A tube having the proper d-c resistance at the operating current must be selected for V_2. If the tube resistance is somewhat less than that required for the grid resistor of the oscillator, a resistor may be added between the cathode of V_2 and the oscillator grid to make up the difference. This resistor, however, reduces the ability of the circuit to stop the oscillator promptly. This disadvantage can more than be overcome by placing a capacitor across it. The leading edge of the r-f pulse will, however, be considerably greater in magnitude than the trailing edge.

Improved Control Circuit

An additional refinement, shown at the right in Fig. 3, will give a nearly flat-topped r-f pulse and con-

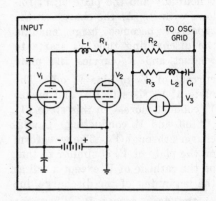

FIG. 3—Square-wave keyer using diode to get improved control

siderable improvement in control of the oscillator. Here V_2 must have a low d-c resistance; R_2 is the amount required to obtain the proper total resistance for the grid of the oscillator, C_1 is a capacitor of at least 10 times the oscillator grid circuit to ground capacitance, L_2 is an inductance whose value depends on the degree of flatness required of the r-f pulse, and R_3 is a resistance of sufficient magnitude to provide more than critical damping for the L_2C_1 circuit.

When the oscillator starts oscillating, the grid current will flow mainly through R_2, but some will flow into C_1 which gradually charges up until it has the same potential across it as R_2. At the end of the pulse, the cathode of V_2 will go more negative. Due to the diode,

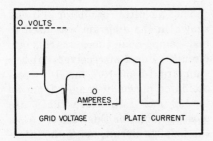

FIG. 4—Typical oscillator oscillograms obtained when circuit of Fig. 3 is used for keying

C_1 will likewise go more negative, as will the oscillator grid. The oscillator can thus be shut off even though the maximum potential across V_2 may be less than the d-c potential on the oscillator grid while oscillating.

Waveforms

With 807 tubes for V_1 and V_2, using pentode and triode connections respectively, about 750 volts can be developed across V_2 with an 850-volt power supply. This 750 volts will easily keep two 15E transmitting triodes cut off with more than 10,000 volts on their plates. Figure 4 shows the variation in voltage of the 15E grids during the pulse. The tubes started oscillating before the grid voltage could rise to ground potential. On oscillating, the operating potential was minus 1,100 volts. At the end of the pulse, V_2 drove C_1 sufficiently

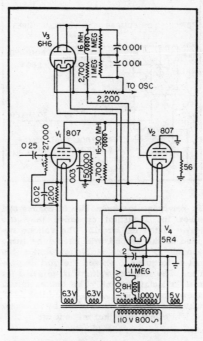

FIG. 5—Complete circuit for keying an oscillator using two 15E triodes

negative that it was able to drive the oscillator grids negative enough to stop oscillation. The grid potential quickly returned to minus 750 volts.

The right-hand side of Fig. 4 shows the oscillator plate current when two 10-microsecond pulses spaced by 10 microseconds were used. Decreasing the inductance of L_2 will shorten the duration of the hump on the top of the pulse, but will increase its amplitude. The peak output power of the transmitter exceeded 7.5 kw at 750 mc.

Complete Practical Circuit

Figure 5 shows the complete circuit diagram as used on the transmitter just described. One slight change from Fig. 3 that should be mentioned is the addition of the 56-ohm resistor between the screen grid of V_2 and ground. This was done to prevent arcs at the tube seal, where the control grid to screen grid spacing is small on an 807. These arcs were due to the superposition of r-f voltage on the large video pulses, probably due to the too-long lead lengths.

Transitron Oscillator

A SPECIALLY-DESIGNED TETRODE or a standard pentode can be operated with the second grid acting as the anode of an oscillator and the plate acting as an electron reflector; the potential of the reflector controls the transit time and hence the frequency of oscillation, as described by Jerome Kurshan in a paper entitled The Transitron, An Experimental A.F.C. Tube, presented before the National Electronics Conference in November and published in the *RCA Review* for December.

Used as the local oscillator in an f-m receiver (88–108 mc) with automatic-frequency control, an experimental tube showed a sensitivity of 100 kc per volt, thus counteracting warmup drift at the high-frequency end of the band by a factor of 4.5. Tests of commercial miniature tubes in the accompanying circuit showed that the 6BE6 with its third (r-f signal) grid as reflector and biased to at least 20 volts negative was one of the strongest oscillators. The 9001 gave the greatest control sensitivity, but oscillated very weakly; the 6AK5 performed most reliably but had low control sensitivity. A special Transitrol tube was built and tested in the circuit shown in the diagram; its performance correlated well with theoretical expectations.

Transit-Time Frequency Control

Because of the greater need for afc in the vhf region (30–300 mc) than in the lower-frequency bands, a simple means of controlling the frequency of a local oscillator is needed. Although a reactance modulator can be used, it entails an additional tube in the receiver.

The pulling of the local oscillator frequency by changes in the bias on the r-f signal grid, an effect sometimes observed in converters, can be used as the basis for afc. The frequency pulling arises because, as the bias changes, electrons are variously reflected back to the oscillator section where they interact with the electrodes and space charge to produce a changing susceptance across the oscillator circuit. To make use of the effect, the tube is so operated that electrons leave the cathode, pass through the control grid, are accelerated by the screen, are possibly reflected by the reflector, and finally reach the anode. By changing the potential on the reflector, the transit time of the electrons between grid and anode can be altered. By deriving a direct voltage from the discriminator of an f-m receiver and using it to control the reflector, afc is obtained without an additional tube.

Operation

An analysis of the oscillator shows that a small capacitance in its resonant circuit is desirable for control sensitivity, although then there will be considerable warmup drift because interelectrode capacitance is a large fraction of the resonant-circuit capacitance.

In practice, it is desirable to keep the voltages on the anode and the control potentials small for large control sensitivity. The reflector spacing in the experimental tube was adjusted to obtain the optimum response with these conditions, but

CIRCUIT FOR COMPARING COMMERCIAL TUBES

TRANSITROL TUBE USED IN EXPERIMENTAL AFC OSCILLATOR FOR F-M RECEIVER

To determine the suitability of commercial tubes for Transitrol operation they are tested in the top circuit. The voltage applied to the second grid should be large enough to produce stable oscillation but not so large as to exceed the grid dissipation. The reflector voltage is adjusted for zero reflector current. The bottom circuit shows the oscillator using a modified 6BE6 which reduced warmup drift by a factor of 4.5 from that without afc

some commercial tubes have such spacings that, by suitable choice of their electrodes and potentials, they can be used with reasonable sensi-

tivities, such as the 6BE6 previously mentioned.

Circuit for Testing Tubes

The Colpitts oscillator circuit shown in the diagram was used to test commercial tubes in this afc circuit. For f-m receivers with a standard i-f of 10.7 mc, the local oscillator normally ranges from 99 to 119 mc. Miniature tubes are most suitable for this range. Also, the Colpitts circuit, using the interelectrode capacitances for feedback and with the cathode grounded, is the simplest to use at these frequencies. For transit-time control, it is important that the cathode be at ground potential.

Unfortunately, neither end of the tuned circuit is at ground. It is necessary for this application that there be an r-f field between the second grid and the reflector, otherwise the transit of the electrons would effectively terminate when they passed the second grid (anode), because thenceforth they could not induce voltage in the resonant circuit. Practically, it is simplest to have the reflector at r-f ground, which requires that the cathode also be at r-f ground to avoid reflector current due to electrons that would be emitted at the negative peaks of cathode voltage.

Twin Oscillator

By TY KIRBY

THE TWIN OSCILLATOR described here was designed primarily as a stable oscillator which would be variable over a narrow band of frequencies. The theory of the twin is simple. Two oscillators are built on the same chassis using identical parts. The physical arrangement is made such that both oscillators are subjected to identical variations in voltage, temperature, humidity and other conditions. Then if there is any drift both oscillators should

drift the same amount in the same direction.

One of these oscillators is padded with zero temperature coefficient capacitors to operate on a frequency slightly lower than the other. The feedback is then adjusted so both tubes operate on the same part of their curves and drift the same amount under varying conditions. The outputs of the two oscillators are combined and the difference between them used as our output

frequency. Thus although any oscillator will drift slightly, as long as its twin drifts the same amount in the same direction at the same time, the output frequency is constant.

It was decided to build a twin whose harmonics would cover the amateur bands. The two halves of a 6SN7 were used in Clapp circuits for the twin oscillators, followed by a 6SN7 mixer and a 6SJ7 doubler. The unit was adjusted for balance in the center of its range and a series of one hour runs made to determine the amount of drift. The resulting drifts after one hour:

Low end of band, 16 cps per mc (negative); center of band, 0 cps per mc; and at the high end of band, 15 cps per mc (positive). The band in this case was 2 mc to 1.75 mc. Tests were run over a period of several weeks to determine at which frequency the drift would be the least. This was found to be 1.850 mc. The oscillator was set at this frequency on Friday at 10 p.m. and left running until the following Monday at 8 p.m. at which time the frequency was measured and the drift found to be 12 cycles (6 cps per mc approximate).

The unit was built on a 10 × 14 × 3 chassis with the power supply on a separate chassis to keep away unnecessary heat. The coils and variable capacitors were taken from surplus TU-10-B tuning units and used without alterations. All fixed capacitors used were zero temperature coefficient or silver mica types.

The coils are mounted on feed-through insulators above the chassis and a shield measuring 10 × 8 × 6 inches covers both coils. The outside of this shield is covered with asbestos to keep external heat away from the coils and the inside cover of the shield is covered with

asbestos to aid in keeping the temperature on both coils the same.

The variable oscillator was padded to operate from 6.375 to 6.5 mc. The fixed oscillator is padded to operate at 5.5 mc. Since padding the variable capacitor changes the feedback in this Clapp circuit, part of the padding was done from the grid end of the coil

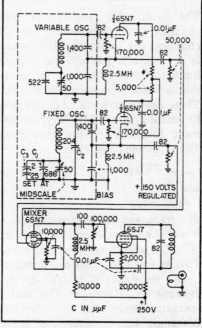

Schematic diagram of highly stable twin oscillator with output from 1.75 to 2 mc

to ground (C_2 in diagram) and these padding capacitors (C_1 and C_2) so proportioned that the plate current of the two oscillators was the same.

Because one oscillator operates at a different frequency than the other and tends to drift the same percentage rather than the same amount (in cycles), a 25-$\mu\mu$f silver mica capacitor (0.002 positive drift) was connected in series with a 2-$\mu\mu$f zero temperature coefficient capacitor and placed in the fixed oscillator circuit (C_3 in diagram). This brought the drift to zero in the center of the band chosen.

If the twin is to be used as a VFO in a CW transmitter the mixer circuit should be keyed. Since the oscillators are not on the output frequency and not keyed there is neither backwave nor chirp.

Although Clapp circuits were used for the twin oscillators any stable oscillator circuit would work. The less drift the individual oscillator circuits have the easier it is to compensate for the difference in drifts due to the difference in frequencies. Standard parts were used but parts which were used in both oscillators were individually matched since commercial tolerances are not close enough to serve the purpose.

Wide-Range Sweeping Oscillator

Wobbled audio output or variable single tone is obtained over a 20-to-1 frequency range by means of Thyrite or Varistor elements in a modified Wien-bridge circuit. A thermistor stabilizes bridge amplitude

By LOUIS A. ROSENTHAL

THE variable-frequency audio oscillator described uses a modified Wien network with silicon carbide nonohmic resistors as part of the frequency-determining element. By controlling direct current through the nonlinear resistors the frequency of oscillation can

be varied through a range of better than 20 to 1. A nonlinear thermistor element in the bridge stabilizes the amplitude of oscillation and insures good sinusoidal waveform. Although the equipment was designed for telemetering, it can be applied wherever large frequency

deviations are required.

A number of articles [1,2,3] have described various methods, most of which are incapable of large deviations or lack amplitude stabilization. Without amplitude control poor waveform may result, because distortion will adjust the loop gain to unity. Vacuum tubes have been used as variable-impedance elements but do not allow simple circuit configurations and are limited in the range of nonlinearity.

Basically all schemes consist of an amplifier, feeding back regeneratively through a variable phase-shift network. The circuit oscillates at a frequency at which the loop phase shift is zero and the loop amplification is unity. The phase shift network must be modulated so as to vary the phase shift and so the frequency. Since the phase-shift network may also change its attenuation with frequency, the loop gain will have to readjust itself automatically. The phase-shift network described is found to have

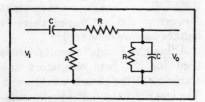

FIG. 1—Modified Wien phase-shift network used for frequency control

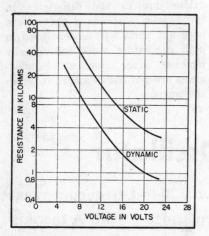

FIG. 2—Static and dynamic resistance as a function of voltage for GE 8399401G1 Thyrite

a constant attenuation and is readily phase modulated.

Phase-Shift Network

Figure 1 is the a-c equivalent of the phase-shift network used. Resistor A is necessary for modulation purposes and resistors R are actually silicon-carbide nonohmic

resistors called Thyrite by General Electric and Varistor by Western Electric[4]. The frequency at which the network produces zero phase shift is

$$\omega_0 = \frac{1}{RC}\left(1 + \frac{2R}{A}\right)^{\frac{1}{2}} \quad (1)$$

and the voltage attenuation at this point is

$$\frac{V_0}{V_1} = \frac{1}{3 + R/A} \quad (2)$$

The modulating resistor A will change the attenuation as R changes; the minimum attenuation is $\frac{1}{3}$. Since R has a usable upper limit the presence of A increases the lowest frequency obtainable. These limitations can be eliminated by making A another Thyrite element identical to the other two. The equations are then

$$\omega_0 = \sqrt{3}/RC \quad (3)$$

and

$$V_0/V_1 = 1/4 \quad (4)$$

The frequency varies inversely with R and the attenuation is a constant of 0.25 providing the individual Thyrite elements track one another.

The resistance R is actually the dynamic resistance at the static operating point for the Thyrite. Although the dynamic resistance changes with voltages, keeping the phase-shift network at a low voltage amplitude point in the feedback

loop minimizes the harmonic generation. Thyrite is a voltage sensitive nonlinear element. Its volt-ampere characteristic is very closely of the form

$$V = kI^n \quad (5)$$

where n is generally between 0.2 and 0.4. The static resistance is

$$R_s = V/I = kI^{n-1} \quad (6)$$

and the dynamic resistance or slope of the volt-ampere characteristic is

$$R_d = dV/dI = knI^{n-1} = nR_s \quad (7)$$

It can be seen that the dynamic resistance is n times the static resistance. The dynamic resistance is the resistance to be used in the frequency equations since it represents the a-c impedance at the operating point. Figure 2 is a plot of the experimentally-determined static and calculated dynamic resistance as a function of d-c voltage. For the Thyrite used (GE 8399401-G1) the static characteristic was very closely $V = 80\,I^{0.27}$. An applied voltage of 20 volts will dissipate the rated power of 0.1 watt and it would appear that the usable dynamic resistances can vary from 1,000 ohms up to infinity. Actually because of the modulation scheme the maximum voltage was about 16 volts and the minimum 2 volts. Two volts corresponds to a current of about 4 microamperes flowing through the Thyrite ($R_d = 130$,-

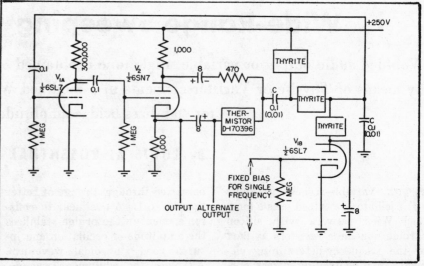

FIG. 3—Complete circuit diagram of the oscillator. Range is changed by choice of capacitors (C). See Fig. 5 for frequency characteristics

000) and is the best cutoff condition for the modulator tube (e_s = −10 volts). This very large variation of resistance will allow corresponding frequency changes.

The three Thyrite elements are connected in series with the supply voltage and a triode modulator tube as shown in Fig. 3. The same direct current passes through all three elements and it was observed that the d-c voltage drops followed one another within 5 percent. Negative voltages applied to the grid of the modulator will reduce the current flowing through the Thyrite, increase the dynamic resistance, and so decrease the frequency.

Amplitude Stabilization

Since the nonlinear elements do not track perfectly, the attenuation can change from the theoretical value of 0.25. Amplitude stabilization will keep the oscillation level constant and insure good waveform. For a simple approach, a nonlinear bridge is used. Referring to the circuit diagram, the bridge consists of two 1,000-ohm arms, a thermistor and a comparison resistor of 470 ohms. The bridge is fed through a phase inverter. Initially the cold thermistor resistance is high and the bridge is unbalanced, resulting in a high loop amplification: Oscillations build up, increasing the power dissipated in the thermistor, decreasing its resistance, and bringing the bridge closer to balance. At the stable operating point the loop amplification is unity. Any tendency for the amplitude to increase or decrease will be offset by the bridge output decreasing or increasing, respectively.

The mechanism can be further explained by referring to Fig. 4, which shows the bridge characteristic as experimentally determined. It is plotted in terms of output voltage as a function of applied voltage. It requires about 3.35 volts to balance this particular bridge. The thermistor operates in its negative-temperature-coefficient and negative-differential-resistance region

and reduces its resistance as the power dissipated in it increases. The remaining loop amplification, which is the product of the amplifier gain and loss in the phase-shift network, is superimposed as a straight line of slope equal to the reciprocal of loop amplification. The common intersection is the operating point resulting in the bridge being sufficiently unbalanced to produce an output of 0.22 volt. As the loop amplification varies, the bridge output, as well as operating amplitude, will change to a much lesser degree depending on the slope of the bridge characteristic at the operating point. A greater slope and higher loop amplification result in greater stability. The rapidity with which the amplitude stabilizes depends on the thermal time constant of the thermistor. Elements such as lamps with positive temperature coefficients can be used if the positions of the comparison resistor and nonlinear element are reversed.

However, elements with negative-differential-resistance regions result in bridges with better stabilization properties. If the loop gain were not to change with frequency there would be no readjustment in amplitude necessary and correspondingly no limit to the rate of frequency modulation. It should be noted that the bridge nonlinear element is really linear at the frequency of oscillation and is nonlinear only to average amplitude or

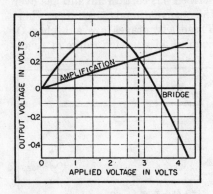

FIG. 4—Amplitude stabilizing bridge characteristic with superimposed loop amplification. The bridge operates at the common intersection with an output of 0.22 v and applied voltage of 2.8 v

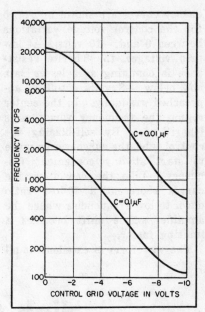

FIG. 5—Frequency versus control-grid potential for two different phase-shift network capacitances

power instead of instantaneous amplitude as in the case of Thyrite.

Practical Circuit

In the circuit of Fig. 3, a triode voltage amplifier with a gain of 52 drives the amplitude-stabilizing bridge through a phase inverter. The bridge contains two electrolytic capacitors in order to eliminate d-c and keep the bridge balanced. The bridge and phase inverter offer a low impedance to the phase-shift network whose impedance level can vary considerably. The modulator tube is bypassed so as to put the shunt Thyrite element at a-c ground potential. After the phase-shift network, the loop is closed. It is important that the amplifier proper have negligible phase shift for the variable frequency range so that all phase shift takes place in the frequency-determining network. Voltages measured at various points in the circuit for a frequency of 1 kc were as follows: input to V_1, 0.051 v; output V_1, 2.66 v; bridge output, 0.208 v; phase-inverter cathode, 1.48 v. The gain of the amplifier is therefore 52.2, the phase-shift network attenuation is 0.245 and the bridge is operating close to the point described in Fig. 4. Frequency curves are shown in Fig. 5 for the control voltage variations between 0 and −10 volts. At low grid voltages, the Thyrite resistance is changing at a lesser rate and below −8 volts cutoff is approached gradually. In the center region the frequency variation is logarithmic. By self-biasing the control tube, the curve can be made to start at any convenient frequency. Like the capacitors the curves represent a 10-to-1 ratio down to low frequencies where the amplifier phase shift becomes a limiting factor.

The waveform is excellent at all times and the amplitude never changes by more than 2 percent in these typical frequency ranges. Frequency stability depends on the power-supply regulation and the temperature coefficient of the Thyrite which is about −0.5 percent per degree centigrade[5]. The particular circuit described was used up to 100 kc and with better high-frequency amplifier characteristics the range can undoubtedly be extended. Other nonlinear elements can provide a variety of frequency characteristics.

Thanks are extended to the United States Air Force, Watson Laboratories, who sponsored this work under Contract No. AF28-(099)-33. The assistance of H. Zablocki, Research Assistant at Rutgers University, is appreciated.

REFERENCES

(1) M. Artz, Frequency Modulation of Resistance-Capacitance Oscillators, *Proc. IRE*, p 409 June 1943.
(2) H. S. McGaughan, and C. B. Leslie, A Resistance-Tuned Frequency Modulated Oscillator for Audio Frequency Applications, *Proc. IRE*, p 974, Sept. 1947.
(3) T. A. Peterson, Jr., A Method of Transmitting Voltage Information by Means of Frequency Modulation, unpublished Master's thesis, Rutgers University Library, 1949.
(4) F. Ashworth, W. Needham, and R. W. Sillars, Silicon Carbide Non-Ohmic Resistors, *IEE Journ.*, 93, p 385, 1946.
(5) Thyrite, a General Electric Resistance Material, Bulletin GEA 4138A.

High-Q Variable Reactance

A cathode-coupled dual triode provides wide reactance variation, wide frequency deviation and higher Q when combined with a tuned circuit than a conventional reactance tube. Circuits of a frequency-modulated oscillator operating at one megacycle and an f-m audio-frequency oscillator are given

By J. N. VAN SCOYOC AND J. L. MURPHY

REACTANCE-TUBE circuits have found an increasingly large field of use in recent years with the advent of frequency modulation and automatic frequency control, and with the expansion in use of industrial electronic equipment and instrumentation. Unfortunately these circuits do not have a very high Q and the range of linear variation of reactance is limited. The basic principle of the variable reactance to be discussed has been described in the literature previously[1,2]. However, the practical methods used to obtain improved results are believed to be new.

The electronic reactance to be described has certain advantages over the conventional reactance tube. These advantages are a higher Q, coupled with a wide range of reactance variation, and simplicity. The circuit has been found quite useful in frequency-modulated oscillators operating both at audio and radio frequencies and in variable-frequency RC type filters. In addition to the variable-reactance circuits, two frequency-modulated oscillators are described, one operating at radio-frequency using the basic circuit and one operating at audio fre-

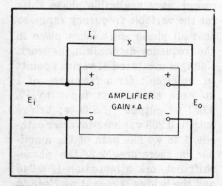

FIG. 1—Functional diagram of variable reactance

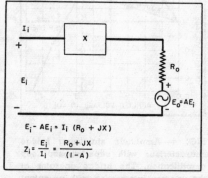

FIG. 2—Equivalent circuit of Fig. 1 for analysis

$$E_i - AE_i = I_i (R_0 + JX)$$

$$Z_i = \frac{E_i}{I_i} = \frac{R_0 + JX}{(1 - A)}$$

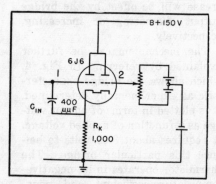

FIG. 3—Cathode-follower reactance-tube circuit

quencies using the new circuit.

Principle

The basic circuit [1,2] consists of a feedback amplifier with a reactance connected in the feedback loop from output terminals to input terminals as shown in Fig. 1. The input impedance is a function of the feedback reactance and the gain and output impedance of the amplifier.

In the equivalent circuit of Fig. 2, it is assumed that the input impedance of the amplifier is very high. The amplifier is replaced by an equivalent generator having an open-circuit voltage AE_i and an output resistance R_o equal to the output impedance of the amplifier.

The current flowing into the input terminal is:

$$I_i = \frac{E_i - AE_i}{R_o + jX} = \frac{E_i (1 - A)}{R_o + jX} \quad (1)$$

where A is the open-circuit gain (gain with X equal to infinity) of the amplifier. The impedance presented at the input terminals is therefore

$$Z_i = \frac{E_i}{I_i} = \frac{R_o + jX}{(1 - A)} \quad (2)$$

This equation shows that the input impedance is a function of the loop impedance including the output resistance, and the factor $(1 - A)$ where A represents the gain of the amplifier without feedback.

Examination of Eq. 2 shows that for positive values of A (even number of stages or a cathode follower) the impedance Z_i has the same sign as $R_o + jX$ if the gain is less than unity, and the opposite sign if the gain is greater than unity. For negative values of A (odd number of conventional amplifier stages) the sign of Z_i is the same as that of $R_o + jX$ for values of A either greater or less than unity. A negative resistance can, of course, produce oscillation and this circuit is used in RC-tuned oscillators.

The reversal of sign of the reactance results, in the case of an inductor, in a reactance that varies directly with frequency (as for a positive inductor) but one in which the current leads the voltage instead

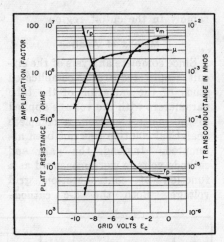

FIG. 4—Characteristics of a single section of a 6J6 tube vary considerably with change in grid voltage

of lagging it. Similarly, for a capacitor, a reactance which varies inversely with frequency, as in the case of the positive capacitor, is obtained but the current lags the voltage.

The effective Q of the circuit, X/R_o is independent of A as may be seen from Eq. 2. However, if R_o is a function of amplifier gain, as in the case of a variable load resistance amplifier, the Q will vary with the gain. A high Q may be obtained by making the amplifier output impedance small in compari-

son to the feedback reactance.

To obtain a variable reactance as a function of a control signal, this control signal may be used to change the gain of the amplifier in some way. For static use, a potentiometer gain control could be used, or some other means such as changing tube transconductance could be used to vary the gain of a stage or several stages of the amplifier.

The load resistance of one or more stages may be used to control the gain. The load-resistance and transconductance variation could be accomplished either statically or dynamically. A combination of load variation and amplifier-transconductance variation is used in the cathode-follower circuit described here.

Dual-Triode Cathode Follower

Figure 3 shows the schematic diagram of a dual-triode variable reactance circuit; one section of the tube functions as a cathode-follower amplifier, and the other as a cathode follower used as a variable load resistance for the first. The only circuit elements required in addition to the tube are a cathode resistor, a feedback reactor and the necessary grid returns.

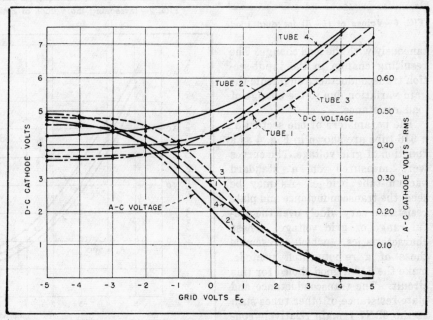

FIG. 5—Cathode voltages when a peak signal of one volt is applied to the grid of the input triode. The applied plate voltage is 150 volts and the cathode resistor is 1,000 ohms

Triode 1 with the feedback loop consisting of *C* is the cathode-follower amplifier which will be called the input section. Triode 2 is the variable or control tube used to vary the gain of triode 1. The cathode-to-ground impedance of triode 2 functions as a variable load resistance for triode 1, and this resistance is controllable by the voltage applied to the grid of triode 2. This variable load resistance appears in parallel with the common cathode resistor used to carry the plate current and provide bias for the two sections.

Due to the direct coupling between the two sections, an increase in the control-section grid voltage produces a decrease in the input-section bias, thus changing the transconductance of triode 1 simul-

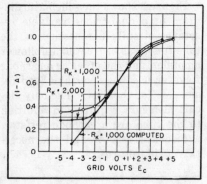

FIG. 6—Values of (1—A) for dual triode

taneously with the load change. The resulting change in the input-section transconductance augments the gain variation due to the change of load resistance.

The parameters of one section of a 6J6 tube are shown in Fig. 4 as a function of grid voltage. The curves were measured on a standard vacuum-tube bridge. As may be seen, the transconductance and plate resistance vary widely over the useful range of grid voltage. These characteristics, which resemble those of a remote-cutoff pentode, make the 6J6 a good choice for this circuit. The transconductance and plate resistance of other tubes such as the 6SN7 remain relatively constant over most of the useful range of grid voltage, and change more

rapidly in the cutoff region.

Method of Analysis

Since complete analysis of the circuit would require a complicated study of the variation of the tube parameters with the voltage applied to the control section, a complete analytical solution has not been attempted. Instead, the gain and cathode voltage were measured as a function of control-section grid voltage. Both the d-c cathode

voltage and the a-c cathode voltage due to a signal of 1.0 volt peak applied to the input section grid were measured on four sample tubes and the results are shown in Fig. 5.

As the control section grid becomes more positive relative to ground, the negative bias on that section is reduced. Simultaneously, the negative bias on the input section is increased. The control section output resistance, which is roughly equal to $1/G_m$, is reduced

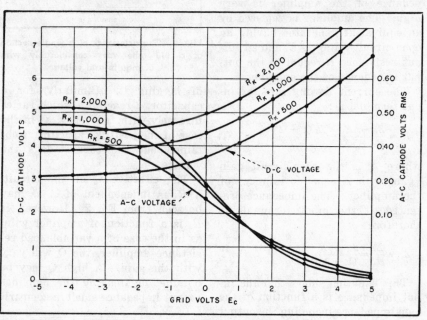

FIG. 7—Increasing the values of cathode resistor provides higher gain

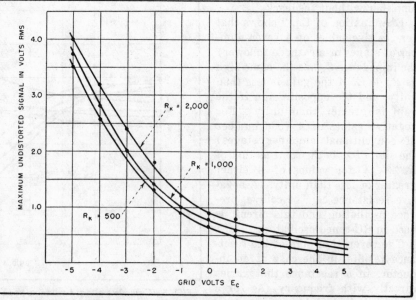

FIG. 8—Distortion level for the three values of cathode resistors

since the transconductance is increased. The increase in negative bias on the input section reduces the transconductance of that section, and consequently reduces the gain. Thus the gain is reduced by two means.

At negative values of control-section voltage, that section presents a high resistance as a load to the input section, increasing the gain. This gain is also increased as a result of maximum transconductance of the input section at small values of negative bias. This effect

istics. These families of curves were taken with a common cathode-resistance of 1,000 ohms.

The factor $(1 - A)$ as a function of grid voltage applied to the control tube is shown in Fig. 6. The two S-shaped curves were measured with two values of cathode resistance, while the third curve was computed from measured tube parameters. The calculated curve was obtained by calculating the gain for each value using the correct tube constants as obtained from Fig. 4. These curves show a total variation

Figure 7 shows curves of d-c and a-c cathode voltage for 500, 1,000 and 2,000-ohm cathode resistors. Otherwise, the conditions were the same as those of the previous curves. The higher values of cathode resistance gave higher figures of gain since the effect of the fixed resistor was reduced.

Linearity

Figure 8 shows the maximum signal which can be applied to the amplifier grid (triode 1) without producing perceptible distortion of

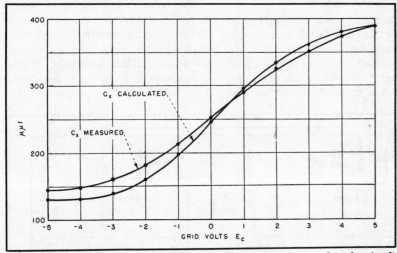

FIG. 9—Input capacitance of tube 1 at 1,000 cycles when connected in the circuit of Fig. 3

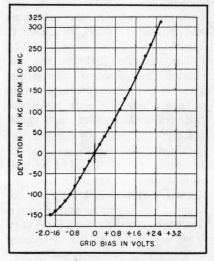

FIG. 11—Frequency deviation of the one-megacycle oscillator

is shown by the family of curves of the a-c voltage at the cathode. The four tubes varied rather widely in their static and dynamic characteristics.

of the factor of the order of three to one. The curves show good agreement except near the end, where the control tube grid is cut off.

the cathode voltage waveform. At extremely high values of positive voltage on the control section, the allowable input voltage is small. This is because the input section is operating near cutoff with a small effective load resistance, and the tube parameters vary throughout a cycle of applied voltage.

No trouble is experienced with negative voltages on the control section, since the effective load resistance is nearly equal to the resistance used in the cathodes. In applications of this circuit, several volts have been applied to the input grid without observing any ill effects due to the harmonic currents drawn. This is, of course, primarily a function of the circuit to which the reactance is connected and its imped-

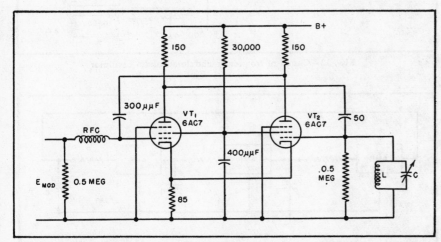

FIG. 10—One-megacycle f-m oscillator using a two-stage amplifier as a variable reactance

ance at the frequency of the harmonics.

To verify the theory, values of capacitance were calculated and measured for the circuit of Fig. 3. The measurements were made on a standard capacitance bridge at a frequency of one kilocycle. The capacitance was calculated by using some of the data previously shown of cathode voltage as a function of control voltage. When this was known, the parameters of each section were determined from the curve. These values were then substituted into the equation for input capacitance. There was a fair agreement between the calculated and measured values, as shown in Fig. 9.

The deviation between the calculated and measured values was greatest at the two extremes of grid voltage where the plate resistance and transconductance vary most rapidly. An input capacitance was obtained that was linear over ± 10 percent for a change of control-section grid voltage of ± 0.5 volt. A total variation of 3 to 1 was obtained. The Q was measured with a Q meter and was found to vary from 30 to 50 in the frequency range of 50 to 75 kilocycles.

R-F Oscillator

Figure 10 shows a radio-frequency frequency-modulated oscillator using a two-stage amplifier as a variable reactance. This circuit operates at a carrier frequency of one megacycle. Amplifier gain, and hence, amplifier input reactance, is controlled by changing the transconductance of VT_1 by impressing the modulating voltage on the grid of this tube. A 50-μμf capacitor is used for the feedback reactance.

The plate load and common cathode resistor values are proportioned to produce a gain of approximately unity with no modulating voltage. From Eq. 2 it may be seen that the reactance is infinite for no modulation, a negative capacitive reactance for positive swings of modulating voltage (gain greater than unity), and a positive capacitive reactance

for negative swings of modulating voltage (gain less than unity).

The frequency deviation from one megacycle as shown in Fig. 11 was linear to approximately 80 kc on either side of the center frequency, while the maximum frequency was 1,310 kc and the minimum 850 kc. Thus a frequency range of 1.54 to 1 was obtained. The linear variation was obtained with a grid-voltage variation of ±0.8 volt, and the total variation was obtained by varying the voltage applied to the grid from −1.8 to +2.6.

Audio F-M Oscillator

Figure 12 shows the application of the circuit of Fig. 3 to an audio-frequency f-m oscillator. This circuit has been used to produce linear frequency deviations of ±17 percent when operated at center fre-

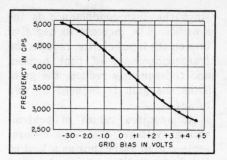

FIG. 14—Frequency deviation of the audio oscillator is linear for about 10 percent each side of the center frequency

quencies varying from 3 to 7 kilocycles.

The circuit is illustrated functionally in Fig. 13 and consists of three low-gain amplifier stages connected in a ring and separated by phase-shifting networks. Three tubes were used instead of a single tube as in the usual phase-shift os-

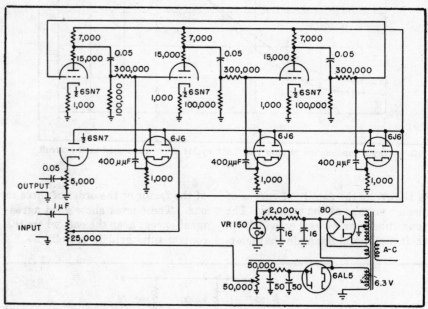

FIG. 12—Circuit of frequency-modulated audio oscillator

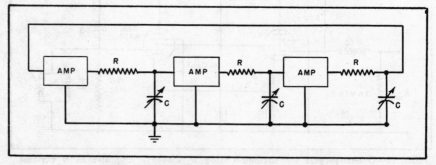

FIG. 13—Block diagram of f-m audio oscillator

cillator in order to operate all reactances at an equal voltage level. The carrier voltage at the grids of the reactances was approximately two volts.

The frequency variation of one of these oscillators is shown as a function of grid voltage in Fig. 14. The output frequency was linear over a region of ±10 percent of the center frequency which was four kilocycles in this particular case. The total variation obtained

was approximately 2,320 cycles. The deviation from linearity was only 0.5 percent at extremes of ±17 percent of the center frequency, and tests with square-wave modulating signals showed the transient response to be good.

Other applications of the dual-triode reactance circuit include remote tuning (1.6 to 1 range), tuning of RC frequency-selective circuits and filters, production of

phase modulation and for self-balancing bridges.

Acknowledgement is gratefully made to E. H. Schulz for suggestions during the course of the work and assistance in preparation of this paper.

REFERENCES

(1) H. J. Reich, The Use of Vacuum Tubes as Variable Impedance Elements, *Proc. IRE*, 30, p 288, June 1942.
(2) H. J. Reich, "Theory and Application of Electron Tubes," McGraw-Hill Book Company, Inc., New York, 1944, p 214.

Citizens Band Signal Generator

Construction details of a signal source designed to facilitate development work on the Citizens Band. The unit contains a tunable concentric-line resonator in a Colpitts oscillator circuit using a subminiature tube

By WALTER C. HOLLIS

FRUSTRATION in developmental and experimental work at the Citizens Band frequencies due to lack of a signal generator caused the construction of the instrument to be described.

The complete generator forms a unit that may be built at a cost for components in the neighborhood of $100. It consists of an oscillator which may be grid modulated, a calibrated variable attenuator and a regulated power supply. The circuit diagram is given in Fig. 1.

The generator contains a subminiature 6K4 tube in a Colpitts oscillator circuit. The tank circuit for this oscillator is of the concentric-line resonator type and is tuned by means of a variable air capacitor. The plate of the 6K4 shunt feeds the high side of the tank circuit.

A substantial part of the circuit inductance is contained within the tube and its plate and grid lead inductance. It is therefore necessary to keep the plate and grid lead lengths down to ¼ inch to obtain an upper frequency limit of 475 megacycles.

The cathode and filament are supplied through two self-resonant chokes which have been experimentally adjusted for best oscillator operation. The lead length is not critical. The oscillator may be externally grid modulated at the terminals shown. This connection contains an R-C filter to prevent r-f leakage through the modulation circuit.

The oscillator is coupled through a wall in its resonator into a waveguide-below-cutoff attenuator. This is a Measurements Corporation model M-234 r-f attenuator.

Construction Details

The oscillator and supply are contained in a shielded sheet-brass compartment directly attached to the M-234 attenuator chassis. The oscillator is assembled within a separate shield can mounted within the main shield compartment. Figure 2 illustrates the construction of the oscillator and shield.

The oscillator resonator is constructed of machined brass parts and is of the coaxial-line type. The resonator is a first model of the out-

put resonator for the transmitter described in the November 1947 issue of ELECTRONICS. As in the construction of any signal generator, all joints must be very carefully soldered to prevent leakage.

The power supply is mounted on a sheet-brass partition which is soldered to the main shield compartment. The grid connection is brought out to terminals on the front panel through an R-C filter. The tuning control for the oscillator is brought out to the tuning dial by means of an insulated shaft. The shielding of the signal generator is completed by means of a removable shield cover.

Frequency Calibration

The transmitter previously described was used in conjunction with a communications receiver and a 1N34 crystal to obtain the frequency calibration for the signal generator. Figure 3 illustrates the calibration method.

The output of the transmitter is used as a local oscillator for the crystal mixer which beats the frequency of the signal generator down

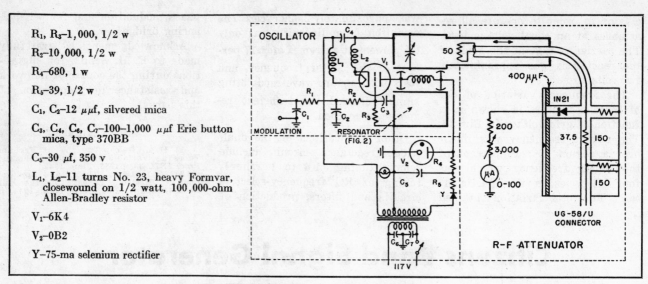

R₁, R₃–1,000, 1/2 w

R₂–10,000, 1/2 w

R₄–680, 1 w

R₅–39, 1/2 w

C₁, C₂–12 μμf, silvered mica

C₃, C₄, C₆, C₇–100–1,000 μμf Erie button mica, type 370BB

C₅–30 μf, 350 v

L₁, L₂–11 turns No. 23, heavy Formvar, closewound on 1/2 watt, 100,000-ohm Allen-Bradley resistor

V₁–6K4

V₂–0B2

Y–75-ma selenium rectifier

FIG. 1—Complete circuit of the generator

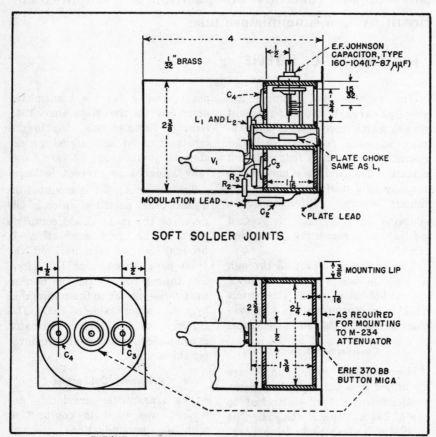

FIG. 2—Mechanical details of oscillator and shield

to a low frequency which may be amplified and detected by the receiver. The receiver is tuned for the strongest signal obtained from the signal generator. The frequency at which the signal generator is oscillating is equal to 465 mc plus or minus the frequency to which the receiver is tuned. If the oscillator is started with the tuning capacitor set at full capacitance it will be operating below 465 mc and as tuning is accomplished the frequency will increase. This method will supply complete frequency calibration data for marking the tuning dial.

This same setup was used to check the warm-up time and the plate-voltage stability. A check of the warm-up drift showed that the oscillator was within 0.5 mc below its final frequency of 473 mc within one minute. Complete stability was reached within five minutes. The plate-voltage stability was found to be 25 kc per volt.

The oscillator was modulated and tested using the receiver previously described (ELECTRONICS, March 1948). It was found that little frequency modulation was introduced, as evidenced by the decrease in audio output as the signal level of the signal generator was increased. The limiters in the receiver became more effective as the signal level was increased, reducing the effect of amplitude modulation. However, frequency modulation is undisturbed by this effect. Therefore it is believed that the residual frequency modulation of this signal generator is quite low.

The author appreciates the help of Jerry Mintner of Measurements Corp. who conducted tests of the final unit. A considerable electro-static field was observed around the tuning dial and the shield cover joint and he suggested a length of tubing around the insulated tuning shaft, forming a waveguide atten-uator; and bolting of the cover about every half inch.

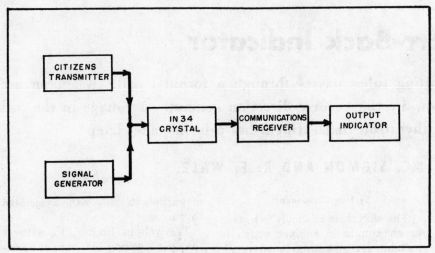

FIG. 3—Setup of equipment for calibration of generator

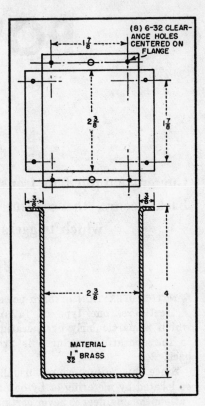

Details of oscillator shield can

POWER SUPPLIES

Arc-Back Indicator

Current supplied to transmitting tubes passes through a toroidal coil. When an arc back occurs, the current flow in the reverse direction generates a voltage in the coil which triggers a thyratron that extinguishes a neon panel lamp

By L. C. SIGMON AND R. F. WALZ

IN THE OPERATION of high-power rectifiers, one type of failure which is particularly exasperating to the operating engineer is arc-back.

Since this failure cannot usually be located by metering or by observation, the engineer is never certain that the tube which is replaced in an effort to correct the trouble is the one which is failing.

Many devices are available to indicate the passage of inverse current through each tube but, until recently, none has been found to indicate only the failing tube. This is explained by the fact that, when an arc-back occurs in a rectifier tube, the overload on other tubes in the rectifier may cause them to pass inverse current thereby resulting in the indication of such current in several tubes simultaneously. The equipment to be described herein does not have this fault inasmuch as it will indicate only the first tube to pass inverse current.

A schematic diagram of the instrument is shown in Fig. 1. This diagram shows only the first two and last stages of the unit but it is normally supplied with six identical stages. The dashed lines on the schematic indicate the two major assemblies of the arc-back indicator, the upper block containing the electronic assembly and the lower block the indicator. A third assembly consists of the toroidal coupling coils.

System Components

The electronic assembly is housed in an aluminum cabinet which is suitable for mounting in any position. The indicating unit mounts an indicating lamp for each position, a test switch for each circuit and a reset switch. The coupling coil is toroidal in shape and designed to be mounted over the existing bus structure in a rectifier. This is the only component to be mounted in the rectifier unit, and modification of the rectifier circuit is not required.

The electronic circuit for each stage is identical and comprises a type 2D21 thyratron, V_1, a type NE-2 gas discharge tube, V_2, an input divider consisting of resistors R_2 and R_3, and an r-f filter consisting of resistor R_1 and capacitor C_1. The cathodes of all stages are connected together and return to ground through the reset switch, S_2, and resistor R_8. Positive potential is applied to the cathodes through resistor R_8 which maintains an initial bias so that the thyratrons are normally non-conducting.

When a positive pulse of sufficient amplitude is applied to the input circuit of any thyratron by its associated coupling coil, the thyratron is triggered and conducts current. The thyratron current, passing through resistor R_9, increases the bias on all the tubes so that a similar input voltage applied to any other tube will not be of sufficient

magnitude to trigger the associated thyratron.

The voltage limiter, V_3, assures that the blocking bias cannot be exceeded irrespective of the magnitude or direction of the current flowing through the bus in the center of the coupling coil and thereby prevents indication of sympathetic arc-back in other tubes of the rectifier. The operation of the type thyratron used is of sufficiently high speed compared to the time separation of pulses from other tubes passing inverse current to insure indication of only the first tube to arc-back.

The indicating circuit comprises resistors R_5, R_6, and R_7, and pilot lamp V_4. Under initial conditions, the plate supply voltage is applied through resistor R_5 to the voltage divider consisting of resistors R_6 and R_7. These resistors permit the pilot lamp to be illuminated when the associated thyratron is non-conducting. When the thyratron is triggered, the current passing through resistor R_5 decreases the voltage applied to the pilot lamp and it is extinguished, thereby indicating the associated thyratron is conducting.

The coupling coil, T_2, has many turns of wire around a core of high-permeability transformer alloy. Its core is saturated by current from the plate supply passing through the coil, resistor R_4, and test switch S_1, to ground. Capacitor C_2 connects the coupling coil to the voltage limiter and the input circuit of the associated thyratron. The coupling coil operates on the principle that unidirectional current passing through the bus in the center of the toroid, when properly poled, will act to increase the saturation and, because of the magnetic properties of the core, will fail to generate any voltage in the coil.

Current passing in the reverse direction, however, will act to decrease the saturation and, when the effects of the two currents are such that the saturation approaches zero, a voltage is generated in the coupling coil. This voltage is used to trigger the associated thyratron.

The test switch, S_1, is a normally closed, momentarily operated switch which is used to open the circuit carrying the saturation current through the coupling coil. The sudden çessation of current resulting from operation of the test switch causes the magnetic field in the coupling coil to collapse thereby generating an induced voltage which is applied to the thyratron as an equivalent to an arc-back signal. Operation of this switch tests the coupling coil circuit establishing that current is flowing and shows that the thyratron and associated indicating lamp are functioning normally.

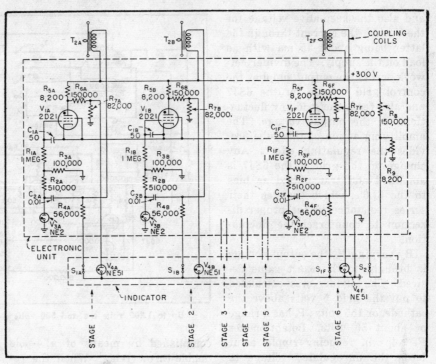

FIG. 1—Circuit of the first two and last stages of the electronic unit and indicator

The reset switch, S_2, is a normally closed, momentarily operated switch which is used to open the cathode circuit of the thyratrons. When operated, it opens this circuit thereby stopping the flow of current through any conducting thyratron. When released the circuit is restored but, as the thyratrons are now nonconducting, the circuits are ready to indicate the reception of

another signal.

The use of an arc-back indicator results in the saving of "down" time in the event of this type of trouble as it permits instant location of the defective tube. Replacement of a good tube, erroneously believed to be the source of arc-back failure, is eliminated, permitting the operation of rectifier tubes to the end of their useful life.

Versatile Power Supply

By WILLIAM B. MILLER

BOTH direct and alternating voltages for meter testing are provided by the circuit shown. The a-c output is continuously variable from 0 to 1,200 volts and the maximum d-c output is fixed and regulated at 500 volts. Lower d-c voltages are obtained by means of a variable voltage divider which allows smooth control down to zero volt.

Low ripple was not a factor in the design and only ordinary filtering was used. However, the action

of the regulator section and a small amount of feedback resulted in a measured ripple of 0.4 millivolt. Regulation was important and is quite good. After the output was set at 500 volts, it held with no perceptible change, with a line variation from 90 to 125 volts and a load variation of from 0 to 200 milliamperes.

Four 6L6G's, triode connected, are used in parallel as the series regulators, and a 6SJ7 as the ampli-

fier. Resistors in each plate lead of the 6L6's equalize the current distribution, and resistors in each grid lead help stabilize and limit the grid current. A total of 200 ma may be safely drawn from this combination.

The 6SJ7 control amplifier was considered as an r-f tube and care in wire placement was used to eliminate erratic operation and unwanted oscillations. Resistors R_2 and R_3 supply the screen voltage and also the keep-alive voltage for the VR150, the current through the latter being about 15 ma with no load on the supply. The divider network across the output supplies the control grid voltage for the 6SJ7 and also feeds the grid any fluctuations in the output voltage. The amplifying action of this tube provides the regulating effect. Any change on the grid of the 6SJ7 is amplified and transmitted as bias to the 6L6's, which changes their series resistance in the proper direction to counteract the fluctuation.

By varying P_1, the output voltage is brought to the exact value desired. The divider was calculated to put the grid 5 volts above the cathode, or 155 volts; P_1 has a range of about 50 volts. Potentiometer P_2 helps in reducing ripple, as it feeds the unregulated voltage to the regulated side and any ripple will be partially cancelled due to the 180-degree phase difference between the two.

Resistor R_1 and capacitor C_1 aid considerably in ripple reduction. A 500,000-ohm potentiometer was used for R_1 and adjusted for minimum ripple voltage. If the supply is used where the load changes rapidly, a 4-μf 600-volt oil-filled capacitor across the output helps in maintaining regulation.

A-C Output

The change from d-c to a-c is ac-

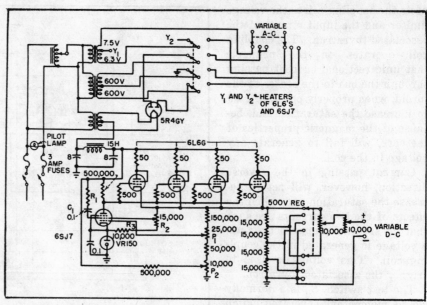

Up to 1,200 volts a-c and 500 volts d-c are available from the power supply

complished by means of a 4-pole double-throw relay. When the relay is energized, it disconnects the high-voltage windings from the rectifier tube and makes them available by means of a switch. The Variac, connected to the primaries of one filament transformer and the plate transformer, controls the a-c output. When the switch selects the filament transformer, a-c from 0 to 7.5 volts is available at the terminals. With half of the plate winding switched in, up to 600 volts may be had. With the full winding, 1,200 volts are available; each range being continuously variable. The Variac is turned down whenever a change is made to prevent arcing at the relay contacts.

The resistance network across the output divides the 500 volts d-c into four ranges, each range being approximately a 125-volt step, depending on the current being drawn. Thus for the first range the voltage is 0 to 125, the second from 125 to 250, the third from 250 to 375 and the last from 375 to the full 500. The arrangement of the potentiometers gives a very smooth control between ranges and allows voltages as low as 0.05 to be easily obtained. The two 10,000-ohm potentiometers are General Radio type 314A, rated at 8 watts.

Thyratron Replaces Vibrator

THE CIRCUIT of an electronic converter that supplies alternating current for powering radio and other electronic units is shown in the diagram. It operates from a six-volt battery and contains no moving parts.

Other types of tubes than the 2051 shown may operate as well. Cold-cathode types might permit instant starting and no power loss

in heating the filament. The inventor of the circuit, Carl R. Peterson of Los Angeles, California, has used a UTC universal output transformed as L_1 and L_2, with the 0 to 8-ohm tap as L_1 and 8 to 500-ohm tap as L_2. Low ohmic resistance and high inductance would provide greater output. The circuit may be of interest to designers of truly portable television

receivers as a picture tube anode supply. A patent has been applied for.

With switch S_2 closed and S_1 depressed momentarily, current will flow from the battery through L_1 and R. The current is limited in value by the resistance R and the resistance of the inductive winding. When S_1 is opened and left in that position, an induced voltage appears across C and tube V. This voltage will be in series with the battery, and will either aid or oppose the battery voltage on each alternate cycle.

When both are in a positive direction with respect to the anode of the tube, the voltage will be sufficient to ionize the gas and the tube will then conduct current in that one direction. The gas-filled tube may be considered as a switch of zero resistance, and a back emf of about 5 volts. Therefore both the induced current and current from the battery will flow in the circuit.

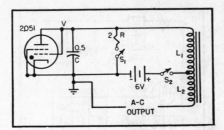

Simple thyratron circuit provides high-voltage a-c output

When the induced voltage plus the battery voltage falls to about 12 volts, the tube will extinguish and thus effectively open the circuit. With the circuit open, the field in L_1 will collapse, the in-

duced voltage will ionize the tube and the cycle will repeat until S_2 is opened. The entire circuit is analogous to that of an ordinary ignition circuit with the exception that the breaker points are replaced by the gas-filled arc tube.

The output of the transformer may be rectified and filtered in the usual manner. The unit has been used to operate an ordinary a-c radio with 6V6 output tube, and the energy is sufficient to operate it in a satisfactory manner with good volume on local stations. There is no noise or hum present in the output.

Stable Electronic Voltage Regulator

By PETER G. SULZER

ELECTRONIC VOLTAGE REGULATORS have been employed when a d-c supply having excellent regulation and stability is required. It is the purpose of this paper to describe a circuit which produces a substantial improvement in performance with but little increase in complexity.

The regulator under consideration consists of a voltage-control tube, a d-c amplifier, a stable voltage standard, and a means for comparing the controlled voltage with the standard voltage. A popular scheme[1,2] is that of Fig. 1 A, which contains a control tube, V_1, a voltage amplifier, V_2, and a constant-voltage glow tube, V_3. Comparison occurs in the grid-cathode circuit of V_2. Analysis has shown[3] that one requirement for good regulation is high gain in the voltage amplifier. Thus a pentode is usually employed for V_2, or the cascode amplifier[4] has been used. Higher gain may be obtained with the cascade amplifier[5] of Fig. 1B. It will be noted, however, that cathode degeneration occurs in V_2 and V_3. In order to realize the full gain capabilities of the two-stage amplifier the circuit of Fig. 1C has been devised. Here both cathodes see a low impedance

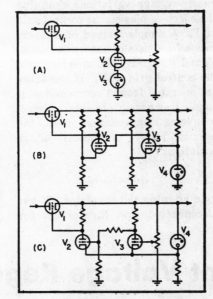

FIG. 1—Basic voltage regulator circuit diagrams

through the glow tube V_4, which is used as the voltage standard. The control grid of V_3 is connected to a voltage divider connected across the output of the regulator. Therefore the output-voltage variations are applied to both cathodes, and it can be seen that, as a result, the effective voltage gain of V_3 is decreased by unity. This, however, is of little consequence when high-μ tubes are employed.

Performance

To calculate the performance of the regulator, consider the equivalent circuit shown in Fig. 2A, where e_i and e_o are the input and output voltages respectively, R_p and μ refer to the control tube (V_1 in Fig. 1C), e_s is the standard voltage, A_o is the voltage-amplifier gain, $1/N$ is the voltage-divider attenuation, and R_L is the resistance presented by the load. Considering incremental voltages,

$$\frac{\Delta e_i - \mu \left[A_o \frac{\Delta e_o}{N} + \Delta e_o \right]}{R_p + R_L} = \frac{\Delta e_o}{R_L} \quad (1)$$

Rearranging, it is found that

$$\frac{\Delta e_o}{\Delta e_i} = \frac{1}{1 + \mu + \dfrac{R_p}{R_L} + \dfrac{\mu A_o}{N}} \quad (2)$$

where $\Delta e_o/\Delta e_i$ is defined as the input regulation. It is desired to minimize this quantity, which can be accomplished conveniently by increasing A_o.

The output regulation can be specified in terms of the equivalent source resistance R_i. Considering the regulator as an amplifier having negative voltage feedback, it can be shown[6] that the source resistance

$$R_i = \frac{R}{1 + A\beta} \quad (3)$$

where R is the output resistance of the amplifier in the absence of feedback, A is the amplifier voltage gain for the same condition, and β is the fraction of the voltage fed back. In the circuit of Fig. 1C, V_1 can be considered as a cathode follower of output resistance $\dfrac{R_p}{\mu + 1}$ and voltage gain $\dfrac{\mu R_L}{R_p + (1 + \mu) R_L}$. Substituting,

$$R_i = \frac{\dfrac{R_p}{\mu + 1}}{1 + \left(\dfrac{A_o}{N}\right)\left(\dfrac{\mu R_L}{R_p + (1 + \mu) R_L}\right)} \quad (4)$$

For the practical circuit of Fig. 2B, where $A_o = 4,000$, $N \approx 2$, $\mu = 5$, and $R_p = 750$ ohms, one obtains from Eq. 2 and 4, $\Delta e_o / \Delta e_i \approx 1/10{,}000$, and $R_i \approx 0.06$ ohm. These calculations were made for a 50-ma load ($R_L = 5,000$). Thus a 50-volt input change would appear as a change of but 0.005 volt at the output, while the output voltage will change 0.003 volt as the load current is increased from 0 to 50 ma.

An improvement in the performance of the circuit can be obtained by increasing A_o through regeneration. A resistor connected between the plate of V_2 and the grid of V_3 will accomplish the desired result. In this manner A_o can effectively be made infinite, with resulting perfect regulation.

Circuit

If the circuit given above is in-

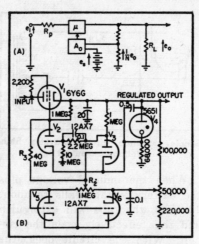

FIG. 2—Stabilized voltage-regulator circuit maintains constant output voltage for ten-percent line-voltage fluctuations and load variations from 0 to 80 ma.

corporated into a power supply, it is found that the output voltage will still vary as the line voltage is changed. This is caused by heater-voltage variations changing the effective bias on the control grid of V_3. A simple method of compensation [7] consists of inserting diodes V_5 and V_6 in Fig. 2B, in series with the control grid of V_3. If the tubes are operated from a common heater supply it is possible to obtain almost complete compensation over the normal range of heater-voltage variations.

Adjustment

In aligning the regulator, R_3 was disconnected, and R_2 was set for zero diode compensation. The control R_1 was set for the desired output (between 225 and 275 volts). The d-c input of the regulator was then varied over a range of 50 volts, and R_3 was selected for zero output-voltage variation. The diode-compensation control was next set for minimum output-voltage change as the line voltage was changed ± 10 percent.

Performance

A final check of performance showed the output voltage to be constant within 0.02 volt for ± 10 percent line-voltage variations and for load currents from 0 to 80 ma, the maximum current for the 6Y6G. The output voltage was constant within 0.025 volt (with fixed load current) over a period of one day. The output impedance was less than 0.2 ohm at all frequencies below 200 kilocycles.

REFERENCES

(1) U. S. Patent No. 2,075,966 (A. W. Vance).
(2) RCA Application Note No. 96, August, 1938.
(3) F. V. Hunt and R. W. Hickman, On Electronic Voltage Stabilizers, *Rev. Sci. Instr.*, **10**, p 6, Jan. 1939.
(4) ibid. (3).
(5) RCA Tube Handbook HB-3. Listed under tube-type 5651.
(6) H. F. Mayer, Control of Amplifier Internal Impedance, *Proc. IRE*, **27**, p 213, Mar. 1939.
(7) G. E. Valley, Jr., and Henry Wallman, "Vacuum-Tube Amplifiers", McGraw-Hill, N. Y., 1948.

Filament Voltage Regulator

A NOVEL circuit for stabilizing tube heaters is employed in the design of a differential analyzer by R. L. Garwin of the University of Chicago. One section of the analyzer makes use of a d-c feedback amplifier connected as an integrator.

The most difficult problem in the design was the input behavior of the d-c amplifier, that is, grid current and grid-cathode potential changes. It was felt that the use of

standard receiving tube types was an important advantage worth considerable effort to achieve. Grid current was finally reduced to less than 10^{-9} amp without tube selection by using a 6AK5 at 100-μa plate current.

The grid-cathode potential was stabilized by regulating the average heater power to better than 0.1 percent by the scheme illustrated in the accompanying diagram. In this circuit, the filament of the first

diode is operated at such current that the emission is temperature-limited. It is then easily shown that the sensitivity of the space current to heater voltage variation gives about two-volt change in plate potential for 0.1 percent heater voltage change. This error signal is then amplified and applied through the power output tube and transformer. By this means, it is made to maintain a constant heater voltage.

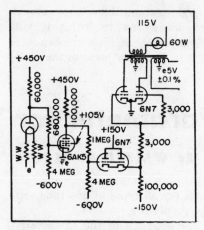

Circuit for regulating a-c heater of amplifier tube

Regulated Voltage Divider

By WILLIAM B. BERNARD

IN MANY electronic circuit applications it is desirable to have a voltage-divider system with good regulation. This may be needed to protect circuit components from high voltages during starting periods or it may be needed to insure proper circuit operation during steady-state operation.

When the current drain from the intermediate tap is small, VR tubes can be used to insure good regulation. When the current drain is high an electronically regulated power supply or a resistive voltage divider with a high bleeder current may be used. Both of these systems suffer from some disadvantages. The electrically regulated supply is complicated and the range over which the output voltage may be varied is small. The bleeder system is very wasteful of power and power supply components of a higher rating are needed to support it.

If the requirements placed on regulation of the intermediate output voltage are not too stringent, most of the benefits of a regulated supply without all the complications can be obtained. If a stable high-voltage supply is available and good but not perfect regulation of the in-

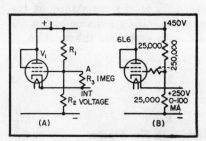

FIG. 1—The basic circuit is shown at A. Typical values of circuit B apply when the power supply bleeder resistor is used for the voltage divider

termediate voltage is desired, the circuit of Fig. 1 is simple and satisfactory. With a triode-connected 6L6 the output impedance will be about 200 ohms. This is far lower than can be obtained from a bleeder system using a reasonable bleeder current.

Resistors R_1 and R_2 are selected to give a voltage at point A just a little below the desired intermediate voltage. The value of R_1 and R_2 should be such that the grid circuit resistance is at least 100,000 ohms to protect the grid if an extremely heavy load is placed on the intermediate supply. If R_1 and R_2 are lower in value to act as a bleeder to stabilize the high-voltage supply,

a resistor in series with the grid lead should be added to make the grid circuit resistance sufficiently high, as shown in B.

If the only reason for desiring good regulation is to prevent the application of abnormally high voltages on the components fed from the intermediate circuit while the tubes are warming up and if poorer regulation during the operating can be tolerated, a resistor may be added in the plate circuit of V_1 to reduce the plate dissipation of the tube.

If R_1 and R_2 are replaced with a potentiometer of suitable rating

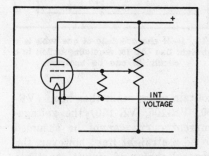

FIG. 2—Almost any desired value of intermediate voltage is obtained with this arrangement

(Fig. 2) the output of the circuit can be varied over almost the entire range from zero to the value of the high voltage.

A tube for use in this circuit must of course have ratings high enough to stand the voltage current and dissipation to which it will be subjected. A high tranconductance is desirable because the cathode output impedance is roughly equal to $1/g_m$. The heater supply must be furnished from a separate well-insulated secondary.

Optimum Parameter for VR Tubes

By WALTER R. BERG

CIRCUIT CONSTANTS of the familiar gas tube voltage regulator can be adjusted to give a maximum possible regulation. This analysis is to determine the optimum conditions. The straight line current-voltage characteristic shown in Fig. 1A of neon gas tube voltage regulators such as the 991 and VR-75 makes a simple mathematical analysis possible. In the use of regulators that

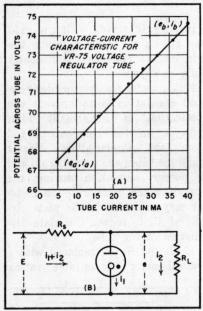

FIG. 1—If characteristic of gas tube is a straight line (A), its regulating action in a circuit (B) can be analysed

contain gases other than neon (VR-90, VR-105, VR-150) the voltage-current curve cannot be assumed to be a straight line; however, the general choice of circuit constants as derived in the following analysis

holds for all types of gas tube voltage regulators.

The equation of the characteristics line is

$$e = ai_1 + b \qquad (1)$$

where

$$a = \frac{e_b - e_a}{i_b - i_a} \qquad (2)$$

and

$$b = e_a - ai_a \qquad (3)$$

Figure 1B represents a typical gas tube voltage regulator circuit. In it

$$E = (i_1 + i_2) R_s + e \qquad (4)$$

where R_s is the resistance of the current limiting resistor commonly used with stabilizer tubes. Also

$$e = R_L i_2 = ai_1 + b \qquad (5)$$

$$i_1 = \frac{e - b}{a} \qquad (6)$$

$$i_2 = \frac{e}{R_L} \qquad (7)$$

Rewriting Eq. 4 gives

$$E = \left(\frac{e - b}{a} + \frac{e}{R_L} \right) R_s + e \qquad (8)$$

or

$$e = \frac{aR_L E + bR_L R_s}{R_L R_s + aR_s + aR_L} \qquad (9)$$

Equation 9 is the expression for

the regulated voltage as a function of the supply voltage and the circuit parameters.

Differentiating Eq. 9 gives

$$\frac{de}{dE} = \frac{aR_L}{R_L (R_s + a) + aR_s} \qquad (10)$$

Substituting in Eq. 9 and 10 gives

$$\frac{de}{dE} = \frac{ea}{aE + bR_s} \qquad (11)$$

For the best regulation $de-dE$ should be made as small as possible; for perfect regulation $de-dE$ should equal zero. In the design of voltage regulator circuits e and a should be made small and b, E, and R_s should be made as large as possible. An analysis of Fig. 1B shows that R_s can be made larger if the value of R_L is increased. In other words, the regulation becomes better as the load current is decreased. In adjusting the circuit constants for maximum regulation it should be remembered that the above mathematical analysis holds only over the working range of the gas tube used. Table I shows the results of tests on the VR-75 tube of Fig. 1A used in the circuit of Fig. 1B.

Table I—Measured Regulation

E	R_L	R_s	e	ΔE, change in input voltage	Δe, change in output voltage
VOLTS	OHMS	OHMS	VOLTS	VOLTS	VOLTS
145	∞	15,500	67.40	20	0.25
165	∞	15,500	67.65		
230	∞	32,500	67.40	20	0.15
250	∞	32,500	67.55		
230	3,000	5,850	67.40	20	0.60
250	3,000	5,850	68.00		

PROPAGATION

VHF Field Intensities

Nomograph shows fields in microvolts per meter for transmitter powers up to 500 watts, antennas up to 500 feet, over obstructions as high as 10,000 feet in the frequency range between 20 and 260 mc

By E. A. SLUSSER

IN PLANNING a new vhf point-to-point radio circuit, it is first necessary to make some estimate of the expected transmission between the two points in question in order to determine the feasibility of such a circuit. Likewise, in planning a new vhf mobile system the expected coverage over flat land and into shadowed areas must be predetermined. These estimated transmission figures can be used to assist in the selection of equipment and location of transmitter sites. Such estimates are usually made by means of profile maps and transmission nomographs.

Previous nomographs for estimating field intensities in the vhf frequency range have been made for small segments only of the total band of frequencies, thus necessitating several charts to cover the entire band. This nomograph enables one to select a given frequency in the range between 20 and 260 mc and estimate the field intensity for either transmission over smooth land or transmission over paths involving shadow losses. It assumes either horizontal or vertical polarization over land and horizontal polarization over sea water. It also assumes 50-watt transmitters and half-wave antennas elevated 40 feet above the ground, but supplementary conversion data is given for other powers and antenna heights.

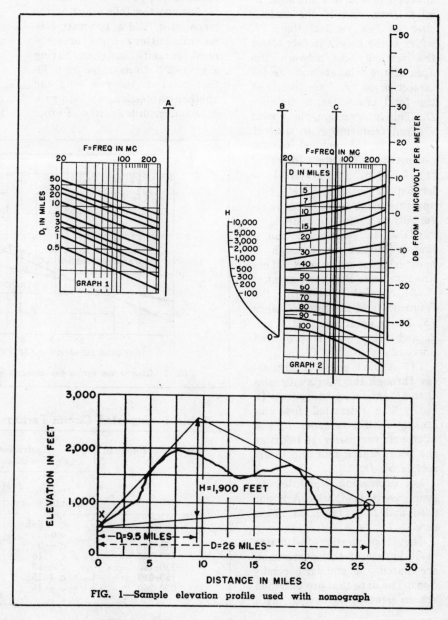

FIG. 1—Sample elevation profile used with nomograph

To use the nomograph, it is necessary to draw an elevation profile of the intervening terrain between the two proposed station sites. An example is shown in Fig. 1. A triangle is constructed by drawing two lines from the station sites, X and Y, each tangent to the nearest hill or obstruction that blocks the line-of-sight path. A base line is also drawn to intersect the two sites, and a vertical line is drawn through the apex of the triangle and intersecting the base line.

The information taken from this figure includes: D_1, which is always the shortest distance in miles from one of the station sites to the vertical line; H, which is the height in feet along the vertical line between the apex of the triangle and the intersection of the base line; and the total transmission distance D. This information, along with a given frequency F in the vhf range, can be applied to the nomograph. The steps follow:

(1) A point on graph 1 is located representing (F, D_1), and this point is projected horizontally to a point on scale A.

(2) H is determined and a line is constructed through H and the point on scale A. This line intersects B at some point.

(3) A point representing the frequency and the total distance (F, D) is determined on graph 2, and this point is projected horizontally to scale C.

(4) A line is constructed passing through the points on scales B and C and intersecting scale D.

(5) The estimated field intensity in db, referred to one microvolt per meter, is taken at the point where this line intersects scale D.

For estimating field intensity over smooth land, scale A is not used and H is taken as being zero.

The transmission estimates made by use of this nomograph are based on standard conditions. The data that are obtained are in general agreement with experience for smooth or mountainous terrain. The factors affecting vhf transmission are both natural (such as meteorological effects, type of soil and surrounding vegetation) and artificial (for example, antenna height, antenna gain, transmitter power and transmission-line loss). The latter items can be taken into consideration when making an estimate and a new equivalent field intensity (equivalent on the basis of a half-wave antenna) can be found.

A sample calculation can be made between locations X and Y by using the profile given in Fig. 1. Assume the following: at the transmitter end a 100-watt 150-mc transmitter using a three-element parasitic antenna having a gain of 6 db mounted on a 90-foot pole; on the receiving end another three-element 6-db-gain antenna mounted on a 30-foot

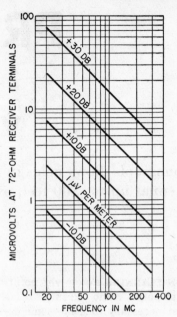

FIG. 3—Conversion graph for receiver input voltage

pole; a combined transmission-line loss of 3 db at both ends.

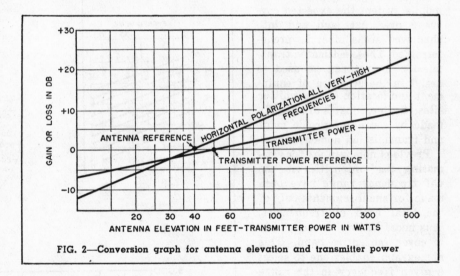

FIG. 2—Conversion graph for antenna elevation and transmitter power

Table I—Expected Circuit Performance With Average Receiver

Frequency Range in Mc	Equivalent estimated field intensity in db referred to $1\,\mu$v per meter		
	Probably Unsatisfactory	Questionable	Probably Satisfactory
20–40	< − 5db	− 5 to + 5db	> + 5db
40–70	< 0	0 to + 10	> + 10
70–100	< + 5	+ 5 to + 15	> + 15
100–120	< + 10	+ 10 to + 15	> + 15
120–160	< + 10	+ 10 to + 20	> + 20
160–220	< + 15	+ 15 to + 20	> + 20
220–260	< + 15	+ 15 to + 25	> + 25

The answer is + 14.5 db.

By comparing the estimated data with the receiver input level requirements one can determine whether or not the circuit will be probably satisfactory. For the average receiver the performance can be taken from Table I.

In making the above comparison one must take into consideration the amount of man-made noise present in the receiver area. The above figures are based on average noise condi-tions but in extremely noisy areas it may be necessary to in-crease the figures by about 20 db.

In order to compare the above data with receiver sensitivity, it may be desirable to convert field intensity, which is given in terms of db above one microvolt per meter, to microvolts appear-ing at the receiver terminals. This can be done by means of Fig. 3. This figure assumes a half-wave antenna connected to the receiver terminals (72 ohms input) by means of a zero-loss transmission line. The voltage (for half-wave antennas) ap-pearing on the receiver termi-nals is 0.32LE where L is the length of the antenna in meters and E the field intensity in mi-crovolts per meter.

For the previous example, + 14.5 db equivalent field inten-sity at 150 mc corresponds to ap-proximately 1.7 microvolts at the receiver terminals.

Calculating UHF Field Intensities

Curves based upon accepted propagation concepts facilitate theoretical prediction of television field intensities between 470 and 890 mc until more experience is obtained. Data on nulls and maxima resulting from path differences are included to show their location in miles from the transmitter

By FREDERICK W. SMITH

THE RECENT allocations proposals by the FCC for commercial television broadcasting in the band from 470 to 890 mc have centered attention on propagation problems at these frequencies. In order to facilitate the prediction of theoreti-cal ground-wave field intensities in this band, the group of charts pre-sented here has been prepared.

The methods for the calculation of field intensities employed were originally proposed by Norton[1] and have been conveniently summarized by Terman.[2]

Field Near Transmitter

The equation for field intensities in the immediate vicinity of the transmitting antenna for the ultra-high frequencies under considera-tion is given by Terman[3] as

$$\text{Field Intensity, } E = \frac{2 E_0 P^{\frac{1}{2}}}{d} \sin \frac{2\pi ha}{\lambda d} \quad (1)$$

where E_0 is the reference field in-tensity produced at a distance d of one mile for an effective radiated power P of one kilowatt, and h, a and λ are the heights of the trans-mitting and receiving antennas and the wavelength, respectively.

The reference field intensity se-lected by the FCC as an f-m and tv standard is that developed in the equatorial plane of a half-wave an-tenna under the conditions specified above, or 137.8 millivolts per meter. Such an antenna has a power gain of 1.641 when compared to an iso-tropic radiator.

Using this value for E_0 and sub-stituting 186,200 miles per sec ÷ f or (c/f) for λ, with h and a in feet and f in megacycles, Eq. 1 can be reduced to

$$E = \frac{275,600}{d} P^{\frac{1}{2}} \sin \theta \text{ microvolts per meter}$$

$$\text{where } \theta = 6.92 \times 10^{-5} haf/d \text{ degrees} \quad (2)$$

It can be seen from Eq. 2 that for a fixed distance and receiving antenna height, a single value of field intensity will result for a given frequency-transmitting antenna height fh product. Thus, where Eq. 2 applies, a transmitting antenna height of 1,000 feet at 450 mc will produce the same field intensity as 500 feet at 900 mc, other factors being equal.

This relationship has been em-ployed to simplify the construction of the field-intensity chart, which is similar in many respects to previ-ous charts published by the FCC for field-intensity calculations in the vhf band. Here, the product fh serves as the independent variable, which permits the use of a single chart for the entire frequency band under consideration.

Phase Interference

Near the transmitting antenna, a series of oscillations will occur in the field intensity as a result of phase interference due to differing path lengths traversed by the space wave and ground-reflected wave components of the signal. This effect is indicated by the sine term of Eq. 2, which will oscillate between unity and zero in value as θ reaches successive values of 90, 180, 270 degrees, and so on. The nulls and maxima thus produced will become much more frequent with decreas-ing distance. However, the latter will always be tangent to a curve along which the field intensity var-

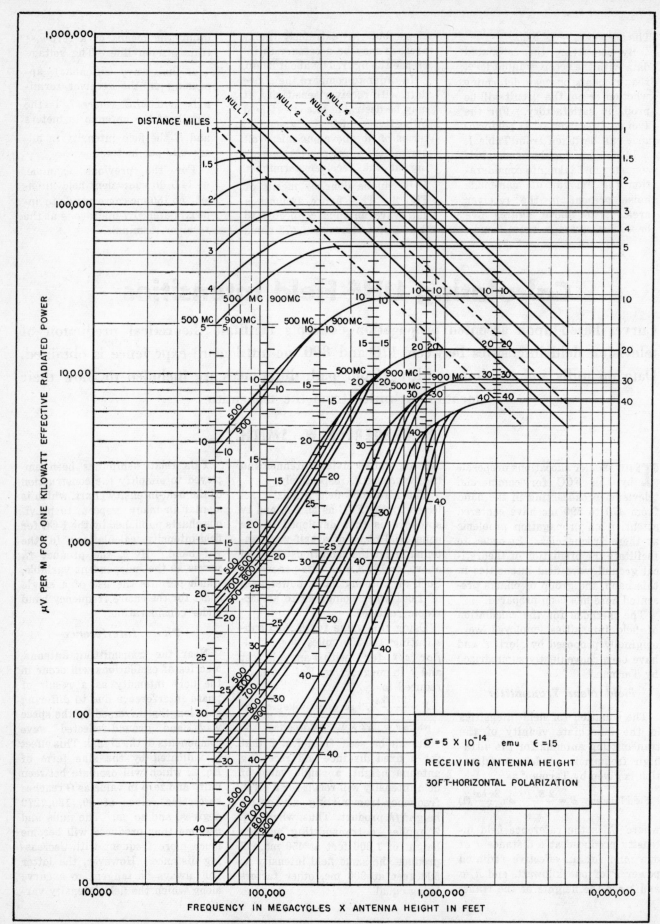

FIG. 1—Theoretical ground-wave signal range for 470 to 890 mc

ies inversely with distance. Such a curve can therefore serve as a guiding upper limit when the graph is used to secure a plot of E as a function of d.

The approximate distances at which the above mentioned nulls occur for various fh products can be estimated from the null lines that have been drawn for the first five nulls. These null points may be more exactly determined from the smaller graph, Fig. 2, which represents the distance to the various maximum and null points as a function of fh. The dotted lines adjacent to the first null line in Fig. 1 serve to indicate the points at which the field intensity curves will start to fall from and return to the inverse distance curve on either side of the first null, giving some idea of the behavior of the field-intensity curves in a null region.

As the transmission distance increases, nulls cease to appear, and field intensities will progressively diminish, varying as the inverse square of the distance when θ has decreased to 20 degrees or less. This is seen in Eq. 2 where sin θ may be replaced by θ itself for the values of θ just mentioned, causing d to be squared in the denominator.

Equation 2 may be used with accuracy until θ equals ten degrees, or until the radio line-of-sight horizon has been reached. Beyond these limits a different expression must be employed which provides field intensities in the diffraction region where the receiving antenna is below the line-of-sight. In order to obtain the continuous curves that appear in Fig. 1, smooth transition curves were drawn between the field strengths calculated for line-of-sight conditions and the field strengths calculated for the diffraction region.

It should also be noted that values shown in Fig. 1 for fh products of 10^6 or more are approximate only.

Diffraction Region Fields

Field intensities in the diffraction region where the receiving antenna is below the line-of-sight are computed by means of an ex-

pression due to Norton and given by Terman[4] as:

$$E = F_1 F_2 E_{su} \qquad (3)$$

where E_{su} is the surface wave intensity at the point on the earth's surface below the receiving antenna as calculated from Eq. 10, par. 2 of the same reference[4], and F_1 and F_2 are the appropriate height factors for the transmitting and receiving antennas as given by Eq. 20, par. 3 of the source above.

It is apparent from Fig. 1, that in the diffraction region the frequency-height product relationship no longer holds, and as a result separate distance scales have been provided for 500 and 900 mc, with the addition of curves for 600, 700, and 800 mc at the 20, 30 and 40-mile points as an aid to interpolation.

Prediction Vs Measurement

Unfortunately, the theoretical calculation of field intensities at these frequencies fails to take into account various factors such as terrain irregularities, shadowing or phase differences in signals arriving at a given point by multipath propagation. Also neglected are effects important at larger distances such as fading, day-to-day variations due to changes in the refractive index of the atmosphere, and tropospheric reflections.

Initial uhf field measurement surveys in the New York[5], and Washington[6,7] areas have indicated that

actual uhf field intensities observed are likely to be lower than those predicted theoretically. However, it is evident that much more investigation will be required before local deviations from the theoretical can be predicted with any accuracy.

Using the Chart

The field intensities developed at any distance up to forty miles for one kilowatt of effective radiated power may be read directly from the ordinate of Fig. 1 for any frequency-transmitting antenna height product along the abscissa. For example, an fh product of 100,000 will produce approximately 54 millivolts per meter at a distance of four miles for an erp of one kw for all frequencies in the band, and at thirty miles, 253, 212, 170, 141 and 124 microvolts per meter for 500, 600, 700, 800 and 900 mc respectively.

For other values of P, the ordinate scales must be shifted in proportion to $P^{\frac{1}{2}}$ as is done when using the charts published by the FCC for the vhf bands.

Where Eq. 2 is valid, Fig. 1 may be compared directly with the FCC curves. Citing the same example, at a distance of four miles, 54 millivolts per meter will also be obtained from the FCC curves for 82 mc at 1,220 feet, 98 mc at 1,020 feet and 195 mc at 513 feet.

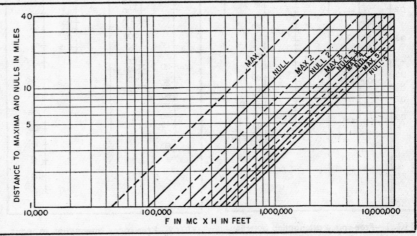

FIG. 2—Distance in miles to maxima and nulls

REFERENCES

(1) K. A. Norton, The Calculation of Ground-Wave Field Intensities over a Finitely Conducting Spherical Earth, *Proc. IRE*, 29, p 623, Dec. 1941. See also FCC Report 39920, March 18, 1940.

(2) F. E. Terman, "Radio Engineers' Handbook," McGraw-Hill Book Co., 1943, sec. 10, par. 1, 2 and 3.

(3) Reference 2, sec. 10, par. 3, Eq. 24 (b).

(4) Reference 2, sec. 10, par. 3, Eq. 18.

(5) G. H. Brown, J. Epstein, and D. W. Peterson, Comparative Propagation Measurements; Television Transmitters at 67.25, 288, 510 and 910 megacycles. *RCA Review*, 9, No. 2, June 1949.

(6) G. H. Brown, Field Test of Ultra-High-Frequency Television in the Washington Area. *RCA Review*, 9, No. 4, Dec. 1948.

(7) J. Fisher, Field Test of UHF Television, ELECTRONICS, p 106, September 1949.

Predicting Performance of UHF and SHF Systems

Graphic method determines suitability of a location for use as a transmitter or receiver site for uhf and shf transmissions. Takes into consideration such factors as free-space attenuation, topographic and atmospheric conditions, and absorption

By E. A. SLUSSER

IN SELECTING transmitter sites, the propagation conditions at a proposed location must be considered. This can be done by means of mathematical formulas and nomograms. For the uhf and shf regions a number of required nomograms are contained herein, as well as the procedure to be followed in making a calculation.

Four items must be considered in determining space attenuation.

These are: the attenuation that would exist in free-space, the topographical conditions, the atmospheric conditions, and absorption.

In making actual estimates for proposed sites, locations are chosen on the basis of topographical characteristics, assuming the effects of absorption to be negligible and allowing a safety margin for atmospheric changes. The following discusses the four factors that affect

attenuation, with particular emphasis on the free-space and topographic factors, which are the most important.

Free-Space Factor

Free-space propagation is defined as the propagation which occurs in a homogeneous medium which is both unbounded and non-dissipative. In actual practice, a criterion which determines free-

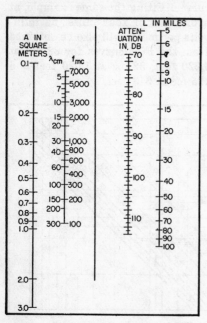

FIG. 1—Free-space attenuation between two identical antennas in terms of effective areas

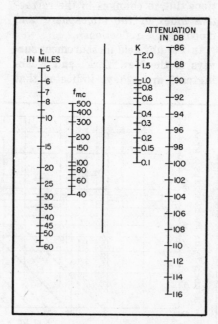

FIG. 2—Free-space attenuation in terms of effective antenna areas when the effective areas are expressed as $K\lambda^2$

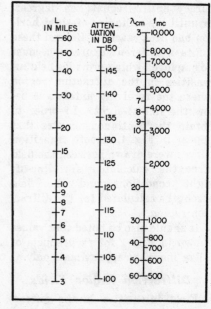

FIG. 3—Attenuation between two isotropic antennas separated by a distance of L miles

space propagation is to have no objects project into the first Fresnel zone. This first zone is bounded by points for which the transmission path from the transmitter to receiver is greater than the direct path by one-half wavelength.

The attenuation that occurs in free space can be expressed in terms of different variables and, for a particular case, one formula may be more advantageous than another.

The free-space attenuation in terms of effective antenna areas between two identical antennas is:

$$10 \log \frac{P_t}{P_r} = 10 \log \frac{2.33 \, L^2}{f^2 A^2} \times 10^{11}$$
$$= 113.7 + 20 \log L - 20 \log fA \qquad (1)$$

where f is expressed in mc, L in miles, and A in sq meters (A is the effective antenna area $K\lambda^2$). The above equation is shown solved by the nomogram in Fig. 1.

For use in Eq. 1, the effective area of the antennas must be calculated. In general, the effective area of an antenna is $1.64 G\lambda^2/4\pi$ where G is the gain over a dipole radiator. Some specific examples are included in Table I.

Frequently the effective area of

an antenna is expressed as $K\lambda^2$. When this is the case, the path attenuation can be expressed as:

$$10 \log \frac{P_t}{P_r} = 10 \log \frac{28.8 \, L^2 f^2}{K^2}$$
$$= 14.6 + 20 \log Lf -$$
$$= 20 \log K \qquad (2)$$

where L is in miles and f in mc. Figure 2 is a nomogram for the solution of Eq. 2.

The path attenuation between two isotropic antennas expressed in terms of power ratio is:

$$\frac{P_t}{P_r} = 4.55 \times 10^3 f^2 L^2$$
$$10 \log \frac{P_t}{P_r} = 36.6 + 20 \log Lf \qquad (3)$$

where L is in miles and f in mc. Figure 3 is a nomogram for the solution of Eq. 3.

In the case of actual antennas having gains of G_t and G_r, the path attenuation becomes:

$$\frac{P_t}{P_r} = \left(\frac{P_t}{P_r}\right)_{isotropic} \times G_t \, G_r \qquad (4)$$

The gains of a few typical antennas are included in Table I for use in Eq. 4.

For identical parabolas, we find that:

$$10 \log \frac{P_t}{P_r} = 20 \log 345 \frac{L\lambda}{D^2}$$

$$= 50.76 + 20 \log L\lambda - 40 \log D \qquad (5)$$

where L is in miles, D (parabola

Table I—Approximate Gains of Various Antennas

Antenna	K	Gain in Db Referred to Isotropic	Gain in Db Referred to Half-Wave Dipole
Isotropic	0.08	—	− 2
Half-Wave Dipole	0.13	+ 2	—
2-Element Parasitic	0.40	+ 7	+ 5
3-Element Parasitic	0.88	+10	+ 8
4-Element Parasitic	1.30	+12	+10
5-Element Parasitic	1.64	+13	+11
Dipole-Fed Parabola	—	Use Fig. 5	Subtract 2 db from values obtained from Fig. 5

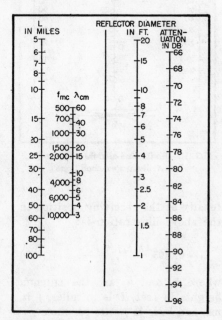

FIG. 4—Attenuation between two parabolic antennas in terms of reflector diameter in feet

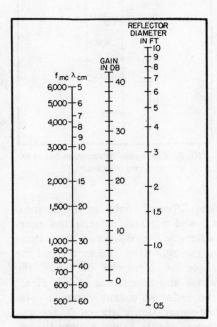

FIG. 5—Apparent power gain of a parabolic antennas in terms of reflector diameter in feet

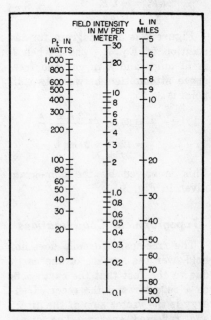

FIG. 6—Field intensity in millivolts per meter for a half-wave dipole at a distance of L miles

diameter) is in feet, and λ in cm. This formula is solved in the nomogram given in Fig. 4. The apparent power gain of a parabola is given by the nomogram in Fig. 5.

The maximum field intensity from a half-wave dipole in free space is given by the expression:

$$E_o = \frac{60 \pi l I}{\lambda L}$$

where E_o = field intensity at a distance L in volts per meter, l = effective length of the antenna in meters, I = antenna current in amps, and λ = wavelength in meters. Any other consistent system of units may be used also.

For a half-wave dipole, the effective length is λ/π, and the radiation resistance is 73 ohms so, when L is in miles, E_o in millivolts per meter, and P_t in watts, the field intensity is:

$$E_o = \frac{4.35 \sqrt{P_t}}{L} \tag{6}$$

This expression is solved in the nomogram given in Fig. 6.

For a properly terminated one-half wave dipole of length d, the voltage in microvolts appearing across its terminals for a given field intensity is:

$$V = \frac{d E_o}{\pi} = \frac{\lambda E_o}{2 \pi} \tag{7}$$

Figure 7 is a nomogram for the solution of Eq. 7. Thus, when L is in miles and λ in cm, the free-space attenuation between two dipoles is:

$$10 \log \frac{P_t}{P_r} = 20 \log \frac{1.23 L \times 10^6}{\lambda}$$
$$= 121.8 + 20 \log L - 20 \log \lambda \tag{8}$$

This is solved by the nomogram given in Fig. 8.

Topographical Considerations

The free-space formula does not hold over the surface of the earth due to the fact that the earth acts as a reflector and the received energy is the vector sum of the direct and reflected energy. The direct energy travels the distance L and the reflected energy the distance S.

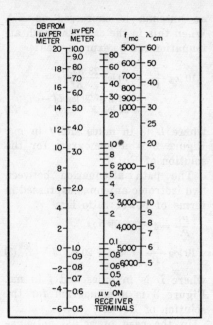

FIG. 7—Field intensity in terms of microvolts on half-wave antenna

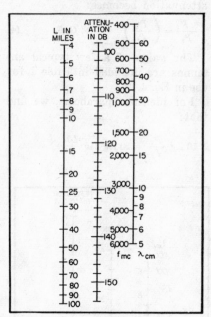

FIG. 8—Free-space attenuation between two dipoles

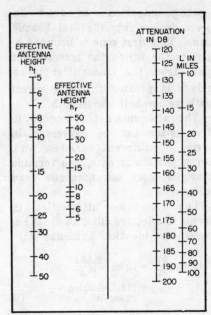

FIG. 9—Attenuation between two dipoles assuming ground reflections

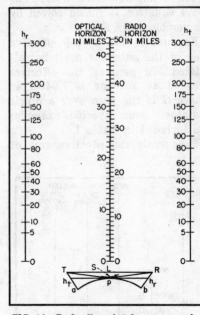

FIG. 10—Radio line-of-sight nomograph. Insert illustrates conditions

The difference between the horizontal and vertical polarization characteristic depends upon the nature of the reflection, the earth, and the angle of incidence β. Thus the phase and magnitude of the direct and reflected energy depends upon the separation distance L, the antenna heights h_t and h_r, and the reflection coefficient of the earth.

It can be shown that the field intensity at the receiving position in the above illustration is:

$$E_1 = 0.0105 \frac{h_t h_r f \sqrt{P_t}}{L^2} \tag{9}$$

where h_t and h_r are the antenna heights in feet, L is in miles, f in mc, and E, is in μvolts per meter.

From the above, we can develop a formula for direct transmission between two dipoles in terms of distance and antenna heights:

$$10 \log \frac{P_t}{P_r} = 20 \log \frac{1.7 \times 10^4 \, L^2}{h_t \, h_r}$$

$$= 144.6 + 40 \log L - 20 \log h_t h_r \qquad (10)$$

where h_t and h_r are in feet and L in miles. Figure 9 is a nomogram for solution of Eq. 10.

In order that Eq. 9 and 10 be valid, β must be small for horizontal polarization at uhf (less than 10 degrees); for vertical polarization over earth or fresh water β must be less than 1 degree; and over sea water less than 0.15 degree. The antennas must be elevated at least $1\frac{1}{2}$ λ above the earth plane, and h_t and h_r must be the effective heights of the antennas. Effective antenna height is explained in the discussion of radio horizons. Furthermore, the phase angle arising from the path difference between the direct and reflected waves must be less than about 30 degrees. This latter condition is satisfied if $h_t h_r / L\lambda < 7$ where h_t and h_r are in feet, L in miles, and λ in cm.

Optical and Radio Horizons

Two factors account for reception beyond the optical horizon; namely, refraction and diffraction. At uhf and shf, the effect of refraction predominates within the horizon.

For ranges just within and beyond the horizon, the effect of diffraction becomes of increasing importance. (Hence, for ranges near the horizon, somewhat inconsistent results may be obtained between Eq. 10 and 14 since the first considers only reflection or refraction while the latter equation considers mainly diffraction and average refraction.)

Refraction results in bending of the energy and is caused by the earth's atmosphere. This bending is equivalent to increasing the earth's diameter by about $33\frac{1}{3}$ percent of average conditions. Over smooth earth a transmitter antenna at height h_t and a receiver antenna at height h_r are therefore, in radio line of sight provided the spacing in miles is less than

$$\sqrt{2 \, h_t} + \sqrt{2 \, h_r} \; .$$

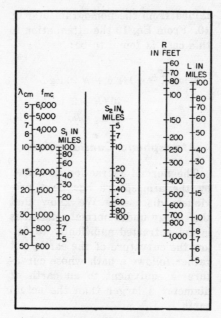

FIG. 11—Nomogram for determining Fresnel zone radius

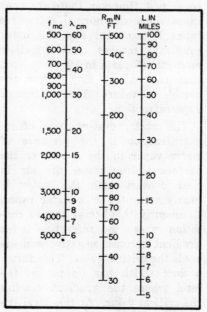

FIG. 12—Maximum radius of Fresnel zone

Both optical and radio line-of-sight distances can be determined for given antenna heights from the nomogram given in Fig. 10.

Let us consider the effect of refraction on the radio horizon as used in Eq. 10, thus taking into account both the curvature of the earth and the average refraction.

The conditions that exist are shown in Fig. 10. The intersection

of a tangent plane through a point P and the antenna supports determines the effective heights (h_t and h_r) of the antennas. The values of a and b can be determined by means of the line-of-sight nomogram (Fig. 10). A line is drawn on the nomogram between the total tower heights on the antenna height scales. Parallel to this line another line is drawn so as to intersect the radio line-of-sight scale, at a value equal to the actual distance L. The values of a and b are read at the points where this line intersects the antenna height scales. The value of h_t and h_r are then found by subtracting a or b from the respective total tower heights.

It is these effective antenna heights that should be used in Eq. 9 and 10.

Fresnel Zone Clearance

To have free-space propagation, the first Fresnel zone must clear all obstacles in the transmission path.

The first Fresnel zone is bound by points for which the transmission from the transmitter to the receiver is greater than the direct path by one-half wave length. These points generate an ellipsoid. The radius R of the first zone at any point in the transmission path located at distance S_1 from the transmitter and S_2 from the receiver is given by the formula: $R^2 = S_1 S_2 / \lambda$ where all quantities are expressed in the same units. When R is in ft; λ in cm; S_1, S_2, and L in miles:

$$R = 13.2 \sqrt{\frac{\lambda \, S_1 \, S_2}{L}} \qquad (11)$$

A nomogram for solution of this expression is given in Fig. 11. Radius R is a maximum when $S_1 = S_2$, and this is given by the formula $R_m = 1{,}140\sqrt{L/f}$. $\qquad$ (12)

In actual use R_m is usually computed and a line is drawn a distance R_m below the direct line-of-sight path between antennas on a profile to determine if this line clears all obstacles. This method is easier than construction of an ellipse. If there is an obstacle protruding over the R_m line, it can be investigated on the basis of the first Fresnel ellipsoid using the nomogram in Fig. 11.

Shadow Losses

Equation 9 indicates that the field intensity varies directly as the frequency so that for a given distance and antenna height, as the frequency is increased, less radiated power is required for a given field intensity. Beyond the horizon this is not the case, as it has been found that the frequency varies inversely as some exponential power of the distance, the latter increasing rapidly with frequency. In fact, the exponent increases so rapidly with frequency that transmission into shadow areas in the uhf and shf regions is impractical. It has been found empirically that the following expression can be used for calculating field intensity near or beyond the horizon:

$$E_o = \frac{0.0105 \sqrt{P_t}\, h_t\, h_r\, f\, L_H{}^{N-2}}{L^N} \quad (13)$$

where: E_o = field intensity in mi-

Table II—Approximate Noise Figures for Receivers

Frequency	Good Receiver 10 log F	Average Receiver 10 log F
<200 mc	5 db	10 db
200– 1,000 mc	8 db	13 db
1,000– 5,000 mc	14 db	19 db
5,000–10,000 mc	17 db	22 db

crovolts per meter, P_t = power transmitted in watts, h_t and h_r = actual antenna heights in feet, L_H = distance to the optical horizon in miles, L = total distance in miles, and f = frequency in mc.

The factor N is taken from Fig. 13. This curve takes into consideration both diffraction and average refraction. Within the horizon the exponent N is equal to two regardless of the frequency so that $L_H{}^{N-2}$ equals unity. Distance L_H can be ob-

tained from the nomogram of Fig. 10. From Eq. 13 the attenuation in this case is found to be:

$$10 \log \frac{P_t}{P_r} = 144.6 + N\, 20 \log L$$
$$- 20\,(N-2)\log L_H$$
$$- 20 \log h_t/h_r \quad (14)$$

Atmospheric Considerations

The normal refraction produced by the atmosphere has been previously discussed. We know that the energy under normal conditions is not refracted sufficiently to follow the curvature of the earth, but rather follows a path whose curvature is equivalent to an earth of diameter ⅓ larger than the actual earth.

The normal refraction is the refraction with which we are most concerned. However, there are some cases when the normal refractive index is exceeded and the index gradient reaches the requisite strength (5 parts in 10^8 feet) such that the energy may follow the earth's curvature. This is termed superrefraction.

The most prevalent cause of superrefraction is the presence of water vapor in the air. Over the surface of the ocean the air in near contact with the water is nearly saturated with water vapor. Frequently, this brings about a condition where the refractive index gradient becomes negative and exceeds the critical value. This forms a duct which has its top at the level where the gradient reaches the critical value. At this level the energy will just follow the curvature of the earth. It should be noted that ducts have no observable effect on the propagation of low frequencies and generally speaking, their effects are confined to frequencies in the 1,000-mc range and above.

Superrefraction may occur over land. In this case it occurs during a radiation fog. The latter is caused by the cooling of land at night by radiation, causing a thin layer of cold air to be formed just above the surface of the ground, re-

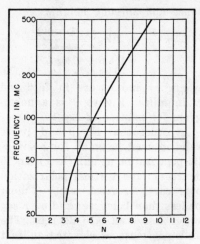

FIG. 13—Factor N is used in predicting field intensities near or beyond horizon

sulting in an abnormally large index of refraction in the lower layers of air.

The effect of duct formations between two microwave stations whose antennas are directed on the basis of the normal radio line-of-sight path might be to decrease slightly the signal intensity at one of the stations, but the observed effect is usually negligible.

Absorption

For all practical purposes, the absorption of energy by the atmosphere in the uhf region can be considered negligible. It does increase, however, in the shf region. The chief cause of absorption is the presence of water in some form. Curves are included in Fig. 14 to show the effect of rain and fog or clouds. It can be seen from these that the absorption increases quite rapidly with frequency, but that even a heavy rain gives little effect on any of the presently used communication frequencies.

Variations in the atmosphere result in changes in the atmospheric and absorption factors and are the chief cause of fading. Information on the amount of fading experienced under various conditions is far from complete. However, measurements made over an extended period of time at several locations indicate that for distances under 45 miles and with temperate weather conditions, fades of 20 db or greater occur only about 0.1 percent of the time on the vhf and shf frequencies. For longer distances, fades of 20 db or greater occur a larger percentage of the time. As a practical system design figure, a margin of 20 to 25 db should be allowed to provide for fading.

Overall System Calculations

The foregoing sections have developed various nomograms for predicting uhf and shf propagation. It remains to tie this data together in a form such that it may be used to predict whether or not a proposed path can be satisfactorily covered by a given uhf or shf system.

In general, the difference between the overall system gain G_s and the path attenuation α_p gives a safety margin that is used to improve the signal-to-noise ratio S/N of the output signal and to provide a safety factor S_f to protect against fading. Thus:

$$S/N + S_f = G_s - \alpha_p \qquad (15)$$

where all of the quantities are expressed in db. (The following neglects any noise improvement factor *nif* that is obtained by use of some modulation systems and hence, is somewhat pessimistic.) The overall system gain G_s

$$G_s = G_e + G_t + G_r \qquad (16)$$

where G_e is the equipment gain, G_t the gain of the transmitting antenna, and G_r the gain of the receiving antenna.

Any properly designed receiver for these frequencies should have sufficient gain to operate on signals comparable in amplitude to the receiver noise output referred to the receiver input, and it can be shown that

$$G_e = 10 \log P_t - 10 \log K\,T\,\Delta f - 10 \log f$$

Hence, the margin to provide for a desired output signal-to-noise ratio plus a safety factor to protect against fading is:

$$S/N + S_f = 10 \log P_t - 10 \log f$$
$$- 10 \log K\,T\,\Delta f$$
$$- (\alpha_p - G_t - G_r) \qquad (18)$$

where the various terms in this equation are all expressed in db.

From Eq. 18 the following method is obtained for determining whether or not a point-to-point path will be reliably spanned using a particular equipment:

(1) From the available transmitter output power P_t calculate 10 $\log P_t$.

(2) Estimate the term 10 log F for the receiver noise figure using the approximate values given in Table II.

(3) Calculate $KT\Delta f$. (Since $K = 1.38 \times 10^{-23}$ joules per deg K and a normal value for T is 290 K, this becomes approximately $4 \times 10^{-21}\,\Delta f$ where Δf is the receiver bandwidth in cps).

(4) Determine whether or not free-space propagation conditions exist. This can be done by plotting a profile of the proposed path and checking for adequate first Fresnel zone clearance of the nearest obstacle by means of the nomograms of Figs. 12 or 13.

(5) Calculate the term $(\alpha_p - G_t - G_r)$ by one of the following methods:

Free-space propagation. If free-space propagation conditions exist, this can be calculated equally well in three different manners. These are:

(a) Use Fig. 1 to determine the attenuation. The effective antenna area required by this nomogram may be taken from the figures given in Table I.

(b) Use Fig. 3 to determine the attenuation between two isotropic antennas. Then subtract from this

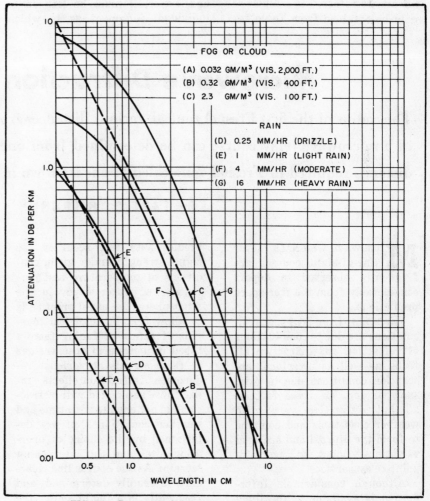

FIG. 14—Curves illustrate effect of rain and fog on shf absorption

the gains of the antenna arrays actually used and, hence, determine $(\alpha_p - G_t - G_r)$. The gains for various arrays referred to an isotropic antenna may be obtained from Table I.

(c) Use Fig. 8 to determine the attenuation between two dipoles. Then subtract from this the gains of the antenna arrays actually used and, hence, determine $(\alpha_p - G_t - G_r)$. The gains for various antennas referred to a dipole antenna may be obtained from Table I.

Line-of-sight conditions. If free-space propagation conditions do not exist, but radio line-of-sight conditions still prevail, Fig. 9 should be used to find the attenuation between two dipoles. Then the gains of the antenna arrays actually used should be subtracted to determine $(\alpha_p - G_t - G_r)$. The gains of various arrays referred to a dipole can again be obtained from Table I.

Shadow conditions. If radio-line-of-sight conditions do not exist, Eq. 14 can be used to obtain the attenuation between two dipoles. Then the gains of the antenna arrays actually used should be subtracted to determine the value of $(\alpha_p - G_t - G_r)$. The gain of various arrays referred to a dipole are given in Table I.

Attempts to check values obtained by either Fig. 9 or Eq. 10, with values obtained from Eq. 14 for ranges close to the distance to the horizon, will lead to inconsistent results since the nomogram of Fig. 9 (or Eq. 10) considers only refraction and ground reflection while Eq. 14 mainly considers diffraction. Within the horizon Fig. 9 is to be used and beyond it Eq. 14, but in the crossover region encompassing ranges near the horizon both effects exist and, hence, it must be left up to individual judgment as to which

method applies.

(6) From the foregoing and Eq. 18 find $S/N + S_f$. From this subtract a value of S_f equal to 20 or 25 db, since this is a reasonable system design figure to use to provide for fading. The value of S/N then found gives the worst signal-to-noise ratio that should normally be obtained over a path served by this radio equipment; that is, it is the value that will exist under conditions of maximum fade. Experience will have to determine what is permissible here. Offhand, a value of 35 db should be quite satisfactory.

(7) If f-m is used, the above S/N will be improved by an amount equal to $10 \log 3m^2$ where m is the deviation ratio.

The author wishes to acknowledge the assistance of Edward Daskam in the preparation of the original manuscript.

Microwave Diffraction Charts

The radius of the first Fresnel zone at various distances from the nearest terminal end of a microwave relay course can be determined from one nomogram. The adjusted distance required in Fresnel zone calculations is shown in the second alignment chart

By EARL D. HILBURN

MICROWAVE SIGNALS over line-of-sight courses are frequently observed to depart considerably from the free-space predictions.

Variations from free-space calculations are due to combinations of refraction and diffraction effects, as well as occasional absorption conditions due to rain, snow or fog. Of these factors, all but diffraction vary with weather conditions and combine to form the diurnal and seasonal variations noted in point-to-point relay services.

Although considerable information is available in the literature to enable the engineer to

predict with fair accuracy the signal strength under given conditions of temperature and percentage of water vapor in the atmosphere, the usual practice is to allow certain empirical margins of safety or fading factors based on long-term observations of relay signals at various frequencies. Diffraction effects, unlike those associated with refraction, do not change with time and weather conditions but are determined by the choice of operating sites and the intervening terrain. As the course line clearance is readily determined, and frequently is a factor under the engineer's control, diffraction

factors are of practical interest in most microwave relay installations.

Fresnel Zone

From diffraction theory,[1] when a wave strikes an intervening object a spherical wavefront radiates from the edge of the obstruction. The field intensity at any point beyond the obstruction is thus dependent upon the vector sum of the direct and scattered wavefronts reaching the receiver. A Fresnel zone may be defined as a circular zone about the direct path at such a radius that the distance from a point on this circle to the receiving

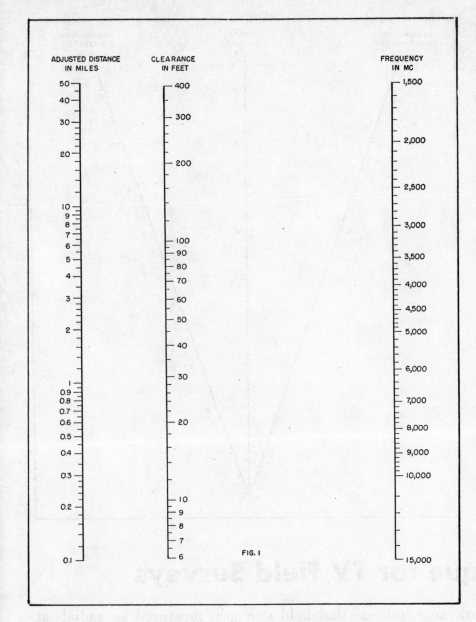

ADJUSTED DISTANCE IN MILES — CLEARANCE IN FEET — FREQUENCY IN MC

FIG. 1

values due to the fact that the phase shift along a line from the transmitting antenna to the top of the obstruction and from there to the second antenna is about one-half wavelength greater than the phase shift of the direct path and some signal reinforcement is obtained.

Figure 1 indicates directly the radius of the first Fresnel zone as a function of distance and operating frequency. The construction shown assumes a plane wave (that the spherical wave has expanded to the point where the front is flat over the diameter of the diffraction zones).

The results given by this chart hold true only if the obstruction is very close to one end of the course. For accurate results at any point along the path, the setting on the distance scale should be adjusted in terms of the results given by Fig. 2. This enables the retardation on both parts of the circuit to be taken into account. Figure 2 is a simple reciprocal nomogram and, as the scales are linear, they may be multiplied by different decimal factors as required.

For example, to find the clearance required for a good microwave path, assume an operating frequency of 7,000 mc, a total course length of 11.5 miles and a principal obstruction 3 miles from the transmitter.

A line connecting 3 and 8.5 on the outside scales of Fig. 2 gives an adjusted distance of 2.2 miles. Connecting this point with 7,000 mc on Fig. 1 shows a required clearance of 40 feet at the point in question.

In addition to determining easily the requirements for a good optical path, these alignment charts permit making quantitative studies of signal intensity conditions under various diffraction conditions including grazing or even badly obstructed courses where the receiver may be in a shadow area.

The principal course obstruc-

point has a path length that is some multiple of a half wavelength longer than the direct path. Hence, according to Fresnel's zone theory, all the even-numbered zones will send wavefronts to the receiver in opposite phase to all those from odd-numbered zones.

The effective field intensity at the receiver will rise and fall above and below the free-space value as the scattered waves alternately reinforce and cancel the direct wave. The energy reaching the receiver from a given zone is proportional to the

area of that zone and inversely proportional to the distance from the receiver. As the width of the rings making up the zones decreases rapidly as the radius of the circles increases, the first few zones are the only ones of any practical importance in diffraction studies of radio waves.

It has been stated [2] that a good optical path for microwave transmission is one with full first-Fresnel-zone clearance. With such an optimum path the signal strength at the receiver (excluding meteorological effects) is somewhat better than free space

tion should be plotted showing the projected area normal to the direct course between stations. The Fresnel zones should be drawn in as circles about the dot representing the course path, the radii being obtained from the charts. (While the nomograms show only the first zone radius, values for higher-order zones may be obtained by multiplying the indicated value by the square root of the number of the zone being considered.)

Having drawn the zone areas, with respect to the masking obstruction, the net field intensity may be obtained by integrating the area of the exposed zones. This can be accomplished graphically by means of the Cornu spiral.[3] In this manner, the departure from free-space values may be accurately estimated for any course.

REFERENCES

(1) Charles F. Meyers, "The Diffraction of Light, X-Rays and Material Particles", J. W. Edwards Co., 1949.
(2) Kenneth Bullington, Radio Propagation at Frequencies Above 30 mc, *Proc. IRE*, 35, p 1,122, Oct. 1947.
(3) C. R. Burrows and S. S. Atwood, "Radio Wave Propagation," Academic Press Inc., 1949.

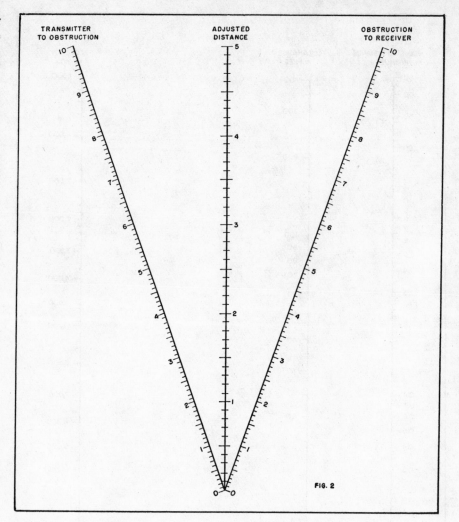

FIG. 2

Technique for TV Field Surveys

Data taken in the New York area indicate that field strengths measured on radials at 10-feet antenna height are not truly representative of actual service rendered. Traverse measurements are suggested and measured height factors reported

By JOHN F. DREYER, JR.

WHEN a field-strength survey of a television station is made, two purposes are usually in mind. The first is to satisfy the FCC that the station performs in accordance with the specifications of the construction permit, the second to assure the management of the station that a satisfactory signal is available to the majority of the population lying within the service area.

These two purposes are not necessarily served by the same set of measurements. In fact, the purpose of this article is to point out that measurements made along radials in accordance with FCC standard proof-of-performance procedure may give too optimistic a picture of coverage.

Standard survey procedure has recently been described in detail[1]. Briefly, the procedure is as follows: At least eight radials are drawn from the station, either at 45-degree intervals, or following roads at approximately 45-degree intervals. Profile graphs are drawn along these radials and the average elevation over the 8-mile distance from 2 to 10 miles is calculated. The height of the transmitting antenna above this elevation is taken as a reference and the expected field strength, for the given value of radiated power, is computed by reference to FCC coverage charts.

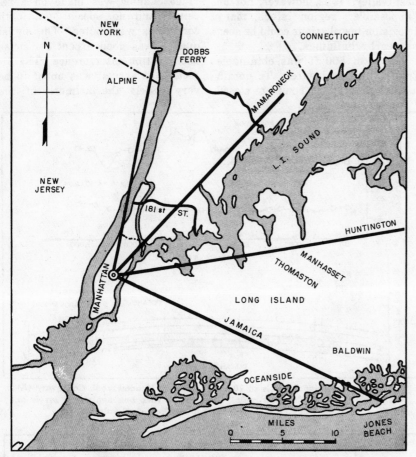

FIG. 1—Four radials and two traverses employed in making the measurements for the survey

Contours are drawn through the 500-microvolt points on the radials. It is presumed that the 500-microvolt signal is available throughout the area enclosed by this contour.

After the station is in operation, measurements of actual field strength must be made, and the values shown to agree within reasonable limits, with the predicted values. The FCC recommends that mobile measuring equipment be used, with an omnidirectional receiving antenna about 10 feet above the ground. The field values so measured must be cor-

rected to represent the actual field strength 30 feet above the ground, the latter value being the nominal height of antennas installed in homes. Simple theory, acceptable to the Commission for this purpose, states that the field strength should increase linearly with height. Thus, if field-strength measurements are made at 10 feet the stated values for 30 feet would be three times as great.

When the terrain between the station and the point of reception is flat and free from obstructions the measured and predicted values are usually found to be in reasonable agreement. But when rough terrain or massive obstructions are encountered, two discrepancies appear. First, the field increases at a rate less than proportional to the antenna height. Second, the values of field strength measured along

the radials are generally higher than those measured at locations between the radials. The latter effect probably is accounted for by the fact that roads along radials generally follow the gaps and valleys in the terrain, hence the obstructions between the station and the points of measurement on radials are generally smaller than those at other points.

Figure 1 is a map of a portion of the New York metropolitan area. Five television stations in Manhattan lie within the center circle. Station WATV, on channel 13, is located just off the map, 16 miles west of the center point. Four radials are shown and are referred to as the Jamaica radial, the Huntington radial, the Mamaroneck radial and the Alpine radial.

At the FCC hearing held in Washington Dec. 1, 1948, the writer submitted an analysis of 66 measurements made on the two Long Island radials. These measurements were made on channels 7 and 11 by the cluster method[2]. At each point, the signals at 10 ft and 30 ft were observed. The ratio of the signal strengths at these heights are plotted in Fig. 2. The ratios cover a wide range. At one point, the signal at 30 ft was 0.7 of that at 10 ft while at the other extreme, the 30-ft signal exceeded the 10-ft value by 12 to 1. When analyzed on probability paper, the distribution seems to be random, with a median value of 2.2.

Very Flat Country

In an attempt to arrive at a more comprehensive understanding of the height factor several other areas were investigated by a similar method, namely readings of signals recorded on tape in a moving vehicle. In a given area, a recording was made while the vehicle moved slowly around a closed course with the antenna at 10 ft. This procedure was then immediately repeated with the antenna at 30 ft.

A section of the Meadowbrook Causeway, about 2,500 feet long, was selected. Referring to Fig. 1, this location is near the end of the Jamaica radial in the center of a coastal marsh with no hills, houses or overhead wires, located 22½ miles from a transmitter operating on channel 11. The car was operated at approximately 2 miles per hour, or 3 feet per second. The time constant of the recording system was 3.5 seconds.

Checks were made at the beginning and end of each run to determine if the station output had changed appreciably. Most measurements were made on the sound signal of the station in question,

dicate that the height factor is determined principally by the terrain in the vicinity of the receiver.

The same procedure was followed at Thomaston, 14 miles out on the Huntington radial. As may be seen from the contour, Fig. 4, this region is at the bottom of a fairly deep valley. It is, however, not an "impossible" region, since many television installations could be seen on nearby buildings.

A run of 500 ft was obtainable free of overhead wires. To obtain a better average, a complete closed

circuit was made twice, giving a total travel of 2,000 ft. The tape was divided into 20 sections and the values plotted. The signals in this case at 30 ft were hardly different from those at 10 ft, the median value of the ratio being 1.05.

Observation of the signals on the video channel was made on a receiver and no special multipath conditions were noted. The signal quality was good except for noise and ignition interference. The direction of arrival was noted to be very closely the azimuth of the

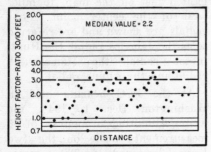

FIG. 2—Height factors on channels 7 and 11, along Jamaica and Huntington radials

since the picture signal is apparently subject to variation when cameras are switched. Otherwise, the behavior of the sound and picture signals is very similar.

The recording tape was divided into 20 sections and the average value of each section plotted, as shown in Fig. 3. Twenty-one signal ratios were calculated. It was found that 50 percent of these ratios exceeded 2.94 (the median value). This is in very close agreement with the theoretical value of 3.0. With the car stationary, at the center of the run, measurements were made of the signal at 15, 20, 25 and 30 ft, on channels 4 and 11. (The results are plotted in Fig. 6A.) It is interesting to note how precisely linear is the height factor for this flat type of terrain. Another height vs signal measurement was made in very similar terrain at Heckscher Park, 30 miles further east. The distance of over 50 miles puts the Manhattan stations well below the horizon. These measurements (Fig. 6B) would in-

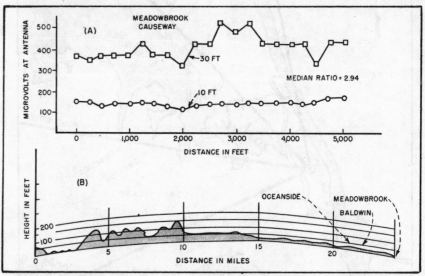

FIG. 3—Average signal levels at 10 and 30 feet at Meadowbrook Causeway (A) and profile (B) of the Jamaica radial. The median ratio between signal levels at 30 and 10 feet is 2.94, close to the theoretical value

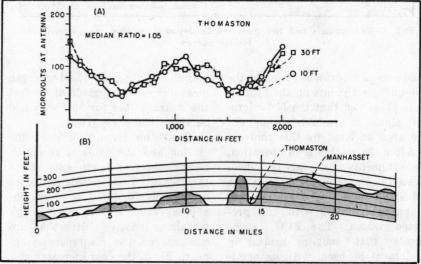

FIG. 4—Average signal levels (A) and profile (B) of the Huntington radial. The median value of the 30/10 ratio is only 1.05 in this case, reflecting the fact that the observation point (Thomaston) is well shadowed

transmitter. The signal path apparently was one of refraction over the top of the hill.

Measurements were also made in a cluster with the car stationary

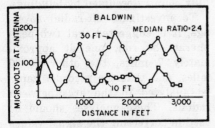

FIG. 5—At Baldwin, on the Jamaica radial, the median signal ratio was 2.4 (see position on profile in Fig. 3B)

and antenna heights of 10, 15, 20, 25 and 30 ft on channels 4 and 11. (One typical location is illustrated in Fig. 6C.)

Another location, 18 miles out in a residential part of Manhasset was checked. This point lies on relatively high ground but the terrain is covered with trees (no foliage at the time) and detached frame dwelling of approximately 30 ft height.

No recorder run was possible because of overhead branches and wires but the cluster measurements indicated conditions not very different from those in the valley. (A typical position is illustrated in Fig. 6D).

Residential Flat Country

On the Jamaica radial at 22 miles, a residential development in Baldwin was investigated. This seemed representative of suburban communities. The streets are winding, lined on both sides with two-story frame dwellings, with trees of about 25-ft height (no foliage when the measurements were made.) A recorder run around a closed circuit of 3,000 ft without overhead obstructions was feasible. When the recordings were analyzed, the median value of the ratio was 2.4, as shown in Fig. 5.

A recorder run of about 100 ft length was made in the vicinity of Oceanside. This is only about 1½ miles from the Baldwin location and the neighborhood is very much the

same. The 30 to 10 ft ratio was 2.25.

Figures 6E and 6F illustrate the signal-versus-height factor at the Oceanside location on New York stations (peak video signals were used in this case).

Radial vs. Peripheral Measurements

During the course of several surveys in the New York area during the past year, it has been observed that, in built-up regions, the signal on radial avenues is much greater than on cross streets. It seemed likely that this condition might also occur in hilly rural areas, because

vehicle surveys following radial roads naturally follow valleys, rivers, and notches in hills. To investigate this possibility, measurements were made on portions of the Alpine and Mamaroneck radials straddling the Bronx, nearby New Jersey and Westchester regions (See Fig. 1).

The Alpine radial (principally along route US 9W) lies on top of the Palisades and has a clear signal path. The Mamaroneck radial traverses flat country in the Bronx and follows the Boston Post Road fairly close to Long Island Sound. It encounters some hills at its outer end.

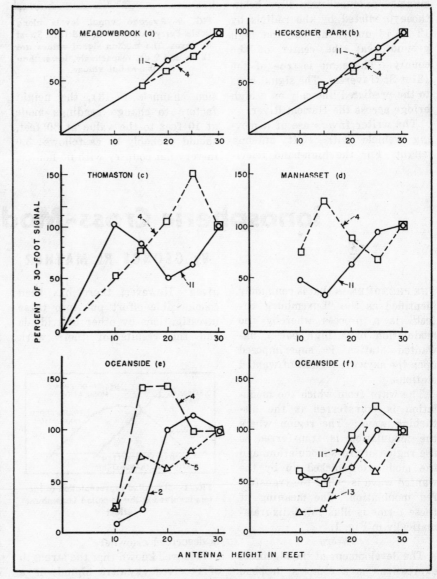

FIG. 6—Variation of signal with height at various locations, on channels 4 and 11 (a-d) and on all New York channels (E-F)

Recorder measurements taken on these radials are presented in Fig. 7. The readings are given as μv per m at 10 ft in db above 100 μv per m.

For comparison, portions of two traverses (peripheral paths) were measured, one on roads approximating an arc at 9 miles radius and the other at about 19 miles radius. The measurements on the traverses are presented in Fig. 8. In this figure, the straight lines represent the signal level as judged from the values on the two radials.

On the Mamaroneck-Dobbs Ferry traverse, through the center of suburban Westchester, the measured signals fell substantially below those predicted by the radials by 12 to 18 db, rising only on high ground near the center of the county. The same is true of the 181st St traverse. The signal rises to the predicted line only on a high bridge across the Harlem River.

The writer favors use of a moving vehicle with 10-ft antenna height. For the high-band televi-

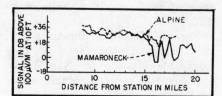

FIG. 7—Average signal levels along Mamaroneck and Alpine radials

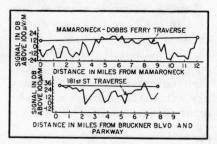

FIG. 8—Average signal levels along Dobbs Ferry-Mamaroneck and 181st Street traverses. The median signal values are 12 db and 9 db, respectively, lower than the radial values

sion channels (7-13), the height factors to change readings made at 10 feet to the value at 30 feet, should probably be as follows: 3.0 in very flat country with no houses,

trees or other obstructions; 2.3 in very flat country occupied by small buildings and trees; 1.1 in regions deeply shadowed by hills; intermediate values between 1.1 and 2.3 for hilly country occupied by buildings.

To investigate off-radial coverage, it is suggested that two peripherals be run, one at approximately 7 miles, the other at 20 miles, and that the recorder tapes be analyzed in the arcs between radials. These analyses should be used in correcting the signal values obtained on the radials.

The survey car should include a collapsible 30-ft. antenna for spot checks of the height factor. Multipath transmission should be investigated photographically at appropriate points on the peripherals.

REFERENCES

(1) J. B. Epperson, Television Field Intensity Measurements, ELECTRONICS, p 78, March 1949.
(2) Goldsmith, Wakeman and O'Neill, A Field Survey of Television Channel 5 Propagation of New York Metropolitan Area, *Proc. IRE*, p 556, May 1949.

Ionospheric Cross-Modulation

By GEORGE R. MATHER

THE PHENOMENON that is commonly identified as the "Luxemburg Effect" is a process whereby the modulation of a high power unwanted station is superimposed upon the skywave signals of wanted stations.

The wave from which the modulation is transferred is the disturbing wave: The region where the modulation is transferred is the region of cross modulation, and the modulation picked up by the wanted wave is called the transferred modulation. The meaning of these terms is illustrated diagrammatically in Fig. 1.

Theory

The development of the algebraic expressions is a complex problem and for the purpose of this report only a brief explanation will be

given. However, there has been considerable effort put into these investigations by other individuals and the results of their work

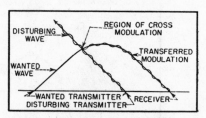

FIG. 1—Simplified representation of factors involved in the so-called Luxemburg effect

is described elsewhere[1,2].

It is well known that the strength of received skywave signals is a function of the absorption of the wave by the ions in the ionosphere.

The absorption in turn is proportional to the collisional frequencies of the ions and this is closely related to the thermal energy of the ions.

Consider then, the relation between the thermal energy of an electron and the presence of a radio wave. When a radio wave traverses the ionosphere there is an exchange in energy and some of the energy of the radio wave is transferred to the electron. Thus the agitational energy of the electrons is increased to a value greater than the thermal energy. When the agitational energy of the electron exceeds the thermal energy the statistical balance is upset and energy is transferred from the electron to the molecules at each collision. This results therefore in an overall increase in the mean thermal energy level and there is an accompanying increase in the collisional frequencies of the ions or indirectly an increase in the absorption coefficient of the ionosphere.

If a second wave now traverses this disturbed portion of the ionosphere it is apparent that it will be subject to a degree of attenuation due to the presence of the first disturbing wave. If the disturbing wave is removed there is an immediate decrease in the attenuation of the wanted wave. Thus a repetition of this process will permit observation of the phenomena of ionospheric cross modulation.

If, however, it is not convenient to pulse modulate the disturbing wave the desired end is achieved by simply amplitude modulating the disturbing wave. This will result in an alternate heating and cooling of the electrons and there will be a periodic variation of the absorption of the wanted wave. The wanted wave will therefore appear modulated and this transferred modulation may be detected on reception of the wanted wave.

Method of Observation

In order to observe the ionospheric cross modulation an experiment was devised making use of broadcasting stations KYW and WRVA on 1,060 kc and 1,140 kc respectively. The geometry of the experiment is illustrated diagrammatically in Fig. 2. The directional characteristics of the KYW transmitter are utilized so that the effective disturbing power is approximately 113 kilowatts.

The experiments were conducted at 2:00 a. m., EST from June 6 to June 10, 1950 inclusive and were of twenty minutes duration. The transmitter at KYW modulated its carrier to depth of 98 percent with a 100-cps tone. KYW operated with the tone on four minutes and off one minute throughout the test. At 2:15 a. m. KYW cut its carrier.

A receiver in Ottawa was tuned to WRVA 1,140 kc, which operated unmodulated on June 6 and 7 and modulated 30 percent with a 440-cps tone on June 8, 9 and 10.

A radio wave analyzer was used in conjunction with the Ottawa receiver to detect and measure the amplitude of the 440 cycle tone and the transferred one hundred cycle tone.

In addition a second receiver in

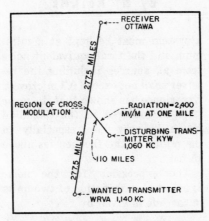

FIG. 2—Experimental setup for studying ionospheric cross modulation

Ottawa made field strength recordings on WRVA and the time that KYW cut its carrier was marked on these records.

The transfer of the one hundred cycle tone to the WRVA carrier was detected on each of the five nights. The tone was audible in the speaker and was detected by the wave analyzer.

On the latter three tests it was found that the WRVA carrier was modulated to a depth of 0.60 to 0.75 percent by the transferred one hundred cycle tone.

There was no noticeable change in WRVA field strength when KYW cut its carrier.

The transferred modulation was subject to various degrees of stability from intermittent on one or two nights to steady (except for normal fading) on the first two nights.

Precautions Taken

The use of the wave analyzer eliminated any possibility of a confusion of the transferred tone with any background hum (power supply) that may be present. It was verified that the transferred tone disappeared immediately upon the removal of the modulation from the KYW carrier.

To establish that the phenomenon was not local in origin several checks were made of stations adjacent to the 1,140-kc channel, however, the transferred tone was present only on the WRVA carrier.

The audio tuning of the wave analyzer was varied and there was no signal detected at frequencies other than 100 cycles (exceptions of course was 440 cycles).

This may be considered one of the most consistent phenomenon observed in ionospheric studies in that the transferred tone was detected on each of five consecutive nights. The transfer was evident throughout various degrees of absorption but the dependance on absorption, if any, could not be determined.

The transfer of the audio signal was effected by a disturbing power of approximately 113 kw at KYW. Assuming a linear relationship between power and transferred modulation, modulation of a wanted carrier to a depth of 10 percent would be possible with a disturbing power of a megawatt.

Available literature on the subject indicates that a greater transfer of modulation, then detected in these investigations, is to be expected. This leads us to conclude that perhaps the conditions of these tests were not optimum and more satisfactory results would be obtained with a mobile receiver. A disturbing transmitter operating on a lower frequency would also contribute to a greater degree of transferred modulation.

It is the desire of the author to extend an expression of gratitude to the Federal Communications Commission and the operators of KYW and WRVA for their kind assistance and co-operation which made the experiment possible.

REFERENCES

(1) L. G. H. Huxley and J. A. Ratcliffe, A Survey of Ionospheric Cross Modulation, *The Proceedings of the Institution of Electrical Engineers*, **96**, Sept. 1949.
(2) L. G. H. Huxley, Ionospheric Cross Modulation at Oblique Incidence, *Proceedings of the Royal Society*, **200**, 1950.

Atmospheric Noise Measurement

Observations of atmospheric noise down to 0.3 microvolt per meter between 75 kilocycles and 30 megacycles require receivers with special preamplifiers. Antennas are integrally mounted with the remote preamplifiers and connected by coaxial cables to recording equipment. Design data are given for a noise signal generator

By H. REICHE

BECAUSE of the scarcity of long-term information on radio propagation and atmospheric noise in Canada, there has been, within the last few years, an accelerated program of research in this field.

The equipment to be described is used for the continuous measurement of noise levels as low as 0.3 microvolt per meter over the frequency range from 75 kilocycles to 30 megacycles. It comprises six modified communication receivers, a control chassis for channel selection and all major switching operations, attenuators, a graphic recorder, and a noise-signal generator. The antennas are mounted on the boxes that house the wide-band amplifiers, and are remotely located, being connected to the measuring equipment through coaxial cables.

The apparatus illustrated is outlined in the block diagram of Fig. 1.

Preamplifier Design

Because no suitable antenna could be obtained having a flat characteristic over the required frequency range, the frequency spectrum was divided into three ranges, each covering about 10 megacycles. By making the lengths of the antennas 15, 22, and 30 feet respectively, it was possible to keep the sensitivity of each individual antenna reasonably constant over its frequency range without resonance at any frequency. Variations in gain are known and taken into account when making final calculations for the noise strength.

The main problem in the design of a suitable amplifier lies in the fact that the noise figure for such

a system must be kept at a minimum and the total equivalent noise from all sources including the receiver shall not exceed 0.3 microvolt. Experience has shown that the noise level encountered in the Canadian North is very low, especially in the region of the frequencies above 15 mc.

The expression for the noise figure of a combination of two units in cascade is given by

$$N_{AR} = N_A + (N_R - 1)/G_A \quad (1)$$

when N_{AR} is the noise figure of amplifier and receiver in cascade, and G_A is the amplifier gain. It follows that the gain of the amplifier should be high. The first amplifier stage is the major noise contributing factor and should have good stability and low noise level.

Sources of Noise

The principal noise sources of the first stage are shot-effect noise, developed in the plate of the tube, and thermal agitation noise, which results from the equivalent input noise resistance of the tube and circuit. Thermal agitation noise becomes negligible if the equivalent noise resistance is not higher than 400 ohms. Numbers of different tubes were subjected to tests to determine their equivalent noise resistance and suitability for use in

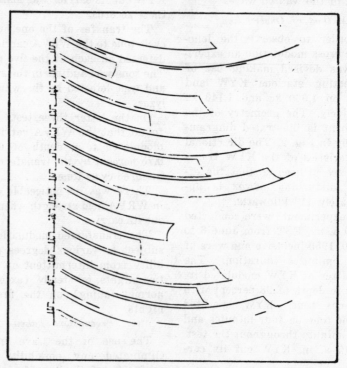

Representative record of two complete cycles of noise on six sequential frequencies

the first preamplifier stage. The noise resistance of a pentode showed approximately 700 to 1,500 ohms and, therefore, such a tube could not be used for this purpose. A 6AC7 connected as a triode showed a noise resistance of only 200 ohms, making this tube suitable for the first stage of the amplifier. The 6AK5 is a

tion. The complete arrangement represented by triodes V_1 and V_2, is termed the Wallman circuit[1].

The noise level of such an amplifier can be calculated and from the obtained results it may be seen that the thermal noise is of very small magnitude as long as the input resistance is kept low.

12×10^3 micromhos. Substituting these values in Eq. 3 the noise current of the first tube is then

$$I = 0.280 \text{ microampere}$$
or $$V = 0.179 \text{ microvolt}$$

The plate load impedance is equal to $1/S_m$ or 83 ohms.

To obtain the required bandwidth and amplification, the Wallman circuit is followed by a wide-band amplifier. To achieve a bandwidth of about 10 mc with a frequency response of ± 0.5 db over the entire range, a degenerative amplifier employing voltage feedback and staggered tuning was designed. The output was taken from a cathode follower, V_7, to match the 73-ohm impedance of the succeeding attenuators. The network consisting of R_3, R_4, and R_5 serves the purpose of providing proper match to the noise signal generator which is fed into the preamplifier at that point. The complete amplifier is housed in a watertight case with a strip-heater included to prevent condensation when operating the equipment at low temperature.

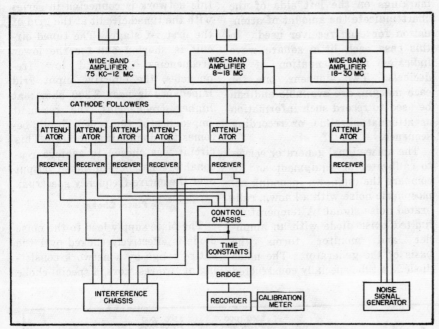

FIG. 1—Block diagram of the atmospheric noise-recording setup. Receivers are automatically switched

Receivers

Because the amount of noise passing through the receivers will depend on the effective noise bandwidth of the circuits, the six sets were carefully aligned to eliminate any possibility of variation in this bandwidth. For this purpose the selectivity control and avc control were fixed and the bfo was cut out entirely. The effective noise bandwidth B of the i-f amplifier of each set was then calculated from the equation

$$B = \int_0^\infty |G/G_o|^2 \, df \qquad (4)$$

where G is the gain at frequency f and G_o the gain at resonant frequency.

The input resistance of a type AR88LF receiver, while nominally 200 ohms, actually varies widely around this value. On a typical set, values as low as 60 ohms at 4.4 mc and as high as 350 ohms at 30 mc have been measured with an impedance bridge. Therefore it is necessary to introduce a resistance network at the input to reduce

similar type of tube and may be used if connected as a triode. Although the triode has the advantage of a low noise level, the Miller effect presents a problem in the design. The grid-to-plate capacitance is increased by a factor of $(G + 1)$, G being the voltage gain of the stage. Using a 6AC7 as a triode with an input capacitance of 11 μμf and a gain of 7, this capacitance becomes about 70 μμf because of the Miller effect. By making the gain of the first stage unity, the capacitance increases only to twice its value through the Miller effect, and any variations in the input capacitance are small when performing such operations as changing tubes. Having thus selected the design, in Fig. 2, of the first stage, the following circuit is a grounded-grid amplifier, employing another 6AC7 as a triode. This tube provides full amplifica-

The equivalent thermal agitation noise current can be computed from the following equation:

$$\overline{I^2} = 4KTG \, df \qquad (2)$$

and the equivalent shot-noise current from equation

$$\overline{I^2} = 4KTRS_m^2 \, df \qquad (3)$$

where $\overline{I^2}$ = mean-square current
K = Boltzmann's constant
T = absolute temperature (usually assumed 20 C)
G = total conductance at tube input
df = bandwidth in cycles
R = equivalent shot-noise resistance
S_m = tube mutual conductance

Assuming the bandwidth to be 10 kc we obtain from Eq. 2

$$\overline{I^2} = 1.62 \times 10^{16} G$$

and if the input resistance, $R_i = 1/G$ we obtain a thermal agitation noise of $I = 0.0127 \, (R_i)^{\frac{1}{2}}$ microamperes. For the equivalent mean-square shot noise we get

$$\overline{I^2} = 1.62 \times 10^{16} R S_m$$

Assume the equivalent shot-noise resistance R is 200 ohms and S_m is

these variations. The resistance seen by the input cable in this case varies only from 71.5 to 78.0 ohms. Although this arrangement involves a considerable loss of signal strength at all frequencies, the overall gain available is ample to take care of it. The noise output of the receiver is taken from the second detector stage as a rectified d-c voltage.

The major components of the control chassis are the sequence timing motor and selector switches that allow the six sets to be sampled in any required sequence. Each receiver is sampled for a period of 25 seconds, one complete sequence being completed in 3 minutes. A conventional R-C time constant provides a 60-second time delay for measuring average noise level. The time constant can be switched off for recording noise peaks. The recording meter is connected to the output of the time constant network by way of a balanced bridge circuit. The diagram in Fig. 3 shows this

circuit which can be adjusted by varying the screen voltages on the tubes with the control R_6.

Recording the Noise

A sample of the recording chart illustrated shows two complete cycles of recorded noise levels, using six different frequencies. The markings on the left side of the chart indicate the amount of attenuation for each receiver used. In this case each little square wave indicates an attenuation of 20 decibels. Two sidepens, one for each margin, are available and can be used to record such information as attenuation, time, or recording sequence.

The noise signal generator serves to calibrate the equipment and to compare the unknown incoming atmospheric noise with a known, calibrated noise signal. A temperature limited noise diode with an amplifier and monitor forms the basis of the generator. The noise diode is a tube specially constructed

for this application. It has a pure tungsten filament with high current capacity. The load impedance of the noise diode consists of a 3,300-ohm resistance in parallel with 40 $\mu\mu$f capacitance, as shown in Fig. 4.

Noise Generator Connection

At frequencies from 2 to 30 mc, this network is connected in series with the tuned circuit at the grid of the first r-f stage. The tuned circuit is shorted out for the lower frequencies. Thus at low frequencies, the effective input grid impedance is near 3,300 ohms; at higher frequencies, the resonant impedance of the tuned circuit becomes the dominating factor. This circuit was chosen to achieve reasonable constancy of noise output over the entire frequency spectrum.

Plate Choke

The plate supply lead to the noise diode is effectively choked over the entire range by a network consisting of two resistors, a special choke

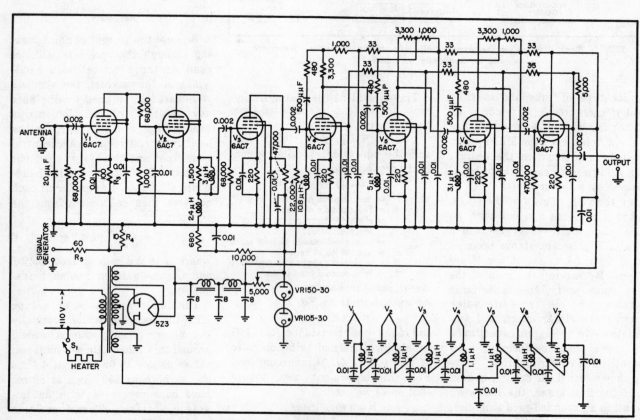

FIG. 2—Circuit diagram of the wide-band amplifier located at the antenna

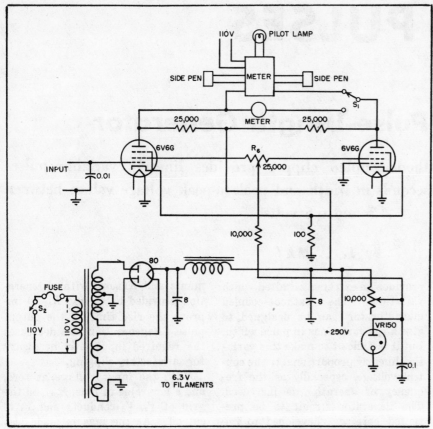

FIG. 3—Recording bridge circuit, balanced by adjustment of R_6

tor is in rms microvolts

$$(B_n)^{1/2} \times \left(M/(B_o)^{1/2} \right) = \text{Noise in rms (5)} \\ \text{microvolts per} \\ B_n \text{ cycles} \\ \text{bandwidth}$$

Conversion of microvolts to microvolts per meter can be made via the formula relating the two units. For a given antenna length h and given wavelength λ we obtain

$$\text{Microvolts} = \frac{h}{2} \frac{\tan \frac{\pi h}{\lambda}}{\frac{\pi h}{\lambda}} \text{ microvolts per meter} \quad (6)$$

A number of other factors have to be taken into account when calibrat-

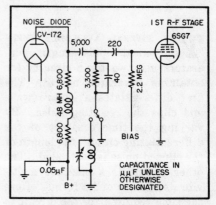

FIG. 4—Noise-initiating circuit for calibrating generator

ing the equipment but a detailed description of the entire calibration procedure would be beyond the scope of this paper.

Acknowledgement

The writer wishes to express his thanks to R. A. Chipman of McGill University for his contribution and suggestions.

REFERENCE

(1) H. A. Thomas and H. V. Cottony, Report CRPL-5-1, Central Radio Propagation Laboratory, National Bureau of Standards, Washington, D. C.

and a bypass capacitor. The noise diode is followed by two r-f sections and the output is taken from a cathode follower stage to the preamplifiers.

The i-f section of a receiver is used for monitoring purposes. Its gain has been made invariable by introducing cathode biasing. The conversion gain of the mixer stage in front of the i-f amplifier remains satisfactorily constant over the frequency range. One meter indicates the noise diode current, and another shows the noise output of the generator.

The calibration will depend on the accuracy and stability of the equipment. If M microvolts of a sinusoidal signal are required at the input of the monitor mixer for full scale output and the noise bandwidth of the monitor is B_o cycles per second, then $M/(B_o)^{\frac{1}{2}}$ is the monitored noise voltage in rms microvolts per cycle bandwidth. The atmospheric noise signals are usually expressed in terms of microvolts per meter for a noise bandwidth of B_n. Therefore the atmospheric noise signal that gives the same recorded reading as a signal from the genera-

PULSES

Variable Pulse-Length Generator

Regeneration added to a cathode-coupled clipper provides linearly variable pulses ranging from 0.5 to 24 microseconds in width and peak-to-peak voltage values between 4.5 and 6.5 volts

By J. C. MAY

THE SEVERAL AVAILABLE TYPES of variable-pulse-length generators use two basic circuits for obtaining a variable output. The first differentiates a square wave and clips the resulting pulse. By varying the time constant of the differentiating circuit, the length of the clipped pulse is controlled. The other circuit is a one-shot multivibrator in one of its forms. Here the time required for the circuit to return to equilibrium, after receiving an input pulse, determines the pulse length.

In some applications, such as pulse-width modulation, it would be convenient to vary the pulse width linearly over a wide range as a function of some voltage or current. The phantastron[1] gives a linear variation controllable by a voltage but provides an extremely limited width variation. The cathode-coupled multivibrator[2] can be designed to give large variations in pulse width. But it is difficult to make this variation linearly proportional to the control voltage, especially as the frequency of operation is increased. The generator circuit to be presented here was developed to improve the linearity between pulse width and control voltage while permitting the widths to be continuously varied throughout the repetition period. The circuit operates by adjusting the level at which a sawtooth voltage is clipped.

Basic Circuit

The basic circuit of the generator, shown in Fig. 1, is the cathode-coupled clipper developed by Goldmuntz and Krauss[3] with regeneration provided by C_c and R_{L1} to improve the rise time of the output pulse. Regeneration also decreases the required input level necessary for satisfactory clipping.

With the input voltage at zero, and a low value of bias, E_{cc1}, on the grid of V_1, V_2 conducts and V_1 is cut off. As the bias is made less negative V_1 starts to conduct. Its current causes a rise of cathode potential, which subsequently causes V_2 to be cut off. Regeneration aids this switching process. Tube V_2 will remain cut off until the grid bias on V_1 is decreased to a point below cut-off. While it is not physically possible to provide sufficient regeneration to cause V_2 to cut off exactly as V_1 starts to conduct, the change required in grid 1-to-

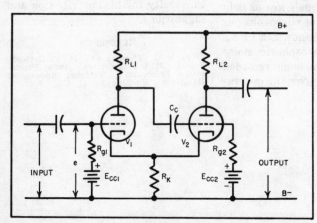

FIG. 1—Basic cathode-coupled clipper circuit with regeneration provided by C_c and R_{L1}

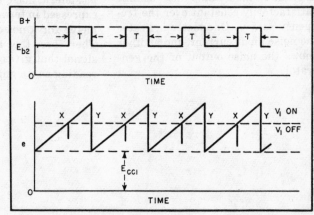

FIG. 2—Applied-voltage wave showing mechanism of pulse generation

ground voltage, e, necessary to change V_2 from "on" to "off" can be made in the order of a volt. For this reason, the switching level is indicated as a single line in Fig. 2.

Now suppose that the applied voltage, e, is a sawtooth voltage oscilloscope, is not ideal but its linearity is sufficient for its intended purpose. A triangular waveform would also be suitable but it is usually more difficult to obtain.

The minimum pulse width attainable with the circuit constants of over the full width range. The pulse height varies from 4.5 volts peak-to-peak at maximum pulse width to 6.5 volts at minimum pulse width. The variation in height could be further decreased by a decrease in regeneration at the expense of increased rise time of the output pulse.[3]

Pulse width as a function of E_{cc1} is shown in Fig. 4. Curve A rise time is good but the width varies in a nonlinear manner since grid current flows in V_1 for a portion of the cycle. To prevent grid current from flowing, a larger cathode resistor is used and, to offset the decrease in output, a larger load resistor is used in the plate circuit of V_2. Linear output of large amplitude and poor rise time of curve B is thus achieved. The compromise solution gives the results of curve C which has sufficiently good linearity, reasonable output, and rise time satisfactory for most purposes. The sensitivity of the pulse generator (sensitivity being defined as the ratio of change in pulse width to the change in control voltage E_{cc1}) will vary inversely with the magnitude of the sawtooth voltage. By reference to Fig. 2 it will be seen that E_{cc1} has to change by a small

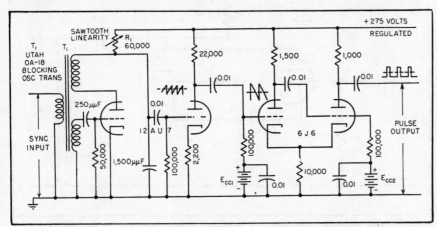

FIG. 3—Blocking-oscillator sawtooth generator feeding the variable-length pulse generator

plus the d-c bias E_{cc1}. If the peak value of e is never sufficient to cause V_1 to conduct, no change occurs in the plate circuit of V_2. In Fig. 2, e causes V_2 to start conducting at point x, to continue conducting for a time, T, and then to cut off at point y. A positive pulse of duration T will appear at the plate of V_b. By further increasing e, T can be made to increase linearly with E_{cc1} if the sawtooth voltage is linear. When the time, T, is equal to the period of the sawtooth, the output pulse will drop to zero because V_2 will be cut off for the full period.

Applied Voltage Requirements

The minimum sawtooth voltage required is about 10 volts peak-to-peak and may be obtained from any convenient source such as the time-base voltage from an oscilloscope. However, for experimental purposes, a simple blocking-oscillator saw-tooth generator[4] was built and is shown, together with the variable-length pulse generator in Fig. 3. The waveform of the sawtooth generator, as taken from the display on a Tektronix Model 511

Fig. 3 is 0.5 microsecond. This is limited primarily by the sharpness and jitter of the sawtooth voltage. The maximum pulse width with a 40-kilocycle repetition rate is 24 microseconds. Voltage E_{cc2} is initially adjusted to a value that will permit E_{cc1} to control the pulse

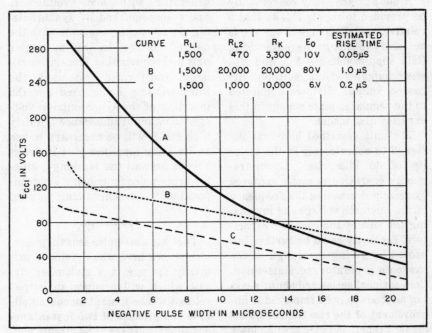

CURVE	R_{L1}	R_{L2}	R_K	E_O	ESTIMATED RISE TIME
A	1,500	470	3,300	10V	0.05μS
B	1,500	20,000	20,000	80V	1.0 μS
C	1,500	1,000	10,000	6V	0.2 μS

FIG. 4—Pulse width as a function of grid bias for various circuit constants

amount, roughly equal to the peak-to-peak value of the sawtooth voltage, to get 100-percent change in width when the amplitude of the sawtooth is small. As the sawtooth amplitude is increased the change in E_{cc1} must also be increased to provide 100-percent change in pulse width.

As shown in Fig. 2 the trailing edge of the pulse remains fixed and the leading edge is moved out as E_{cc1} increases in magnitude. If it should be desirable to reverse this operation the polarity of the sawtooth voltage should be reversed. The leading edge will then remain fixed and the trailing edge of the pulse will move.

Measurement of Pulse Width

The point-by-point accuracy of the pulse-width measurement is limited by the procedure used in this investigation. A Browning Sweep Calibrator Model GL-22 with 0.5-microsecond markers was used as the width indication. Markers of 0.1-microsecond width are available with this instrument but they had insufficient amplitude for this particular work. With reasonable care, the 0.5-microsecond markers give reliable, repeatable data.

A d-c amplifier may conveniently be provided to supply E_{cc1} so that a relatively small change in voltage is necessary to change the pulse width. Grid supply voltages E_{cc1} and E_{cc2} were supplied from suitably bypassed voltage dividers connected to the regulated plate supply in this experimental model.

The unit described here was designed to operate only in the vicinity of 40 kilocycles. Lower-frequency operation is easily achieved by merely decreasing the frequency of the sawtooth voltage and increasing the size of the coupling capacitors. Linearity could be further improved by giving the design of the sawtooth generator more attention. Conventional series and shunt peaking methods may be employed if improvement of the rise time or an increased repetition rate of the pulses is desirable. Without any changes

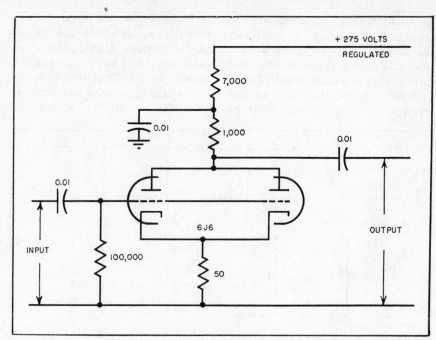

FIG. 5—Pulse amplifier with gain of 5, giving maximum output of 25 volts peak-to-peak

the unit has been operated at 100 kilocycles.

A simple pulse amplifier is shown in Fig. 5. This has been used where larger pulse output has been desirable. It introduces no perceptible pulse distortion when the external shunt load capacitance is 20 micro-microfarads.

Synchronization of this pulse generator with some voltage is easily accomplished by synchronizing the sawtooth generator with the desired voltage. In this particular unit a three-winding blocking-oscillator transformer was used, the third winding being used for the insertion of the synchronizing voltage.[5] The input impedance is fairly high but it will be necessary to use an isolating amplifier if it is desirable to prevent the blocking-oscillator firing pulse from being superimposed on the synchronizing voltage.

Applications

The variable-pulse-length generator shown here was developed primarily for use in a multiplier circuit which will produce an output voltage whose instantaneous amplitude is a product of two instantaneous input voltages. The circuit may be used for pulse-width modulation

where the modulating voltage is superimposed on E_{cc1};[6] it also can produce variable pulse delay where the pulse to be delayed is used to synchronize the pulse generator and the delayed output pulse is obtained from the differentiated generator output. This operation is analogous to conventional flip-flop delay multivibrator action but has wider, more linear control of the delay time. Variable pulse delay can be used as a basis for modulation (pulse-position modulation).[6] Two of these pulse generators could be connected in cascade to provide an extremely flexible variable-delay, variable-width gating circuit. The first unit would supply variable delay, the second variable gate width. The movable edge of the variable-width pulse may be differentiated to provide a pulse variable in time to be used to control the ignition time of a thyratron or ignitron circuit.[7] Control by a d-c voltage of the thyratron or ignitron current is readily assured over a full half-cycle of anode voltage.

In any of the above systems the pulse output can be made to be a triggered output. That is, if a sawtooth generator were employed that was not free-running but delivered a sawtooth only upon the reception of a synchronizing pulse, pulse output would depend directly on the repetition rate of the synchronizing voltage. This is not readily accomplished with the blocking-oscillator sawtooth generator shown here but several other forms are available.[8],[9]

The author wishes to thank H. L. Krauss of Yale University for suggesting this type of circuit and for his help and criticism during the investigation.

REFERENCES

(1) MIT Radar School Staff, "Principles of Radar," Second Edition, Chapter II, Article 16, McGraw-Hill Book Co., New York, N. Y.
(2) MIT Radar School Staff, "Principles of Radar," Second Edition, Chapter II, Article 15, McGraw-Hill Book Co., New York, N. Y.
(3) L. A. Goldmuntz and H. L. Krauss, Cathode-Coupled Clipper Circuits, *Proc. IRE*, 36, No. 9, p 1172, Sept. 1948.

Also O. H. Schmitt, A Thermionic Trigger, *Jour. Sci. Instr.*, 1938, XV, p 29.
(4) D. G. Fink, "Principles of Television Engineering," First Edition, p 473, McGraw-Hill Book Co., New York, N. Y.
(5) Radiation Laboratory Series, 19, "Waveforms," Section 6-4, p 218, McGraw-Hill Book Co., New York, N. Y.
(6) F. E. Terman, "Radio Engineering," Third Edition, p 776, McGraw-Hill Book Co., New York, N. Y.
(7) J. G. Skalnik, A Pulse-Controlled Thyratron, ELECTRONICS, p 120, Dec. 1949.
(8) Radiation Laboratory Series, 19, "Waveforms," p 273, McGraw-Hill Book Co., New York, N. Y.
(9) Radiation Laboratory Series, 21, "Electronic Instruments," Section 18-7, p 641, McGraw-Hill Book Co., New York, N. Y.

Sync-Separator Analysis

Response of a sync separation circuit to the nonsinusoidal composite television signal is analyzed. Equations are given for circuit design and calculated values are compared with measured values for monoscope and broadcast test pattern inputs

By W. HEISER

CIRCUITS used for sync separation are not complex in nature but their response to the composite television signal is quite different from that which a conventional sinusoidal analysis would show.

The requirements for an ideal sync separation system are threefold, namely:

(1) The sync pulses should be entirely free of any video signal or the blanking pedestal.

(2) The horizontal sync pulses should all have the same amplitude and shape; moreover, the vertical sync and equalizing pulses should be consistent in their waveforms also.

(3) A reasonable amount of noise immunity should be achieved in the separating system.

These requirements should be met for all conditions of modulation, percent sync and picture content that are within the FCC requirements.

The sync separation circuit to be analyzed is shown in Fig. 1. The input signal at point A is a composite video signal with positive sync pulses and the sync pulses alone are obtained at point B. With the proper choice of the constants in the grid circuit, the grid of the 6AG5 will restore in the sync pulse region.

The location of the restoring point in the sync pulse region is dependent upon the ratio R_2/R_1 as will be shown subsequently. The tops of the sync pulses are removed since grid current is drawn during this time, attenuating that portion of the sync above the restoring level by the ratio of r_g to R_2 (see Fig. 2), while the bottoms of the sync pulses and the video signal are removed since they are below the low cutoff point (-1 to -1.5 v) established by the low plate and screen voltages of the 6AG5.

With the grid of the 6AG5 restoring near the blanking level the noise immunity of this circuit is quite good. However, restoring in this region rather than near the sync tips tends to make the restoring level more critical since changes in the restoring level due to variations in the average video signal or the advent of the vertical sync pulses will cause a variation in the shape or width of the sync pulses at the output of the sync clipper since the sync pulse is trapezoidal rather than rectangular in shape.

The variation due to changes in the average video signal is usually slow enough to be negligible, while that due to the vertical sync pulses may be eliminated by using a large enough coupling capacitor as will be shown later. While increasing C above a certain minimum value does not affect the restoring level, it will decrease the immunity of the cir-

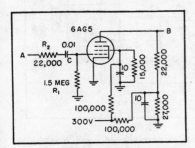

FIG. 1—Sync clipper circuit analyzed in text

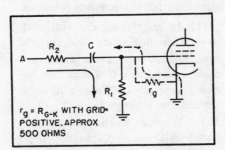

FIG. 2—Solid arrow shows discharge path for C and dashed arrow the charging path

cuit to some types of noise.

Pulse Amplitude

The magnitude of the sync pulses desired at the output of the clipper as well as the size of the input composite signal play a large part in determining how far down from the sync tips we may restore without having video and pedestal present in our clipped sync output. For example, with a 25-v peak-to-peak composite signal at point *A* with 20-percent sync, or 5 v of sync, we will only have 30 percent, or 1.5 v of sync at the clipper grid if we are restoring 70 percent down.

To keep the sync clean, the cutoff point of the tube, determined largely by the screen voltage, must be closer to zero than —1.5 v, or we must restore closer to the sync tips with perhaps some decrease in noise immunity. With the cutoff point

capacitance has no effect on the restoring level when the vertical sync pulses are not considered.

(4) The change in restoring level due to the vertical sync pulses with various values of coupling capacitors larger than the value found in item 3 above.

(5) The minimum value of the coupling capacitor to eliminate this change in restoring level during vertical sync pulse time.

Restoring Level

For these calculations we need only consider that portion of the circuit shown in Fig. 2. For the first three computations the input signal at point *A* is as shown in Fig. 3. The concept of an average level (K_A) for the video signal is not strictly rigorous unless we have a constant video signal such as given by a test pattern. Since all meas-

We may neglect r_g as compared with R_2.

For purposes of computation, the idealized signal is shown in Fig. 4. Then E and E' represent the charge on capacitor C at the end of the discharge and charge times respectively. Since the voltage across C at the end of the charge time equals the voltage at the beginning of the sync pulse plus the amount the capacitor is able to charge up, we may write Eq. 1. Similarly, we may write Eq. 2 by noting that the voltage across C at the end of the discharge time is equal to the voltage at the beginning of the discharge minus the amount the capacitor has discharged during the time interval.

$$E' = E + (E_c - E)(1 - e^{-t_1/R_2 C}) \qquad (1)$$
$$E = E' - [E' - E_c(1 - K_A)]$$
$$(1 - e^{-t_2/R_1 C}) \qquad (2)$$

To simplify the notation let

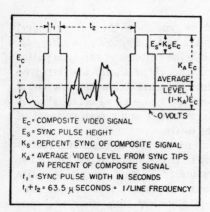

FIG. 3—Composite video signal fed to circuit of Fig. 2

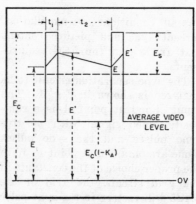

FIG. 4—Idealized input signal used for analysis of the circuit action

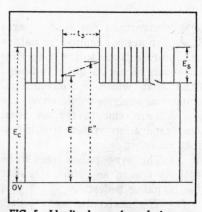

FIG. 5—Idealized waveform during vertical blanking time

closer to zero the magnitude of the sync pulses in the output will be less.

It is proposed to show a method for calculating the following:

(1) The restoring level at the grid of the clipper tube, assuming for the present that the vertical sync pulses have no effect on this level.

(2) The variations in this restoring level with different values of percent sync in the composite video input signal and with changes in average picture content.

(3) The value of the coupling capacitor above which any increase in

urements made in this article were taken using a test pattern and since the variations in the restoring level from line to line are small, the average level K_A is taken over a complete field for the purpose involved.

(1) In calculating the restoring level when neglecting the vertical sync pulses two assumptions are made. Capacitor C discharges between sync pulses through $R_1 + R_2$ toward the average level, $E_c (1 - K_A)$. We may neglect R_2 as compared with R_1. Capacitor C is charging during the sync pulses toward the sync tips through $R_2 + r_g$.

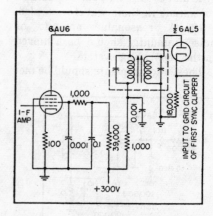

Circuit of narrow-band sync amplifier and sync detector that caused rounding of pulses shown in Fig. 6

$$\frac{t_2}{R_1 C} = x \quad \text{and} \quad \frac{t_1}{R_2 C} = y$$

Then
$$E' = E_c - (E_c - E) e^{-y}$$
$$= E_c (1 - e^{-y}) + E e^{-y} \quad (3)$$
$$E = E_c (1 - K_A) + E' e^{-x} - E_c$$
$$(1 - K_A) e^{-x} = E_c (1 - K_A)$$
$$(1 - e^{-x}) + E' e^{-x} \quad (4)$$

It is immaterial whether we solve at this time for E or E' since they are almost equal.

Solving for E by inserting Eq. 3 in Eq. 4,

$$E = E_c \left[1 - \frac{K_A (1 - e^{-x})}{1 - e^{-x} e^{-y}} \right] \quad (5)$$

To simplify Eq. 5, consider the series

$$e^z = 1 + z + \frac{z^2}{2'} + \frac{z^3}{3'} + \dots .$$

As long as z is less than 0.1 we may use the approximation $e^z \approx 1 + z$ with an error less than 1 per-

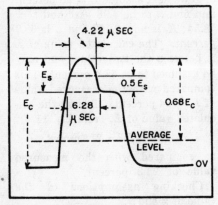

FIG. 6—Horizontal sync pulse at clipper grid with the tube removed from its socket shows rounding

cent. If x and y are less than 0.1,

$$1 - e^{-x} = 1 - \frac{1}{1+x} = \frac{x}{1+x}$$

and
$$1 - e^{-x} e^{-y} = \frac{x + y + xy}{(1+x)(1+y)}$$

Let us define $K_1 = \frac{1 - e^{-x}}{1 - e^{-x} e^{-y}}$

$$= \frac{x}{x + \frac{y}{1+y}}$$

If we restrict y to being 0.05 or less we may then approximate with less than a 5-percent error by calling

$$K_1 \approx \frac{x}{x+y}$$

Substituting the values of x and y and simplifying,

$$K_1 = \frac{1}{1 + \frac{R_1}{R_2} \frac{t_1}{t_2}} \quad (6)$$

so Eq. 5 becomes

$$E = E_c (1 - K_A K_1) \quad (7)$$

Let us define the restoring level as $L = (E_c - E)/E_s$. Examination of Fig. 4 shows that when this ratio is zero we are restoring at the top of the sync tips and when it is 1 we

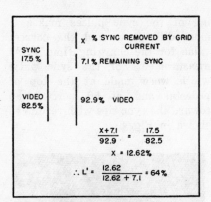

FIG. 7—Sample calculation of measured restoring level

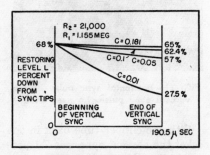

FIG. 8—Exponential change in restoring level during vertical sync pulses with various values of C

are restoring at the blanking level. Using Eq. 7 and $E_s = K_s E_c$

$$L = \frac{K_A K_1}{K_s} \quad (8)$$

Change in Restoring Level

(2) Examination of Eq. 8 shows that the restoring level moves closer to the blanking level with a whiter picture (K_A increasing) and/or a decrease in the percent sync in the input signal (K_s decreasing).

(3) Examination of Eq. 6 shows that K_1 is independent of C as long as our assumption of y being 0.05 or less holds. This means that for

any set of constants R_1 and R_2 the restoring level is independent of C as long as it is greater than the value given below. This, as stated previously, does not mean that the

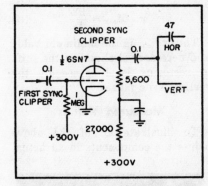

Circuit of second sync clipper whose output feeds the horizontal discriminator and vertical integrator

value of C will not affect the change in restoring level due to the vertical sync pulses.

For $y < 0.05 = t_1/(R_2 C)$

$$C'_{min} = \frac{20 t_1}{R_2} \quad (9)$$

(4) During the time when the vertical sync pulses are present, capacitor C of Fig. 2 is charging toward the sync tips. This charging time may be assumed to be $3H$ or 190.5 μsec (see Fig. 5). The voltage E'' on the capacitor at the end of the vertical sync pulses is the voltage at the beginning plus the amount the capacitor charges or

$$E'' = E + (E_c - E)(1 - e^{-t_3/R_2 C})$$

The restoring level at the end of the vertical sync pulses L_v expressed as percent of sync down from the sync tips is then

$$L_v = \frac{E_c - E''}{E_s} = \frac{(E_c - E)}{E_s} e^{-t_3/R_2 C} \quad (10)$$

But $(E_c - E)/E_s = L$, the restoring level considering only horizontal sync pulses. We have therefore

$$L_v = L e^{-t_3/R_2 C} \quad (11)$$

Equation 11 shows the change in the restoring level after the vertical sync pulses.

(5) In a manner similar to that in which Eq. 9 was developed we may compute a value of the coupling capacitor C necessary to reduce the

change in restoring level after the vertical sync pulses to a 5-percent change.

From Eq. 11, $e^{-t_3/R_2C} = 0.95$

$$\text{or} \quad \frac{t_3}{R_2C} \approx 0.05$$

$$\text{or} \quad C''_{min} = \frac{20t_2}{R_2} \quad (12)$$

Thus C''_{min} is the minimum value of C necessary to eliminate the shift in restoring level caused by the vertical sync pulses.

Measured Values

To illustrate all of the above points the components in an actual

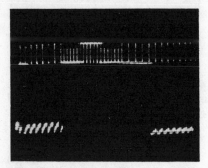

FIG. 9—Composite video signal at clipper grid with tube out

circuit were measured as 21,000 ohms for R_2, C of 0.01 μf and R_1 as 1.5 megohms. Measurements were made at the sync clipper grid with a suitable oscilloscope to measure sync pulse width and percent sync without excessive loading of the grid resistance R_1. Since the probe used with the scope had an input impedance of 5 megohms, this is taken into account by using a value of 1.155 megohms for R_1, the value of a parallel combination of 1.5 meg with 5 meg.

Using an r-f monoscope signal the percent sync was 17.5 percent (K_s = 0.175) and the average level measured down from the sync tips was 68 percent ($K_A = 0.68$) at the clipper grid with the tube removed. The relatively low percentage of sync and the rounding of the sync pulses as shown in Fig. 6 are due to a narrow-band sync amplifier used for greater noise immunity in the particular receiver on which these tests were made. This round-

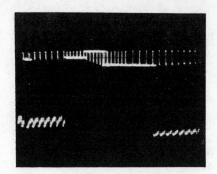

FIG. 10—Composite video signal at clipper grid showing restoring level

ing of the sync pulses makes it more difficult to find the correct value for the charging time, t_1, so measurements of the sync pulse width were made at the top of pedestal and at 50 percent up toward the sync tips with results as shown in Fig. 6.

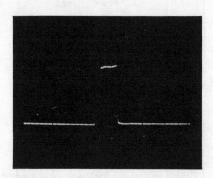

FIG. 11—Horizontal sync pulse before vertical sync pulse, 7.4 μsec wide

With the clipper tube back in the socket the percent sync was 7.1 percent before the vertical sync pulses and 14.0 percent after these pulses. From these readings we may find the measured restoring levels in percent down from the sync tips as

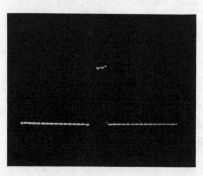

FIG. 12—Horizontal sync pulse after vertical sync, 5.2 μsec wide

shown in Fig. 7. The results are $L' = 64$ percent and $L_v' = 23.3$ percent.

To calculate the restoring levels we must know t_1 and t_2. When the sync pulses do not have a fast rise time a trial and error method for finding t_1 must be used. When the sync pulses are trapezoidal in shape with a fast rise time a close estimate of t_1 may be made; however this trial and error method should give more accurate results. Let us first assume $L = 65$ percent. Then interpolating linearly from Fig. 6 for t_1 between the bottom of the sync pulse and the 50-percent point we have $t_1 = 4.84$ μsec and $t_2 = 58.66$ μsec.

Putting the values into Eq. 6, $K_1 = 0.1805$. From Eq. 8, $L = K_1K_A/K_s = 70.2$ percent. Since this does not check with our assumed value of L we next assume $L = 68$ percent and find t_1 to be 4.96 μsec and $t_2 = 58.54$; K_1 is now 0.177 and L is 68.7 percent. The calculated value of L is between the two values and may be assumed to be 68.4 percent. This compared with the measured value of $L = 64$ percent. To find the calculated value of L_v from Eq. 11,

$$L_v = L\,e^{-t_3/R_2C} = 27.5 \text{ percent,}$$

as compared with the measured value of 23.3 percent.

Checking assumptions of the value of x and y,

$$x = t_2/(R_1C) = 0.0051 \text{ and } y = t_1/(R_2C) = 0.0236.$$

Since x is less than 0.1 and y is less than 0.05 the assumptions are verified.

Coupling Capacitor

Using Eq. 9, we may find for particular values of R_1 and R_2 the value of capacitance above which any increase in capacitance has no effect on the restoring level when the vertical sync pulses are neglected. This value is

$$C'_{min} = 20t_1/R_2 = 0.0047 \ \mu f.$$

The larger the value of C, the less will be the change in restoring level due to the vertical sync pulses. To compute this necessary value of C to reduce this restoring level change to 5 percent from Eq. 12,

$$C''_{min} = 20t^3/R_2 = 0.181 \ \mu f.$$

Figure 8 shows the effect of various values of the coupling capacitor on the restoring level change during the vertical sync pulses. These curves were found using Eq. 11 with R_2 of 21,000 ohms.

As a further check, measurements were made on WCBS with a test pattern. The results of this and the above work are shown in Table I. The calculated and measured values of the restoring levels check well within the accuracy of the measurements.

Shown in Fig. 9 and 10 are photographs of the composite signal at the sync clipper grid with the tube out and with it in. This illustrates

Table I—Calculated and Measured Values

	WCBS	Monoscope
With 6AG5 Clipper Out		
Percent sync—K_s	24%	17.5%
Average level from sync tips—K_A	66%	68%
Width of hor. sync pulse at bottom	6.74 μsec	6.28 μsec
Width of hor. sync pulse at 50% point	4.34 μsec	4.22 μsec
With Tube in Socket		
Percent sync at clipper grid before vertical sync pulse	12%	7.1%
Percent sync at clipper grid after vertical sync pulse	20.6%	14.0%
Measured Restoring Levels		
Before vertical—L'	56.8%	64 %
After vertical—L'_s	18.0%	23.3%
Calculated Restoring Levels		
Before vertical—L	53 %	68.4%
After vertical—L_s	21.4%	27.5%

the restoring level variations with $C = 0.01 \ \mu f$. The photographs of Fig. 11 and 12 show the horizontal sync pulses before and after the vertical sync pulse respectively after another stage of amplification which has widened both pulses slightly.

The sync pulse before the vertical sync pulse is 27.7 percent wider than the one after this pulse; this may cause some trouble in the afc circuit for the horizontal sweep. Figure 8 shows that in order to eliminate this effect the coupling capacitor should be at least 0.1 μf when $R_1 = 1.155$ meg and $R_2 = 21,000$ even though the noise immunity may suffer somewhat.

The writer thanks Bernard Amos for his comments and encouragement in the writing of this article.

Improved Vertical Synchronizing System

Positive interlace, freedom from line pairing and increased noise immunity without critical adjustments result from use of large-amplitude steep-fronted pulses for vertical synchronization. The pulses are derived from a simple circuit containing a germanium diode and a single triode

By ROBERT C. MOSES

THE RELATIVELY POOR performance of vertical sync circuits is indicated by the difficulty often encountered in obtaining accurate and stable interlace free of drift, line pairing and the necessity for frequent and critical adjustment of television receivers.

With a few exceptions, present vertical sync circuits are essentially unchanged from those used in receivers of prewar vintage. Many of the shortcomings of these systems come about as a result of the method used for segregation of the vertical sync pulses from the composite sync signal. Almost without exception, this is performed by resistance-capacitance integration or equivalent means.

Integration with a resistance-capacitance network having a time constant suitable for complete elimination of the horizontal pulses produces a slowly rising serrated wavefront which reaches its maximum amplitude in approximately 190 microseconds. Because, with sync pulses of this shape, the triggering point of the vertical deflection oscillator is not positively determined with respect to time, stable and carefully controlled operating conditions of the latter are required if accurate interlacing is to be maintained.

Improved Rise Time

A material improvement in both vertical sync stability and interlace performance would result were the triggering pulses steep-fronted and of fairly large amplitude. Moreover, if a circuit responsive only to pulses of greater than a certain duration were placed between the sync clipper and the vertical deflection circuits, both horizontal pulses and short-duration noise pulses occurring during the field scanning interval would be rejected and the noise immunity of the entire system improved.

The circuit to be described performs the functions of pulse segregation, amplification, limiting, and sharpening, to yield a series of large-amplitude, steep-fronted pulses in rigidly controlled phase relationship to the transmitted vertical sync signal.

Theory of Operation

Figure 1 shows a block diagram

of the improved sync system, while Fig. 2 indicates the significant waveforms drawn against a relative time scale.

Part A of Fig. 2 is a section of the standard sync signal at a time corresponding to the end of one interlaced field, and shows the last two horizontal sync pulses, twelve equalizing pulses and six vertical sync pulses. The approximate durations of these pulses are 5 μsec, 2.5 μsec and 27 μsec respectively.

The mixed line, equalizing, and field sync pulses are applied in positive polarity to a resistance-capacitance differentiating network having a carefully chosen time constant. The network passes with negligible attenuation the leading and trailing edges of all pulses. Charge storage in the capacitor during the pulse interval, however, introduces an appreciable droop in the flat top of each pulse, and causes the trailing edge to undershoot the pulse base line. It can be shown that the amplitude of the undershoot is a function of both the width of the applied pulse and the time constant of the network.

For a single-stage resistance-capacitance network, the amplitude of the undershoot may be expressed by:

$$E = V - \left[\frac{V}{\epsilon^{t/RC}}\right]$$

where E = amplitude of pulse undershoot, V = amplitude of applied pulse, t = width of applied pulse in μsec, RC = time constant of network in ohms-μf, and ϵ = 2.71828, the base of natural logarithms.

For a cascaded network containing n identical stages,

$$E = V - \left[\frac{V}{(\epsilon^{t/RC})^{\frac{n(n+1)}{2}}}\right] \text{ to a close approximation}$$

The equations relate the amplitude of the pulse undershoot to that of the applied pulse, and are strictly valid only where the network is driven from a zero-impedance generator, and is terminated by an infinite impedance.

In a practical case, the source and terminating impedances may vary over wide limits. Use of a cascaded multistage network reduces the effect of variations in the former by making the output waveform less dependent upon the characteristics of the generator.

The composite sync signal is passed through a two-stage resistance-capacitance network, each stage of which, neglecting the terminating impedances, has a time constant equal to the width of one vertical sync pulse or 27 μsec.

The effective constants of the network are then such that the undershoot amplitudes become

$$E_o = (V - 0.136V) = 0.864V \text{ for the}$$
27-μsec vertical pulses, and

$$E_o = (V - 0.705V) = 0.295V \text{ for the}$$
5-μsec horizontal pulses

where E_o is the amplitude of the undershoot developed across the final resistive element. For convenience in terminology, these undershoots may be called inverse pulses.

The ratio of amplitudes of the inverse vertical to inverse horizontal pulses is approximately 2.9 to 1. For equalizing pulses and noise pulses of duration shorter than 5 μsec, this amplitude ratio is increased.

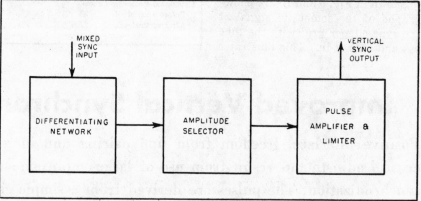

FIG. 1—Block diagram of system for producing steep-fronted pulses

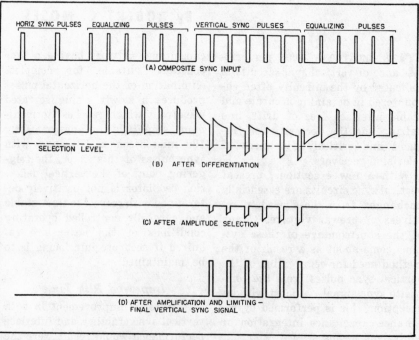

FIG. 2—Waveforms of composite sync input and changes produced by the system

Amplitude Selector

The output of the resistance-capacitance network consists of positive-going high-frequency components of the applied sync signal, together with the inverse vertical, inverse equalizing, and inverse horizontal pulses in the opposite polarity. This waveform, shown in Figure 2B, is applied to the cathode of a biased diode amplitude selector.

The cathode of the amplitude selector diode is maintained at a fixed positive potential with respect to its anode, and is nonconductive both for positive-going input signals and for negative signals of small amplitude. The positive cathode bias is adjusted to be somewhat greater than the peak amplitude of the inverse horizontal pulses. The latter, together with the inverse equalizing pulses and

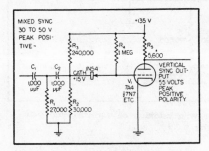

FIG. 3—Complete circuit contains a crystal diode and triode tube

any short-duration noise pulses, are therefore rejected by the diode.

During the vertical sync pulse interval, the higher amplitude inverse vertical pulses developed by the network drive the diode into conduction. As shown in Fig. 2C, a series of six steep-fronted negative pulses occurring in time coincidence with the trailing edges of the applied vertical sync pulses appear at the anode of the amplitude selector diode. These have durations approximately equal to the width of the serrations in the vertical sync block, 4.7 μsec, and a recurrence rate of 31,500 pps, twice the line scanning frequency.

Pulse-Width Gate

From the above discussion, it is apparent that the combination of the R-C network and amplitude selector function as a pulse-width actuated gate, developing pulses at its output only when the input pulse duration exceeds a certain fixed value. Particularly effective pulse-width discrimination is obtained if the applied pulses are

Table I—Operating Characteristics

	Input Pulses	Output Pulses
Amplitude	40 v, peak	55 v, peak
Polarity	positive	positive
Rise time	0.8 μsec	0.9 μsec
Decay time	0.7 μsec	1.1 μsec
Pulse width	27 and 5 μsec	4.8 μsec
Pulse flatness	———	better than 2%
Keying frequency	60 cps	———
Repetition frequency	31,500 pps	31,500 pps
Number of pulses	———	6
Threshold level	———	17.5 peak sync input
Interference components on pulse baseline	———	1.5 v, p-p, approx

squared and amplitude stabilized, as is generally the case in a practical receiver application.

The negative-going inverse vertical pulses at the anode of the diode are applied to the input of a triode pulse amplifier, the operating conditions of which are such that pulse limiting and sharpening takes place. Because the grid is returned through a high resistance to the plate supply, it assumes a very slightly positive potential with respect to the grounded cathode. This assures conduction of the tube in the absence of signal.

With the grid slightly above ground, a very effective clamping action takes place at the input of the pulse amplifier. The grid is prevented from being driven more positive, thus assisting materially in rejecting any positive-going high-frequency sync pulse components which may leak through the amplitude selector. At the same time, the d-c axis of the pulse is restored and held rigidly near ground potential.

Since the peak amplitude of the inverse vertical pulses applied to the pulse amplifier is more than sufficient to drive the grid to cutoff, the final inverted output pulses at the plate are squared and sharply clipped at the same level. The tube therefore acts as a limiter in both positive and negative directions.

The pulse train of Fig. 2D becomes the final vertical synchronizing signal, the amplitude of which may be made as large as desired, and the rise time of which is limited only by the bandwidth of the preceding video amplifiers and sync auxiliaries of the receiver.

Circuit Details

Figure 3 shows the complete schematic diagram of the system. Capacitors C_1 and C_2, together with resistors R_1, R_2 and R_3 comprise the two-stage differentiating network. The values of these components are such that each stage of the network has the required 27-μsec time constant. Resistors R_2 and R_3 also serve as a voltage divider across the B supply, and maintain the cathode of the amplitude selector diode at a suitable positive potential.

The amplitude selector is a type 1N54 germanium diode. This type is characterized by high forward conductance together with unusually high resistance in the reverse direction, that is, with the cathode positive. Materially improved operation of the circuit is obtained with a germanium diode in this position, since the extremely low interelectrode capacitance of 1-$\mu\mu$f greatly reduces feed-through of undesired high-frequency components existing at the output of the differentiator. In addition, the increased conductance afforded by the germanium diode provides a substantially higher pulse amplitude across the relatively low grid-cathode impedance of the pulse amplifier. This improves the limiting action of the latter at low signal levels.

The circuit constants have been selected for a supply voltage of +135 volts, and an input pulse peak amplitude of 40 volts. Inasmuch as resistors R_2 and R_3 provide a positive bias of 15 volts at the cathode of the amplitude selector diode, the circuit as a whole has a threshold of operation somewhat above this level of input sync pulse. Since upward of 30 volts are generally available at the output of the final sync amplifier, this threshold lies considerably below the video level at which a picture having satisfactory contrast is obtained.

Triode V_1 operates as a pulse limiter and sharpener, with a voltage gain of slightly over five times. The relatively low plate load resistance, 5,600 ohms, affords adequate amplifier response to pulses having rise times as short as one microsecond.

Although a substantial improvement in pulse rise time could have been effected by inductive peaking in the plate circuit, this was not considered sufficiently advantageous to warrant the additional circuit complication.

Connection to Oscillator

Figure 4 is the schematic diagram of a typical vertical deflection circuit of the blocking-oscillator type, together with the vertical pulse separator system described. The preferred method of connection between the two is shown. The secondary of the blocking oscillator transformer T_1 is effectively a part of the plate load of V_1, and acts to further shape the sync pulses as well as to retain their sharp leading edges.

Because the plate resistance of V_1 in parallel with its load resistance represents an effective impedance of only a few thousand ohms in series with the a-c grid return of the oscillator, including the pulse amplifier as a portion of the oscillator circuit in no way affects normal operation of the latter. Injection of sync in this manner

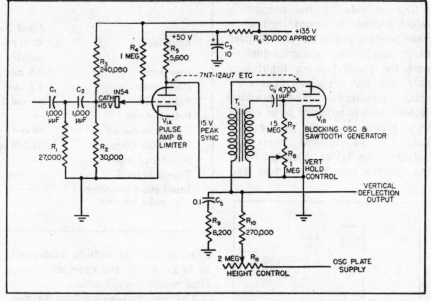

FIG. 4—Typical vertical blocking oscillator with addition of vertical sync pulse separator

offers the further advantage of extreme simplicity.

Sync Amplitude

The peak amplitude of vertical sync pulse developed at the plate of V_1 depends upon the effective supply voltage at the junction of R_5 and R_6. Although a maximum of 55 volts of sync is available if R_6 were omitted, it may in some cases be found that more satisfactory operation of the blocking oscillator itself will be obtained with peak sync amplitudes of 10 or 15 volts.

The network consisting of C_3 and R_6 provides a means of adjusting the output pulse amplitude without affecting the pulse rise time; R_6 and C_3 also supply a measure of decoupling at the plate of the pulse amplifier. The time constant of this network should be long with respect to the field repetition

period, and in general should be not less than 0.05 second.

With component values indicated in Fig. 4, the pulse amplifier operates at a quiescent plate voltage of 35 volts and a plate current of 2.9 ma. Under these conditions, the tube develops between 12 and 15 volts of sync pulse across the plate load, and requires but 4 volts of negative swing at the grid for complete limiting.

Pulse segregation with a system of this type has several additional advantages. Vertical synchronizing with pulses whose leading edges have a large time rate of change greatly minimizes interlace instability and eliminates the necessity for critical adjustment of the vertical oscillator frequency during and after warmup. The resulting accuracy of synchronizing is not nearly so dependent upon maintaining a constant amplitude of applied sync pulses as is that obtained with the usual R-C integrator system. This is because the shape of the final triggering pulse is completely independent of the input pulse amplitude over a very wide range. Rigid control of the latter is not so essential.

Integrator sync systems require

that conditions before and after transmission of the broad-topped vertical sync pulses in the composite sync signal be identical for odd and even line fields. This necessitates the insertion of two groups of six equalizing pulses. Because the method of pulse segregation described does not depend upon integration, the equalizing pulses are unnecessary. This suggests that a degree of simplification could be effected in the composite sync signal.

An improvement in noise immunity in the vertical sync circuit may be realized, because short-duration noise pulses which occur during the field scanning interval will affect the circuit in exactly the same manner as normal horizontal sync pulses and will be rejected by the amplitude selector. Such noise rejection increases the vertical sync stability of the receiver under adverse noise conditions, and virtually eliminates frame splitting and picture roll.

Operating Data

The major electrical operating characteristics of the circuit are shown in Table I. Figure 5 shows scale waveform tracings taken at

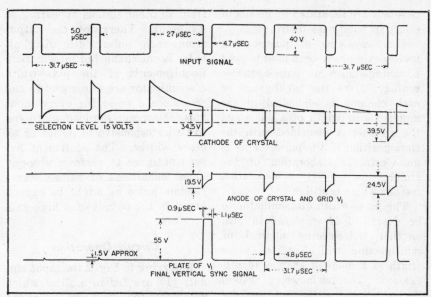

FIG. 5—Waveforms produced at designated points in the circuit

significant points throughout the system. These were obtained directly from a Tektronix model 511-A wide-band oscilloscope. To permit more accurate measurements, resistor R_6 of Fig. 4 was temporarily shorted out, allowing maximum amplitude of output pulse to be developed.

All data are taken with a simulated sync signal consisting of keyed 27-μsec and 5-μsec pulse trains. The pulse repetition frequency and keying frequency are 31,500 pps and 60 cps respectively.

Measurements were made with a plate supply voltage of 135 volts and the total current was 10.7 ma with R_6 removed.

The author acknowledges with thanks the valuable assistance of M. C. Pease of Sylvania Electric Products Inc. in the preparation of this paper.

Pulse-Width Discriminator

Designed specifically for use as a channel decoder in a multiplex communications system, this discriminator handles input pulses 20 to 100 microseconds wide. Also useful for measuring width of rectangular and other waveforms

By A. A. GERLACH AND D. S. SCHOVER

A MAJOR PROBLEM exists in the method of multiplexing or mixing information channels together at the sending end of a telemetering system and identifying these channels at the receiving end, whether the transmission of information is accomplished by wire or radio link.

Many methods are now employed successfully in telemetering systems of varying complexity and factors involved in the choice of a particular mode of multiplexing are usually dictated by the nature of the intelligence to be transmitted and the degree of equipment complexity that is to be tolerated.

Multiplexing Methods

One widely used method is the subcarrier system where a separate carrier signal, usually in the supersonic or low r-f range of frequencies, is assigned to each information channel. The channel information is superimposed on the carrier signal by amplitude or frequency modulation and all carrier signals are transmitted through a common transmission medium to the receiving station where the individual

This work was performed under contract with the United States Department of the Air Force.

channels are separated by means of selective band-pass filters.

Many systems of pulse-coding multiplexing have been used to good advantage such as pulse-sequence coding. Here the intelligence of each channel is embodied in the amplitude or width of a pulse and the channel is identified with the time position of the pulse. This is an electronic elaboration of the simple mechanical commutation method which is still in use.

The pulse-width discriminator to be described is employed in still another pulse-coding method of multiplexing which utilizes pulse width as a mode of channel identification. The telemetering system for which the equipment was de-

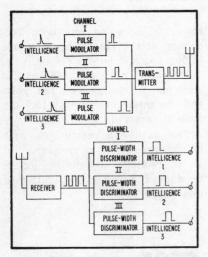

FIG. 1—Block diagram of three-channel telemetering system using pulse-width channel coding

veloped required that three channels of information be relayed by a vhf radio link and that all three channels contain information which originally appeared as pulses. The desired information would be the pulse frequency. Since the pulse-repetition rate of each channel was an independent function, pulse-position coding methods were ruled out and a pulse-width coding system was used. A block diagram of the system is shown in Fig. 1.

The function of the pulse-width discriminator in the system is to separate the information channel for which the discriminator is set

from all other signals appearing at its input. Therefore, the output from each pulse-width discriminator is one channel of information. Requirements of the pulse-width discriminator are to respond to and reproduce a pulse for every input pulse of a predetermined width and to be unresponsive to pulses of all other widths. The equipment has been designed to perform properly under conditions of rather severe random noise as might be experienced in the output of a high-gain receiver.

Circuit Operation

Referring to Fig. 2 the input signals (1) are fed to a slicer which separates the spurious variations such as receiver noise from the intelligence signals. The output pulses of the slicer (2) have various widths corresponding to the information channels transmitted. This output is fed to two different circuits, one with a differentiator input stage and the other with an inverter-clipper input stage. The positive output of the differentiator (4) is used to trigger a one-shot multivibrator which provides a gating pulse of predetermined width (9) to the coincidence tube. This gating pulse is delayed for a period of time after the start of the input pulse equal to the width of the input pulse.

The output of the slicer is also inverted (3), differentiated (5) and used to initiate a delay multivibrator whose width is a controllable

parameter of the discriminator unit. The output of this multivibrator (6) is differentiated and appears as a negative pip (7) at the trailing edge of the delay multivibrator used to trigger a second gate multivibrator.

The output from the second gate multivibrator (8) is delayed for a period of time after the start of the input pulse equal to the width of the delay multivibrator pulse. Outputs of the two gate multivibrators (8) and (9) are fed to a coincidence tube which conducts only during the coincidence time of the two gate pulses. The coincidence tube will therefore trigger the output multivibrator only for a given input pulse width and this width is a controllable adjustment of the disdiscriminator unit.

Figure 3 illustrates the sequence of operations on the input intelligence shown in proper time orientation. The various numbered waveforms are related to the number points in the block diagram, Fig. 2. Three different pulse inputs are shown—one to which the discriminator is set to respond, one shorter and one longer than the properly selected pulse width. Waveforms 8 and 9 of Fig. 3 illustrate the proper and improper gating conditions for coincidence.

Circuit Details

The details of the circuitry involved in accomplishing the desired objectives are illustrated in Fig. 4. Slicing of the input signals is ob-

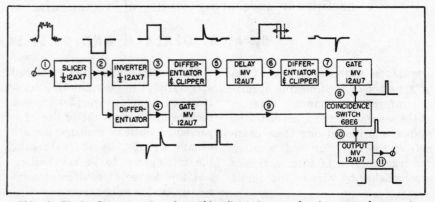

FIG. 2—Block diagram of pulse-width discriminator showing waveforms at successive stages

tained by biasing the grid of the first half of a 12AX7, V_{1A}, about 14v below cutoff. This allows for slicing of the center three volts out of a 30-v input; the rectifier action of the tube suppresses the top half of the pulse. For other input voltages the bias may also be adjusted to allow selection of the center three volts of the input pulse. The positive input pulses appear at the plate of V_{1A} inverted and cleaned of any receiver noise.

The inverted pulses are fed simultaneously to the grid of V_{1B}, inverted again and then differentiated by the 50-$\mu\mu$f capacitor and 51,000-ohm resistor. The resulting positive pip triggers the gate multivibrator consisting of both halves of V_6.

The output at the plate of V_{1B} is differentiated by the R-C network and the positive pip triggers the delay multivibrator consisting of both halves of V_2. The negative pip at the grid of V_{2A} is suppressed by a germanium crystal so as not to influence the width of the delay multivibrator pulse. The width of this delay pulse is controlled by an

adjustment of the grid resistor of V_{2B} which determines the time constant of the multivibrator.

The output of V_{2B} is again differentiated through an R-C network and this time the resulting negative pip is fed to the plate of V_{3A} to trigger the gate multivibrator consisting of both sections of V_3.

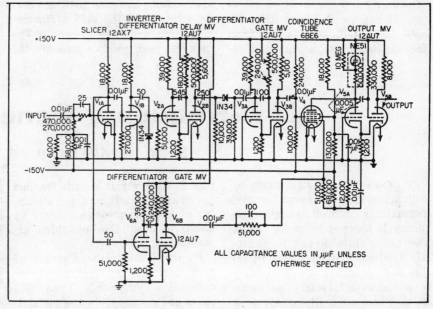

FIG. 4—Schematic diagram of the pulse-width discriminator

The positive pip at this point is suppressed by the germanium crystal connected between the plates of V_{2B} and V_{3A}. The width of this gate pulse is internally controllable in order to provide a sensitivity control for the discriminator.

The coincidence tube, V_4, is a pentagrid converter with inputs at the first and third grids. The first grid is biased at about 23v negative and the third grid is biased at about 56v negative. Either bias alone is sufficient to cut the tube off but when the outputs of the two gate multivibrators occur simultaneously at the grids of V_4 the tube conducts, supplying a trigger impulse to the output multivibrator consisting of both sections of V_5. A neon lamp is incorporated in the output circuit to indicate when coincidence at V_4 is achieved.

The power-supply requirements for the discriminator consist of a positive and a negative 150-v sup-

ply and a 6.3-v filament supply. The positive 150-v supply drain is 48 ma and the negative supply drain is 7 ma. The filament current is 1.7 amp.

The circuit illustrated in Fig. 4 has been constructed and tested with both a direct video input and a modulated r-f signal which was de-tected by a receiver and fed to the pulse-width discriminator. In either case the circuit performed very satisfactorily and exhibited excellent stability over a prolonged period of operation.

In the circuit shown, the delay multivibrator is adjustable in width over a range of from 20 to 100 μsec by a calibrated front-panel adjustment. The width of the gating pulses may be varied by an internal adjustment over a range of from 2 to 12 μsec. For a 3-channel multiplexing system employing pulse widths of 30, 60, and 90 μsec it was found that a sensitivity range of ± five μsec was very satisfactory. This allows for instabilities due to slight pulse-width and pulse-amplitude variations and yet provides ample guard bands between channels.

The pulse-width discriminators were constructed as small compact plug-in units which may be removed

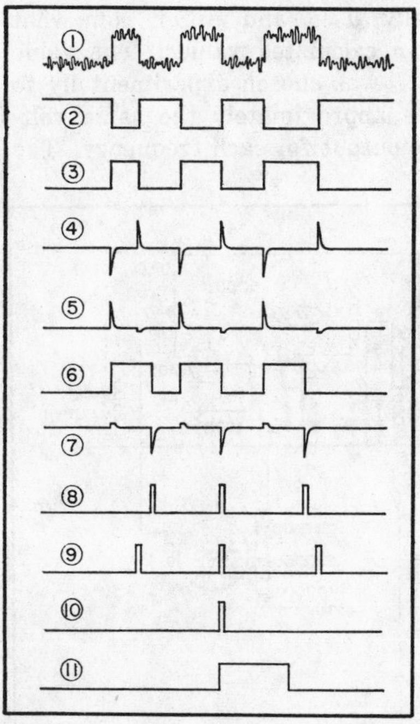

FIG. 3—Waveform relations in pulse-width discriminator. Waveforms (8) and (9) show the proper and improper gating conditions for coincidence

and replaced in a minimum of time. Miniature tubes are employed throughout as well as turret-type sockets to make the units light and compact.

Conclusions

The pulse-width discriminator described exhibits both a high degree of stability and simplicity of operaton. It has the ability to discriminate the intelligence pulses from the random noise background occurring in high-gain receivers. Although the unit was designed to handle pulses in the range of 20 to 100 μsec wide, modification of the network components will allow the range to be extended.

The units discussed were intended for intelligence channel decoders in a multiplex communication system; however, their use may be extended to the field of instrumentation and measurement. The unit has been used to measure the width of rectangular pulses, and, due to the clipping action of the input circuit, it may be employed to measure the pulse width of other waveforms. This circuit has, in general, turned out to be a very useful addition to the laboratory pulse equipment used by the authors. For this measurement application it is recommended that a more accurate vernier-type control be employed in place of the simple dial arrangement shown.

Low-Frequency Generator

By W. G. SHEPARD

THE GENERATION of sine waves by ordinary electronic means becomes increasingly difficult as the frequency is lowered below 10 cycles. The phase-shift circuit is generally used but elaborate care in design and construction is necessary to achieve satisfactory performance. Since a multivibrator is a more dependable low-frequency oscillator, operating down to almost any slowness, it was decided to use the output wave of a multivibrator and shape it into essentially a sine wave.

First a large square-wave voltage was generated by triggering an Eccles-Jordan flip-flop circuit from the multivibrator, this being easily done because the triggering signal can be applied to both grids. By incomplete integration, essentially a triangular wave is obtained. Since this wave contains no even harmonics and only 1/9 third and even less higher harmonics,

$$Y = 8/\pi 2\ E(\cos x + 1/9 \cos 3x + 1/25 \cos 5x \ldots),$$

a simple filter system will reduce the harmonics to negligible value.

Such a sine-wave generator is most easily constructed for a single frequency and is not very well suited for continuously variable frequencies over a wide range because of the increasing attenuation of the filter as the frequency is raised. However, it is quite feasible to construct a unit covering a number of fixed frequencies selected by means of a suitable switching arrangement.

Figure 1 shows the diagram of such a circuit as constructed for calibration purposes. Type 6J6 tubes are employed in the multivibrator and flip-flop circuits, the multivibrator receiving its plate supply from a regulated source for greater frequency stability. Capacitor C_3 and R_3 form the triangular wave and V_3 is a cathode follower inserted to lower the impedance. Two filter circuits, C_4R_4 and C_5R_5, are so proportioned that the third harmonic is attenuated in each about three times as much as the fundamental, leaving about one or two percent third and practically no higher harmonics. For simplicity only three switch positions are shown in the diagram, but values are given in the table for 10 frequencies. These are the values actually used and differ somewhat from calculated values. The value of C_5 was chosen experimentally to give approximately the same voltage output for each frequency. The

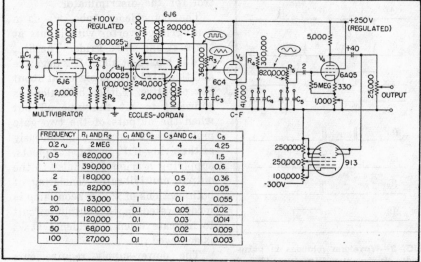

FREQUENCY	R_1 AND R_2	C_1 AND C_2	C_3 AND C_4	C_5
0.2 ∿	2 MEG	1	4	4.25
0.5	820,000	1	2	1.5
1	390,000	1	1	0.6
2	180,000	1	0.5	0.36
5	82,000	1	0.2	0.05
10	33,000	1	0.1	0.055
20	180,000	0.1	0.05	0.02
30	120,000	0.1	0.03	0.014
50	68,000	0.1	0.02	0.009
100	27,000	0.1	0.01	0.003

FIG. 1—Schematic of sine-wave generator producing frequencies from 0.2 to 100 cycles

cathode circuit of V_4 contains a control allowing for further minor adjustments in output voltage. The output voltage, after being amplified by the 6AQ5 tube, is about 14 volts at the input to the attenuator.

Since the generator, as constructed, is used for calibration work, some method was necessary to make sure that the output voltage is approximately the same for each frequency. Since the frequency is too low for the use of a meter, a small cathode-ray tube is used as an amplitude indicator. The vertical and horizontal plates are tied together to increase the sensitivity of the tube. Since this causes the spot to move back and forth diagonally, the tube must be rotated 45 degrees to give a horizontal spot movement.

Sine and Square-Wave Generator and Selective Amplifier

By GEORGE ELLIS JONES, JR.

BASED UPON a half-lattice R-C type all-pass filter[1,2,3] a wide-range sine-wave generator has been designed and constructed which, in conjunction with a regenerative coupled cathode clipper amplifier[4], delivers both a sine and a square wave of about 28-volt peak-to-peak amplitude from about three cps to one hundred six kc.

The circuit is essentially that of Villard[3] but modified to include more direct coupling for better low-frequency characteristics and cathode-follower stages for improved isolation and low-impedance sources necessary for extending the high-frequency range.

Six controls are used. Switch 1 establishes the frequency range and ganged rheostats R_2 and R_3 give a fine control of frequency (a shaft rotation of 180 degrees providing a 20 to 1 frequency change). Potentiometer R_4 controls the amount of feedback and the amplitude of the generated sine wave. When this control is set so that just insufficient feedback is available to maintain oscillation, the circuit from attenuator R_1 to potentiometer R_4 acts as a sharp filter, passing the frequency at which oscillation would occur were more feedback used.

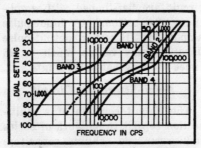

Typical calibration curve for generator-amplifier shown in circuit diagram

Potentiometer R_5 controls the output amplitude of the sine wave and potentiometer R_6 similarly controls the square-wave output amplitude.

REFERENCES

(1) Chance, et al., "Wave Forms", p 137, Radiation Laboratory Series, McGraw-Hill Book Co., Inc., New York, 1949.
(2) E. W. Rosentreter, Single-Signal Single-Sideband Adaptor, ELECTRONICS, p 124, Jul. 1948.
(3) O. G. Villard, Tunable A-F Amplifier, ELECTRONICS, p 77, Jul. 1949.
(4) L. A. Goldmintz and H. L. Krause, Proc. IRE, p 1172, Sep. 1948.

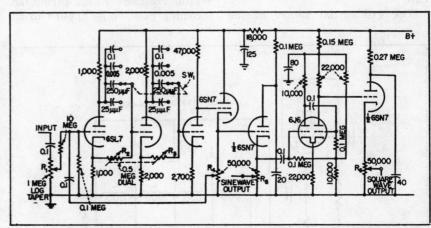

Circuit diagram of sine and square-wave generator and selective amplifier capable of delivering up to 28 volts peak-to-peak from 3 cps to 106 kc

Improved Pulse Stretcher

Duration of pulses is increased as much as 25 times, with output amplitude remaining proportional to input. Flat-topped output is provided by a delay line charged by crystal rectifiers driven by a cathode follower. Sample design equations are given

By JAMES F. CRAIB

INCREASED DURATION of pulses in a series without change in their relative amplitudes is often desirable in design of pulse circuits. Pulse stretching, as distinguished from multivibrator action, retains information in the relative amplitudes of successive pulses.

One common method of stretching pulses is shown in Fig. 1A. For a positive-pulse input at terminal 1, the rectifier conducts only for the pulse duration. The capacitor charges to nearly peak pulse voltage during the pulse duration and slowly discharges through the high resistance during the interval between pulses.

In this type of stretching, the output pulse can never have a flat top because the stretched portion of the pulse is fundamentally the exponential discharge of the R-C circuit.

The exponential nature of the discharge results in a residual signal lasting much longer than the duration of the useful output. The trailing end of one pulse may overlap the beginning of the next pulse and reduce its effective amplitude. In an extreme case this phenomenon is the basis for power-supply filter operation.

A new type of stretcher is shown in Fig. 1B. Output pulses from this circuit are flat-topped with amplitudes proportional to input-pulse amplitudes. However, output-pulse duration may be as much as 25 times the original pulse length.

Pulse-Stretcher Circuit

The circuit consists of a multi-section repetitive network of series inductors and shunt capacitors forming a delay line. Sections of this line are parallel charged by crystal rectifiers which permit an incoming pulse to be applied to all shunt capacitors simultaneously and charge them to nearly the amplitude of the incoming pulse. With no pulse input, the rectifiers become high resistances and the line is left with all capacitors charged equally.

When the line discharges through a short circuit at its end, a negative step of voltage (from line potential to zero) progresses down the line discharging each capacitor in turn. The output pulse, which has been at maximum since the line was charged, is terminated when the discharging action reaches the open end of the line.

Input and output waveforms are shown superimposed in Fig. 1C. The output pulse rises as rapidly as the capacitors are charged and nearly as fast as the input-pulse rise time. When the discharge step reaches the open end of the line, it tends to appear at double amplitude, shown dotted in Fig. 1C. However, the rectifiers prevent a negative excursion and the pulse ends abruptly at the base line.

The end of the pulse is more rounded than the beginning because of distortion of the step wave as it travels down the line. This distortion is usually permissible but with less distortion a line would have a wider passband and introduce less delay per section. To obtain the same delay more sections would be required. The trailing edge of the pulse may be as round as possible to save size, weight and cost of components.

Choice of Impedance Levels

Flatness of the pulse top is affected by any leakage that may discharge the capacitors before the

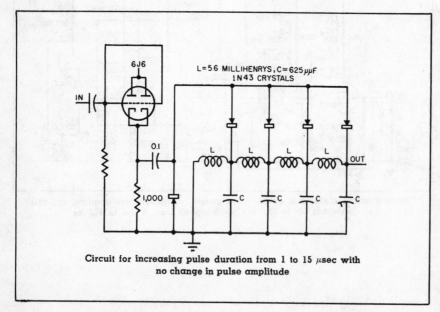

L = 5.6 MILLIHENRYS, C = 625 μμF
1N43 CRYSTALS

Circuit for increasing pulse duration from 1 to 15 μsec with no change in pulse amplitude

discharge wave reaches them. Back resistance of the crystals is one source of leakage and line impedance should be limited to about one-tenth the back resistance or about 10,000 ohms for 1N43 crystals.

Another source of leakage is the output circuit fed by the line. The stretcher is usually connected directly to a vacuum-tube grid without a blocking capacitor but if such a capacitor is used, the grid resistor must be as large as possible. Low line impedance will reduce relative leakage through the grid resistor but will increase the current necessary to charge the line.

The stretcher is usually driven by a cathode follower whose cathode impedance, in series with the forward resistance of the rectifiers, varies from 50 to 200 ohms. The time constant formed by the cath-

ode impedance and the parallel combination of line capacitors should be short enough so that the capacitors charge within the duration of the incoming pulse. The driving tube must be capable of delivering the peak current that will flow during the charging period.

These considerations are not easily subject to analytical prediction because cathode impedance and rectifier forward resistance change with current during the charging period. A good design provides for the necessary grid drive at the instant the pulse is applied to the grid, as the capacitors are then uncharged. Cathode impedance may then be assumed to be some average value and the charging time constant calculated for this value.

With stretched-pulse durations of one to twenty μsec, it is practical

to use a 6J6 cathode follower with both halves in parallel and a line impedance between 5,000 and 20,000 ohms. To properly swing the crystals between low forward resistance and high back resistance it is necessary to operate with pulse amplitudes of at least two volts. Values lower than this give stretched pulses whose tops are not flat because of line discharge by the crystals.

Pulses of the order of ten volts are about the maximum that can be handled by a 6J6 cathode follower with these circuit values. Higher-amplitude pulses may have rise times rapid enough to drive the cathode follower into its grid-current region. This is permissible only if a low-impedance grid circuit or satisfactory d-c restoration is provided.

Stretching may be increased by operating several stages in cascade. However, a cathode follower is then needed between stages to provide power gain and impedance matching.

Superposition of Pulses

When a second pulse, equal in amplitude to the first pulse, is applied to the stretcher before the first pulse has completely passed through the circuit, the output amplitude will remain constant during the total stretching interval.

If the second pulse is either larger or smaller in amplitude than the first, the output amplitude will be that of the first pulse until the second is applied when it will change to the amplitude of the second and remain there for the rest of the total stretching interval. These actions are shown in Fig. 2.

Many designs for a circuit which generates pulses of special shapes are possible through the use of unequal charging voltages on successive stages and by charging the line with a series of pulses of various amplitudes.

If the input pulse is of constant amplitude and duration, series resistors may be used to vary the charging potential of various sec-

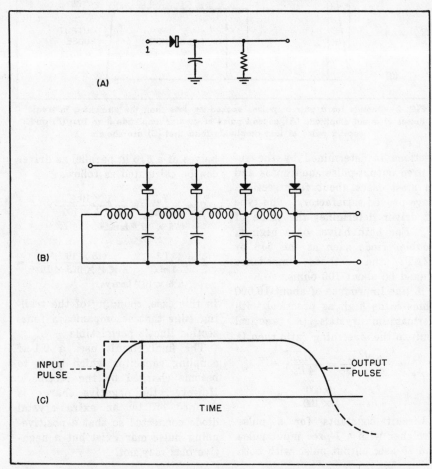

FIG. 1—Usual form of R-C pulse stretcher (A), improved type utilizing a delay line (B) and input and output waveforms for improved circuit (C) showing the sharpening of the end of the output pulse by rectifier damping

tions of the line. For varying pulse amplitude and duration, it is necessary to obtain rapid charging by the use of separate cathode followers.

When the pulse is accompanied by a background of noise, the noise-pulses are stretched so that a constant d-c level is established. In most circuits this level is discarded by coupling capacitors so that the apparent signal-to-noise ratio is improved.

As the noise level approaches the signal level the signal may be degraded by short noise pulses whose amplitudes are nearly the same as the signal. These pulses may reduce crystal back resistance momentarily, permitting the capacitors to discharge. As a result, the signal is degraded into a sawtooth and becomes lost in noise. The signal-to-noise ratio at small values is not improved by the stretcher and may even be reduced slightly.

Design Equations

In the design equations of a pulse stretcher the following terms will be used: T_s, stretching interval; T_p, input pulse duration; R_k, impedance of a driven source (usually the cathode impedance of a cathode follower); L, inductance per section of network; C, capacitance per section of network; and n, number of sections of network.

The input pulse duration should be at least four time constants to insure adequate charging of the capacitors

$$T_p = 4 R_k n C$$

The stretching interval will be the delay of the network or approximately

$$T_s = n \sqrt{L C}$$

Solving these two equations for line constants gives

$$C = \frac{T_p}{4 n R_k}$$

$$L = \frac{T_s^2}{16 n^2 C}$$

In practice, the number of line

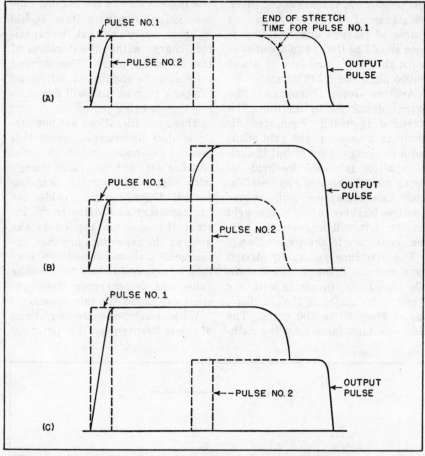

FIG. 2—Outputs for a pair of pulses spaced by less than the stretching interval. Pulses of equal amplitude (A), second pulse of greater amplitude than first (B) and second pulse of less amplitude than first (C) are shown

sections is determined by the required output-pulse squareness and in most cases about four sections have proved satisfactory. The type of driver determines the value of R_k. For both halves of a high-g_m double triode such as the 6J6 or 12AT7 the cathode impedance should be about 100 ohms.

A line impedance of about 10,000 ohms is as high as practical with germanium crystals. A practical limit to the stretching ratio then is

$$\frac{T_s}{T_p} = \frac{n \sqrt{L C}}{4 n R_k C} = \frac{\sqrt{L/C}}{4 R_k} =$$

$$\frac{Z_o}{4 R_k} \cong \frac{10,000}{4 \times 100} = 25$$

Circuit constants for a pulse stretcher with a 1-μsec input pulse and 15-μsec output pulse with both

halves of a 6J6 in parallel as driver can be calculated as follows

$$C = \frac{T_p}{4 n R_k} = \frac{1 \times 10^{-6}}{4 \times 4 \times 100} = 625 \times 10^{-12} \text{ farads}$$

$$L = \frac{T_s^2}{4 n^2 C} = \frac{(15 \times 10^{-6})^2}{4 \times 4^2 \times 625 \times 10^{-12}} = 5.6 \times 10^{-3} \text{ henrys}$$

In this case, rounding of the trailing edge that accompanies a four-section line is permissible.

The final circuit uses a 0.1-μf coupling capacitor which tends to become charged by the rectifiers. However, the negative charge is drained off by an extra crystal diode connected so that a positive-going pulse may exist but a negative bias may not.

Pulse Rise and Decay Time Measurement

By ALLAN EASTON

PRECISE MEASUREMENT of rise and decay characteristics of pulses is a necessary adjunct to their expanding application. Various characteristics of pulses are defined in Fig. 1. The rise or decay time can be measured by one of the common methods illustrated in Fig. 2. If

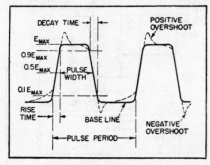

FIG. 1—Principal features of pulses show times to be measured

the pulse is symmetrical, that is the rise and decay times are substantially equal, an elliptical sweep can be used[1]. However when the pulse has a very steep rise or a very rapid decay, the pulse itself can be used as the sweep to obtain accurate time measurements.

Basic System of Measurement

Figure 3 shows two alternate arrangements of the measuring equipment. The trigger used to initiate the test pulse may be derived from a free running trigger generator or from a frequency divider driven by a high-frequency source. In the former case a pulsed oscillator is required to provide the measuring frequency. In the latter instance the high-frequency oscillator from which the trigger is derived may be the source of the measuring frequency.

The pulse whose rise time is to be investigated is connected to the horizontal plates of the cathode-ray tube. Thus the pulse provides the sweep. The pulse is simultaneously passed through a differentiating

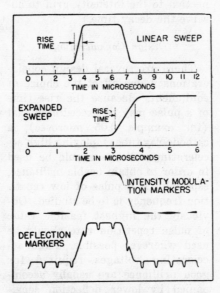

FIG. 2—Several techniques are frequently used to measure pulse rise or decay time. The top two methods depend on a linear sweep for a time base; the bottom two use time interval markers

network whose output is connected to the cathode-ray tube grid or cathode.

Before the pulse begins to rise, the beam of the cathode-ray tube is stationary and appears as a bright spot marked A in Fig. 4A. (assume for the moment the calibrating oscillator is not operating). As the pulse voltage rises, the spot sweeps across the screen at a velocity proportional to the rise time and for a distance proportional to the peak voltage and deflection sensitivity. The pulse eventually reaches the peak voltage and remains at this value for a while causing the bright spot at B, after which it sweeps back to the starting point A until the next cycle. Both rise and decay times contribute to the total deflection while the periods of relatively constant amplitude cause only bright spots. This fact should be contrasted with the other methods mentioned above wherein rise and decay times occupy only a very

small percentage of the screen trace.

Now suppose the marker oscillator, which is synchronized with the initiating trigger, is connected to the vertical plates of the cathode-ray tube. This connection is analagous to the familiar use of sinewaves for sweep calibration. Figure 4B shows a possible result. The display in this figure still has limited utility because it contains both the forward and return traces superimposed, which may prove confusing. Blanking of the return trace is the purpose of the differentiating circuit.

It is well known that a pulse passed through an R-C circuit of proper time constant (sufficiently short compared with the pulse width) results in a pair of pulses, one positive and one negative. The times of occurrence of the pair of pulses coincide with the rise and decay times of the input pulse. If the output of the differentiating circuit is connected to the intensity

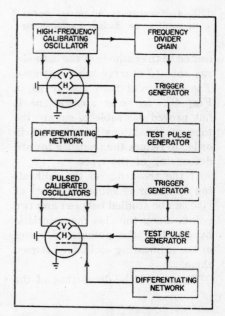

FIG. 3—The measuring technique can be accomplished by several arrangements of equipment

grid of the cathode-ray tube, the positive pulse will cause brightening of the trace and the negative pulse dimming. When the grid is initially biased near cutoff, then brightening will result for a time corresponding to the rise time of the test pulse. (If a negative test pulse is used the output of the differentiating circuit should be connected to the cathode of the cathode-ray tube to observe the rise time). The trace will then appear as in Fig. 4C. In some applications it has proved desirable to square the tops of the intensifying pulses in order to reduce the tendency toward defocusing of the trace.

If the frequency of the calibrating oscillator is known, the rate of rise can be studied between any two points along the rise characteristic by counting the number of cycles of the calibrating oscillator between them.

To observe the decay time of the

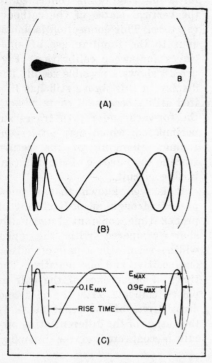

FIG. 4—Appearance of traces produced on oscilloscope during measurements

test pulse, the output of the differentiating circuit may either be inverted or connected to the cathode of the cathode-ray tube. (A negative test pulse would require connection to the intensity grid to observe the decay time.)

Design Considerations

There are several design considerations which affect the choice of equipment. Because the rise time of a pulse may be exceedingly fast (for example 0.05 microsec), a cathode-ray tube employing high accelerating voltages should be used in order to obtain usable brilliance, especially if a pulse of low repetition frequency is to be studied. Obviously the highest feasible value of pulse repetition rate should be used wherever possible. High accelerating voltages required for good brilliance are usually accompanied by lower deflection sensitivity although new tubes with 20,000 volts of accelerating potential and high deflection sensitivity are available commercially[2]. Thus a fairly large peak pulse voltage is needed to secure sufficient deflection. If small pulses are to be measured, a pulse amplifier is essential but usually will distort the rise time of extremely fast pulses. This defect is common to most methods of rise time measurement.

It is, of course, not essential that the measured pulse be connected to the horizontal plates of the cathode ray tube. The vertical plates may be preferred.

The calibrating oscillator may take several forms; the commonest is a free running oscillator operating at a fairly high frequency. (For example, a 100 mc oscillator will give 10 marker cycles when observing a pulse with a 0.1 microsec rise time, whereas a 10 mc oscillator will give 10 cycles with a pulse of 1 microsec rise time.) The use of a chain of synchronized sinewave oscillators[3] makes it possible to obtain

division from 100 mc down to trigger frequency, with each oscillator providing a frequency division of ten to one, or better yet, five to one. A fundamental circuit diagram of a suitable synchronized sinewave frequency dividing oscillator is shown in Fig. 5. It is also possible to utilize a pulsed oscillator as a source of calibrating frequency[4].

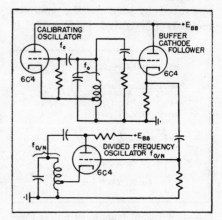

FIG. 5—A synchronized frequency dividing oscillator can be used to obtain a pulse triggering signal co-ordinated with the deflection signal

Numerous variations of the principles outlined in this paper are possible. No attempt has been made to show particular circuit arrangements as these details will depend on the types of pulses to be measured and the available laboratory equipment. Also the equipment arrangement for a laboratory measurement will differ considerably from that for measuring and standardizing production pulse generators.

REFERENCES

(1) Allan Easton, Measuring Pulse Characteristics, ELECTRONICS, p 150 Feb 1946.
(2) I. E. Lempert and R. Feldt, The 5RP Tube, Intensifier Type CR Tube for High Voltage Operation, *Proc Inst Radio Engrs*, p 432 July 1946.
(3) C. W. Carnahan and H. P. Kalmus, Synchronized Oscillators as FM Limiters, ELECTRONICS, p 109 Aug 1944.
(4) Allan Easton, Pulse Modulated Oscillator, ELECTRONICS, p 125 March 1947.

Steepness of Pulse Fronts

By MILTON D. RUBIN

MOST ANALYSES of pulsed circuits assume that the wavefront of the pulse is a step function, such as

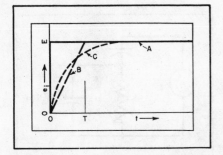

FIG. 1—Pulse front can be approximated by a step function (curve A), a linearly rising front (curve B), or an exponentially rising front (curve C)

curve A in Fig. 1. Actually it is physically impossible for a voltage or current to change instantaneously from one value to another. Therefore a wavefront cannot have infinite slope as implied by this function. There are cases in which this assumption of a perfectly square pulsefront leads to erroneous results. In these cases the following analysis gives better results with no greater complexity.

Linearly Rising Pulse Front

Often it is appropriate to assume an infinite slope as a first approximation, and to interpret the results accordingly. However when this approximation gives incorrect results (One of the principal cases being an analysis of pulse differentiation), a second approximation to the solution, a linearly rising pulsefront such as curve B in Fig. 1, which is close enough to be of great practical help, can be assumed. A fairly complete analysis of this problem has assumed exponential rise of the pulse, such as Curve C in Fig. 1, which might be considered as a third and even closer approximation[1].

Nevertheless, assumption of a linear rather than exponential rise

may, at times, be more accurate, as the rise is often linear until just before flattening out, particularly when peaking circuits are used.

What the practical electronic designer prefers is a few rules of thumb for quick application to various cases, especially when numerous stray effects need to be considered and the circuit values are not accurately known.

Assume a linear rise of the pulse. By way of illustrating the approach, a simple R-C circuit, shown in Fig. 2, is considered because of its simplicity and wide application. Likewise, the essentials of the mathematical analysis are given because of their simplicity and because the method can be used for other circuits.

The voltage rises from 0 to E in time T, therefore the rate of rise is E/T, and the input voltage is $e_i = Et/T$. The current can be found by dividing the operational transform expression for the voltage by

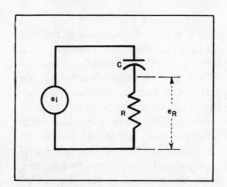

FIG. 2—Curves in Fig. 3 pertain to this simple but common circuit

the operational transform for the impedance, and solving for the current by known equivalences (The operational transform method, giving direct solutions of pulse transmission problems, should be at every electronic engineer's fingertips.), or by contour integration in the complex plane. The expression for the voltage by the operational

transform method[2,3], for the rise period, is therefore E/Tp, where p is the well known operator. The impedance is $R + 1/Cp$, thus

$$i :: \frac{E/Tp}{R + 1/Cp} \qquad (1)$$

where :: denotes operational transform equivalence. The solution is

$$i = (CE/T)(1 - \epsilon^{-t/RC}) \qquad (2)$$

Usually we are interested in the voltage across the resistor. This voltage is

$$e_R = (RCE/T)(1 - \epsilon^{-t/RC}) \qquad (3)$$

which is of the form of curve C in Fig. 1.

Interpretation of Results

To interpret this equation into practical rules of thumb, let us consider several cases, realizing that for the present we are considering only the rise period.

First, for t considerably less than RC

$$e_R = Et/T \qquad (4)$$

Thus the voltage follows and is equal to the input voltage, as it also has this equation. If T is considerably less than RC, then the whole wavefront is transferred faithfully across the resistor.

For the second case, consider T approximately equal to RC. Then $t = T = RC$, substituting in Eq. 3.

$$e_R = (RCE/RC)(1 - \epsilon^{-1}) = 0.6321E \qquad (5)$$

or e_R is approximately $(2/3)E$. The voltage across the resistor thus rises exponentially to about $(2/3)E$, and there is some differentiation and loss in voltage.

For the third case, consider when the wavefront rises to its full value in time $t = T = 3RC$. Here again the voltage rises exponentially to its final value, which is, from Eq. 3

$$e_R = (E/3)(1 - \epsilon^{-3}) = (0.95/3)E \qquad (6)$$

or e_R is approximately $(1/3)E$. In this case we have lost 2/3 of the voltage, and are now in the region in which many differentiating circuits work. The analysis indicates that, unless the rise time of the input voltage is about the same as or less than the time constant of the differentiating circuit into which it is working, much of the voltage is lost in passing through the circuit.

For the fourth case, consider a rise time very much larger than RC. For $t = T = aRC$, where a

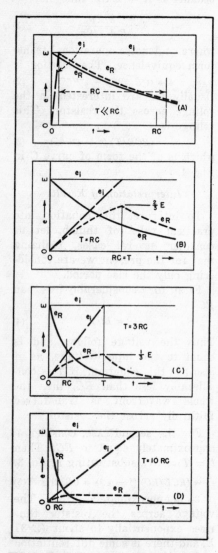

FIG. 3—Comparison of response to square-wave to that of linearly rising wavefront for various pulse periods relative to the circuit time constant shows considerable difference for relatively long pulses

$= 7$ or greater, the exponential term in Eq. 3 becomes less than 0.001, and the voltage rises in time T to $e_R = E/a$. For example, consider the case of $a = 10$. When the input voltage wavefront reaches

its full value of E at $t = T = 10RC$, the voltage across the resistor reaches within better than 0.01 of one percent of its maximum value of $0.1E$. Actually the voltage has reached 95 percent of this value at $t = 3RC$ thus

$$e_R = (E/a)\,(1 - \epsilon^{-3}) = 0.095E \qquad (7)$$

These four cases are illustrated in Fig. 3. The solid e_i curves are the square input voltage; the solid e_R curves are the output voltage (Fig. 2) resulting from such an input. The dashed e_i curves are a linearly rising input voltage; the dashed e_R curves are the output from such an input. In Fig. 3A there is little difference between the output obtained from a square or a linearly rising waveshape. However in Fig. 3B there is a noticeable difference. In Fig. 3C and especially Fig. 3D there are no similarities. The errors resulting from assuming a squarewave are obvious.

Until now we have been discussing the rise period. After the input voltage has reached its maximum at time T, it remains constant for the duration of the pulse, and the voltage across the resistor falls exponentially, in accordance with the equation

$$e_R = E_R\epsilon^{-(t-T)/RC} \qquad (9)$$

where E_R is the maximum voltage reached across the resistor, and time is still measured from the origin of the pulse front. At the tail of the pulse, a similar differentiated pulse appears with opposite polarity. We have used the term differentiation somewhat loosely, as the center portion of the differentiated pulse, between the two spikes, must be included in the concept of differentiation as applied to pulses.

Rules of Thumb

Comparing the results from assuming a linearly rising pulsefront with those resulting from assuming a perfectly square pulsefront (Fig. 3), we see how misleading the latter assumption can be. For example, in case four, the output voltage approaches very closely the true mathematical differential of the in-

put wave, except for amplitude, as the input wave is Et/T and the output is $e = E/a$ during the rise time.

Rules of thumb for anticipating pulse response of circuits are therefore as follows:

(1) If the time constant of the circuit is much greater than the rise time of the pulse, the pulse-

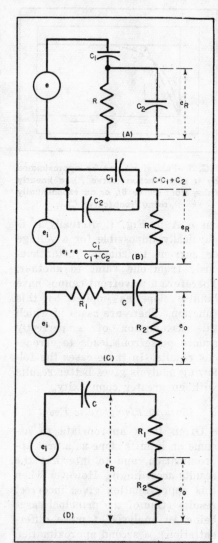

FIG. 4—Several circuits, slightly more complex than that of Fig. 2, can be analysed by the exact same technique. Other more complex circuits can be analysed by analogous techniques

front is transferred across the circuit with slight loss in voltage (Fig. 3A).

(2) If the time constant of the circuit is about equal to the rise time of the pulse, the voltage out-

put maximum is about ⅔ of the input (Fig. 3B).

(3) If the time constant of the circuit is ⅓ or less of the rise time of the pulse, the output voltage is approximately this fractional proportion of the input (Fig. 3C and 3D).

Practical Applications

There are several practical points which should be considered regarding the effect of the associated physical circuits to which the above differentiating circuit is connected. First, R should represent the complete effective load on the differentiating circuit. Second, usually some capacitance exists across the resistor, shown as C_2 in Fig. 4A. In this case, by application of Thevenin's theorem, there results Fig. 4B, to which we can apply the results arrived at above. The voltage produced across R by placing C_2 in parallel with C_1, and replacing the input voltage with the reduced input voltage $e_i = eC_1/(C_1 + C_2)$,

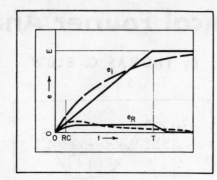

FIG. 5—Comparison of results assuming a linearly or an exponentially rising wavefront shows that they give results of the same order of magnitude

as shown in Fig. 4B, is the same as in the original circuit (Fig. 4A).

Third, the above analysis assumes that the output resistance of the generator supplying e_i is negligible in comparison with R. If this is not so, we can reduce it to this case as follows. In Fig. 4C, R_1 is the output resistance of the source, and R_2 is the load resistance. This circuit is exactly the same as Fig. 4D.

Thus the results of the previous analysis apply by using the value of $R_1 + R_2$ as R to get e_R, and then multiplying by the ratio $R_2/(R_1 + R_2)$ to get the actual output voltage e_o.

Figure 5 illustrates, for the sake of comparison, an exponential pulse front (dashed e_i) with a time constant of one half the rise time of the comparable linear pulse front (solid e_i) shown with it. The output voltage across the resistor due to the exponential pulse front (dashed e_R) may be compared with that due to the linear front (solid e_R) as an indication of the reliability of the second order approximation compared to the third order one. The assumption of linearly rising pulse front is quite reliable.

REFERENCES
(1) G. P. Ohman, Square-Wave Differentiating Circuit Analysis, ELECTRONICS, p 132 Aug 1945.
(2) Gershon J. Wheeler, Laplace Transforms for Electronic Engineers, ELECTRONICS, p 304 Feb 1945.
(3) N. W. McLachlin, "Complex Variable and Operational Calculus with Technical Applications", McMillan Co., 1944, Chapter 10.

Voltmeter for Pulses

HIGH INPUT IMPEDANCE is obtained in a vacuum tube voltmeter for use with pulses by the accompanying circuit. Basically it is a conventional diode rectifier, using the first section of a 6SN7 with grid tied to plate, followed by a cathode coupled amplifier (cathode follower). Other tube combinations might be better (perhaps a 6SQ7). Amplifier grid bias is adjusted, depending on the plate supply voltage, to approximately cut off the amplifier plate current.

Capacitor C is charged through the diode during a positive pulse. The charge then leaks off through resistors R_G and R_c. However, the

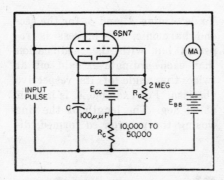

Voltmeter responds equally well to pulses from one to 20 microseconds duration

triode section of the 6SN7 then passes current developing a voltage across R_c to oppose the discharge of the capacitor. The time constant of the output circuit is thus increased. This increase of time constant of the actual circuit over that of the passive circuit elements alone approaches the amplification factor of the amplifier tube as R_c approaches the internal tube resistance. Because of the increased time constant of the output circuit, the capacitor can be small, thus increasing the input impedance of the voltmeter. Indication can be either by a plate milliammeter as shown, or by a conventional voltmeter across R_c. (A High Impedance Pulse Voltmeter, D. E. Howes, *Rev Sci Inst*, p 322 Nov 1945)

Graphical Fourier Analysis

By THOMAS C. BLOW

PERIODIC FUNCTIONS can be analyzed into their harmonic contents by several methods. Simplified schedules[1] are available that shorten numerical step-by-step integrations[2] but a graphical method that is short and accurate enough for engineering purposes is simpler. In addition, as will be seen from the following description, only a few ordinates need be used when determining the lower order harmonics.

Vector Addition

The accompanying diagram shows how the analysis is performed with a protractor and scale. The first ordinate a_1 is laid off from the origin in the direction specified by its abscissa, 30 deg in this illustration. Successive ordinates are laid off end to end in their respective directions. Ordinates of negative values such as a_5 through a_{11} are, of course, laid off in the negative direction. The line closing the polygon is then the desired coefficient A_1, but multiplied by $n/2$ where n is the number of ordinates used in the analysis, 12 in this case. The angle ϕ_1 is the angle between the resultant and the vertical axis.

The coefficient and angle so determined are substituted in the equation

$$F(\theta) = A_0 + A_1\sin(\theta + \phi_1) + A_2\sin(2\theta + \phi_2) + A_R\sin(R\theta + \phi_R)$$

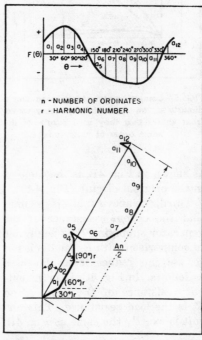

At the top is shown a wave to be analysed; twelve ordinates are constructed at 30 deg intervals to illustrate the technique. Below is shown the construction by which the amplitude and phase angle of the fundamental are graphically determined

To determine A_2 and ϕ_2 for the second harmonic, the process is repeated but with the modification that each ordinate is laid off at twice the angle of its respective abscissa. For example, a_1 is laid off at 60 deg. The length of the line closing the polygon so formed, divided by $n/2$, is A_2; its angle to the vertical is ϕ_2. The third harmonic coefficient will be found by laying off the ordinates at three times their respective angles.

For the steady state component A_0 the algebraic average of the ordinates is taken and divided by n. For the case of R = $n/2$ the line closing the polygon should also be divided by n instead of $n/2$ and the angle will always appear in this case to be 90 deg. However, in actual practice such a condition will not be encountered because the number of ordinates must be at least three to four times the highest order harmonic to be analysed reliably. Fewer ordinates can be used in determining the lower harmonics but, in any case, a sufficient number should be employed to adequately describe any abrupt variations during the cycle. Also, the analysis is greatly facilitated by the use of a universal protractor for making the graphical construction.

REFERENCES

(1) R. P. G. Denman, 36 and 72 Ordinate Schedules for General Harmonic Analysis, ELECTRONICS, p 44 Sept. 1942.
(2) A. V. Eastman, "Fundamentals of Vacuum Tubes", McGraw-Hill Book Co., New York, 1941. A good example of the step-by-step integration method is presented in Appendix B.
(3) J. R. Ashworth, A Simple Graphical Method for the Harmonic Analysis of a Cyclic Function, Electrician, p 888, 67, 1911.

Pulse-Sinewave Converter

By W. M. CAMERON

ALTHOUGH in most apparatus using pulse techniques the desired end result is in pulse form, there are exceptions such as in pulse frequency-modulation systems and radar radio links where sinewave output is desired. A simple and useful method of converting the output pulses to sinewaves is to produce a positive and a negative exponential, which are then folded to produce a wave having approximately sinusoidal charactertistics. The circuit for doing this requires few components.

Wave Synthesis

Several practical considerations suggest the sort of converter most suited to this problem. The pulse energy, when averaged over a recurrence cycle, is quite low. Thus, although low-pass filters are conventionally used to obtain sinewaves from pulses, it would be preferable that the converter contain an internal power source to furnish an output of reasonable amplitude. This requirement implies the use of vacuum tubes, but the number of tubes should be held to a minimum. The converter output should have reasonably low harmonic content, so that additional filtering can be a minimum, but cannot use resonant circuits for this purpose because the output frequency should be a function of the pulse rate.

Figure 1 shows a circuit that meets these requirements. The first tube is biased to cutoff. A positive pulse on its grid causes C_1 to discharge through the tube for the duration of the pulse, after which it charges slowly through R_1. The exponential wave thus obtained is applied through an R-C network to the grid of V_2. The plate circuit of this tube also has a long time constant that prevents any sharp discontinuities from appearing in the output wave. The curves on the

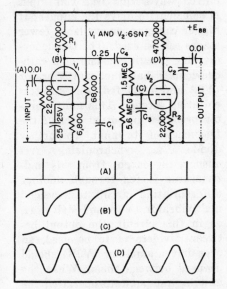

FIG. 1—Circuit for converting pulses to sinewaves is simple and more compact than a passive filter. Component values are for a representative application

diagram show the waveforms at various points when the circuit is operating at the frequency for which the second harmonic is the least. With an input pulse of 30 volts peak, the output has an amplitude of about 17 volts peak to peak.

Design and Performance

For tube and component values as shown in Fig. 1, the values of C_1 and C_2 for least second harmonic distortion at frequency f_H are given approximately by the empirical formula

$$C_1 = C_2 = 3.70 \times 10^6 \, (f_H^{-1.08}) \, \mu\mu F$$

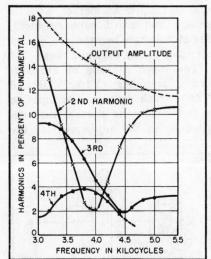

FIG. 2—Measured variations of voltage output and percent harmonics show performance of pulse-to-sinewave converter

and C_3 is ten percent of this value. The coupling capacitor C_4 should be kept large so that it does not introduce appreciable phase shift. Part of the justification for this approximate formula is that the impedances in the circuit are adjusted to produce only slight loading on previous loops in the networks. The approximation is within ten percent of the rigorous result, which is commensurate with the tolerance of commercial components.

Other factors than component values influence the waveform. With plate supply voltages of 200, 150 and 100 volts the corresponding second harmonics were 15, 17.3 and 20 percent at 2,200 cps. Values

ranging from 14.5 to 21 percent were found at the same frequency when other tubes of the same type were substituted. Figure 2 shows the harmonic content from a typical converter (measured on a General Radio type 636-A Wave Analyzer) expressed as a percentage of the fundamental. Four converters operating within the band from 500 to 4,000 cps but having different f_H were tested. The second harmonic present at f_H was 2.7, 3.2, 4.0 and 2.1 percent respectively.

In planning an adaptation of this converter for other ranges or tube complements, the two functions of the circuit should be kept in mind. The part of the circuit to the left of C_4 produces an exponential wave from the pulse input. A large exponential voltage change across C_1 is desired and will be obtained when the impedance of R_1-C_1 is high and V_1 has low plate resistance and high emission capability; a sharp cutoff tube requires lower input pulses than a remote cutoff type. The part of the circuit to the right of C_4 is a dynamic filter in which R_2 is in series with the plate resistance of V_2 during both charging and discharging of C_2, the voltage change across C_2 being effected by varying the plate resistance. With other tubes, R_2 should be chosen for best filter action. While one might obtain the required filtering with a passive L-C network, the size of the inductances necessary at these frequencies that will match a driving impedance in the order of 0.5 megohm is the main drawback.

When the electronic converter circuit is used in frequency-modulation equipment, the deviation should be limited to five percent of the recurrence frequency. A circuit of this type was used successfully in a pulse frequency-modulation system that carried audio frequencies to 2 kc on a mean recurrence frequency of 5 kc.

Multifrequency Synchronizer

By ROBERT K-F SCAL

PULSES repeating at multiples or fractions of the input signal frequency are produced by a versatile synchronizing unit that is useful for calibration and measurement in a variety of control and laboratory applications. The unit can be driven by the power line or by an external oscillator at a frequency in the subsonic, sonic or ultrasonic range. For example, the equipment has

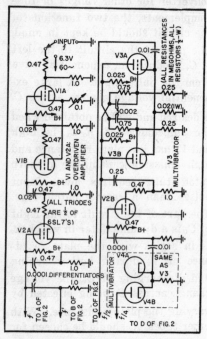

FIG. 1—Input and divider portions of synchronizer; second multivibrator is same as first; connections go to correspondingly marked leads of Fig. 2

been used to produce range markers. It delivers an output that can be adjusted in amplitude and made to have a rectangular, square, or impulse waveform.

Straightforward Circuit

The circuit uses only resistance and capacitance, hence there can be no frequency drift as there might be if resonant circuits were used. Triodes are used throughout; almost any type is suitable, but the high-gain dual type is preferable.

The circuit values shown here are for a 60 cps input; they are not particularly critical.

Functionally the unit consists of four sections: the input, the multiplier, the divider, and the output. Figure 1 shows the input and divider; Fig. 2 shows the multiplier and output. Although the circuit shown provides five output frequencies (the fundamental, its second and third harmonics, and its second and third subharmonics), the circuit can be extended, or restricted, to any required range.

The input consists of an overdriven amplifier (V1A, V1B and V2A) which converts the input to a rectangular or square wave depending on the adjustment of the

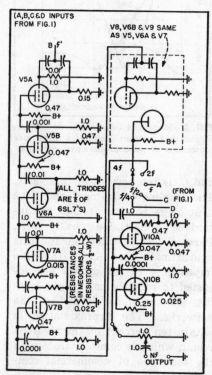

FIG. 2—Leads A, B, C and D come from corresponding leads of Fig. 2. Multipliers (one shown in detail) and output portions of synchronizer are shown here

cathode resistor. If a fixed input voltage is used, this resistor can be

fixed at the value giving the required waveform. One volt input is sufficient to drive the clipper; if higher voltages are available, fewer stages can be used. The frequency-dividing circuit consists of a cathode-coupled half-shot multivibrator (V3A and V3B) fed from a differentiating circuit. This multivibrator produces an output of half the frequency of its input. To further divide the synchronizing frequency, the output from this multivibrator is fed through another differentiating circuit to a second multivibrator (V4A and V4B). If, as in this circuit, the output between dividers is to be used, an over-driven amplifier (V2B) should be used between them. When the unit is first put into operation the dividing circuits may need adjusting to assure that they are not triggered by stray pickup. The circuit can be laid out and adjusted so that the tubes need not be shielded, but if the equipment is to be used near apparatus producing strong pulses, shielding from external pickup is essential.

Frequency Multiplier

The novel multiplying circuit shown in Fig. 2 is an alternate-pulse inverter that inverts only the positive pulses of a wave train consisting of alternate positive and negative pulses. Pulses shown in Fig. 3 are applied to both grid and cathode of the inverter (V5A), which is effectively self-biased practically to cutoff. A positive input pulse affects the grid, producing a negative pulse in the plate circuit. A negative pulse affects the cathode, also producing a negative pulse in the plate circuit. The following two stages (V5B and V6A) eliminate positive pulses appearing in the plate circuit and shape the negative pulses. Because a grounded-grid amplifier (V6A) is used in this shaping circuit, the pulses out of it are positive.

To obtain a rectangular or square wave at the multiplied rate, the output pulses can be fed to a multivibrator. If further multiplication is required, the pulse output is fed through a differentiator to another alternate pulse inverter (V8, V6B, and V9). A buffer and shaping amplifier (V7A and V7B) is advisable if the output from the first multiplier is to be used externally as well as for driving another multiplier. The grid circuit of the output (V7B) is adjusted to give the required wave shape.

As shown here the unit provides only one frequency at a time. If several frequencies are to be used, additional switching and output amplifiers can be added to obtain all frequencies simultaneously if desired. The single output amplifier used here consists of an overdriven stage (V10A) to limit the voltages of all frequencies to the same level. The output switch selects rectangular or square waves from the output of this amplifier, or pulses produced by feeding the signal to the cathode follower (V10B) through a differentiator. Additional circuits can be used to improve the waveform if desired.

Spacing of the output pulses from the alternate pulse inverter is the same as the input spacing. If the inverter is used to drive a single-

shot multivibrator, it will be necessary to adjust the multivibrator to obtain the required output; for example, to obtain a symmetrical square wave. Although the dividing and multiplying circuits are not sensitive to frequency, the coupling circuits of the multipliers are; they will have to be adjusted if the input frequency is changed. A unit employing an input frequency equal to the highest required frequency and using only dividers is, therefore, more versatile than one using both dividers and multipliers.

Power requirements for the unit are small. The maximum output voltage is dependent on the B+ voltage, which can be from 250 to 300 volts for the 6SL7's or higher if 6SN7's are used. A 5Y3-GT/G or selenium rectifier can be used with a single-section filter. A regulator may be desirable because the output is sensitive to supply voltage. Transients on the B+ line may trigger the multivibrators. Therefore, if, as is most likely, an electrolytic filter is used across the output of the power supply, it should be bypassed with either a small paper or mica capacitor to offer low impedance to high frequencies. If an external power supply is used, the capacitors should be across the B+ at the synchronizer to by-pass stray pulses picked up from the supply line, even if it is shielded.

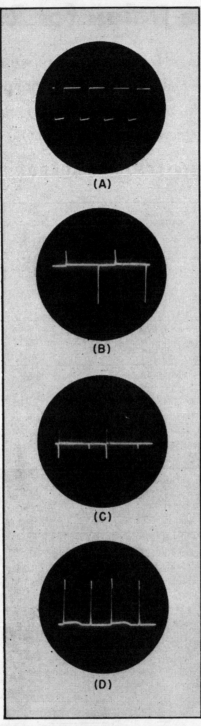

(A)

(B)

(C)

(D)

FIG. 3—Oscillographs show waveforms at critical portions of synchronizer. (A) output of overdriven amplifier, (B) input to alternate pulse inverter, (C) output of alternate pule inverter, and (D) output of shaping amplifier

Variable Pulse Delay for Radar Ranging

Accurate, continuously-variable or fixed pulse delay unit may be used in radar ranging, navigation, propagation studies and other similar techniques. Delay is obtained locally or remotely with range from a few microseconds to several milliseconds with a maximum error of 0.3 microsecond

By JAMES F. GORDON

Although there are several methods for obtaining variable pulse delays, many of them become impractical where a number of general requirements must be met. It is possible to design a multivibrator-type delay[1] for periods extending from a few microseconds up to several milliseconds. These delays are entirely satisfactory for applications not requiring high stability or calibration accuracy.

For short periods of fixed delay, both real and artificial delay lines

This article is based on a paper presented at the 1950 National Electronics Conference. The Conference paper will appear in the *NEC Proceedings*.

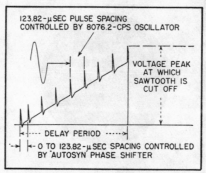

FIG. 1—Basic sawtooth time delay

are generally satisfactory. Other methods of creating pulse-type delays may be considered such as the phantastron,[1,2] mercury delay lines,[3]

and other types wherein an ultrasonic delay[4] may be accomplished.

One of the requirements of such a delay unit may be to establish pulse delays of the order mentioned above while maintaining a calibration accuracy which is independent of the repetition rate of the reference input pulse. A system which may be made reasonably insensitive to repetition rate is that used considerably in the past several years as a means of creating a pulse delay.[5]

A brief review of the general function of such a system is as follows: A delay reference input pulse

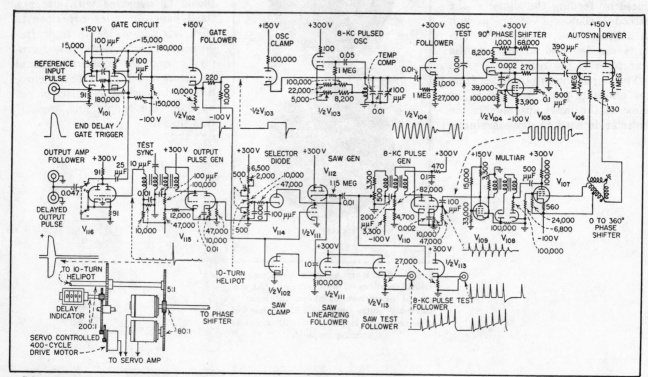

Schematic diagram of pulse delay unit. Output pulse has a width of one μsec and a peak value of 70 volts. Delay is variable from a few μsec to several milliseconds

is made to trigger, simultaneously, a sine-wave oscillator circuit and a sawtooth generator. The oscillator feeds a 0 to 360-deg variable phase-shifting circuit, the output of which feeds a pulse generator. The pulse generator output consists of pulses, one for each cycle of the sine-wave oscillator. These pulses are super-imposed upon the sawtooth circuit and appear as shown in Fig. 1.

By making the sawtooth generator trigger itself after it reaches a predetermined peak value, saw-tooth plus superimposed pulse, and by using this peak trigger voltage to develop an output pulse, a time delay is realized. The time delay is essentially equal to the period of the total sine-wave oscillations represented by the pulse spacings on the sawtooth.

By changing the point at which the sawtooth generator triggers itself, it is possible to create a delay which is adjustable in steps, each step equal to one cycle of the sine-wave oscillator. By virtue of the phase shifter following the pulse sine-wave oscillator circuit it is possible to superimpose upon this saw-tooth, pulses equally spaced by one cycle of the sine-wave following the first pulse.

The first pulse at the base of the sawtooth will be spaced a period from the start of the sawtooth by a 0 to 360-deg value depending upon the setting of the phase shifter. By suitably adjusting the sawtooth stopping point and by setting the phase shifter it is possible to super-impose any number of pulse spacings plus any part of a pulse space on the sawtooth. If the sawtooth cut-off point is made to increase in synchronism with the corre-sponding sine-wave phase shifter, the delay period as indicated will be continuously adjustable. Since this is accomplished in practice by a mechanical linkage, the unit is referred to as an electromechanical pulse delay unit.

In a unit designed on the fore-going basis the total pulse delay accomplished is the same as a num-ber of individual delays, all of which are not immediately appar-

ent. One of the general sources of such individual delays results from the existing condition in all pulsed timing equipments that any pulse must necessarily have a finite rise period. The designer should make all pulses in the delay chain have as short a rise period as possible and the amplitude should be gener-ous in all cases to reduce the total delay in any system and the trig-gering action sensitivity to ampli-tude variations. Sensitivity of this sort is often responsible for a type of annoying pulse phase modulation generally referred to as jitter. Long term variations of the same type result in reset inaccuracies.

The total delay effected by a unit of this type must take into consid-eration the delay introduced by the character of the delay reference input pulse and by the effect of the

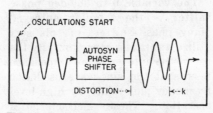

FIG. 2—Input and output waveforms for autosyn phase shifter. Resulting distortion is not dissipated until the end of the first two cycles

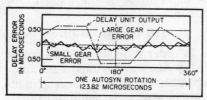

FIG. 3—Relationship between electrical error and mechanical error due to the gear train of the counter

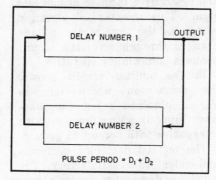

FIG. 4—Stable and adjustable pulse gen-erator consisting of two delay units con-nected back to back

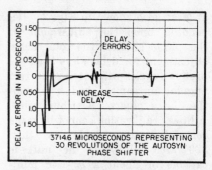

FIG. 5—Total calibration error of a typical delay unit over a range of 3714.6 micro-seconds plotted at each autosyn revolution except for the two points indicated. The two delay-error points shown were plotted from more frequent readings

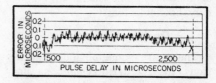

FIG. 6—An automatically traced error curve for a carefully balanced and adjusted unit over a 500 to 2,500-microsecond delay

delayed output pulse characteris-tic upon the circuit to which the unit is connected. The total unit delay in microseconds for a given control setting may be expressed as

$$D = d + k + m + 10^6/360f \,(\theta + \rho)$$

where

d is the delay in microseconds due to the character of the input pulse, the effect of the output pulse on the driven circuit and the delay caused by triggering characteristics within the circuit

θ is the phase angle due to sine-wave oscillator phase shifter

ρ is the total degrees of sine-wave oscillator duration between second and last pulses on sawtooth, (see Fig. 1 and 5.)

f is the sine-wave oscillator fre-quency in cycles

k is the additional delay, positive or negative, created by waveform distortion of the initial cycles fol-lowing triggering of the sine-wave oscillator, (see Fig. 2 and 6.)

m is the delay due to errors in the mechanical system

As shown in Fig. 2, the oscilla-tor output is clean and harmonic free following the initial time t, and should have a total harmonic distortion of less than 1%. The sharp wave front caused by start-ing the sine wave creates a wave-form distortion following the auto-syn phase shifter that is not dissi-pated until after the first two cycles at least, also shown in Fig. 2. Depending upon the adjustment of the phase shifter, the total delay adjustment for delays less than the first two cycles will not have correct angular agreement and k will either be a plus or a minus value. A linear calibration cannot be made for delays appreciably less than 360 μsec, although the unit is capable of about a 30-μsec minimum delay. A variation in the phase balance of the 90-deg phase shifter by a value of 1 deg will create an error of ± 0.4 μsec. For delays extending beyond the region of distortion shown in Fig. 2, k may be neglected.

Design Limitations

There are some obvious limitations to the arrangement as described. The method requires a very stable sine-wave oscillator and a faithful sine-wave phase shifter.[5] The method also requires a rigid means of developing pulses from the sine-wave oscillator which are phase locked to the sine-wave oscillator. Increasing the delay period accentuates these requirements.

A limitation is presented by the maximum amplitude of linear sawtooth that may be generated. This maximum amplitude determines the minimum sawtooth pulse spacing which may be accommodated on the sawtooth without danger of ambiguous pulse selection. This in turn determines the frequency of the sine-wave oscillator.

For the unit described here, the sine-wave oscillator operates at 8,076.2 cycles resulting in a voltage separation on the sawtooth of approximately 3.5 volts. This represents a peak sawtooth voltage of 3.5 $\times$ 40 or 140 for the maximum delay of 40 pulse spaces and is the condition for a delay of approximately 5,000 μsec. The delay is readily accomplished with miniature vacuum tubes and low supply voltages.

Sine-Wave Oscillator

The sine-wave oscillator shown in the circuit diagram is a pulsed Hartley type. It is rendered opera-

tive by removing the impedance of a cathode-follower-type clamp from across its tank circuit as soon as a reference input pulse is applied to the unit. The oscillator feedback network is adjusted to maintain a sine-wave oscillation at the peak direct voltage determined by the energy stored in the inductance at the time of release. The oscillator is made inoperative by replacing the oscillator clamp across it at the end of the delay period.

To obtain both short and long-term stability the oscillator is arranged to include a high-Q inductor, well shielded and rigidly mounted within a magnetic shield. Temperature compensation is provided. The 90-deg phase-shifter circuit is utilized primarily because it requires only one R and one C and is less critical to adjust.

The variable 0 to 360-deg phase shifter is the familiar autosyn.[6] Many phase shifters of this sort utilize a rotating capacitor.[5] By the use of the autosyn, a low impedance results at the sine-wave oscillator frequency plus relatively high-level operation. These characteristics are desirable in order to reduce the total tube requirements. The phase accuracy of the arrangement can be made to be of the order of 10 minutes.

Use of the Multiar

In order to phase-lock the pulses to the sine-wave output of the autosyn phase shifter, a form of multiar[7] is used. The multiar has the advantage of being regenerative for voltage increments of one sign and insensitive to those of opposite sign. This creates a situation where, as the sign of the voltage changes through zero, the circuit becomes immediately operative.

In the multiar circuit shown, the conduction which triggers V_{100} is obtained when the sine-wave input is going from positive to negative with respect to ground.

The method described performs well enough to be satisfactory. The multiar output pulse drives a conventional pulse generator which functions to maintain both a con-

stant level output and a low-impedance pulse source to feed the pulses to the sawtooth generator.

The sawtooth generator utilizes a single feedback follower to provide a linear charging current for the sawtooth capacitor. The linearity resulting is of the order of one-tenth of one percent. Precision resistors and capacitors are used in the circuit.

A triode may be used instead of a selector diode. There is a greater stability in the cut-off characteristics of a biased diode which reduces the hazards of pulse skipping.

A second conventional parallel-triggered blocking oscillator type of pulse generator provides an output pulse. The pulse is shaped and made available as either a positive or negative pulse to feed a 90-ohm line.

To provide rigid synchronization of the triggered functions in the circuit, an Eccles-Jordan bistable type of biased multivibrator[8] is rendered conducting in one direction by the delay reference input pulse. This is referred to as a gate circuit and it remains conducting until one delay period has been completed. The output pulse resulting from the delay function triggers the Eccles-Jordan circuit back to its original position to await the next delay reference input pulse. The gate circuit control to the sine-wave oscillator and sawtooth is accomplished by means of a cathode follower to minimize loading effects on the gate circuit.

The smallest disturbance to any part of the circuit is likely to affect the stability and hence the accuracy. Since in order to operate and calibrate it is necessary to observe circuit functions, two follower tubes are built into the unit as nonloading test connections. The follower tubes allow examination of the sawtooth and the 8,076.2-kc derived blocking-oscillator output pulse.

Unit Construction

The chassis is mounted in a temperature-controlled oven so that all thermosensitive components associated with the accuracy of the delay are kept at a constant temperature. To improve the uniformity of component temperature, a small air circulator is incorporated within the oven.

By utilizing a counter and suitable gearing, it is possible to arrange a means of directly reading the delay period to which the unit is adjusted. Accuracy of the reading depends upon the accuracy of the gearing between the counter indicator and the delay control shaft. The accuracy is excellent with precision gearing. The error curve for a 120-μsec section of the total delay range is shown superimposed upon the gear error in Fig. 3. The long-period cyclic gear error as indicated by the dotted line may be attributed to a large gear in the mechanical part of the system. The short-period cyclic error may be attributed to a smaller gear and other mechanical errors.

The linearity of the unit as a function of the position of the control shaft is degraded by the "run out" in the gearing driving the indicator but is a minor factor. By careful balancing of the 90-deg. phase shifter, the measured results

shown in Fig. 6 may be obtained. Here, the gear-train error becomes predominant.

Remote Control

The unit may be operated remotely by a servo system comprising a coarse and fine autosyn system which is designed as an integral part of the unit. The error curve of Fig. 3 does not take into account the errors in the servo system. These errors must be added algebraically to the results obtained with direct control of the unit.

Units of the type described are applicable in radar ranging, navigation, propagation studies, coding, and other similar techniques. A novel application is the use of two such units to trigger each other to form a very stable pulse generator as shown in Fig. 4. In this arrangement the pulse output period is equal to $D_1 + D_2$ and may be varied by changing the period of either or both of the delays. It is necessary to start the action by causing either of the units to generate a pulse. If either of the units fail to deliver a pulse, the oscillation ceases. The probability of fail-

ure during normal operation is so remote as to be insignificant.

The successful development of the unit described is due to the contributing efforts of H. A. Straus, J. M. Miller, Jr., C. G. McMullen, E. C. Nunn, E. L. Gray, W. G. Chenoweth and G. M. Trinite.

REFERENCES

(1) S. Seely, "Electron-Tube Circuits," McGraw-Hill, 1950. Chance, Hughes, MacNichol, Sayre and Williams, "Waveforms," 19, Rad. Lab. Series, McGraw-Hill, 1949.
(2) F. C. Williams and Moody, Jour. Inst. Elec. Engrs., 93, p 1,188. 1946.
(3) H. J. McSkimin, Theoretical Analysis of the Mercury Delay Line, Jour. Acoustical Soc. of America, July 1948.
(4) Rad. Lab. Series (Ref. 1). H. B. Huntington, A. G. Emslie and V. W. Hughes, Ultrasonic Delay Lines I, Jour. Franklin Inst., 1, p 245, 1948. V. Hughes, A Theory of the Supersonic Delay Line, Rad. Lab. Report No. 733, Sept. 15, 1945. H. B. Huntington, The Theory and Performance of Liquid Delay Lines, Rad. Lab. Report No. 792, Sept. 21, 1945. F. A. Metz, Jr. and W. M. A. Anderson, Improved Ultrasonic Delay Line, ELECTRONICS, July 1949.
(5) L. A. Meacham, Timer for Radar Echoes, Bell Lab. Record, June 1947.
(6) E. D. Cockrell, "Industrial Electronic Control," McGraw-Hill, 1944.
(7) Rad. Lab. Series, (Ref. 1).
(8) W. H. Eccles and F. W. Jordan, Radio Review, 1, p 143, 1919. O. S. Puckle, "Time Bases", John Wiley, Inc., 1943, Cruft Electronics Staff, "Electronic Circuits and Tubes", McGraw-Hill, 1947. H. J. Reich, "Principles of Electron Tubes," McGraw-Hill, 1941.

Improved Ultrasonic Delay Lines

Forged magnesium-alloy delay lines developed as memory devices have bandwidths as great as 4 mc at a carrier frequency of 10 mc. The attenuation is the least so far available in practical lines. Special clamping of S-cut ADP crystal transducers is described

By F. A. METZ, JR. AND W. M. A. ANDERSEN

THE ULTRASONIC DELAY LINE is a device developed during World War II to store intelligence for periods of several milliseconds and is now used in high-speed digital computers and other devices.

The construction and operation of a typical delay line is shown in Fig. 1. The crystals have a resonant frequency in the range of 10 to 30 mc. The intelligence to be stored modulates the carrier frequency.

The first delay lines used employed liquids as transmitting media, but the many disadvantages of liquids caused a search to be made for a suitable solid.

During the war much effort was spent in finding solids with low ultrasonic absorption for use in constructing ultrasonic delay lines. An account of this work, and the solid delay lines constructed, are to be found in the report of D. L. Aren-

berg[1]. A complete bibliography of previous work is also given in his report.

At the end of the war, Arenberg's conclusions were that fused quartz offered the best transmission qualities of any known substance, but that the length of delay was limited by the size of the blanks available. It was also difficult to machine properly, and great angular accuracy of the reflecting faces was necessary to prevent the generation of spurious signals resulting from inaccuracies.

Single crystals showed good ultrasonic transmission, but when polycrystalline media such as steel, tungsten, fine-grained aluminum and magnesium were tried, their absorption was too high for delay-line purposes. Magnesium alloys were not considered at that time.

The Delay Medium

The objective of our investigations was to find a medium from which lines having 3 milliseconds or more delay could be constructed, operating at a carrier frequency of 10 mc or higher, and having a bandwidth greater than 2 mc. At the time these studies were initiated, there was no solid that would give this performance. Fused quartz was acceptable, except that 2,000 μsec was the longest delay obtainable without strong spurious signals.

Many materials were tested to de-

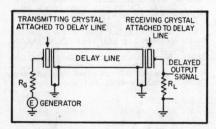

FIG. 1—Elementary delay line, showing how signal is transmitted by input transducer and delayed output having same waveform is received

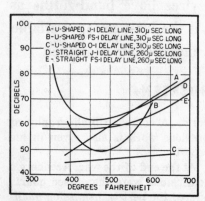

FIG. 2—Successive annealings at increasing temperatures change the attenuation

termine their suitability. Some results are shown in Table I. The velocity measurements were taken

with a Sperry Reflectoscope at a frequency of 10 mc.

To determine whether the attenuation was low enough in the metal, test lines having about 500-μsec delay were constructed and the losses in the crystals and medium measured. In all measurements taken, mismatch and cement losses were of the order of 30 db.

This attenuation was sufficient to reject all materials listed in Table I except fused quartz and the magnesium alloys O-1, J-1 and FS-1. These materials were far superior to any of the others, the transmission being best in the order named. For example, a J-1 delay line, delay 397 μsec, at carrier of 10 mc had an attenuation of 40 db; and an FS-1 delay line, 970 μsec, at 10 mc, had an attenuation of 50 db. These measurements were made with 1,500-ohm resistors and a resonant coil shunting the crystals. The shear mode was used in both cases, with the crystals cemented to the magnesium alloy. No end cells were used. Other examples include a straight rod of O-1 alloy, delay 329 μsec, with attenuation of 35 db when untreated. After heat treatment at 450 F, the attenuation was 30 db, and the pulse shape improved. A straight rod of FS-1 alloy, with a delay of 330 μsec, had an attenuation untreated of 38 db; upon treatment at 450 F attenuation dropped to 32 db, with improved pulse shape.

The next series of tests was made

using rods bent into the shape of a U. Three rods of J-1, FS-1, and O-1 were heated to 400 F and bent. Before heat treatment the attenuations at 10 mc were FS-1, 67 db; O-1, 47 db; and J-1, 75 db.

The rods were then heat treated and tested after the temperature

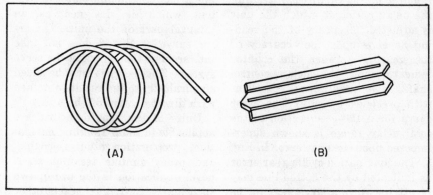

FIG. 3—Two of the experimental folded forms of delay lines used. Various conformations were tried in developing compact units

was raised in steps. The results are shown in Fig. 2. If plots had been made at lower temperatures minima could have been found for O-1 (C) and J-1 (A) also.

To determine these minima, readings were taken on two other samples of J-1 (D) and FS-1 (E). These curves are also plotted in Fig. 2. There is little agreement in these curves. It seems that 500 F is a good annealing temperature, but the results vary too much in the two samples to arrive at any general conclusion. The composition of commercial alloys is not constant enough to determine the best heat treatment. Laboratory samples of these alloys will probably give consistent results.

As an illustration of the great variation in transmission properties, one long rod tested showed a signal internally reflected several times that was delayed 4,950 μsec, with an attenuation 47 db below the input pulse. But in the compact, folded configurations used in these experiments, 1,600 μsec is the upper limit that can be relied upon using commercial alloys. Two of the configurations used are shown in Fig. 3.

Another type of treatment to improve transmission in magnesium and the alloys mentioned above was hot forging with a drop hammer forge. The pressure used was approximately 5 tons per square inch.

The first sample treated by forging was a billet of pure magnesium 10 centimeters long. The results obtained are illustrated in Fig. 4, the transmitted pulse being shown at 4A. Before forging, the signal could not be seen, placing the atten-

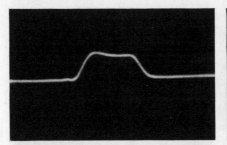 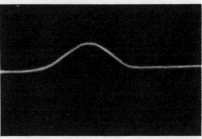

FIG. 5—A 1-microsecond 10-mc pulse, at left, and the corresponding received pulse through a magnesium delay line using cemented-quartz AC-cut transducers

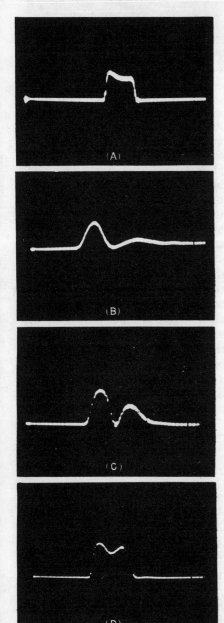

FIG. 4—Change in transmission characteristics after successive forgings. The transmitted pulse is shown at (A). See text for explanation of (B), (C) and (D)

uation above 90 db. After the first forging at 550 F, and heat treatment, the attenuation was 61 db, with a change in wave shape as shown at 4B. After the second forging the received pulse was down 68 db as at 4C. The third forging, not illustrated, showed an increase in attenuation but a somewhat better pulse response. The fourth forging, at 500 F, showed marked improvement in pulse response with attenuation at 61 db, as indicated in 4D.

Before treatment the grain size of the magnesium was small and very jumbled. After the final forging, the grain size was larger, and more orderly in arrangement. The amount of inclusion was not changed.

A sample of J-1 alloy was also forged that had good transmission, but poor pulse reproduction. After passing through the same treatment as the pure magnesium, the pulse reproduction was much improved.

Upon microscopic examination, the grain size proved to be unchanged after forging, being smaller than the pure forged magnesium. The compound was more evenly distributed between grains after forging. The sample had an attenuation of 38 db, and was 10 centimeters long.

In addition to the transmission and pulse fidelity of the medium, the change of delay time of the signal with temperature is of importance in using these devices. This condition was measured by mounting a delay line made of FS-1 alloy 10 inches long inside an oven and the change in delay time measured. The change in delay time with tem-

perature proved to be linear, and the total delay time for a sample of length L is given by

$$D_{Mg} = L (8.34 + 0.0021T)$$

T being the temperature in degrees centigrade, and 8.34 being the delay per inch at 0 C.

In Report 745, Radiation Lab., MIT, Jacobson obtained for a mercury delay line.

$$D_{Hg} = L (17.42 + 0.0052T)$$

where the symbols have the same meaning as before. From these relations the temperature coefficient of delay of mercury is 2.99×10^{-4} sec per sec per deg C while for FS-1 alloy it is 2.52×10^{-4} sec per sec per deg C. The coefficient for mercury is 18.7 percent greater than that of FS-1 alloy.

The shear mode of vibration was found to be the best type for solid delay-line application. Since the bars used were many wavelengths wide, there was no velocity dispersion present in the bar. The use of the shear mode has the advantages of less spreading of the sound beam in the medium, decreased velocity of propagation, and a noticeable improvement in signal-to-noise ratio of the delay line.

Shear Crystals

Since the shear mode gives a polarized wave, only a portion of the noise originating in the medium affects the receiving crystal. The computed gain in signal-to-noise ratio over the compressional mode is 4.97 db.

These advantages have been realized in practice, and use of the longitudinal mode has been discontinued in solid delay lines.

The first delay lines constructed using magnesium alloys used AC-cut quartz crystals as transducers. The crystal capacitance was tuned out with an inductance, and the resulting resonant circuit loaded with a 1,500-ohm resistor to improve the response. The crystals were cemented to the magnesium alloy with a thin film of phenyl benzoate, which is applied melted and cools to form an adherent layer.

Bandwidth of Lines

Although the attenuation in these delay lines was low, a measurement of the response showed the bandwidth to be 0.8 mc at a carrier frequency of 10 mc. This is entirely inadequate for many applications of the device.

Since the typical pulse response of the delay line, shown in Fig. 5, was not satisfactory, it appeared that this might be improved by a different choice of crystal. According to the current theory used in delay-line design,[2,3,4] for optimum bandwidth the ratio of the acoustic impedances of the magnesium to the crystal should be equal to the square root of 2. The crystal should have a high dielectric constant and a high piezoelectric constant for good coupling of energy into the medium.

The crystal chosen was S-Cut ADP (Ammonium Dihydrogen

* Swann[5] shows that the acoustic output is theoretically a nonlinear function of applied emf, and that the relative prominence of harmonics increases with acoustic loading.

Phosphate, $NH_4H_2PO_4$) which is nearly ideal from these considerations. Its constants are: piezoelectric constant, 24×10^{-10} cm per volt; sound velocity in crystal, 2.02×10^5 cm per sec; acoustic impedance, 3.6×10^5 acoustic ohms; dielectric con-

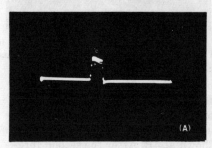 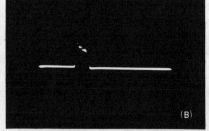

FIG. 6—A 1.5-microsecond 10-mc pulse, at left, and the pulse received after a delay of 225 microseconds, using S-cut ADP crystal transducers

stant, $K_x = 55$; $K_z = 14.5$.

This cut is derived from Z-cut by rotation about the X axis, 45 deg off the Y axis, and vibrates in thickness shear.

The thickness constant for this crystal is fairly small, and blanks were available at a resonant frequency of 1 mc. To operate at 10 mc, the 1-mc blank was cemented to the magnesium, as in the case of the quartz crystal, and then lapped down in a special jig to the required frequency. There was considerable improvement over quartz, but the results were still inadequate.

The results are shown in Fig. 6. From the rise time of the delayed pulse, the estimated response is seen to be somewhat greater than 1.2 mc.

This is not considered adequate except for fairly wide pulses.

It was apparent that the bandwidth obtained was much less than that predictable using existing theories—both in the case of quartz and ADP crystals. While there is good reason to question the adequacy of the existing theories describing the bandwidth of loaded piezoelectric crystals when the loading is as heavy as occurs in delay lines,* it was also felt that the effectiveness of the cement bond might be a limiting factor in the obtainable bandwidth.

Mason and McSkimin[6] show that slippage due to poor bonding between the crystal and delay line can be considered as a shunt capacitance across the delay line. In the equivalent circuit they use for illustration it is obvious how improper bonding limits the bandwidth of a delay line. Since a wide bandwidth is required in the storage of narrow pulses it became evident that radi-

Table I—Characteristics of Delay-Line Materials

Material	ρ (grams per cu cm)	V_L (cm per sec $\times 10^5$)	V_T (cm per sec $\times 10^5$)	V_R (cm per sec $\times 10^5$)	σ	E (dynes per sq cm $\times 10^{11}$)
FS-1 Extruded Magnesium..	1.690±0.020	5.473±0.012	3.030±0.013	2.800	0.279±0.004	3.07±0.19
J-1 Extruded Magnesium...	1.700±0.030	5.673±0.013	3.010±0.013	2.793	0.304±0.004	4.02±0.19
AM3S Magnesium.........	1.735±0.002	5.787±0.029	3.095±0.015	2.870	0.300±0.006	4.32±0.07
M-Extruded Magnesium....	1.750±0.010	5.758±0.011	3.092±0.010	2.866	0.297±0.002	4.34±0.05
0-1 Extruded Magnesium...	1.817±0.002	5.800±0.029	3.041±0.015	2.825	0.310±0.005	4.40±0.06
Fused Quartz.............	2.198±0.004	5.926±0.030	3.751±0.019	3.395	0.166±0.006	7.30±0.12
Pyrex...................	2.226±0.001	5.574±0.028	3.436±0.017	3.127	0.194±0.010	6.27±0.12
Plate Glass..............	2.510±0.010	5.769±0.029	3.426±0.017	3.137	0.227±0.008	7.32±0.14
2SO Aluminum...........	2.713±0.005	6.349±0.023	3.105±0.016	2.900	0.343±0.004	7.02±0.10
Molybdenum.............	10.09±0.03	6.286±0.031	3.348±0.016	3.106	0.302±0.004	29.4±0.5
Tungsten................	19.25±0.01	5.183±0.026	2.873±0.014	2.654	0.278±0.006	40.6±0.6

ρ = density
V_L = longitudinal velocity
V_T = transverse velocity
V_L and V_T correspond to those computed using the bulk modulus of elasticity

V_R = Rayleigh wave velocity (computed from V_L and V_T in this table)
σ = Poisson's ratio
E = Young's modulus

cal changes would have to be made in order to remove the limitations of solid delay lines using cemented crystals. Efforts made in this direction resulted in the development of a pressure mounted crystal with which control of the bonding between the crystal and the delay line is secured by varying the pressure applied to the crystal through a pressure block. This pressure block has the additional function of absorbing spurious reflections. A further result of the development of pressure-mounted crystals was extreme ruggedness and resistance to changes due to elevated temperatures.

Figure 7 shows the possible design of a pressure-mounted crystal which, while mechanically simpler than designs actually used, indicates clearly the function of the various parts. Using pressure-mounting methods similar to that illustrated, it was found that the acoustic response of the delay line was as great as 62.5 percent. This measurement was made using r-f modulated by 400 cycles and tuning out the shunt crystal capacitance as the r-f frequency was varied. This bandwidth was considerably greater than could be obtained in practice due to limitations imposed by the purely electrical characteristics of the delay line.

The receiving end of a delay line with the necessary attached circuit elements is shown in Fig. 8. Shunt

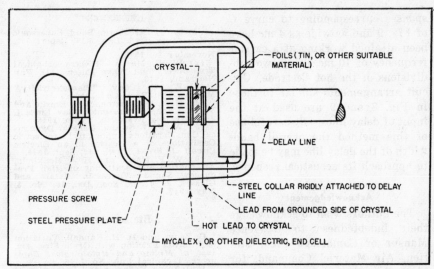

FIG. 7—Improved method of pressure-mounting a quartz crystal to a solid delay line

capacitance of the crystal and any necessary stray capacitance is denoted by C_0. A tuning coil L is used to tune out C_0 at the carrier frequency used. The resistance R is used to broaden the frequency response of L and C_0 in parallel. In practice, R cannot usually be made much smaller than 500 ohms.

In Fig. 8, curve A typifies the acoustic response of the delay line-crystal combination, B the frequency response of the parallel C_0, L, and R combination and curve C typifies the overall frequency response of the delay line in conjunction with the necessary electrical circuit elements. Although these curves are not drawn to scale, they show that with clamped crystals the overall bandwidth is now limited by

the electrical circuits that must be used at the terminations of the line.

An arrangement used to broaden the overall frequency response of a delay line is indicated in Fig. 9. It will be noted that the hot electrode of the crystal is now divided and that each division is separately tuned and damped. In the illustration the signals applied to the two grids of the tube are mixed electronically and the amplified resultant appears at the plates of the tube. This output is depicted by curve C in Fig. 9. Curve A is the same as that in Fig. 8 and the two curves B are the responses appearing at the two grids of the mixer. In practice, as many as four subdivisions of the hot electrode of the crystal have been used. Overall re-

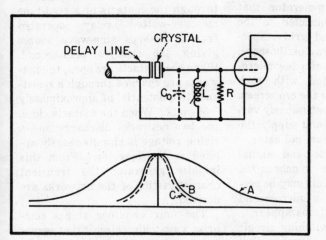

FIG. 8—Output circuit and characteristic curves for a delay line using conventional electrodes

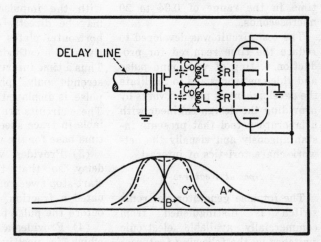

FIG. 9 — Divided-electrode output circuit and delay-line characteristics

sponses curresponding to curve *C* of Fig. 9 and as wide as 4 mc have been attained working at a carrier frequency of 10 mc, using two sub-divisions of the hot electrode. Circuit arrangements similar to those in Fig. 8 and 9 are used at the input of delay lines. By careful use of this method the overall band-width of the delay line may be made to approach its acoustical response.

Acknowledgement

The authors wish to acknowledge their indebtedness to Lawrence Mansur of Cambridge Field Station, Air Materiel Command, for his cooperation and many helpful suggestions in this work. Acknowledgement for their contributions at various times to this work is also due Eric B. Hansell, Leo F. Epstein and Gilbert W. Bett.

REFERENCES

(1) D. L. Arenberg, Solid Supersonic Delay Lines, Rad. Lab. MIT Report 932, November 30, 1945.
(2) W. P. Mason, "Electromechanical Transducers and Wave Filters," D. Van Nostrand, 1942.
(3) W. G. Cady, "Piezoelectricity," McGraw-Hill Book Co., 1946.
(4) H. B. Huntington, A. G. Emslie and V. W. Hughes, Ultrasonic Delay Lines I, *J. Frank. Inst.*, 245, No. 1, Jan. 1948.
(5) W. F. G. Swann, General Dynamical Considerations Applied to Piezoelectric Oscillations of a Crystal in an Electric Circuit, *J. Frank. Inst.*, 242, Sept. 1946.
(6) W. P. Mason and H. J. McSkimin, Attenuation and Scattering of High Frequency Sound Waves in Metals and Glasses, *J. Acous. Soc. Am.*, 19, No. 3, May 1947.

BIBLIOGRAPHY

C. Zener and R. H. Randall, Variation of Internal Friction with Grain Size, *Am. Inst. of Mining and Metallurgical Engineers*, Technical Pub. No. 1146.
H. Jeffreys, Reflexion and Refraction of Elastic Waves, *Roy. Astron. Mon. Nat. Geophys. Suppl.* No. 7, p 331, Jan. 1926.
Jeffries and Archer, "*Science of Metals*," McGraw-Hill Book Co., 1927.
N. F. Budgen, "Heat Treatment and Annealing of Aluminum and Its Alloys," Sherwood Press, Cleveland, Ohio, 1933.
R. L. Wegel and H. Walther, Internal Dissipation in Solids for Small Cyclic Strains, *Physics*, 6, p 141, 1935.

Alfred von Zeerleder, "The Technology of Magnesium and Its Light Alloys," 2nd ed., Gustav Fock, New York, 1936.
C. Zener, Internal Friction in Solids, *Proc. Phys. Soc.*, London, 52, 1940.
A. Beck, "Technology of Magnesium and Its Alloys," F. A. Hughes & Co. Ltd., London, 1943.
A. Gemant, Frictional Phenomena XIII, *J. Appl. Phys.*, 14, p 204, 1943.
F. Seitz, "Physics of Metals," McGraw-Hill Book Co., 1943.
L. Bergmann, "Der Ultraschall," 3rd ed., Edwards Brothers, Ann Arbor, Michigan, 1944.

R. I. Jacobson, A Measurement of Supersonic Velocity in Mercury at 15 Megacycles per Second as a Function of Temperature, Rad. Lab. MIT Report 745, 20 Sept. 1945.

W. G. Cady, Piezoelectric and Ultrasonic Phenomena in the Ultrasonic Trainer, Final Report to MIT, OSRD contract OEMsr-262, Sept. 30, 1945.
American Magnesium Corporation, Properties of Magnesium Products, 1946.
Macelwane and Sokon, "Introduction to Theoretical Seismology," John Wiley & Sons, 1946.
Ultrasonic Delay Lines, *J. Acous. Soc. Am.*, 20, No. 1, Jan. 1948.
A. G. Emslie, H. B. Huntington, H. Shapiro and A. E. Benfield, Ultrasonic Delay Lines II, *J. Frank. Inst.*, 245, No. 2, Feb. 1948.
W. Roth, Scattering of Ultrasonic Radiation in Polycrystalline Metals, *J. Appl. Phys.*, 19 No. 10, Oct. 1948.
Crystal Research Laboratories, Interim Engineering Reports, Contract W28-099 ac110, July 1946 to Dec. 1948.

Radar Delay Network Tester

A COMBINATION impulse generator and electronic switch for testing radar component networks was described by T. R. Finch of Bell Telephone Laboratories at the 1949 IRE National Convention. This test facility may be used to test any network that can be arranged to store a d-c charge, such as delay and pulse-forming networks with delay, pulse duration and response rise time in the range of 0.04 to 20 microseconds.

The test circuit was developed to reduce the time required for production testing of wide-band pulse and video networks and to facilitate the development of new networks by providing the design engineer with a laboratory tool that presents instantaneously and visually the network characteristics of interest.

Special Features

The impulse generator-electronic switch is distinguished from commercially available electronic switches by the following features:

(1) It provides an impulse generator which energizes the networks under test and discharges these networks through a zero-impedance switch, resulting in pulse patterns related to the transmission characteristics of the networks. These microsecond pulse patterns are repeated at a rate of 480 pulses per second.

(2) It provides a start-stop sweep and beam intensifier synchronized with the impulse generator that may be directly connected to the horizontal plates and grid respectively of a cathode-ray oscilloscope. Thus a time interval of a few microseconds only, phased with each pulse, is displayed on the cro screen. These circuits are continuously variable in trace speed and supply the time base for the visual indicator.

(3) Provides wide-band signal delay so that the synchronized start-stop sweep circuit may be actuated a fraction of a microsecond before the pulse patterns appear.

(4) Provides a switching circuit which is positively synchronized with the impulse generator and sweep circuit. Thus switching synchronization and adjustment is unnecessary.

Operation of Circuit

The accompanying block diagram illustrates the basic circuit performance. The impulse generator is so arranged that the standard network and the network under test can be discharged simultaneously through the contacts of a reed-type mercury-wetted relay operated from a 240-cps sine-wave source giving 480 closures per second. When the contacts are open, the networks are charged through a resistance to a potential of approximately −50 volts. When the contacts close, the two networks discharge and a rising voltage is simultaneously applied to the inverter. From this impulse generator the transient characteristics of the networks are derived.

The four amplifier stages comprise a switching circuit that serves to commutate signals characteristic of the networks under test, so that first one signal and then the other is impressed on the screen of the cro, at a sufficiently high rate of switching that both characteristics seem

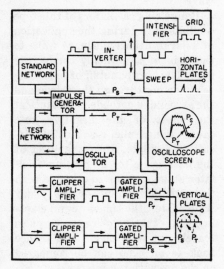

Block diagram of tester

to appear simultaneously.

The sweep circuit merely provides the time scale for the plot that appears on the cro screen.

Switching Action

The clipper amplifiers receive 240-cycle input voltages from the oscillator, one 180 degrees out of phase with the other, and convert these into square waves 180 degrees out of phase. These square waves are locked with the frequency of relay contact closures since both are driven from the same oscillator. However, the contacts make two closures per square wave cycle and are approximately 90 degrees out of phase with the leading edge of each square wave.

The spiked pulse signals generated in the impulse generator by the networks under test are applied through gain controls to the control grids of the gated amplifier tubes, while the square-wave voltages of the clipper amplifiers are applied to the screen-grids of these tubes. With 125-volt square-wave amplitudes with respect to ground and a 100-volt positive d-c bias on the screen grids, the screen voltages alternate between +225 and —25 volts with reference to ground. The gated amplifier tubes are normally cathode-biased so that with no signal on the control grids and +225 volts on the screens only a small amount of plate current flows and

very little screen current. When the signal pulses appear simultaneously on the respective control grids, the screen of one tube will be +225 volts and the other —25 volts hence one tube will conduct and the other will be blocked. Due to the phase relationship of the screen voltage (180 degrees out of phase), the signal voltages are interlaced in the common plate circuit as first one signal is amplified and then the other. Thus, each signal appears at the rate of 240 pulses per second on the screen.

The start-stop sweep circuit is initiated at the same time that the signal pulses are generated. Since it requires approximately 0.2 microsecond to produce the linear sweep voltage, a wide-band delay network is inserted in the common plate circuit of the gated amplifier tubes to provide 0.5 microsecond delay so that complete pulse patterns are shown.

For most conditions of operation, the intensity control on the cro is set so that there is no visible spot on the screen, and intensity voltage is provided by a 6AC7 in the intensifier stage only during the sweep interval.

Radar Range Calibrator

Design of an instrument for calibrating in production the concentric rings of a ppi indicator used for estimating distance. Range ring pulses generated in the radar are compared on a triggered oscilloscope with spaced pulses from a crystal-controlled calibrator

By ROBERT L. ROD

RADAR EQUIPMENTS utilizing the plan position indicator (ppi) type of visual presentation have superimposed upon the polar diagram a series of concentric circles or range rings which enable range estimations to be made to particular targets of interest. Depending upon the range scale in use, these rings are generally spaced 0.5, 1.0, 5.0, or 10 statute or nautical miles apart. Those objects which appear

on the ppi between range rings may be fixed in range by interpolation. In order to insure the maximum in accuracy, the indicated distance to any ring as measured from the center of the cathode-ray tube, or zero range, is maintained well within one percent of the true range.

Range ring pulses, which intensity-modulate the ppi tube to form the rings, are generally formed by squaring the output of a shock-

excited ringing oscillator by means of several amplifiers and differentiation of the resultant square wave. By correct choice of parallel resonant oscillator circuit components, the period of sine-wave output is made equal to the desired time interval between successive range rings. In production testing of radars it is necessary to utilize a simple and rapid system for precisely tuning the resonant circuit to the correct frequency.

Applications

The test instrument to be described permits range ring pulses generated in the radar to be compared with spaced pulses generated by a highly accurate calibrator. Thus, when the radar range ring pulses are in exact time coincidence with those obtained from the calibrator, the slug-tuned inductance in the radar range ring generator that determines the resonant frequency of the ringing is precisely adjusted. A standard triggered-sweep oscilloscope is used for making the necessary visual comparison checks.

The range calibrator may be conveniently used with any radar system that can be locked in synchronism with some submultiple of the test instrument's nautical or statute mile fundamental frequency of either 80.86 or 93.12 kilocycles. Radars utilizing free-running multivibrators or blocking oscillators to establish their pulse recurrence frequencies (prf) may be locked in step with the calibrator without altering repetition rates by more than a few hundred cycles during the calibration period. When both the radar and the calibrator are locked in synchronism, it is possible to align fixed and variable range rings as well as to measure the time duration of various waveforms throughout the radar. By modulating the Z-axis of a triggered oscilloscope with the calibrator pulses, a waveform under observation will be intensity-modulated by a series of dots spaced one or five miles apart, selected at will. Time intervals can then be accurately measured with a minimum of difficulty.

Systems used to generate range ring pulses are described in the literature. However, it is well to review one common type briefly. In Fig. 1, a typical circuit is shown wherein a pulsed ringing oscillator produces a damped sine wave. The period of the sine wave is made equal to the desired time interval between the range ring pulses which are developed by the following squaring, differentiating and blocking oscillator circuits. By the use of a reasonably high-Q resonant circuit in the cathode of the ringing oscillator, it is possible to produce five or more usable cycles having, for example, a period of five nautical miles, or 62.4 microseconds, between successive cycles. By center-tapping the inductance and adding a feedback triode, the oscillator can be made to have constant amplitude output for each cycle during the ringing time.[1] Sufficient amplification following the damped ringing oscillator will produce a practically perfect square wave.

Range ring oscillators of this type oscillate only during the application of a large negative square wave to the grid of a normally conducting tube. The abrupt cutoff of plate current flowing through the triode and the associated cathode inductance at the onset of the negative gate causes the parallel resonant LC circuit to oscillate. Since the onset of the gate pulse to the ringing oscillator stage is made to coincide with the pulsing instant of the radar transmitter, the time interval elapsing while the radio-frequency pulse travels out to a target and thence back as an echo can be compared on the ppi with the interval between successive range rings.

Accuracy

Neglecting such factors as the linearity of the ppi sweep, accuracy of the range rings is dependent upon the following factors:

(A) The resonant frequency of the ringing oscillator.

(B) The degree of amplification following the pulsed oscillator.

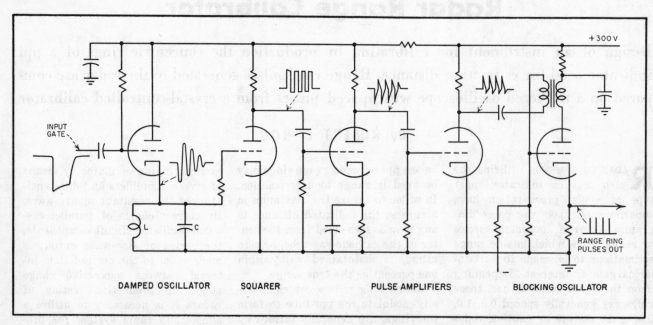

FIG. 1—Typical radar range ring pulse generator and voltage waveforms produced at the various stages

(C) The leading edge fall time of the negative gate used to ring the oscillator.

(D) The preciseness of all timing sequences throughout the radar system, generally known as system time delay.

It is the purpose of this paper to deal with an extremely accurate method for adjusting the resonant frequency, A, of the ringing oscillator. Factors B, C, and D may be accounted for by careful design so the end result will be the production of pulses coinciding with both the radio-frequency transmitted pulse and the start of the ringing, and the following 2π, 4π, 6π, and so on, points of the sine wave.

Inasmuch as the ringing oscillator is pulsed but part of the time, a direct comparison between the damped sine-wave frequency and a known frequency standard is cumbersome unless some provision is made for phasing and synchronizing the two waveforms. It is also impractical and inaccurate to preset the slug-tuned inductance against its particular capacitor outside the chassis by methods normally used for adjusting resonant circuits.

A practical device for calibrating range ring pulses is the instrument shown in Fig. 2 as a block diagram. Functionally, the range calibrator delivers a continuous series of sharp negative calibration pulses spaced either one or five miles apart, and a simultaneous series of negative synchronizing pulses occurring at a repetition rate one-fifth the frequency of the precision crystal oscillator. The synchronizing pulses are used in one application to lock a free-running radar master multivibrator into step with the sequence of operations occurring in the calibrator. Thus, the calibration pulses may be compared directly with those generated by the radar range ring generator.

Circuit Details

The complete circuit is given in Fig. 3. A 6V6 tetrode crystal oscillator, V_1, is used in the calibrator as the range ring frequency standard. The fundamental frequency is 80.86 kilocycles for nautical and 93.12 kilocycles for statute miles. (81.84 kilocycles corresponds to 2,000 yards.)

Following the crystal oscillator is a 6AC7 squaring amplifier, V_2, and a free-running blocking oscillator, V_{3A}, locked, one for one, to the fundamental crystal frequency. Output of this blocking oscillator is fed out of the unit through a single amplifier, V_{4B}, as negative calibration pulses spaced one mile apart. Alternately, pulses spaced five miles apart can be obtained by interposing a counting-down blocking oscillator, V_{4A}, and an isolation cathode follower, V_{6B}, between the one mile pulse generator, V_{3A}, and the output amplifier, V_{4B}. The additional blocking oscillator counts down by a factor of five to deliver 5-mile calibration pulses.

As shown in Fig. 3, part of the crystal oscillator output is also applied to a 360-degree phase shift network composed of a phase-shifting transformer and a precision variable phase-shift capacitor. By the use of this network, a voltage is developed at the grid of V_{3B} which may differ in phase with the output of the oscillator anywhere from zero to 360 degrees, depending upon the position of the rotor. To secure linear phase shift against rotor rotation, with little if any change in amplitude, the circuit must be carefully balanced. The 90-degree phase shift elements must be chosen[2] so that at the fundamental frequency, the resistance, R, equals the capacitive reactance of capacitor C.

The phase-shifted sine-wave at V_{3B} is amplified, as before, to synchro-

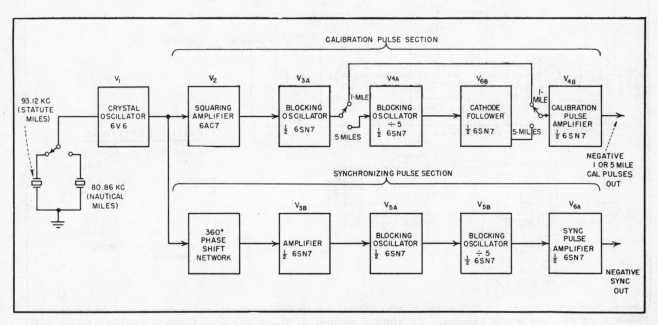

FIG. 2—Block diagram of the precision radar range calibrator

nize the free-running blocking oscillator, V_{5A}, one for one to the fundamental frequency. Output pulses from V_{5A} are divided in repetition frequency by five in the following blocking oscillator, V_{5B}, to produce radar synchronizing pulses occurring at a frequency of 18.62 or 16.17 kilocycles, respectively, for the statute and nautical mile cases. Tube V_{6A} amplifies and inverts the synchronizing pulses, the control sync determining pulse amplitude delivered to the radar.

A great advantage in placing the phase shift network in the synchronizing pulse generator section, as compared to the original approach which located the shifter in the calibrating pulse section, is the elimination of errors created by phasing network distortion. Since it is imperative that the sine wave fed

to the calibration pulse section be kept absolutely free from distortion for precise results, the location of the phase shift device to the noncritical synchronizing pulse circuit, in the final design, helped to improve the linear relationship between phase shift and the physical position of the rotor.

Radar Calibration Procedure

The phase shifted synchronizing pulses are fed out of the calibrator at intervals of 72.0 microseconds, when using the nautical mile crystal. The free-running multivibrator in the Radiomarine CR-101 Radar, for example, operates at a prf of approximately 3,000 cycles per second on the shorter ranges of 1.5 and 5 miles, equivalent to a period of about 333 microseconds. By coupling the synchronizing pulses into

the multivibrator at correct amplitude, the radar will lock in at a somewhat higher pulse recurrence frequency of about 3,470 cycles on every fourth sync pulse. This prf increase is of minor consequence, since higher recurrence frequency is maintained only during the calibration period.

Similarly, when the CR-101 is operated on its longer ranges of 15 and 50 miles, the prf of the radar system is quartered to 750 cycles, corresponding to a period of 1,333 microseconds. Every 18th sync pulse then locks the unit in step, a change of about 115 cycles in the pulse recurrence frequency.

The procedure used to adjust the radar range rings is relatively simple. Negative synchronizing pulses from the calibrator are applied to the radar master multivibrator.

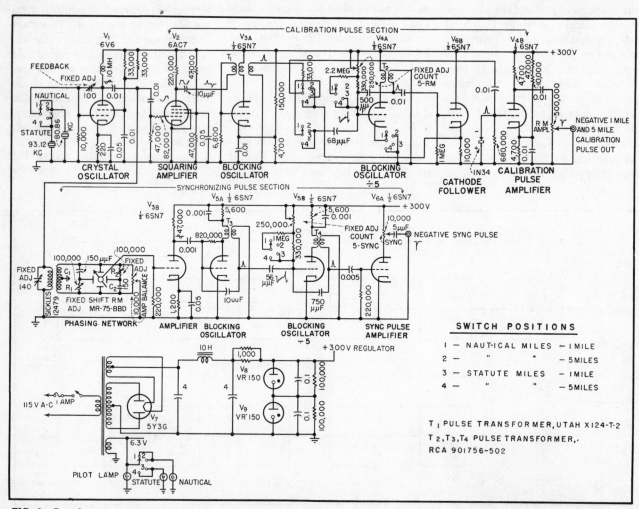

FIG. 3—Complete circuit of the instrument. All switches are ganged. The phasing network contains a butterfly-type capacitor

Meanwhile, positive radar range ring pulses are fed to the upper vertical deflection plate of a triggered-sweep oscilloscope. Negative calibration pulses are then applied to the lower vertical deflection plate. After the radar has been locked to the calibrator by adjusting the synchronizing pulse amplitude, both sets of marker pulses will be visible on the oscilloscope, inverted in polarity.

Adjusting the phase-shifting capacitor appears to move the calibration pulses along the sweep. This is done until two pairs of successive pulses are coincident or close to coincidence above one another. The slug-tuned inductance in the ringing oscillator circuit is then adjusted so that the spacing between radar range ring pulses approaches that between the precision pips.

Slight adjustments must be made in phasing during this operation to insure that the reference markers remain coincident. At the exact alignment point, all the leading edges of all the various pulses will coincide. The synchroscope during this operation is triggered by the radar system so that its sweep and the radar trigger start simultaneously.

For estimating the duration of various pulse waveforms through the radar, the procedure is slightly altered. A waveform of interest is observed on a triggered-sweep oscilloscope intensity modulated in the Z-axis by the markers from the calibrator. At intervals of either one or five miles, the sweep will brighten up, forming a series of bright spots superimposed on the waveform. The phase-shift capacitor is rotated until any one spot

coincides with the start time of the waveform. The time duration to any point of interest thereafter can be read in 1 or 5 mile steps. Interpolation between one-mile markers can be fairly accurately performed by noting the traverse of the phase-shift capacitor. Since every 360 degrees of rotation corresponds to one additional mile of spot movement, small angular displacements are practically proportional to equivalent fractions of a mile, providing that the phase-shift network is accurately aligned.

REFERENCES

(1) MIT Radiation Laboratory Series, "Radar System Engineering", p 522, McGraw-Hill Book Co., New York, N. Y.
(2) "Pulsed Oscillator and Phase Shifter," MIT Radiation Laboratory Report 63-23, July 22, 1943. Available from O.T.S., Dept. of Commerce, PB-No. 3942, Title E-15.

Radar Test Generator

Triggered or free-running pulses and c-w signals are provided from 47 to 76 mc for testing radar and other wide-band i-f circuits. Output is variable from 0.1 microvolt to 0.1 volt with pulse widths of 0.25, 0.5 and 1 microsecond

By KEEFER S. STULL

DURING THE DEVELOPMENT of sensitivity time-control circuits for a new radar set, it was found that a special pulsed signal generator with continuously variable output voltage over a wide range and a very low c-w background level was needed. Such an instrument was designed and built for laboratory use and has been employed in many applications.

The generator has either pulsed or c-w output, from 0.1 μv to 0.1 volt, into a 50-ohm load over a frequency range of 47 to 76 mc. It can be triggered or operated free-running and gives output pulses of ¼, ½, or 1-μsec duration. The output attenuator is direct reading and the instrument has an output

meter for calibration purposes.

Circuit Analysis

The r-f section uses a push-pull variable-frequency Hartley oscillator which is capacitively coupled to a push-pull power amplifier. The amplifier is driven class C and has a self-resonant tank coil which is loaded to give approximately a 15-mc bandwidth with a center frequency of 60 mc. The tank coil is arranged to feed energy into a short section of wave guide operating below cutoff which is used as a calibrated attenuator.

In order to get good energy transfer into the guide with a uniform wave distribution, the coil is wound with a flat face mounted

very close to the guide opening. A movable pickup loop in the attenuating guide is made from a 50-ohm resistor to give the proper source impedance to feed a 50-ohm coaxial cable. This cable ends on the front panel and must be externally terminated in a 50-ohm load.

The r-f section is completely enclosed in a tight silver-plated box internally subdivided into four sections. The output tank is carefully isolated in one of these subdivisions to prevent stray oscillator pickup and thus reduce the c-w background level during pulsed operation. All power wires enter the r-f section through button-type feedthrough capacitors and series 60-mc traps which are completely isolated along with the pulse-forming line in another one of the subdivisions. The oscillator and modulator wiring is in the third section while the fourth contains the tubes, each with an individual shield.

Output Measurements

A 1N21C crystal and a 200-μa meter with a variable resistor in series, see Fig. 1, are used to measure the output voltage during c-w operation. With the pickup loop in the end of the waveguide near the output coil, the voltage at the output terminal is over 0.1 volt, which is high enough to give a large reading on the output meter. This amount of output can be accurately measured by some external means and then the meter calibrated accordingly.

The meter gives no useful indication for outputs below 0.01 volt and it would be difficult to measure lower output accurately by other means, particularly in the microvolt region. However, if some higher value of output is known exactly, then all lower values can be accurately determined because of the known exponential rate at which a signal decreases in amplitude with distance along a wave-

guide operated below the cut-off frequency.

The dial which moves the pickup loop can be directly calibrated in output voltage providing its index can be adjusted to give a correct reading at some high value of output.

One good method of measuring the output voltage is with a thermistor bridge. The thermistor must be shunted with a noninductive resistor to give a parallel resistance of 50 ohms for proper termination. The bridge power reading must then be corrected for the power lost in the shunt resistor to give full output power. The voltage is found from the formula $E = \sqrt{PR}$.

The output meter can also be calibrated without applying power to the signal generator by feeding an audio signal into the r-f output terminal to simulate an r-f signal. If a frequency of about 10 kc is used, it should be high enough to give crystal characteristics corresponding to r-f conditions but still low enough to be measured with a vtvm.

It is necessary to gate the circuit to give a clean pulsed r-f signal of known amplitude. It is not practical to gate the oscillator or ampli-

fier control grids because then there will be a reaction on the oscillator frequency. It is necessary for the oscillator to run continuously under the same load conditions for stable operation. Therefore 6AS6's were chosen for the r-f amplifiers because their high suppressor transconductance permits them to be suppressor modulated.

It was found that when the amplifier grids were being excited by the oscillator, the plate current could be completely cut off with approximately -5 volts on the suppressors and as the suppressor voltage was increased from -5 volts up to $+12$ volts, the plate output would increase almost linearly. Any further increase in suppressor voltage causes only a slight change in output, see Fig. 2. When the suppressors are driven positive there

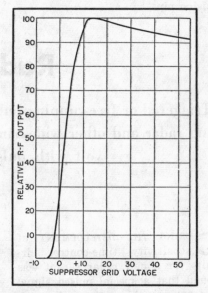

FIG. 2—Characteristic curve of 6AS6 class-C r-f amplifier with constant control-grid excitation

is a flow of current in the suppressor circuit, therefore they must be driven from a fairly low impedance.

Pulsed Output

For pulsed output the 6AS6's have a suppressor bias of -7 volts which keeps the plate current safely cut off. If the suppressors are then gated with a positive pulse having an amplitude greater than 19 volts,

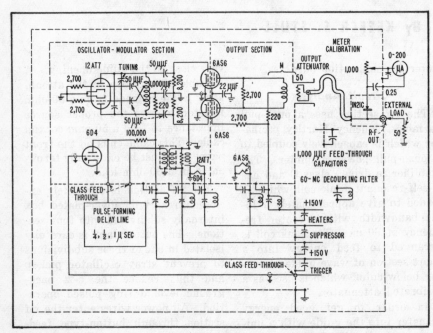

FIG. 1—Schematic diagram of the r-f section of the radar test generator

the peak output will be fairly constant because of the saturation effect of the suppressor as mentioned previously. This makes it possible to get a measureable peak pulse amplitude, for if the tubes are operated c-w with more than +12 volts on the suppressors the c-w output will equal the peak pulsed output and can be measured, as described previously.

When the amplifier plate current is cut off by the suppressor, the cathode current is not greatly affected, and it all tends to flow to the screen grids. To prevent excessive screen dissipation under these conditions the screen current is decreased by feeding the screens through a series resistor to drop their voltage. However, when an output pulse is required, and the suppressors are driven positive, the screen voltage must rise instantly, thus greatly limiting the size of the screen by-pass capacitor that can be used. A compromise must be reached between r-f degeneration and a screen-circuit time constant which will allow it to follow short pulses.

The modulator consists of a gas triode used to discharge a lumped-circuit pulse-forming line of variable length coupled to the suppressors of the 6AS6's through a pulse transformer. The number of L-C components in the line can be switched from the front panel for pulses of 1, $\frac{1}{2}$ and $\frac{1}{4}$ μsec duration.

The positive pulse output is sufficient to drive the suppressors well into saturation. The d-c bias on the grid of the modulator can be adjusted from the front panel between the limits of −7 and −33 volts for best operation. The d-c bias for the 6AS6 suppressors is selected by the pulse—c-w switch.

For c-w operation, a bias of +20 volts is obtained from a voltage divider to allow the 6AS6's to operate at suppressor saturation. For pulsed operation a bias of −7 volts is applied, just enough to safely hold the 6AS6 plate current cutoff except when positive pulses are supplied from the modulator.

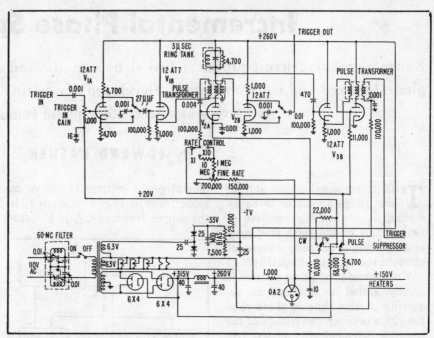

FIG. 3—Schematic diagram of the power supply and trigger chassis for the generator

Trigger and Power Circuits

The remainder of the instrument, consisting of trigger and power circuits, is built on a separate chassis, see Fig. 3. The triggering pulse for the modulator is obtained from a driver in the form of a blocking oscillator which is biased to prevent a free-running condition. The driver is triggered by a cathode follower whose input is the voltage across a ring tank in the plate circuit of a triggering blocking oscillator. The circuit is arranged so that the cathode-follower grid does not swing positive until approximately 3 μsec after the ring tank is excited by the triggering blocking oscillator. This triggering blocking oscillator also drives a phase-splitting tube directly, without delay, to give either a positive or negative external trigger output. This is useful for triggering a synchroscope just before the r-f output pulse so that its effect can be easily observed in a test circuit.

The triggering blocking oscillator can be allowed to run free over a frequency range of approximately 70 to 10,000 cps or a negative bias can be applied to its grid for external triggering. The external positive or negative trigger pulses are fed through a gain control, phase-splitting tube, phase-selector switch, and cathode follower to drive the triggering blocking oscillator. When the pulse—c-w switch is in the c-w position the triggering blocking oscillator is made inoperative by opening its cathode circuit. This switch also chooses proper bias for the 6AS6 suppressors and compensates for the different current requirements of pulsed and c-w operation.

The plate supply uses two 6X4's in parallel in a full-wave rectifier circuit with a capacitive input filter to give +260 direct volts. An OA2 is used to supply +150 volts regulated to the r-f section. The heater winding plus another 6.3-volt winding are connected in series to drive a voltage doubler using selenium rectifiers to supply the negative bias voltages required. The a-c input is fused and passes through a shielded 60-mc filter to prevent r-f from leaking out along the power line.

The author wishes to acknowledge the cooperation of Richard Whitehorn and Malcolm Clark in the design and construction of this instrument.

Incremental Phase Splitter

Range simulator circuit produces two signals at the same frequency but differing in phase by fixed and equal amounts. Developed for testing radar equipment, the device serves as a laboratory phase standard

By EDWARD KASNER

THE incremental phase splitter and range simulator to be described is a circuit productive of two signals of the same frequency and differing in phase by a series of discrete increments of equality.

The incremental phase splitter is ideally suited to applications requiring precise time or phase relationships between two signals of the same or harmonically related frequencies. A few of its possible applications are the simulation of radar and loran data, generation of accurate synchronizing signals for the production of delay gates and timing pulses, and use as a laboratory phase standard.

Range Simulator

The circuit was developed as a target range simulator to facilitate the development of radio ranging equipment.

An 81.94-kc sine wave, corresponding to 2,000 radar yards per cycle, is employed as the ranging system's time base. The phase displacement between the transmitted and received timing signals is determined by their transmission time through space and is directly proportional to target range. In order to function as a calibrating range simulator, the circuit must provide two 81.94-kc sinusoidal signals, one fixed in time and the other variable through a series of angular displacements corresponding accurately to the required range test points. The ranging system's test points are: 0, 400, 800, 1,200, and 1,600 yards. The corresponding phase displacements between the transmitted and received signals are: 0, 72, 144, 216, and 288 degrees.

The basic circuit of the incremental phase splitter is shown in block form in Fig. 1 wherein f_s is the source frequency, f_o is the out-

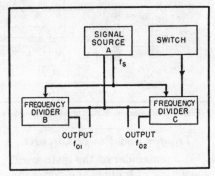

FIG. 1—Block diagram of a basic phase splitter

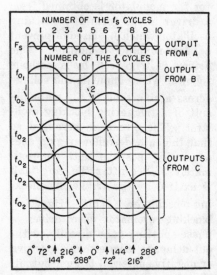

FIG. 2—Phase relations in the incremental phase splitter

put frequency, N is required number of phase increments, and $f_s = N f_o$. The circuit consists of signal source, A, of frequency f_s; a constantly operating frequency divider, B, synchronized by A and dividing its output frequency by N; and another frequency divider, C, identical to B but provided with means whereby its operation may be momentarily interrupted. The circuit operates as follows. Divider B provides the fixed, or reference phase. Divider C provides the incrementally variable phase. A momentary contact switch is wired into C in such a manner as to render it inoperative when the switch is closed. Upon releasing the switch, divider C again becomes operative, synchronizing with A in one of N phase relationships. This is graphically illustrated by Fig. 2 in which $N = 5$.

The generalized values of the N phase relationships the $\theta + 0$, $\theta + [360/N]$, $\theta + [2(360)/N]$, $\dots \theta + [(N-1) 360/N]$ degrees, where θ represents the residual phase displacements between the

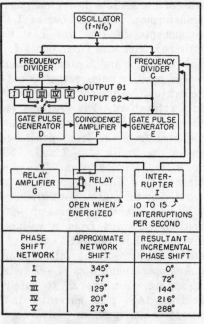

FIG. 3—Phase splitter allowing predetermined selection

PHASE SHIFT NETWORK	APPROXIMATE NETWORK SHIFT	RESULTANT INCREMENTAL PHASE SHIFT
I	345°	0°
II	57°	72°
III	129°	144°
IV	201°	216°
V	273°	288°

outputs of B and C when the incremental displacement equals zero. The value of θ reduces to zero when B and C are synchronized at identical points in time on the signal from A. The phase selection sequence cannot be predetermined in this ba-

lected signal from the phase-shift networks, the resultant output pulses from the coincidence amplifier, F, energize relay H via its control amplifier, G. This action immediately disconnects the interrupter and stabilizes the circuit at

repeatedly actuated and the new indicated ranges are recorded.

This process is repeated until all five check points have been recorded. If desired, one of the simulator signals can be inverted in phase to provide five more check

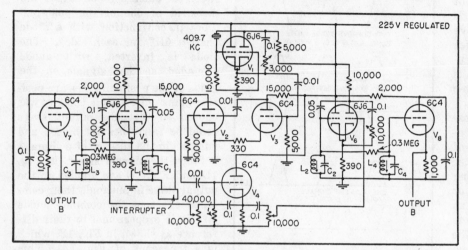

FIG. 4—Schematic of the incremental phase splitter with frequencies chosen for radar range simulation

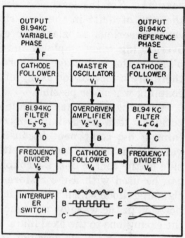

FIG. 5—Block diagram and waveforms for the circuit of Fig. 4

sic circuit because of the random nature of the synchronization of C to any one of five cycles of A.

Figure 3 illustrates a method whereby any one of a predetermined series of angular increments can be selected at will. Blocks A, B and C comprise the oscillator-divider combination previously described. Here, again, $N = 5$. Divider B feeds five networks that shift the phase of its output to a few degrees less than the required incremental displacements. The output of the selected network is fed to a gate pulse generator, D, via the selector switch. Divider C also feeds a similar pulse generator, E. The two pulse generators feed a coincidence amplifier, F, which produces one pulse per cycle only when the two gate pulses overlap in time. A continuously acting interrupter, I, throws C in and out of operation, thus permitting C to synchronize repeatedly to any one of the five cycles of A at random. When the output of C is such that it is approximately in phase with the se-

the required incremental phase shift.

Figure 4 illustrates a practical version of the circuit shown in Fig. 1. Tube V_1 is a 409.7-kc crystal master oscillator; V_2 and V_3 are overdriven amplifiers which decrease the rise time of the synchronizing signal and thus minimize phase jitter between outputs. The cathode follower, V_4, couples the synchronizing signal from $V_2—V_3$ to the two frequency dividers, V_5 and V_6. The low source impedance of V_4 prevents interaction between V_5 and V_6. The Crosby[1] two-terminal, resistance-stabilized oscillators[2] are excellent frequency dividers, readily synchronized and of good sinusoidal waveform. Filters $L_3—C_3$ and $L_4—C_4$ feed reasonably pure sine waves to the output cathode followers, V_7 and V_8.

In use, the simulator signals are fed to the range-determining circuits in place of the transmitted and received signals. After zero-setting the range indicator, the interrupter switch connected to V_5 is

points: 200, 600, 1,000, 1,400, and 1,800 yards. Error curves relating actual and indicated range can be readily plotted from the recorded data.

Accuracy after a brief warm-up is such that no short-time change in the incremental phase shift is detectable by conventional methods. Because of the phase-sensitive nature of the resonant filters, the circuit exhibits a gradual drift of θ, the residual constant. Since drift compensating arrangements are many, and fairly well known, they are not considered here.

Many incremental phase-splitter applications require the generation of a pair of pulses occurring at a known repetition rate and displaced from one another by one of a series of discrete time increments. This requirement can be met by replacing the sinusoidal frequency dividers with multivibrators and differentiating their outputs.

REFERENCES

(1) M. G. Crosby, Two Terminal Oscillators, ELECTRONICS, p 136, May 1946.
(2) F. E. Terman, "Radio Engineering," McGraw-Hill Book Co., New York, p 371, 1937.

Double-Ended D-C Restorer

By D. A. BELL

DIRECT-COUPLED AMPLIFIERS are apt to be inconvenient for a number of reasons. Not the least of these is the risk of drift in the first stage causing serious unbalance or even overloading when amplified and applied to the last stage. There is therefore a motive for using an a-c coupling whenever possible.

When the signal has periodic excursions to a fixed limit but contains a d-c component because of varying amounts of signal on either side of the center line, a-c coupling can be used with a d-c restorer or clamping diode which fixes the mean position of the wave by reference to the excursions to the fixed limit. The name clamping diode does not seem to have come into general use, but is very expressive of the function of the diode in clamping one limit of the waveform to a fixed voltage level.

Probably the most familiar example of the d-c-restoring technique is to television video amplifiers, where the line sync pulses provide a repeated excursion to a fixed limit. There are cases, however, where the requirement is rather to keep the signal symmetrically balanced (in amplitude) on either side of the datum line, in spite of differences in proportion of time spent with either polarity.

The best example of this is a telegraph signal working on a mark and space basis represented by signals of opposite polarity. Figure 1A represents a hypothetical signal having the times spent on space and mark in the ratio 3 to 1 but with equal and opposite amplitudes of $+1$ and -1. Figure 1B shows the result of passing a repeated signal of this form through an a-c coupling (capacitor and leak). The datum line has shifted so as to produce equal areas on either side of zero, instead of equal amplitudes.

Now the problem is to get the datum line back into the center of

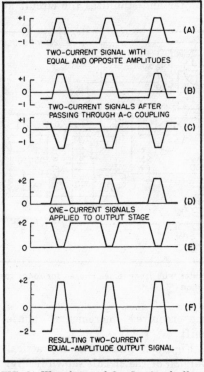

FIG. 1—Waveforms of 3-to-1-ratio of off-to-on telegraph signal, and effects of a-c coupling networks and d-c restoration circuits

the waveform, so that a relay or other device will operate exactly in the center of the transition from mark to space. This would not be important if the waveform were square, but in practice the reversals take a finite time and any departure from a symmetrical datum line will change the ratio of mark-to-space times. A distortion of mark-to-space time ratio of this kind is called bias distortion by telegraph engineers.

The desired result can be achieved by the circuit shown in Fig. 2, which includes a double-ended d-c restorer and operates as follows. The first tube is simply a phase-splitter, so that in addition to the waveform shown in Fig. 1B we have the inverted waveform of Fig. 1C. Each of the waveforms is applied to a d-c restorer consist-

ing of the coupling capacitor between the phase-splitter output and the grid of one of the push-pull tubes in conjunction with a diode (half a 6H6 for each side). The diode is inverted, with anode grounded, so that signals on the grids of the pushpull tubes are positive-going only. (This polarity was chosen so that the output stage could be fairly heavily biased and run cool in the absence of a signal.)

Since the signals shown in Fig. 1D and Fig. 1E are applied to the output stage in pushpull, their combined effect in the common anode circuit is proportional to their difference as shown in Fig. 1F, which is a true copy of Fig. 1A. This waveform may be viewed by connecting the points Y_1 and Y_2 directly to the plates of a cathode-ray tube. It will not be seen if the points are connected to the input terminals of an oscilloscope having capacitor-coupled input, since the introduction of this a-c coupling destroys

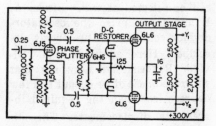

FIG. 2—Circuit diagram of double-ended d-c restoration amplifier

the d-c-restored condition which has been achieved in the amplifier. A striking demonstration of the efficacy of the system is given by having a changeover switch to give either direct or capacitive coupling from the points Y_1 and Y_2 to the plates of the cathode-ray tube.

For more practical use the loads in the anode circuit of the output stage may consist of the two halves of the windings of a telegraph relay or recorder.

Besides allowing a telegraph signal to be amplified in a-c-coupled stages and d-c-restored in the final stage, this circuit might be used for converting single-current (Fig. 1D) to double-current (Fig. 1F) signals.

As mentioned above, a telegraph relay must change over at a signal amplitude exactly half way between the mark and space levels in order to avoid bias

distortion of the signals, and with double-current working the changeover should occur at the neutral point of zero current. But in single-current working, where space is indicated by zero current, the changeover must occur at half the mark amplitude to avoid distortion.

This is normally achieved by biasing the operating point of the relay to half the signal amplitude, and therefore requires adjustment for

any change of signal amplitude. By using the phase-splitter and double-ended d-c restorer, either with or without preceding a-c amplification, a symmetrical two-current output is obtained. This has the advantage of operating a relay at neutral bias, so that it changes over at zero current and its operation does not require adjustment for signal amplitude.

RECEIVERS

Receiver Gain Nomograph

Permits rapid determination of maximum required voltage gain when bandwidth and noise figure, required input to detector and antenna resistance are known

By PETER G. SULZER

THE NOMOGRAPH permits rapid determination of the maximum required voltage gain of a radio receiver. Factors which enter into such a calculation are the resistive component of the antenna impedance, the bandwidth and noise figure of the receiver, and the required input to the detector.

The available power from the resistive component R of the antenna impedance is 4×10^{-21} watts per cycle of bandwidth at 290 Kelvin[1]. This permits calculation of the equivalent rms noise voltage E_1 at the receiver antenna terminals. The receiver, however, will have noise sources of its own, making the true equivalent input voltage greater than E_1. If E_1 is multiplied by $F^{0.5}$, where F is the noise figure of the receiver, the true equivalent input voltage E_2 is obtained. The maximum useful voltage gain of the receiver is that which will bring E_2 up to the level at which it is desired to operate the detector. Then, if the detector is to operate at a level E_d, the voltage gain A can be found by dividing E_d by E_2. These operations are carried out on the nomograph, as illustrated by the following example:

Suppose it is desired to design a radar receiver to work from a 50-ohm transmission line. The i-f bandwidth is to be 1 mc and the detector is to operate at a level of 2 volts so that signals weaker than noise will not be discriminated against by the curved detector characteristic. It is hoped to obtain a noise figure F of 10, and it is desired to find the required voltage gain with that assumed noise figure. Joining 50 ohms on the R scale with 1 mc on the BW scale by means

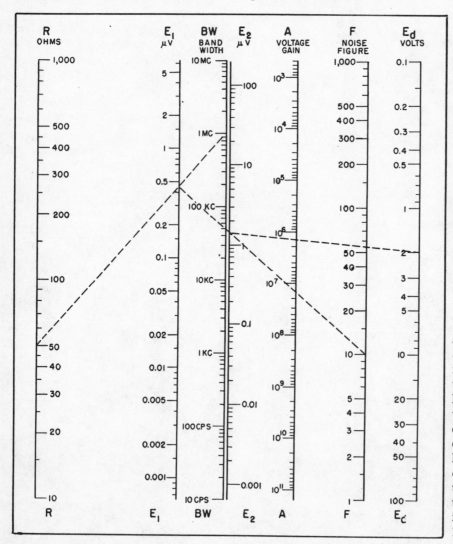

of a straight-edge, it is found that $E_1 = 0.44$ microvolts. Connecting this point on the E_1 scale with 10 on the F scale, $E_2 = 1.4$ microvolts. Then, joining 1.4 microvolts on the E_2 scale with 2 volts on the E_d scale, A is found to be 1.4×10^6. Thus a voltage gain of more than 1,000,000 is

required between the antenna terminals and the output of the last i-f stage.

It should be noted that the above calculations assume an impedance match at the antenna terminals. For best noise figure, a mismatch is usually desirable[1]. The resulting error in design can

usually be absorbed by the necessarily large tolerance in gain which must be made to allow for variations in tubes and components.

REFERENCE

(1) H. T. Friis, Noise Figures of Radio Receivers, *Proc. IRE*, p 419, July, 1944.

Receiver Noise Nomograph

Over-all noise figure of radio or radar receiver is quickly found when noise factors of first two sections and gain or loss of first section are known

By CHESTER W. YOUNG

IN THE DESIGN of radio and radar receivers, it is often advantageous to determine quickly the feasibility of using components at hand. The following nomograph was developed for this purpose, and is based on two well-known formulas[1,2]

$$\overline{NF}_{(1+2)} = \overline{NF}_1 + \frac{\overline{NF}_2 - 1}{W_1} \qquad (1)$$

$$\overline{NF}_{mix} = Lt \qquad (2)$$

where $\overline{NF}_{(1+2)}$ is noise factor (in power) of overall receiver, $\overline{NF}_1$ is noise factor of first network, $\overline{NF}_2$

is noise factor of second network, $\overline{NF}_{mix}$ is noise factor of mixer, W_1 is gain (or loss) of first network, L is loss of mixer and t is noise temperature (ratio) of mixer.

The nomograph can be used with either a mixer followed by an i-f amplifier as the second network or

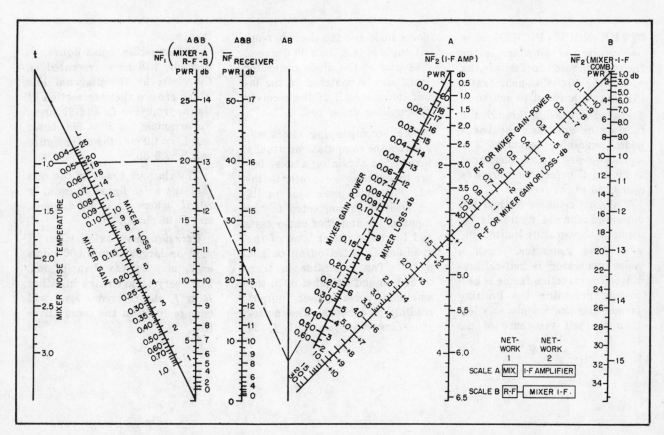

with an r-f amplifier followed by a mixer-i-f amplifier combination whose overall noise factor can be worked prior to adding the r-f amplifier. Scale A is used if the first network has a gain (or loss) less than one and Scale B is used if it has a gain greater than one.

How to Use Nomograph

Place a straightedge on desired values on A and B scales to locate turning point on AB scale. Using this turning point and value on A scale (or B scale), read final value on adjacent A scale (or B Scale; use A scales together or B scales together). The L and t scales are used to determine noise factor of the mixer.

Example: If required range for system with a given transmitted power requires over-all noise figure to be 13.65 db (noise factor of 23.2), what is minimum noise figure which crystal mixer can have if it has a loss of 13 db, and can this be used with an existing 3-db i-f amplifier?

Starting on left side of nomograph, align straightedge with noise temperature of 1.0 and mixer loss of 20, and read $\overline{NF}_{mix}$ as 20. Using this and overall $\overline{NF}_{receiver}$ value of 23.2, find turning point on AB. Using turning point and 13-db (mixer gain of 0.05) loss point on slant A scale, read 0.65 db for NF_2 on vertical A scale, as maximum permissible noise figure.

REFERENCES

(1) S. N. Van Voorhis, "Microwave Receivers," **Vol. 23** of *MIT Radiation Lab Series*, p 2.
(2) Torrey and Whitmer, "Crystal Rectifiers," **Vol. 15** of *MIT Radiation Lab Series*, p 30.

Noise Figure Chart

Gives noise figure directly in decibels from value of noise-generator diode current required to double the noise power output of an amplifier from its no-input value. The input impedance of the unit under test is the other parameter

By EUGENE D. JAREMA

THE NOISE FIGURE of a receiver or amplifier is the factor, expressed in decibels, by which the signal-to-noise ratio existing in a resistive source is degraded in passing through the receiver or amplifier, the bandwidth remaining constant. The signal-to-noise ratio is measured at 20 deg C before the source is connected to the receiver.

The most common method for determining noise figures is by using a temperature-limited diode noise generator. Such a noise generator is self-calibrating. No correction factor is necessary, providing the limiting frequencies are considerably less than the self resonance of the

noise diode and the electron transit angle is less than 90 degrees. The load of the diode generator must also be matched to the input impedance R of the receiver or amplifier under test.

The accompanying chart eliminates the computations usually involved in obtaining a noise figure by the noise-generator method. The noise generator in its off position is connected to the input of the amplifier under test, and the noise power level of the amplifier is noted on an output meter. The generator is then turned on and adjusted until the amplifier noise power output reading is doubled. The noise-generator diode current I_A is

then noted.

The amplifier noise figure, in decibels, will be represented on the chart by the diagonal line which crosses the intersection of the appropriate I_A and R lines. For example, let $R = 300$ ohms and $I_A = 1.0$ ma; the noise figure will be 7.8 db.

The chart is based on the fact that the noise figure is equal to $20I_A R$, where I_A is in amperes and R in ohms.

Occasion may arise when R may be larger than 1,000 ohms or I_A may be less than 0.1 ma. For every cycle change in either R or I_A the reference level will change 10 db in the same direction.

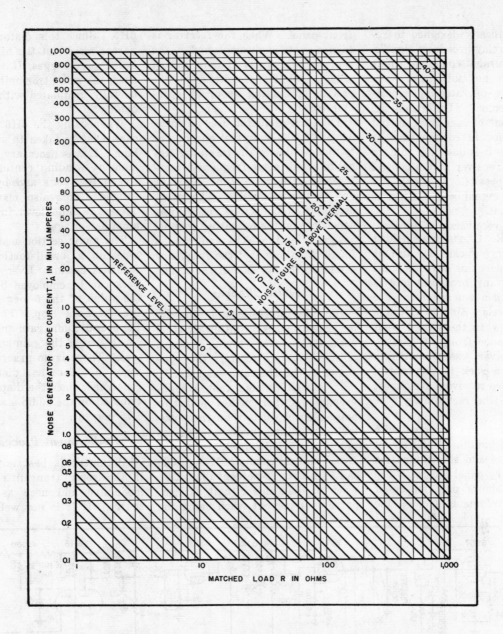

Remote Pickup Broadcast Receiver

Crystal-controlled 26-mc receiver can be used by inexperienced personnel to receive remote broadcasts from scenes of emergencies, sporting events, and other on-the-spot affairs. Extreme simplicity insures reliability and ease of operation and servicing

By ADELBERT A. KELLEY

SOME ENGINEERS at the smaller broadcast stations do not appreciate the advantages of adding relay broadcast equipment to their station facilities. Such equipment provides a means for direct broadcast from any point where wire lines are not available, and is particularly adapted to on-the-spot coverage of fires, floods, parades, or certain sports such as golf.

The equipment does not have to be complicated or expensive. Transmitters are commercially available but there are no receivers on the market specifically designed to receive 26-mc relay broadcast signals. General coverage communications receivers are not satisfactory unless they are operated by experienced personnel. Unfortunately, broadcast control operators are not always trained in communications techniques so it is desirable to have as simple a receiver at the control position as possible. It should not drift off the signal or be subject to misadjustment.

Two such receivers are in operation at WINR. One is in a shielded portable carrying case for use at the end of a wire line near the point of origin of any broadcast and is provided with a v-u meter for use in setting levels. Since a wire line is used only when the special event is some distance from the studios, another receiver was permanently mounted in a rack in the control room. The two receivers are almost identical and the rack unit will be described.

The receiver was designed with simplicity in mind. This meant crystal control and the elimination of unnecessary panel controls. The photograph shows only an on-off switch and volume control on the front panel. When the receiver is turned on, it is always tuned on the center of the relay channel and it will not drift off either in the process of heating up or by operator error.

The local oscillator uses an inexpensive 8,500-kc crystal and triples to the low side of the incoming signal to avoid image-frequency interference with the 27-mc amateur and diathermy band. The exact oscillator frequency is, of course, dependent on the operating channel assigned by the FCC and can be found by taking ⅓ of the frequency 470 kc on the low side of the signal.

Noise Silencer

Ignition interference in the 26-mc region makes a limiter a virtual necessity. After trying several noise-silencer circuits, the one shown in the diagram was used.

It is well to note that a high-vacuum rectifier makes a better noise-silencer diode than the popular germanium diode due to its practically infinite back resistance. As a practical example, 1N34 diode caused nearly 30-percent distortion when used in this circuit as compared to 1 percent when using the

6H6. Since this distortion is apparent mostly at the higher modulation percentages, if the 1N34 is used, the relay transmitter can not be fully modulated without loss of quality.

When using the 6H6 diode some care must be taken to avoid heater hum. It was necessary to bias the filament winding center tap positive a few volts and bypass it to ground. This also materially reduces the hum level in the audio amplifier stages.

The audio section uses two pentodes in a low-distortion inverse-feedback circuit. Even more feedback can be employed by reducing the value of the 5-meg resistor in the feedback loop. This reduces the overall audio gain and might be considered if the gain seems excessive. There is no practical advantage, as far as distortion is concerned, since the distortion contributed by the audio stages is only 1.75 percent.

Alignment Procedure

Alignment is best accomplished if the relay transmitter is tone modulated and used as a signal source. If it is not well shielded,

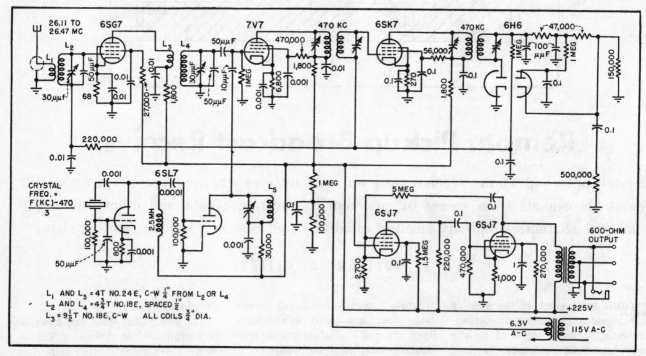

Complete schematic of 26-mc crystal-controlled receiver for remote pickup broadcasts

it should be moved some distance from the receiver to avoid overload. A crystal of the proper frequency is inserted in the crystal socket and oscillation checked by measuring the grid voltage of the tripler stage. It should be − 15 v as measured by a vtvm. The i-f transformers are

then aligned to the correct frequency by using a standard signal generator.

The relay transmitter is turned on, modulated, and the signal is tuned in by varying the tuning of the i-f transformer trimmers. The i-f tuning is the only tuning adjust-

ment that will compensate for a crystal slightly off-frequency so the final i-f adjustment will be some frequency around 470 kc. After the relay signal is located, all the i-f and r-f trimmers are peaked.

Television Front-End Design

Design equations for several types of r-f amplifier stages of a television receiver are derived and illustrated. Emphasis is placed on the problem of optimizing the signal-to-noise ratio while satisfying gain, bandwidth and adjacent-channel rejection require ments

By H. M. WATTS

THE CIRCUITS to be considered in this paper are the r-f amplifier and mixer portions of a receiver intended to operate in the standard 12 television channels.

The design is based on inductive tuning, the design process being the same whether the tuning is continuous or in steps. It is not intended to prove the superiority of certain circuit configurations over others, but rather to indicate the factors to be considered and the method of evaluating them in the design process.

Initial Premises

Initial premises in the design are the exclusive use of 6.3-volt miniature tubes, the use of 75-ohm coaxial-cable input and output and the use of a 26-mc intermediate frequency.

To review FCC standards, the vestigial sideband character of the transmitted signal is such that the receiver would ideally have the response characteristic shown in Fig. 1 for reception of signals on channel 2. Note that the sloping response in the vicinity of the picture carrier is linear and that the response is 50 percent at picture-carrier frequency.

It is not important what the fre-

quency is at A and at D, but only that A be within the channel and that the curve between A and D is such that when the area ABC is pivoted about B until A coincides with D the resultant response curve is flat from 55.25 mc up to 59.25 mc. (For instance, the dashed curve ABD would be quite acceptable.) The reason for this is that the equivalent video response curve for any modulated-carrier amplifier is obtained by adding the percent response at $f_c + f_m$ (where f_c is the carrier frequency and f_m is the modulating frequency) to the response at $f_c - f_m$ and plotting the resulting sum against f_m for all values of f_m between zero and the frequency corresponding to full sideband width. Thus, for the example of Fig. 1, the equivalent video response at 100 kc is equal to the sum of the r-f response at 55.15 and that at 55.35 mc, while the equivalent video response at 1 mc is the sum of that at 54.25 mc and that at 56.25 mc. Invariably the smoothest curve AD implies the best phase response.

Figure 1 shows that the maximum possible equivalent video bandwidth would be slightly less than 4.5 mc since the best that can be done below 55.25 mc is to provide a

response supplementing the upper sideband to give a flat equivalent video response, and since the response of the picture channel is necessarily zero at the sound transmitter frequency. The maximum realizable equivalent video bandwidth will therefore be taken as 4

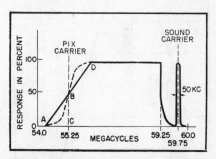

FIG. 1—Ideal response characteristic for receiving channel 2. For other channels, substitute the appropriate frequencies

mc wide at the 6-db-down points.

With 55.25 mc as the bottom of the received band (the frequency below midband at which gain is 6 db down) which is 4 mc wide, the band center for this channel is 57.25 mc, and the band center of the receiver will correspondingly be 3.25 mc above the bottom of any channel to which the receiver is tuned. As will be shown late maximum gain and bandwidth are obtained with minimum capacitance shunting the load circuit of an amplifier stage, so the circuits will be resonated by tube and wiring capacitances alone and the circuit inductance will be changed to change stations.

Synchronous single-tuned interstage networks will be considered rather than coupled circuits or stagger-tuned circuits, even though the latter two are theoretically better. It has been proven that both of the latter circuits provide a greater usable bandwith for a given gain, but the stagger-tuned system is difficult to track properly over the specified range, and the coupled-circuit system requires one additional tuning element per interstage.

Figure 2 shows the computed variation in scalar impedance of a parallel *RLC* circuit over a band of frequencies centered at the antiresonant frequency of the *LC* combination. The scalar impedance has

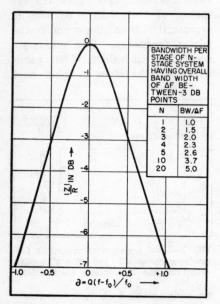

FIG. 2—Plot of normalized scalar impedance of parallel *RLC* network having a Q of 10 at resonance

been shown in terms of 20 log_{10} $|Z|/R$, or simply db down from the impedance at resonance, and frequency has been presented as Q times the percent deviation from antiresonant frequency.

For this circuit, Q is defined as the ratio $R/\omega_o L$ where ω_o is the

antiresonant radian frequency.

The significance of Fig. 2 is that in any system of cascaded amplifiers having single-tuned load circuits, the gain of each stage will vary with frequency in the manner shown by the curve. If each of three identical stages were 3 db down in gain at the extremes of a band of width Δf centered about a frequency f_o, the unit as a whole would have a gain 9 db down (from that at f_o) at the extremes of the band Δf.

Data derived from the curve have been tabulated to the right of the curve, showing the bandwidth per stage required for an *N*-stage system to have an overall bandwidth of Δf between the —3 db points.

Preliminary investigation shows that two tuned circuits (through which the signal must pass) will be used in any r-f head using a grounded-grid r-f amplifier, and three tuned circuits will be used in other r-f head configurations. It will be assumed arbitrarily that for an overall receiver bandwidth of 4 mc between —6 db points, the i-f amplifier will be allowed —3 db from maximum gain and the r-f head will be allowed —3 db from maximum gain at the edges of the 4-mc band. According to the table of Fig. 2, each tuned circuit in an r-f head having a grounded grid r-f stage must be 6 mc wide, and each tuned circuit must be 8 mc wide in other r-f heads.

So far, the discussion has neglected the matter of reception of the 59.75-mc sound carrier with its ±25-kc deviation under 100-percent modulation. Since the sound carrier is 2.5 mc from the resonant frequency of the tuned circuits, a study of Fig. 2 reveals that the gain is down 4.4 db from maximum gain at sound carrier frequency for an r-f head having a grounded-grid stage, and 4.2 db down for other heads. This loss relative to picture-channel midband gain can be made up in the high-gain sound i-f amplifier since it is relatively

easy to obtain extra gain in narrow-band circuits.

Noise Considerations

In practice, the designer considers each noise source along the path of the signal from the input up to the point in the circuit at which new noise contributions are trivial in importance due to the increasing magnitude of the signal and the noise from earlier circuits. We must start, therefore, with a block diagram, Fig. 3, and determine the level of the signal and of the noise for as many points along the circuit as seems necessary.

It will be necessary to develop certain gain and grid-equivalent noise-resistance equations that do not appear in the literature, and to bring out carefully the difference between the correct manner of combining the noise powers from each of two actual resistances and the correct manner of combining noise power from a real resistance with that of a fictitious resistance.

Pentode R-F Amplifier

There are four basic circuits from which to choose: the conventional pentode r-f amplifier of Fig. 4, the grounded-grid amplifier of Fig. 5, the cathode-follower amplifier of Fig. 6, and the cathode-coupled amplifier of Fig. 7. The pentode amplifier will be discussed first, calculating the tube-noise equivalent resistance referred to the grid, then the optimum antiresonant resistance of the circuit connected to the grid will be computed. Then it will be shown how the noise powers from the real and the equivalent resistances combine, the optimum plate circuit antiresonant resistance will be computed and signal and noise voltages will be referred from the grid to the plate.

To facilitate calculation, the actual tube with its shot effect, current-division noise, and other sources of noise voltage is replaced by a theoretically noiseless tube in whose grid circuit there is a fictitious resistor having a thermal-agitation noise voltage which pro-

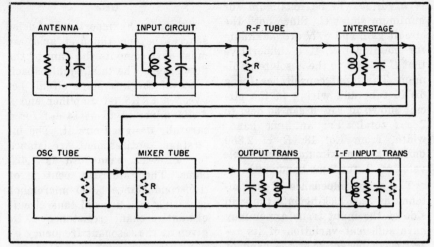

FIG. 3—Noise analysis block diagram. Symbol R denotes a fictitious noise-equivalent resistor

duces the same noise voltage in the output of the theoretical tube as there is in the output of the actual tube. This fictitious resistor, the grid-equivalent noise resistor of

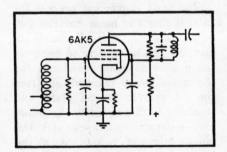

FIG. 4—Pentode r-f amplifier

the tube, is a legitimate and accurate equivalent because the noise energy of a resistor has essentially the same flat frequency spectrum as the tube noise. The value of the use of an equivalent noise resistor lies in the fact that noise powers add directly, rather than noise voltages adding directly. Therefore, noise-resistance values may be added directly as though the resistors were in series, and the total noise voltage computed accordingly.

As an equivalent of the situation wherein noise-powers from a real and a fictitious resistor must be added together, assume that two different resistors of value R_a and R_b generate noise in the grids of two identical noiseless amplifiers

using pentodes having infinite r_p. Assume that each amplifier has a voltage gain, A, and that the amplifiers have a common load of R_L. Then the total noise voltage across the load resistor is given by

$$E_{np} = (P_n R_L)^{1/2} \qquad (1)$$

where P_n is the total noise power produced in R_L by the two tubes. As shown later, the thermal-agitation noise voltage from a resistor R_a can be expressed as

$$E_a = K(R_a)^{1/2} \qquad (2)$$

The power produced in the plate load due to a noise voltage E_a at the grid is

$$P_a = \frac{A^2 E^2_a}{R_L} \qquad (3)$$

The total power P_n can be expressed

$$P_n = P_a + P_b \qquad (4)$$

where P_b is defined by Eq. 3 with subscript b substituted for a. Substituting for P_a and P_b from Eq. 3 in Eq. 4,

$$P_n = \frac{A^2}{R_L}(E^2_a + E^2_b) \qquad (5)$$

We can now substitute Eq. 5 in Eq. 1,

$$E_{np} = [A^2(E^2_a + E^2_b)]^{1/2} \qquad (6)$$
$$E_{np} = A(E^2_a + E^2_b)^{1/2} \qquad (7)$$

Now, substituting from Eq. 2 in Eq. 7,

$$E_{np} = A[K^2(R_a + R_b)]^{1/2} \qquad (8)$$

But $\quad E_{np} = AE_{ng} \qquad (9)$

so $\quad E_{ng} = K(R_a + R_b)^{1/2} \qquad (10)$

The artifice of two tubes having a common load resistor emphasizes the fact that these two noise contributions (one from a real resistor, one from a fictitious resistor) could not react on each other earlier in the circuit than the plate load. In the case of two real resistors connected in parallel in a given circuit, the equivalent resistance of the two is computed from the well-known parallel relationship

$$R = R_a R_b / (R_a + R_b) \qquad (11)$$

and the noise voltage is simply computed for the equivalent resistor.

Further Development

For the grounded-cathode pentode amplifier circuit of Fig. 4, the grid-equivalent noise resistance is given by[1]

$$R_{eq} = \frac{I_p}{I_k}\left(\frac{2.5}{G_m} + \frac{20 I_s}{G_m^2}\right) \qquad (12)$$

where I_p, I_k, and I_s are the d-c plate current, d-c cathode current, and d-c screen current respectively, and G_m is the plate transconductance in mhos. In the case of a 6AK5 tube operated at $E_p = 75$ v, $E_{sc} = 75$, $E_g = -0.6$, $I_p = 6.0$ ma, $I_s = 1.5$, $G_m = 5,000$ micromhos, then $R_{eq} = 1,360$ ohms.

From the thermal-noise-voltage equation[2],

$$E = 2(KT\Delta f)^{1/2} \times (R)^{1/2}, \qquad (13)$$

where

$K = $ Boltzman's constant $= 1.374 \times 10^{-23}$ joules per degree K.

$T = $ absolute temperature of resistor in degrees Kelvin.

$R = $ resistive component of impedance across which voltage is developed.

$\Delta f = $ bandwith of circuit through which noise voltage is transmitted. (This definition of Δf as the overall receiver bandwidth differs from that shown ordinarily because we have specified that the receiver as a whole has a bandwidth of 4 mc, which makes it unimportant whether noise components exist in the r-f section over a greater band than 4 mc).

We find that for $T = 300$ degrees Kelvin and $\Delta f = 4$ mc,

$$E = 0.26\,(R)^{1/2} \text{ microvolts} \tag{14}$$

For the calculated value of R for the 6AK5, $E = 9.6$ microvolts. This is the tube-noise voltage referred to the grid, not the grid-circuit noise voltage.

From classical transformer theory, E_{grf}, the signal voltage at the grid of the r-f stage is:

$$E_{grf} = E_{ant}\,(R_g/R_{ant})^{1/2} \tag{15}$$

where E_{ant} is signal voltage from the antenna, R_{ant} characteristic resistance of the antenna transmission line, R_g antiresonant resistance of the grid circuit (this quantity is directly measurable with an r-f impedance bridge as opposed to R in Eq. 12). It is evident that for maximum signal at the grid the value of R_g should be as high as possible. Further, if we compare Eq. 14 with Eq. 15 we see that the ratio of signal voltage at the grid to noise voltage from R_g is not dependent on the value of R_g. On the other hand, an increase of R_g will bring about an increase in E_{grf} and noise voltage from R_g together, with respect to the tube-noise voltage which is not dependent on R_g. As a result, the net S/N ratio is improved due to the tendency for the tube-noise voltage to become relatively insignificant. Thus an increase in R_g improves both gain and S/N. We must now determine just how large R_g can be made without violating any of the design requirements.

H. W. Bode shows[3] that for a constant-shunt C and R, regardless of location of the pass band of a network in the frequency spectrum,

$$\Delta f \propto 1/RC \tag{16}$$

where f is the bandwidth of the circuit in cps, R is the shunt resistance of the circuit, and C is the shunt capacitance of the circuit. In the case of a simple parallel RLC circuit,

$$\Delta f = 1/2\pi RC \text{ cps} \tag{17}$$

where f is the frequency at which the scalar impedance is 3 db down from maximum value, or

$$R = 1/2\pi\,(\Delta f)C \tag{18}$$

From the equation it is evident that since the required bandwidth is fixed, R will be maximum for minimum shunt C. Since both the circuit gain and S/N are maximum for maximum R, it is imperative that C be held to the absolute minimum. The input capacitance for a 6AK5 tube and wiring in the circuit shown in Fig. 4 can be held to 7 $\mu\mu$f total. For an 8-mc bandwidth, from Eq. 18, $R = 2,850$ ohms, the maximum permissible value of R_g for 8-mc bandwidth.

The shunt impedance of the antenna as seen looking into the grid side of the input transformer may have sufficient variation of its reactive component over the band of a given channel to render it worthy of close scrutiny. It has been found that the reactance variation is small enough that the antenna does not narrow the receiver pass band, but on the other hand it is not small enough to allow the antenna to be properly treated as a pure resistance over the pass band of a given channel.

Inasmuch as it is necessary to match the antenna to the grid circuit to prevent reflections on the line, if the antenna impedance were purely resistive over the band the effective resistance shunting the circuit would be halved by connecting the antenna into the circuit, and the reactance would be unaffected. In such an event the r-f stage grid circuit would have twice the bandwidth previously computed. With present antennas it appears not to be good design practice to depend on the antenna for band widening, but it is surely permissible to use the reduced grid circuit antiresonant resistance in computing resistor noise voltage. The latter voltage is therefore 9.8 microvolts. The total noise voltage at the grid of the 6AK5 amplifier is then $E_{ng} = 13.7$ microvolts.

If the impedance of the antenna transmission line is 75 ohms, from Eq. 15, $E_{sg} = 6.16 \times E_{ant}$ microvolts. Thus, a signal of 22.2 microvolts at the antenna would yield a S/N ratio of 10 if there were no noise contributions of importance beyond the r-f amplifier grid.

Gain

To assess the importance of noise sources beyond the first grid, we must next compute the gain of the first stage. The total shunt capacitance of the interstage circuit between a 6AK5 r-f amplifier and a 6AK5 mixer is about 14 $\mu\mu$f for a carefully designed circuit. The interstage antiresonant resistance for an 8-mc bandwidth is 1,425 ohms. The gain of a pentode of transconductance 5,000 micromhos operating into a tuned tank circuit of antiresonant resistance R is given at the resonant frequency by

$$A = G_m R = 7.12 \tag{19}$$

The signal voltage at the 6AK5 amplifier plate is then

$$E_{sp} = A E_{sg} = 43.8\,E_{ant} \tag{20}$$

Similarly, the noise voltage at the plate due to r-f stage tube noise and grid-circuit noise is

$$E_{np} = A E_{ng} = 97.5 \text{ microvolts} \tag{21}$$

The most convenient process for introducing the noise contribution of the interstage circuit resistance and the mixer tube is to compute the noise-equivalent resistance for the noise power transmitted from the r-f grid to the r-f plate, and then add to this quantity the interstage circuit resistance and the noise-equivalent resistance of the mixer tube. The r-f stage noise-equivalent resistance referred to the plate can be computed from Eq. 14 as follows:

$$R_{np} = \left(\frac{E_{np}}{0.26}\right)^2 \tag{22}$$

where R_{np} is the desired resistance referred to the plate, and E_{np} is the noise voltage at the plate from the grid, as before. Substituting from Eq. 21 in Eq. 22,

$$R_{np} = A^2 (E_{ng})^2/(0.26)^2 \tag{23}$$

and, substituting for E_{ng} from Eq. 14,

$$R_{np} = A^2 R_{ng} \tag{24}$$

wherein R_{ng} represents the total noise resistance in the r-f grid circuit and tube. Then $R_{np} = 141,200$ ohms.

This value of equivalent noise resistance is quite large compared to the values of circuit impedance and equivalent tube-noise resistance encountered so far. Therefore we can at least make a good first approximation to the correct S/N ratio of the complete unit without any further data. This approximate r-f head S/N ratio can be computed from the data given, $S/N = E_{sg}/E_{ng} = 0.450\ E_{ant}$. Although it is current practice to express the S/N characteristic of a receiving system by use of the system noise figure, it is more convenient to use S/N voltage ratio as defined above for purposes of calculation, and then convert to noise figure as a final basis for comparison.

To summarize the data computed

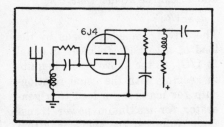

FIG. 5—Grounded-grid triode-amplifier

on the 6AK5 grounded-cathode r-f amplifier, $E_{sp} = 43.8\ E_{ant}$, $R_{np} = 141,200$ ohms. We find later that for the case of a 6AK5 grounded-cathode amplifier coupled to a grounded-grid mixer the interstage capacitance is only 7 $\mu\mu$f, so that the interstage resistance level can be doubled, which doubles the r-f gain and yields $E'_{sp} = 87.6\ E_{ant}$, $R'_{np} = 564,800$ ohms.

Triode Grounded-Grid Amplifier

Next consider the grounded-grid triode amplifier circuit of Fig. 5. The noise-equivalent resistance of a triode grounded-cathode amplifier referred to the grid is given by Terman[4] as

$$R_n = 3/G_m \text{ ohms} \tag{25}$$

Using Eq. 14 the equivalent noise voltage at the grid of the tube is

$$E_{ng} = 0.26\ (R_n)^{1/2} \text{ microvolts} \tag{26}$$

However, in the grounded-grid amplifier, as in any other amplifier having impedance in the cathode circuit, the application of an a-c

voltage e_n between grid and ground will produce an a-c plate current,

$$I_n = \frac{\mu\ e_n}{r_p + Z_L + Z_K\ (\mu + 1)} \tag{27}$$

where I_n is the resultant plate current, r_p is the a-c plate resistance of the tube, Z_L is the load impedance between plate and ground, Z_K is the impedance connected between cathode and ground, and μ is the amplification factor of the tube. In response to the current I_n, there will be a voltage E'_{nc} from cathode to ground,

$$E'_{nc} = E_{ng} \frac{\mu Z_K}{r_p + Z_L + Z_K\ (\mu + 1)} \mu v \tag{28}$$

which refers the noise voltage to the true input of the grounded-grid amplifier. Since both plate load and cathode circuit are resonant at the same frequency, at the center of the transmission band of the amplifier, Eq. 28 becomes

$$E'_{nc} = E_{ng} \frac{\mu\ R_K}{r_p + R_L + R_K\ (\mu + 1)} \mu v \tag{29}$$

where R_K is the resistive component of impedance connected between cathode and ground. However, the input impedance of a grounded-grid amplifier at resonant frequency is given by Jones[5] as

$$R_1 = \frac{r_p + R_L}{\mu + 1} \text{ ohms} \tag{30}$$

and the input transformer must match this resistance if reflections are to be avoided in the transmission line to the antenna. Then,

$$R_K = R_1$$

$$R_K = \frac{r_p + R_L}{\mu + 1} \tag{31}$$

Substituting for R_K from Eq. 31 in Eq. 29 we have,

$$E'_{nc} = E_{ng} \frac{\mu\frac{(r_p + R_L)}{(\mu + 1)}}{r_p + R_L + (\mu + 1)\frac{(r_p + R_L)}{(\mu + 1)}}$$

$$E'_{nc} = E_{ng} \frac{\mu}{2\ (\mu + 1)} \text{ microvolts} \tag{32}$$

It can be shown in general that

$$E'_{nc} = E_{ng} A_{gk} \text{ microvolts} \tag{32.1}$$

where A_{gk} is the gain from grid to cathode that would be obtained if a signal were injected between grid and ground. Equation 32

shows the value of the tube noise voltage of a grounded-grid triode amplifier referred to the cathode circuit for the particular case where the cathode load resistance matches the input resistance of the tube. To simplify the equation for circuits using a tube of μ appreciably greater than 1,

$$E'_{nc} = \frac{E_{ng}}{2} \tag{33}$$

Comparing Eq. 33 to Eq. 26 and 25, for the particular value of R_K selected,

$$R'_n = \frac{R_n}{4} \tag{34}$$

and

$$R'_n = \frac{0.75}{G_m} \tag{35}$$

where R'_n is the noise equivalent resistance (of a grounded-grid amplifier stage) referred to the cathode.

If desirable or necessary to provide a different cathode impedance than R_1 in Eq. 30 the noise resistance changes. In general, referring to Eq. 26 and 32.1 we have

$$R'_n = R_n A_{gk}^2 \tag{24.2}$$

From inspection of Eq. 29, if μ is much greater than one, then for those circuits in which R_K is of the same order as, or greater than, $(r_p + R_L)$, we can write approximately,

$$E'_{nc} = E_{ng} \tag{36}$$

For this grounded-grid r-f amplifier circuit, however, we must match the input circuit to the antenna, so the equivalent noise resistance is given by Eq. 35. For a 6J4 operated at 15 ma of plate current, $G_m = 0.012$ mho, $r_p = 4,500$ ohms, and $\mu = 54$, so that $R'_n = 62.5$ ohms.

Since the plate-circuit impedance of a class-A amplifier is the actual load impedance shunted by the a-c plate resistance of the tube, in the case of the triode amplifier the correct antiresonant impedance of the load circuit proper is appreciably higher (for a given bandwidth) than for a pentode. The 6J4 triode has substantially the same output capacitance as the 6AK5, so that the same interstage antiresonant resistance of 1,425 ohms is required. With an a-c plate resistance of 4,500 ohms, the load circuit itself should have an antiresonant resistance of 2.080 ohms (R_L in Eq. 30). Substituting the proper values in Eq. 31, $R_K = 120$ ohms. The total noise resistance in the input (cathode) circuit is then 122.5 ohms, since $\frac{1}{2}R_K$ ($\frac{1}{2}$ because of the shunting effect of the antenna) and R'_n add directly as required by Eq. 11.

If we change notation in Eq. 15 to refer to R_K instead of R_g, and E_K instead of E_g, we have

$$E_{Kggrf} = E_{ant}(R_K/R_{ant})^{1/2}, \text{ or } E_{sK} = 1.27 E_{ant}$$

The tube gain is simply the ratio of R_L to R_K, since the same signal current flows through both plate load and cathode circuit. Thus,

$$A = R_L/R_K = 17.35 \tag{37}$$

The signal voltage at the plate of the grounded-grid r-f amplifier is then

$$E_{sp} = A E_{sK} = 22.0 E_{ant} \tag{38}$$

The total cathode noise resistance referred to the plate circuit is, Eq. 24, $R_{np} = 36,800$ ohms. To perform the same input circuit S/N calculation (as a first approximation to the receiving system S/N), already done for the 6AK5: $E_{nk} = 2.87$ microvolts, and $S/N = E_{sk}/E_{nk} = 0.442 E_{ant}$.

A signal of 22.6 microvolts at the antenna would be required for an S/N of 10. Note that S/N is better for the 6AK5 grounded-cathode amplifier than it is for the 6J4 grounded-grid amplifier thus far. On the other hand, the 6J4 cathode circuit has a very interesting characteristic. Since R_K is 120 ohms, and the shunt capacitance across the cathode circuit totals about 7 μμf, we find from Eq. 17 that $\Delta f = 1/2\pi RC = 190$ mc. This means that the cathode circuit may be tuned to 135 mc and there is no need for adjustment to receive stations between 54 and 216 mc.

We shall later show that $R_L = 4,500$ ohms is desirable for the 6J4 grounded-grid r-f when used with a 6J4 grounded-grid mixer, and for

that condition, $R_K = 164$ ohms, $R_{ant} = 144.5$ ohms, $E_{sk} = 1.48 E_{ant}$, $A = 27.5$, $E_{sp} = 40.7 E_{ant}$, $R_{np} = 104,500$ ohms, and $S/N = 0.475 E_{ant}$.

Cathode-Follower Amplifier

In the cathode-follower r-f amplifier circuit of Fig. 6, the optimum step-up ratio for the output transformer is needed in addition to the other calculations encountered in the previous circuits.

When an a-c grid-to-cathode voltage of E_{gK} volts is applied to a cathode follower whose load resistance, R_K, is small compared to the a-c plate resistance, the resultant cathode current is

$$I_k = E_{gk}G_k \tag{39}$$

where G_k is the cathode transconductance. The voltage across a cathode load, R_K, is E_K where

$$E_K = I_K R_K = E_{gK}G_K R_K \tag{40}$$

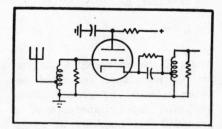

FIG. 6—Cathode-follower r-f amplifier

The grid-to-ground voltage that was required to produce this cathode voltage is

$$E_g = E_{gK} + E_K = E_{gK}(1 + G_K R_K) \tag{41}$$

and the gain from grid to cathode is

$$A_{cf} = E_K/E_g = G_K R_K/(1 + G_K R_K) \tag{42}$$

From Eq. 15 the step-up from antenna to grid is $A_1 = (R_1/R_{ant})^{\frac{1}{2}}$ and the step-up from cathode to output resistor R is $A_2 = (R_2/R_K)^{\frac{1}{2}}$ where R_K is the load resistance presented to the cathode by the output transformer.

The total gain of the cathode-follower amplifier from antenna to R_2 is

$$A = A_1 A_{cf} A_2 \tag{43}$$

Substituting for A_{cf} and A_2, each of which is dependent on R_K,

$$A = \frac{A_1 G_k (R_k R_2)^{1/2}}{1 + G_k R_k} \tag{43.1}$$

To determine the value of R_K for maximum gain the derivative of A with respect to R_K is set equal to zero. The gain A_1 is dependent on R_K only by virtue of the dependence of input capacitance of the tube on the grid-to-cathode gain, A_{cf}, which is in turn dependent on R_K. The degree of dependence of A_1 on R_K is so slight that A_1 changes only 20 percent as R_K goes from zero to infinity, so we shall assume A_1 to be invariant with R_K in performing the differentiation. Then

$$\frac{dA}{dR_k} = A_1 G_k (R_2)^{1/2} \times \frac{d}{dR_k}[(R_k)^{1/2}/(1 + G_k R_k)]$$

and it can be found that

$$R_k = 1/G_k \tag{44}$$

The driving impedance seen by the load of a cathode follower is equal to $1/G_K$, so the above result is quite in keeping with the usual relationship for matching a load to a generator for maximum power transfer. Note that the above condition has no relation to the condition for maximum power output from a cathode follower when the available input signal is unrestricted. Substituting for R_K from Eq. 44 in Eq. 43.1, we have

$$A = \frac{1}{2}A_1 (G_K R_2)^{1/2} \tag{45}$$

$$A = \frac{1}{2}(G_k R_1 R_2/R_{ant})^{1/2} \tag{46}$$

Having obtained the basic gain equation for the circuit, we can evaluate the signal and noise transmissions to the output. The cathode-follower r-f amplifier grounded-grid mixer combination would not require an interstage transformer, so we need only consider the combinations involving a straight pentode mixer or a cathode-coupled mixer in computing the value for R_2. For both the 6AK5 pentode mixer and the 6J6 cathode-coupled mixer, the input capacitance of tube, socket, and wiring is about 7 μμf, so R_2 must be 2,850 ohms for an 8-mc bandwidth. Using either the 6J6 (sections paralleled) or the 6J4 as r-f stage, the G_K is 12,000 micromhos for an obtainable operating condition. The output transformer ratio $R_2/R_K = R_2 G_K = 34.2$ impedance ratio. With such an impedance step-up, the 5 μμf cathode-to-ground capacitance of the cathode-follower adds only 0.146 μμf to the capacitance loading across R_2, so we may neglect it.

The input capacitance to either a 6J6 or a 6J4 cathode follower is about 6 μμf so R_1 is 3,320 ohms for an 8-mc bandwidth.

The cathode follower gain is then $A = 19.5$.

Computing the tube noise-equivalent resistance from Eq. 25, since the presence of cathode feedback does not modify the inherent S/N of the tube, $R_n = 3/G_K = 250$ ohms. The grid-circuit antiresonant resistance is made up of the transformed antenna resistance in parallel with the 3,320-ohm damping resistor, or 1,660 ohms net noise resistance. The total noise resistance effective in the input circuit is $R_{nt} = R_n + R_1 = 1,910$ ohms.

The amplified and transformed total noise resistance at the ouput side of the output transformer can be computed with the aid of Eq. 24,

$$R_{n2} = (A_{cf}A_2)^2 R_{nt} \quad (47)$$

By Eq. 43, 45, 47,

$$R_{n2} = 1 G_k R_2 R_{nt} = 16{,}350 \text{ ohms} \quad (48)$$

From Eq. 26 the noise voltage across R_2 (excluding the noise from R_2 itself as well as the mixer noise which is yet to be computed) is $E_{n2} = 33.3$ microvolts.

Since the gain is 19.5, $S/N = AE_{ant}/E_{n2} = 0.585\ E_{ant}$. A signal of 17.1 microvolts at the antenna would produce an S/N of 10 for this circuit if there were no further noise contributions.

Remembering that R_1 in Eq. 30 represents the input resistance to a grounded-grid stage, and that R_K in Eq. 42 is the load resistance of a cathode follower, the choke in the cathode lead (Fig. 7) is made antiresonant with stray capacitance at the center of the transmission band, so that to a close approximation $R_1 = R_K$.

Then, using the equations, the overall gain of the cathode-coupled amplifier is

$$A_{cc} = \sqrt{\frac{R_g}{R_{ant}}} \left[\frac{G_{m1}R_L}{1 + G_{m1} \times \dfrac{r_{p2} + R_L}{\mu_2 + 1}} \right]$$

For a bandwidth of 8 mc per interstage, the required damping resistor value is calculated from Eq. 18 to be 1,400 ohms. Likewise, for the same bandwidth in the antenna-to r-f grid transformer, a damping resistor value of 3,320 ohms is required.

For the 6J6, G_m is 5,000 micromhos, r_p is 6,600 ohms, and μ is 33, so $A_{cc} = 21.4$.

To calculate the signal-to-noise voltage ratio of the cathode-coupled amplifier, we need to combine the noise contributions of the two tubes. The equivalent noise resistance at the high side of the antenna-to-grid transformer is half of the damping resistor value, or 1,650 ohms. The grid-equivalent noise resistance of the cathode-follower stage having a G_K of 5,000 micromhos can be readily computed to be 600 ohms. Adding these, the total noise resistance is 2,250 ohms.

The ratio of cathode voltage to grid voltage in the cathode follower is 0.541, and the value of grid circuit noise resistance transmitted to the cathode of the cathode follower is

$$R_{n1} = A^2_1 R_n = 658 \text{ ohms} \quad (24)$$

To introduce the noise contribution of the grounded-grid section of the cathode-coupled amplifier, we must use the relationship given by Eq. 29,

$$E'_n = E_n \frac{\mu R_K}{r_p + R_L + R_K(\mu + 1)}$$
microvolts

In this application R_K, the cathode load for the grounded-grid section, is the output impedance of the cathode-follower section. Since the output impedance of a cathode follower is the same as the input impedance of a similar tube used as a grounded-grid amplifier with no plate load, we may use Eq. 30 in the form, $R_o = r_p/(\mu + 1)$ ohms, where R_o represents the dynamic portion of the output impedance of a cathode follower. Using previously quoted values for a single section of a 6J6, $R_o = 194$ ohms.

Substituting this value for R_K in Eq. 29 along with other values previously given, $E'_n = 0.452E_n$. Making use of Eq. 26, we find that $R'_n = 0.205\ R_n$. Since R_n has already been computed to be 600 ohms, $R'_n = 123$ ohms. This value of R'_n can now be added to the 658-ohm contribution of the input transformer and cathode follower to give the total noise contribution of both tubes and the input circuit, viewed at the common cathode point, as 781 ohms. Applying Eq. 24 again to determine the value of the above noise resistance as viewed at the final output point of the cathode-coupled amplifier, we have $R_n = 27,600$ ohms where 5.95 is the cathode-to-plate gain of the grounded-grid section as determined in the computation of A_{cc}. The noise voltage in the output can be computed using Eq. 26, ignoring the noise from the interstage transformer and the mixer, $E_{np} = 43.2$ microvolts and $S/N = 0.495\ E_a$.

For operation with a grounded-grid mixer (Fig. 10c), R_L should be 2,850 ohms. For this condition A_{cc} is 39.1 for the combination with the 6J4 mixer, A_{cf} is 0.580 (ratio of grid voltage to cathode voltage in the cathode follower), R_{n1} is 757 ohms, E'_n is $0.420E_n$, R'_n is 0.1765

Table I—Amplifier Circuit Summary (Excluding Interstage and Mixer Noise)

Circuit	Tube	Voltage Gain	S/N	Output R_n
Grounded-Cathode	6AK5	43.8	$0.450E_a$	141,200
		87.6	$0.450E_a$	564,800
Grounded-Grid	6J4	22.0	$0.362E_a$	55,000
Cathode-Follower	6J4	19.5	$0.585E_a$	16,350
Cathode-Coupled	6J6	21.4	$0.495E_a$	27,600
		39.1	$0.537E_a$	78,500

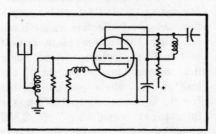

FIG. 7—Cathode-coupled r-f amplifier

R_n, R'_n is 106 ohms, the noise resistance contribution of the transformer and cathode follower is 757 ohms, the total noise resistance seen at the common cathode is 763 ohms, R_{n1} is 78,500 ohms (viewed at the final output point of the cathode-coupled amplifier), the cathode-to-plate gain of the grounded-grid section is 10.14, E_{np} is 72.8 microvolts, and S/N is $0.537E_a$.

Pentode Mixer

E. W. Herold shows[6] that G_c, the conversion transconductance of a pentode plate detector having signal and oscillator voltages both introduced at the control grid, is

$$G_c = 0.23G_o \qquad (49)$$

if the oscillator voltage swings the mixer from zero bias to cutoff and G_o is the cathode transconductance of the tube, that is the change in

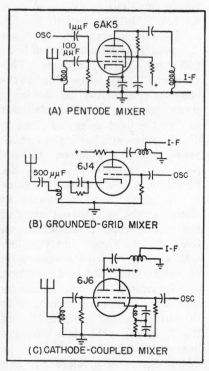

FIG. 8—Several mixer circuits for use without an r-f stage

(A) PENTODE MIXER

(B) GROUNDED-GRID MIXER

(C) CATHODE-COUPLED MIXER

cathode current per-unit-change in grid voltage. Since Herold has made the assumption that G_o and I_o are 1.25 times the corresponding plate transconductance and plate current (a valid approximation for

many pentodes) for purposes of this paper we may express Eq. 49 in terms of G_m by a suitable change of constants. Thus,

$$G_c = 0.287\, G_m \qquad (50)$$

With a peak G_m of the 6AK5 mixer of 0.01 mho, the conversion transconductance is $G_c = 0.00287$ mho.

To transform the signal down to a 75-ohm impedance level for transmission to the i-f amplifier, we may either tap down on the plate coil for the output, or make use of a small (5 μμf) capacitance series resonant with the net inductive reactance of the plate tank. The latter method has the advantage of simpler coil construction and the disadvantage of adding about 50 percent to the capacitance shunting the circuit. In the interests of maximizing gain and bandwidth, we will then use the tapped coil, or autotransformer circuit.

If the output of the mixer were impressed on a purely resistive 75-ohm load, the total capacitance shunting the mixer plate circuit is the (approximately) 5-μμf output capacitance of the mixer. However, the actual load connected to the output will be a second r-f transformer whose resonant-frequency input impedance is 75 ohms resistive. If **we use an autotransformer** to terminate the receiving end of the output coaxial, its net effect on the mixer plate circuit will be to connect in shunt the grid circuit of the first i-f amplifier stage. Assuming the use of such an input transformer and a 6AK5 first i-f amplifier, the total effective capacitance shunting the mixer plate circuit will be 14 μμf, which will call for a net antiresonant resistance of the load of 1,425 ohms (see calculation for 6AK5 amplifier-to-6AK5-mixer interstage) consisting of 2,850 ohms shunted across the mixer plate circuit and 2,850 ohms across the first i-f stage grid circuit. The conversion gain, A_c, is the product of conversion transconductance and load impedance, so $A_m = 4.09$.

The mixer plate transformer must be designed to transform

from a 2,850-ohm level to a 75-ohm level so there will be a voltage step-down from mixer plate to coaxial output jack. The net voltage gain from the grid of the mixer to the coaxial output jack is $A'_c = A_m (75/2850)^{\frac{1}{2}} = 0.664$.

For the 6AK5 mixer of Fig. 8, the noise resistance is shown by Herold[6] to be R_{nm}, where

$$R_{nm} = \left(15 + 21\frac{I_o}{G_o} \right) G_o \qquad (51)$$

and where I_o and G_o refer to zero bias cathode current and cathode transconductance of the mixer tube respectively. Changing from G_o to G_m as before,

$$R_{nm} = \frac{12 + 16.8\, I_p/G_m}{G_m} \qquad (52)$$

For a 6AK5 tube at a screen voltage of 120 volts, the zero-bias plate current is 20 ma and the zero bias transconductance is 10,000 micromhos or 0.01 mho. Therefore, by Eq. 29 the tube noise equivalent resistance referred to the grid is $R_{nm} = 4,560$ ohms.

Table I and the data computed for the 6AK5 mixer form Table II, which summarizes the features of the 6AK5 mixer in combination with various r-f amplifiers. The quantity, R_{int}, used in Table II is the sum of mixer equivalent-grid noise resistance and interstage noise resistance; while R_n is the sum of R_{int} and the output noise resistance for the appropriate r-f amplifier as listed in Table I. The quantity R_n $(A'_c)^2$ is in turn equal to R_n referred to the coaxial output jack of the unit.

Technically, before computing E_n, we should add the transformed total noise resistance of the first i-f input circuit plus the first i-f tube equivalent-grid noise resistance, but practically the term is negligible (2,850 ohms circuit resistance plus 1,360 ohms first i-f tube grid equivalent-noise resistance equals 4,210 ohms which is transformed in impedance in the ratio 75/2,850 to yield 111 ohms effective at the coaxial cable jack).

The 6J6 Mixer Circuit

For the 6J6 mixers of Fig. 9, the equivalent noise resistance is[6]

$$R = 13/G_o \qquad (53)$$

for the mixer section of the tube, where G_o is the zero bias transconductance in mhos of the tube. An additional source of noise in this circuit is the triode section that is used to transmit oscillator voltage to the mixer proper. The noise resistance of a triode is (Eq. 25) $R = 3/G_m$, where G_m is the average transconductance of the tube in mhos. To a reasonable approximation, the average transconductance is equal to half of G_o, the peak transconductance, so we may write

version gain $A_c = 2.59$.

The cathode circuit may be either a low-impedance-level selective-narrow-band circuit resonated at local oscillator frequency, in which case it must be tuned from station to station; or it may be a broad-band circuit, in which case it cuts the conversion gain to one half (this can be proved by use of Eq. 27 to determine the gain of a tube whose cathode load impedance is the cathode output impedance of a similar tube) but does not have to be tuned. The conversion gain for the 6J6 mixer with a wide-band cathode circuit is therefore 1.30. Since we use the same impedance transfor-

Grounded-Grid Mixer

The grounded-grid mixer shown in Fig. 10 has several features that require an analysis quite different from that for the pentode. In the case of the circuits of Fig. 10A and 10C it is found that the impedance level of the amplifier plate load can be doubled (for the same overall r-f head bandwidth) thus doubling amplifier gain. Assuming that the input impedance to the mixer is about 80 ohms and that the input capacitance is 7 $\mu\mu$f, the bandwidth of the mixer cathode circuit is approximately 285 megacycles. From a different viewpoint, the circuit behavior can be summarized by saying that the grounded-grid mixer

Table II—Summary of Performance of 6AK5 Mixer with Various Amplifiers

R-F Amplifier	Tube	R_{rf}	R_{int}	R_n	$R_n (A'_c)^2$	E_n	Gain	S/N
Grounded-Cathode	6AK5	141,200	6,000	147,200	65,000	66.3	29.1	$0.440E_a$
Grounded-Grid	6J4	55,000	6,000	61,000	26,900	42.6	14.6	$0.343E_a$
Cathode-Follower	6J4	16,350	7,400	23,750	10,470	26.6	13.0	$0.489E_a$
Cathode-Coupled	6J6	27,600	6,000	33,600	14,800	31.6	14.2	$0.449E_a$

Table III—Performance of 6J6 Mixer with Various Amplifiers

R-F Amplifier	Tube	R	$R(A'_c)^2$	R_{nt}	E_n	S/N	Total Gain
Pentode	6AK5	145,500	25,650	266,760	42.5	$0.433E_{ant}$	18.40
Grounded-grid	6J4	59,300	10,470	10,580	26.8	$0.345E_{ant}$	9.24
Cathode-Follower	6J4	20,100	3,540	3,650	15.7	$0.521E_{ant}$	8.18
Cathode-coupled	6J6	31,900	5,630	5,740	19.7	$0.456E_{ant}$	8.98

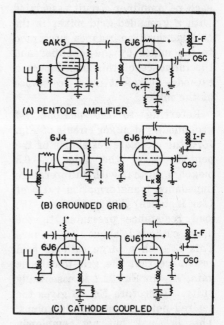

(A) PENTODE AMPLIFIER

(B) GROUNDED GRID

(C) CATHODE COUPLED

FIG. 9—Circuits employing a 6J6 mixer. For narrow-band cathode circuit at (A), C_K or 100 $\mu\mu$f is added and L_K is adjusted to resonate with C_K at the oscillator frequency. For wide-band cathode circuit at (B), L_K is adjusted to resonate with stray capacitance

the total noise resistance for the twin-triode mixer as

$$R_c = 19/G_o \qquad (54)$$

Under the intended operating conditions, the peak transconductance, G_o, of a 6J6 is 6,500 micromhos so, $R_c = 2,920$ ohms. As in the case of the 6AK5 mixer, the tube noise resistance is small but not negligible, compared with the total noise resistance in the plate of the preceding r-f stage.

The conversion transconductance is[6]

$$G_c = 0.28 \, G_o = 0.00182 \text{ mho.} \qquad (55)$$

Since the output capacitance of the 6J6 is substantially the same as that of the 6AK5, the same load impedance can be used and the con-

mation ratio in the 6J6 mixer plate circuit as in the 6AK5 mixer circuit, (the two tubes have practically the same output capacitances), the gain of the 6J6 from signal grid to coaxial output jack is $A'_c = 0.42$ for the switched cathode circuit and 0.21 for the fixed cathode circuit.

We may repeat the process used in setting up Table II for the 6AK5, this time introducing the quantity R_{nt} which is equal to $R(A'_c)^2$ plus the transformed noise resistance of the first i-f stage, 111 ohms. In Table III, the figures given are for the tunable cathode circuit. For fixed-tuned operation, the gain figures are half of those shown.

input provides no significant capacitive loading on the r-f amplifier-mixer interstage.

In the case of the grounded-grid amplifier grounded-grid-mixer combination of Fig. 10B, it is not only possible to increase the impedance level of the amplifier plate load, but it is also conceivable that some impedance lower than the maximum allowed by the bandwidth would give a maximum gain for the **overall unit** due to the interaction of the stages on each other.

In the case of the cathode-follower r-f amplifier grounded-grid-mixer, the circuit is indistinguishable from a cathode-coupled mixer operating without an r-f amplifier except for one point. The single point of difference between the two circuits is the choice of the plate to be used for output. This "no r-f cathode-coupled mixer" configuration is the better so we shall drop the cathode-follower r-f grounded-grid-mixer combination and discuss its twin in a later section.

The primary feature that requires individual treatment for each r-f amplifier circuit associated with a grounded-grid mixer is the cathode load impedance presented to the mixer by the amplifier and the influence of this impedance on cathode-equivalent noise resistance of the mixer.

Referring to the pentode r-f grounded-grid-mixer circuit of Fig. 10A, the a-c plate resistance of the pentode is of the order of 0.3 megohm, so that with an interstage impedance transformation ratio of (for instance) 3,000:100 ohms, the load resistance presented to the mixer cathode is about 10,000 ohms. This is such a large cathode load resistance that the grid-to-cathode gain, A_{gK} in Eq. 32.1 is essentially unity. Therefore Eq. 53 gives the desired noise resistance, 867 ohms. This is small but not completely negligible compared to the output noise resistances of other amplifiers.

In the 6J4 grounded-grid r-f 6J4 grounded-grid-mixer combination we are faced with the problem of providing maximum voltage transfer to the input impedance of the mixer. Since the plate load impedance of a mixer is very low at the signal frequency, the input impedance of the grounded-grid mixer is simply $1/G_m$, a constant. There exists the possibility that either the maximum-voltage transfer requirement or the bandwidth requirement may fix the interstage transformer

ratio. An analysis reveals that the total gain from antenna to mixer output jack is given by

$$A = G_c \left[R_{IF} \times \frac{\mu_1 + 1}{G_{m2}} + \frac{R_L}{r_{p1} + R_L} \right]^{1/2}$$

where R_L is the load resistance presented to the r-f amplifier plate by the interstage transformer, G_c is the conversion transconductance of the mixer, and μ_1 and r_{p1} refer to the r-f tube. It is apparent that as R_L ranges from r_{p1} to ∞ the gain in-

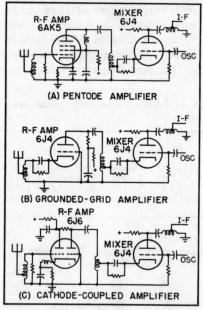

FIG. 10—Three types of r-f amplifiers feeding a 6J4 grounded-grid mixer

creases only 40 percent, so that there is no great advantage in using a high transformer ratio. If we use $R_L = r_{p1} = 4,500$, the interstage bandwidth is 10 mc so the interstage gain is down 0.7 db at 2 mc each side of carrier frequency, and according to Fig. 2, the mixer plate circuit is permitted a bandwidth as small as 4/0.85 or 4.7 mc. Resistor R_{IF}, the mixer plate resistor, is then 2,420 ohms total for a 14-$\mu\mu$f mixer plate circuit total capacitance.

From the above, the mixer input impedance is 80 ohms, so the r-f plate-to-mixer cathode voltage transformation ratio is $A_T = 0.1675$ for the 6AK5-6J4 and the 6J6-6J4 combinations, and $A_T = 0.1330$ for the 6J4-6J4 combination.

At the 6J4 mixer cathode we thus have the following voltages and resistances:

R-F Amp	Mixer	E_s	R_n
6J4 G-G	6J4	5.41 E_{ant}	2,850 ohms
6AK5 G-C	6J4	14.7 E_{ant}	16,700 ohms
6J6 C-C	6J4	6.55 E_{ant}	3,150 ohms

The conversion transconductance, G_c, is 0.0042 mho, so for the 6J4-6J4 combination, the conversion gain A_c is 10.14, and for the 6AK5-6J4 and 6J6-6J4 combinations $A_c = 5.88$.

The voltage ratio for the mixer plate to coaxial output transformer is $A_o = 0.176$ for the 6J4-6J4, and $A_o = 0.231$ for the 6J6-6J4 and 6AK5-6J4 combinations.

The net mixer-cathode to coaxial-output gain is then $A = A_s \times A_c = 1.79$ for the 6J4-6J4 combination, and $A = 1.36$ for the other combinations.

The voltages at the coaxial output jack are tabulated below:

R-F Amp	Mixer	E_s	E_n	S/N
6AK5	6J4	20.0 E_{ant}	45.8	0.436 E_{ant}
6J4	6J4	9.70 E_{ant}	25.0	0.388 E_{ant}
6J6	6J4	8.90 E_{ant}	20.0	0.445 E_{ant}

No R-F Amplifier

If each of the three mixers were operated with no r-f stage as shown in Fig. 8 we would have a somewhat different picture. We lack only a formula for noise resistance of a 6J4 mixer having a 75-ohm cathode circuit resistance. Substituting this value of R_K and previously known values for the other factors in Eq. 29, the noise **voltage is 46.9 percent of that** for a grounded-cathode triode mixer. Equations 26 and 53 show that $R'_n = 2.76/G_c$. For the 6J4 with $G_c = 0.015$ mho, $R'_n = 191$ ohms.

All of the data required for the various mixer circuits operating with no r-f amplifier are tabulated below.

6AK5 Mixer, Fig. 8A

Tube noise resistance referred to grid	4,500 ohms
Grid circuit antiresonant resistance.	3,540 ohms
Total noise resistance at grid	6,270 ohms
Noise voltage at grid	20.6 μv
Gain, antenna jack to grid	6.87

Gain, grid to output jack.......... 1.72⌉
Total grid noise resistance referred
  to output....................... 18,550 ohms⌉
Total noise resistance at output.... 18,660 ohms
Noise output voltage.............. 35.5 μv
Signal output voltage.............. 11.8 E_{ant}
Signal-to-noise ratio.............. 0.332 E_{ant}

6J4 Mixer, Fig. 8B

Tube noise resistance referred to
  cathode......................... 191 ohms
Input circuit resistance........... 75 ohms
Total input noise resistance....... 230 ohms
Total input noise voltage......... 3.94 μv
Gain, cathode to output jack...... 1.93
Total input noise resistance referred
  to output....................... 857 ohms
Total noise resistance at output.... 968 ohms
Noise output voltage.............. 8.09 μv
Signal output voltage.............. 1.93 E_{ant}
Signal-to-noise ratio.............. 0.239 E_{ant}

	Switched Cathode Coil	Fixed Cathode Coil
6J6 Mixer, Fig. 8C		
Tube noise resistance referred to grid.........	2,000	.....
Grid circuit antiresonant resistance..............	6,300	.....
Total noise resistance at grid.................	5,150	.....
Noise voltage at grid....	18.7	.....
Gain, antenna jack to grid	9.17	.....
Gain, grid to output jack.	0.75	0.375
Total grid noise resistance referred to output.....	2,900	725
Total noise resistance at output..............	3,010	836
Noise output voltage....	14.3 μv	7.52 μv
Signal output voltage....	6.88 E_{ant}	3.44 E_{ant}
Signal-to-noise ratio.....	0.480E_{ant}	0.457E_{ant}

The associated i-f amplifier should be designed to have as much of the required gain of the receiver as stability against regeneration will permit. For the particular conditions existing in this case, it has been found practical to have a gain of 100 db, or a voltage step-up of 100,000 to 1, in the combined i-f and video amplifier. Since a video output of 40 volts is sufficient to fully modulate the kinescope grid for most tubes, an i-f input of 400 μv is needed. It has been experimentally determined that a signal-to-noise voltage ratio of 20 db or 10 to 1 is necessary for good reception. This means that the r-f and mixer should provide at least enough signal gain that there will be an accompanying 40 μv of noise at the coaxial output jack. If the signal-to-noise ratio is expressed as $S/N = KE_{ant}$ and if S/N is set equal to 10, then $E_{ant} = 10/K$. The minimum acceptable r-f section gain is then that needed to bring E_{ant} up to a 400-μv level, $A_{min} = 400/E_{ant}$ and $A_{min} = 40K$. From these data we can set up **Table IV.**

Table IV—Summary of Tubes and Circuits

R-F Amplifier	Mixer	Gain	K	A_{min}	Tuned Circuits
6AK5 G-C	6AK5	29.1	0.440	17.6	2
6AK5 G-C	6J6 (fixed cath)	9.2	0.433	17.3	2
6AK5 G-C	6J6 (tuned cath)	18.4	0.433	17.3	3
6AK5 G-C	6J4	20.0	0.436	17.5	2
6J4 C-F	6AK5	13.0	0.489	19.6	2
6J4 C-F	6J6 (fixed cath)	4.1	0.521	20.8	2
6J4 C-F	6J6 (tuned cath)	8.2	0.521	20.8	3
6J4 G-G	6AK5	14.6	0.343	13.7	1
6J4 G-G	6J6 (fixed cath)	4.6	0.345	13.8	1
6J4 G-G	6J6 (tuned cath)	9.2	0.345	13.8	2
6J4 G-G	6J4	9.7	0.388	15.5	1
6J6 C-C	6AK5	14.2	0.449	17.95	2
6J6 C-C	6J6 (fixed cath)	4.5	0.456	18.3	2
6J6 C-C	6J6 (tuned cath)	9.0	0.456	18.3	3
6J6 C-C	6J4	8.9	0.445	17.8	2
None	6AK5	11.8	0.332	13.3	1
None	6J6 (fixed cath)	3.44	0.457	18.3	1
None	6J6 (tuned cath)	6.88	0.480	19.2	2
None	6J4	1.93	0.239	9.6	0

Summary

Table IV shows that the 6AK5 mixer is the only mixer with no r-f stage that has almost as much gain as A_{min}, although the 6J6 with tuned cathode has one of the best signal-to-noise ratios of all circuits considered. Of the combinations employing a 6J4 grounded-grid r-f amplifier, only the 6J4-6AK5 combination has more gain than A_{min}.

One surprising point demonstrated by these data is the lack of signal-to-noise superiority of the 6J4 grounded-grid amplifier compared to the 6AK5 amplifier. The reason is that the low input impedance to the grounded-grid stage permits only a small signal voltage step-up before the signal finds itself on common ground with tube noise for all further amplification.

Of those combinations using a 6J4 grounded-grid amplifier, the 6AK5 mixer provides most gain, with only one tuned circuit and with a slight margin over the minimum acceptable gain. Another possibility brought out by the data in Table IV is that of using a grounded-grid 6J4 r-f amplifier followed by a 6AK5 r-f amplifier and a 6AK5 mixer where the total range of frequencies over which the unit is to work does not exceed 190 mc, and where maximum obtainable gain is needed. Such a combination would have a voltage step-up

of 548 or a gain of 54.8 db (which would reduce required i-f and video gain about 70 db), a signal-to-noise ratio of 0.496 E_{ant}, and would require only two tuned circuits.

Of the several mixers operated with a 6AK5 r-f stage, although all combinations have a gain of $\frac{2}{3}$ or more times A_{min}, the 6AK5 mixer provides the most gain with nearly the same S/N and the minimum number of tuned circuits. The 6AS6, which is a 6AK5 having the suppressor brought out to a separate pin, could be used as a mixer with oscillator voltage injection at the suppressor. This circuit would reduce the capacitance shunting the amplifier-mixer interstage, which would make possible a slightly higher interstage impedance and increase gain, but a lower conversion transconductance (due to screen dissipation limitations) would produce about the same overall gain and signal-to-noise ratio as the 6AK5 mixer. Pentagrid mixer tubes such as the 6BE6 have such low conversion transconductance as to be out of the question.

The 6J4 c-f r-f combinations exhibit the best obtainable S/N ratios, but unfortunately at the expense of gain. The 6J4 c-f r-f-6AK5 mixer provides a very good S/N of 0.489 E_{ant} with a gain only 3 db short of A_{min}.

Although the 6J4 as a grounded-grid mixer without r-f amplification and the 6AK5 mixer operated with no r-f amplification look good on the basis of tube and tuned-circuit economy, both should be vigorously rejected on the basis of excellent capability of transmitting oscillator power to the antenna.

REFERENCES

(1) F. E. Terman, "Radio Engineers' Handbook", McGraw-Hill Book Co., first ed., fifth impression, Eq. 42., p 294, 1943.

(The term $gm2$ is a typographical error.)
(2) Reference 1, Eq. 116, p 477.
(3) H. W. Bode, "Network Analysis and Feedback Amplifier Design", D. Van Nostrand Co., Inc., p 213, 1945.
(4) Reference 1, p 294.
(5) M. C. Jones, "Grounded-Grid Radio Frequency Voltage Amplifiers", Eq. 5, Proc. IRE, p 423, July 1944.
(6) Reference 1, p 572.

Transit-Time Effects In Television Front-End Design

By H. M. WATTS

PAPERS analyzing transit-time effects in high-frequency tubes[1] show only qualitative correlation between theory and practice for most tube types. The 6AK5, and a few tube types not generally used in present-day television design, show good agreement between predicted and measured transit-time effects, while the 6J4, the 6J6 and others do not.

It has been shown[2] that the effects of transit-time loading for a grounded-cathode amplifier are as follows:

$$Y_{in} = G_1 + jB_1 + G_T \qquad (1)$$

where Y_{in} is the total input admittance seen by the driving circuit, $G_1 + jB_1$ is the input admittance of the passive elements of input circuit, and G_T is the transit-time loading conductance.

$$G_{Teq} = \beta G_T \qquad (2)$$

where β is the ratio of equivalent noise temperature of G_T to room temperature and G_{Teq} is the equivalent noise conductance of transit-time loading.

$$F = 1 + \frac{1}{G_s}[G_1 + G_T + R_{eq}(Y_T + G_T)^2] \qquad (3)$$

where G_s is the equivalent admittance of the signal source, R_{eq} is the grid-equivalent noise resistance of the tube excluding transit-time noise, $Y_T = G_s + G_1 + jB_1$ and F is the noise figure of the first stage.

This noise figure is defined as the ratio of total noise power in the output circuit to the noise power output due to Johnson noise in the signal source admittance.

Noise Figure

The noise voltage output from a source resistance R is $E = \sqrt{4KTR\Delta f}$ and the maximum noise power that can be delivered to an equal load resistor R is $E^2/4R = KT\Delta f$, so that the available noise power from an input circuit of noise figure F is $FKT\Delta f$, and Δf is the effective bandwidth of the receiver, which is 4 mc.

The quantity β has been shown

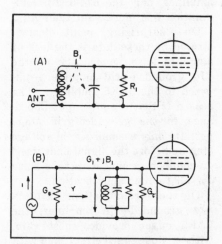

FIG. 1—Actual input circuit (A) of typical television front end and equivalent circuit (B) showing antenna replaced by a current source of transformed shunt conductance G_s

to be about 5 and the transit-time loading conductance has been shown to vary as the square of frequency for the 6AK5 and the few other tubes which fit transit-time noise theory, so that as frequency increases, induced noise plays an in-

creasingly important role. It will be noted that Eq. 3 has a minimum value, or best noise figure, when Y_T is minimum. A reasonable approximation where the input circuit has a wide band width compared to the overall system is to assume $B_1 = 0$, so we will use this approximation in the following work.

If we define ρ by

$$\rho G_{in} = G_1 + \beta G_T \qquad (4)$$

Eq. 3 can be put in the form

$$F = 1 + \frac{G_{in}}{G_s} \left[\rho + R_{eq}G_{in}\left\{1 + \left(\frac{G_s}{G_{in}}\right)^2\right\} \right] \qquad (5)$$

From inspection of Eq. 5, it would appear that there may be a value of G_s that will minimize F. This has been shown to be the case[3]. The optimum value G_s' is given by

$$G_s' = \sqrt{(\rho + R_{eq}G_{in})\frac{G_{in}}{R_{eq}}} \qquad (6)$$

The corresponding optimum noise figure is

$$F' = 1 + 2\sqrt{(\rho + R_{eq}G_{in})R_{eq}G_{in}} \qquad (7)$$

The idea of mismatching generator to amplifier in order to optimize F is an excellent one for many purposes, but unfortunately it is somewhat impractical in television receivers because the accompanying signal reflections on the antenna transmission line destroy the picture detail at the picture output. We shall next consider the consequences in degradation of noise figure of matching antenna to receiver and the consequences in antenna lead-in reflections of optimizing noise figure.

Effect of Matching on Noise

If we match receiver to antenna, the transformation ratio of the input transformer of Fig. 1A is so adjusted that the value of transmission line impedance transformed to transformer output level G_s is equal to G_{in}. Then Eq. 5 reduces to

$$F = 1 + \rho + 2 R_{eq} G_{in} \qquad (8)$$

As an example, consider a 6AK5 having $R_{eq} = 1,350$ ohms operating at a frequency where effectively $G\tau = 0$, with $R_1 = 2,850$ ohms so that $G_{in} = G_1 = 350 \times 10^{-6}$ mhos. From Eq. 4, $\rho = 1$, and we compute $R_{eq} G_{in} = 0.472$, so that $F' = 2.67$. If on the other hand we let $G_s = G_{in}$, we find $F = 2.94$, so that optimum transformation yields a noise figure smaller in the ratio 1.1 to 1 or 0.4 db better than matched impedances.

For a 6AK5 at 200 mc, $G\tau \cong 500 \times 10^{-6}$ mhos, so that for a circuit needing only 350×10^{-6} mhos of shunt conductance in order to provide sufficient bandwidth we would minimize G_1 in Eq. 1. For an input coil Q of 150 at 200 mc, if tuning capacitance is $7\,\mu\mu f$, $G_1 = 60 \times 10^{-6}$ mhos, so $G_{in} = 560 \times 10^{-6}$ mhos. From Eq. 4, $\rho = (G_1 + \beta G\tau) \div (G_{in}) = 4.4$, and we compute $R_{eq} G_{in} = 0.755$, so from Eq. 7, $F' = 4.95$ and from Eq. 8 $F = 6.91$. Thus the degradation of noise figure due to matching impedances rather than optimizing, for a 6AK5 grounded-cathode amplifier at 200 mc, is a factor of 1.39 or approximately 1.4 db.

Reflections in Transmission Line

The reflection coefficient R of a transmission line can be computed from the relationship

$$R = \frac{Z_o - Z_R}{Z_o + Z_R} \qquad (9)$$

where Z_o is the characteristic impedance of the line and Z_R the terminating resistor.

From Eq. 6 we find that for the 6AK5 at 200 mc, $G_s' = 1,460 \times 10^{-6}$ mhos, so $R_s' = 685$ ohms. For the same conditions, $G_{in} = 560 \times 10^{-6}$ mhos so $R_{in} = 1,790$ ohms. But R_{in} is Z_R and R_s' is Z_o in Eq. 9 so $R = (685 - 1,790)/(685 + 1.790) = -0.446$

Most common television receiving antennas match the associated transmission line poorly over a few of the channels, so that a reflection from the receiver end of the transmission line would be re-reflected at the antenna. If we were to have the same mismatch at the antenna as at the receiver in the example above, we would have at the receiver input the desired signal plus an additional wave train of one-fourth the amplitude but delayed by the round-trip travel-time of the antenna lead-in.

Considering the possible variability of antenna output impedance

Table I—Noise Figures for Typical Television Front-End Circuits[4]

R-F Amp	Mixer	Power Ratio	F db	F Tuned Gain	Tuned Circuits
Grounded-Cathode Input Circuit					
6AK5	6AK5	4.17	6.20	29.1	2
6AK5	6J6	4.31	6.34	9.2*	2
				18.4**	3
6AK5	6J4	4.25	6.28	20.0	2
Cathode-Follower Input Circuit					
6J4	6AK5	3.38	5.29	13.0	2
6J4	6J6	2.98	4.74	4.1*	2
				8.2**	3
Grounded-Grid Input Circuit					
6J4	6AK5	6.86	8.36	14.6	1
6J4	6J6	6.86	8.36	4.6*	1
				9.2**	2
6J4	6J4	5.36	7.29	9.7	1
Cathode-Coupled Input Circuit					
6J6	6AK5	4.00	6.02	14.2	2
6J6	6J6	3.88	5.89	4.5*	2
				9.0**	3
6J6	6J4	4.08	6.10	8.9	2
No R-F Circuit					
None	6AK5	7.33	8.65	11.8	1
None	6J6	3.88	5.85	3.44*	1
None	6J6	3.51	5.45	6.88**	2
None	6J4	14.13	11.5	1.93	0

* Fixed-Cathode Mixer Circuit
**Tuned-Cathode Mixer Circuit

over the band as well as the variability of antenna lead-in lengths, the choice between design for best noise figure and best input impedance is assuredly a matter of design judgment.

Total Noise Voltage

In a previous paper[4] signal-to-noise figures (K) were calculated for various types of commonly used television front-end circuits, such that $E_s/E_n = KE_{ant}$. If we wish to compute the total noise voltage that would have to be present at the input of a noiseless receiver in order to provide the same noise output as the receiver under scrutiny, we set $E_s/E_n = 1$ so that $KE_{ant} = 1$. But under this circumstance, the total equivalent noise voltage at the antenna is equal to the signal voltage E_{ant} so then $E_n = 1/K$.

This means that the noise power present in the receiver input is $E_n^2/R = 10^{-12}/K^2 R$ watts, where R is the input resistance at the antenna terminals (75 ohms) and the factor 10^{-12} converts the signal to volts. The total Johnson noise power in a matched input resistor was previously shown to be $KT\Delta f$ (here K is Boltzmann's constant, not the K mentioned above) which is 1.65×10^{-14} watts for a 4-mc bandwidth.

From the definition of noise figure then,

$$F = \frac{10^{-12}}{1.65 \times 10^{-14}\ K^2 R} = \frac{0.808}{K^2}$$

In terms of this formula we can now express the previously-mentioned signal-to-noise figures in terms of noise figures as shown in Table I.

Transit-Time Effect

The manner of combining the transit-time component of noise factor with the other components is not simple and for the tubes for which $G\tau$ is known only with poor accuracy it is not worth the trouble. We rewrite Eq. 8 to include $G\tau$ explicitly,

$$F = 1 + \frac{G_1 + \beta G\tau}{G_1 + G\tau} + 2 R_{eq} (G_1 + G\tau) \qquad (10)$$

where $G_1 + G\tau$ is held constant, as long as possible, against increase of $G\tau$ by decreasing G_1. It will be noted that as $G\tau$ increases the second term increases smoothly from 1 to β (which is 5), and the third term does not begin to increase until G_1 has reached its minimum value, after which the increase is linear with $G\tau$. For the 6AK5 the third term rose from about 1 to about 1.5 as $G\tau$ rose from 0 to the value at 200 mc. Since R_{eq} is much smaller in triodes this term is even less significant for the 6J4 and 6J6 over the range of interest.

Conclusions

Thus we see in a general way that the effect of inclusion of transit-time effect is to add a number about equal to 4 to the noise figure, for the vicinity of the frequency where $G\tau$ equals the desired value of G_{in}. If we select from Table 1 the four circuits utilizing the 6AK5 mixer, simply as a basis for comparison,

Table II — Noise Figures for Various R-F Amplifiers Used With 6AK5 Mixers

R-F	Amp.	F $G\tau = 0$	Est. F 200 mc	Est. F db
6AK5	Gr. Cath.	4.2	8.2	9.1
6J4	Cath. Fol.	3.4	7.4	8.7
6J4	Gr. Grid	6.9	10.9	10.4
6J6	Cath. Coupl.	4.0	8.0	9.0
None	——	7.3	11.3	10.5

and estimate F by arbitrarily adding the number 4 to each noise figure, we obtain the data shown in Table 2.

We note on inspecting Tables 1 and 2 that the effect of transit-time (as estimated) is to tend to level the differences between the various circuit combinations, so that for increasingly high frequencies the reduction of noise from sources other than transit-time becomes diminishingly important.

REFERENCES

(1) C. J. Bakker, Fluctuations and Electron Inertia, *Physica*, **8**, Jan. 1941.
(2) G. E. Valley, Jr. and H. Wallman, "Vacuum Tube Amplifiers," MIT Radiation Laboratory Series, **2**, McGraw-Hill Book Co., Inc., N. Y., 1948.
(3) Wallman, Macnee and Gadsden, Low-Noise Amplifier, *Proc. IRE*, **36**, p 700, 1948.
(4) H. M. Watts, Television Front-End Design, Part II, ELECTRONICS, p 106, May 1949.

Television Remote Tuner

By VIN ZELUFF

A CONSIDERABLE PORTION of the author's spare time has been spent in experimental work on television receiver circuits. Several times a need has arisen for a quick comparison-check of the on-the-air performance of a newly built front end. Removal of one front end and temporary wiring and mechanical mounting of a second unit whose performance is known has consumed valuable time.

A front end that can be quickly connected or coupled to the i-f stages of a receiver under test obviates this difficulty. A unit constructed for the purpose contains its own power supply for heater and plate voltage and provides output at the picture signal i-f frequency. This self-powered front end serves equally well as a signal source for testing experimental i-f strips.

Other Use

Use of large-screen picture tubes in home television receivers imposes difficulty in critical tuning of the receiver while standing at the tube screen. Because of the large picture near to the eye, adjustments made at the set often result in dissatisfac-

tion when the owner goes to his seat at the proper viewing distance. He must then return to the set location to readjust or change the station.

A more convenient arrangement results if a remote tuning unit is installed at the viewing position. Selection of station and fine tuning can then be done while comfortably seated at this location.

Ideally, such a tuner would require a minimum of connections to the receiver and would be removable to allow the receiver to operate normally with its own front end when desired.

Because this is also required of the comparison front end contemplated, it was decided to construct a tuner that would serve both purposes. As representative

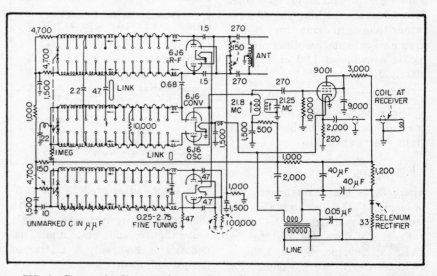

FIG. 1—Circuit of self-powered tuner. If used with transformerless receivers an isolation transformer is needed

of the most popular design, the receiver selected to be controlled was an RCA 630 type.

A 630 front end was fitted into a small aluminum box and a selenium-rectifier power supply added.

Coupling Problem

The major barrier to operation of a separate self-powered tuner is the difficulty of coupling the high-impedance plate circuit of the converter stage to the grid circuit of the first i-f stage with leads of possibly several feet in length. Link coupling from the remote converter tube to the first i-f stage appeared most convenient because it required no direct connection to the receiver except for a possible common ground lead.

The bar to link coupling is the mechanical arrangement of the plate coil in the coupling system between the converter plate circuit and the grid circuit of the first i-f stage. This coil is mounted inside of a large diameter form on which the sound trap and sound i-f take-off coil is mounted. Any link coil would need to be wound on this outer form, at a considerable distance from the inside coil. In addition, it would need to be fixed in position and would not be readily removable if the remote tuner were to be operated on another receiver.

Experimental link coils wound on both the converter plate coil of the tuner and the receiver proved that the degree of coupling was insufficient; not enough signal voltage was developed at the grid of the first i-f stage.

A simple method of obtaining low-impedance output and sufficient voltage from the remote unit is the addition of a cathode follower to its converter output. The circuit of the complete remote tuner unit is shown in Fig. 1. No components in the RCA front-end need to be changed; it is only necessary to complete the grid return of the r-f amplifier and supply operating potentials to the tubes. The normal capacitor coupling from the converter plate circuit feeds the grid of the cathode-follower stage. Although the latter presents lower capacitance than the grid of the usual i-f stage there'was no noticeable effect on the tuning of the plate coil.

Link coupling is used at the receiver. The signal produced in the cathode follower output circuit is fed through 75-ohm RG-59/U coaxial cable to a four-turn coil wound on a fiber form. Its diameter is $1\frac{5}{8}$ inch and length is 3 inches. This form fits readily over the large sound trap coil of the 630-type chassis.

The considerably greater field produced by the cathode driver stage provides signal voltage at the grid of the first i-f stage nearly equal to that of the directly connected front-end in the receiver. The selector switch of the latter is usually set to an unused high-band channel to prevent beat interference.

Cable length has been as great as forty feet when used for demonstration purposes. Open test leads up to five feet long have been used on a bench and fed between other chassis and equipment cabinets without affecting the picture received.

Smaller coupling coils have been used in feeding other types of i-f systems and occasionally the open coaxial lead has been connected to the grid of the first i-f stage when picture quality was not a factor but it was necessary to determine whether the i-f stages were operating. When used with a receiver having an intercarrier sound system, the 21.25-mc trap on the tuner coil can be open circuited. This may also be advisable with receivers having conventional sound i-f systems unless they are tuned to 21.6 or 21.8 mc.

Television Receiver Transient Analysis

Response of entire television receiver to 100-kc square waves provides convenient method of production quality control. Results, normally plotted on graph paper, can be shown as composite video on picture tube

By JOSEPH FISHER

THE ability of a television receiver to reproduce fine detail and sharp transitions without excessive ringing or smear may be judged by the response of the receiver to a 100-kc square wave. In order that the transient response of the entire receiver from antenna terminals to the picture-tube grid may be determined, this equipment provides means of modulating a standard television picture carrier with the square wave. In addition, a marker generator places time dots upon the oscilloscope presentation so that rise time, transient ringing, and smear can be accurately measured.

Equipment

The transient analyzer comprises four units used in conjunction with three pieces of commercial test gear. The analyzer itself is made up of a regulated 150-volt power supply, a square-wave clipper, a modulator and a marker generator. The complete test setup employs in addition a Ferris model 18C r-f signal generator, a Measurements Corp. model 71 square-wave generator and a Tektronix model 511 cathode ray oscilloscope. For accurate measurement of the transient response of the receiver, the inherent distortion in the measuring equipment must be minimized.

In operation, a 100-kc square wave (5-μsec pulse) produced by the generator operating at maximum output is applied to the input of a three-stage clipper shown in Fig. 1. The rise time of the signal produced by the square-wave generator is 0.2 μsec. The clipper unit reduces this rise time to 0.05 μsec. Signals of either polarity are available at the output, and the amplitude may be varied from zero to two volts peak-to-peak.

The output of the clipper unit is connected to one of two balanced modulators. One of these is for an intermediate frequency of 26.6 mc. The other is for television channel 2 (55.25 mc).

The r-f generator is connected to the modulator input as shown in the circuit diagram of Fig. 2. The bandwidth of the input circuit is ± 10 mc, while the bandwidth of the output circuit is ± 15 mc. Modulation is applied to the cathodes of the two 6BH6 tubes. For overall transient tests the depth of modulation should be about 30 percent, so that any peculiarities of vestigial side-band transmission near 100-percent modulation are avoided.[1,2] A signal input of 0.6 volt peak-to-peak applied to the cathode circuit produces 30-percent modulation.

With the r-f generator attenuator set to 100,000 μv, the open circuit voltage across the 300-ohm balanced output of the modulator is approximately 20,000 μv. Since the percentage modulation of the analyzer remains constant as the r-f input voltage is changed, the output level of the modulator may be changed by means of the r-f attenu-

ator on the generator. If desired, the r-f generator may be left at 100,000 μv and resistance pads having known attenuation inserted in the 300-ohm balanced line connect-

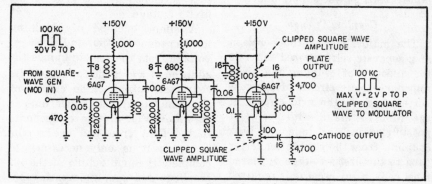

FIG. 1—Diagram of the square-wave clipper that reduces rise time of test pulses

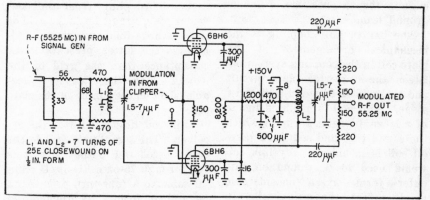

FIG. 2—Modulator for television channel 2 is driven by r-f signal generator and modulated by output of square-wave clipper, Fig. 1

ing the output of the modulator to the antenna terminals of the television receiver under test. The modulator unit can be used as a double-sideband r-f picture generator by impressing a composite video signal on the modulation input terminal. The video signal must have negative sync.

The two-stage vertical amplifier in the test oscilloscope has a rise time of 0.05 μsec, a frequency response within 3 db from 5 cycles to 8 mc, and a minimum amount of overshoot. The probe supplied with the oscilloscope has an input resistance of 10 megohms shunted by 12 $\mu\mu$f. The input capacitance of a picture cathode-ray tube such as the 12LP4 is about 6.0 $\mu\mu$f.

At first thought, it would seem possible merely to replace the c-r tube with the probe when measur-

ing overall transient response. However, most television receivers use series peaking between the final video amplifier tube and the c-r tube grid, and circuits of this type are critical to end capacitance. To eliminate this source of measurement error, c-r tube bases are supplied that have a built-in R-C compensated attenuator, consisting of a 7-megohm resistor shunted by a 15-$\mu\mu$f capacitor. To make measurements, the tube socket is unplugged from the tube base and the socket is plugged into the adapter. The scope probe is then connected to the adapter output connection. This method of measurement insures that the capacitance terminating the lead to the picture-tube grid is the same when either the picture tube or the adapter is used.

A marker generator shown in Fig. 3 is incorporated to place time dots on the oscilloscope presentation so that rise time and transient ringing can be measured accurately. The 20-mc oscillator voltage, producing dots spaced 0.05 μsec apart, is connected to the cathode input of the test oscilloscope. To insure that the dots will remain stationary a quenched oscillator is used. The positive gate, a pulse lasting for the duration of the triggered sweep, is connected to the input of the marker oscillator from the test oscilloscope. The 20-mc oscillator employs a 12AU7 tube held in a non-oscillating state by means of the diode damping across the plate coil. The positive gate pulse raises the cathode potential of the diode damper and the circuit goes into oscillation for the duration of the pulse.

When measuring over-all transient response from antenna terminals to cathode-ray tube grid, for receiver comparison, the following standards have been used:

(1) modulation depth of 30 percent

(2) transition from black to white

(3) 2 μsec sweep

(4) synchronous time dots spaced 0.05 μsec apart

The photograph (A) shows the transient response and test pattern of a receiver in a misaligned condition. The rise time is approximately 0.2 μsec with a definite smear axis lasting for approximately 0.6 μsec. The distance between dots is 0.05 μsec and corresponds to approximately one-hundredth of an inch displacement on a ten-inch picture tube.

The illustration (B) shows the transient response and test pattern of a receiver that is in better alignment. The rise time is approximately 0.17 μsec and the angle of the smear axis is much less than for the first receiver. The transient analyzer was used as a double-sideband television signal generator and was modulated with composite video from a monoscope signal source to obtain the picture illustrated in these photographs.

Recording Transients

A permanent record of the transient response of a given receiver can be obtained either by photo-graphing the oscilloscope presentation or by transferring the response indicated on the scope to graph paper.

A Paillard Bolex Model H-16 camera using Super XX 16-mm reversible film is used to photograph the trace. A hood between the camera lens and the screen eliminates ambient light. The distance between the camera lens and tube face is 42 cm, and pictures have been taken at f:1.5 with an exposure time of 1/30 sec. The oscilloscope used has a green filter and piece of transparent plastic mounted in front of the tube face. The top edge of the plastic is coated with red lacquer and illuminated by a small lamp. Lines scribed in the face of the plastic sheet appear red and are used as calibration marks. To indentify the photograph a small square area is sanded so as to transmit red light, and a semitransparent piece of paper with the identifying number marked in ink is pasted over this area. The illustrations show a receiver identifying number at the lower left-hand corner. The oscilloscope presentation is held to 2 cm to prevent overload on any receivers having an excessive amount of overshoot.

A faster method of recording the information is to transfer the scope presentation to graph paper. It is most conveniently done by scribing nine short horizontal lines on the left side of the plastic between the 2-cm calibration lines. The time dotted transient response curve can then be moved bodily through these calibration lines by adjustment of the oscilloscope controls. The vertical position of each dot as it is moved past the calibration lines is then recorded on graph paper. The X axis of the graph used contains forty equal divisions spaced 3/16 inch apart, each equal to a time interval of 0.05 μsec. The Y axis contains ten equal divisions also spaced 3/16 inch apart. After some experience is gained using this method it is possible to plot the transient response in a few minutes.

Single-Pulse Testing

For more detailed studies of transient response it is advantageous to modulate the analyzer with a composite video signal containing mixed sync, mixed blanking and a single 5-μsec pulse located in the center of each scanning line. The block diagram of the equipment used to produce this signal is shown in Fig. 4.

Horizontal driving pulses from a standard sync generator are applied to two cathode-coupled multivibrators indicated as MV 1 and MV 2. The first multivibrator produces a rectangular pulse with a duration of 30 μsec while the second multivibrator produces a pulse having a duration of 35 μsec. These pulses are differentiated and inverted and the trailing edge of MV 2 is used to trigger MV 3, which produces the 5-μsec test pulse. The trailing edge of MV 1 is used as a trigger for the oscilloscope. The pulse output of MV 3 is applied to a two-stage clipper to achieve a rise time

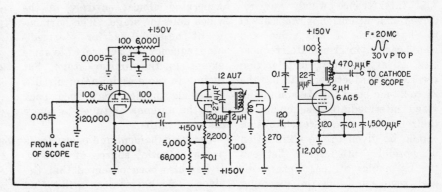

FIG. 3—Marker generator puts time dots on trace accurately to measure rise time and transient ringing effects

of 0.05 μsec with a minimum amount of overshoot. This test signal is applied to a specially designed line mixing amplifier to produce a composite video signal including sync and blanking. This signal can be used to modulate the transient analyzer or may be applied directly to the input of a video amplifier for measurement of its transient response.

Since the scope trigger impulse leads the test pulse by 5 μsec the same dotted type of presentation is obtained.

The equipment described is a double-sideband generator. All transmitters operating in this country employ vestigial-sideband transmission in which all modulation frequencies three-quarters of a megacycle below picture carrier are rapidly attenuated. Our measurements have shown that receivers having a good transient response from the double-sideband generator

produce a good quality picture from a standard television transmitter.

Equal Performance

The original television standards were formulated on the premise that a receiver having the standard RMA selectivity curve, in which picture carrier is located at the 50-percent response point should work

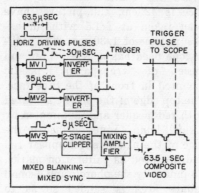

FIG. 4—Method of single-pulse testing using composite video signal

equally well whether receiving a double-sideband signal or a vestigial-sideband signal. As reported by others, the presence of the sideband filter in the transmitter gives rise to a slight leading signal and some smear.

Other writers have advocated the use of phase correction in television transmitters to correct both the distortion introduced by the sideband cutting and the high-frequency cutoff of standard television receivers. The use of such circuits would require industry agreement, a standard station monitor, and the establishment of definite transient standards for television broadcast stations. It would certainly represent an avenue of improvement for television.

REFERENCES

(1) R. D. Kell and G. L. Fredendall, Selective Sideband Transmission in Television, *RCA Review*, p 425, April 1940.
(2) R. D. Kell and G. L. Fredendall, Standardization of the Transient Response of Television Transmitters, *RCA Review*, p 17, March 1949.

Internal Television Receiver Interference

Minimum interference from harmonics of sound and video carrier intermediate frequencies is provided when 21.75 mc is used for the sound i-f. Harmonic-generating capabilities of the video detector are analyzed and optimum frequencies given for intercarrier and

41-mc operation

By B. AMOS AND W. HEISER

ONE TYPE of television picture interference which has received little attention is that caused by harmonics of the video and sound carrier intermediate frequencies. A large majority of television receiver manufacturers still use the 21 to 26-mc band for the sound and video intermediate frequencies of their receivers and consideration should be given to the elimination of possible interference between the harmonics of these intermediate frequencies and the incoming television signal.

The harmonics of the video car-

rier intermediate frequency are generated almost entirely in the video detector stage. The harmonics of the sound carrier intermediate frequency are generated to some extent in the limiter stage, but mainly in the discriminator circuit. These harmonics may feed back into the antenna or tuner by many different paths.

Common filament and power leads are a potential source of trouble. It has also been observed that the video i-f harmonics will feed through the video amplifier and appear on a lead to the cathode-ray

tube socket. Since this is usually near the antenna input connection, feedback may take place along this path. The use of a dual diode, such as the 6AL5, for the video detector and d-c restorer furnishes another path by which these harmonics may reach the leads to the crt socket and then the tuner input.

This problem has become increasingly more important as the sensitivity of receivers has been increased. Use of a single video amplifier, because of economic reasons, necessitates relatively high level video detection, with correspondingly larger magnitude of the video i-f harmonics. The built-in antenna has also served to emphasize the importance of this problem, since obviously a receiver with a self-contained antenna will be more susceptible to interference from these internal harmonics than one

amplifiers and therefore their effect will probably not be noticeable in the video output signal. Since at least part of the 3.85-mc beat on channel 10 will come through the video i-f pass band, we have five channels where harmonic interference may occur.

tion. Figure 4 shows the simplified video detector with the diode resistance neglected and the output voltage waveform for an unmodulated input signal at 26.4 mc of one volt zero to peak.

Schade (*Proc. IRE*, Aug. 1943) has given a method for determin-

FIG. 1—Interference from third video i-f harmonic on channel 5

FIG. 2—Eighth sound i-f harmonic on channel 7 produces a 50-kc beat

FIG. 3—Eighth sound i-f harmonic on channel 7, a 1.55-mc beat for 22.1 mc.

which has its antenna located some distance away. The wide-spread use of unshielded 300-ohm transmission line also increases the possibility of interference from this source.

Harmonics Involved

To illustrate this type of interference in more detail, consider a typical television receiver with a sound carrier i-f of 21.9 mc and a video carrier i-f of 26.4 mc. Table I lists the video carrier frequencies of the twelve television channels, the harmonic present on a particular channel, and the frequency of the beat resulting from the harmonic and the video carrier for the above intermediate frequencies.

The table shows that seven of the twelve television channels have an i-f harmonic existing within their bandwidth. The harmonics existing on channels 3 and 6 give beat frequencies much greater than the 3.5-mc bandwidth of usual video i-f

Figure 1 shows the 1.95-mc beat from the third harmonic of the video i-f interfering with the channel 5 signal. Notice that this interference pattern may be easily mistaken for local oscillator radiation.

Figure 2 shows the 50-kc beat between the eighth harmonic of the sound i-f and the channel 7 signal.

Figure 3 illustrates the interference of this same harmonic on channel 7 for a sound i-f of 22.1 mc, the resulting beat frequency being 1.55 mc. Note that this interference is quite similar to that obtained from an external f-m signal. The harmonics falling in channels 8, 10 and 13 are similar in nature.

In most television receivers, the video detection, because of the relatively large signal required to drive a single video amplifier and the high intermediate frequency which makes small amounts of capacitance important, may be essentially regarded as being peak linear detec-

ing this waveform. Since at point P the discharging capacitor voltage equals the steady state voltage, no transient will occur. After solving for B, it is only necessary to make a Fourier analysis of the output waveform to determine the magnitude of the harmonics. Unfortunately, it has been found that these results do not check experimentally and that the diode resistance must be considered for representative video detector loads.

Detector Analysis

Figure 5 shows the simplified video detector with the diode resistance R, considered. While this resistance will vary with the magnitude of the input signal, for our purposes it will be considered as the average slope of the diode characteristic over the input signal range. The steady-state a-c relations of the load circuit for a sine-wave input are shown at the left of Fig. 5. The alternating waveforms are shown on the right-hand side of the figure.

Note that the steady state current now leads the input voltage by a smaller angle, θ, than before. Since the steady-state capacitor voltage still leads the current by the same angle, θ', as before, we now have the capacitor voltage leading the input voltage. At point P the transient capacitor voltage equals the input voltage and the diode starts conducting. However, since this voltage is different from the a-c steady-state capacitor voltage, a transient effect will take place. We will assume that this dies out by the end of the diode conduction time so that at point Q, the transient and steady-state capacitor voltages are equal.

Assume also a sine-wave variation for the capacitor voltage during the diode conduction period. The angle B may be found in the same manner as before except that θ now has a different value because of the diode resistance.

Figure 6 shows the output waveform alone with its two equations. A Fourier analysis of this waveform was made. Figure 6 gives the results of this analysis for the third and seventh video i-f harmonics generated in a typical video detector by a 3-volt peak input signal.

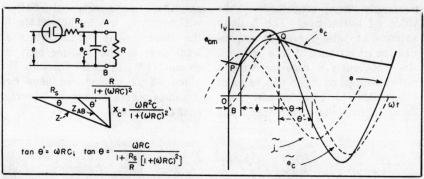

FIG. 5—Simplified video detector with diode resistance

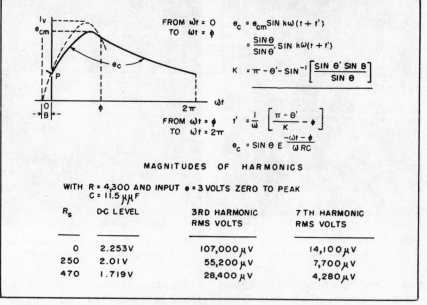

FIG. 6—Output waveform and representative magnitudes of video i-f harmonics

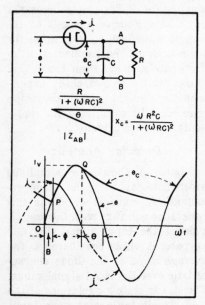

FIG. 4—Simplified video detector neglecting diode resistance

TABLE I
Harmonics of I-F Present on Channels 2—13 Video I-F = 26.4 Mc Sound I-F = 21.9 Mc

Channel	Video Carrier	Harmonic Falling in Channel	Harmonic in Mc	Beat Frequency
2	55.25 Mc			
3	61.25	3rd Sound I-F	65.7	4.45 Mc
4	67.25			
5	77.25	3rd Video I-F	79.2	1.95
6	83.25	4th Sound I-F	87.6	4.35
7	175.25	8th Sound I-F	175.2	0.05
8	181.25	7th Video I-F	184.8	3.55
9	187.25			
10	193.25	9th Sound I-F	197.1	3.85
11	199.25			
12	205.25			
13	211.25	8th Video I-F	211.2	0.05

The results are given for three values of diode resistance for purposes of comparison; the actual tube used, a 6AL5, was considered as having a resistance of 250 ohms. The results obtained for the 6AL5 checked experimentally. From the relatively large magnitude of

the beat frequencies from the harmonics of the video i-f signal as the video i-f is varied.

A study of these two figures will show that a sound-carrier intermediate frequency of 21.75 mc (video i-f = 26.25 mc) appears to give the most reduction in number

tends to aggravate the problems due to the sound i-f harmonics, because of the introduction of additional feedback paths to the tuner.

Intercarrier Sound

The use of intercarrier sound substantially reduces the chances of

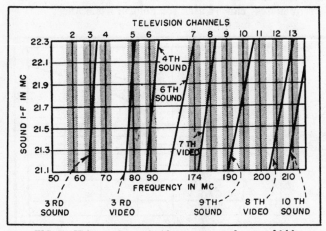

FIG. 7—Video and sound i-f harmonics as the sound i-f is varied

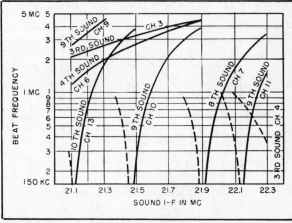

FIG. 8—Beat frequency versus sound i-f. Dotted lines in this and Fig. 9 and 10 indicate harmonic below video carrier

these harmonics, it can be seen that only a small fraction need reach the tuner to interfere with a weak incoming signal. By increasing the time constant of the load so that the output voltage variation between cycles is reduced, the magnitude of the harmonics will be decreased. However, then the load capacitor will be unable to follow high modulation frequencies near 3.5 mc, and distortion will occur.

Minimum Beats

One possible means of reducing the interference caused by these harmonics is to select intermediate frequencies in the 21 to 26-mc band for the sound and video i-f amplifiers that give the least number of objectionable beat signals. Figure 7 shows the location of the various harmonics falling in the twelve television channels as the sound carrier intermediate frequency is varied from 21.1 to 22.3 mc (video i-f varies from 25.6 to 26.8 mc).

Figure 8 shows the frequency of the various beats from the sound i-f harmonics as the intermediate frequency is varied. Figure 9 gives

of objectionable harmonics. With these intermediate frequencies the beat frequencies under 3.5 megacycles are:

(1) A 1.5-mc beat on channel 5 due to the 3rd video i-f harmonic.

(2) A 2.5-mc beat on channel 8 due to the 7th video i-f harmonic.

(3) A 2.5-mc beat on channel 10 due to the 9th sound i-f harmonic.

By moving the sound carrier i-f from 21.9 mc to 21.75 mc, the number of objectionable harmonics has been reduced from five to three.

The amplitude of these harmonics is such that interference may only be noticed under weak-signal conditions. The use of shielded cable for the antenna lead-in and careful chassis layout will minimize this interference. It may be necessary to use a series or parallel resonant trap to stop the 3rd video i-f harmonic from feeding back to the tuner under most signal conditions on channel 5. The other harmonics, being much smaller in amplitude, may usually be eliminated by proper lead dress and adequate bypassing. The use of two diodes of a triple diode-triode tube, such as a 6T8, for the sound discriminator,

interference from any sound i-f harmonics since now these may only be generated in the video detector where the sound carrier is of relatively low amplitude. Therefore the only i-f harmonic interference is due to the video i-f harmonics as shown in Fig. 9.

By selecting a video intermediate frequency of 25.6 mc and using intercarrier sound, the possibility of harmonic interference is almost eliminated since the frequencies of the two offending harmonics lie almost outside the video i-f passband.

The use of intermediate frequencies in the vicinity of 41 mc makes the selection of the actual frequency much less critical than in the 22-mc region. Figure 10 shows the beat frequencies from both sound and video i-f harmonics that are possible for sound intermediate frequencies from 40.9 to 41.6 mc. Notice that only three harmonics fall into any of the twelve television channels. If intercarrier sound is specified, the only harmonic which must be suppressed for the above range of sound i-f is the 4th video i-f which falls on channel 8. Consequently, the exact selection of the sound i-f frequency, say at 41.25 mc, can be dictated by other considerations.

It is also possible, if the tuner image rejection ratio is not sufficiently large (as it may be on the high television channels) for i-f harmonics existing above the local oscillator frequency to cause interference in the picture. For example, consider a receiver tuned to channel 9, with a sound carrier i-f of 21.75 mc, the local oscillator frequency will be 213.5 mc. The eleventh harmonic of the sound i-f is 239.25 mc. The 25.75-mc beat between these two frequencies can possibly appear in the picture (as a 0.5-mc beat) if a feedback path exists. These harmonics, lying above the local oscillator frequency, will not usually cause trouble. However, the possibility of interference from this source should be recognized.

The authors wish to thank Carl Quirk for helpful assistance.

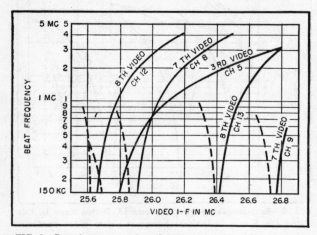

FIG. 9—Beat frequencies from harmonics of the video i-f signal plotted against change in the video i-f

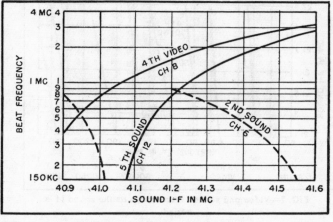

FIG. 10—Beat frequencies from both video and sound i-f harmonics using an i-f near 41 mc

F-M Receiver Design Problems

A survey of design and production techniques, including an evaluation of limiter-discriminator, ratio, and synchronized-oscillator detectors. Hum reduction and the tracing and elimination of regenerative effects in i-f and r-f stages, particularly for a-c/d-c receivers, are described

By E. C. FREELAND

A NUMBER of problems arise in the design of f-m receivers as compared with those for a-m only. Because the f-m system is capable of handling greater dynamic range, the power output of the audio amplifier must usually be about twice that for a-m, and the extended frequency range requires up to 15,000 cycles frequency response.

Distortion must be held to less than 5 percent and efforts must be made to eliminate high-order distortion. A de-emphasis circuit must be switched in for f-m to compensate for the predistortion introduced at the transmitter to improve the high-frequency signal-to-noise ratio. The de-emphasis element takes the form of an R-C low-pass filter with a 75-microsecond time constant for the requisite 6-db-per-octave audio attenuation.

Audio and modulation hum may arise in the filament circuit. Heater-to-cathode leakage in detectors employing balanced discriminators or ratio detectors may cause hum problems in production because one of the cathodes is above ground for audio frequencies. Insofar as a-c/d-c receivers are concerned, the detector must be placed at the low end of the filament string.

Filament-to-grid emission in the converter and local oscillator tubes of a-c/d-c receivers has been found to be a possible cause of frequency-modulation hum in the local oscillator. The use of a low value of grid leak in the order of 15,000 ohms has been found quite helpful. The converter tube should be located next to the second detector in the filament string in order to minimize the a-c filament-to-grid potential. The presence of frequency modulation in the local oscillator is readily detected by applying to the converter grid first an unmodulated i-f signal and then an unmodulated r-f signal and noting the increase in audible hum.

Detector Systems

There are three types of f-m detectors generally used in commercial receivers. They are: the balanced discriminator which is usually preceded by a limiter; the ratio detector which uses a balanced discriminator in a circuit arrangement which accomplishes noise re-

the result that the a-m noise modulation is materially reduced. Resistors R_2 and R_3 are chosen to give screen and plate voltages in the order of 5 to 40 volts to obtain the desired limiter characteristic.

The desired discriminator characteristic shown in Fig. 1C is obtainable with approximate transformer constants such that L_1 equals L_2, M is twice that for critical coupling, and Q is 50 for an i-f frequency of 10 mc. The magnitude of L_1 and L_2 determines the voltage output and is about 5 to 10 mh in commercial design.

The vector diagrams in Fig. 1D show how the voltage output is de-

diagram for the ratio detector. Here, a-m rejection is obtained by a double diode circuit in conjunction with a balanced discriminator transformer which has special electrical constants. The addition of a capacitor C_3 for storage of stabilizing voltage and the reversal of the diode D_1 are the most significant circuit changes over that of the ordinary balanced discriminator. In addition, the diode conductance should be high and the diode load resistors low so as to load the secondary windings L_2 to a point where the secondary Q is approximately one-fourth the unloaded Q.

The open circuit voltage across L_2 is made large compared to that across L_3. The application of the diode load should then reduce the voltage across L_2 such that it is equal to about 75 percent of the voltage across L_3. This effect is illustrated in the vector diagram in Fig. 2B, which also gives the approximate turns relation required to simulate the conditions of this vector relation. Coil L_1 is made large in comparison to L_3 so as to match more nearly the plate resistance of the i-f amplifier and to minimize the effect of the diode load on the primary Q. The value of M is made less than critical so that E_2, within limits, will be a direct function of the diode load.

The application of a carrier signal to the primary of the discriminator transformer will now charge C_3 to a d-c voltage equal to $E_{D1} + E_{D2}$ and this charge will follow low rates of change in carrier level. However, suppose that the carrier level is suddenly increased as by a burst of noise. Capacitor C_3 will essentially act as a short-circuit, consequently the diodes will impose a heavy load on L_2 and the voltages E_{D1} and E_{D2} will increase only by a small fraction of the carrier increase caused by the noise. Conversely, if the carrier level is modulated downward by the noise, C_3 remains charged and reduces the diode current, which results in an increase in E_{D1} and E_{D2}. If the downward modulation drives the

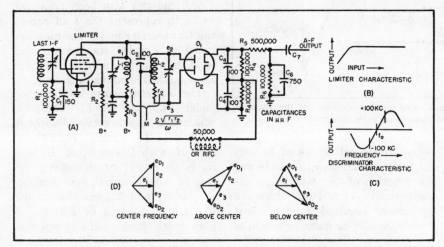

FIG. 1—Limiter-discriminator f-m detector circuit. The graphs show operational characteristics; the vector diagrams explain instantaneous effects

duction without the use of a limiter; and the synchronized-oscillator type of frequency detector, the commercial form of which is known as the Bradley detector, giving noise reduction without a limiter.

Figure 1A shows a schematic for the limiter and balanced discriminator form of detector. Amplitude-modulation limiter action is obtained by the use of a low time constant circuit of the order of 15 microseconds in the grid of the limiter tube and by the proper adjustment of plate and screen voltages to obtain a flat saturation characteristic, as shown in Fig. 1B. The opposing noise voltage appears across the low time constant circuit R_1C_1, with

veloped as the signal goes through its frequency modulation cycle. Voltages e_2 and e_3 are added at 90 degrees to the primary voltage e_1 through C_2 when at the center frequency. As we move off resonance, the phase of the secondary voltage shifts with respect to that of the primary, a difference in diode voltage is obtained and an incremental d-c voltage is produced across resistors R_4. Circuit R_6C_6 in conjunction with R_5 serves as an attenuator and de-emphasis network. The values given are approximately as required for the average audio amplifier of a radio receiver.

Ratio Detector

Figure 2A shows the schematic

diode current to zero, then L_2 is open-circuited and no increase in opposition noise voltage is possible.

The lower the value of R_1 and the greater the Q of L_2 the more downward modulation the detector can handle. However, the lower the value of R_1 the less sensitive is the detector and the greater is the possibility of distortion due to incor-

adds these voltages. Thus the output of the ratio detector is given as one-half E_{D2} minus E_{D1}.

Since no audio voltage can appear across the stabilizing capacitor, the ground can be shifted to the optional location and thus permit the use of a cathode common to that of the first audio tube. However, this arrangement does not

concerned. These balancing resistors are of the order of 1,000 ohms.

Equivalent Circuit of Ratio Detector

Figure 3 may help further to clarify the operation of the ratio type of detector. Figure 3A shows the equivalent circuit under center-frequency conditions, with batteries substituted for rectified and applied voltages. Resistors are substituted for the various impedances. The values shown are only relative for the purpose of illustration and bear no absolute relation to the actual detector circuit. Batteries B_1 and B_2 are fictitious voltages which replace the i-f plate current of the driver stage. The diode load has also been relocated so as to represent the load across the transformer and a one-megohm resistor occupies its conventional location so as to simulate as nearly as possible the actual detector.

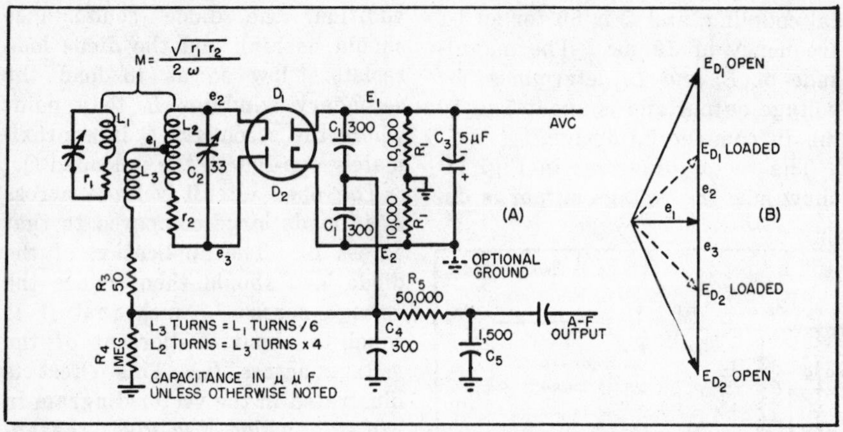

FIG. 2—Ratio detector for f-m. Transformer turns ratios are given and the vector diagram indicates optimum transformer performance

rect phase relations in the transformer. A good compromise design using approximately the constants shown will handle up to 60 percent of downward modulation.

The audio voltage appears across R_4 which, so far as operation is concerned, may be an open circuit and is shown only as a means of clarifying the functioning of the circuit. When the carrier frequency is at its center value the voltages E_{D1} and E_{D2} are equal, and since the two diode currents are in opposition, no voltage will be developed across R_4.

Now as modulation moves the carrier off center frequency such that E_{D1} decreases and E_{D2} increases, the current through R_4 due to E_{D1} is decreased. This is equivalent to an increase being caused by a voltage in opposition to that due to E_{D1}. Since E_{D2} represents such an opposition voltage, the two changes in diode currents produce a resultant change in voltage across R_4 equivalent to connecting the two diode voltage increments in parallel, while a balanced discriminator

permit the effective use of balancing resistors between the diode and the junction of the stabilizing capacitor and load resistor which are sometimes required for the best results insofar as noise rejection is

The diagram shows the detector under a stabilized condition, wherein B_3 may be removed without changing the circuit conditions. Now if, with B_3 connected, B_1 plus B_2 is increased or decreased the change in current will flow through B_3 plus R_{D1} and R_{D2} and the change in E_{D1} and E_{D2} will be 1/100th of that which would occur if the sta-

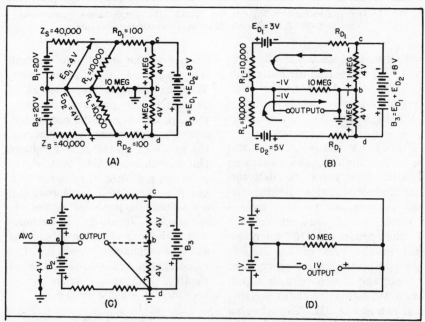

FIG. 3—Simplified diagrams of the ratio detector, with batteries representing voltages and resistances representing impedances

bilizing voltage B_3 were not present. It is seen that a-m has little effect on E_{D1} and E_{D2}.

Figure 3B shows the relations at off center frequency for a change in diode voltages of one volt, Fig. 3D shows voltages in parallel.

Figure 3C shows the equivalent of a circuit used with a grounded cathode. Since the ground has effectively moved from zero to plus four volts with respect to point a and the voltage from a to d is proportional to the carrier strength, point a delivers an avc voltage equal to half the charge on the stabilizing capacitor.

The importance of electrical balance of the secondary of the discriminator transformer cannot be overstressed. The transformer parameters, particularly the impedance of the secondary and its coupling to the primary, are also deserving of careful consideration for the best possible a-m rejection.

A signal generator capable of delivering a signal with simultaneous amplitude and frequency modulation will be of great help. The frequency modulation should be of the order of 100 cycles at ±75-kc deviation and the a-m of the order of 1,000 cycles at 50-percent modulation so that it is possible, by the use of a high-pass filter, to measure the a-m component of the audio output voltage in the presence of the output due to frequency modulation. This filter should have sufficient attenuation to reduce the reading on the output meter, due to f-m, to a negligible value compared to that due to a-m. This check for attenuation can be made by switching off the ampli-

tude modulation and reading the output through the filter when frequency modulation is applied. A synchronized scope pattern of the discriminator characteristic will also show the presence of a-m by

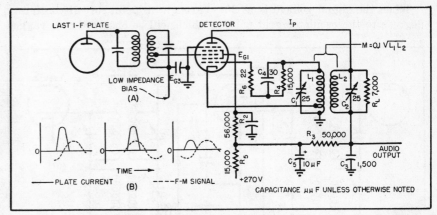

FIG. 4—Typical synchronized-oscillator f-m detector. Plate-current and signal relations are shown at B

giving a wide line. The proper interpretation of this pattern will be of value in determining the f-m/a-m ratio. A ratio of 30 to 1 in voltage, which is about 30 db, is considered satisfactory for field performance. The ratio should be checked at various levels of input.

Figure 4 shows a circuit arrangement which is applicable to the Bradley synchronized-oscillator type of detector. The oscillator circuit may be of the Colpitts or Hartley type, the particular requirement being that it run under class C conditions. The tube is a pentagrid type with the element structure of such design as to give the special characteristics required for best operation as a synchronized-oscillator type of detector and noise rejection.

Frequency modulation as required to maintain lock-in is obtained from a 90-degree component of the oscillator signal injected across L_1 by L_2. The magnitude is controlled by the change in oscil-

lator plate current I_p. The control of magnitude of the 90-degree component is accomplished by changing the total effective bias of E_{G3} plus E_{G1}. This 90-degree component will appear as a capacitance or an inductance across L_1C_1, dependent upon the polarity of L_2. Therefore the reversal of L_2 reverses the phase of the audio output in reference to the carrier modulation.

In most cases the capacitive polarity for L_2 gives the best results and is determined by observing the oscillator frequency when changing the bias E_{G3}. If the phasing is correct, the oscillator frequency will increase with more negative bias.

Load resistance R_L damps L_2 such that its Q is approximately 10. This damping prevents changes in phase of the 90-degree component during the application of frequency modulation to the oscillator under lock-in conditions. When the circuit parameters are properly adjusted, a straight line is obtained between the break-out points and the output is independent of the input.

Figure 4B illustrates the method by which the effective bias of $E_{G3} + E_{G1}$ is made to vary with modulation. This method produces an audio component of plate current through R_3C_3, the amplitude of

Table I—Approximate Performance Data for ±22-KC Deviation

Type of F-M Detector	Location of Measurement	Sensitivity in μV	Output Voltage
Ratio	Driver Grid	100,000	0.3
Bradley	Driver Grid	75,000*	2.0
Limiter and Balanced Discriminator	Limiter Grid	10×10^6	5.0

* Lock-in sensitivity for ± 75 kc

which is a direct function of the carrier deviation. It is to be noted that the time constant of R_3C_3 is 75 microseconds, as required to supply the proper de-emphasis correction to the audio response curve.

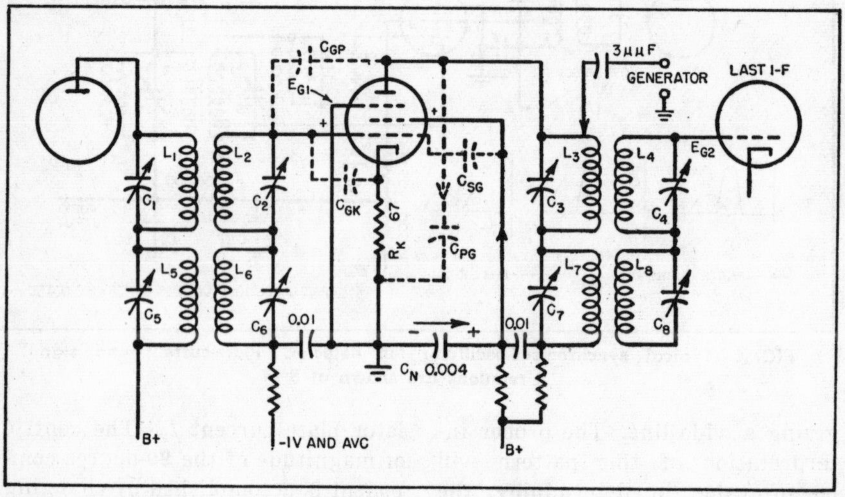

When the signal voltage is at 90 degrees to the oscillator grid pulse

caused by this phase shift is not sufficient to provide the magnitude of 90-degree component required to deviate the oscillator so that it is in step with the carrier, break-out occurs and the audio output goes through a point of discontinuity which will be observed as a ragged

and performance requirements. It is possible to realize a gain of 2 in the antenna stage, and for the r-f stage a gain of 10. Although the theoretical maximum is considerably higher, it is difficult to realize, because of tube loading and other circuit losses that are difficult to control. Keeping these factors in mind, we can estimate the gain requirements and the number of stages to be used in the i-f system.

FIG. 5—Representative a-m and f-m intermediate-frequency stage with notations for discussion of regenerative effects

no change in plate current will take place. It should be remembered, however, that a fictitious capacitance or inductance is present across L_1C_1 under this steady-state condition. The oscillator frequency is in part determined by this 90-degree component as well as L_1C_1 and the padding of C_1 must be such as to compensate properly.

Now let us apply modulation to the carrier such that its frequency is shifted by a small incremental change, and such that the phase shifts in such a direction as to approach the in-phase condition. A small increase in plate current takes place, resulting in a corresponding increase in the 90-degree component of oscillator current across L_1C_1. This change in turn produces enough change in oscillator frequency to satisfy the conditions around the loop.

The converse takes place when the modulation is such as to move the frequency in the opposite direction, as indicated by the out-of-phase condition shown in Fig. 4B. When the change in plate current

type of distortion. When break-out occurs, either the phase shift has gone through 90 degrees or the tube has reached saturation.

While the lock-in sensitivity of this type of detector is as low as 0.3 volt, full advantage of this sensitivity cannot be realized because of the fact that it is necessary to drive G_3 from a source impedance of a few thousand ohms in order to reduce stray oscillator voltage on G_3 due to capacitance coupling in the tube. Experience has shown that excessive oscillator voltage on G_3 introduces objectionable distortion. A more complete description appeared in the October 1946 issue of ELECTRONICS, p 88.

It is seen from Table I that the choice of the f-m detector has a direct bearing on the requirements of the i-f amplifier, particularly so far as gain is concerned. Whether or not an r-f stage is used also affects the gain requirements and overall stability of the i-f system.

The antenna sensitivity may vary between two and 75 microvolts, depending on the price class

Figure 5 shows a typical double-channel i-f stage capable of handling either f-m or a-m signals. The a-m trimmers C_5, C_6, C_7 and C_8 act as bypasses for the 10.7-mc f-m signal, while L_1, L_2, L_3 and L_4 are of negligible impedance at the a-m i-f.

The stage gain at optimum coupling is given by

$$A = E_{G2}/E_{G1} = \frac{G_M (Z_3 Z_4)^{1/2}}{2 + (Z_3/R_p)} \qquad (1)$$

when Z is $\omega L Q$, $L_3 L_4$ is in the order of 8 to 12 microhenrys and Q is about 50 for the average receiver. In most cases the term Z_3/R_p can be neglected. The attenuation at plus and minus 100 kc in a stage employing a transformer with a Q of 50 and adjusted for critical or optimum coupling is 1.2 to 1. It is desirable, from the standpoint of facilitating production padding and field operation in any one of the previously discussed detector systems, to maintain the coupling at slightly less than the critical value.

Regeneration

In many cases the chief problem pertaining to the i-f amplifier is that of regeneration. The cause of regeneration is difficult to locate because in many cases no analytical method seems to be available by which its source can be located.

It is helpful to consider a regenerative or degenerative amplifier as one having a portion of the output signal coupled back to the input in some particular phase relation to the original. Rather than feed the original signal in at the first stage of the amplifier, let it be applied to the last stage in such a manner that the regenerative as well as the original signal will be amplified.

This effect is accomplished as shown in Fig. 5 by applying the so-called original signal from the generator through a small capacitor about 3 μμf to the terminal of L_3, C_3 being adjusted to compensate for the additional capacitance across L_2. The front end of the amplifier has previously been tuned and the detector converted to an a-m type by opening one diode or stopping the oscillator. When the diode is removed, an equivalent capacitance should be substituted in its place to maintain correct tuning. With an amplitude-modulated signal, it is now possible for the audio amplifier to indicate relative signal amplitudes. The feedback signal, if present, is readily removed by shorting L_2 with a 0.01-μf capacitor. The presence of feedback will be indicated by a change in amplitude of the detected audio output.

When the amplifier circuits are tuned exactly to the frequency of the applied signal, the phase angle between the feedback signal voltage and that of the applied signal is usually some multiple of 90 degrees. If under these conditions the feedback is not in phase with the applied signal, the tuned circuits will seek a new frequency such that the several small phase shifts in each circuit will add up to bring the feedback voltage almost in phase with the applied signal. Under this condition the apparent maximum gain is not at the true resonant frequency of the tuned circuits and the selectivity curve becomes unsymmetrical, or if the feedback is of sufficient magnitude the amplifier will oscillate at some frequency, usually within $(1 \pm 2/Q)$ times the resonant frequency of the tuned circuits. If the feedback is small, and at 90 degrees to the applied signal, it may only change the symmetry of the selectivity curve, and it will then be necessary to check for the presence of feedback at frequencies slightly off resonance. The check is still made by observing the change in output due to shorting L_2 with a 0.01-μf capacitor.

The application of this method to the solution of a regenerative problem is relatively straightforward. Since there is no longer dependence upon the front end of the amplifier to provide a source of signal, it is possible to disconnect or short-circuit any point ahead of L_3 without affecting anything other than the regeneration.

To locate the source of feedback,

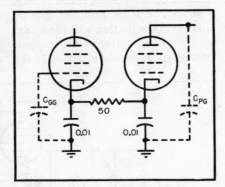

FIG. 6—B-minus decoupling circuit

start at the first stage and, with a 0.01-μf capacitor, bypass successively the grids and plates of each stage until a change in output signal level is noted. Such a point is a source of feedback, but not necessarily the only one.

If the amplifier is oscillating it will be necessary to proceed down the line until a point is reached where the bypass kills the oscillation. Having located the point at which regeneration occurs, it then becomes only a matter of inserting the necessary filtering, providing the feedback is in the low-potential end of the circuit. If it is in the high-potential end, other methods of correction must be applied.

The most familiar type of regeneration, which occurs in the high-potential end of i-f amplifier impedances, is that resulting from grid-to-plate capacitance. The advent of the screen grid tube eliminated, for a time, this type of regeneration, but as better i-f transformers were developed and the individual stage performance improved, it again became the limiting factor so far as stage gain is concerned. This style

of feedback can be found in most low-cost broadcast receivers and manifests itself as an unsymmetrical selectivity curve.

An indication of the magnitude of feedback due to the grid-to-plate capacitance (C_{GP}) is given by

$$\frac{A_f}{A} = \frac{1}{1 - (C_{GP} Q_2 A / C_2)} \qquad (2)$$

when A_f is gain with feedback owing to C_{GP}. It is approximate because it does not include the phase angles which vary with the degree of feedback and approach 90 degrees as the magnitude of the feedback is reduced.

Consider a possible example where C_{GP} is 0.004 μμf, Q_2 is 50, C_2 is 24 and A is 60. By substitution it is found that the amplification with feedback present is twice that without feedback, while good design practice calls for this ratio to be less than about 1.3 to 1. If the overall design is such as to require the maximum possible i-f stage gain, the use of neutralization is a means of reducing the feedback due to grid-to-plate capacitance.

Neutralization

A convenient means of neutralizing the grid-to-plate capacitance involves obtaining an out-of-phase voltage on the screen with respect to that of the plate. The screen-to-control-grid capacitance C_{SG} then sets up a voltage across L_2 in opposition to that of the feedback voltage caused by the grid-to-plate capacitance. The polarity signs in Fig. 5 indicate the conditions of instantaneous polarity as required for conditions of neutralization.

The out-of-phase voltage to be applied to the screen is best obtained by making the screen bypass C_N common to the plate bypass. Now C_N, in combination with the plate-to-ground capacitance C_{PG}, forms a voltage divider across L_3 and the current is in such direction as to obtain the necessary phase reversal across C_N. For purposes of clarity, C_{SG} is assumed small in comparison to C_2 and hence shows only the approximate relation required for balance

$$C_N = C_{PG} \, C_{SG}/C_{GP} \qquad (3)$$

Since C_{PG} is not readily determined and the lead inductance of C_N is also a factor, the conditions for balance are more exactly determined by experimental methods than by calculation from the theoretical equation. Because the 3-μμf coupling capacitor adds to the plate-to-ground capacitance, a more accurate balance will be obtained if this capacitor is reduced to about 1 μμf and its leads dressed down towards the chassis to keep the grid-to-plate capacitance at a minimum. It will then be necessary to readjust C_3 for maximum output to compensate for the change in coupling capacitance. Now with L_1 shorted, observe the effect of C_2 on the output. If C_N is too large the circuit will be under-neutralized and the output will be observed to increase and then decrease as the phase of the feedback is changed by tuning C_2 through resonance from the high-frequency side. The converse is true if the circuit is in the underneutralized condition.

When the correct value of C_N is inserted no change in output will be observed as C_2 is tuned through resonance. The value of C_N may vary from minus 25 to plus 50 percent without increasing the feedback ratio beyond about 1.3 to 1 providing the ratio without neutralization does not exceed 2 to 1, but since allowance must be made for other variables, a tolerance on C_N of minus 10 to plus 25 percent is preferred.

Feedback in F-M Sets

The common type of overall regeneration due to common coupling in the B-plus circuits is familiar to most engineers and need not be discussed here. There is, however, a new problem in the B-minus circuits which will be encountered when designing an f-m receiver incorporating the familiar a-c/d-c circuit in which the chassis is isolated from the power circuits. Figure 6 shows the circuit elements involved in this type of feedback and a filter for eliminating it. The plate-

to-ground capacitance C_{PG} sets up a voltage across the 0.01-μf capacitor connected between ground and cathode of this stage. In the absence of the 50-ohm filter resistor, this voltage would be applied between the grid and cathode of the previous stage through its grid-to-ground capacitance C_{GG}.

Experience would lead one to think that the value of the capacitor between cathode and ground in Fig. 6 should be increased, but a little further investigation will show that a 0.01-μf capacitor will resonate with half-inch leads at about 10 mc.

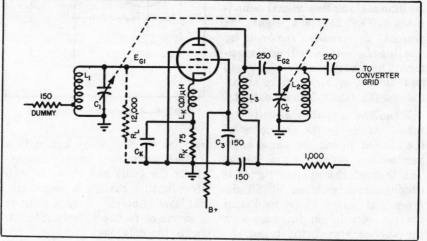

FIG. 7.—R-f stage for a-m and f-m receiver, arranged for discussion of regenerative effects

The choice of this particular value of capacitor for most of the bypass requirements in the i-f amplifier of f-m receivers is then apparent. It is necessary to depart from conventional a-m technique so far as the B-minus circuit is concerned, by adding filter sections between the cathodes of successive amplifier stages.

Filament Feedback

Similar problems to that of the B-minus circuit also exist in the series filament string of a-c/d-c receivers, the feedback being due to the capacitance between the filament and cathode and the filament and grid. In the solution of this problem, series chokes are used and the bypasses are returned to the cathode rather than ground in

order to avoid modulation hum due to a-c potential on the floating chassis. Filters of this type are also often required in a-c receivers to reduce feedback currents carried by the parallel filament circuits.

The combination of the low capacitance used in the tuned circuits of the i-f amplifier and the construction used in high G_m tubes increases to a marked degree the effect of the change in input capacitance when avc is applied to the grid. The proper choice of cathode resistor R_K will introduce an apparent negative capacitance designated as ΔC in the expression

$$R_K = \Delta \, C/C_{GK} \, G_M \qquad (4)$$

This negative capacitance diminishes with G_m at approximately the same absolute rate as that of the positive input capacitance. The value shown in Fig. 5 is approximately that required for correction of input capacitance change of the average i-f stage employing a high G_m tube.

The choice of a converter is somewhat dependent upon overall design considerations. The triode is known to have a much lower equivalent noise resistance than a pentagrid type and therefore will be the most likely choice if no r-f stage is contemplated for one or both bands. If an r-f stage is included as part of the design, a pentagrid converter may give slightly better performance in f-m gain and r-f input resistance.

The chief regeneration problems associated with the converter are the so-called hot spots which are identified as highly regenerative portions of the band. They apparently arise from the oscillator coupling to the i-f through the filament or B-plus leads to produce an antenna frequency, which in turn is coupled back to the antenna or r-f circuits. Bypassing of the hot filament or B-plus leads to chassis through a small self-resonant capacitor of about 100 μμf has been found to be effective in removing this type of regeneration.

R-F Amplification

If an r-f stage is used, degenerative as well as regenerative problems will be encountered. Because the phase relations cannot be maintained so that the two effects cancel, it is necessary to treat each as an individual problem and apply independent solutions.

The acorn tube makes the most

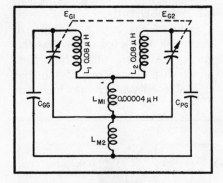

FIG. 8—Circuit to indicate capacitor-shaft coupling

reliable type of diode voltmeter, but still imposes a loss across the tuned circuit. A small series capacitor will reduce the loss, but at the same time reduces the voltmeter sensitivity. Keep leads short.

The gain of the r-f stage shown in Fig. 7 is given by

$$A = G_M \omega L_2 Q_2 \qquad (5)$$

Special design precautions must be taken even to approach this theoretical value. An amplifier tube

working at these frequencies has a low input resistance caused by transit time and the voltage across the cathode-lead inductance L_K. The grid-to-cathode capacitance C_{GK} couples this cathode voltage to the grid circuit in degenerative relation to the applied signal. If the cathode lead is assumed to be one inch long with a diameter of 0.05 inch, the relation

$$L_K =$$
$$0.005\, l \left[2.3 \log_{10} \left(\frac{4l}{d} + \frac{d}{4l} - 1 \right) \right] \quad (6)$$

shows it to have an inductance of 0.01 microhenry. Inserting this value in the equation

$$R_L = 1/\omega^2\, G_M\, L_K\, C_{GK} \qquad (7)$$

and assuming that the grid-to-cathode capacitance of the tube is 5 μμf, while the G_m is assumed to be 4,000 micromhos, gives an apparent load resistance of 12,000 ohms. The shunt impedance of L_1C_1 is found to be about 10,000 ohms and hence R_L has the effect of reducing the Q of the tuned circuit by a factor of approximately two to one.

The effect of the input admittance on the circuit Q of L_1C_1 is readily verified by observing the voltage change across L_1 as the tube is turned on with the signal generator loosely coupled to L_1C_1 through a 2-μμf capacitor. If the loading is of the magnitude indicated by the previous calculations, the voltage will drop about two to one with the r-f tube hot as compared to that with the tube cold. Part of this loading depends upon the transit time of the electrons between the grid and cathode.

The net effect of the tube on the Q of the input circuit can be largely compensated by inserting, in series with the cathode, a small resistor R_K. If C_K is very small and R_K large in comparison to L_K, the phase angle of the feedback will be shifted such that R_L is replaced by a negative capacitance which affects only the value of C_1. If the impedance between cathode and ground has a capacitive phase angle, R_L will be negative, and if sufficiently so, the circuit will oscillate. When a proper adjustment of the cathode

impedance is made, the generator voltage across L_1C_1 will not be affected by turning the heater of the r-f tube on or off.

The importance of short leads and low inductance in common circuit paths is important in r-f stages that employ the conventional type of f-m tuning capacitor. The circuit elements involved are arranged in Fig. 8, where L_{M1} is the mutual inductance to be considered as replacing the coupling in the capacitor owing to common currents through the rotor shaft and frame of the tuning capacitor. The inductance of a ground lead represented by L_{M2} indicates how coupling exists due to the stray ground capacitances of the grid and plate circuits. While this inductance, for the same degree of feedback, can be about five times that of L_{M1}, it will be shown that it is important to use the best possible grounding on the rotor shaft and frame of the tuning capacitor.

Suppose that L_{M1} is physically represented by a copper rod 1/32 inch in diameter and 1/64 inch long. While Eq. 6 cannot be rigorously applied to such small dimensions, we find by substitution that the inductance of L_{M1} is approximately 0.00004 microhenry. Using the relation

$$A_f/A = 1/[1 - (L_M\, Q_1\, A/L_2)] \quad (8)$$

if the stage gain A is assumed to be 20 and Q_1 is 100, it is found that the right-hand denominator becomes zero and a condition of oscillation exists. This analysis, like that of the previous problem relative to i-f regeneration, is only approximate because it does not include the phase angle of the feedback which varies with the degree of feedback and approaches 90 degrees as the feedback approaches zero.

This type of regeneration might be analyzed by a similar procedure to that described for feedback in the i-f amplifier stage. The signal from the generator is applied across L_2 through a small capacitor and its amplitude observed on a high-frequency diode voltmeter connected directly across L_2. If regeneration is present the deflection of the diode voltmeter will change with the tuning of a trimmer across C_1 while C_2 is adjusted for resonance. Regeneration may be due to mutual coupling between the coils, capacitance coupling between the circuits, or mutual coupling owing to common currents in the tuning capacitor. Correction of these various conditions is straightforward. To eliminate the coupling in the tuning capacitor entirely, it may be necessary either to use insulated rotor sections in the gang capacitor or replace it with permeability tuned coils.

Few Crystals Control Many Channels

Local oscillator of multichannel superheterodyne receiver used for aircraft communication and navigation is crystal controlled on 120 channels by only 10 crystals. Conditions for minimum number of crystals, frequency spacing, and stability are described

By W. R. HEDEMAN, JR.

RADIO RECEIVERS, to be sufficiently stable in the very high frequency portion of the spectrum, require crystal control. However, to provide separate crystals for each channel is often impractical.

The need for simplicity is especially great in aircraft equipment operating in the 108 to 132 megacycle band, in which such avigational facilities as localizers and omnidirectional ranges, and such communicational facilities as tower and airways channels and domestic and international operational stations are located. An aircraft flying from coast to coast in the United States can use as many as forty frequencies in this band, if it stays on the same company airway; if the plane is interchanged between companies at terminal points on the way, more frequencies would be used. All these frequencies should be crystal controlled.

To minimize the required number of crystals both to reduce production cost and simplify servicing, a crystal saver circuit has been devised for use in the Bendix MN-85 vhf navigation system receiver.

Circuit Principle

The basic problem to be solved in aircraft receiver design is to provide crystal control on the 120 channels spaced every 200 kilocycles throughout the 108 to 132 mc band. Each frequency must be maintained to better than 0.01 percent. Control must be established using a small number of self-contained crystals, retaining simplicity of design, and providing ease of maintenance and reliable performance. To meet the requirements of frequency stability, a superheterodyne receiver is necessary. This discussion is concerned only with producing the required number of crystal-controlled local oscillator frequencies to obtain the desired number of channels, and does not consider overall receiver design problems.

Consider Fig. 1; the variable oscillator is the receiver local oscillator. It is a free oscillator, capable of being tuned over the frequency band required. The radio-frequency tuning circuits are ganged and tracked with the local oscillator tuning. The actual frequency-rotation curve is unimportant, but an approximation to straight-line frequency-rotation is helpful in stabilizing tuning motor control circuits.

Some of the output of the variable oscillator is fed to the first frequency converter where it is combined with the output of the first crystal oscillator from which one

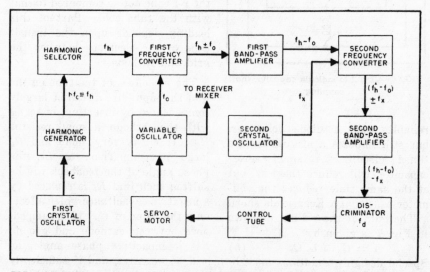

FIG. 1—Variable oscillator of receiver is stabilized on any one of 120 channels in the vhf aircraft band by means of this crystal saver circuit

harmonic is selected by means of fixed tuned selective circuits. The first band-pass amplifier passes the difference frequency of the output from the first frequency converter on to the second frequency converter into which is also fed the output from the second crystal oscillator. This oscillator may be at any one of a number of frequencies as determined by its crystal selector. The second band-pass amplifier passes the difference frequency of the output from the mixer second frequency converter. Output from this band-pass amplifier is fed to a number of fixed tuned discriminators, of the Foster-Seeley type, to obtain d-c output which feeds the control tube. The latter, in turn, operates the servomotor.

Output from the discriminator provides intelligence for frequency correction and for initial tuning. If f_o is the frequency of the variable oscillator, f_h is the frequency of harmonic selected, f_x is the frequency of second crystal oscillator, and f_d is the frequency of discriminator, then

$$f_o = f_h + f_x \pm f_d \qquad (1)$$

when the system is balanced by being on frequency. Either the plus or the minus sign can be selected as the stable frequency position by changing the sense of the servomotor. Thus by a few changes of several variables, many frequencies can be crystal controlled.

Servomotor Control

To explain the motor control circuit it is helpful to examine a simplified form such as is shown in Fig. 2, which shows only a variable oscillator driven by a motor, with a discriminator to determine the oscillator frequency. The direction of motor rotation is determined by relay contacts HC, LC, their coils being energized from the output of the discriminator, through the control tube. Normal plate current of the control tube without discriminator output is sufficient to energize LC only, in which condition the motor will not run.

The discriminator output will reverse in polarity depending on whether the oscillator frequency is above or below the discriminator frequency. If discriminator output is negative, plate current in the control tube will decrease and LC will drop out, causing the motor to run in one direction. If discriminator output is positive, plate current in the control tube will increase and both HC and LC will be energized, causing the motor to run in the opposite direction. Thus the oscillator frequency is maintained equal to the discriminator frequency.

Figure 3 shows the next step in expanding the system, and

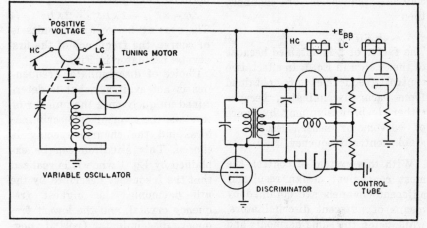

FIG. 2—Basic control circuit maintains variable oscillator at center frequency of discriminator by relay-actuated motor tuning

shows how the plus or the minus sign for the discriminator frequency is chosen. The discriminator, instead of being fed directly from the oscillator, is fed from the output of a frequency converter. The converter mixes the output of a crystal oscillator, and the oscillator to be controlled. A low-pass filter in the converter plate circuit passes the difference frequency. If the oscillator frequency differs from the crystal frequency by the discriminator frequency, the motor does not run. The oscillator frequency may be either greater or less than the crystal frequency to obtain this result. But only one position is stable, depending upon the motor polarity. For, if the os-

cillator frequency is the smaller, then an increase in oscillator frequency decreases the difference between oscillator and crystal frequencies, while if the oscillator frequency is the greater an increase in its frequency will increase the difference between oscillator and crystal frequencies. Thus, by reversing motor polarity, two stable oscillator frequencies are obtained for each crystal used.

In tuning a system of this type, normal procedure is to start the local oscillator tuning from one limit of the frequency band, and to allow it to sweep the band. As its frequency changes, it will pass a position where Eq. 1 will be satisfied; here the servomotor will stop. If for any reason the frequency of the local oscillator changes, the motor again will drive to retune the local oscillator.

In order to save wear and tear on the motor, it has been found advantageous to control frequency only coarsely by the motor tuning, and to obtain fine frequency control by means of a reactance tube operated by the output from the discriminator. Whenever the range of control of the reactance tube is exceeded by slow frequency drifts, the motor restores mechanical tuning to the center of the range of control of the reactance tube. The reactance tube also eliminates frequency-modulation of the local oscillator due to vibration or to other causes, because, being completely electrical, it can act fast enough to eliminate such modulation.

Number of Frequencies

The number of frequencies which can be selected for control is equal to the number of combinations of harmonics, crystals, and discriminators which can be obtained. But for any combination there is one, and only one, stable local oscillator frequency. If H is the number of harmonics used, X is the number of crystals, D is the number of discriminators and N is the number of control frequencies or channels, then

$$N = 2HXD \qquad (2)$$

The factor of 2 is obtained because of the $\pm$ sign in Eq. 1. In effect, two control frequencies are obtained from each discriminator, because either algebraic sign may, by choice of servomotor sense, describe a stable control frequency.

With this system of control, the most convenient design results if adjacent channels are obtained by means of adjacent discriminators, while using the same harmonic and crystal. If x is the channel spacing, then x is also the discriminator frequency spacing designated as Δf_d. If there are D discriminators,

then the spacing between crystals Δf_x is

$$\Delta f_x = D\Delta f_d = Dx \qquad (3)$$

After using all discriminators once, the next higher crystal frequency is selected, and the discriminators are used again. This selection is repeated until the highest frequency crystal has been used, whereupon discriminator polarity is reversed. The lowest frequency crystal then is re-employed with all of the discriminators, but this time the discriminators are used in the reverse order with respect to frequency. The same thing is done with the remaining crystals. If, then, there are X crystals, the spacing between harmonics

$$\Delta f_h = 2Xf_x = 2XD\Delta f_d = 2XDx \qquad (4)$$

The spacing between harmonics is, of course, the frequency of the first crystal oscillator in Fig. 1.

Choice of discriminator frequencies is not arbitrary, but is determined uniquely once the number of crystals, the number of discriminators, and the channel spacing is chosen. This situation can be explained by Eq. 1 when it is realized that the frequency described by the nth harmonic, the highest frequency crystal, and the lowest frequency discriminator (polarity negative) must be adjacent to the frequency described by the nth harmonic, the lowest frequency crystal, and the lowest frequency discrimi-

nator (polarity positive). If these frequencies are f_1 and f_2, respectively then, from Eq. 1

$$f_1 = n\Delta f_h + f_{x\,max} - f_{d\,min} \qquad (5)$$

and

$$f_2 = n\Delta f_h + f_{x\,min} + f_{d\,min} \qquad (6)$$

Furthermore $f_2 - f_1 = x$ because these frequencies are adjacent. Then, subtracting Eq. 5 from Eq. 6

$$f_2 - f_1 = x = f_{x\,min} - f_{x\,max} + 2f_{d\,min} \qquad (7)$$

or

$$f_{d\,min} = \frac{x + f_{x\,max} - f_{x\,min}}{2} \qquad (8)$$

but

$$f_{x\,max} - f_{x\,min} = (X-1)\Delta f_x \qquad (9)$$

That is to say, the difference between the maximum and minimum crystal frequencies is equal to the frequency spacing between crystals, times the number of spaces (the number of crystals less one). But from Eq. 3, $\Delta f_x = Dx$, therefore Eq. 9 becomes

$$f_{d\,min} = \frac{x + (X-1)Dx}{2}$$
$$= \frac{x(1 + D(X-1))}{2} \qquad (10)$$

Equation 10 means that discriminator frequencies are chosen uniquely once channel spacing, number of discriminators, and number of reference crystals are chosen.

Choice of harmonic and crystal frequencies is determined, to some extent, by the local oscillator. The lowest oscillator frequency should be above the highest crystal frequency. The lowest crystal frequency should be above the passband of the first amplifier of Fig. 1, and the highest harmonic frequency should be below its pass-band. This arrangement of frequencies eliminates the possibility of spurious conversion products in the frequency monitoring circuits. With the arrangement shown a 2-to-1 frequency coverage ratio is the maximum possible. However, several other arrangements are possible, by means of which the coverage can be extended to 4-to-1 or 8-to-1.

The usual choice of the number of harmonics, crystals, and discriminators is that which leads to the

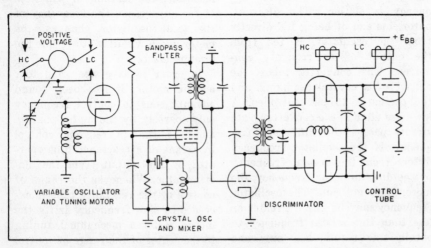

FIG. 3—Frequency stabilization is obtained by beating variable oscillator against crystal oscillator; compare with Fig. 2

smallest total number of elements, and is accomplished if they are all equal in number. If this number is n, then, from Eq. 2

$$n = (N/2)_{11} \qquad (11)$$

Equation 11 is not a necessary condition, and may be departed from if, by such departure, other and more desirable benefits can be obtained; for example, direct channel frequency reading from a simple control box.

Frequency Stability

To estimate frequency stability factors it is necessary to inquire into the values of f_h, f_s, and f_d over the frequency band. From Eq. 10

$$f_{d\ min} = (x/2)(1 + DX - D) \qquad (12)$$

Then, if $D \geq 1$

$$f_{d\ min} = (x/2)DX \qquad (13)$$

From Eq. 4 $f_h = 2XDx$; therefore

$$f_{d\ min} < \Delta f_h/4 \qquad (14)$$

indicating that Δf_h must be considerably less than the absolute frequency f_o because f_h is only a part of f_o. Also $f_{d\ min}$ must then be only a very small part of f_o, because it is less than $\frac{1}{4}\Delta f_h$, as shown in Eq. 14. Thus very large percentage errors in the absolute value of f_d will cause only very small percentage errors in f_o.

The principal frequency error, therefore, will be that owing to errors in f_h and f_x. These frequencies are crystal controlled, and can be held to ±0.005 percent individually by means of temperature controlled ovens. The resultant frequency error due to f_h and f_x collectively will also be ±0.005 percent because these frequencies are of the same algebraic sign in Eq. 1.

Considerable research into the construction of fixed frequency discriminators has revealed a method of construction which provides frequency compensation for temperature changes by means of choice of materials having the proper thermal coefficients of expansion to hold the relative positions of active parts fixed over a very wide temperature range. This construction avoids the

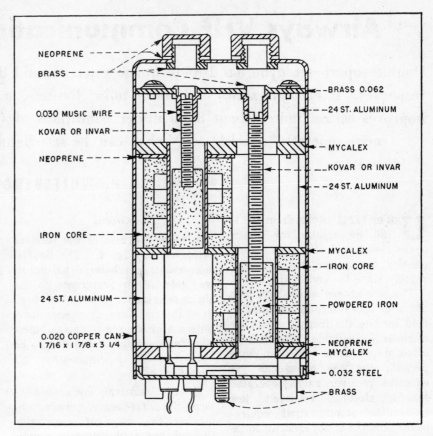

FIG. 4—Discriminator is constructed of compensating materials to insure stability

use of temperature coefficient capacitors to obtain temperature compensation; by it and because of the high Q obtained, only ±0.2 percent of the discriminator center frequency need be allowed for center frequency drift plus reactance tube control. This error will be not greater than ±0.002 percent of the local oscillator frequency. The reactance tube will allow ±2 percent of the band covered in mechanical detuning before affecting output frequency by more than the allowable deviation. Figure 4 shows the discriminator construction.

Under the worst conditions, using ±0.005 percent crystals and a ±0.2 percent discriminator, a final frequency stability of better than ±0.007 percent can be obtained by this circuit over a very wide range of frequencies.

The above circuit lends itself quite readily to remote control over

a very few wires. The description of a radio frequency channel is accomplished by the selection of one harmonic, one crystal, and one discriminator. This effectively breaks channel selection down into successive steps, each step being finer than the one preceding. If it is desired to effect a remote choice of ten possibilities, then ten leads plus a remote switch can be used. In the case at hand, if there were four each harmonics, crystals, and discriminators, then four leads for each variable plus one ground lead, and three remote four-position switches will suffice for the control of 128 channels. In the practical case for the 108 - 132 megacycle receiver, 7 harmonics, 10 crystals, and 2 discriminators are used. The switches in this case are arranged coaxially for conservation of space and ease of reading.

Airways VHF Communications Receiver

Double superheterodyne has 100-db image rejection and 80-db attenuation of spurious responses. It employs series and shunt noise limiters, a noise-balancing circuit that improves series limiter about 8 db under conditions of CAA specified noise test and carrier-operated squelch relay that can be set slightly above ambient noise

By ARTHUR H. WULFSBERG

USE OF FREQUENCIES from 108 to 136 megacycles for air-to-ground communications and aeronautical navigation has expanded rapidly since the end of the war.

The advantages which have won vhf wide acceptance in the aviation field include the increased number of channels available, freedom from atmospheric noise which in turn permits the use of simple yet effective receiver carrier-operated squelch circuits, relatively low transmitter power output requirements, and the use of small airborne antennas of low aerodynamic drag and relatively constant impedance over the frequency range.

To implement the changeover from medium high frequencies to vhf for such functions as Federal Airways enroute communications and airport traffic control in accordance with the recommendations of the Radio Technical Commission for Aeronautics (RTCA), the Civil Aeronautics Administration has recently procured a large number of single-channel vhf fixed-tuned ground station receivers (CAA Type RUQ) specially designed and manufactured to its specifications.

The equipment specifications reflect the wide experience of CAA engineers in this field; in addition to the usual requirements regarding sensitivity, selectivity, frequency stability and rejection of spurious responses, high standards of performance with respect to cross-modulation, desensitization due to strong off-frequency signals and rejection of the effects of pulse-type interference were specified.

Circuits

A block diagram of the receiver is shown in Fig. 1. The double-conversion superheterodyne circuit was selected in preference to the single-conversion type. The high first intermediate frequency permits a high degree of image rejection (approximately 100 db) to be obtained with a single-stage r-f amplifier.

Use of a relatively low second intermediate frequency permits obtaining the required selectivity through use of a two-stage amplifier employing only three double-tuned transformers and also contributes appreciably to the overall frequency stability of the receiver. It has been found that even with very careful compensation of the last i-f circuits, the temperature drift of this section can contribute as much to the overall frequency drift of a high-stability vhf receiver as do variations in crystal oscillator

frequency. The use of a low final intermediate frequency is therefore advantageous.

Although double-conversion systems are usually regarded as being more susceptible to spurious response troubles than single-conversion circuits, careful selection of crystal and intermediate frequencies and provision of adequate selectivity in the r-f, i-f and frequency-multiplier circuits has resulted in obtaining better than 80 decibels attenuation of all spurious responses including image and i-f responses.

The r-f amplifier stage consists of a single pentode operating in conjunction with three capacitor-tuned circuits employing miniature air-dielectric variable capacitors. Removable grooved pins are inserted in holes in each capacitor shaft to provide dial pointers and rotation stops.

To achieve a high degree of selectivity in the input circuit for reduc-

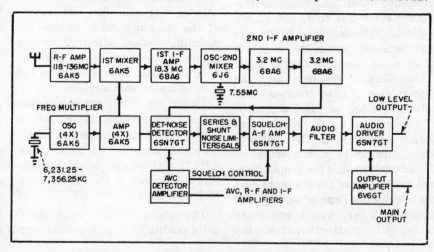

FIG. 1—Arrangement of stages and frequencies in the vhf fixed-tuned receiver

tion of cross-modulation and desensitization effects, this circuit is operated with relatively loose coupling both to the single-turn antenna coupling link and to the grid of the r-f amplifier tube. The high operating Q of the input tuned circuit makes it possible to operate several receivers from a common antenna, the input coupling links of the receivers being operated in series using connecting cables approximately one-half wavelength long. Tests made with several multiple-receiver systems typical of control tower installations indicated very little loss of sensitivity with up to five receivers being operated with frequency separation as low as 200 kilocycles.

The first frequency conversion takes place in a pentode mixer operating with grid injection. To obtain optimum conversion gain and noise figure, this tube is operated at relatively low plate and screen voltages, approximately 50 and 30 volts respectively. The injection signal is obtained from a crystal oscillator-frequency multiplier system consisting of an oscillator-quadrupler and a second quadrupler.

The crystal unit is a hermetically sealed fundamental mode unit of the CR-18/U style operating without temperature control. Crystal oscillator frequency is held to 0.005 percent over the range −10 C to +60 C. Two capacitor-tuned circuits are employed at output fre-

quency to provide a high degree of rejection to signals of undesired crystal harmonic frequencies.

The output of the first mixer circuit is coupled to a single-stage first i-f amplifier employing a pentode and two double-tuned transformers operating at 18.3 megacycles. The second frequency conversion takes place in an oscillator-second mixer circuit which uses a double triode. The crystal oscillator circuit operates at 7.55 megacycles; the second harmonic of this frequency is mixed with the 18.3-megacycle signal to produce the 3.2-mc second intermediate signal which is amplified in a two-stage amplifier. Three double-tuned transformers operating at slightly less than critical coupling provide the desired selectivity characteristics. A conventional diode detector circuit is used.

To achieve a high degree of rejection of impulse-type noise with regard to its effects on receiver desensitization and squelch operation as well as audio output, the special noise limiter circuit shown in Fig. 2 was developed.

Noise Limiter

In addition to the conventional series diode automatic noise limiter, a shunt diode limiter is employed to reduce the effects of noise impulses on the avc and squelch circuits. This diode is biased to about −15 volts and presents a low-impedance path to ground to any

noise impulses exceeding 100 percent upward modulation. This prevents the application to the avc detector of strong impulses which normally desensitize the receiver by generating undesired avc voltage. Since the avc circuit also controls the squelch circuit, undesired opening of the squelch in the presence of noise is also materially reduced.

The audio noise remaining in the output of the series diode limiter is reduced further by coupling a noise signal of opposite polarity in series with the output circuit of the limiter. This noise signal is developed in an infinite-impedance type detector which is biased so that signals of normal modulation are not detected.

The noise output of the receiver is approximately 20 decibels below normal output at 30-percent modulation when tested according to the CAA specified method. The method calls for the application of 10-microsecond r-f pulses at 1,000 pulses per second with amplitude up to 1.0 volt superimposed on a 100-microvolt unmodulated carrier. The use of the noise-balancing circuit results in an improvement of about 8 decibels over the performance of the series diode limiter alone under conditions of this test.

Automatic Gain Control

The avc detector-amplifier circuit shown in Fig. 3 develops a delayed

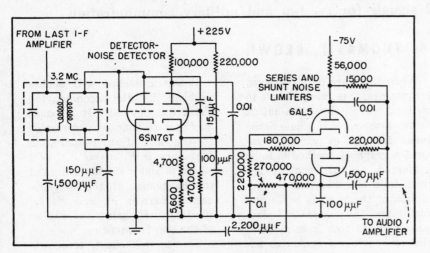

FIG. 2—Detector and noise limiter circuits

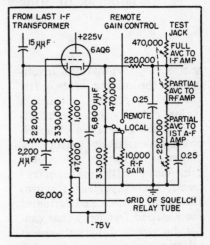

FIG. 3—AVC detector and amplifier

and amplified gain control voltage. In this circuit one diode section operates as a detector circuit, the d-c output of which is applied to the grid of the triode section which operates as a cathode-loaded voltage amplifier. The output voltage is coupled to the avc time constant circuit through the second diode section.

With no carrier applied to the receiver, about 50 volts positive appears on the cathode; this voltage is not applied to the avc line because of the unidirectional characteristic of the output diode. When a signal developing approximately 8 volts audio detector bias is applied, the conduction of the triode circuit is cut off sufficiently to produce a negative cathode voltage which appears on the avc line and increases with increasing signal level. The 1,000-ohm cathode resistor provides d-c degeneration which improves the stability of the circuit and renders it less sensitive to variations in tube characteristics.

An amplified d-c control voltage for operation of the carrier-operated squelch relay tube is also supplied by this circuit. Since this

voltage is not affected by the avc time constant circuit, virtually instantaneous operation of the squelch relay is obtained.

Because of the amplification of the control signal, the squelch circuit completely opens or closes with less than 20-percent change in input signal. This permits the squelch-opening threshold of the receiver, as determined by the setting of the r-f gain control, to be set only slightly higher than the ambient electrical noise level of the receiver location. In addition to the contacts required for audio silencing, the relay is provided with contacts for operation of a panel lamp and external apparatus.

A-F Stages

The audio amplifier circuits are conventional resistance-capacitance and transformer-coupled circuits. A low pass pi-section filter attenuates all frequencies above the normal communications range.

Two audio output amplifiers are provided; one has low-level output for operation with 600-ohm telephone lines, and the other provides up to one watt for operation of

loudspeaker circuits.

The main output amplifier is provided with 12-decibel inverse voltage feedback to improve output regulation. Operation of up to five speakers is possible with negligible change in level when one or more speakers are switched in or out of service. All power input, audio output and control leads are filtered to eliminate possible interference due to any externally applied r-f signals.

Approximately 2,000 type RUQ receivers are now being placed in service in control towers and airways communications stations operated by the Civil Aeronautics Administration. A typical control tower installation includes receivers operating at 121.5 mc for emergency, 121.9 mc for airport utility, 122.5 mc for private aircraft control, and at one frequency in the range 118.1 to 121.3 mc for air carrier traffic control. Airways communications stations will normally be equipped for reception on 121.5 mc, 122.1 mc and 126.7, for emergency, private aircraft enroute and air carrier enroute communications, respectively.

Mixer Harmonic Chart

Chart speeds identification or prediction of spurious frequencies resulting from beating of various harmonic terms in mixer output when one input frequency is **variable as in wide-band signals for tv, f-m and military communication**

By THOMAS T. BROWN

IN MANY APPLICATIONS involving the mixing of two frequencies to produce a third, a major difficulty often encountered is the generation of spurious frequencies by beating together of harmonics. When near coincidence with the required terms, these spurious frequencies cause audible modulation of the required frequency that cannot be removed by subsequent selective circuits.

When there are only two fixed frequencies, it is fairly simple to write down all the combination terms involved. If one of the input frequencies varies, however, a graphical method is to be preferred, as this enables the immediate identification or prediction of the various beats and facilitates the choice of frequency ratios free from modulation or spurious frequencies adjacent to the wanted terms.

It was in dealing with such a problem that the accompanying chart was devised. It is based on the fact that the expression for the value of any combination frequency is $F_s = mF_o \pm nF_x$, where m and n are the orders of the harmonics of the two frequency sources F_o and F_x respectively, F_x being the higher of the two frequencies.

To use this chart, trace upward from the ratio F_o/F_x of the two primary frequencies to the heavy difference line $F_x - F_o$ or the heavy sum line $F_x + F_o$, depending on which output component is being used. From this intersection, trace up and down to the nearest slant lines; from each one, trace left to read the F_s/F_x value for that spurious combination frequency. Alternatively, the spurious frequencies can be figured from the identi-fying notations on the two near-est lines. Where intersections of two slant lines are nearest to the desired intersection, a beat audio modulation equal to the frequency difference

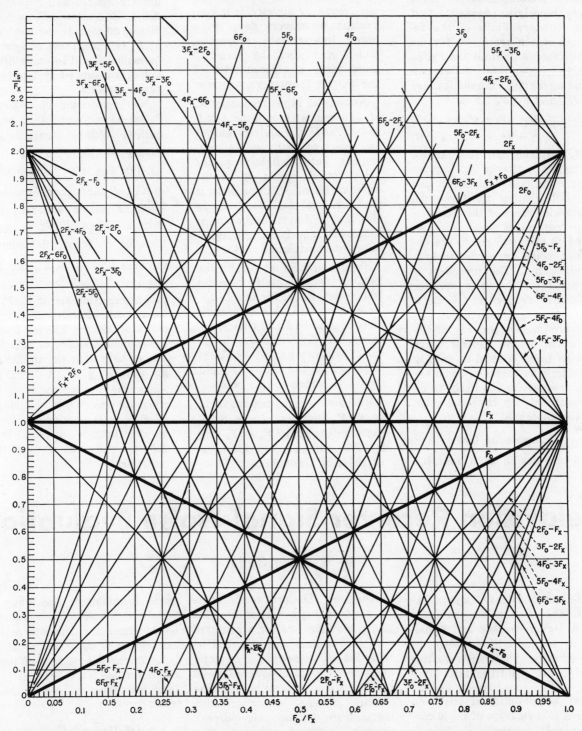

Mixer chart, with F_o and F_x as mixer input frequencies (with F_x the higher) and F_s as desired output frequency. Lines intersected when tracing straight up from value of F_o/F_x represent combination frequencies, values of which can be found either from labels on lines or from scale of ordinates. Only intersections near desired combination (sum or difference) need be considered. When F_x is fixed, ordinate scale can be marked to give frequency directly.

will be produced.

Some problems may require the use of an expanded region of the chart showing higher combination terms. This may readily be constructed to any scale without plotting the whole curve from the origin. Assuming that the boundary limits of the required region are F_{s1}/F_x for the lower frequency limit and F_{s2}/F_x for the upper limit, the corresponding limits on the abscissa are F_{o1}/F_x and F_{o2}/F_x. Now

$$F_s = mF_o \pm nF_x \qquad (1)$$

$$F_o/F_x = [(F_s/F_x) \mp n]/m \qquad (2)$$

Substituting the four known boundary limits in Eq. 2 gives four equations involving m and n. Substituting for these the harmonic orders of the combination frequencies which it is desired to plot, two points are obtained which are connected by a straight line. This procedure is repeated for the main sum or difference frequency ($m = n = 1$) and other desired pairs.

A preliminary scrutiny of the structure of the general chart will be found helpful in quickly showing what order of combination frequencies are likely to be encountered in the particular region concerned.

Example of Use

In the design of a repeater station for a vhf relay, it is common practice to receive the transmission at a given frequency and retransmit at a slightly higher or lower frequency to reduce feedback difficulties. Rather than convert the input to the output frequency directly, it is convenient to convert down to a lower intermediate frequency, which may then be amplified more easily and reconverted to the output frequency.

Assume an input frequency F_x of 250 mc with a 3-mc bandwidth, and a required output frequency of 240 mc. A convenient intermediate-frequency value for F_s would be in the order of 50 mc. The problem is to choose local oscillator frequencies that will avoid radiation of spurious frequencies and minimize intermodulation distortion.

Trying first 50 mc for F_s, the local oscillator value F_o becomes 200 mc and F_o/F_x for this is 0.8. Tracing upward, this is immediately seen to be a bad choice, because the desired main difference frequency line $F_x - F_o$ intersects both the $4F_o - 3F_x$ and $5F_x - 6F_o$ lines at this point.

By inspection, the nearest value of F_o/F_x that it is in a clear space on the heavy $F_x - F_o$ line is 0.775, which corresponds to an i-f value of about 55 mc. Trac-

ing vertically up and down from the intersection of the 0.775 ordinate with the $F_x - F_o$ line, we find that the nearest spurious frequencies occur at $F_s/F_x = 0.33$ and 0.12. Their values are quickly figured as $F_s = 0.33 \times 250 = 83.5$ mc and $F_s = 0.12 \times 250 = 30$ mc. If the bandwidth of F_s is 3 mc, these 83.5-mc and 30-mc beats will be easily filtered out of a 55-mc i-f system by the tuned circuits.

Now converting up again, let F_o be 55 mc and let F_s be the desired 240-mc output frequency, so that $F_x = 240 - 55 = 185$ mc, the frequency required of the second local oscillator to get a sum-frequency output. Then F_o/F_x is 0.298. Tracing up from this value to the sum line $F_x + F_o$, the two nearest spurious frequencies to this intersection are at $F_s/F_x = 1.4$ and 1.2. For 1.4, the output is $1.4 \times 185 = 259$ mc due to the combination $2F_x - 2F_o$. For 1.2, we have both $4F_o$ and $3F_x - 6F_o$ giving $1.2 \times 185 = 222$ mc. Since the bandwidth is 3 mc, adequate selectivity should not be difficult to provide at 240 mc to discriminate against these 259-mc and 222-mc spurious components.

Television Receiver Signal-Noise Evaluation

By D. O. NORTH

THE OBJECT OF THIS PAPER is to formulate the relation between input picture signal strength and signal-noise appearing in the post-detector video circuits. The transformation of electrical quantities into luminance of the viewing screen, and the relative acceptability of television pictures as a function of noise content are not discussed.

Pre-Detector Considerations

A receiver, tested with a dummy antenna at standard temperature T_o yields a noise factor[1] F. This means that the receiver, when used with this dummy antenna, can be regarded as noise-free. The total noise output is in effect considered to originate in thermal noise of the dummy antenna, whose effective temperature is for this purpose taken to be FT_o, as shown in Fig. 1A.

If the voltage gain from open an-

tenna terminals to the input terminals of the detector be taken as $G(f)$, where for convenience G is assumed to be unity for frequencies lying in the flat portion of the receiver's video filter (Fig. 1B), the total rms noise voltage at the detector input is

$$e^2_n = \int G^2(f)\, \overline{de^2} = 4kFT_o\, R_a \int G^2(f)\, df$$
or

$$e_n = \sqrt{4kF\, T_o\, R_a \Delta f} \qquad (1)$$

where $\Delta f = \int G^2 (f) df = 4.0$ mc by calculation from Fig. 1B.

The noise voltage will still be this amount when a real antenna of the same impedance replaces the dummy, provided the real antenna looks into space which exhibits a noise temperature T_o. Otherwise one must replace F by

$$F' = F + \frac{1}{L} \left(\frac{T_a}{T_o} - 1 \right) \qquad (2)$$

where T_a is the noise temperature of space and L is the insertion loss of a line connecting the real antenna to the receiver $(1 < L < \infty)$.

Suppose an existing signal field is producing, during the synchronizing pulse, an rms voltage e_c at the open end of the feed-line, as shown in Fig. 1C. If the receiver is properly tuned this carrier will lie halfway down the sloping skirt of the filter, as shown in Fig. 1B. Hence the carrier voltage produced at the detector input will be $e_c/2$.

Post-Detector Considerations

Assuming unity voltage gain from input to output of a linear detector, the peak detector output during synchronizing pulse and in the absence of noise is $\sqrt{2}\ e_c/2 = e_c/\sqrt{2}$. The standard black-white modulation occupies 60 percent of the spread between peak of synchronizing pulse and zero level. Hence, the peak-to-peak video signal is $0.6\ e_c/\sqrt{2}$ and the rms video noise is $\sqrt{4kF'T_oR_a\Delta f}$. Now let S be the

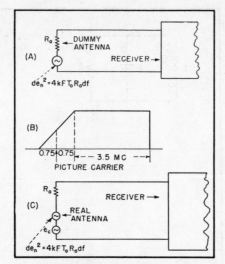

FIG. 1—Measurements of noise factor in television receivers require the use of dummy antennas whose impedance duplicates that seen looking into the open end of the feedline from the real antenna

ratio of peak-to-peak video signal to rms video noise. Then

$$e_c = \frac{\sqrt{2}}{0.6}\ S \sqrt{4kF'T_oR_a\Delta f} \qquad (3)$$

which is the formulation sought.

Setting $k = 1.37 \times 10^{-23}$ joule per degree, $T_o = 290$ degrees Kelvin, $\Delta f = 4 \times 10^6$ sec^{-1} we may rewrite Eq. 3 as

$$e_c\ (\mu v) = 10.5\ S \sqrt{F'}\ \sqrt{\frac{R_a}{300}} \qquad (4a)$$

or

$$e_c\ (db\ above\ 1\ \mu v) = 20.4 + S\ (db) +$$

$$F'\ (db) + 10 \log \frac{R_a}{300} \qquad (4b)$$

As a numerical illustration of Eq.

4, suppose one wants $S = 31.6$ (30 db). If F' (power) $= 15.9$ (12 db) and $R_a = 300$ ohms, then e_c must be 1,328 μv (62.4 db above 1 μv), and half of this or 664 μv must appear on the input terminals of the receiver if it happens to be matched to the feeder.

Conversion of e_c into field strength can be made in straightforward fashion, involving line-loss, impedance transformations and effective length of the antenna. It should particularly be noted that Eq. 4 is valid whether or not the receiver be matched to the antenna feedline; it is important that measurements of F on the bench employ a dummy antenna whose impedance, within the television channel, duplicates that seen looking into the open end of the feedline from the real antenna, because F is a function of this impedance, though usually not a very strong one.

The field intensity expressed in decibels above 1 microvolt per meter is

$$E = 14.8 + S + F' + L +$$

$$20 \log \left(\frac{f}{100} \right) - G \qquad (5)$$

where S is the ratio of peak-to-peak video signal to the rms noise in db, F' the noise factor in db, L the transmission line loss in db, G the gain of the antenna relative to half-wave dipole in db, and f the frequency in megacycles.

REFERENCE

(1) Absolute Sensitivity of Radio Receivers, *RCA Review*, p 332, Jan. 1942.

Selectivity Calculations

Equations, nomograph and chart relate 3-db bandwidth to Q, R, L and f for single parallel-tuned circuits, show effect of adding single or double-tuned circuits, and give bandwidth of up to ten cascaded circuits at attenuation levels up to 100 db

By HAROLD J. PEAKE

USE of the accompanying nomograph and curves allows rapid solution of bandwidth and selectivity problems involving one or more tuned circuits

such as those employed in selective amplifiers.

The material given relates the following quantities: the number of tuned circuits, the half-power

bandwidth of one circuit and the overall bandwidth at any attenuation level. Both single-tuned and double-tuned circuits are considered. For the case of double-tuned circuits, equal primary and secondary Q's with critical coupling are assumed; in either case, all circuits are assumed to be resonant at the same frequency.

In a simple parallel-tuned circuit like that shown in Fig. 1, let R represent the losses in L and C combined with the external loading resistance. Disregarding the loss in C, the Q of this circuit is

$$Q = f_o/\Delta f. \qquad (1)$$

where f_o is resonant frequency and Δf is 3-db bandwidth, both in the same units of frequency. For example, if a tuned circuit resonant at 30 mc is required to have a 500-kc bandwidth, then $Q = 30/0.5 = 60$ is the required Q of the inductor.

If it is desired to adjust the bandwidth by resistance loading,

$$Q = R/2\pi f_o L \qquad (2)$$

Here R is in ohms, f_o is in cycles per second, and L is in henrys. For example, if a 0.75-mc bandwidth with a center frequency of 30 mc is to be obtained with a 1-microhenry coil of $Q = 60$, Eq. 2 gives the shunt resistance due to the coil loss as $R_1 = 2\pi f_o LQ_1$ $= 2\pi \times 30 \times 10^6 \times 10^{-6} \times 60 =$ 11,300 ohms. From Eq. 1, the final Q desired is $Q = f_o/\Delta f = 30/0.75$ $= 40$, which corresponds to a final shunt resistance of $R = QR_1/Q_1 = 40 \times 11,300/60 =$ 7,530 ohms. Now, there remains to determine what resistance R_2 paralleled with $R_1 = 11,300$ ohms produces a shunt resistance $R =$ 7,530 ohms. This is calculated by $R_2 = RR_1/(R_1 - R) = 7,530$ $\times 11,300/(11,300 - 7,530) =$ 22,600 ohms, the required load resistor value.

The 3-db bandwidth of the tuned circuit is also calculable from

$$\Delta f = 1/2\pi RC \qquad (3)$$

where, if R is in ohms and C is in farads, Δf is in cycles per second. In the preceding example, $f_o = 30$ mc and $L = 1\mu h$, requiring that $C = 28 \mu\mu f$. Then, since $R = 7,530$ ohms, Eq.

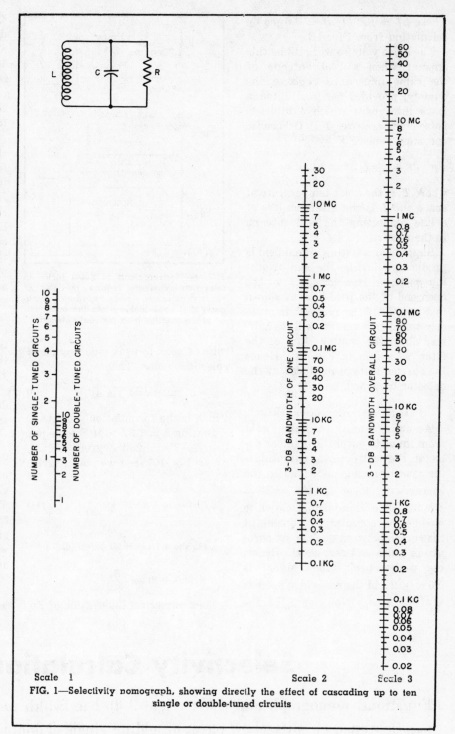

FIG. 1—Selectivity nomograph, showing directly the effect of cascading up to ten single or double-tuned circuits

3 gives $\Delta f = 1/2\pi \times 7,530 \times 28 \times 10^{-12} = 0.75$ mc. This equation is very useful for bandwidth calculation when the external load resistance is much less than the shunt resistance determined by the coil Q; that is, when the effect of the latter resistance can be disregarded.

The preceding discussion applied only to single circuits of the type shown in Fig. 1. The nomograph has been prepared to facilitate bandwidth calculations for amplifiers having several such tuned circuits, all individual circuits having the same resonant frequency and bandwidth. On the nomograph a straight-edge intersecting the three scales connects corresponding values of number of circuits, 3-db bandwidth of one circuit and 3-db overall bandwidth of the combination. The left-hand scale has two sets of gradations, one for single-tuned circuits and one for double-tuned circuits. This nomograph allows determination of any one of the three quantities if the other two are known or assumed.

Example 1. Find the overall bandwidth (at the 3-db response points) of four single-tuned circuits, each with a 3-db bandwidth of 1 mc. Connecting 4 on the left-hand markings on scale 1 with 1 mc on scale 2, read 0.42 mc on scale 3.

Example 2. Find the bandwidth of each transformer if five are to be used to obtain a bandwidth of 0.3 mc. Connecting 5 on the right-hand markings on scale 1 with 0.3 mc on scale 3, read 0.34 mc on scale 2.

Example 3. Find the number of single-tuned circuits required for an overall bandwidth of 1 mc if each circuit has a 2-mc bandwidth. Connecting 1 mc on scale 3 and 2 mc on scale 2, read approximately three circuits on the left-hand side of scale 1.

Other Attenuation Levels

To determine the bandwidth of cascaded circuits at attenuation

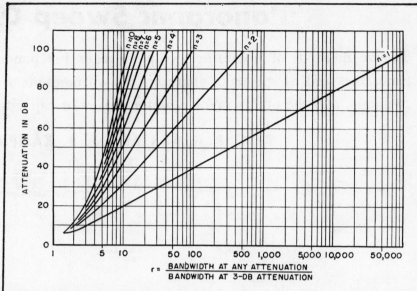

FIG. 2—Chart giving bandwidth at any attenuation up to 100 db in terms of that for 3 db attenuation, for cascading of up to ten single-tuned circuits

levels other than 3 db, use of Fig. 2 is helpful. Here is plotted the ratio of the bandwidth at any attenuation on the vertical scale to the bandwidth at the 3-db level; the number of single-tuned circuits n is the parameter. To determine the ratio r for double-tuned circuits, take the square root of r as read from Fig. 2.

For example, to obtain the 80-db bandwidth of five single-tuned circuits, read $r = 16$. If the 3-db bandwidth were 2 mc, then the 80-db bandwidth is $2 \times 16 = 32$ mc. If the circuits were transformers instead of single-tuned circuits, the 80-db bandwidth would be $2\sqrt{16} = 8$ mc.

Since the values of r at the 6-db points cannot be accurately read from Fig. 2, it is noted here that for single-tuned circuits the 6-db bandwidth is equal to the 3-db bandwidth multiplied by

$$\sqrt{\frac{4^{1/n} - 1}{2^{1/n} - 1}}$$

where n is the number of circuits. For double-tuned circuits the radical becomes a fourth root instead of a square root.

Panoramic Sweep Circuits

Twelve methods of obtaining sweep voltages for panoramic receivers, f-m signal generators and r-f spectrum analyzers. Two methods are electronic, one is electrodynamic, and the others involve motor drives of capacitors, disks or potentiometers

By C. B. CLARK AND F. J. KAMPHOEFNER

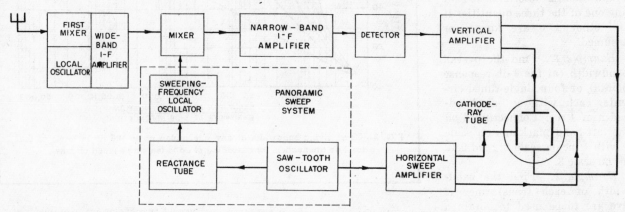

DOUBLE SUPERHET—Most widely used type of panoramic receiver. Second oscillator is frequency-modulated by reactance tube. Each of band of signals entering receiver will beat with local oscillator and pass through wide-band i-f amplifier. At second mixer, each signal is mixed in turn with output of sweeping oscillator, to form series of signals which pass through narrow-band amplifier and eventually appear as vertical deflection on c-r tube. Since oscillator frequency is function of sweep voltage, signals will be positioned across base-line according to their original frequency. No moving parts, but there is limit to sweep bandwidth.

As with other panoramic receivers which operate on receiver i-f, this scheme is useful in identifying signal images and other spurious responses. If receiver is tuned in given direction (say increasing frequency), all true responses will move across the screen from right to left. Image responses will move in opposite direction. Harmonic responses (signals beating with harmonics of receiver local oscillator) may be identified by the rate at which trace moves across screen as receiver is tuned.

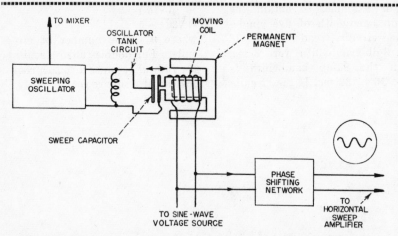

VIBRATING SWEEP SYSTEM—Similar to that in dynamic loudspeaker, driving sweep capacitor whose capacitance change is proportional to displacement from center position. Since coil displacement is proportional to voltage across coil, change in frequency of sweeping oscillator will also be proportional to voltage across coil. Sine wave is used to drive coil, resulting in sinusoidal variation of frequency with time. Spot displacement is linear with frequency, since sine wave is also used for sweep. Since there are two responses per cycle, phase-shifting network is used to make the two traces coincide on c-r screen. One advantage of this type of circuit is that amount of frequency swing is easily adjustable.

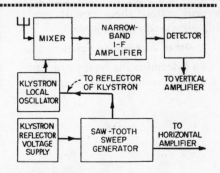

KLYSTRON SUPERHET—Applying sawtooth voltage in series with klystron reflector-voltage supply varies local oscillator frequency at sawtooth frequency. Since circuit has no image rejection, center frequency of narrowband i-f amplifier must either be made so low that the two responses nearly coincide, or so high that image response is rejected by mixer or antenna circuits. Also, there is no way of identifying images by their direction of motion on c-r tube as receiver is tuned, which can be done with all other circuits described.

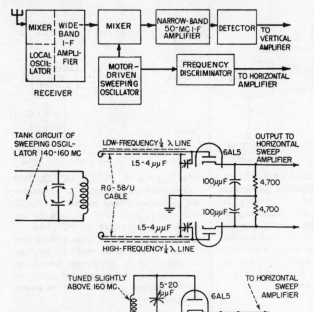

RECEIVER

MOTOR-DRIVEN OSCILLATOR—Useful in receivers where band to be swept is greater than that obtainable by reactance tube method. Frequency modulation of oscillator is accomplished by motor-driven capacitor. Sweep voltage is obtained by coupling frequency discriminator to oscillator. Oscillator output must be constant over frequency range, as discriminator is sensitive to amplitude as well as frequency changes. A ratio detector circuit can be used, although this refinement is not usually necessary.

Example 1—Use with microwave receiver having 200-mc i-f amplifier with bandwidth of 20 mc. To minimize spurious responses caused by harmonics generated in mixer, 50-mc value is chosen for narrow-band amplifier and range of 140 to 160 mc for sweeping oscillator.

Discriminator has two resonant circuits coupled to oscillator, each having separate detector. One circuit resonates just above highest frequency of oscillator, and other is just below lowest oscillator frequency. At center frequency, diode outputs cancel; at other frequencies they combine to give direct voltage which varies linearly with frequency.

Example 2—Useful at frequencies where it is difficult to maintain simple lumped-constant circuits. Output of resonant-line discriminator is balanced with respect to ground, permitting grounding outer conductors of both coaxial lines. No phase-inverter stage is needed to push-pull amplifier for c-r tube. Output of discriminator is about 0.5 volt per mc. With discriminator-type sweeps, oscillator frequency can be varied in any convenient way, without following any definite law of frequency vs time.

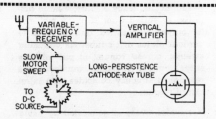

MOTOR-DRIVEN POTENTIOMETER—Used where low sweep frequency is allowable. Sweep voltage is obtained by coupling a potentiometer (which may be horizontal centering control) to motor drive. Received signals will remain visible 5 to 10 seconds, so motor drive must tune receiver through entire frequency band in less than 10 seconds. If there is no backlash in mechanical system, signals received on return sweep will coincide to form single trace. Especially useful where wide frequency band must be covered and receiver must have high sensitivity.

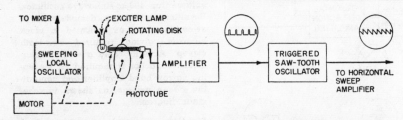

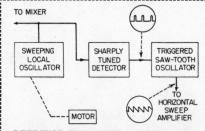

PHOTOTUBE-TRIGGERED SWEEP—May be used if sweep rate of local oscillator does not vary widely. Hole in motor-driven disk should be shaped to give as sharp a light pulse as possible, to avoid jitter in horizontal sweep voltage. Does not require close tolerances between disk and phototube.

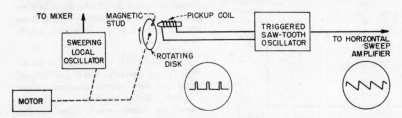

MAGNETICALLY TRIGGERED SWEEP—Trigger pulse is generated by magnetic pickup coil. By careful design of magnetic circuit, enough voltage can be developed to trigger sweep oscillator directly. Mechanical tolerances must be close if device is to generate stable sweep voltage.

DETECTOR-TRIGGERED SWEEP—Part of output from sweeping local oscillator is fed to detector that is tuned to minimum frequency of oscillator. Output voltage pulse is thus generated each time sweeping oscillator frequency equals that to which detector is tuned, at end of oscillator range. This pulse is used to trigger sweep oscillator.

As with other triggered sweeps, sweep speed must be maintained reasonably constant. If speed changes greatly, saw-tooth oscillator may trigger at slightly different phase, causing jitter in horizontal trace. Also, if sweep speed is low, sweep becomes nonlinear, affecting frequency calibration of c-r tube.

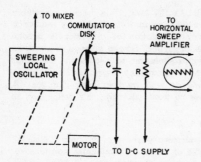

MOTOR-DRIVEN COMMUTATOR—Simple and quite practical if sweep speed is not high. Capacitor C charges through R while brushes are running on insulated section of commutator. When conducting segments come under brushes, C discharges through commutator, giving saw-tooth sweep voltage across C. Sweep voltage can be made large enough to apply to c-r tube plates directly without amplification.

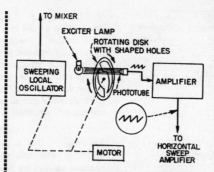

PHOTOELECTRIC SWEEP GENERATOR—Amount of light reaching phototube is determined by size of opening in rotating disk. By properly shaping opening, desired saw-tooth output can be obtained. Since no RC circuits are involved, sweep is practically independent of sweep rate. Main objection to this type of circuit is that exciter lamp supply must be regulated.

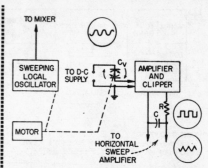

CLIPPED-WAVE SWEEP GENERATOR—Motor-driven capacitor C_v modulates d-c supply at sweep frequency. Amplifier output is clipped to form square wave and integrated by RC circuit to form a back-to-back saw-tooth wave. Resistor R should be made larger than reactance of C at sweep frequency. Must be operated at constant speed, as output voltage is proportional to sweep frequency.

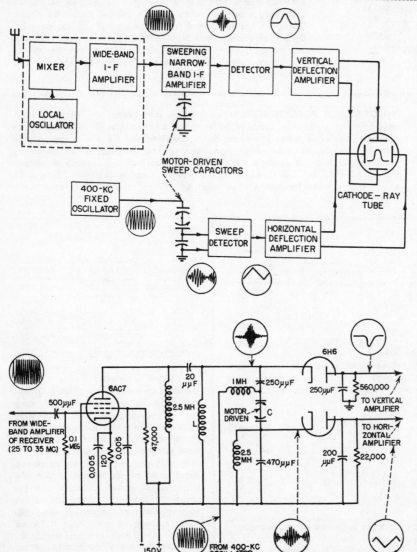

SWEEPING I-F AMPLIFIER—Used successfully in receiver having i-f of 30 mc and a 10-mc bandwidth. Output of wideband i-f amplifier is fed to narrowband i-f amplifier, frequency of which is determined by motor-driven capacitor. Resonant frequency of narrow-band amplifier is varied from 25 to 35 mc, and its output is rectified and applied to vertical plates of c-r tube. As capacitor sweeps across range, output of this stage varies, reaching maximum as resonant frequency coincides with input signal frequency.

Horizontal sweep is generated by using rotating capacitor to amplitude-modulate voltage from 400-kc sine-wave oscillator. Resulting voltage is demodulated in sweep detector, as indicated in block diagram, giving required saw-tooth sweep. Actually, only a single motor-driven capacitor is required for sweeping narrow-band amplifier and generating sweep voltage, as shown in schematic diagram.

Blanking of c-r tube is not required since sweep voltage has same value for given position of capacitor regardless of whether frequency of narrow i-f stage is increasing or decreasing. The sweep rate can be made very low or even zero and presentation will still be correct, providing d-c deflection amplifiers are used.

Resolution of 1 mc can be obtained with 10-mc sweep width described, using ordinary lumped-constant circuit elements. Better resolution can be obtained by using coaxial line circuits, although these are bulky unless intermediate frequency is considerably higher than 30 mc.

Drift-Cancellation Circuit

By FREDERICK A. SCHANER

IN THE DEVELOPMENT of communication receivers in the frequency range of 0.5 mc to 56 mc, especially those for the Armed Services, there are generally three common requirements: Extremely high image and spurious response rejection ratios across the entire tuning range, a high order of oscillator stability, and symmetry of the skirts of the i-f pass band around the center frequency in the order of ± 2 percent. The first requirement can be most readily dealt with through the application of the principle of double conversion throughout the frequency range above 8 mc.

In the case of oscillator stability, it is possible to develop a local oscillator with excellent frequency stability through the use of the so-called Clapp oscillator circuit. Frequency multipliers may be used in cases of high tuning ratio per band where the Clapp oscillator itself is unsatisfactory.

Considering the difficulties in maintaining almost perfect symmetry of the i-f pass band skirts around the center frequency, the first step is to maintain a fixed center frequency. The problem of asymmetry becomes greater as the bandwidth of the pass band decreases and is most acute in the cases where crystal filters are employed to set up the pass band. In the hypothetical case of a 455-kc i-f crystal filter with a bandwidth 100 cycles wide at the 6-db points, a shift in center frequency of a few cycles ahead of the crystal filter will result in an asymmetrical selectivity curve at the output of the filter. Another important step in the solution of this problem is to eliminate regeneration in the entire i-f system so that any change in coupling in the case of a variable bandwidth i-f system will not affect the center frequency.

Figure 1 shows a block diagram of the drift cancellation circuit. This circuit employs triple conversion and hence solves the image rejection problem.

Constant-Frequency Output

The figures superimposed on the connections between the various blocks of the diagram show a simple arithmetical analysis of the principle of drift cancellation. These figures represent a case where the r-f system of the receiver is connected to a primary standard adjusted to 18 mc. The local oscillator is assumed to be operating 4 mc above the r-f and has drifted 87 cycles. This signal is fed into the broad-band i-f amplifier and also into the second mixer. A signal generated by the 455-kc crystal oscillator which employs a crystal of the CR-26/U type is also fed into the second mixer.

The output of the second mixer, which is now 3,545,087 cycles, is fed into a narrow-band amplifier. The output of the i-f amplifier, 4,000,087 cycles, and the output of the narrow-band amplifier, 3,545,087 cycles, are fed into the third mixer with a resultant output of 455,000 cycles. Thus each cycle of local oscillator drift results in a change of one cycle in the frequency of the signal passing through each of the two amplifiers feeding the third mixer and the difference remains at 455-kc.

The output of the third mixer feeds the regular 455-kc amplifier.

The crystal of the reference oscillator is capable of maintaining

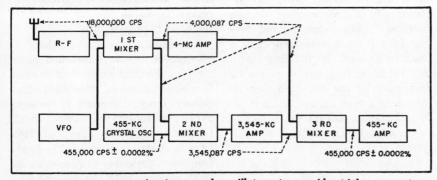

FIG. 1—Arrangement of mixers and oscillators to provide triple conversion

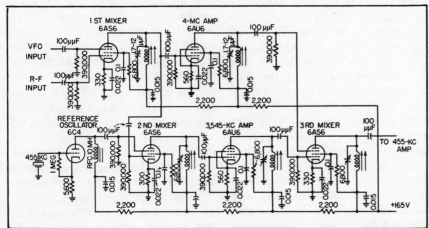

FIG. 2—Complete circuit forms a unit that may be added to a conventional communication receiver

an accuracy of 0.0002 percent per megacycle or slightly less than one cycle in 455 kc. Hence the drift

cancellation circuit eliminates the effect of local oscillator drift on the intermediate frequency and pro-

vides an accurate i-f center frequency. A diagram of the complete circuit is shown in Fig. 2.

Heterodyne Eliminator

Beat-note interference is attenuated by means of a frequency converter which inverts the numerical order of all frequencies either side of a desired carrier and places the off-frequency interference on the cut-off side of an asymmetrical filter

By J. L. A. McLAUGHLIN

OVER-CROWDING of the radio-frequency spectrum has led to the development of a number of signal-separating devices for use in conjunction with standard communications receivers.

The unit described in this article is capable of high attenuation of interference close in frequency to that of a c-w or modulated carrier, with no loss in transmitted intelligence. The system has been employed extensively in radio intelligence work where standard communication receiver selectivity proved to be inadequate.

Principle of Operation

This particular type of heterodyne eliminator is known as an asymmetrical off-frequency inverter, and is suitable for both phone and c-w reception. The circuit diagram, excluding power supply and audio amplifier, which are conventional, is shown in Fig. 1.

The unit is suitable for use with a communications receiver having an i-f of approximately 455 kc. No receiver realignment or circuit changes are required. The inverter is connected to the receiver by a small coaxial cable, the end of which has an insulated loop. This loop is placed over the plate pin of the first i-f amplifier tube and the tube replaced in its socket.

The block diagram, Fig. 2, illustrates the functions of the elements employed. The front end of the system is the off-frequency inverter

(mixer), which consists of two crystal-controlled oscillators either of which will convert the desired carrier to a frequency of 50 kc.

When the oscillator lower in frequency than the desired carrier is employed the numerical order of all off-frequencies will remain unchanged. However, when the oscillator higher in frequency is substituted the numerical order of the converted off-frequencies will be inverted. Should the desired carrier be off the center frequency a positive amount in the first case, this error will appear negative in frequency by the same amount in the second case. This holds true for all frequencies off the symmetrical center frequency of the system.

Filter Design

An asymmetrical high-pass filter is connected to the output of the off-frequency inverter. When an undesired carrier is present in the high-pass side of the filter, it can be frequency shifted to the cut-off side by switching oscillators, whether or not it originally was above or below the desired carrier frequency. In the case of a phone signal, one side of this asymmetrical filter's selectivity is suitable for attenuation of off-frequencies close enough to produce beat-notes and yet broad enough on the other side to permit the passing of speech frequencies without attenuation. This passband can of course be extended

to permit high-fidelity reception.

Toroidal coils make possible the design of a compact high-pass filter with attenuation characteristics suitable for this service. The unit used is sealed in a $2\frac{1}{2}$ x $2\frac{1}{2}$ x 4-inch case. The desired high-pass attenuation characteristic is supplied by two medium-Q 50-kc transformers. They also supply sufficient attenuation to reduce the return peaks on the cutoff side of the fixed high-pass filter.

The high attenuation in the cut-off side of the asymmetrical filter also supplies the selectivity needed for elimination of the audio-frequency image inherent in heterodyne c-w reception. The overall frequency response curve of this filter is shown in Fig. 3. The beat-frequency oscillator is preset at 49 kc to produce with the desired signal an audible beat-note of 1,000 cycles. The audio-frequency image will therefore result from a signal of 48 kc. It will not be heard, since this frequency is down more than 100 db.

The actual value of attenuation of the heterodyne beat-note will depend on the rectifying action of the detector. This action will be influenced by the relative strength of the two signals appearing at the detector's input. Under normal receiving conditions, rectifying action of the detector with regard to the desired signal will be linear. However, in the case of the audio-frequency image the high attenua-

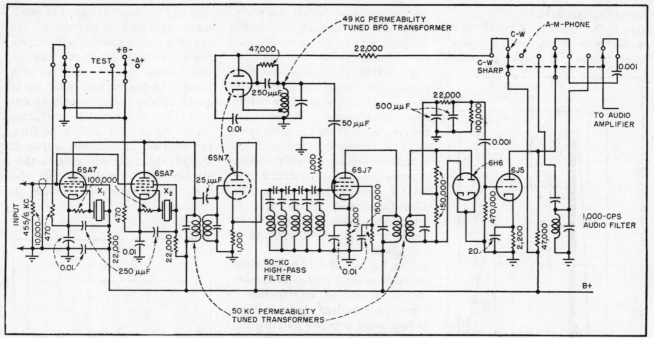

FIG. 1—Schematic diagram of off-frequency inverter. Crystals X₁ and X₂ operate 50 kc above and below the i-f frequency

tion of the filter will weaken this signal's energy to a point where the detector's action becomes square law. These factors must be considered in evaluating the attenuation of beat-note interference both in c-w and phone reception.

To achieve the selectivity required for c-w reception, a sharply peaked audio filter after detection is more practical and economical than attempting to obtain this selectivity in the 50-kc filter. If this filter is made asymmetrical, signal

frequencies can be inverted here as in the first filter by switching the off-frequency inverter oscillators in the front end of the system. Figure 4 shows the response curve of a commercial 1,000-cycle filter suitable for this use. It has an attenuation of approximately 40 db per octave, which makes its asymmetrical frequency characteristics 2-to-1 in db. In other words, an interfering signal 200 cycles above the frequency of the desired one will produce a beat-note of 1,200 cycles in

one off-frequency switch position with an attenuation of 10 db. In the opposite switch position the beat-note is changed to 800 cycles and an attenuation of approximately 20 db is achieved. This 2-to-1 asymmetrical filter gives high selectivity with good economy.

It is well known that extremely selective circuits have a tendency to ring on c-w signals, which destroys their usefulness. An asymmetrical filter, however, will provide considerably more useful selectivity before this ringing state is reached.

Tuning Technique

The tuning of a c-w signal on an asymmetrical off-frequency inverter receiver is simpler and faster than on a conventional type.

The asymmetrical off-frequency inverter eliminates the need for two variable c-w controls found essential in communications receivers for elimination of the audio-frequency image and off-frequency interference. (The variable BFO and the crystal filter phasing control). The phasing control provides a form of asymmetrical response. Because the standard communications receiver lacks the ability to

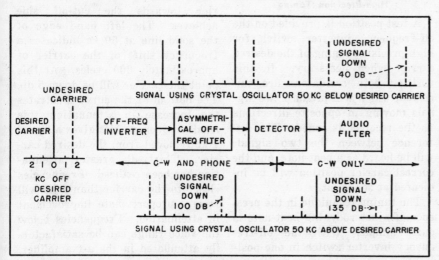

FIG. 2—Simplified block diagram of heterodyne eliminator showing effects of circuit components on undesired carrier with and without off-frequency inversion

invert off-frequencies, it is necessary in the presence of interference in the broader side of the crystal filter, to move the phasing control

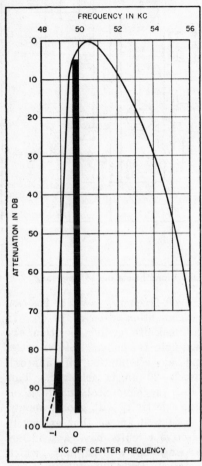

FIG. 3—Frequency response curve, showing attenuation of off-frequencies

to this side for attenuation. These variable adjustments are superfluous in the asymmetrical off-frequency inverter system.

The usefulness of the system for phone reception in the presence of interference is obvious. However, to be practical a sound tuning technique for location of the desired phone signal's carrier in the correct position of the asymmetrical filter has to be employed. In some earlier models, suitable for high-fidelity reception, a tuning indicator connected to a sharply peaked 50-kc carrier amplifier was employed.

Another scheme which suggested itself was the use of a locked-in oscillator to supply an exalted carrier. Such devices are commonly employed in single-sideband communication, where channel separation is sufficient to preclude heterodyne interference. However, in the type of work we are more interested in, where communication is always imperiled by off-frequency interference, the exalted-carrier system proved impractical. Too often the close-in off-frequency interference takes control of the locked-in oscillator, destroying its usefulness.

The tuning of a desired phone signal in present models is by aural means. When no interference is present the desired signal is tuned to maximum response and intelligibility as in normal receiver practice. This is made possible by peaking the nose of the response curve. By rocking the tuning control slightly the operator can sense the cut-off side of the filter by the rapid attenuation feel of this side, compared to the other. The correct location of the carrier (50 kc) will of course be toward this cut-off side, slightly below peak response. A good operator will, with practice, be able to hit this point with high accuracy. However, a tuning error of plus or minus 500 cycles is permissible.

High-Precision Tuning

A test position is provided on the off-frequency inverter switch for high-precision tuning of the desired carrier when necessary. In this position both oscillators are employed, which will produce two signals moving in opposite directions as the receiver is tuned. The difference between the two signals will be heard as a beat-note, and the correct carrier position will be indicated at zero-beat.

The tuning technique in the presence of a heterodyning beat-note is quite simple. With the off-frequency inverter switch in one posi-

tion and the receiver tuned to maximum beat-note interference, the opposite switch position will remove the heterodyne. Since the side the interference was originally on, with respect to the carrier, may be in doubt, this procedure should be followed in both switch positions. When the correct switch position for greatest attenuation is found, a slight detuning will give further attenuation, particularly if the beat-note interference is low in frequency.

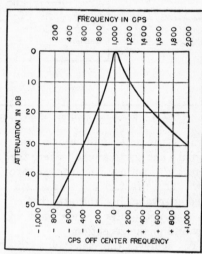

FIG. 4—Frequency response curve for 1,000-cps audio filter

Figure 3 shows the increase in attenuation to low frequencies a slight detuning of the desired carrier towards the cut-off side achieves. The left hand edge of the solid line at 50 kc indicates a frequency shift of the carrier of approximately 300 cycles. At this point the carrier will be down 5 db. The bottom of the curve illustrates the increase in attenuation this small frequency shift gives a signal 1 kc removed from the desired carrier. Thirty-db greater attenuation has been realized. Frequencies closer to the carrier than 1 kc will receive proportionate improvement in attenuation. Frequencies below the voice range can be satisfactorily attenuated in the a-f amplifier.

Remote Control for Radio Tuning

By S. WALD

A noticeable trend in architecture and planning for modern homes is the increased use of built-in broadcast receivers. Their popularity has encouraged the author to investigate the possibilities of remote tuning devices and their application to standard broadcast receivers. The unit discussed in subsequent text and illustrated in the accompanying diagrams has been found to be highly effective, providing for both push-button and continuous remote tuning.

The schematic of the system is shown in Fig. 1. Alternating plate and grid voltages are applied to two miniature thyratrons in a push-pull circuit. The voltage between grid and cathode of each tube lags the corresponding plate voltage by approximately 115 degrees. Thus, each tube fires during a little less than one-half of the positive plate voltage excursion.

The induction motor working windings causes increased heating, it is nevertheless beneficial. The superposition of a continuous current converts the shape of the induction motor speed-torque curves so that the rotor speed is easily controllable by the stator voltage, and it provides a damping or anti-hunt torque proportional to the angular velocity of the rotor, thus preventing overshooting and the resulting continuous mechanical oscillation known as hunting.

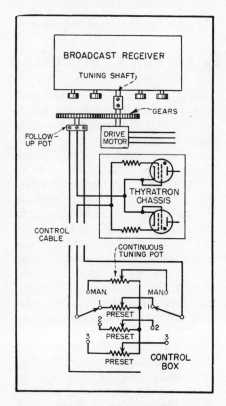

FIG. 2—The continuous tuning potentiometer is calibrated in frequency. The switching may be accomplished by a multi-position rotary switch or a bank of push-buttons

The fixed a-c grid bias is made as low as possible without causing the grid to lose control, and the phase angle is made to approach 90 degrees. A single R-C network is used to supply this grid bias at a

phase angle close to optimum value from the heater winding on the transformer.

Using a radio receiver with the servo-device incorporating a 15-watt Holtzer-Cabot gear head induction motor to drive the 4-gang tuning capacitor, the unit was capable of resetting to within 1,000 cycles at 1,000 kc.

The physical and electrical requirements for potentiometers suitable for use in the control and follow-up circuits are not severe. The unit used for the continuous tuning function should be a wire-wound, high resolution potentiometer having at least 5 to 7 turns of wire per degree of rotation. Preset potentiometers are employed for rapid channel selection. In the circuit shown, one potentiometer per station is required.

The components contained in the control box consist of a number of preset potentiometers, a rotary switch or bank of push-buttons and a continuous tuning potentiometer which is calibrated in frequency.

The circuit is shown in Fig. 2. In operation, one adjusts each potentiometer for each station. Thereafter, whenever the switch connects a particular potentiometer in the circuit, the gang capacitor in the radio receiver chassis is rotated to its correct position for station selection.

Hum Reduction

Intensive investigation of problem results in useful circuit design data for minimizing hum from alternating magnetic fields, electrical leakage, input circuit wiring and heater-cathode leakage current

By ARTHUR F. DICKERSON

SOURCES of hum fall into two broad classifications: hum arising from causes external to the tube which act either upon the tube or upon the components of the circuit, and hum arising within the tube as a result of its characteristics. The first classification covers hum from alternating magnetic and electrostatic fields and from leakage and stray capacitances in the circuit wiring, while the second includes heater-to-cathode leakage and the action of the heater field within the tube.

The most common sources of alternating magnetic fields are transformers and chokes. There are also fields surrounding the wires carrying the heater current and the a-c primary supply, but these fields are extremely small by comparison. The intensity of the field in air at a distance of one inch from a single wire carrying one ampere is in the order of 0.08 gauss, while the stray flux from transformers may be more than a hundred times greater than this value.

The amount of stray flux for a specific transformer is determined by the design of the core and is practically constant over the normal load range. It is difficult to assign a general value to the magnitude of stray flux since it is dependent largely upon the quality of the transformer. However, the order of magnitude for average-quality transformers is 5 to 10 gauss at a distance of two inches from the core in the active portion of the flux pattern.

Figure 1 shows the flux pattern for a transformer with E-type core laminations. This pattern is quite similar to that of an air-core coil, except for modification due to the iron core of the transformer. The pattern is represented as if the transformer were suspended in air. The presence of a chassis of magnetic material will have little effect upon the portion of the field which is two inches or more above the chassis, but the field in the region of the chassis will be extended due to the lower reluctance path. Some advantage may be gained in this respect by the use of vertical-mounting transformers in preference to the half-shell types of construction.

The flux concentration point at which the major portion of the flux leaves and enters the core is located at the ends of the core segment on which the winding is made. This point is further from the chassis in the vertical-mounting transformers, thus reducing the extension of the field. The directional properties of the stray flux are also more favorable in transformers of the vertical-mounting type than in transformers of the half-shell type regardless of the material used in the chassis.

Hum In Receivers

An alternating magnetic field was applied to each tube of three different receivers, which ranged from communications types to commercial five-tube table models and included both f-m and a-m reception. The antenna was disconnected and the gain control advanced all the way. The field intensity was then increased until the hum level became audible above the noise. This was repeated individually for each tube in the set.

It was found that in most cases a field of 50 gauss rms would produce audible hum when applied to the r-f amplifier, converter, i-f amplifiers, or the first audio stage. The power-output stage, and the detector or discriminator stage in circuits employing separate tubes for detector and first audio were

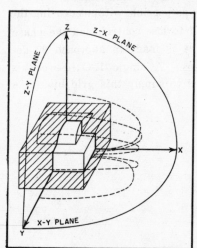

FIG. 1—Stray flux pattern for transformer with E-type core laminations

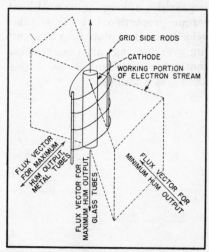

FIG. 2—Tube with concentric type construction

not affected by fields as high as 150 gauss rms.

Since it has been shown that a representative figure for escape flux from a power transformer is 5 to 10 gauss, it would seem that the tube itself offers no particular problem as to hum. In many cases this may be true. However, the value of 5 to 10 gauss was given for a distance of two inches from the core of the transformer, and the field intensity increases inversely as the square of the distance from the transformer. The fields in the immediate vicinity of the transformer are therefore quite high, and placement of critical tubes in this region should be avoided.

In addition, the final measurements in the test outlined were made aurally, and the hum components, both 60 and 120 cycles, were less audible than the higher-frequency noise which was used as

arbitrary unit (microvolts-per-gauss referred to the grid) has been selected since it takes into account the gain of the tube under test as well as the strength of the field, and in addition is more easily referred to the signal level at which the tube is expected to operate.

The hum level of the pentode-type amplifier does not increase linearly with an increase of field intensity, but varies at a rate somewhere between the first and second power of the field intensity, depending upon the reference level of the magnetic field. Thus, for glass-type pentodes, a hum level of about 250 microvolts-per-gauss (referred to the grid) may be expected at field intensities of around 45 gauss, while at 5 gauss the figure drops to around 20 microvolts-per-gauss. Values for comparable metal-type pentodes are in the order of 5 microvolts-per-gauss

construction is shown in a cutaway view in Fig. 2. A major portion of the electron stream can be considered bidirectional along a line which is perpendicular to the plane of the grid side rod supports at the cathode. The magnetic field will deflect the electron stream a maximum when the flux is perpendicular to the path of the electrons. These maximums occur when the flux vector is coaxial to the tube, or when perpendicular to the tube axis and in the plane of the grid side rods. As a general rule, metal tubes and glass tubes which have nonmagnetic side rods show a maximum in the direction normal to the tube axis, while those with magnetic side rods have a maximum in the axial direction, the difference between the two conditions being in the order of 6 to 10 decibels in voltage. Example:

	Axial Flux Hum Voltage at Plate of Tube	*Normal Flux Hum* Voltage at Plate of Tube
6SJ7GT	1.5	0.5
6SJ7	0.02	0.04

The minimum hum condition for all types occurs when the flux vector is perpendicular to the tube axis and normal to the plane of the grid side rods. The minimum is down 30 to 40 decibels from the maximum in glass types and 10 to 20 decibels in metal types, the difference arising from the distortion of the field in the metal type which prevents a sharp minimum.

Since the minimum occurs only

Common Sources of Hum and Their Solutions

Cause of Hum	Maximum Hum Level at Grid	Solutions
Modulation of plate current by stray flux from power transformer		Proper orientation of tube with respect to power transformer
Glass pentode	2.00 mv	Selection of proper size plate load resistance. (See text)
Glass triode	0.30 mv	
Metal pentode	0.10 mv	
Metal triode	0.02 mv	
Heater-to-grid leakage across socket	10 to 15 μv for each megohm of grid resistance and each volt rms of heater above ground	Use of double-ended tubes. Adjustable ground position on secondary of filament transformer
Leakage or induced voltages in closed loops of the input circuit	Up to 75 μv	Use of double-conductor input cable as shown in Fig. 5
Heater-cathode leakage	Currents of 0.04 to 1.0 microampere	Adequate bypassing of cathode for power frequency. Use of low cathode impedances

a reference. In the fields of audio work this is a legitimate criterion, but in measurement and control equipment the hum must be considered on the basis of its rms value.

A considerable amount of data has been taken on several different tube types under varying field intensities and circuit conditions. A few representative figures may be quoted for general guidance. An

and increase only slightly between 5 and 45 gauss due to shielding effect of the metal envelope. Triode types show hum levels of around 30 microvolts-per-gauss at 45 gauss, and 7 microvolts-per-gauss at 5 gauss.

The orientation of the tube elements in a magnetic field determines largely the influence that the field will have upon the output of the tube. A tube of concentric-type

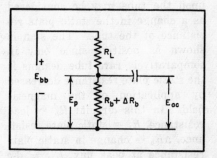

FIG. 3—Equivalent circuit for a tube operating in a magnetic field with no signal on the grid

when the flux is directed perpendicular to the tube axis, rotation of the tube socket is not effective in removing hum when the flux vector is parallel to the tube axis. It is possible to rate a transformer on the basis of the direction of stray flux vectors in the area adjacent to the transformer, normally occupied by tubes. In this respect the vertical-mounting transformer is superior to the half-shell type, since more of its flux is perpendicular to the usual tube mounting axis in the space occupied by the tube elements.

If a tube is operated in an alternating magnetic field, the hum output is a function of the strength of the field, the constants and voltages of the circuit, and the characteristics of the tube. Consider a tube operating in a magnetic field without a signal on the grid. The equivalent circuit is shown in Fig. 3. The effect of the field

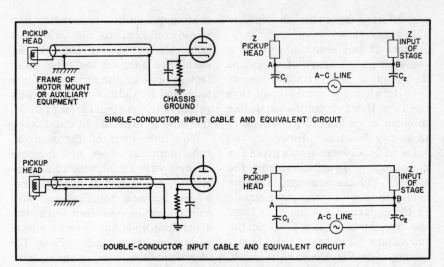

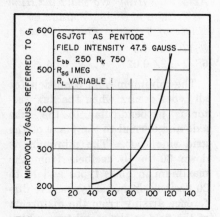

FIG. 4—Variation of hum with gain in a typical pentode amplifier

upon the tube may be considered as a change in the static plate resistance of the tube. The sign is shown as positive since only in comparatively rare tube designs is the static plate resistance decreased by application of the magnetic field. In this circuit: R_L = load resistance, R_b = static plate resistance, ΔR_b = change in static plate resistance at peak flux, E_{bb} = d-c plate supply voltage, E_b = static plate voltage, E_{ac} = peak-to-peak hum output voltage and I_b = static plate current.

Let the subscript 1 refer to

FIG. 5—Actual and equivalent input circuits for single and double-conductor shielded input cable. Reduced hum is achieved with double-conductor cable

normal operation (that is, operation in the absence of a magnetic field) and subscript 2 refer to operation at peak flux value. Then:

$$E_{ac} = (I_{b1} - I_{b2})R_L \qquad (1)$$

$$I_{b1} = \frac{E_{bb}}{R_L + R_b} \qquad (2)$$

$$I_{b2} = \frac{E_{bb}}{R_L + R_b + \Delta R_b} \qquad (3)$$

Substituting Eq. 2 and 3 in Eq. 1

$$E_{ac} = \left(\frac{E_{bb}}{R_L + R_b} - \frac{E_{bb}}{R_L + R_b + \Delta R_b} \right) R_L \quad (4)$$

$$= \frac{E_{bb} R_L \Delta R_b}{(R_L + R_b)(R_L + R_b + \Delta R_b)} \qquad (5)$$

$$E_{b1} = \frac{E_{bb} R_b}{R_b + R_L} \qquad (6)$$

$$\Delta R_b = K R_b \qquad (7)$$

where K is a function of static plate voltage and flux density.

Substituting Eq. 6 and 7 in Eq. 5

$$E_{ac} = \frac{K E_{b1} R_L}{R_b + R_L + K R_b} \qquad (8)$$

$$K R_b << (R_b + R_L) \qquad (9)$$

Eq. 8 may be written

$$E_{ac} = K \frac{(E_{b1} R_L)}{(R_b + R_L)} \qquad (10)$$

Experiment has indicated that K is a function of $1/E_b$ within the normal limits of E_b encountered in a resistance-coupled amplifier. If the peak value of flux remains constant, for a specific tube:

$$K E_b = \text{a constant} \qquad (11)$$

Then

$$E_{ac} = \frac{R_L}{(R_L + R_b)} \times \text{a constant} \quad (12)$$

If the tube is a triode, the static plate resistance R_b is fairly constant for different values of R_L, and in addition R_L is usually much larger than R_b. Equation 12 indicates that if this is the case, E_{ac} is reasonably independent of the circuit values.

In the case of a pentode, R_b decreases with an increase of R_L and since R_b and R_L are of the same order of magnitude:

E_{ac} is a function of

$$\frac{R_L}{(R_L + R_b)} \times \text{a constant} \quad (13)$$

It will be noted that this expression for hum output voltage is quite similar to the familiar formula for output signal voltage:

$$E_o = \frac{\mu E_g R_L}{R_L + R_p} \qquad (14)$$

in which case μE_g represents the constant. The major difference is that R_b in the hum formula is static plate resistance, E_b/I_b, while R_p in the signal-voltage formula is dynamic plate resistance.

It has been shown that in the usual application for triodes ($R_L \gg R_b$ or R_p) the output hum level is relatively independent of the plate load resistance, as is also the gain. Hence, for triodes, the hum level referred to the grid is constant for a given value of flux.

In pentodes, R_b varies inversely with R_L, and R_b remains practically constant over the flat portion of the plate characteristics. Thus, if R_L is increased, assuming R_L and R_p of like magnitude, the gain increases by an amount less than the increase in R_L, but the hum output increases directly as R_L. The hum level referred to the grid of a pentode increases, therefore, with an increase of the plate load resistance as demonstrated in Fig. 4.

The output from metal types was approximately 40 decibels down in voltage from that of glass types. The placement of a close-fitting iron shield over the glass tube reduces its hum to within 2 or 3 decibels of the metal type.

The wave form of hum output for the metal type is for the most part fundamental, with a small amount of second harmonic, while for the glass type it is second harmonic with varying amounts of higher-order even harmonics. This represents an advantage for the metal type when viewed from an audibilty standpoint, since a 120-cycle note is much more readily heard than a 60-cycle note. A 60-cycle note, to sound as loud as a 120-cycle note, must be about 3 decibels greater in power.

Electrical Leakage

The leakage impedance between socket pins contributes hum to stages with a-c heaters to a degree dependent upon grid-circuit impedance, pin placement, socket material and heater-to-grid capacitance. Consider a voltage divider made up of the leakage impedance from heater to grid pin ($Z_{leakage}$) and the impedance from the grid to ground (Z_{grid}). The voltage which appears across this divider is determined by the wiring of the heaters, and the portion of this voltage which appears at the grid is determined by the ratio of grid-circuit impedance to leakage impedance. Since normal Z_{grid} is much smaller than $Z_{leakage}$, the voltage at the grid is almost directly a function of the grid-circuit impedance and in-

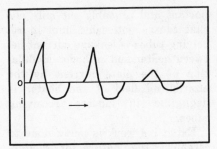

FIG. 6—Typical waveforms of heater-cathode current

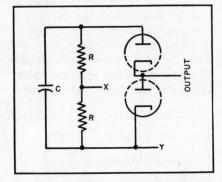

FIG. 7—Basic ratio-detector circuit

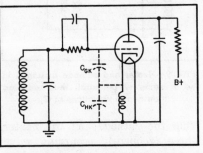

FIG. 8—Variations of C_{HK} may cause hum through frequency modulation of local oscillator

versely a function of the leakage impedance.

Isolantite-type sockets have the highest leakage impedance, which is almost entirely capacitive reactance. Next best are polystyrene, mica-filled Bakelite and black Bakelite, in that order, with varying amounts of resistive components. Since the leakage impedance is predominantly capacitive even in the worst sockets, the elimination of harmonics in the heater supply is of great importance. The leakage impedance decreases for the higher-order harmonics. In addition, the gain of the stage is usually greater. Thus a sine-wave heater voltage appears as a sine-wave output at the plate, but

a complex wave at the heater is reproduced with greater harmonic content at the plate. Representative values of hum to be expected from this source are 10 to 15 microvolts at the grid for each volt of heater potential above ground with a 1-megohm grid impedance.

When one pin of the heater is grounded there is a single source of leakage voltage, which arrives at the grid leading the heater voltage by 90 degrees. When the heater is above ground in a series string, the leakage from both pins arrives in-phase at the grid. However, if the heater is operated from the secondary of a power transformer with the center-tap grounded, the leakage from the two pins arrives at the grid out-of-phase, but with different magnitudes. This partial bucking effect may be utilized completely by grounding the heaters through the center tap of a potentiometer with the outside arms connected to the heater supply, and then adjusting the ground tap for cancellation of the two leakage voltages.

Double-ended tubes such as the 6J7 offer a distinct advantage in the problems of hum from leakage since their grid connections are well removed from the heaters. As an example, the 6J7 has one-tenth the hum of the 6SJ7 in this respect.

Input-Circuit Wiring

Careful attention to the wiring of input circuits will frequently reduce the hum of low-level amplifiers. Figure 5 shows the equivalent circuits for single and double-conductor shielded input cable. Units C_1 and C_2 are leakage capacitances to the a-c line in the amplifier and in the auxiliary equipment. For the single-conductor cable a closed circuit is made which has a portion of the grid-return lead in the loop. This closed circuit may act either as an electrical-leakage path or as a magnetic loop, depending largely upon the line connections and the size of the leakage capacitances.

The resistivity of ordinary shield braid over a single conductor is roughly 0.003 ohm per foot. Capacitors C_1 and C_2 then must be rather large to produce an appreciable voltage drop along the shield. However, in the case of a grounded line, C_2 becomes a direct connection and C_1 may be as high as 0.1 microfarad due to the line-isolation capacitors in certain types of equipment. With a grounded 115-volt line, 0.1-microfarad leakage will produce 50 microvolts across three feet of shield.

Frequently the leakage path of C_1 and C_2 is shorted out by a ground strap between the two chassis or some other direct connection. In this case the closed circuit acts as a magnetic loop subject to the stray flux of the equipment. Hum levels as high as 75 microvolts at the grid have been encountered in tests from this source.

The use of two-conductor shielded cable as shown isolates the input circuit from any closed loop which the shield may make with auxiliary equipment, and thereby prevents a voltage drop which may appear along the shield from being reflected through the pickup impedance to the grid. This principle can also be appplied to the use of ground straps.

The careful elimination of all closed loops in the grounding connections will frequently reduce the hum level of the equipment. Ground connections inside the chassis follow the same pattern, so that the cathode-grounding point and the ground end of the grid circuit should always be connected at the same point on the chassis and should be independent of other circuits, except at the chassis point.

Sources Within the Tube

The heater is the only tube element intentionally carrying alternating current at the power frequency. The heater for indirectly-heated-cathode types is coated with a ceramic-like material to insulate it from the cathode sleeve which encloses it. Of several possible ways for alternating current exciting the heater to act upon the other elements and cause hum, the most im-

portant and probably the only one that causes noticeable hum in receiving tubes is leakage current between heater and cathode. Modulation of the plate current by the alternating field of the heater is negligible in modern receiving tubes.

Extensive work is being done to establish the nature of heater-cathode leakage current but the information is not yet complete. It may be stated that the current is due mainly to a combination of three phenomena: capacitive coupling between heater and cathode, direct (more or less resistive) leakage between them and emission

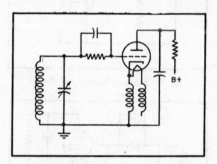

FIG. 9—Heater and cathode arranged to be at same r-f potential, thus reducing hum due to variations of C_{HK}

from the cathode and the heater. Three frequently occurring waveforms of heater-cathode leakage current are shown in Fig. 6 and these indicate that this current is rich in harmonic content.

If the cathode is grounded, current will not affect operation. The same holds for an adequately by-passed-cathode-resistance condition. However, there are numerous cases such as cathode followers, phase inverters, and detectors where the heater-cathode leakage current will cause a voltage drop across the cathode resistance if the heater is returned to ground. To present satisfactory design data it is necessary to consider this current.

The heater-cathode impedance is so large when compared with the normally used cathode resistance that the current source may be considered as a constant-current generator. In tubes which are manu-

factured with an aim to minimizing heater-cathode leakage, current of 0.04 microampere is common where the heater voltage is 6.3 volts rms and where the cathode is returned to one end of the heater through a resistance. In some types such as output tubes, where hum requirements are less severe, this current may be as high as 1.0 microampere. Fortunately the degenerative action of an unbypassed cathode resistance tends to lessen the effect of the leakage current.

A frequently used circuit in f-m sets is the ratio detector. The schematic circuit is given in Fig. 7. The ground is connected either at point X or at point Y. The former is called a balanced ratio detector. The hum due to heater-cathode leakage current is 3 or 4 times greater with a balanced circuit than with the unbalanced circuit obtained when point Y is grounded. The hum increases, of course, with increased resistance values. Also, the larger the resistances, the greater the difference between the balanced and the unbalanced circuit. This is due to the loading effect of the diodes.

The increased use of the higher-frequency television and f-m bands has presented an unusual problem of hum arising in the local oscillator. Figure 8 shows a circuit diagram of a typical high-frequency local oscillator. The a-c heater supply causes the heater-to-cathode

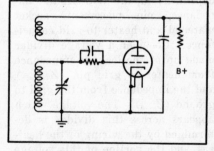

FIG. 10—Tuned-grid tuned-plate oscillator with grounded cathode to minimize effect of variations in C_K

capacitance, C_{HK}, to vary at the power frequency. This arises from either thermal variations of the heater insulation or from mechanical vibration of the heater, possibly from a combination of the two.

Since the heater-to-cathode capacitance appears in series with the grid-to-cathode capacitance, C_{GK}, across a portion of the grid tank, any repeating variation of C_{HK} will cause the oscillator frequency to vary. At the higher frequencies the capacitance in the grid tank is extremely small so that a small change of C_{HK} will vary the oscillator frequency enough to produce an f-m signal in the i-f strip. It has been estimated that a heater-cathode capacitance change of one part in two million in television channel 13 will produce audible hum at the loudspeaker.

Figures 9 and 10 show two methods for minimizing hum from this source. In Fig. 9 the heater and cathode of the oscillator tube are operated at the same r-f potential. This method has proved satisfactory up to 200 mc. The tuned-grid tuned-plate circuit of Fig. 10 enables the cathode to be operated at ground potential.

TRANSMISSION LINES

Open-Wire Line for F-M

Relatively inexpensive 240-foot untuned line feeds commercial 10-kw transmitter output to high-gain antenna. Installation is more efficient than coaxial lines of comparable power handling capabilities and is substantially unaffected by the weather

By JOHN W. ECKLIN

AT this station we have had a number of transmission line problems that may well be common to those faced by engineers in other f-m stations of comparable power. A solution to be described has increased the calculated effective radiated power from 31 to 36 kw.

When the station first went on the air at the present site in 1947 transmitter power of 1 kw was used although an increase to 10 kw transmitter power was contemplated. A 1⅝-inch coaxial line was purchased which was expected to carry 10 kw. However, when the 10-kw rig was connected to the line there was an arc-over and the standing-wave ratio climbed to 3 to 1. This condition was caused by moisture in the line. The importance of keeping the line air tight and under a small amount of pressure cannot be overemphasized. The line, which lasted only a few years, could have been used indefinitely had not this one little item been overlooked and had the line been inspected once a year.

Costs and efficiencies were calculated and it was decided to install a two-wire line. The efficiency for 1⅝-inch coax on the 240-foot run required was 88 percent, for 3⅛-in., 92.5 percent. For two-wire line, the efficiency calculated to better than 98 percent. Because of previous experience with 1⅝-in. and its efficiency the choice lay between 3⅛-in. and two-wire line. The cost of

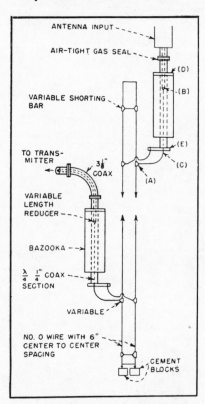

FIG. 1—Overall line and matching methods. Elements A through E are shown in detail in Fig. 2

two-wire line was estimated to be $1,000 which was much lower than the 3⅛-in.

The construction of the two-wire line called for several approximations, for while text books give formulas for calculating quarter wavelengths, specific information on correction for different spacings,

one-line size, and so on couldn't be found.

Number 0 wire spaced six inches was used for the line. By formula, $Z_0 = 276 \log b/a$ so that for this case, $Z_0 = 432$ ohms. The 10-kw transmitter and 4-bay antenna had output and input respectively of 51.5 ohms unbalanced to ground. The problem was to match the balanced two-wire line of 432 ohms to the 51.5-ohm unbalanced line. This was done by using a bazooka which is essentially a 1-to-1 transformer, for taking care of the balanced-to-unbalanced to ground condition and a quarter-wavelength coaxial matching section as an impedance matching device.

The necessary Z_0 for the quarter-wave length transformer is the geometric mean between the Z_0 of the two-wire line and the coax; $Z_0 = (Z_s Z_r)^{\frac{1}{2}} = 149$ ohms. By using 3⅛-in. coax and a ¼-in. bronze welding rod for a center conductor, the matching section was taken care of ($Z_0 = 138 \log b/a$ which in this case gives 149 ohms).

Since the transmitter is only 30 feet from the tower, it was decided to mount a bazooka at both the top and the bottom instead of having a horizontal run. For running the two-wire line up the tower, braces were made at the top and the bottom variable from 25 to 30 inches from the tower (our frequency is 101.3 mc). The wire is threaded at the top and two holes of 0.35-in.

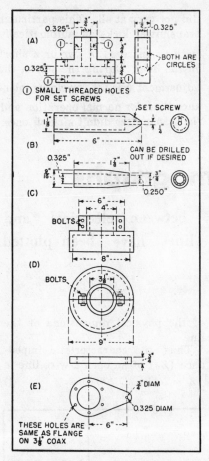

FIG. 2—Dimensions of the parts used for matching sections and line attachment

diameter drilled in the top and bottom brace.

At the top, where the wire is threaded, four nuts are used. One is used at the underside of the top brace to hold a copper bar snug against the brace. Three nuts are used on top of the brace to give less chance of stripping the threads on the wire and letting it fall. At the bottom, after passing through the 6-inch-spaced holes on the brace, a 300-pound concrete weight is placed on each wire to keep it taut.

To maintain the wires the proper distance from the towers, and to prevent their swaying, quarter-wave shorted standoff insulators are used at staggered distances averaging 20 feet. If each insulator is separated by exactly the same distance a mechanical resonance may be set up during a bad windstorm causing the wire to vibrate.

When these standoffs are exactly quarter-wave at the operating freqency they have a high impedance which is a pure resistance.

Half-inch bronze round stock was used, and for our frequency they were made 30 in. long, of which 8 in. was threaded. Then by drilling two half-inch holes 6 inches apart in a horizontal crosspiece of the tower, and by using two nuts, one on each side of the tower crosspiece, we had a variable quarter-wave standoff insulator. On the tower facing the line a copper strap, 8 inches long by $1\frac{1}{2}$ in. wide with holes drilled identical to those in the tower, is placed. This gives a good low resistance short raising the Q and the effective impedance and providing a low-loss standoff. These were tuned with the swr meter in the transmitter. They can be calculated, however.

A perfect short would have to be 18 in. in diameter but the crosspieces of the tower don't even approach this figure. If the short is the same size as the material in the standoff then the six inches of the short has to be taken into consideration in the length of the standoff. With a perfect short, the standoff will be a quarter wavelength from the tower. When it was assumed that the crosspieces were a perfect short, this turned out to be true within the limits of experimental error. We used a velocity constant of 0.96 and the formula for a quarter wavelength in inches given by $2{,}950 \times V/f_{mc}$.

When connected according to calculations, this line had an swr of 1.8 to 1. The change was made from the old $1\frac{5}{8}$-in. coax to the two-wire line with no loss of time on the air. None of the different units was critical. With additional tuning the swr was brought down to 1.4 to 1.

Constructing the Bazookas

For best results the diameter of the bazooka should be two to three times the diameter of the coax. We used a diameter of nine inches. A bazooka isn't at all critical as to

length; if designed for 100 mc it will work satisfactorily over the f-m band. For best results and lowest swr it should be adjusted to exact frequency. Flat copper sheet $\frac{1}{8}$ in. thick and 30 in. wide was rolled and silver soldered for a diameter of 9 in.

Figure 1 (section D) and Fig. 2D show the construction of the bazooka short-circuit. The distance from the bottom of the bazooka to the connector (Fig. 1 and 2E) shouldn't be over two or three inches. The length of the bazooka from the short is calculated in inches by the formula $2{,}950 \times 0.96/f_{mc}$.

The 149-ohm impedance transformer was constructed as follows. A four-foot length of $3\frac{1}{8}$-in. coax (outer conductor) was used which also is part of the bazooka. A length of center conductor equal to $(2{,}950 \times 0.96/f_{mc}) + 5$ inches was cut and the reducer in Fig. 1 and 2B inserted. To this is added the $\frac{1}{4}$-in. welding rod with the adapter reducer shown in Fig. 1 and 2C.

The $\frac{1}{4}$-in. welding rod should be silver soldered to the No. 0 line with the adapter (Fig. 2C) before starting any of the transformer construction. The connector shown in Fig. 1 and 2E is used to maintain the 6-in. line spacing. The two No. 0 wires, one from the connector in Fig. 2E and one from the adapter in Fig. 2C are connected to the two-wire line with the connectors shown in Fig. 2A.

It is important to keep the leads from the bazooka to the two-wire line the same length and spaced 6 inches. The No. 0 wire leading from the connector (Fig. 2E) is threaded and a nut placed on each side of the connector.

The matching section is supported by the use of a commercially available gas seal. Such a unit is generally placed between two lengths of coaxial line at the output of a transmitter. By this means, pressure is maintained up the exterior line even though in the transmitter building it isn't kept air tight. Besides holding up the impedance-matching transformer this unit also makes it possible to pressurize the antenna. On the flange in the gas seal used for joining the center conductors, a hole is tapped and a small set screw is placed through the center conductor of the coax into this tapped hole. The

same method is employed with the center conductor and the reducer in Fig. 2B. The matching section is supported by tightening the set screw on the ¼-in. conductor.

Luckily, after the installation, we had a bad storm with plenty of rain, hail and a 50-mph wind. The swr

did not vary at all. This particular transmitter kicks off automatically with an increase in swr or a short in the line. During the storm, the adjustment was set for closer tolerance than for normal operation and the transmitter didn't kick off once.

R-F Transmission-Line Nomographs

Ten equations commonly used to compute relationships between electrical and mechanical properties of radio-frequency transmission lines have been plotted as convenient nomographs

By PHILLIP H. SMITH

IN radio engineering, nomographs permit the saving of considerable time, particularly where the repeated solution of mathematical equations is required. They are especially well suited to portraying the relationships between the many electrical and mechanical properties of radio frequency transmission lines since these relationships may generally be expressed by relatively simple mathematical equations. Ten of the most useful of these equations have been plotted as nomographs as a convenience to the radio engineer. Each of these is discussed briefly and the formulas are given to permit an evaluation beyond the accuracy of the nomograph should this be desired in any particular case. The derivation of the formulas is based upon certain simplifying assumptions which are generally considered justifiable for radio-frequency transmission lines.

1. Characteristic Impedance of Transmission Lines

For radio-frequency transmission lines where the losses per wavelength are relatively small, the charactertistic impedance is essentially a pure resistance. The characteristic impedance is numerically equal to the square root of the ratio of the distributed inductance to the distributed capacitance per unit

length. Since both of these parameters are uniquely related to the physical size and spacing of the conductors, it is possible to express the characteristic impedance in terms

of the physical dimensions of the line.

Thus, the characteristic impedance (Z_0) of an open 2-wire line is

$$Z_0 = 276 \log_{10}(2D/d) \text{ ohms} \qquad (1)$$

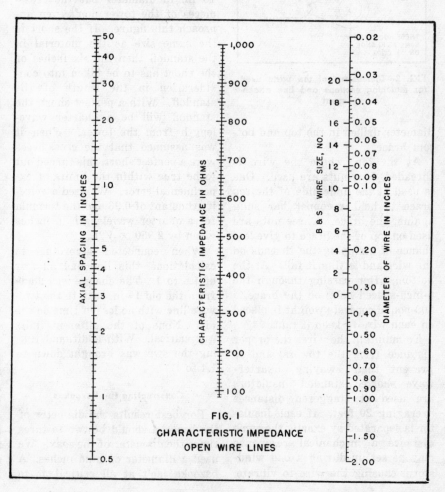

FIG. I

CHARACTERISTIC IMPEDANCE
OPEN WIRE LINES

where D is the wire separation on centers and d is the wire diameter, both in the same units. Figure 1 shows the characteristic impedance of an open 2-wire line as a function of the conductor dimensions and their center-line spacing.

2. Characteristic Impedance of a Coaxial Line

The characteristic impedance (Z_0) of a coaxial transmission line is

$$Z_0 = 138 \log_{10} (D/d) \text{ ohms} \qquad (2)$$

where D is the inner diameter of the outer conductor and d is the outer diameter of the inner conductor. This applies only to a line where the medium between conductors is predominantly a gas, such as air, at low pressures.

If the coaxial line is filled with a uniform dielectric material other than a low pressure gas, the characteristic impedance is reduced by a factor equal to $1/k^{\frac{1}{2}}$, where k is the relative dielectric constant of the material. For a line with bead insulators at small uniform intervals, the effective dielectric constant (k_e) may be computed from the following

$$k_e = (k t + s)/(t + s) \qquad (2a)$$

where t is the thickness of one bead, s is the spacing between two beads, both t and s in the same units; and k is the relative dielectric constant of the bead. A number of optimum values for the characteristic impedance of coaxial lines exist which are based upon different considerations such as the maximum power handling capability and the minimum loss. Several of these optimum values are indicated along the characteristic impedance scale on the right hand side of the nomograph. Fortunately, all of these optimums are relatively broad in their characteristics and a considerable departure can generally be tolerated for any particular application.

Figure 2 shows the characteristic impedance of a gas dielectric coaxial transmission line as a function of the two conductor diameters.

3. High-Frequency Resistance of a Coaxial Line

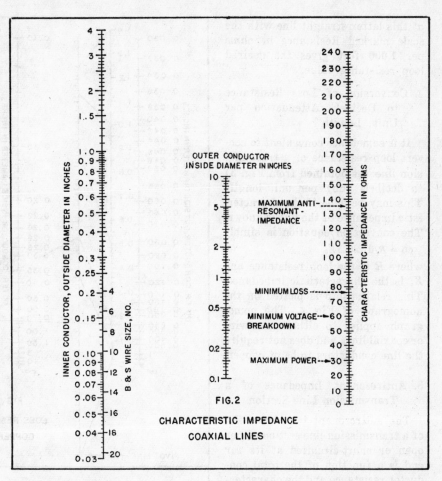

FIG. 2

CHARACTERISTIC IMPEDANCE
COAXIAL LINES

The high frequency resistance of a coaxial transmission line is one of the principal factors which determine the attenuation along the line. It is also one of the factors which determine the maximum anti-resonant impedance and the minimum resonant impedance of a line section when used as a circuit element. The high frequency resistance of a coaxial line is a function of both conductor dimensions and of the frequency (due to skin effect). It is also a function of the resistivity of the material of which the conductors are made.

For copper coaxial lines the high frequency loop resistance (R) is

$$R = 0.0315 f^{1/2} \left[\frac{1}{d} + \frac{1}{D} \right] \text{ ohms}$$
$$\text{per 1,000 feet} \qquad (3)$$

where f is the frequency in kilocycles, D is the inner diameter of the outer conductor in inches, and d is the outer diameter of the inner conductor in inches.

For conductors other than copper, the high frequency resistance is proportional to the square root of the ratio of the resistivity of the conductor to that of copper.

Figure 3 shows the resistance of a copper coaxial line as a function of the conductor dimensions and the frequency. Dielectric losses, which are negligible in a gas dielectric line, are not included.

The nomograph on Fig. 3 is used as follows: draw a straight line connecting points on the first and fourth scales from the left, which show, respectively, the line conductor diameters. Obtain the intersection of this line with the second scale marked Size Factor. Now project this intersection to a corresponding point on the third scale marked Pivot Line, as shown in the example on the nomograph. Finally, connect this new pivot point with a straight line intersecting the desired value on the sixth or frequency scale. The intersection of this latter straight line with the scale marked Resistance in ohms per 1,000 feet gives the desired loop resistance value.

4. Conversion of Loss Resistance to Decibels Attenuation per Unit Length

It is sometimes convenient to convert loop resistance of a transmission line (as obtained from **Fig. 3**) to decibels (db) per unit length. This may be done if the characteristic impedance of the line is known. The conversion equation is simply

$$db = R/0.23025 Z_0 \qquad (4)$$

where R is the loop resistance and Z_0 is the characteristic impedance. This relationship is plotted on the nomograph of Fig. 4. The nomograph applies to either open-wire or coaxial lines and does not require the line conductors to be of copper.

5. Antiresonant Impedance of a Transmission Line Section

The antiresonant impedance Z_{AR} of a transmission line section either open or short-circuited at its far end is a function of the total conductor resistance and the characteristic impedance of the section. The relationship is

$$Z_{AR} = 2 Z_0^2/R \text{ ohms} \qquad (5)$$

where Z_0 is the characteristic impedance and R is the resistance of the antiresonant line section.

The shortest antiresonant line section is one-quarter wavelength long (short-circuited at its far end) and accordingly this will have the highest antiresonant impedance. A line section one-half wavelength long (open-circuited at the far end) will have only half as high an antiresonant impedance because its resistance R is twice as great.

Figure 5 shows the antiresonant impedance of a transmission line as a function of the total resistance and the characteristic impedance of the section. The nomograph applies equally to either coaxial or open wire lines.

The resonant impedance of a transmission line section is simply one-half of its total resistance (ob-

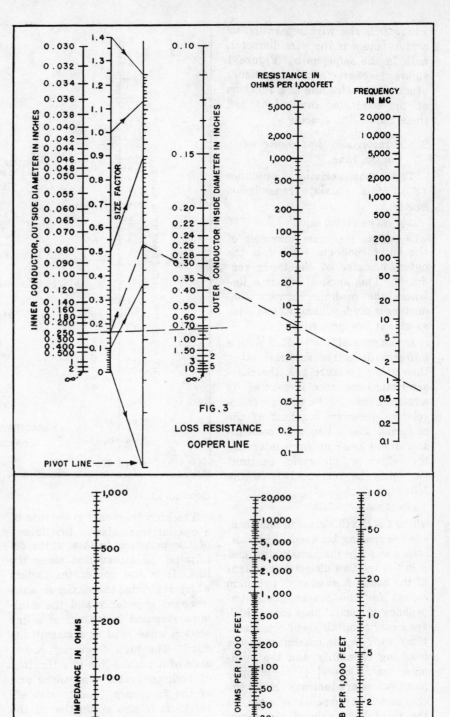

FIG. 3

LOSS RESISTANCE COPPER LINE

FIG. 4

RESISTANCE VS DB

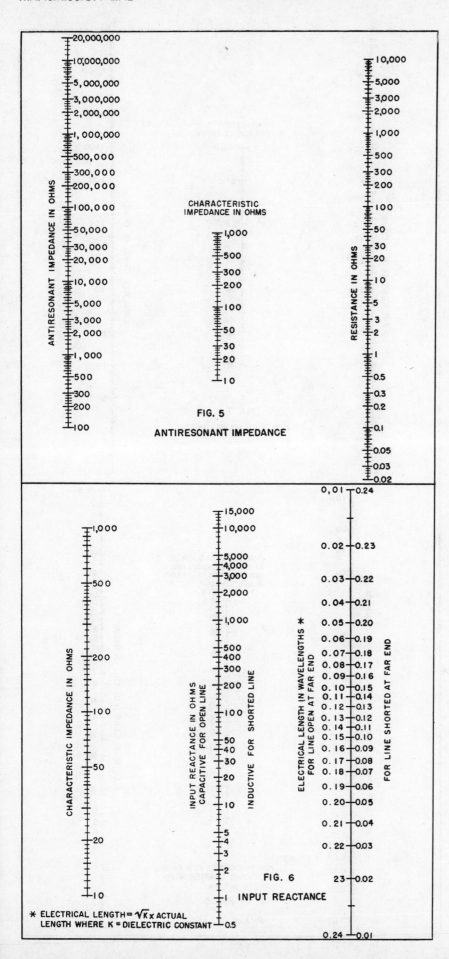

CHARACTERISTIC
IMPEDANCE IN OHMS

FIG. 5

ANTIRESONANT IMPEDANCE

FIG. 6

INPUT REACTANCE

* ELECTRICAL LENGTH = √K x ACTUAL
LENGTH WHERE K = DIELECTRIC CONSTANT

tained from Fig. 3); accordingly, no nomograph has been plotted for this.

6. Input Reactance of a Transmission Line Section

A short length of transmission line is sometimes used as a reactance element in high-frequency circuits. The input reactance is a function of the electrical length of the line section and its characteristic impedance. The reactance varies between values essentially equivalent to plus and minus one half of the antiresonant impedance (obtained from Fig. 5). In air or gas dielectric coaxial lines, the electrical length is very nearly the same as the physical length measured in terms of free space wavelengths. A dielectric other than a gas results in a reduction in the length of the wave in the line which is proportional to the square root of the average dielectric constant. Thus a polyethylene coaxial cable with a dielectric constant of 2.5 will be electrically $(2.5)^{\frac{1}{2}}$ or 1.6 times as long as if the dielectric were a gas.

The electrical length and the characteristic impedance of a line section as well as its termination (either open circuit or short circuit) determine the magnitude and sign of the input reactance. For an open-wire or coaxial line section, open-circuited at its far end, the input reactance X_s is

$$X_s = -Z_0 \cot (360 \, l/\lambda) \text{ ohms} \qquad (6)$$

where l/λ is the electrical length in wavelengths and Z_0 is the characteristic impedance.

For an open-wire or coaxial line section, short-circuited at its far end, the input reactance X_s is

$$X_s = Z_0 \tan (360 \, l/\lambda) \text{ ohms} \qquad (6a)$$

Figure 6 shows the input reactance of an open or short-circuited transmission line section as a function of the electrical length, the characteristic impedance, and the termination.

7. Quarter - Wave Transmission Line Impedance Transformers

Impedance transformations are often made along radio-frequency transmission lines by employing a quarter-wave section of transmission line of selected characteristic impedance as an impedance transformer. When such a line section is terminated in a pure resistance its input impedance will be a pure resistance which depends upon the load resistance value and the value of the characteristic impedance of the quarter-wave line section.

Figure 7 shows the input resistance R_s of a quarter-wave open wire or coaxial line section terminated in a pure resistance load. The relationship is

$$R_s = Z_0^2/R_l \text{ ohms} \qquad (7)$$

where R_l is the terminating resistance and Z_0 is the characteristic impedance.

8. Current-Phase Relationship Along a Transmission Line

The phase relationship of the current from point to point along a radio-frequency transmission line will be uniform with length only when the line is terminated in an impedance equivalent to its characteristic impedance; otherwise the phase will vary nonuniformly along the line.

Figure 8 shows the phase relationship of the current at the sending end of a line, with respect to the current in a resistance load, as a function of the ratio of the load resistance to the characteristic impedance of the line, and of the effective length of line. The relationship is

$$\phi = \arctan\left[\frac{R_l}{Z_0}\tan\left(360\,\frac{l}{\lambda}\right)\right] \quad (8)$$
degrees

where R_l is the load resistance, Z_0 is the characteristic impedance and l/λ is the electrical length in wavelengths.

The current in the load will always lag the current at the sending end of a transmission line. It will undergo exactly 180 degrees of phase shift in each electrical half-wave length regardless of the ratio of the load resistance to the characteristic impedance.

9. Voltage Gradient along a Coaxial Line

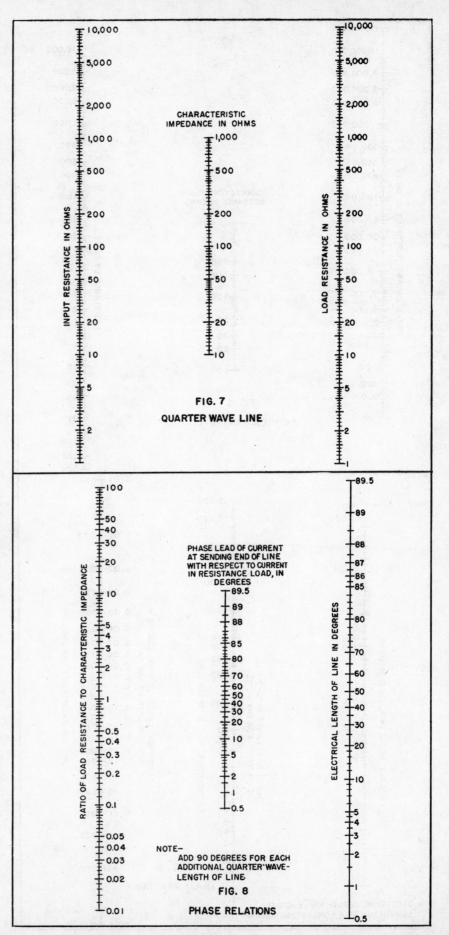

CHARACTERISTIC IMPEDANCE IN OHMS

INPUT RESISTANCE IN OHMS

LOAD RESISTANCE IN OHMS

FIG. 7
QUARTER WAVE LINE

RATIO OF LOAD RESISTANCE TO CHARACTERISTIC IMPEDANCE

PHASE LEAD OF CURRENT AT SENDING END OF LINE WITH RESPECT TO CURRENT IN RESISTANCE LOAD, IN DEGREES

ELECTRICAL LENGTH OF LINE IN DEGREES

NOTE—
ADD 90 DEGREES FOR EACH ADDITIONAL QUARTER-WAVE-LENGTH OF LINE

FIG. 8
PHASE RELATIONS

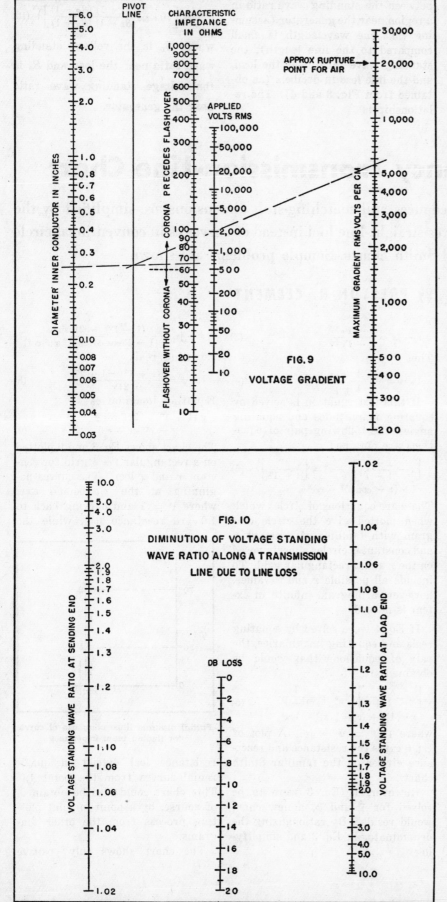

FIG. 9
VOLTAGE GRADIENT

FIG. 10
DIMINUTION OF VOLTAGE STANDING
WAVE RATIO ALONG A TRANSMISSION
LINE DUE TO LINE LOSS

In a coaxial transmission line the maximum voltage gradient occurs at the surface of the inner conductor. When this gradient exceeds the critical value of approximately 20,000 volts (rms) per cm, breakdown will occur in the form of either corona or arcover. If the characteristic impedance of the line is less than the optimum breakdown value of 60 ohms, arcover will occur without corona—if it is more than 60 ohms, corona will precede arcover.

Figure 9 shows the maximum voltage gradient G_{max} on a coaxial line as a function of the characteristic impedance of the line, the physical size of the inner conductor and the applied voltage. The relationship is

$$G_{max} = 47.2E/dZ_0 \text{ rms volts per cm} \quad (9)$$

where E is the applied rms voltage, d is the diameter of the inner conductor in inches, and Z_0 is the characteristic impedance.

This nomograph is used as follows: first, connect with a straight line points on the first and third scales from the left which represent the inner conductor diameter and the characteristic impedance (see example on nomograph). The intersection of this line with the second scale labeled Pivot Line is next connected with a second straight line passing through the desired point on the fourth scale labeled Applied Volts, RMS. The intersection of this second straight line with the fifth scale gives the desired value for the gradient on the surface of the inner conductor in rms volts per cm.

Bead insulators may cause higher gradients in their vicinity resulting in premature voltage breakdown particularly if they fit loosely on the inner conductor.

10. Diminution of Standing Wave Ratio Due to Line Loss

A high-frequency transmission line whose characteristic impedance is not matched by the load impedance will have standing waves along its length. The standing wave ratio in the vicinity of the load will be numerically equal to the ratio of the load resistance to the characteristic impedance (or its reciprocal if this is less than unity). If the line has attenuation, there will be a gradual diminution of the standing wave ratio in the direction of the generator.

Figure 10 shows the relationship

between the standing wave ratio in a region near the generator (assuming that the wavelength is small compared to the line length), the standing wave ratio near the load, and the line loss in decibels (as obtained from Fig. 3 and 4). The relationship is

$$db = \left[10 \log_{10} \frac{(S_L + 1)(S_G - 1)}{(S_L - 1)(S_G + 1)} \right]^{1/2} \quad (10)$$

where S_L is the voltage standing wave ratio near the load and S_G is the voltage standing wave ratio near the generator.

High-Frequency Transmission-Line Chart

Determination of input impedances and matching-stub dimensions are simplified by the use of this chart which features straight-line loci instead of curves as in conventional circle diagram and Smith charts. Sample problems are shown

By PRESTON R. CLEMENT

THE CIRCLE DIAGRAM and the Smith chart[1,2] are convenient methods for solving input impedance and matching-stub problems on high-frequency dissipationless transmission lines. However, by properly manipulating the equations of which these two charts are a plot, a third chart can be developed which has the advantage that in working such problems a straight-line locus is followed in the chart, rather than a curved one.

If a given transmission line has a length s, phase shift β radians per unit length, characteristic impedance R_c, and receiving end impedance $\bar{Z}_R$, then the impedance at the sending end is given by the well-known formula

$$\bar{Z}_s = R_c \frac{1 + \Gamma \epsilon^{j(\psi - 2\beta s)}}{1 - \Gamma \epsilon^{j(\psi - 2\beta s)}} \quad (1)$$

where $\Gamma \epsilon^{j\psi}$ is called the reflection coefficient of the line and is equal to the ratio of the reflected component to the incident component of voltage at the load. In terms of impedance

$$\Gamma \epsilon^{j\psi} = \frac{\bar{Z}_R - R_c}{\bar{Z}_R + R_c}$$

Letting $\phi = \psi - 2\beta s$

$$\bar{Z}_s = R_c \frac{1 + \Gamma \epsilon^{j\phi}}{1 - \Gamma \epsilon^{j\phi}} \quad (2)$$

To achieve a per unit basis, let $\bar{Z}_s/R_c = r + jx$. Then Eq. 2 becomes

$$r + jx = \frac{1 + \Gamma \epsilon^{j\phi}}{1 - \Gamma \epsilon^{j\phi}} \quad (3)$$

Thus

$$\Gamma \epsilon^{j\phi} = \frac{r - 1 + jx}{r + 1 + jx} \quad (4)$$

If this last equation is solved by equating magnitudes and equating angles, the following pair of equations are obtained

$$\left[r - \frac{1 + \Gamma^2}{1 - \Gamma^2} \right]^2 + x^2 = \left[\frac{2\Gamma}{1 - \Gamma^2} \right]^2 \quad (5)$$
$$r^2 + (x - \cot \phi)^2 = \csc^2 \phi$$

These are equations of circles which when plotted give the circle diagram with families of constant Γ and constant ϕ circles superimposed on the r and x rectangular grid. To include all possible r and x values, however, a diagram infinite in extent is needed.

If Eq. 4 were solved by equating reals and equating imaginaries, the pair of equations that would be obtained are

$$\left[u - \frac{r}{1 + r} \right]^2 + v^2 = \frac{1}{(1 + r)^2} \quad (6)$$
$$(u - 1)^2 + (v - 1/x)^2 = 1/x^2$$

where $\Gamma \epsilon^{j\phi} = u + jv$. A plot of Eq. 6 gives the resistance and reactance circles on the familiar Smith chart.

However, if Eq. 3 were to be solved for Γ and ϕ, a new chart would result. By rationalizing the denominator in Eq. 3 and simplifying

$$r + jx = \frac{(1 - \Gamma^2) + j2\Gamma \sin \phi}{(1 - \Gamma \cos \phi)^2 + \Gamma^2 \sin^2 \phi} \quad (7)$$

Equating reals

$$\cos \phi = \frac{r(1 + \Gamma^2) - 1 + \Gamma^2}{2\Gamma r} \quad (8)$$

Equating imaginaries

$$x(1 + \Gamma^2) - 2xr \cos \phi - 2\Gamma \sin \phi = 0 \quad (9)$$

The chart shows Eq. 8 and 9 plotted on a rectangular Γ - ϕ grid for constant r and x loci. The curves beginning at the right-hand axis where $\Gamma = 1$ and curving back to 1,0 are reactance loci, while the

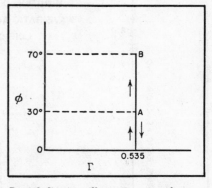

Partial diagram illustrating use of curve for finding input impedance

resistance loci extend in quasi-radial curves from the point 1,0. This chart could also be obtained, of course, by a point-to-point plotting process from the other diagrams.

The chart shows only positive

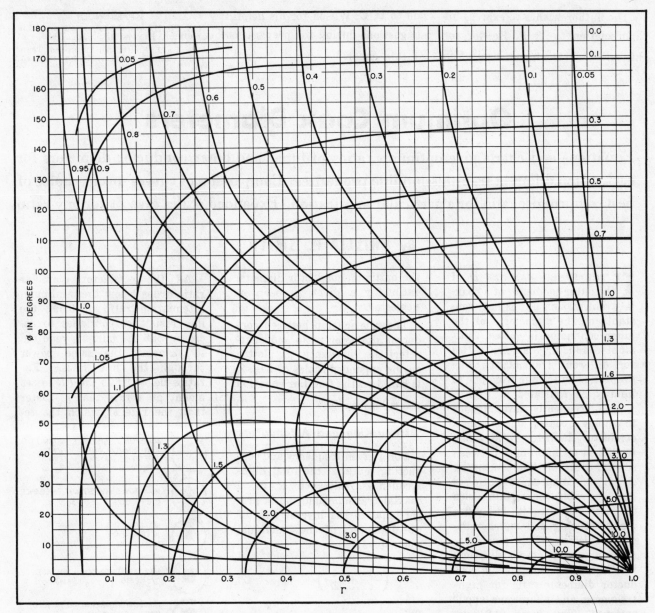

values of x. From Eq. 9 it is seen that if x were chosen negative and ϕ negative, (or ϕ greater than 180 deg), the equation has merely been multiplied through by (-1). Therefore, to complete the chart, a second half-chart could be drawn for negative values of x, with ϕ ranging from 0 to -180 deg, but it would be merely a reflection of the chart shown about the Γ axis, and therefore not necessary, as the following example shows.

EXAMPLE 1. Calculation of input impedance. Let $R_c = 250$ ohms, $\overline{Z}_R = 500 + j375$ ohms, and $\beta s \pm 50$ deg. Then $\overline{Z}_R/R_c = 2 + j1.5$ and

the chart shows a reflection coefficient of approximately $0.535/30$ deg. This corresponds to $\overline{A}$ below. Now subtract $2\beta s$ or 100 deg from 30 deg, giving -70 deg. We may read the proper value at $\phi = +70$ deg, keeping in mind that x would be negative in the other half chart.

Thus following the straight Γ line of 0.535 down to zero and back up to B or 70 deg, we read $0.77 - j1.1$. Therefore, $\overline{Z}_s = 250\,(0.77 - j1.1) = 192 - j275$ ohms.

EXAMPLE 2. Single-stub impedance matching. If $R_c = 250$ ohms and $\overline{Z}_R = 80 - j60$ ohms, then

$R_c/\overline{Z}_R = 2 + j1.5$. This locates the same point as in example 1. Following the constant Γ line downward (corresponding to moving away from the load to zero and then upward, we would reach unit conductance when $\phi = 63$ deg. Thus $\beta s = (30\ \text{deg} + 63\ \text{deg})/2 = 46.5$ deg, or at a distance 46.5 deg$/\beta$ from the load, the stub should be placed. The susceptance at that point is approximately -1.25 mho, and the point 0, $+1.25$ corresponds to about 77 deg. Thus the length of a shorted stub at that point should be $2\,(77$ deg) or 154 deg and for an open stub, 154 deg -90 deg $= 64$ deg.

The author wishes to express his appreciation to V. P. Hessler for his encouragement and inspiration and to D. G. Wilson for his helpful suggestions during the preparation of this paper.

REFERENCES

(1) P. H. Smith, Transmission Line Calculator, ELECTRONICS, Jan. 1939.

(2) P. H. Smith, An Improved Transmission Line Calculator, ELECTRONICS, Jan. 1944.

Optimum Coax Diameters

Equations and charts give optimum ratios of inner and outer conductor diameters for each of ten different transmission line properties. Comparison of curves speeds choice of best compromise ratio for a particular application. Expanded scales give Z_0 for any ratio

By PHILLIP H. SMITH

IF THE INNER DIAMETER D of the outer conductor of a coaxial transmission line is held constant and the diameter d of the inner conductor is varied, optimum conductor diameter ratios for different transmission line properties will range from one to infinity as indicated in Fig. 1.

It is frequently advantageous to employ a coaxial line having a conductor diameter ratio which results in a compromise between several desirable line properties. A single compromise ratio is also desirable for certain fields of use because it simplifies manufacturing and merchandising problems. These considerations have led to standardization, in effect, of a single coaxial conductor diameter ratio for high-frequency and microwave applications.[1] This ratio (2.3) results in a nominal characteristic impedance of about 50 ohms. For many specific coaxial line applications, however, the design engineer may find it desirable to employ a conductor diameter ratio which will give more nearly optimum results.

The derivation of the optimum ratios is briefly described and optimum values are indicated to one part in ten thousand. In all cases the medium between conductors is assumed to be a gas with a dielectric constant approaching unity, and any effect of inner conductor supports upon the optimum conductor diameter ratio for a given property is neglected.

The relationship between conductor diameter ratio and characteristic impedance, as plotted on the expanded scales of Fig. 2, is based on the familiar equation

$$Z_0 = 138 \log_{10} (D/d) \qquad (1)$$

Attenuation and Attenuators

For a given frequency and conducting material the total high-frequency resistance R of a coaxial transmission line is proportional to the inverse sum of the diameters of the individual conductors:

$$R \approx \left(\frac{1}{d} + \frac{1}{D} \right) \qquad (2)$$

This equation shows that minimum resistance of a line of given outer conductor diameter D occurs when ratio D/d approaches unity. Minimum resistance does not, however, accompany minimum attenuation. As the conductor diameter ratio approaches unity the resistance approaches 0.435 times the resistance of a line having minimum attenuation, as seen from Fig. 3.

Minimum attenuation, commonly referred to as loss in a coaxial transmission line, occurs when ratio D/d is 3.592. This ratio corresponds to a characteristic impedance of 76.64 ohms.

As the conductor diameter ratio drops below the minimum-attenuation ratio of 3.592 the line resistance continues to decrease but the current required to transmit the same power through the line rises. For ratios below 3.592 the I^2R losses mount at a rate that is faster than the rate at which the re-

MAXIMUM RESISTANCE, MINIMUM Q AND MINIMUM ANTIRESONANT IMPEDANCE, MAXIMUM RESONANT IMPEDANCE $D/d \doteq \infty$ $Z_0 \doteq \infty$

MAXIMUM ANTIRESONANT IMPEDANCE $D/d = 9.185$ $Z_0 = 132.9$

MAXIMUM Q AND MINIMUM ATTENUATION $D/d = 3.592$ $Z_0 = 76.64$

MAXIMUM BREAKDOWN VOLTAGE $D/d = 2.718$ $Z_0 = 59.93$

MINIMUM TEMPERATURE RISE OF INNER CONDUCTOR $D/d = 1.835$ $Z_0 = 36.38$

MAXIMUM POWER CARRYING CAPABILITY $D/d = 1.648$ $Z_0 = 29.94$

MINIMUM RESISTANCE, MINIMUM Q, AND MINIMUM RESONANT IMPEDANCE $D/d \doteq 1.000$ $Z_0 \doteq 0$

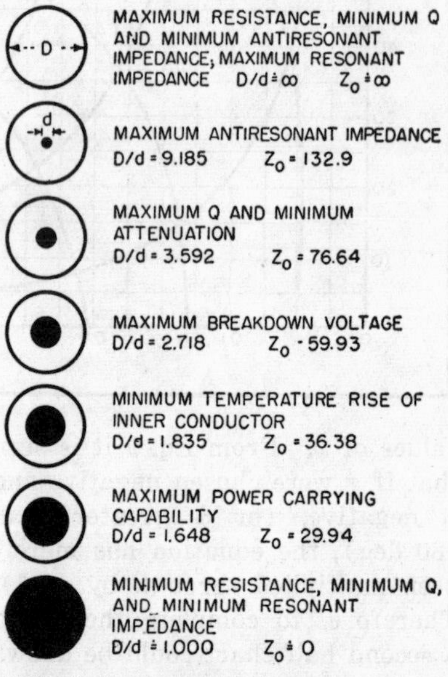

FIG. 1—Quick picture of optimum coaxial conductor diameter ratios

sistance decreases. The attenuation constant of the line and not the resistance alone determines the overall attenuation.

The attenuation constant α of a high-frequency transmission line is

$$\alpha = R/2 Z_0 \qquad (3)$$

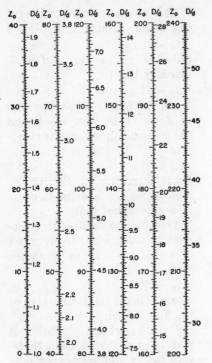

FIG. 2—Characteristic impedance in ohms of gas-filled coaxial line for various conductor diameter ratios

Substituting Z_0 from Eq. 1,

$$\alpha = \frac{R}{276 \log_{10} (D/d)} \qquad (4)$$

But from Eq. 2 R is proportional to $[(1/d) + (1/D)]$. Substituting this for R in Eq. 4, we obtain

$$\alpha = K \frac{(1/d) + (1/D)}{\log_{10} (D/d)} \qquad (5)$$

where K is a proportionality factor. The conductor diameter ratio corresponding to minimum attenuation is obtained by mini-

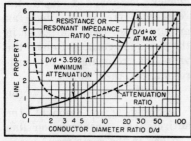

FIG. 3—Solid-line curve gives effect of D/d on ratio of resistance or resonant impedance of line to that of line having minimum attenuation. Dashed-line curve gives effect of D/d on ratio of attenuation of line to that of line having minimum attenuation

mizing α with respect to D/d.

The increase in attenuation[2] as a result of departing from the optimum ratio of 3.592 is obtained from Eq. 5 when the proportionality factor K equals log $3.592/(3.592 + 1)$ or 0.121. Figure 3 shows this graphically.

Heat, Voltage and Power

The optimum conductor diameter ratio of a coaxial line based on temperature rise of the inner conductor may, with certain simplifying assumptions, be computed by multiplying the attenuation constant, as expressed by Eq. 5, by the area ratio of outer to inner conductor per unit length (which equals the ratio of diameters) and then minimizing

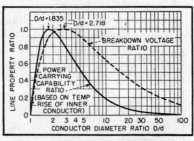

FIG. 4—Solid-line curve gives effect of D/d on ratio of power-carrying capability of line to that of line having maximum capability. Dashed-line curve gives effect of D/d on ratio of breakdown voltage to that of line having maximum resistance to breakdown

with respect to D/d. An optimum ratio of 1.835 is thus obtained, which corresponds to a characteristic impedance of 36.38 ohms.

The calculated penalty[3] in decreased power-carrying capability based on a constant temperature rise of the inner conductor, for departing from this optimum ratio, is shown on Fig. 4. The penalty in increased temperature rise of the inner conductor for departing from the ratio 1.835 will vary for different conditions of inner and outer conductor emissivity and thermal properties of the surrounding media, and therefore can be evaluated quantitatively only in specific cases.[3]

A coaxial transmission line will withstand maximum applied voltage between conductors when their diameter ratio is 2.718, which corresponds to a characteristic impedance of 59.93 ohms. This is determined by minimizing the formula for the voltage gradient at the surface of the inner conductor, where breakdown first occurs, with respect to D/d. The gradient g in volts per cm at the surface of the inner conductor[4] is

$$g = \frac{2E}{d \log_e (D/d)} \qquad (6)$$

where E is the applied voltage and e is the Napierian base (2.718). The reciprocal of g gives a quantity which is proportional to the ratio of the breakdown voltage of a line to that of a line having maximum resistance to breakdown. This is plotted on Fig. 4 as a function of the conductor diameter ratio.

Maximum power-carrying capability of a concentric transmission line occurs when the conductor diameter ratio equals $\sqrt{e}$ or 1.648, which corresponds to a characteristic impedance of 29.94 ohms[5]. This assumes that the frequency is within a range (usually below about 50 mc) where voltage breakdown rather than overheating of the inner conductor governs the maximum power rating of the line. This ratio is also optimum from the power-carrying standpoint at higher frequencies under most conditions of pulsed operation where the average power is small as compared to the peak power.

In order to calculate the maximum power-carrying capability ratio, based on a limiting voltage gradient on the inner conductor, we note first that the applied voltage across a transmission line terminated in its characteristic impedance is a function of the characteristic impedance and the power P in the line:

$$E = \sqrt{PZ_0} \qquad (7)$$

But the characteristic impedance

as given by Eq. 1 may also be expressed as

$$Z_0 = 60 \log_e (D/d) \qquad (8)$$

Substituting into Eq. 7,

$$E = \sqrt{60\,P} \times \sqrt{\log_e (D/d)} \qquad (9)$$

The gradient at the surface of the inner conductor for a given applied voltage is given by Eq. 6. Substituting the above equivalent for E into Eq. 6 we obtain the following expression for the gradient at the surface of the inner conductor for a given power

$$g = \frac{2\,\sqrt{60\,P}}{d\,\sqrt{\log_e (D/d)}} \qquad (10)$$

The conductor diameter ratio which permits the transmission of a given power with minimum voltage gradient, and hence maximum power transmission when voltage gradient is the limiting factor, is obtained by minimizing g, as given in Eq. 10, with respect to D/d. We then obtain $(D/d) = \sqrt{e} = 1.648$. The square root of the reciprocal of the gradient as expressed in Eq. 10 gives a quantity which is proportional to the ratio of the power-carrying capability of the line to that of a line having a maximum capability, based on minimum voltage gradient on the surface of the inner conductor. This is plotted as a function of the conductor diameter ratio in Fig. 5.

Antiresonant Impedance

The maximum antiresonant impedance of coaxial transmission line sections is obtained when the conductor diameter ratio is 9.185, which corresponds to a characteristic impedance of 132.90 ohms.[6] The antiresonant impedance of a transmission line section is, in general

$$Z_{AR} = Z_0/\alpha \qquad (11)$$

where α is the attenuation constant of the line. Substituting the value for Z_0 given by Eq. 1,

$$Z_{AR} \approx \frac{\log_{10} (D/d)}{\alpha} \qquad (12)$$

Combining this with Eq. 5 then gives

$$Z_{AR} \approx \frac{\log^2_{10} (D/d)}{(D/d) + 1} \qquad (13)$$

The conductor diameter ratio which provides a maximum antiresonant impedance for a line section is obtained by maximizing Z_{AR} with respect to D/d.

The absolute value of the antiresonant impedance for a transmission line of optimum conductor diameter ratio (9.185) may be computed from

$$Z_{AR} = 3,428.82/R \qquad (14)$$

where R is the total resistance of the line section.

Resonant Impedance

Minimum resonant impedance of a coaxial line section is obtained when the conductor diam-

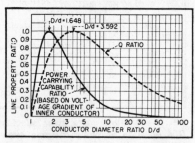

FIG. 5—Solid-line curve gives effect of D/d on ratio of power-carrying capability of line (based on voltage gradient of inner conductor) to that of line having maximum capability. Dashed-line curve gives effect of D/d on ratio of Q of line to that of line having minimum attenuation

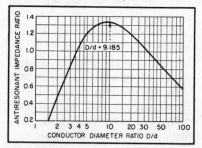

FIG. 6—Effect of D/d on ratio of antiresonant impedance of line to that of line having minimum attenuation

eter ratio approaches the limiting value of unity. As the ratio approaches this limiting value the characteristic impedance approaches zero.

The resonant impedance of a line section is, in general,

$$Z_R = \alpha Z_0 \qquad (15)$$

Substituting the value for Z_0 given by Eq. 1

$$Z_R \approx \alpha \log_{10} (D/d) \qquad (16)$$

From Eq. 5, α is proportional to $(1/d) + (1/D)/\log_{10} (D/d)$ and the resonant impedance is therefore

$$Z_R \approx (D/d) + 1 \qquad (17)$$

From inspection of Eq. 17, Z_R approaches a minimum value as D/d approaches unity.

The absolute value of the resonant impedance for a given set of conditions may be computed from

$$Z_R = R/2 \qquad (18)$$

where R is the total resistance of the line section.

From inspection of Eq. 2 it may be seen that R (and therefore Z_R) is minimum when $d = D$ or $D/d = 1$.

The minimum antiresonant and the maximum resonant impedance of a coaxial transmission line section is obtained when the conductor diameter ratio becomes infinitely large, which corresponds to an infinitely large characteristic impedance. As may be seen from Eq. 13 and 17, this occurs when D/d becomes infinitely large. This is shown, with respect to a line having minimum attenuation, on Fig. 3 and Fig. 6.

Q Ratio

If in a tuned circuit the frequency is changed from the resonant frequency by an amount Δf so that the power in the circuit is reduced to half the value at resonance (or antiresonance), then

$$Q = f/2\,\Delta f \qquad (19)$$

Defining Q of resonant (or antiresonant) transmission line sections in the same way,[6]

$$Q = \frac{Z_0}{R} \times \frac{2\,\pi\,l}{\lambda} \qquad (20)$$

where $2\pi l/\lambda$ is the angular length of the line section in radians and R is given by Eq. 2.

The Q is maximum when R/Z_0 is minimum, but R/Z_0 is proportional to the attenuation of the line as shown in Fig. 3 and therefore the Q is maximum when $D/d = 3.592$.

The Q of a coaxial transmission line section is minimum when the attenuation of the line is maximum. As may be seen from Fig. 3, this occurs when D/d approaches the limiting value, unity, and also when D/d becomes infinitely large.

REFERENCES

(1) RMA Subcommittee on Antennas and R-F Lines—TR-31-2901; RMA Subcommittee on Gas-Filled Transmission Lines—TR-911.

(2) E. J. Sterba and C. B. Feldman, Transmission Lines for Short Wave Radio Systems, *Proc. IRE*, July 1932.

(3) C. R. Cox, Design Data for Beaded Coaxial Lines, ELECTRONICS, p 130, May 1946.

(4) F. W. Peek, Jr., "Dielectric Phenomena in High-Voltage Engineering," McGraw-Hill Book Co., New York, Second Edition, p 28.

(5) P. H. Smith, U. S. Patent No. 2,298,428, issued Oct. 13, 1942.

(6) B. J. Witt, Concentric Tube Lines, *Marconi Review*, p 20, Jan.-Feb. 1936.

Coaxial-Stub Filter

Undesired signals in a coaxial transmission line can be attenuated up to 30 db by connecting two stubs to the line, one for rejection and the other to correct the line impedance. Graphs give approximate stub lengths for any interfering frequency in range from 20 to 200 mc

By JAMES A. CRAIG

COAXIAL LINE stubs often can be effectively used in transmitter or receiver coaxial transmission lines to reduce or trap out specific spurious radiations or interfering signals. Stubs are well worth trying, since they are relatively inexpensive and can be depended upon to furnish up to 30-db additional attenuation to an undesired signal. Two stubs are used, one for rejection and one for correction, as shown in Fig. 1.

Receiver stubs are most easily fabricated from RG-58/U solid dielectric cable. Where stubs are to be used to suppress transmitter spurious radiations, a solid-dielectric cable should be used having the same power-handling capacity as is used between the transmitter and its antenna. The approximate length of the rejector stub for the undesired frequency can be determined from Fig. 2. A piece of cable several inches longer than that called for should be connected into the transmission line as in Fig. 1, as close as practical to the transmitter or receiver.

Use a pick or other sharp-pointed instrument to short-circuit the outer shield to the inner conductor at various points, starting from the outer end of the stub and working inward. Note at which point the short-circuit produces the greatest attenuation of the undesired signal and permanently short-circuit the cable there. Cut off the excess cable. This short-circuit may be best accomplished by collapsing the outer shield around the center conductor and soldering all around.

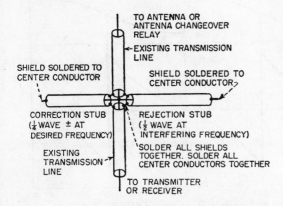

FIG. 1—Method of connecting stubs is same for both transmitting and receiving lines. Put stubs as close as possible to transmitter or receiver

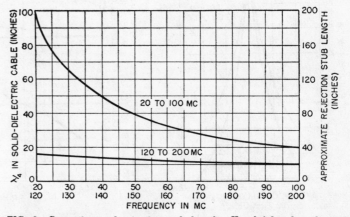

FIG. 2—Correction and rejection stub lengths. Use left-hand scale in connection with Fig. 4 to determine correction stub length, since this is longer or shorter than a quarter-wavelength at some frequencies

As Fig. 3 shows, the rejection stub alone produces a certain amount of attenuation to the undesired signal. This is because it has been tuned to be a shorted half-wave section of line at the undesired frequency. As such, it presents close to zero impedance to this frequency at its point of connection to the main transmission line. However, at the desired frequency, the rejection stub will not be a shorted half-wave section of line and will therefore present either capacitive or inductive reactance to the line and thereby cause some degree of attenuation to the desired frequency. This effect can be overcome by adding a second stub called a correction stub, as shown in Fig. 1.

For various desired versus undesired frequency conditions, the length of the correction stub may vary from almost zero to one-half wavelength. The length of one-quarter wave in solid dielectric cable is also plotted in Fig. 2, to show that the correction stub will be some value between zero and a definite upper limit. In this case, the desired frequency should be used in determining the length of the correction stub. This stub is tuned and is permanently short-circuited as in the case of the re-jection stub, except that the tuning is done to produce the least attenuation of the desired signal.

If the correction stub were to be made exactly one-quarter wave long at the desired frequency, it would present infinite impedance (neither capacitive or inductive) to the desired signal. While being made shorter than a quarter wave it presents progressively less inductive reactance. While being made somewhat longer than a quarter wave it presents progressively less capacitive reactance to the line.

The amount of reactance in either case depends upon how much longer or shorter than a quarter wave the correction stub is made. This length is automatically arrived at in the tuning procedure given above.

Figure 4 shows whether the correction stub will be longer or shorter than the quarter-wavelength shown in Fig. 2. To use Fig. 4, determine what relationship the interfering frequency bears to the desired frequency. As an example, if the desired frequency f is 40 mc and the interfering signal is 25 mc, the interfering frequency would be between $0.5f$ and $0.75f$. The lower curve shows that in this range the reactance presented to the line by the rejection stub is capacitive, and the upper curve shows that the correction stub should present inductive reactance and hence be shorter than a quarter wave, or shorter than the value called for on Fig. 2. The correction stub is thus utilized to balance out the reactance presented to the line by the rejection stub at the desired frequency.

Correction Stub Details

It is not necessary or desirable to show how many inches shorter or longer than a quarter wave the correction stub should be in chart form, since the precise length will be automatically arrived at as the stub is short-circuited in the tuning process. However, the upper curves in Fig. 4 do give the approximate length of the correction stub in terms of wavelength. In the example given above, these curves show that the corrector stub will be less than ⅛ wave long. In this case, it is advisable to start with a quarter-wave length of cable and short it at various points in the vicinity of an eighth wave to find the exact point.

Had Fig. 4 indicated the need for a capacitive correction stub (greater than a quarter wave and less than a half wave), it would be advisable to start with

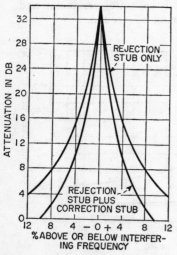

FIG. 3—Attenuation characteristics of stubs

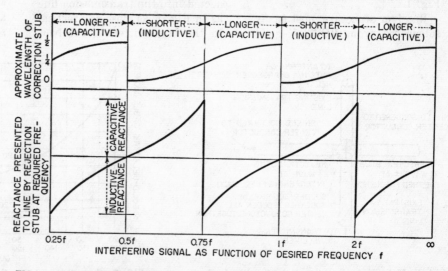

FIG. 4—Curves showing line characteristics with stubs in place, as function of ratio of interfering signal to desired signal

a half-wave length of cable and probe through the predicted point. Figure 4 is to be used chiefly as an aid in predicting the length of the correction stub and to help in visualizing the line conditions with the stubs in place.

A word of caution is advisable in a few specific cases. If the interfering frequency is approximately $\frac{1}{2}$, $\frac{1}{4}$ or $\frac{1}{8}$ of the desired frequency, stubs cannot be used. In these cases, the rejection stub will prove to be a full wavelength or multiple of a full wavelength at the desired frequency and will therefore present high attenuation to the desired frequency as well as to the interfering frequency. On the other hand, if the interfering frequency is exactly twice the desired frequency a correction stub will not be necessary since the one-half wave rejection stub will be an exact quarter wave at the desired frequency and will present infinite impedance to the desired frequency.

Reducing Standing Waves

Bilaterally matched attenuator, interposed between load and generator, reduces vsw ratio seen by generator. Chart shows what attenuation gives the required reduction

By R. E. GRANTHAM

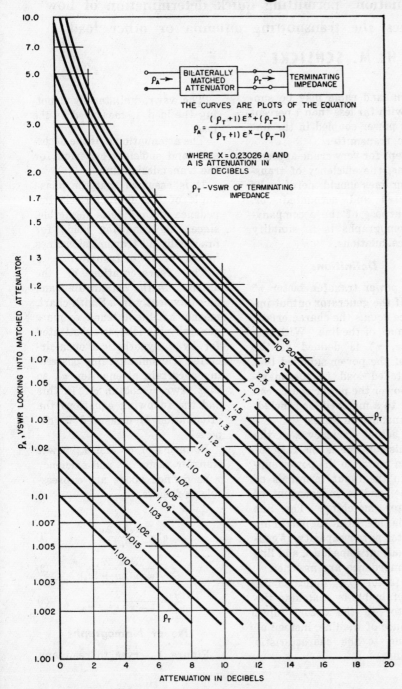

ATTENUATORS are often used in circuits to isolate changes of impedance from impedance-sensitive devices such as klystron oscillators. Also, attenuators are occasionally used in transmission lines to reduce the voltage standing-wave ratio.

For application at ultrahigh frequencies and above, the accompanying graph provides a convenient means of calculating isolation effected by a given amount of attenuation. A condition for the application of the graph is that the attenuator must be bilaterally matched. That is, the vswr must be 1.00 looking into either pair of attenuator terminals if the opposite pair is connected to an impedance having a vswr of 1.00. The attenuator, then, might be one of the bilaterally matched metallized-glass units which are commercially available in both waveguide and coaxial transmission-line types or a suitable length of lossy coaxial transmission line such as the Army-Navy type RG-21/U.

The accompanying graph presents a plot of the vswr looking

into a bilaterally matched attenuator ρ_A as a function of both the vswr of the attenuator terminating impedance ρ_T and the attenuation A, expressed in decibels, of the attenuator.

Assume it is necessary to buffer an oscillator from its load impedance so that frequency changes due to changes in the load impedance are minimized. Assume also that the maximum vswr variation to be tolerated by the oscillator is from 1.00 to 1.16 and that the load vswr variation is from 1.00 to 10.0. Entering the graph with $\rho_T = 10.0$ and $\rho_A = 1.16$, it is found that 10.5 decibels of attenuation is required.

Efficiency of Mismatched Lines

Nomographs relate power transfer ratio and efficiency of extremely short transmission line to vswr and attenuation, permitting quick determination of how much power actually reaches the transmitting antenna or other load

By H. M. SCHLICKE

ENERGY TRANSFER by short transmission lines is often considered to be very close to 100 percent, on the assumption that the transmission line approximates an ideal non-dissipative line and the voltage standing-wave ratio (vswr) approaches 1.

However, this idealization may lead to unanticipated marked differences, even for small deviations from the presumed conditions. If, for example, the load causes a vswr of 1.5 on a line that has an attenuation of only 0.5 db and if the input impedance of the line is matched to the output impedance of the generator, the efficiency is off 11.4 percent. If the generator output impedance were equalized to the characteristic impedance of the line, the efficiency of the line would drop to 85.9 percent. For measurement purposes, deviations of that magnitude are hardly negligible.

This situation deteriorates rapidly for increasing attenuation a_l of the transmission line and for higher vswr. Broadband loads fed over a certain length of transmission line may obtain power only in the order of magnitude of 10 to 50 percent. Electrically short transmitting antennas fed by relatively long transmission lines without matching transformers between

antenna and cable may be supplied with far less than 1 percent of the power coupled in the line by the transmitter.

Except for very crude approximations, the efficiency of transmission lines should therefore be calculated and accounted for. The purpose of the accompanying nomographs is to simplify these calculations.

Definitions

The power transfer factor η^* holds if the generator output impedance equals the characteristic impedance of the line. With this premise, η^* is defined as the ratio of the power supplied to a mismatched load to the maximum power the power source can deliver to a matched load including transmission losses.

The actual efficiency η of the transmission line is the ratio of the load power to the power supplied to the input terminals of the line, and is independent of generator matching. The line input is identical to maximum generator power capacity, if generator output impedance and line input impedance are matched.

The factor η/η^* indicates the gain obtainable by matching the generator to the actual input impedance of the line, instead of matching to the characteristic impedance.

The vswr, unilaterally denoting the load, is measured at the load.

The attenuation a_l is the necessary and sufficient criterion for the transmission line.

It is assumed that the phase angle of the characteristic impedance of the line is negligible, since this condition holds for practically all transmission lines in use for power transfer.

The representation of the antenna in the cotanh diagram, or equivalently in a Smith chart, means that the antenna, or more generally the load, is substituted for by a hypothetical open-circuited transmission line possessing a certain attenuation α_a, so that vswr = cotanh α_a. In this and the following equations the attenuation is measured in nepers.

In terms of a_l and a_a, power transfer factor η^* and efficiency η as defined above are expressible as follows:

$$\eta^* = \frac{2 \sinh 2a_a}{\epsilon^{2a_l + 2a_a}} \qquad (1)$$

$$\eta = \frac{\sinh 2a_a}{\sinh (2a_l + 2a_a)} \qquad (2)$$

$$\frac{\eta}{\eta^*} = \frac{1}{1 - \epsilon^{-(4a_a + 4a_l)}} \qquad (3)$$

Use of Nomographs

Figure 1 serves to read any

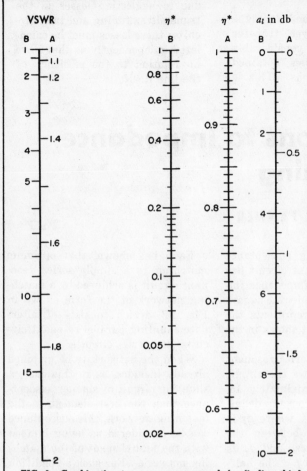

FIG. 1—Combination two-range nomograph for finding third value when any two are known. Use all three scales marked A together for lower ranges of attenuation a and vswr; use scales marked B together similarly for higher ranges

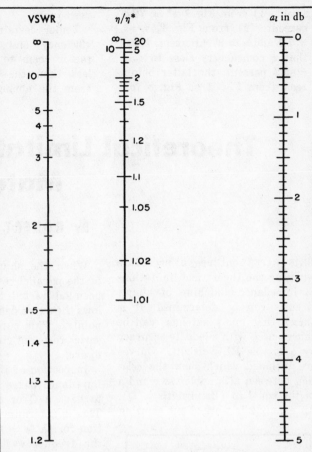

FIG. 2—Nomograph gives directly (center scale) the gain that can be obtained by matching the generator to the actual input impedance of the line, whereas nomograph of Fig. 1 is for matching generator to characteristic impedance of line

one of the three determinants η^*, a_l and vswr, when two of them are known. It should be noted that only the scales with the same letter (A or B) are commensurable.

Figure 2 permits the finding of the multifunctional relation between η and η^*.

Though η can be determined by multiplying η^* (Fig. 1) and η/η^* (Fig. 2), Fig. 3 will often be more convenient. The two-letter designations of the center scales indicate the coordinated outer scales.

Examples

A transmitter with a variable output transformer and a capacity of 100 watts is available. The vswr at the load is 5. What maximum attenuation a_l of the line is tolerable, if 60 watts are required in the load? Answer: η = 60 percent, hence from Fig. 3 a_{max} = 1.15 db.

A transmission line of 0.5 db attenuation feeds an antenna represented by vswr = 2. What is the antenna power relative to the maximum transmitter power, if (1) the transmitter output impedance equals the characteristic impedance of the transmission line, and if (2) line input and generator output are matched impedancewise? An-

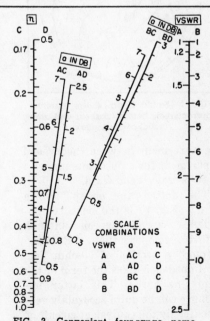

FIG. 3—Convenient four-range nomograph for determining efficiency of transmission line directly when attenuation and vswr are known. Use scales only in combinations indicated

swer: (1) from Fig. 1 $\eta^* = 79.3$ percent; (2) from Fig. 2, $\eta/\eta^* = 1.1$ and $\eta = 87.4$ percent. Note that η comes very close to $\eta_{max} = 89.2$ percent, the latter being read from Fig. 1 or Fig. 3 for

vswr $= 1$.

Under certain conditions the efficiency and power transfer factor seem to be considerably less than the values obtained from the nomographs. This is

due to neglecting losses in the transmitter tuning and tank circuits; these losses must be calculated independently as they have no relation to the efficiency of the line itself.

Theoretical Limitations to Impedance Matching

By ROBERT L. TANNER

THIS PAPER outlines a procedure whereby the theoretical limitations to impedance matching of simple circuits can be determined. It is shown that many antennas can be represented with adequate accuracy by a simple RLC circuit. Curves are included which show the relation between attainable vswr and a factor equal to (Bandwidth $\times$ Q). An example is worked out showing

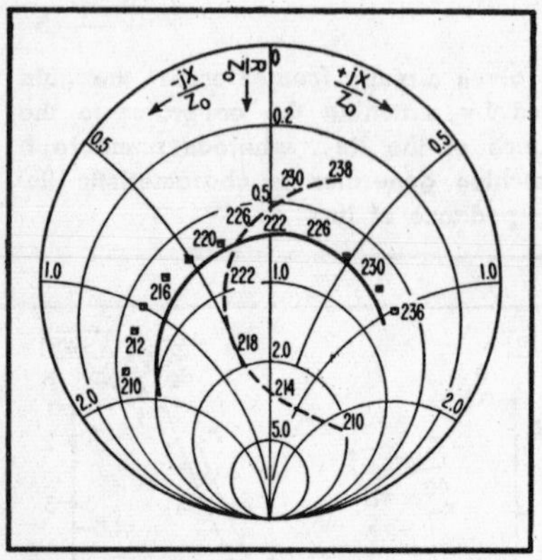

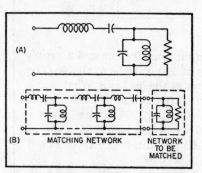

FIG. 1—Smith Chart shows antenna characteristic before (dashed) and after (solid) compensation

the agreement between theory and experiment for a flush antenna with a 10-percent bandwidth.

The dotted line on the Smith Chart (Fig. 1) is the measured impedance curve for an antenna before compensation. Rotation through a section of 50-ohm line, the impedance takes the form of the solid line curve. This latter impedance can be quite accurately represented by the equivalent circuit of Fig. 2A.

When the shunting susceptance of the parallel resonant circuit has been subtracted, the impedance follows the curve defined by the square points. This curve represents the series resonant circuit shown in the figure.

Inspection of the series resonant impedance curve shows the circuit to have a Q of approximately 15. This is determined from the definition for Q, $Q = f_r/\Delta f$, where Δf is the frequency band between the half-power frequencies, and f_r is the resonant frequency. The half-power frequencies are the frequencies at which the series resistance is equal to the series reactance. Inspection of the Smith Chart shows

these frequencies to be approximately 216.5 mc and 230 mc, while the resonant frequency is approximately 222 mc. Thus

$$Q = \frac{222}{230 - 216.5} = 15.3$$

Fano has shown[1] that optimum matching to a simple series resonant circuit is achieved by a matching network of the form shown in Fig. 2B, which consists of alternate shunting parallel resonant circuits, and series circuits.

When the network to be matched already includes, as in this case, a shunting circuit of smaller susceptance than the first element of the matching network, this susceptance can be considered as being lumped with the first element of the matching network. For such a condition the match which can be achieved is the same as when the series circuit alone is to be matched.

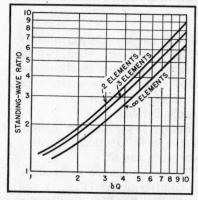

FIG. 2—Equivalent circuit of antenna after rotation through section of line (A) and equivalent circuit (B) of antenna and matching network

FIG. 3—Optimum matching to simple resonant circuit obtainable with network of n elements

The curves of Fig. 3, which are derived from results obtained by Fano, give the optimum match to a simple resonant circuit which can be achieved with a matching network of *n elements*. For the present example the circuit to be matched has a Q of 15.3. The fractional bandwidth δ over which the match is required is defined by the formula $f_2 - f_1/\sqrt{f_2 f_1}$, and in the present instance has the value

$$\delta = \frac{f_2 - f_1}{\sqrt{f_2 f_1}} \quad \frac{234 - 214}{\sqrt{234 \times 214}} = 0.0895$$

thus δQ has the value

$$\delta Q = 15.3 \times 0.0895 = 1.37$$

Referring to the curves of Fig. 3 we see that the optimum match which can be achieved with a two-element matching network (one shunt element and one series element) results in a vswr of approximately 1.5.

Fano shows that

$$\int_{f_1}^{f_2} \ln \frac{1}{\rho}\, df \leqq \text{constant}$$

where ρ = reflection coefficient.

A little study reveals an importance application in this condition. It shows that if the optimum match is to be achieved over the band of frequencies between f_1 and f_2, then the match at any point in that range can not be better than the optimum. Thus, for example, if a perfect match exists at one point in the range, $\rho = 0$ at that point and $1/\rho \to \infty$. Therefore, the contribution to the integral, which represents the area under the curve ln $1/\rho$, is very large for a small range of frequencies in the vicinity of the point. Since the value of the integral is bounded, this means that the contribution at other sections of the range must be small; that is, $1/\rho$ must be small, ρ large, and the match poor.

The performance of the antenna after matching gives substantial confirmation of the theory. The vswr oscillates about the value 1.5. A match better than optimum at the ends of the band has been obtained at the expense of a match poorer than optimum in the center.

The foregoing discussion applies to impedances which can be represented by the circuits of the type shown in Fig. 2A, in which the

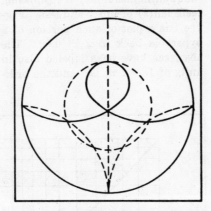

FIG. 4—Impedance curve of network which cannot be matched to value given by Fig. 3

shunting element has susceptance smaller than that required for the first element of the optimum matching network. If the susceptance of the shunt element is larger than this value, the excellence of the match which can be achieved is poorer than the value indicated by the curves of Fig. 3. In terms of the impedance curve on the Smith Chart, too large shunt susceptance means that the impedance curve of the uncompensated impedance is already wrapped too tightly as shown in Fig. 4.

Although the example which has been considered in the above discussion was a series resonant circuit shunted by a parallel resonant cir-

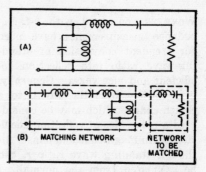

FIG. 5—Counterpart of impedance of Fig. 1 for which matching criteria apply is shown in A. Associated matching network is shown in B

cuit, the curves of Fig. 3 apply equally well to an impedance of the type shown in Fig. 5A.

Furthermore, all the arguments which were applied to the matching of a series resonant circuit apply equally well to the matching of a parallel resonant circuit if reactance is substituted for susceptance, and so on.

Thus, a parallel resonant circuit is best matched by a network such as the one shown in Fig. 5B which begins (at the load end) with a series element.

The match to a circuit such as the one in Fig. 5A is only as good as is indicated by the curves of Fig. 3 if the reactance of the series element is smaller than that required for the first element of the optimum matching network of Fig. 5B.

REFERENCE

(1) R. M. Fano, "Theoretical Limitations on Broadband Matching of Arbitrary Impedances," Technical Report No. 41, MIT Research Lab. of Electronics.

Graph for Smith Chart

By R. L. LINTON, JR.

WORKERS concerned with r-f impedance measurements have need for frequent conversion of standing-wave ratio into reflection coefficient and vice versa. Generally, information finds its way onto a Smith chart[1], which may be considered a polar plot of reflection coefficient k_r in magnitude and phase. Although standing wave ratio r_v can be estimated from the normalized resistance circles on the chart, a more accurate determination may be desired. Particularly at high reflection coefficients, estimates of standing-wave ratio are extremely difficult.

The graph in Fig. 1 provides a simple graphical means of obtaining standing-wave ratios up to 99 in terms of reflection coefficient, or vice versa. Of even greater convenience is the feature whereby the standing-wave ratio may be obtained in terms of transmission coefficient k_t. This parameter is equivalent to the normalized distance in from the outside circumference of the chart, a very easy value to use in dealing with high standing-wave ratios.

The graphical construction may be prepared from memory whenever needed. All that is required is a sheet of two-cycle log paper and a straight edge. The construction is derived as follows.

The well-known formula for voltage standing-wave ratio is written:

$$r_v = (1 + |k_r|)/(1 - |k_r|) \quad (1)$$

Add one to each side of the equation:

$$1 + r_v = (1 + |k_r|)/(1 - |k_r|) + 1 \quad (2)$$

Multiply by $(1 - |k_r|)$:

$$(1 - |k_r|)(1 + r_v) = 2 \quad (3)$$

Replace $(1 - |k_r|)$ by $|k_t|$, the transmission coefficient:

$$|k_t|(1 + r_v) = 2 \quad (4)$$

Let:

$$|k_t| = 1 - |k_r| = x \quad (5)$$
$$1 + r_v = y$$

obtaining for Eq. 4

$$xy = 2 \quad (6)$$

This is the equation for an equilateral hyperbola in Cartesian coordinates. A hyperbola plotted on logarithmic coordinates is a straight line at 45 degrees to the axes. We are interested only in the first quadrant and in abscissas (transmission coefficients) of unity and less. Figure 1 is a plot of such portion of a hyperbola back to $x = 0.02$. The abscissas have been labeled also in units of $1 - x = |k_r|$ and the ordinates have been labeled in units of $y - 1 = r_v$ more useful than y itself. The simple, easily constructed conversion chart results.

REFERENCE

(1) P. H. Smith, An Improved Transmission Line Calculator, ELECTRONICS, p 130, Jan. 1944; J. Markus and V. Zeluff, "Electronics for Engineers," McGraw-Hill Book Co., New York, p 326, 1945.

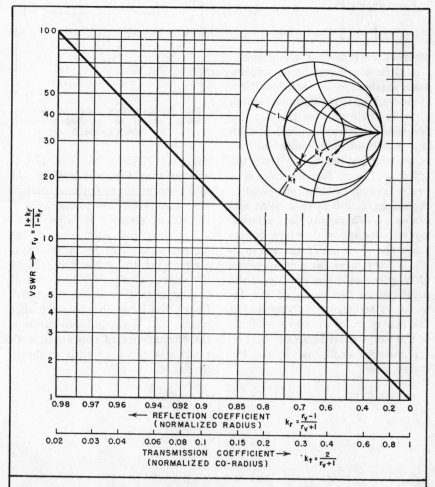

FIG. 1—Graph giving voltage standing-wave ratio vs reflection coefficient based on normalized radius on Smith chart. Graph also gives transmission coefficient based on normalized co-radius, often more useful

Attenuation in Waveguides

Power-handling capabilities and attenuation for the TE$_{1,0}$ mode in the rectangular waveguides adopted as standard by the Radio Manufacturers Association

By HENRY LISMAN

IN A RECTANGULAR copper waveguide with air dielectric and for the TE$_{1,0}$ mode, the attenuation is given by the equation:

$$\alpha_{\text{copper}} = \frac{0.01107}{a^{3/2}} \left[\frac{\frac{1}{2} \frac{a}{b} \left(\frac{f}{f_c}\right)^{3/2} + \left(\frac{f}{f_c}\right)^{-1.2}}{\left\{ \left(\frac{f}{f_c}\right)^2 - 1 \right\}^{1/2}} \right]$$

where α_{copper} = attenuation in db per foot for copper waveguide, a and b are the larger and smaller inner dimensions in cm, f/f_c is the ratio of the frequency transmitted to the cutoff frequency.

If a metal other than copper is used, the attenuation given by the formula should be multiplied by a constant which is equal to the square root of the ratio of the resistivity of that metal to the resistivity of copper. A few values for commonly used materials are:

Aluminum.	1.27	Chromium. 1.27
Brass	2.00	Gold 1.18
Cadmium. .	2.04	Silver 0.95

In the graph, there is plotted a series of curves showing the variation of attenuation, in db per foot, with frequency for the same frequency ranges used in the power curves described below.

The maximum continuous-wave power that a waveguide can carry for the TE$_{1,0}$ mode is given by $P = (E_{max})^2 \, 6.63 \, (10^{-4}) \, ab \, (\lambda/\lambda_g)$ where P = maximum power for the TE$_{1,0}$ mode in watts, E_{max} = maximum permissible voltage gradient (A value of 15,000 volts per cm has been assumed), a and b are the larger and smaller inner dimen-

sions respectively in cm, λ/λ_g is the ratio of the free space wavelength to that in the guide.

This equation gives the theoretical maximum power that a waveguide can handle if the voltage standing-wave ratio is 1 and is valid for particular conditions of humidity and pressure only. Furthermore, the breakdown voltage is also affected by initial ionization, gap width, pulse width and repetition rate and surface points.

In the graph, there is plotted a series of curves showing variation of maximum power that can be transmitted through the various waveguides with frequency for the respective frequency ranges which are obtained from the condition that $1.18 < \dfrac{\lambda}{\lambda_g} < 1.67$.

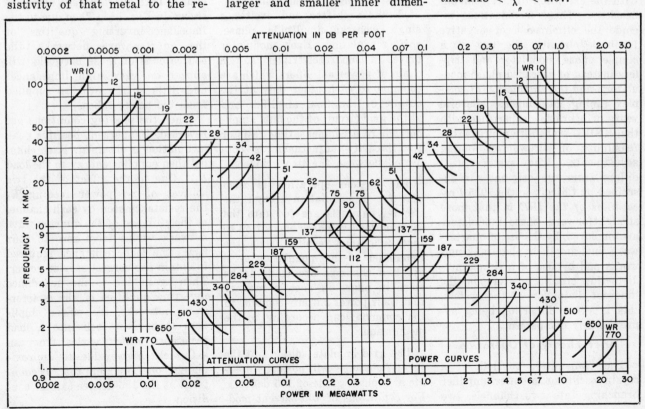

TRANSMITTERS

Five-KW Phase-to-Amplitude Transmitter

Phase-to-amplitude modulation provides high-quality signals with 1.5-percent rms distortion at low and medium audio frequencies and 2.8 at 7,500 cps.   Total power input to transmitter is 13.5 kw for full output

By NORMAN D. WEBSTER

NEED AROSE at station KOH in Reno, Nevada, for a 5-kw a-m transmitter that would fit into an existing building that was originally designed to house a 1-kw transmitter.

It was decided that a phase-to-amplitude modulated transmitter would be used. The 5-kw design finally adopted resembles, to a certain extent, the 50-kw version used at KFBK in Sacramento, California, with the exception of a few simplifications. These modifications include the elimination of negative feedback circuits, the use of a simple phase modulator and triplers instead of cascaded phase modulators, and the elimination of complex tuning mechanisms. Several years of operating experience with the KFBK transmitter prove the feasibility of screwdriver tuning adjustments. The system used differs from the original one described by Chireix in the 1935 *Proceedings of the IRE* in that more straightforward phase modulators are employed, by the use of quarter-wave final-amplifier plate-tank networks and by use of a simple predistorting circuit to overcome the inherent distortion of the system, this inherent distortion being approximately five percent.

Brief Theory of Operation

The transmitter consists of a crystal oscillator, a buffer amplifier branching into two channels, two phase shifters, two frequency triplers, two sets of cascaded class C r-f power amplifiers and output circuits wherein the currents from the two phase-modulated channels are brought together resulting in the production of amplitude-modulated waves.

The output of the buffer amplifier divides into two components of equal amplitude and opposite phase. Each of these two components passes through a manually-operated phase shifter and excites a single constant-amplitude phase-shift modulator. Each modulator drives a separate tripler and a chain of power amplifiers which are common to each other only at the output of the final amplifier and at the grid circuit of the final amplifier where a compensating resistor for linearity adjustment is connected between the two grids.

The system operation is such that for a modulation trough the two r-f channels are fed into the common load in phase opposition so that no output results. Over the remainder of the modulation cycle the two channels are made to be more in phase in such a manner that their power outputs combine in the common load according to the modulation.

The grid or plate voltages of the two r-f channels will normally operate at a phase angle of 135 degrees. For conditions of 100-percent modulation, the phase of one channel is advanced $22\frac{1}{2}$ degrees and the other is retarded $22\frac{1}{2}$ degrees. At this instant the phase difference between channels could be 180 or 90 degrees depending on which channel initially leads or lags the other.

When the two channels are 180 degrees out of phase no voltage will appear across R_L as illustrated in Fig. 1A. This condition constitutes in effect a short circuit of the sink ends of both quarter-wave networks shown in Fig. 1A. Then due to the impedance-inverting qualities of the quarter-wave networks, the source ends of these networks will appear as very high impedances and little energy will be supplied from the power tubes.

When the phasing conditions are reversed, 100-percent positive peak modulation is obtained. Each channel then supplies energy to the load R_L. Due to the effect of the two sources of r-f power feeding R_L the resistance seen by each channel at the sink end of the quarter-wave network varies from zero to four times the load resistance required to obtain the correct carrier power. Then again due to the impedance inverting qualities of the quarter-wave networks, the power amplifiers themselves look into a load resistance which varies from an extremely high value to approximately one quarter that encountered at the 135-degree carrier condition.

Vector Diagrams

Figure 1B is a voltage diagram showing the phase relations of the final plate voltages of the two channels at carrier (solid vectors), at modulation peak (dashed vectors) and at a modulation trough (dotted vectors). Inasmuch as the two channels are connected to R_L in shunt rather than in series, the power relations at the load itself can best be understood by reference to the current diagram of Fig. 1C.

It is seen that the current I_L, flowing through the load is the vector sum of the two channel currents I_1 and I_2. When the relative phase between channels θ is 135 degrees the load current is at its carrier value. When θ is 180 degrees the load current (and consequently the load voltage) is 0, and with $\theta = 90$ degrees, I_L has it maximum value corresponding to a peak of modulation.

Here it also becomes evident that inasmuch as each final tube delivers varying amounts of power at a substantially constant r-f voltage, the phase-to-amplitude system is in reality one of load-impedance modulation. The load presented to the output terminals of the coupling network of channel 1 is

$$Z_{L1} = \frac{E_L}{I_1} = \frac{I_L R_L}{I_1}$$

An examination of Fig. 1C will show that

$$I_L = 2 I_1 \cos \frac{\theta}{2}$$

Thus

$$|Z_L| = \left(2 \cos \frac{\theta}{2} \right) R_L$$

and varies from a short circuit at $\theta = 180$ degrees to $\sqrt{2} R_L$ at $\theta = 90$ degrees.

This gives the absolute value of the complex impedance. Further study of Fig. 1 will show that the phase angle, of the impedance, or the power factor angle, is $\theta/2$. This makes the complete expression for the load impedance as seen by each channel

$$Z_L = \left(2 \cos \frac{\theta}{2} \right) R_L \underline{|\theta/2}$$

or in rectangular form

$$Z_L = \left(2 \cos^2 \frac{\theta}{2} \right) R_L + j \left(2 \sin \frac{\theta}{2} \cos \frac{\theta}{2} \right)$$

$$R_L = 2 R_L \cos^2 \frac{\theta}{2} + j R_L \sin \theta$$

This shows that in addition to the desired resistance variation $2R_L \cos^2 \theta/2$ there is also introduced

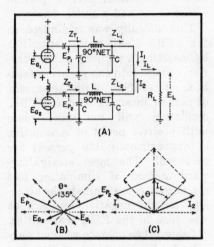

FIG. 1—Basic output schematic and vector diagrams show phase-to-amplitude principle

a reactive component, caused by the circulating current common to the two tank circuits. The reactance will be inductive for one channel and capacitive by an equal amount for the other channel.

Unfortunately these reactive components vary with the operating angle θ making it impossible to balance them out completely over the entire modulation cycle by introducing fixed reactances. However, it is evident that if enough fixed reactance of the proper sign is added to each channel to make the power factor unity at, or slightly below, the operating angle chosen for the proper carrier power, the power factor over the remainder of the modulation cycle will remain good except near the amplitude-modulation troughs where low efficiency is of little consequence.

Final Amplifier

If we assume that each final tube operates as a constant voltage generator, the power drawn from either tube varies inversely as the square of cos $\theta/2$. When the operating angle is chosen so that $\theta/2$ varies over the near-linear portion of the cosine curve, the load impedance and power output vary as the square of the angle of phase separation, which is the desired result.

It is also of interest that in actual practice the loaded Q of the 90-degree final amplifier plate-tank networks may vary from 20 at carrier to 5 for a positive crest of modulation and from 20 to 600 or so depending on the inherent Q of the output networks for a negative trough of modulation. For good fidelity, means must be provided to prevent the loaded Q of the tank, and consequently the r-f plate voltage, from rising above a predetermined value during part of a modulation cycle. This is accomplished at KOH by biasing the final amplifier grids so that plate current flows during a large portion of the positive r-f grid driving half cycles, thus keeping the output tanks loaded by the plate circuits of the output tubes. Such procedure reduces the plate efficiency to approximately 70 percent at carrier level.

A further improvement in r-f voltage regulation is effected by the use of a compensating load resistor R_c connected between the grids of the final amplifier tubes. When conditions of phasing between the two channels of the transmitter are momentarily more in phase less r-f power is dissipated in R_c. This results in an increase of final amplifier grid driving power at the times it is needed or during positive excursions of modulation.

During negative troughs the resistor serves to reduce the driving power and the final amplifier grid bias voltage. This in turn reduces the tendency for the final amplifier r-f plate voltage to rise during the portion of a modulation cycle when the final amplifier plate circuits are practically unloaded. The current through R_c varies approximately as $(2 \sin \theta/2)E_p/R_c$ where E_p is the rms r-f plate voltage of one driver tube. A rather complex vacuum tube r-f voltage regulator is used on the KFBK 50-kilowatt transmitter for the purpose of maintaining a constant r-f voltage at the plates of the final amplifier tubes.

Overmodulation

A very attractive feature of this transmitter not obtainable in other transmitters is that it may be heavily overmodulated without attendant side band interference, since the two phase-modulated channels can never in practice be exactly identical in power output. The carrier, therefore, will not cut off during accidental overmodulation. The positive peaks will continue to rise until the two phase-modulated channels are in phase or until the final amplifier tubes are saturated. Measurements on the KOH transmitter show 10 percent rms distortion at 110 percent positive peak modulation. At double the audio input level required for 100 percent modulation the second harmonic distortion is about 100 percent.

This may be understood from an inspection of Fig. 1C. Here 22.5-degree phase excursions in the two

channels will cause a 180-degree out-of-phase condition and a negative trough of amplitude modulation. Any further phase changes in the same direction will cause the carrier to commence increasing in power. This is a condition that would change an over-all negative feedback circuit momentarily to one of positive feedback with resultant oscillation over a portion of the input audio cycle.

This difficulty was minimized on the KFBK 50-kilowatt transmitter by inserting a properly-phased carrier voltage into the negative feedback r-f rectifier. With the amount of carrier insertion used at KFBK, oscillation will not take place until positive peaks of modulation of approximately 130 percent are exceeded. The most straightforward manner of eliminating this complexity is to eliminate the necessity for the negative feedback as was done in the KOH transmitter.

Designed to operate without negative feedback, this transmitter has a noise level of −59 db below the 100-percent modulation level, an rms distortion at 100-percent modulation of 1.5 percent at low and

medium audio frequencies and 2.8 percent at 7,500 cps. The distortion is predominantly of the second-harmonic variety, which is difficult to detect even with a trained ear.

Conclusion

A year of operation of this transmitter proves it to be stable, reliable and economical of tubes. The total power drain of the transmitter averages 13.5 kilowatts during operation. Although it is more critical of original adjustment than high-level-modulated transmitters, its economy of space, power and tubes and its excellent audio fidelity and its ability for heavy modulation recommend this type of transmitter to those stations having circuit-minded chief engineers and a flair for economy.

The author wishes to thank F. E. Terman and Oswald G. Villard, Jr. of Stanford University and William E. Evans, Jr. for their invaluable assistance in the development of the phase-to-amplitude modulated transmitters discussed in this paper.

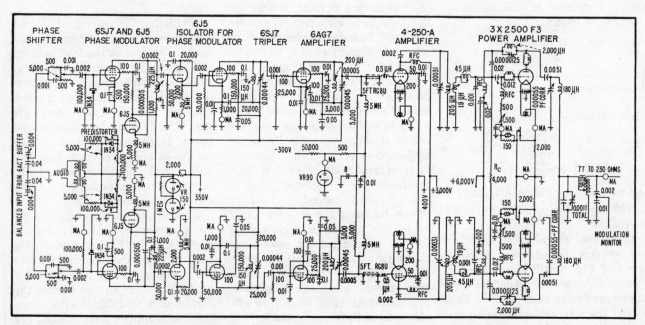

FIG. 2—Schematic of 5-kw phase-to-amplitude modulation transmitter. Two 6AC7's are used as crystal oscillator and buffer

Instantaneous Deviation Control

Audio signal of an f-m transmitter is differentiated, clipped and integrated so that the output wave is identical to the input except for slope limiting. Transmitter frequency deviations are held to definite limits determined by the maximum allowable slope

By MARION R. WINKLER

A FEW YEARS ago the performance of a radio communications system depended primarily on two factors, the power of the transmitter and the sensitivity of the receiver.

Interference between stations or systems was no serious trouble because their operating frequencies were sufficiently separated with unused channels which acted as guard bands. As more services acquired frequency assignments, the number of guard bands decreased.

Concentrated attention has been given to control receiver images and spurious response, receiver radiation and transmitter harmonics. The selectivity of receivers has been greatly improved. The engineering art has reached a point where, today, alternate channels can be used successfully with adjacent channels serving as guard bands. It must be concluded, therefore, that half the available channel space is being wasted.

Phase-modulation transmitters are particularly vulnerable to over modulation. Without control, loud voices, sharp voices, transients, or noise pulses produce wide excursions of the transmitter frequency, extending the deviation into the adjacent channel and even into the alternate channel. For operation on the desired channel, this means loss of intelligibility and a decrease in the signal to noise ratio as the transmitter deviates beyond the pass band of the receiver. Adjacent channel operation will not be possible until the frequency deviation of all transmitters is kept within their assigned channel.

Principle of Operation

In attempting to control the frequency deviation of a phase-modulation transmitter, it is often customary to use conventional amplitude compressors. These devices are not instantaneous. The attack time is slow and the device remains paralyzed after a transient. Even if the audio amplitude is controlled the frequency deviation of the transmitter is not controlled because the frequency deviation of a phase-modulated transmitter is a function of both the frequency and the amplitude of the audio wave.

The desired answer to the problem of controlling frequency deviation would be a device which would virtually place a barrier or limit on the frequency excursions caused by the phase modulator. It is difficult to place such a barrier on the frequency after the radio waves have passed through the phase modulator. However, if an audio wave is synthetically produced, which would graphically look like the frequency deviations produced by the modulator, then barriers could be introduced which would hold the amplitude to certain prescribed limits.

After the audio wave has passed through the amplitude limiting barriers it might be restored by a reversible process to its original form and delivered to the phase modulator.

The manner in which this can be done is illustrated in Fig. 1. This circuit provides instantaneous deviation control (IDC). The synthesized wave is produced by a differentiation circuit. This differentiator is a simple device consisting of only a resistor and a capacitor.

As shown in both the first graph and the second column of illustrated

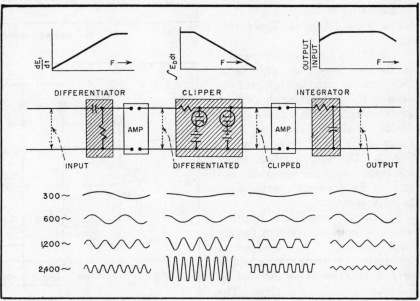

FIG. 1—Basic circuits illustrating the fundamental principle

wave forms, the differentiated voltage is proportional to both the input voltage and the frequency; more precisely it is proportional to the slope or steepness of the input wave. Since the differentiator is a gain losing device it is usually de-

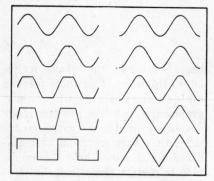

FIG. 2—Sine waves with various degrees of clipping, before and after integrating

sirable to use an amplifier to raise the signal to a suitable level for clipping. This also provides electronic isolation, with zero loading of the differentiator and a more suitable source impedance for the clipper.

The clipper may be a pair of biased diodes, also shown in Fig. 1, which become conducting when the instantaneous peak value of the differentiated wave exceeds the bias. One diode will clip positive peaks and the other the negative peaks. This is shown in the illustrated wave forms of clipped voltage.

After the wave has been operated on by the clipper, the differentiation process can be reversed by passing the wave through an integrator circuit. This is also a simple device consisting again of a resistor and a capacitor as shown in Fig. 1. The second graph shows the response of the integrator circuit to be inversely proportional to the frequency.

The output wave is now identical with the input wave except for the slope limiting. The transmitter frequency deviations will be held to very definite limits as dictated by the maximum allowable slope. The third graph indicates the overall

fidelity of the instantaneous deviation control circuit to be flat over a wide band. The usable bandwidth will depend on accepted tolerances and the frequencies that need to be controlled.

The distortion caused by IDC is quite small. This is illustrated in the output voltage wave form shown in Fig. 1. Distortion is introduced only into those wave fronts which have a slope that exceed a predetermined amount. These distortions in general consist of higher order harmonics which fortunately are eliminated by the integrator to a point where they are readily tolerated.

The distortion introduced in a sine wave can best be understood from a graphical study as shown in Fig. 2. A moderate amount of clipping produces trapezoidal waves with curved sides. After integrat-

ing, the curved sides become the rounded extreme of the alternating current and the flat top becomes the straight line sides of the same current. The rounded portion is identical with the rounded part of the original sine wave before being applied to the differentiator. From a geometric standpoint the only distortion introduced has been over that part of the sine wave which had too great a slope.

Obviously the greatest distortion that can possibly exist would occur when the clipper produces square waves. The output from the integrator would then be a triangular wave having only odd harmonics. The third harmonic would be 1/9th of the fundamental, the fifth harmonic 1/25th of the fundamental and other harmonics trivial.

The distortion introduced by IDC into voice frequencies does not lend

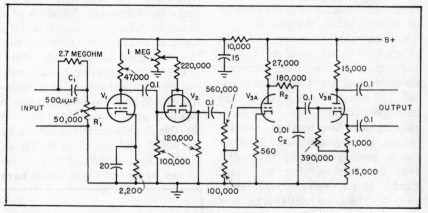

FIG. 3—Fixed station instantaneous deviation control circuit

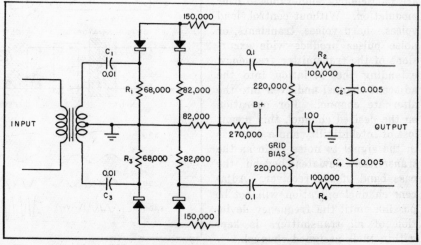

FIG. 4—Circuit of a mobile IDC unit

itself quite so well to such a simple analysis. Many voice frequencies are quite peaked and jagged and can pass through the IDC circuit without having their intelligence content seriously altered yet the transmitter frequency deviation may be reduced by a large margin. The voice level between syllables is usually lower and experiences little or no clipping. It is therefore possible to provide greater deviation for the lower voice levels or greater overall average deviations without exceeding the desired or authorized deviation limits.

Commercial Equipment

In making a practical application of IDC to a transmitter there are a number of considerations which may dictate the final design.

Size, cost, power drain, the fidelity desired and the range of offending frequencies will affect the choice of components and circuits. The type of differentiator, clipper, or integrator may vary considerably from the one illustrated in Fig. 1.

Figure 3 is the circuit diagram of a fixed station IDC unit. Differentiation is accomplished by the capacitor C_1 and the resistor R_1. The clipper circuit differs from that previously described.

The combined diodes are fed a constant direct current. Normally half this current goes through each diode. Any small signal variation, positive or negative, applied to the cathode of the input diode, will normally cause the same variation at the cathode of the output diode. The diodes therefore serve to conduct the variations from input to output. However, if large variations of signal are applied at the input, the first diode will become nonconducting on positive peaks and the second will become nonconducting on negative peaks.

Integration is accomplished by the capacitor C_2 and the resistor R_2. The clipping level, or the deviation, is adjusted by a potentiometer regulating the diode current. The volume level is adjusted at the input where no interaction exists between it and deviation. A resistor shunting C_1 affords some bass compensation. The output is pushpull.

Figure 4 is the circuit diagram of a unit useful for mobile application because of its low cost, small space requirements and low power drain.

This unit is designed to accommodate a carbon microphone in the input and deliver a balanced or pushpull output for the grids of the phase modulator tubes. No amplification is used within the circuit and clipping is performed with germanium crystal diodes. Differentiation is performed with the C_1-R_1 and C_3-R_3 circuits; integration with the C_2-R_2 and C_4-R_4 circuits.

Performance

When the action of an IDC circuit is observed on an oscilloscope connected to the discriminator of a good f-m receiver, the voice wave seems to strike an invisible barrier even when subjected to 20 or 30 db overload. The barrier remains fixed even when subjected to sudden bursts of signal or transients. There is no attack time or paralysis, it is instantaneous. This makes close talking possible thereby reducing background noise. It tolerates a wide range of audio level.

The control prevents transmitters on nearby channels from spilling over into the pass band of system receivers. But more important is the fact that it holds the system transmitted frequency within the associated receiver bandpass response, permitting a higher average modulation level. This results in an increased signal-to-noise ratio and improved reception in fringe area operation.

Adjacent channel operation in the mobile field is now a requirement and it is axiomatic that deviation control is necessary. Since IDC is quite simple, economical, and fool proof, it is destined to see wide application.

Acknowledgement is due John Hultquist who was the first to try the idea, and others who have contributed the commercial developments.

Improving Program-Limiter Performance

Use of delay limiter described prevents sideband splatter on crowded a-m broadcast channels effectively and economically. Fringe area reception is improved, overmodulation peaks are reduced in number and total modulation energy is greater

DONALD W. HOWE, JR.

CERTAIN BROADCAST peak-limiting amplifiers are often unsatisfactory on the present crowded and competitive a-m broadcast channels where sideband splatter has to be prevented to avoid interference with nearby adjacent-channel stations and maximum program level is imperative for effective coverage.

As far as coverage is concerned, it would be possible simply to adjust the limiter output to the 100-percent modulation point and to increase the input to get a high average modulation. Most listeners would never notice the distortion. In this case, the transmitter would be overmodulated for several peaks of each loud beat of music. Even some of the new limiters are subject to this criticism since they avoid transient distortion known as "plop" or "thump" by using an attack time of 50 to 100 milliseconds. This practice gives rise to radiations on several adjacent channels with serious consequences.

The device to be described is the result of efforts to improve the operation of the limiter in use at WARE, rather than incur the greater expense of a limiter that would meet our requirements.

The goal set was the fulfillment of the requirements set forth by Maxwell[1]; essentially zero attack time to prevent even occasional overmodulation, flat output level characteristic, and elimination of transients. Any one requirement may be obtained easily at the expense of the others.

The delay limiter was developed to enable the standard limiter to provide zero attack time with the least possible detriment to the second two requirements. Flat output level and elimination of transients may be secured by proper adjust-

ment and balance of a good standard limiter.

To study the dynamic performance, a standard signal is desirable. The circuit shown in Fig. 1 provides a sine wave whose amplitude can be increased by a known amount on an impulse from an oscillograph switch, the increase occurring where the wave crosses the zero axis. The upper wave in Fig. 2 shows the type of signal produced.

The need for such an electronic switch is shown by the initial transient in Fig. 3. The entire waveform is the response of the limiter as it was received from the factory to a sudden 6-db increase above limiting threshold in a 360-cycle wave. Aside from the mechanical switching difficulties are the defects of the limiter itself: 3.7-db overshoot, about 20-milliseconds attack time and a control ratio (increase in input over increase in output) of 5.5. Such operation cannot provide much increase in program level without serious overmodulation splatter on other stations.

Circuit Development

If the input signal to the limiter were fed through a delay line and the control bias were obtained from a separate amplifier fed from the input to the delay line, the limiter

should be able to anticipate peaks. This simple idea is likely to result in overcontrol and was discarded in favor of the pulse method to be described, which simply speeds up the action of the regular limiter.

Consider a limiter having the general type of circuit shown in Fig. 4. Voltage divider R_1-R_2 provides a diode bias so that the limiter gain will be constant up to the limiting point at which the diodes conduct, producing a gain control bias for the control tube or tubes V_1. In general, the larger this diode bias is in comparison to the control tube bias, the greater will be the control ratio or the flatter will be the output level characteristic.

The diodes operate on peaks and because a finite time always is required to charge C_1, one or more peaks get through the limiter before gain reduction is complete, as shown in Fig. 3. If the diode delay bias could be reduced momentarily just prior to the peak of a too large signal wave, the diodes could rectify on the increasing slope of the large signal and would have C_1 charged to a sufficient degree to anticipate the peak without resorting to a clipping action. This reduction in bias is accom-

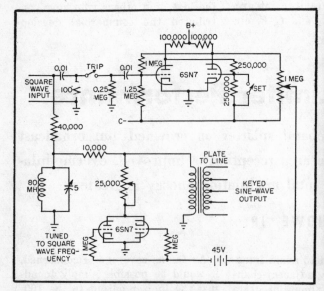

FIG. 1—Circuit to produce increase in amplitude of output sine wave as it goes through zero

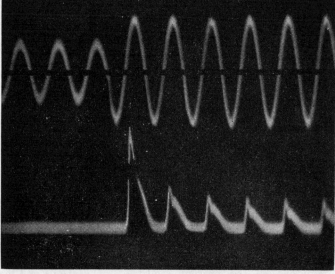

FIG. 2—Delayed standard signal and accelerating pulse. Upper wave is the type produced by the circuit of Fig. 1

plished by a pulse circuit, as shown in Fig. 6.

A block diagram of the whole device, Fig. 5, will perhaps best explain its operation. The heart of the circuit is the 0.25-millisecond delay line, representing with lumped constants, a distortionless telephone line. The number of elements determine the cut-off frequency, about 27,000 cycles here.

To make up for the delay line

that this speed up acts on the negative modulation peaks. A few peaks above 100-percent positive modulation cause no harm. As additional insurance against negative over-modulation, an adjustable clipper is used which does not operate on any steady-state signal but only before the 6L7 gain is automatically reduced. Even then the tops of high peaks are not really clipped but only rounded.

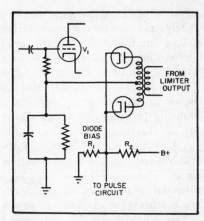

FIG. 4—General type of standard limiter circuit for adapting to delay limiter

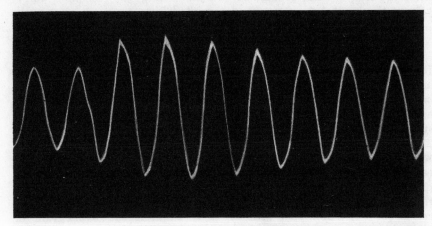

FIG. 3—Performance of a factory-adjusted standard peak limiter to a sudden 6-db increase above threshold.

losses, an additional stage was added and this provided an opportunity to provide compression to aid the peak limiting. The bias amplifier, fed from the cathode of the 6L7, supplies the agc bias and a monitoring output, as well as supplying undelayed signal to operate the pulse-forming circuit shown in Fig. 6.

In the pulse-forming circuit, the 1N56 and its R-C load provide a voltage for the grid of one-half a 6SN7, which follows the envelope of the signal at least on the increasing side. For any steady signal level the 6SN7 is at or near cut-off by virtue of its high bias resistor. On any sudden increase in signal, however, the tube will conduct until the 0.5-μf cathode capacitor is charged, dragging down the diode bias of the standard limiter before the peak of the delayed signal reaches the output of the limiter. No attempt was made to use full-wave rectification but polarities were carefully chosen so

Three time constants are used to provide correct operation with all types of program material. First, the standard peak limiter has essentially zero attack time, and its release time is usually set about 0.25 second. Second, the 6L7 agc has an attack time of approximately one second, controlled by the 0.25-μf capacitor and its 2-megohm charging resistor. Recovery time is twice as long. Third, when a high level continues for several seconds, the 4-μf capacitor becomes charged, preventing full-gain recovery for ten or fifteen seconds.

Adjustment and Operation

Figure 7 shows the complete diagram of the added unit used. The adjustment of the input signal level, input to bias amplifier controlled by R_1, agc voltage controlled by R_2 and the bias on the pulse amplifier controlled by R_3 are somewhat interrelated and must be adjusted with care. It was found that the highest signal received, —20 db, would al-

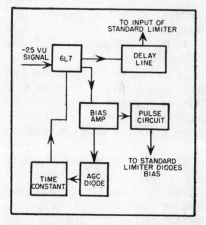

FIG. 5—Block diagram of delay limiter

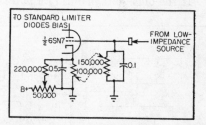

FIG. 6—Pulse-forming circuit used in delay limiter

low a compression of 12 db with no more than 2-percent distortion. The meter in the cathode circuit of the 6L7 provides a measure of compression once calibrated.

Flatness of agc characteristic is controlled by R_2. A high setting of R_2 requires a high setting of the input voltage from R_1. Since a compression action rather than a limiting action is wanted here, R_2 should be set low enough to give a gradual gain reduction. Finally R_3 may be set so that the pulse tube is completely nonconducting except for sudden increases in program level. An oscilloscope on the diode bias of the standard limiter is useful.

A desirable form of pulse is shown in Fig. 2 in relation to a suddenly increased 500-cycle signal out of the delay line. The single panel control shown in the photograph is the input to the bias amplifier R_1. This control in practice provides an adjustment of the average compression carried and is set to zero when making over-all noise and distortion measurements.

The oscillogram, Fig. 2, shows that the pulse starts only a few degrees after the signal goes through zero in a direction such as to produce negative modulation. If the polarity of the standard signal were reversed, making the first large peak in such a direction as to produce negative modulation, the pulse would start only a few degrees after the previous zero. In this case, the pulse reaches its peak of 32 volts about 30 degrees or 0.17 millisecond before the peak of the input signal to the limiter. The bias on the limiter diodes is then decreased from its normal 75 volts to 43 volts.

If the bias voltage during a pulse

is x volts, limiting action will start when the instantaneous value of the input signal is $x/75$ of the normal peak threshold value and should be complete by the time the first peak is reached. Successive pulses after the first are unnecessary and perhaps undesirable since they reduce the steady-state output below the normal value. The oscillogram is not long enough to show the complete disappearance of these pulses when the slow agc has reduced the gain of the input 6L7.

Performance

The unit has been used in conjunction with a Raytheon limiter amplifier and listener response has been gratifying. In many fringe areas where the measured field strengths of other stations are 2 or 3 times the strength of WARE, we have been reported as the loudest signal on the band. This is probably due not so much to the fact that the output of the limiter can be set 3 or 4 db higher without overmodulation as it is due to the reduction of dynamic range by the compressor. Since the service area of a class II, III or IV station is protected from interfering co-channel signals only in excess of −26 db (20 to 1 field strengths),

there is not much point in preserving a dynamic range of more than 20 db. The time constant of the automatic gain control of the 6L7 input stage serves to bring the weaker portions of a program out of the mud and in general leads to greater listener satisfaction.

A more scientific test was made with a ten-minute taped program. It was played through once using the standard limiter alone and again using the complete equipment. Thirty overmodulation peaks as indicated by the modulation monitor flashing lamp were observed in the former case, and only three using the delay line limiter. Furthermore, the total modulation energy as indicated by a thermal integrating wattmeter, was 53 percent greater than for the standard limiter. In both cases the limiter amplifier was operated with 5-db maximum limiting and when the delay limiter was used its average compression was 6 db in addition.

A simultaneous oscillogram of

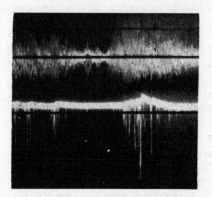

FIG. 8—Program performance of delay limiter showing accelerating pulses for 10 to 15-db limiting

output signal and pulse voltage when the unit was operated on program with more than 10 db peak limiting is interesting, as shown in Fig. 8. Note that practically none of the negative signal peaks exceed the 100-percent modulation line but that many peaks extend above the 100-percent positive modulation line. Since the limiter action is designed to anticipate negative modulation peaks only, positive overshoot may be expected. Proper choice of input signal polarity when

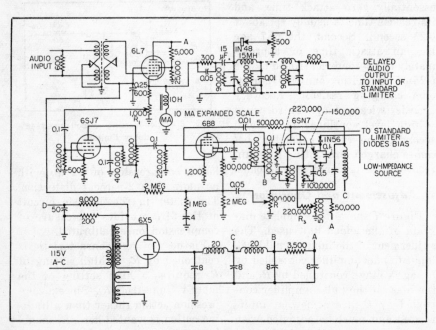

FIG. 7—Schematic diagram of delay limiter

positive and negative peaks are un-equal may result in considerable increase in volume level.

Further Development

Oscillograms taken with the standard test signal were somewhat disappointing in that they showed an overshoot for a small fraction of a cycle. Increased delay may be necessary here or per-haps the pulse circuit should be fed from a cathode follower to avoid output transformer phase shifts.

To prevent a transient rattle in the limiter, it is essential that the gain-controlled tubes be balanced for small and large signals as well as for static current. Individual cathode and screen adjustment together with means for detecting dynamic balance are being installed.

A useful addition would be some means of selecting the polarity of the incoming signal such that the larger peak would always give positive modulation.[2]

REFERENCES

(1) D. E. Maxwell, Dynamic Performance of Peak-Limiting Amplifiers, *Proc. IRE*, Nov. 1947.
(2) R. P. Crosby, Automatic Phase Reversal Amplifier, ELECTRONICS, **14**, p 64, Oct. 1941.

Audio-Input Limiter for Mobile F-M

By LAWRENCE C. FULLER, JR.

INEXPENSIVE AND COMPACT, the audio-input limiter described provides modulation limiting for mobile f-m transmitters. It permits maximum coverage for a given power by providing 100 percent modulation without the dangers of adjacent channel interference and receiver distortion from overmodulation. The limiter avoids the distortion introduced by conventional circuits and may be used in public address systems to prevent acoustic feedback. Its application is restricted to use with a carbon microphone.

Basic Circuit

The microphone shown in Fig. 1 receives direct current from the B

given level. The audio signal is stepped up by the transformer to a higher level, which in some cases is sufficient to modulate the transmitter without further amplification. Part of this audio component is amplified by the triode section of V_2 and rectified by the diode, causing a negative voltage to appear at the grid of V_1 proportional to the average audio-signal level entering the microphone. The louder the audio signal, the more negative the bias,

ing constant output.

Audio Amplifier

Since the audio current is not amplified before reaching the modulator tube, there is no chance

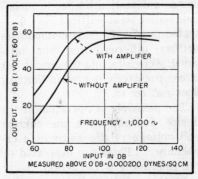

FIG. 3—Curves show effect of amplifier in limiter circuit

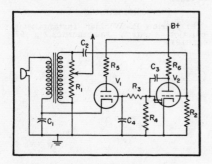

FIG. 1—Basic audio-limiter circuit

supply through V_1 in series with the primary of the audio transformer. Capacitor C_1 completes the audio circuit consisting of the microphone and transformer primary. With no signal into the microphone, the current is set to a

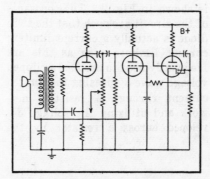

FIG. 2—Limiter circuit with audio amplifier

consequently, the less current will be supplied to the microphone. Since the output of the microphone is proportional to the direct current through it below saturation, the output is reduced and limiting action obtained. For example, if current is reduced to 5 ma by an audio signal, and the signal increased 20 db, the microphone current will be further reduced to 0.5 ma maintain-

for the introduction of microphonics. If amplification were necessary, it would be done at a high audio level as shown in Fig. 2 and the gain would probably be small. The distortion contributed by this circuit depends on the quality of the transformer and can easily be made negligible. The carbon microphone is left as the only source of noise and distortion. The limiting action is good and curves are shown in Fig. 3.

The attack and decay time is dependent on the time constants of R_3, R_4, C_3 and the diode, and can be adjusted to give satisfactory results. First syllable of a word following a pause will over-modulate. This is not very noticeable and is unimportant to intelligibility.

With phase modulation, it is desirable to limit proportional to frequency as well as the amplitude of the audio signal. This may be done by making a differentiating circuit of R_2 and C_2 which will cause V_2 to amplify the high frequencies more than the low frequencies.

Simple Deviation Limiter

By VIRGIL M. BRITTAIN

TO LIMIT the frequency deviation produced by a phase-modulated transmitter, it is necessary to limit the slope of the audio-frequency wave applied to the phase modulator.

A method of slope limiting which consists of differentiating the audio-frequency wave, clipping the voltage peaks from that wave, and then integrating the clipped wave, was described in a recent article.[1]

A somewhat simpler method of slope limiting which is suitable for use as a deviation limiter in phase-modulated transmitters is illustrated in Fig. 1. This method uses neither differentiating nor integrating circuits, and the circuit loss is comparatively low when limiting does not occur.

The principle of operation of the device depends upon the current and voltage relationships in a capacitance. These are expressed by the equation $i = C\,(de/dt)$.

In the equation, it is seen that the current and the derivative of the voltage wave are linearly related. Since the derivative of the

voltage wave is the slope of the voltage wave, the maximum value of the slope may be limited by

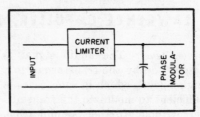

FIG. 1—Basic circuit for limiting current to a capacitor

simply limiting the current flowing in the capacitance to an appropriate maximum value. This leads to a basic circuit as shown in Fig. 1.

A practical form of the circuit is shown in Fig. 2. The constants of the circuit are such that the twin diode is actually a current limiter; current limiters such as this are frequently used to produce a clipped voltage wave by passing the limited current through a resistive network and utilizing the voltage developed across a resistor by the

limited current; however in this case it can be shown by means of an oscilloscope that clipped voltage waves do not exist in the circuit.

When no limiting occurs, the output voltage is only slightly less than the input voltage, and there is very little, if any, phase shift in the circuit.

The device functions very satis-

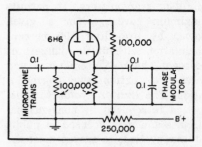

FIG. 2—Practical circuit of deviation limiter

factorily in limiting deviation in a phase-modulated transmitter of the type used for mobile radiotelephone service.

REFERENCE

(1) Marion R. Winkler, Instantaneous Deviation Control, ELECTRONICS, p 97, Sept. 1949.

Transistor Frequency-Modulator Circuit

Use of transistor in frequency-modulation circuit saves a-c filament power, reduces size and weight, requires less a-f driving power and reduces d-c power requirements. Distortion in transistor frequency modulator can be kept as low as in tube modulators

By L. L. KOROS AND R. F. SCHWARTZ

TRANSISTORS, since their introduction several years ago, have successfully been applied in many circuits originally designed to operate with vacuum tubes. Experimental work described here shows suitability of transistors for use as frequency modulators.

The control element of the transistor in this application is the emitter as in conventional amplifier circuits. The controlled element is, however, the internal impedance of the collector-base path. Measurements on transistors show that the internal collector impedance changes between broad limits if the voltage and the current are changed slightly between the emitter and base. The measurements further show that instead of the internal collector impedance being purely resistive, it is actually complex for some values of emitter current.

In some transistors the reactive component of the collector impedance changes its value from inductive to capacitive as the emitter current is changed. In other transistors the sign of the internal collector impedance remains the same within the range of emitter currents used.

The wide variation of internal collector impedance is used to produce frequency modulation in an oscillator circuit. A conventional tube circuit is used for the oscillator. The production of frequency modulation by resistance changes has been proposed before[1,2]. These methods use the variable internal plate resistance of tubes and some resistance-transforming means for coupling variable reactive elements to an oscillator tank.

Circuit Details

The circuit used for the transistor frequency modulator is somewhat simpler. Figure 1 shows the diagram of the experimental setup. The collector circuit of the transistor is fed with direct current through r-f choke L. A capacitor, C_k, not greater than about 1/10 of the oscillator tank capacitor, couples the collector to the oscillator tank. The emitter circuit is biased to class A amplifier service. The audio input is applied to the emitter circuit through series resistance R. This resistance reduces distortion caused by the nonlinear characteristic of the emitter circuit. The transistor cannot develop an audio-output voltage in the collector-load circuit, even if the collector current is varied, because r-f choke L acts as a short-circuit for the audio output. The audio signal applied to the emitter, however, varies the collector resistance between broad limits at an audio-frequency rate. Coupling capacitor C_k is coupled to the tank through the variable internal collector resistance of the transistor and the ground return. The r-f choke in parallel with the collector represents a high r-f reactance and can be neglected.

The coupling capacitor draws more or less capacitive current from the tank according to the instantaneous value of the transistor internal collector resistance. This produces a frequency modulation. The oscillator tank, however, is loaded through C_k with a variable resistance, which is the internal collector resistance. This variable loading effect produces some amplitude modulation. By proper selection of the oscillator tank capacitor, C_t, which should be of low reactance, the amplitude-modulation effect of the variable collector resistance can be kept below any desired value. A high value of reactance for the tank capacitor is needed, however, to produce a large frequency deviation for a given collector resistance variation. A sound compromise is possible between these contradictory requirements.

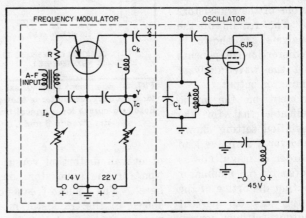

FIG. 1—Transistor frequency modulator provides low-distortion modulation with low d-c and a-f power input requirements. Signal frequencies up to 1.5 mc may be used

Figure 2 shows a typical static linearity curve for a transistor frequency modulator operating at 1.03-mc carrier frequency. During the static deviation measurements the flow of modulation current was simulated by varying the emitter bias-current resistor. Also shown in Fig. 2 is the amplitude variation of the frequency-modulated oscillator tank.

Figure 3A shows the equipment used to test the deviation and static linearity of the circuit. The signal from the oscillator under test is picked up on a communications receiver (with c-w oscillator on) and the receiver output frequency deviations are measured by comparison with a calibrated audio signal generator using Lissajous figures.

The circuit of Fig. 1 was tested for its dynamic performance with a 400-cycle modulating signal. This was done by applying the audio signal to the a-f input terminals and observing the output by means of a discriminator and wave analyzer. Two 6SH7 limiter stages preceding the 6H6 discriminator seemed to give sufficient limiting for all signal levels encountered in this work and assured a linear output response of ±2.5 volts d-c for ±5,000-cps frequency variation with a 0.05-volt rms frequency-modulated input.

A distortion analysis of the modulator was made for three different values of deviation. Figure 3B shows graphically the relationship between the input voltage and the deviation for one of the transistors investigated. The results of the distortion analysis are shown in Table I. The distortion components were read on the wave analyzer at the discriminator output.

A measurement on the audio oscillator indicates that for the maximum deviation setting shown in Table I, and for a resistive load of the same order of magnitude as that represented by the modulator circuit, the output distortion of the audio oscillator was 0.3 percent rms. For output settings corresponding to the lower inputs used, the distortion is so low as to be con-

sidered negligible. No correction was used, therefore, on the data of Table I. Figure 3C shows the plot

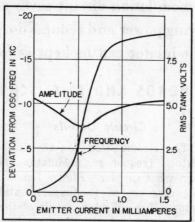

FIG. 2—Curves show linearity of modulation characteristics and effect of modulation on oscillator output amplitude

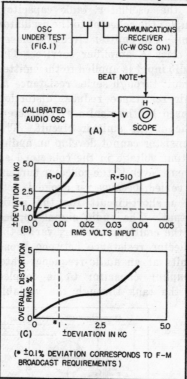

FIG. 3—Equipment used to test transistor frequency modulator is shown in A. Resulting curves for a typical transistor are given in B and C

of overall distortion versus deviation for the transistor considered here. The audio-frequency response of the transistor modulator was measured and is substantially constant from 20 to 15,000 cps for all of the transistors investigated.

The data given in Table I and Fig. 3C show that for a ±0.1-percent deviation of the carrier frequency, which is the upper limit required in the f-m services, the distortion was reasonably low. The interpolated value was only 1 percent rms. Figure 3B shows that the input voltage to the modulator to obtain this deviation was also low. The ±0.1-percent frequency deviation was achieved with about 0.008 volt rms input. The input resistance of the emitter circuit with a 510-ohm series resistor R was about 650 ohms. For maximum deviation the input requirement of the modulator with the linearizing resistor was therefore about −40 db (0 level 1 milliwatt). The input without linearizing resistor was −55 db. The input requirement showed fluctuations in the order of 6 db from transistor to transistor.

Internal Collector Resistance

Two equivalent circuits of the modulator are shown in the insert in Fig. 4. Any collector reactance is included in C_s. This form of representation does not follow the real situation because the coupling capacitor has a predetermined value and the changing element is the collector impedance. It is more convenient, however, to separate the resistive and reactive elements into two groups and to consider the modulator as a series or parallel combination of a capacitor and resistor. The equivalence of the series and parallel representation is expressed by

$$R_s - jX_s = -\frac{R_p jX_p}{R_p - jX_p} \qquad (1)$$

$$\frac{X_s}{R_s} = \frac{R_p}{X_p} \qquad (2)$$

where X_s and X_p are the reactances of C_s and C_p respectively at the oscillator frequency.

For practical purposes, the data which can be measured directly by the easiest method are C_p and ΔC_p, the change of C_p. Resistance R_p can be measured by a Q-meter, and C_s and R_s can be computed.

From Eq. 1 and 2

$$C_s = C_p \; \frac{X_p{}^2 + R_p{}^2}{R_p{}^2} \qquad (3)$$

$$R_s = R_p \; \frac{X_p{}^2}{X_p{}^2 + R_p{}^2} \qquad (4)$$

The frequency deviation Δf is expressed by

$$\Delta f = - \; \frac{f}{2C_t} \, \Delta C_p \qquad (5)$$

If it is found that the calculated $C_s = C_k$, which is the coupling capacitor actually used, the internal collector impedance is purely resistive and its value is identical with R_s. If, however, it is found that C_s is less than C_k it means that the internal collector impedance can be represented by a resistor and capacitor in series. If C_s is greater

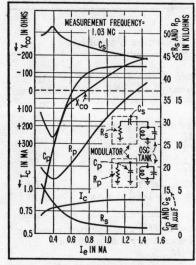

FIG. 4—Curves show relationship between emitter current and other circuit variables for two forms of equivalent circuit

than C_k the internal collector impedance can be represented by a series combination of a resistance and inductance.

The technique used to measure C_p, ΔC_p and R_p consists of the determination of the Q of the network formed by the internal collector impedance and the coupling capacitor C_k connected in series. The frequency modulator part of Fig. 1 is coupled to the Q-meter at X and Y. The inductance of the Q-meter, for obtaining the most exact figures, should be chosen lower than recommended for normal use of the in-

strument at the same frequency, in order to make the Q reading on a convenient range on the meter. If lower inductance is used it is necessary to add capacitors in parallel to the variable capacitor of the Q-meter to tune the circuit to resonance at the investigated frequencies. The techniques of the measurement are as follows: (1) Tune the Q-meter's variable capacitor to maximum Q-reading, before the transistor is inserted in its socket. Read Q_o and C_o. (2) Plug in the transistor and select different emitter current values I_e. (3) Tune the Q-meter's variable capacitor to maximum Q-reading again with each I_e setting and read the $Q(I_e)$ and the changes on the Q-meter capacitor ΔC_p. From the Q readings for the different emitter currents, R_p is computed as

$$R_p = \frac{Q_o Q(I_e)}{Q_o - Q(I_e)} \; X_L \qquad (6)$$

where X_L is the reactance of the Q-meter coil used. To minimize errors due to distributed capacitances and lead inductances, the transistor socket with the coupling capacitor C_k and the r-f feed choke L was built as a compact unit which was directly plugged into the terminals of the Q-meter. A photograph of this frequency modulator unit is shown.

The curves of Fig. 4 show the values of C_p, R_p, C_s and R_s as functions of the emitter current at 1.03 mc for one transistor. The experimental data are presented in Table II. The values of the collector current I_c are also shown in the same figure. The values of C_p and Q were measured, and the values of R_p, C_s and R_s were calculated from Eq. 6, 3 and 4. The reactive component of the internal collector impedance is represented by X_{co}. The computation of X_{co} was done with the expression $X_{co} = X_{ck} - X_s$ where X_{ck} is the reactance of the coupling capacitor and X_s is the reactance of C_s at the r-f carrier frequency. As Fig. 4 shows, the value of the reactive component X_{co} was found to be low compared with R_s. Nevertheless, it had an influ-

ence on the frequency deviation. Reactance X_{co} changed in this case from inductive to capacitive values. There were found, however, transistors where X_{co} was even smaller and the internal collector impedance was, for the main part, resistive. It was also found that the collector resistance and reactance depended upon the electrical history of the transistor. In the investigated cases, however, if the transistor showed amplification properties, the frequency-modulation property also was present.

Figure 4 shows that a large variation of the resistive component of the collector impedance, about 600 to 5,000 ohms, takes place for only a small change of the order of one milliampere in emitter current. Since the emitter resistance is of the order of 100 ohms, only a small input power is required for a relatively large change in collector resistance, as we have previously seen. Such a variation is an interesting feature which makes the transistor especially useful as a frequency modulator.

The transistor frequency modulator may introduce some jittering of the oscillator frequency due to instability of the transistor constants and to temperature changes. If the center frequency of the oscillator is stabilized by means of a discriminator and standard frequency

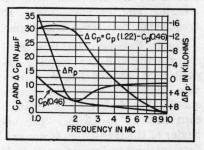

FIG. 5—By careful choice of transistors, operating frequency of frequency modulator can be extended up to 10 mc

source, as is the standard practice for broadcast transmitters, a considerable part of the effect of transistor instability is eliminated.

Modulating Higher Frequencies

The relatively low output power

of the frequency-modulated oscillator cannot be considered as a limitation of the system, because the frequency multiplier stages amplify and multiply the r-f excitation to the necessary power level to excite the f-m power amplifier tube.

To obtain information about the capability of the transistors to modulate oscillators at higher frequencies, several transistors were tried with the previously described Q-meter method at frequencies between 1 and 10 mc. Figure 5 represents typical experimental data. Table III shows the measured values.

The emitter current limits of 0.46 ma to 1.22 ma (with the corresponding collector current units of 0.74 ma to 0.86 ma) were selected to produce high C_p changes around the linear response part of the frequency-modulation characteristic. The R_p values were computed again by Eq. 4. The changes of R_p (ΔR_p) are represented also in Fig. 5. The sign of ΔR_p indicates whether the parallel resistance value is going down with increasing emitter current, in which case ΔR_p is shown as positive, or going up, in which ΔR_p is shown as negative. This increasing or decreasing character depends, in the case of one investigated transistor, upon the applied frequency. In the case of another transistor, R_p decreased with increasing emitter current for all frequencies between 1 and 10 mc.

Figure 5 shows that this transistor unit with the coupling capacitor of 47 $\mu\mu$f has a reasonably high ΔC_p value, and consequently has frequency modulation capability up to 2.5 mc. The behavior of the transistors is not uniform at higher frequencies. It is too early to say what is the upper frequency limit of the transistor in f-m service. Of course the flexibility of the modulator will be higher if the oscillator frequency can be increased. Otherwise, at least one more frequency multiplier stage must be used. This additional

Table I—Overall Measured Distortion

Input Voltage to Modulator (rms volts)	Deviation (± cps)	Distortion Components of 400-cps modulating tone		Overall Distortion (rms %)
		Harmonic	% Fund.	
0.0132	1,350	2nd	0.979	
		3rd	0.769	
		4th	0.419	
		5th	.....	1.32
0.0330	2,850	2nd	1.91	
		3rd	0.800	
		4th	0.450	
		5th	......	2.12
0.0460	3,900	2nd	3.62	
		3rd	0.?75	
		4th	0.?30	
		5th	0.337	3.72

Table II—Measurement of Collector Variables

I_e (ma)	I_c (ma)	Q	C_Q*	C_p ($\mu\mu$f)	R_p (Kilohms)	C_s ($\mu\mu$f)	R_s (Kilohms)	X_{co} (Kilohms)
		106**	177	0	Before inserting transistor			
0.46	0.74	55	165	12	7.37	48.4	5.55	+0.09
0.58	0.78	50	155	22	6.12	51.1	3.48	+0.26
0.75	0.81	54	142.5	34.5	7.12	48.2	2.02	+0.08
0.96	0.84	62.5	136	41	9.84	47	1.26	0
1.22	0.86	70	134.5	42.5	13.35	45.7	0.92	−0.09
1.64	0.86	75.5	134.5	42.5	16.98	44.4	0.74	−0.19

* C_Q is the reading of variable capacitor in Q-meter. A fixed capacitor was used parallel to C_Q to tune the 10-microhenry coil to 1.03 mc.
** The first line represents Q_o, the others $Q(I_e)$.

Table III—Measurement of Frequency Response

f (mc)	Coil (μh)	Q (0.46)	Q (1.22)	C_Q (0.46)* ($\mu\mu$f)	C_Q (1.22)* ($\mu\mu$f)	C_p** ($\mu\mu$f)	ΔC_p ($\mu\mu$f)
1.03	10	55	70	165	134.5	12	30.5
2	5	60	39	204	175	4	29
3	1	56	42	261	243	3	18
4	1	71	40	268	255		13
5	1	72	32	126	120	2	6
7.5	1	71	21	418	414	2	4
10	1	59	20	225	225	1	0

* C_Q (0.46) and C_Q (1.22) represent readings of variable capacitor in Q-meter at 0.46 and 1.22-ma emitter currents.
** C_p is capacitor value represented by transistor at 0.46-ma emitter current.

stage might also be necessary for high-power transmitters due to the low oscillator power. As transistor development advances and the similarity between units becomes greater, the reasonable upper frequency limit and oscillator tank voltage limit for the transistor frequency modulator can be determined.

REFERENCES

(1) A. V. Eastman and E. D. Scott, Transmission Lines as Frequency Modulators, *Proc. IRE*, p 878, July 1934.

(2) B. E. Montgomery, Inductively Coupled Frequency Modulator, *Proc. IRE*, p 559, Oct. 1941.

Extending Linear Range of Reactance Modulators

By FRITZ BRUNNER

LARGE FREQUENCY DEVIATION can be obtained directly from a frequency modulated oscillator by interposing a stage of amplification between the oscillator tank and the grid of the reactance tube.

Principle of Operation

In the basic reactance tube frequency modulated oscillator, a variable reactive current I_R whose magnitude is controlled by the mod-

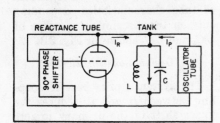

FIG. 1—Basic reactance modulators

ulating signal is supplied through a reactance tube to the tank circuit. The oscillator tube supplies a constant in-phase current I_P to the tank circuit as shown in Fig. 1. Under these conditions the instantaneous frequency is

$$f = \frac{1}{2\pi[L(C + I_R/2\pi fE)]^{1/2}}$$

where L is the inductance of the tank, C is its capacitance, and E is the voltage across it. If the resonant frequency of the tank circuit is

$$f_o = 1/2\pi(LC)^{1/2}$$

the deviation frequency approximates

$$\Delta f = f - f_o \approx -I_R/4\pi EC$$

which shows that the extent of the deviation is directly proportional

to the reactive current supplied by the reactance tube.

In conventional reactance tube f-m oscillators I_R is obtained by shifting the phase of the tank circuit voltage as near as possible to 90 degrees by a resistance-reactance circuit, and using this voltage to control the reactance tube. Unfortunately considerable attenuation is associated with the phase-shifting network, so that the I_R available from the reactance tube is small in comparison to the voltage across the tank circuit. The frequency deviation that can be produced, especially at vhf, despite the greatest possible L/C of the tank circuit, is small. The oscillator must often be followed by several multiplier and converter stages to yield the necessary frequency deviation.

The introduction of an amplifier before or after the phase splitter makes possible greater deviation. Because the phases in this amplifier affect the stability of the oscillator, only one stage can usually be used.

Circuit Simplification

The simplest arrangement is to use the dynamic plate resistance of the amplification tube as the resistance of the phase shifter as is done in Fig. 2A. If this tube has a high plate resistance, the voltage appearing across the reactance is shifted nearly 90 degrees. This reactance can be either an inductance or a capacitance. The reactive current delivered to the tank circuit can be modulated by changing the

effective mutual conductance of one or more of the tubes associated with it.

At very high frequencies only the tube capacitances need be used for the reactive component of the phase shifter. *At higher frequencies the transit time in the reactance tube can supply the 90 degree phase shift so that a single transit-time reactance tube replaces the two tubes.* Otherwise the effect of transit time can be counteracted by adjustment of the phase shifter.

The circuit can be simplified still further by using the oscillator tube

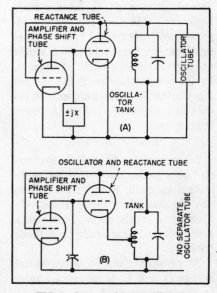

FIG. 2—Improved f-m oscillators

simultaneously as the reactance tube as shown in Fig. 2B.

Practical Execution

To obtain the largest possible

frequency deviation with good stability, it is necessary to limit the amplitude of operation to the linear portion of the grid characteristic of the amplifier. A crystal diode

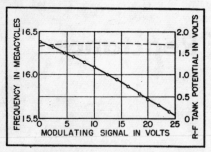

FIG. 3—Typical experimental results

can provide this limiting.

The fact that the tank circuit capacitance is distributed over the several tubes of the system must be taken into consideration. If, at vhf, the inductances of the tube connections are too near that of the tank circuit, and the reactance tube supplies a strong reactive current, oscillation may be unstable. This condition can be avoided by increasing the inductance of the tank circuit, decreasing the tube capacitances, and decreasing the inductances of the connections, possibly by concentrating all the tubes in one envelope.

Using the oscillator tube as the

reactance tube also, and using low transconductance tubes, linear deviation and constant amplitude of oscillation were obtained. Figure 3 shows typical experimental results. At frequencies where the reactances are concentrated in the tank circuit, frequency deviations of 10 percent of the mean frequency can be obtained with reasonably magnitude. Even in the uhf range frequency deviations commonly obtained at lower frequencies can be produced, so that the mean frequency can be regulated without inertia in a wide range by superimposing a control voltage on the modulating voltage.

Frequency Modulator

By GEORGE G. BRUCK

A NEW METHOD for obtaining frequency modulation combines several components of a frequency modulator into one unit. The usual reactance-tube frequency modulator comprises a (1) reactance tube, or tubes if push-pull, (2) double diode demodulator, and (3) inverse feedback loop for linearity and mid-frequency control. These three units can be combined into a single unit giving the circuit of Fig. 1. In the composite circuit the control discriminator is working on the oscillator frequency, not on a lower frequency.

Circuit Behavior

Disregarding L_2 and C_2 the circuit acts as a class-C Hartley oscillator. As such, each grid receives one impulse every cycle. Relatively high grid resistances limit peak grid voltages practically to cathode potential.

At resonance the vector potential across L_2 and C_2 is at right angles to the one across L_1 and C_1, thus, although each grid receives one impulse per cycle, these two voltages are phased differently. Figure 2A shows the vector diagram for the case of perfect resonance. There

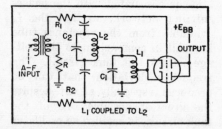

FIG. 1—Frequency modulation is produced by this simple circuit

are two plate current pulses per cycle, one advanced by the same angle that the other is retarded relative to the phase condition of the tank circuit of L_1 and C_1. The circuit is in equilibrium when the tube is oscillating at resonance.

If an a-f voltage is applied in push-pull to the two grids through R_1 and R_2, it alternately increases and decreases the angle of flow on either side of the tube. The contribution on either side of the tube towards the total plate current thus has its phase shifted back and forth, resulting in frequency modulation. Simultaneously, a voltage is established across R_1 and R_2 that tends to counteract the modulating voltage, thus providing negative feedback. The voltage-frequency

characteristic of the circuit is therefore essentially independent of tube characteristics, depending only on the discriminator curve of L_1C_1 and L_2C_2 shown in Fig. 2B.

Design Considerations

The system works best if coupling between L_1 and L_2 reduces the phase shift in the primary to zero in the neighborhood of resonance, which is accomplished with 0.50 transitional coupling. Choosing L_2 three to four times L_1 will give best results. If coupling is too high, the circuit can oscillate at either of two

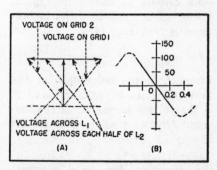

FIG. 2—(A) Grid voltages are symmetrically displaced in phase by action of resonant circuits of Fig. 1. (B) Application of a-f as shown in Fig. 1 produces frequency modulation. Values on coordinates show magnitudes that can be expected

distinct frequencies, both different from the resonant frequency of L_2 and C_2. If coupling is too low, the frequency of oscillation becomes dependent on both circuits, whereas it should, for optimum performance, depend only on L_2 and C_2.

Amount of feedback is controlled by the magnitude of R_1 and R_2. If very little feedback is desired, R_1 and R_2 are replaced by r-f chokes, which must be identical to avoid differential phase shifts.

Output is obtained by inserting a parallel resonant circuit in the plate lead at the point marked on Fig. 1. The circuit lends itself particularly

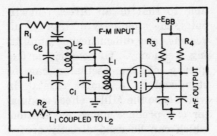

FIG. 3—Modification of the circuit of Fig. 1 gives an f-m discriminator

well to recovery of higher harmonics in the plate circuit and can be used as a frequency-multiplying driver stage. Although the fourth harmonic is the highest that can usually be obtained at the output,

in one circuit operating at about 10 mc the output was 78 mc. Such an arrangement will give full frequency deviation with only a carbon micophone in the primary of the modulation transformer.

The same or a very similar circuit can be used as an f-m phonograph pickup. For reception, the circuit can be operated as a discriminator as shown in Fig. 3 wherein it also acts as limiter, amplifier, and squelcher. It is essentially an oscillator that falls in step with the incoming signal. Audio frequency is recovered in push-pull from the two plates.

Miller-Effect Modulator

By P. L. BARGELLINI

THE INCREASING DEVELOPMENT of communication systems using frequency or phase modulation has stimulated the invention of several forms of modulators. In practical use these modulators suffer from poor carrier stability or great complexity in their stabilizing circuits, and limited ranges of linearity. Because of inadequacies in the reactance-tube modulators being used in experiments with railroad radiophones, especially microphonics in the reactance tube, another type of frequency modulation circuit was devised.

Miller-Effect Modulator

Important properties of a frequency modulator are: (1) inertialess linear frequency controlling element, (2) simple production and injection of voltage for stabilizing carrier frequency, and (3) stability in the presence of mechanical vibration. Requirement (1) calls for an electronic modulating element of considerable simplicity. (The reactance tube suffers from the fact that it can never be a pure reactance, always having some residual resistance.) Requirement (2) is more simply satisfied if the

frequency modulation is produced directly rather than indirectly as in some systems. A triode more adequately fills requirement (3) than a multigrid tube.

The means taken to meet these requirements is shown in Fig. 1A. By it, a pure reactance can be injected into the oscillatory circuit. The quadrature current is simply obtained from the grid-cathode space current of a triode that is excited by the controlled resonant L-C circuit and that has a purely resistive load. Analysis of the circuit shows that, in the general case, the input admittance between grid and cathode has both real and imaginary components. But if the load is purely resistive, as in this special case, and the grid-plate and grid-cathode capacitances are of the same order of magnitude and the product of frequency, grid-plate capacitance, plate resistance and load resistance is considerably less than unity, the input becomes purely capacitive. This input capacitance is equal to $C_{GK} + C_{GP} (1 + A)$, and its dependence on the amplification factor of the tube and plate circuit conditions is familarly known as the Miller effect.

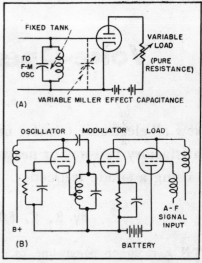

FIG. 1—(A) Basic principle of Miller effect frequency modulator circuit depends on variation of load resistance of tube reflecting a variable capacitance across its input. In practical adaptation of this principle (B) modulator tube is placed across oscillator and has a vacuum tube for load

Pure negative (capacitive) reactance can thus be injected into the tank circuit without the need for phasing circuits or multigrid tubes; the only requirement is that the plate load be purely resistive. To produce the frequency modulation, the gain A of the tube is varied by the additional elements shown at Fig. 1B. The amplification of the modulator tube is varied by placing in its plate circuit another tube as load which behaves as a variable resistance dependent on the audio-frequency signal voltage. The oscillator tube is connected in a Hartley circuit.

Because both cathode and grid of the load tube operate at r-f potentials, it is necessary to use r-f chokes to separate the r-f and a-f portions of the circuit. The battery provides the proper bias for maximum linearity between a-f input, internal resistance of the load tube, and frequency deviation of the oscillator. Drift of the oscillator's center frequency is easily counteracted by superimposing a compensating voltage obtained by usual automatic frequency control techniques on the battery voltage. Although the frequency stability of this circuit is inherently compar-

able to that of all direct f-m circuits, the simplicity of this circuit reduces the difficulties of stabilizing frequency. Of course, the frequency of the oscillator can be stabilized by a quartz crystal, in which case the Miller effect modulator can produce phase modulation, which can be used directly or fed to multiplier stages.

Experiments with Radiophone

This new modulator circuit has been used in equipment built for the Italian State Railways to determine the feasibility of very high frequency radiotelephone communications between a moving train and a fixed ground station. Troubles from microphonics encounted with reactance-tube modulators were eliminated by using the Miller effect modulator and frequency stability was better. These tests were made on carrier frequencies around 110 mc with 40

watts output from the transmitters. For tests the antenna on the train was purposely placed on the coach next to the electric locomotive, as shown in Fig. 2. The electrified sections of the right-of-way use 3,000-volt overhead lines; a train is drawn by a 3,000 hp locomotive.

The transmitter consisted of a Miller effect modulator using a 12J5GT and a 12AH7GT, a 12A6 oscillator multiplier, 12A6 frequency doubler, 832 frequency tripler, and 829B power amplifier. A total frequency multiplication of 18 is obtained to produce a modulation index of 4, which is sufficient to give suitable noise suppression despite the adverse antenna location and the change in signal strength because of the cuts and built-up suburban districts through which the 24 miles of track between Rome and Tivoli pass.

Voice–Operated Switching of Carrier Systems

New all-electronic transfer unit, fast enough to permit break-in between words, provides satisfactory two-way or party-line communication over power line or radio carrier systems using a single frequency. Oscillograms show negligible clipping of speech at start

By R. C. FOX, F. S. BEALE AND G. W. SYMONDS

IN a radio or power line carrier system of communication, break-in operation with all stations on the same frequency speeds operation, eliminates tuning complications, reduces equipment needs and increases the number of communication channels possible in a given frequency spectrum. Automatic break-in can be achieved by use of a voice-operated device for automatic switching, sometimes called vodas.

In earlier power line carrier applications, vodas systems usually produced excessive speech clipping

at the beginning of each period of transmission, because of sluggish interlock circuits. This necessitated waiting before speaking until the other carrier transmitter had shut down.

Satisfactory break-in operation requires that the voice-operated switching device act at high speed in transferring the system from standby condition to the talk or listen condition. It must return the system to standby less quickly, preferably with a choice of time constants, to prevent such action between syllables and words. Also,

the sequence of switching operations should be independent of circuit adjustments and tube characteristics.

In a network of several stations on a power line carrier channel, the first operator to speak actuates his carrier transmitter. This must be made the basis for blocking the remaining transmitters, yet the system must be designed to return quickly to the standby condition so that quick replies and even interruptions of the first speaker can be made.

The electronic transfer unit to be

described closely approaches these qualifications. It was designed for use with conventional power line carrier equipment comprising one receiver and one transmitter, as shown in Fig. 1. The entire system is inserted between a standard two-wire telephone line and a power line coupling network.

Switching Sequences

When no one is talking, the transfer unit places the system in the ready or standby condition wherein both the carrier transmitter and the audio amplifier of the receiver are blocked by bias voltages, as indicated by shading on the boxes in Fig. 1. Either an outgoing audio signal or an incoming r-f signal can, under this condition, reach the transfer unit and initiate the next switching sequence.

If an outgoing audio signal reaches the transfer unit first, this unit acts to remove the blocking bias from the carrier transmitter so the signal can go out over the power line. Simultaneously the transfer unit applies blocking bias to the carrier receiver, to prevent an incoming carrier signal from actuating the transfer unit while the other party is talking.

If an incoming r-f signal reaches the transfer unit first, this unit acts to remove the blocking bias from the audio amplifier of the receiver. Simultaneously the transfer unit blocks the outgoing audio amplifier so an outgoing audio signal cannot actuate the transfer unit. This scheme provides absolute interlocking of sequences at each carrier equipment terminal.

Cessation of either the initiating audio signal or the r-f signal permits the system to revert to the ready condition. Transfer from the transmit condition to the receive condition is never made directly, but always by first returning the system to the ready condition. This feature, coupled with the ability to function at a high speed, permits a rapid-fire conversation to be handled successfully and makes it possible for the speaker to be interrupted by the listener.

Transfer Unit Details

The electronic transfer unit consists of two amplifier channels (with two associated bias rectifiers in each) and a power-oscillator type bias supply, as indicated in Fig. 2. One amplifier channel is designed for audio frequencies, the other for r-f signals. Both terminate in gas-thyratron rectifier circuits arranged to provide the correct control bias voltages in the proper sequence without any adjustments. The gas thyratrons used contain no mercury vapor and therefore will give no trouble at low temperatures. They cannot damage themselves since their anode-supply oscillator limits any surge current to a value considerably less than the peak rating of the tube. The gain of each amplifier channel is controllable to allow adjustment for the noise levels encountered.

One reason for using a power oscillator as bias source is that the associated carrier equipment is designed for operation from a 125-volt d-c source and a separate bias supply is therefore required. The power oscillator output, rectified by the gas thyratrons as and when required, provides voltages that are independent of the primary source of power, hence can be added to it. Another reason for using the oscillator is that its a-c output is conveniently controlled and rectified by thyratron tubes.

The oscillator operates at about

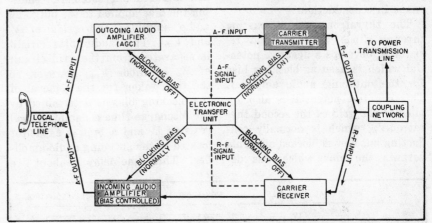

FIG. 1—One complete station of Westinghouse type JY power-line carrier equipment for two-way telephone communication using a single carrier frequency. Required switching operations are performed automatically by voice-operated electronic transfer unit in center of diagram

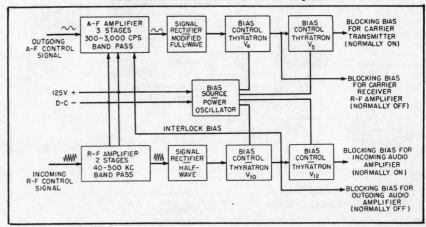

FIG. 2—Electronic transfer unit, which delivers appropriate combinations of blocking bias voltages to carrier transmitter and carrier receiver at a station in response to incoming or outgoing signals. Power oscillator provides bias voltages for thyratrons; only other voltage source is 125 v d-c

10 kc, which is well above the highest audio frequency involved. Filter requirements for the control rectifiers are quite simple at 10 kc. The output transformer for the power oscillator has four independent secondary windings that supply the separate voltages to the four gas-thyratron control tubes.

Circuit of Transfer Unit

The circuit of the transfer unit is shown in simplified form in Fig. 3. Considering the r-f channel first, the amplified and rectified r-f signal is filtered sufficiently to give an adequately smooth d-c firing potential for the first thyratron, V_{10}, which is normally biased to cutoff. When sufficient control grid potential is developed, the thyratron snaps into conduction.

The thyratron current passing through diode V_{11B} and load resistor R_2 develops a negative potential which is used as blocking bias for the outgoing audio amplifier. This negative potential is also applied to the grid of the second thyratron, V_{12}, which is normally conducting but now is blocked off. This permits the bias which was developed across load resistor R_3 to discharge and unblock the incoming audio amplifier, thus permitting the audio output of the carrier receiver to be delivered to the telephone line. This sequence cannot be violated in this direction. The outgoing audio amplifier blocking bias must exist before the incoming audio amplifier blocking bias can be removed, since the output of V_{10} controls the conditions of V_{12}.

The bias developed across R_2 by V_{10} is also applied to the first grid of V_2 to interlock the audio channel against transient disturbances that may arise in the audio circuits connected to this channel.

When the incoming r-f signal stops, V_{10} extinguishes within a few hundred microseconds, removing the bias applied to the outgoing audio amplifier and grids of V_2 and V_{12}. This audio bias circuit is separated from the grid circuit of V_{12} by diode V_{11B}, however, so the time taken for the removal of the blocking bias is determined by the discharge time constant of load resistor R_2 and a bypass capacitor located in the outgoing audio amplifier. This time delay is about five

milliseconds. A similar condition, except that a capacitor must be charged, meantime controls the length of time required to block the incoming audio amplifier; the delay here is about one millisecond. Thus, the sequence of the output bias functions has been reversed by pitting an R-C charge curve of short duration against an R-C discharge curve having a larger time constant.

The trigger-like action of thyratron V_{10} insures that the output control bias voltages will be either full on or full off instead of at some intermediate value. They are independent of the varying level of the r-f input signal which is used as the primary control signal, as long as the minimum level does not drop below the threshold set by the r-f amplifier channel gain control.

The a-f signal amplifier channel of the transfer unit is similarly arranged except that it accepts audio-frequency signals for control and has a fairly sharp 300 to 3,000-cycle bandpass characteristic to help the control system discriminate between noise and useful voice frequencies.

Delay of Release

It is desirable for the transmit condition to occur as soon as possible after the start of speech, to minimize clipping. The equipment accomplishes this in approximately 2.5 milliseconds. Upon cessation of the signal, however, the transmitter control system should have a certain minimum delay of release. Otherwise the transmitter would be keyed on and off by individual cycles of speech, especially fundamental low-frequency components which for a man's voice are between 100 and 200 cycles. The circuit containing double-diode detector V_3 and isolating diode V_{9A} accomplishes this in addition to permitting a choice of four different delay-of-release time settings (by means of two switches). This circuit permits altering the delay of release from approximately 27 milliseconds to about 340 milli-

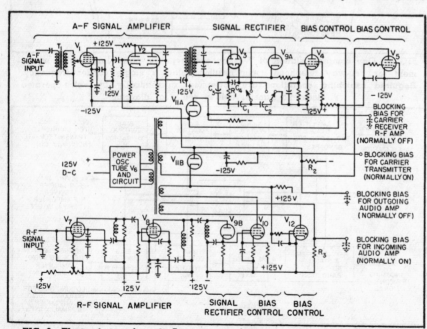

FIG. 3—Electronic transfer unit. Arrangement of stages corresponds to block diagram in Fig. 2. Capacitors shown dotted at blocking bias output terminals are in other units of station equipment but serve to determine time constants for blocking functions indicated. No mechanical relays or other moving parts are used

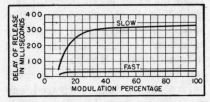

FIG. 4—Average delay of release of carrier transmitter vs percentage modulation. Slow curve compares approximately with amount of delay found in many vodas schemes, while fast curve corresponds to maximum speed at which electronic transfer unit is now arranged. Choice of delay of release time is affected by personal preferences, room and line noise level

seconds without affecting the charge time, and hence the time of transfer to the transmit condition.

The delay-of-release circuit is a modification of a full-wave detector. The amplified audio signal appears at the secondary of audio output transformer T_2 and is rectified by double-diode V_3. The filter for the d-c output of this rectifier is separated into two sections by diode V_{3A}. A small filter, consisting of equal capacitances C_3 and C_4 with load resistor R_1, is connected permanently across the d-c output. Additional capacitors C_1 and C_2 are arranged to be connected into this circuit by two switches to alter the discharge time constant. Due to diode V_{3A}, the charge time constant

with respect to C_3 and R_1 is not affected.

Assume, for instance, even half cycles of output from T_2 to be rectified at V_{3A}. The output voltage across R_1 will rise quickly to its full value because of the small amount of capacitance in C_3. Capacitors C_1 and C_2 are relatively large and require more time to charge to full voltage, therefore the cathode of V_{3A} becomes positive with respect to its anode, isolating C_4, C_1 and C_2 from R_1 and C_3 until the charges become equal.

Action of Release Circuit

After any selected capacitance of C_1 and C_2 has been charged to full voltage, this capacitance then adds to that of C_3 during those instants when the voltage across R_1 drops enough to make the V_{3A} anode positive with respect to its cathode—and both sections of capacitance contribute to the filtering of the then full-wave output.

Upon the cessation of the audio signal and the consequent decay of the d-c output of V_3, the effect of the larger capacitors, C_1 and C_2, is evident. The small fast-time-constant capacitor C_3 would tend to discharge quickly through R_1, but this would place its potential below that of the larger capacitors, which

therefore act through V_{3A} to maintain the voltage across R_1, changing the effective R-C product for the period of the discharge.

Upon application of audio input there is developed immediately a d-c output voltage to fire the first thyratron, V_4. When the audio input is stopped, the d-c output decays rapidly or more slowly according to the delay time chosen, keeping V_4 fired for this delay period.

Figure 4 shows the relationship of delay of release to the percentage modulation of the carrier transmitter. Above 30-percent modulation, the delay of release characteristic is relatively flat. The outgoing audio amplifier employs automatic gain control, which materially assists in obtaining this flat response characteristic.

Oscillogram of Response

Figure 5 is an oscillogram taken with a laboratory setup including two complete power line carrier, single-frequency automatic simplex equipment assemblies, operating over an artificial line providing 80 db of attenuation. Trace 1 is a 60-cycle timing wave. Traces 2, 3 and 4 show the response of the a-f signal channel of the electronic transfer unit.

Trace 2 shows the 1,000-cps audio

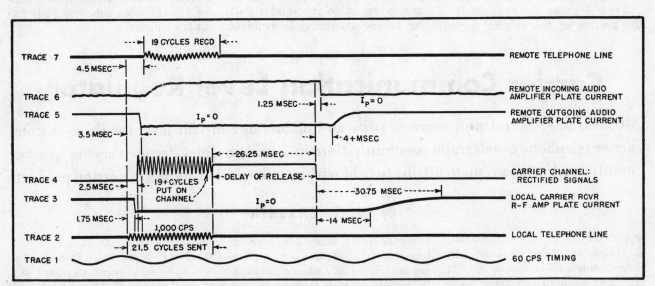

FIG. 5—Operation of electronic transfer unit under test conditions with 21.5 cycles of a 1,000-cps audio signal going out with amplitude sufficient to produce 50-percent modulation of carrier transmitter, with time constants set for faster release. Transfer unit returns system to ready condition fast enough to provide many opportunities for receiving stations to break in

signal, existing for 21.5 milliseconds in the local telephone line, that initiated the sequence of events shown in this oscillogram.

Trace 3 shows how the normal plate current of the r-f amplifier of the local carrier receiver is blocked to zero 1.75 milliseconds after arrival of the audio signal, and shows also how and when it is permitted to restore to normal.

Trace 4 indicates that the local carrier transmitter was delivering a modulated r-f signal to the power line 2.5 milliseconds after arrival of the audio signal, and actually delivered 19 of the 21.5 cycles of the originating signal to the remote listener.

Traces 5, 6 and 7 show the response of the r-f signal channel of the transfer unit at the remote station which receives the signals from the power line.

Trace 5 indicates how arrival of the modulated r-f signal blocks the outgoing audio amplifier there by driving its normal plate current to zero, and shows how this plate current is permitted to restore to normal.

Trace 6 shows (at left) the normally blocked condition of the incoming audio amplifier at the remote station, and shows the unblocking and reblocking of this amplifier in response to the incoming r-f signal.

Trace 7 shows the final result— the portion of the original signal that is actually delivered to the remote telephone line.

For the oscillograms of Fig. 5, the delay of release was set for fast release. With this, the local carrier transmitter stays on for slightly over 26 milliseconds after the audio signal stops. A succeeding audio signal arriving within this interval is fully transmitted. Fourteen milliseconds after stopping the local carrier transmitter's r-f signal, the local carrier receiver starts to unblock, and becomes fully released in about 30 milliseconds. Thus, the total time from stoppage of the initiating audio signal in the local telephone line until the entire two-station set-up is ready to accept another such signal in the opposite direction of transmission is less than 57 milliseconds.

Performance Data

Recordings of conversation held over actual power-line carrier channels using this form of equipment show that on the two shortest delay-of-release settings the listener will have little or no trouble in interrupting the speaker at the transmitting station.

When using the longest delay of release, the transfer action seldom occurs except at the ends of sentences, or between words if long pauses exist. Even with this setting, however, no appreciable waiting before answering is required.

Even an experienced operator, anticipating the stopping of the other speaker and having an answer in readiness (but not actually trying to interrupt the other party), rarely can respond fast enough to speak before the system is cleared and ready to act upon his speech. This is due to the average human response time of 0.2 second. The delay of release to be used is usually a matter of individual preference.

High-speed operation involves use of the shortest delay of release. All other values of delay are long enough to eliminate release between syllables and even words more or less completely, depending upon the characteristics of speech of the persons using the telephone instruments. The choice of release delay has no effect upon the speed of transfer from ready to either the transmit or receive conditions.

The economics of communication facilities do not permit building lines so perfect that all of the original sounds are received by the listener, in the identical form in which they originated. Clipping of one to three milliseconds from the beginning of the speech or signals is rarely missed, since telephone lines and mental reactions sacrifice a larger percentage of the actual original signal and the listener's imagination subconsciously fills in the balance.

Carrier Communication Level Regulator

All-electronic control unit corrects twist and maintains constant level for three-channel carrier telephone or telegraph communication on open-wire lines despite varying weather conditions. Variations up to 20 db are held within 2 db without adding distortion products

By W. S. CHASKIN

IN THE FIELD of carrier communication on open-wire lines, the three-channel, 30-kc carrier system is widely used to add three voice circuits without affecting operation of the existing physical circuit.

Where these lines are long in terms of total attenuation, repeaters are placed at suitable intervals to restore operable levels in the audio material transmitted. Attenuation on such lines, however, is not a constant. It varies in two ways: (1) it increases from dry-to-wet and cold-to-warm weather; (2) it increases more at the high end of the frequency spectrum, in an effect known as twist. This causes the higher-frequency channels to operate in unfavorable weather at relatively lower levels than the lower-frequency channels of the same carrier system.

Automatic regulators have been used to compensate for these effects. However, the pilot regulator described here is one of the first to perform these functions with an all-electronic circuit which permits the elimination of all moving parts, relays, motors and physical contacts from the regulating circuit.

The regulator forms part of a standard rack-mounted carrier unit and consists of three equipment panels: (1) a pilot oscillator which produces pilot-frequency current for transmission on the line from one terminal of the system to another; (2) the regulator itself, which determines attenuation of the pilot frequency on that line and adjusts the level of the terminal or repeater for constant output level regardless of attenuation or twist ahead of it; (3) an alarm which signals the attendant with light and bell when any abnormal operating conditions have exceeded the scope of the regulator.

Pilot Oscillator

The pilot oscillator circuit is given in Fig. 1. One oscillator is used in the transmitting branch of each terminal of a system. When installed in an East terminal (transmitting to the West) it operates on 5.9 kc, whereas at a West terminal it generates a frequency of 29.6 kc.

Stability of both output level and frequency are most important considerations in this oscillator. It uses two 6N7 triodes in a push-pull-parallel circuit, with inductor L_1 and capacitor C_2 in a parallel frequency-determining circuit. Inductor L_1 has an iron-powder pot and adjustable core for fine setting of the pilot-oscillator frequency. Fixed bias is provided by cathode resistor R_1. This resistor is wired to test points as shown to facilitate measurement of plate current in terms of voltage drop.

Positive feedback goes through

capacitor C_1 and variable resistor R_2. A stabilizing variable-bias network maintains constant output level by picking up a voltage from the secondary of transformer T_1, rectifying it in germanium diodes, and filtering it in R_9 and C_4 before feeding it to the grids to create automatic correction for any tendency toward output-level variation.

Jacks J_1 and J_2 are provided for patching-in a 600-ohm db meter for adjusting feedback control R_2 to give correct oscillator level. Pilot-frequency output-level adjustment is made with resistor R_8 to establish the conventional output of minus 49 dbm at jacks J_3 and J_4. This output circuit, consisting mainly of R_{12} and R_8 in series, has an impedance high enough to allow bridging across the input of the transmitting amplifier of the carrier terminal with negligible loss to through transmission. When the pilot-frequency signal leaves the transmitting amplifier its level is 8 dbm.

Arrangement of the output jacks is designed to permit disconnecting the pilot oscillator from the transmitting amplifier when necessary for adjustments or substitution of a test oscillator. An additional carrier-frequency output is pro-

vided to supply current at pilot-oscillator frequency for modulating an extra reduced-fidelity channel available in these systems for use as a service circuit or as a voice-frequency channel for subdivision into a total of nine telegraph subchannels.

Pilot-transmitting filter *PTF*, consisting of L_2 and C_3, is series resonant at the pilot frequency. This precludes the possibility of appreciable pilot-frequency harmonics being present at the transmitting-amplifier input.

Pilot Regulator

The pilot regulator, shown in block form in Fig. 2, is essentially a variable attenuator. One regulator is connected into the carrier-receiving branch of each terminal of a system. Additionally, two are required for each intervening repeater—one to handle each direction of transmission. The circuit arrangement permits switching of the regulating action to either the manual or the automatic section. This provides for emergency operation and for servicing the automatic circuit.

When the control is set for automatic operation, all carrier-band

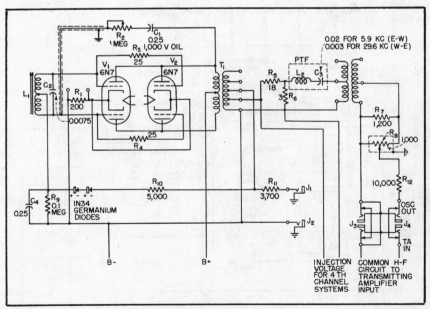

FIG. 1—Pilot oscillator circuit. Pilot-frequency currents originating here are transmitted over the line to determine the amount and kind of attenuation and then control the succeeding repeater or terminal to restore normal level and correct twist

frequencies enter the regulator at the upper right and pass through an attenuation pad, a hybrid transformer, and an amplifier. The output of this amplifier is applied to the input of the terminal receiving

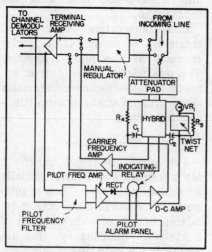

FIG. 2—Block diagram of pilot regulator. Control of attenuation is achieved in the hybrid transformer by the sampled pilot frequency derived from the carrier-frequency receiving amplifier

amplifier whose output is sampled and fed back to the regulator through a pilot-frequency filter, a one-stage pilot-frequency amplifier,

a rectifier and a d-c amplifier. The output of the latter is used to control passage of carrier-band frequencies through the hybrid transformer by the degree of unbalance of the hybrid-bridge circuit.

As bridge balance increases, carrier-band level at the regulator output terminals increases. The bridge in Fig. 2 is composed of R_4 and C_1 balanced by lamp VR_1, R_5, the twist-adjusting network and C_2. Thus, the level of carrier-band frequencies reaching the terminal receiving amplifier, and consequently the subscriber's handset, is determined by the received level of the pilot frequency.

Action of Regulator Circuit

Figure 3 shows the regulator circuit in detail. Again the regulator input is at the upper right. The attenuator is a five-element T pad arranged for strapping into the input with $\frac{1}{2}$, 1, 2, 4, and 8-db attenuation factors which can be combined to match the manual attenuator at the center of its range. The output of the hybrid transformer passes through the carrier-frequency amplifier consisting of V_1 and goes through switch SW_1 to the

carrier terminal receiving amplifier, which is not shown. The sampled output of this amplifier returns to the regulator at the lower right, entering the pilot-regulator filter. This sharp-tuned network feeds the paralleled grids of V_4, the pilot-frequency amplifier. Cathode degeneration and bias in this stage are controlled by C_9 and R_{18} to provide gain adjustment over a 6-db range for centering the pointer of meter-relay RE_1, a Weston type-730 sensitive relay which serves to actuate the alarm when the pilot-frequency level varies beyond the automatic-regulating range for any reason. This combination is also used in adjusting the regulator from time to time as required during normal operation.

After passing through the pilot-regulator filter, which selects the pilot frequency from the carrier band, the pilot frequency is amplified in V_4 and fed to transformer T_4. The output of the main secondary winding is rectified in V_5, a 6H6. Resistor R_{10}, the 6H6 load, feeds an adjustable portion of this rectified signal to the grids of the d-c amplifier stage (V_2 and V_3 in parallel) by way of the adjustable-

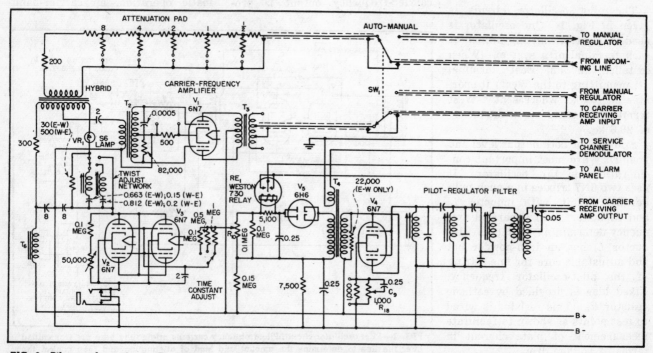

FIG. 3—Pilot regulator circuit. Reactance in the twist network in the right-hand arm of the hybrid bridge gives a frequency-discrimination factor that restores flat frequency characteristics

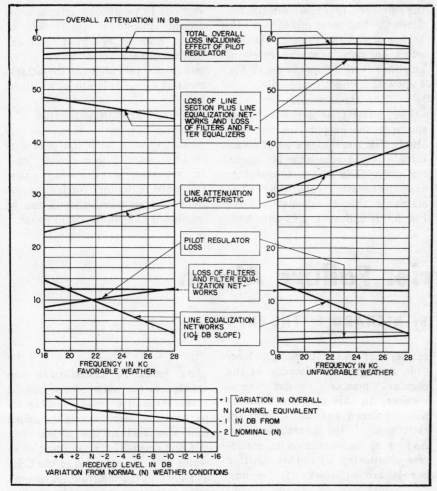

FIG. 4—Total loss over a carrier system, shown as a summation of various related factors. The action of the pilot regulator is to keep overall loss approximately the same under favorable and unfavorable weather operation. Effect of unfavorable weather is shown in lower graph

time-constant network. An additional secondary on transformer T_4 supplies demodulating carrier voltage for the fourth or service carrier channel previously mentioned.

The d-c potential on the grids of V_2 and V_3 is proportional to the received level of the pilot frequency, which thus controls the current flow through lamp VR_1. As current varies, the lamp-filament temperature—and thus resistance—varies and the hybrid-bridge balance is altered, changing attenuation of the carrier frequencies in the hybrid and providing regulation. Because V_2 and V_3 operate as a d-c amplifier, small changes in rectified pilot voltage cause larger changes in current flow through VR_1.

Weather Conditions

Under normal weather conditions the pilot regulator is customarily set for an overall loss of 16 db between regulator input and output circuits. This loss includes pilot-regulator pad loss, regulator-hybrid-bridge loss, and regulator-amplifier gain. At a West terminal the regulator pad is normally strapped for a 10-db loss, the bridge introduces a 31-db loss under normal conditions, and the amplifier contributes a 25-db gain. The result is a 16-db loss. At an East terminal the regulator pad is strapped for a 6-db loss, the bridge operates at a 35-db loss, and the amplifier has a 25-db gain—making the net loss again 16 db. The difference in bridge-circuit attenuation

results from the different frequencies utilized in opposite directions of transmission.

The twist network is a reactance circuit in series with the current-sensitive resistor VR_1 in one arm of the hybrid bridge in Fig. 3. This introduction of reactance makes the attenuation introduced by the bridge circuit dependent on frequency to a degree that can be preset by changing the resonant frequency of the network. Maximum twist correction is obtained when the impedance of the right side of the bridge varies most with frequency or when maximum reactance is in the circuit. No twist correction occurs when the twist network contains no reactance.

Under favorable weather conditions, current through VR_1 is relatively low, and is adjusted by R_{10} to give maximum bridge balance and attenuation (35 db) and increased high-frequency attenuation. The normal slope of the preceding line section adds to this high-frequency attenuation and both are offset by a slope-correction network contained in another portion of the carrier terminal. The resulting level to the amplifier is uniform as to frequency.

Under unfavorable weather con-

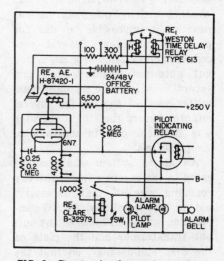

FIG. 5—Circuit of pilot-regulator alarm panel. Action of time-delay circuit at output of 6N7 is such that alarm is energized if operating conditions exceed regulator range for more than 30 seconds, to allow for transient effects on the line

ditions, pilot-current level is reduced, along with all other signals, by increased line attenuation. This raises plate current from the d-c amplifier and increases the resistance of VR_1, unbalancing the bridge to reduce attenuation in the hybrid transformer. Bridge unbalance, however, is most effective at higher frequencies due to action of the series-resonant circuit of the twist network. Thus, the higher-frequency attenuation which occurs here when the bridge is balanced tends to disappear most rapidly as

the bridge becomes unbalanced. Since the line twist increases as the bridge twist decreases, the net effect on signals at the receiving amplifier is nil. The curves of Fig. 4 show this effect graphically.

Alarm System

The meter-type sensitive relay shown in the output circuit of the 6H6 in Fig. 3 actuates a set of alarm signals if the regulator is unable, for longer than 30 sec, to maintain normal operating conditions. The alarm is shown schematically in Fig. 5. It utilizes a 6N7 with both

sections in parallel to actuate a 30-second time-delay circuit RE_1 on either high or low pilot level and thereby give a visual a arm. Terminals are provided for the attachment of external lamps or an alarm bell.

Means are incorporated for silencing the bell but the visual signal remains until the pilot current is restored to a proper level. In repeater installations, where there are regulators for both directions of transmission, both can be connected to a single alarm panel.

Carrier Failure Alarm

By RICHARD E. THORNTON

THIS STATION has an auxiliary transmitter in the same location as the control room and studios, and it became a problem for the studio staff to efficiently employ the auxiliary transmitter when the regular five-kilowatt transmitter went off the air due to power failures and other emergencies.

The regular monitoring system in the control room was capable of being fed off the audio output of a monitoring receiver, but during bad weather and lightning storms was practically impossible to use for program purposes. Several procedures and systems were suggested but were not satisfactory. Upon several occasions the regular transmitter was off the air for several minutes before the studio operator was notified, due to unavoidable complications.

An alarm system was incorporated in the receiver itself, thereby reducing size of unit necessary, wiring, and simplicity. An RC combination was used between the output transformer and the plate of the first audio stage, so that the feedback level would be appreciably more than monitoring level. The output of the receiver speaker, with

carrier on, was not enough, however, to impair monitoring on the regular master control room speaker. In this way, the receiver may be tuned and audio level set satisfactory to the operator on duty. As long as the carrier is on, static-free monitoring off the transmitter bus is accomplished. If, for any

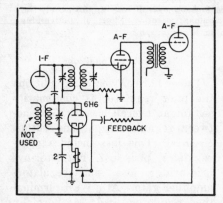

Simple additions to the circuit of a monitoring receiver form a carrier failure alarm

reason, the carrier ceases, the relay switches in the feedback circuit, and the resulting tone signal overrides any level that the monitor may be feeding to master control.

Circuit

An extra i-f transformer was coupled to the plate of the last i-f stage through a small coupling capacitor. The secondary of the added unit was tied to the plates of a H6 and a sensitive relay inserted in series with the cathodes of the 6H6, as shown in the diagram. A one-ma relay performs admirably. A capacitor was tied across the relay winding to prevent chatter due to modulation.

Adjustment of the unit is not critical. The carrier is applied to the antenna input terminals of the receiver and the r-f gain advanced on the receiver to a point slightly beyond that necessary to actuate the relay. This advance is necessary due to the fact that slightly more current is required to reset the relay when the carrier comes back on after a dropout than is necessary for initial adjustment. The i-f transformer is tuned to resonance by means of maximum reading on a 0-5 ma meter in series with the cathodes of the 6H6.

Since installation, there have been no failures of the alarm and it has saved quite a bit of otherwise lost broadcast time.

Reducing Transmitter Out Time

By JAMES H. GREENWOOD

CONTINUITY of service is important to a radio station and the listening public. A minute of silence in the middle of a program may destroy the continuity and annoy the listeners, many of whom would tune in another station.

All of the facilities at WCAE are installed at least in duplicate. Lost time therefore becomes only that time required to isolate the unit in trouble and switch to the alternate unit. This time may be subdivided into four categories; time in which the existence of trouble is observed and realized, time in which to classify or locate the trouble and determine its seriousness, warm-up time for the alternate equipment and actual time involved in switching the alternate equipment into service.

The distribution of time among these classifications varies widely for different types of failure. For some components, the diagnosis and replacement are completely automatic; for others, the human element enters into each step of the process.

At one time, the emergency transmitter at WCAE consumed 45 seconds in warming up. Switching it into service could be accomplished during this time. However, the human element entered into the first two categories mentioned previously and another 15 seconds was added, bringing the total time lost on each occasion of transmitter failure to approximately one minute.

The one-minute loss time has now been reduced to between 12 and 15 seconds. On the surface, it appears to be a gain of four to one

but in listener reaction the gain is much greater, for the first quarter minute of silence is not nearly as annoying as the fourth.

Reduced Warm-Up Time

Warm-up time was reduced to 12 seconds by applying heater current

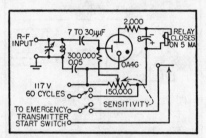

FIG. 1—Schematic diagram of the circuit for starting the emergency transmitter automatically whenever the carrier is interrupted

continously to all heater-type tubes. This practice has not resulted in any observable reduction in useful tube life since only one heater-type tube has been replaced for any cause since 1939 when the system was installed in its original form.

The human element was removed from observing and realizing the existence of trouble by additional circuitry, as shown in Fig. 1. A small sampling antenna and tank circuit excite the grid of an OA4G. In its plate circuit is a relay which starts the emergency transmitter warm up whenever the r-f grid excitation falls below a safe, preset value. This relay does not apply plate voltage to the emergency transmitter.

If the loss of carrier is caused only by a momentary flashover within a tube or a transient arc caused by a lightning discharge,

there is no need for the emergency transmitter and the operator merely shuts it off instead of completing the transfer. Observance of the nature and seriousness of the trouble is accomplished while the equipment is warming up and by the time the decision has been made, the equipment is ready for use.

To reduce the time necessary to switch the alternate equipment into operation, some of the operations performed had to be simplified. The original switching operation consisted of the following steps: removing final-stage plate voltage from the transmitter being taken out of service, switching six circuits from one transmitter to the other (antenna, program input, frequency monitor, modulation monitor, audio monitor and cathode-ray monitor) and applying plate voltage to the transmitter being placed in service.

Controls for most of these operations were grouped at one location. The exceptions were the frequency, modulation and cathode-ray monitors. They were fed from the same sampling antenna which excites the OA4G and therefore indicate operating conditions automatically for whichever transmitter is in use.

With a little practice, all remaining circuits can be switched in a fraction of a second. A completely automatic change-over could have been devised but it would have been considerably more complex and less reliable. Also, it would still require the minimum warm-up time of 12 seconds. The system described retains all of the advantages of human judgment with no added delay.

Series Overmodulation

By ROBERT E. BAIRD

Amplitude modulation in excess of 100 percent can be produced with a series modulator without creating sideband splatter. Several methods have been described for accomplishing such overmodulation (for example: Overmodulation Without Sideband Splatter, O. G. Villard, Jr., ELECTRONICS, p 90, Jan. 1947) and for exceeding 100 percent modulation on positive peaks without exceeding it on negative peaks. Broadcast stations in some localities overmodulate within the five-percent differential allowed by the FCC by slightly unbalancing their class-B linear amplifier. The simple method that is to be described here rounds the negative peaks so that overmodulation cannot occur on them even though over 200 percent modulation may be produced on positive peaks. In this way the break in the carrier that would cause sideband splatter is avoided.

Modulator Tube is Variable Resistor

Series modulation has considerable merit in itself because there are no reactances in the modulator. All that is needed is the proper tube and a power supply giving a little more than twice the rated voltage of the r-f amplifier. Figure 1A shows the basic circuit. The modulator operates like a class-A audio amplifier in that the grid never swings positive. In action, the modulator tube behaves as a variable resistance (with half the supply voltage across it when no audio signal is applied) in series with the modulated r-f amplifier. The variation in resistance acts at audio frequency, approaching zero resistance on positive peaks so that the full power supply voltage (twice the rated voltage of the r-f amplifier) appears across the modulated stage. On negative peaks, cutoff is approached (or reached) so that the tube impedance approaches (or reaches) infinite resistance.

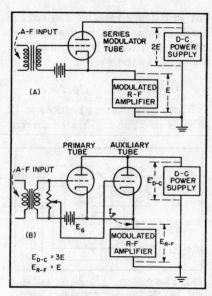

FIG. 1-(A) Conventional series modulator and (B) series modulator with auxiliary tube to suppress negative peaks

Modified Power Supplies

In practice it is found that, because the tube is not absolutely linear, it needs considerably more than half the power supply voltage across it in order to stay in the linear portion of its characteristic and still achieve 100-percent modulation on positive peaks without distortion. As much as 20 percent of the power supply voltage may still be across the modulator tube when 100-percent undistorted positive peaks are being handled by the modulated tube. (This remaining voltage could be considerably reduced by designing a tube for the purpose. The 6AS7G might prove very good in a low power modulator.)

By using several tubes in parallel, it is possible to make a slight change in the circuit that, with proper adjustment, will enable it to accentuate positive peaks and suppress negative peaks. In the circuit of Fig. 1B the grid of the auxiliary tube is shown connected to a tap across the audio input. Although

there may be sufficient signal to cut off the primary tube on negative peaks, the auxiliary tube will still be conductive and hence the resistance of the modulator will not reach infinity and 100-percent modulation on the negative peaks is not attained. If in addition the static voltage drop across the modulator is increased from E to $2E$, it will be possible to furnish $3E$ to the modulated stage on positive peaks, or 200-percent modulation. Under this condition the tap for the auxiliary tube is adjusted so that its grid does not quite reach cutoff on negative peaks, thus 100-percent negative modulation will not be exceeded. Proper adjustment of the tap can be determined with an oscilloscope as shown in Fig. 2.

As is expected, the foregoing procedure introduces some distortion. However, for speech it is not objectionable at 150 percent modulation and does not interfere with the intelligibility at even 200-percent peak positive modulation.

Experimental Equipment

To demonstrate the feasibility of the method, a transmitter using type 10 tubes and having series modulation was modified for the purpose. With conventional 100-percent modulation, 400 volts appeared across the r-f stage and about 600 across the modulator. On 200-percent modulation with suppressed negative peak, about 250 volts appeared across the r-f stage and 750 across the modulator. The ideal values for these respective conditions would be 500–500 and 333–667.

More detailed data were obtained from a transmitter having a single-ended 304TL r-f stage and 304TL's in the modulator. Transformer coupling into the modulator tubes was found necessary to provide a low-impedance d-c grid return. Although a power supply capable of providing nine times the unmodulated carrier power on positive

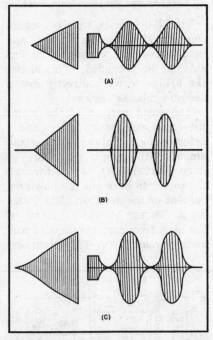

FIG. 2-(A) Conventional 100-percent modulation, (B) unsuppressed 200-percent modulation, and (C) 200-percent modulation with auxiliary tube adjusted to limit negative peaks

peaks may seem excessive, the fact that this power need be provided only on such peaks means that, in practice, the filter capacitors can be relied upon to supply the peaks; the power transformer and filter chokes need be but little larger than for a conventional modulator. The heavier the modulation, the smaller the power dissipated in the modulator tubes. Thus considerable increase in peak power is made possible with negligible increase in power supply. In addition, because series modulation is used, a heavy modulation transformer and speech amplifiers are omitted; a voltage amplifier is sufficient to drive the modulator. The modulator is as shown in Fig. 2A. The accompanying tabulation gives data taken with it for two conditions: (1) two 304TL's in parallel, one having reduced audio excitation, and (2) three 304TL's in parallel, again with one having reduced excitation.

Although this method of suppressing the negative peak so that amplitude modulation in excess of 100 percent can be obtained without sideband splatter may not be desir-

able for high-power transmitters, it is economical for some uses of low-power transmitters. For example, using this method, the watt-hours at the increased voltage, with appropriate batteries, obtainable from such portable equipment as that used by the forestry fire wardens can be increased without increasing the weight of the equipment.

MODULATOR CHARACTERISTICS

Percent Positive Peaks	E_{R-F} Volts	E_{D-C} Volts	I_P Ma	E_G Volts
TWO TUBES				
100	1,050	2,700	370	—120
125	850	2,750	300	—130
150	750	2,750	270	—145
200	650	2,800	240	—165
THREE TUBES				
100	1,100	2,600	380	—117
125	900	2,700	330	—130
150	800	2,800	270	—150
200	700	2,750	240	—165

Percent negative peak modulation: 100

Distortion and Noise Meter

High selectivity possible with standard components in a null T-bridge filter circuit is made use of in a simple, easily built meter for checking noise and distortion of broadcasting and other audio equipment. Suggestions are made for construction and operation

By ROYDEN R. FREELAND

AUDIO DISTORTION and noise measurements, such as must be made on broadcast stations and should be made on public address and other installations, can be taken with the instrument to be described here. It covers the audio range from a fundamental frequency of 50 cps through harmonics up to 50,000 cps and reads noise levels down to —60 db directly.

The rms distortion is measured by suppressing the fundamental frequency and then measuring the

remaining part of the output wave from the equipment under test with a square-law vacuum-tube voltmeter. The rms distortion D_{RMS} of a wave is defined as the effective value of the harmonics divided by the effective value of the fundamental; that is

$D_{RMS} = (I_2{}^2 + I_3{}^2 + I_4{}^2 + \ldots)^{1/2}/I_1$

where $I_2, I_3, I_4, \ldots$ are the effective values of the distortion harmonics and I_1 is the effective value of the fundamental. On the one hand, distortion measuring instruments

based on the suppression of the fundamental are simpler and less expensive than other types. On the other hand, they give only the total rms distortion and are normally convenient only when measuring a few specified fundamental frequencies, such as required by the new FCC rule 3.46(e).

Null T-Bridge Suppresses Fundamentals

The basic suppression circuit of the instrument is a null T-bridge and when balanced it has zero transmission at the balance frequency but very high transmission for harmonics, if the values of the components are properly chosen. With resonant circuits having Q's of three to five, the fundamental can be suppressed while the second harmonic is attenuated less than a decibel. The value of R_s (Fig. 1) must be low if harmonic attenuation is to be kept low.

To obtain balanced conditions of the null bridge, the following equations must be satisfied

$$\omega L_s = 2/\omega C$$
$$R_s = 1/R\,(\omega C)^2$$

For a fixed value of L_s and R_s, R will become larger as C becomes smaller. This will cause R to vary widely when using a single inductance to cover several frequencies.

prises two variable resistances for coarse and fine adjustment. Some frequencies require additional resistance for balance and this is also placed in the circuit by the frequency switch.

All of the bridge elements were obtained from local radio stocks. It was found impractical to calculate the values of the components and then attempt to purchase them. A variety of ready-made inductances could not be found. Most of the inductances available had too high a resistance to produce a usable Q.

For the low frequencies, an ordinary iron core filter choke was tried, but its value changed readily with varying input levels to the bridge. By taking a 15-henry choke

(the second harmonic of any null frequency must be attenuated less than 1 db).

Function and Range of Instrument

The T-bridge is widely used in commercial distortion meters, and is a convenient circuit since one side can be grounded. This allows the bridge to work directly into a vacuum tube as shown.

The vtvm portion of the meter uses four voltage amplifiers and a detector-meter stage. A small amount of current, controlled by ZERO ADJUSTMENT, is fed through the meter to buck out the no-signal current of the detector. The FEEDBACK CIRCUIT provides control of the high frequency response as well as the circuit GAIN. The potentiom-

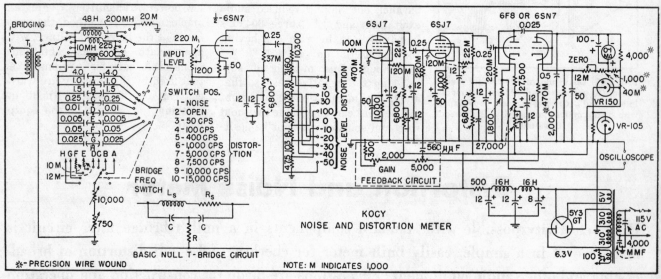

FIG. 1--Complete circuit diagram of noise and distortion checker shows ganged switch for setting rejection frequency of null bridge, distortion and noise level switch and high gain amplifier terminating in detector and meter circuit. The 4.8-henry inductance was made by removing the end portion of the core of a 15-henry choke. Bridge circuit components may be varied to use available parts as long as the Q is kept high enough for less than 1-percent attenuation of any null frequency second harmonic

In practice, R may be controlled somewhat by slightly increasing R_s.

The complete circuit for the noise and distortion meter is shown in Fig. 1. The T-bridge uses three inductances for measuring the eight fixed frequencies, which are chosen to conform to FCC regulations. A different amount of capacitance is required in the bridge for each fundamental and is placed in the circuit by the BRIDGE FREQUENCY SWITCH. The resistance R com-

and removing the end portion of the core this change in inductance was reduced to a negligible value. The inductance of the modified choke was 4.8 henries.

Values of components for the bridge at the eight frequencies as selected by the bridge frequency switch are tabulated in Fig. 1. Actually the values of the components can be varied widely to suit the parts available as long as the circuit Q is sufficiently high

eter following the null bridge controls the INPUT LEVEL to the vtvm and is used for setting the meter reference level. The setting of the step-attenuator, which precedes the first 6SJ7, plus the meter reading gives the total value of distortion or noise. There are six attenuator steps for noise measurements, giving full scale readings of 0, −10, −20, −30, −40, and −50 db. The combination of attenuator setting and meter reading allows noise measurements to below −60 db. Noise measurements to lower values can be made by operating the equipment under test at a level lower than the desired reference level. That is, if the desired measurement is the noise below −60 db, the equipment can be operated, for example, with an output level of −10 db. If the noise were −65 db with a 0 db reference, it would be −55 db with a −10 db reference, which can be read on the instrument.

The attenuator has five steps for measuring distortion. These are calibrated for full scale values of 100, 30, 10, 3, and 1 percent. The 100-percent position is that used for calibration.

The accuracy of the instrument depends upon the accuracy of the attenuator resistors and of the meter scale calibration. Close tolerance resistors can be purchased for the attenuator, or, as done in this case, each value can be made up of several ordinary carbon resistors using a resistance bridge to determine the correct value.

Minimizing Hum and Input Loading

In constructing the noise and distortion meter, precautions were taken to minimize hum pickup by the bridge inductances. The two larger inductances were mounted at slight angles, determined experimentally. No trouble was had with the smallest inductor. High-Q toroidal inductances could be used in such a bridge to minimize hum pickup. However, the small additional hum reduction did not seem to warrant the expense of these coils over those used.

Any hum picked up in the inductances raises the minimum input levels at which satisfactory measurements can be made. Where it is planned to use such an instrument for high-level audio measurements, levels below 0 db will seldom be encountered. At these high levels the small amount of hum picked up by the inductances causes little trouble. The meter described has a hum level down more than 60 db with gain

control in the maximum position. Because the bridge inductances are out of the circuit during noise measurements, their hum pickup

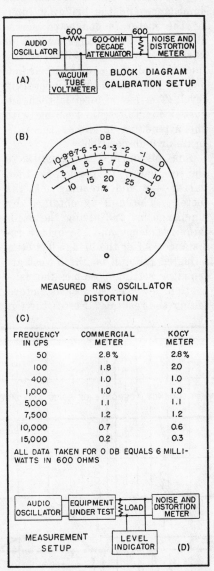

FIG. 2—(A) When the instrument is calibrated, the meter scale will appear as shown (B). Measurements made with the instrument (C) in a test setup (D) compare favorably with those made with a commercial meter

has no effect on these measurements. Residual noise in the meter is more than 80 db below 0 dbm signal.

It can be seen that the balance resistance varies widely. For normal audio measurements where balanced circuits are encountered, a bridging type input transformer

must be used to prevent loading of the circuit under test. The capacitive impedance of the bridge required that a transformer having a low impedance secondary be used to avoid resonant peaks in the low-frequency characteristics of the circuit. The T-bridge may be connected directly across an unbalanced circuit for measurements. The impedance of the circuit connected to the bridge input has very little effect upon the operation of the bridge circuit. Under these conditions the loading effect of the T-bridge on the circuit being measured is substantially that of the balance resistance. At the extreme low frequencies the impedance looking into the bridge increases and is capacitive. As can be seen from the balance equations, R can be increased by increasing L_s and decreasing C while R_s remains constant. To increase R at the low frequencies presents a problem without specially wound inductances.

Calibration and Performance Testing

To calibrate the scale of the output meter, the instrument was set up as shown in Fig. 2A. It was assumed that the audio oscillator had zero internal impedance. The noise-distortion meter was adjusted for a full-scale meter reading with a 1,000-cps signal. The attenuator box was then adjusted to place 10-db attenuation in the circuit in 1-db steps. After the insertion of each db attenuation the meter scale was carefully marked.

Two scales were calibrated for distortion measurements using the standard vtvm to indicate the correct input voltage ratios. The meter scale is shown in Fig. 2B. One scale for noise measurements is marked from 0 db to −10 db. The two distortion scales are marked between 30 percent and 10 percent, and 10 percent and 3 percent. These two distortion scales serve for reading all five distortion attenuator settings.

The frequency response of the meter for each position of the bridge switch was plotted to determine the harmonic frequencies contained in each measurement. The overall response is shown in Fig. 3A. This response curve shows that the meter exceeds the specifications set forth by the FCC.

Response curves for the eight nulls are shown in Fig. 3B. Note that the second harmonic of any null frequency is attenuated less than 1 db.

A direct comparison of the operation of the meter with a commercial instrument was made by making distortion measurements on an inexpensive audio oscillator with both meters under the same conditions (Fig. 2C).

Distortion Measurements

The meter described is used in measurements similar to other noise and distortion meters. An audio oscillator of low harmonic

output is connected to the equipment under test as shown in Fig. 2D. The output of the equipment is terminated in its correct load impedance and the bridging input of the meter is connected across this load. The bridge switch of the meter is set to the desired frequency and the equipment is adjusted for the desired operating level. The meter level is then adjusted for full scale reading with the attenuator in either the calibrate or 0-db position.

FOR DISTORTION MEASUREMENTS the oscillator frequency is then varied for null reading of the meter. The null is obtained by simultaneously adjusting the oscillator frequency and the bridge resistance. After the bridge has been adjusted for null on the lowest attenuator setting possible, the calibration level is rechecked before taking the reading. For distortion

measurements, it is necessary to set the oscillator frequency to at least twice the null frequency when adjusting the calibrate level. If the oscillator or equipment level varies greatly over this range, an external meter must be connected at the input point to insure the input level to the meter is the same for calibration and for the null frequency. After the level is correctly set, the oscillator frequency is reset to the null point and the attenuator adjusted until a reading can be obtained on the meter scale. The combination of the attenuator setting and meter reading indicates the total distortion.

Although the lowest calibrated reading for distortion is 0.3 percent on the 1-percent scale, a lower value can be read by setting the attenuator to the −50 db position. Full scale reading in the position corresponds to 0.316 percent which

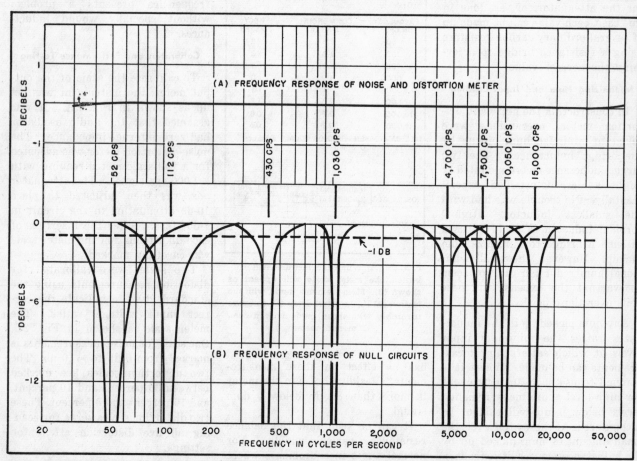

Fig. 3—(A) Frequency response of the meter, with the null bridge bypassed, is flat over the full audio spectrum. (B) The rejection of the null bridge is sufficiently sharp so that second harmonics are attenuated less than a decibel. Problem is to find large inductance with low loss for use at low frequencies

can be easily read on the 3-percent scale.

NOISE MEASUREMENTS are made by setting the frequency switch of the meter in the noise position and adjusting the meter for full scale reading. The signal is then removed from the equipment under test and the input properly terminated. The noise level present may then be read by decreasing the attenuator setting until an indication is obtained on the meter. Again, the combination of the meter reading and the attenuator setting gives the final result.

Distortion measurements taken with the meter indicate the rms total of all components of the input signal which fall within the limits of the frequency range, except the fundamental frequency component, which is rejected by the bridge. The reading of the meter will therefore include the following components:

(1) harmonics, (2) modulation cross products between hum and fundamental, (3) modulation cross products between hum and harmonics, (4) hum components and (5) noise components. The noise and distortion meter sums all these quantities and indicates the ratio of the sum of all undesired components to the fundamental frequency component. If it is desired to determine the distortion due to the harmonic and cross product components alone, either of two methods may be used.

One method is to operate the equipment under test at a high output level. This results in making the hum and noise components small compared to the other components.

The second method is to measure the distortion in the normal manner at the desired output level, then to measure the noise level in db, using the same output level as reference. The db noise level is then converted to percent and the values substituted in the equation

$$H = (D^2 - N^2)^{1/2}$$

where H is total harmonic and cross section distortion in percent, D is distortion in percent and N is noise in percent.

The noise and distortion meter described can be constructed for less than $100.00. This is considerably less than the price of a similar instrument on the commercial market. The meter is capable of reading distortion as low as 0.1 percent and noise to below −60 db within the frequency range 30 to 50,000 cps.

Low-Distortion A-M Signal Generator

One-hundred-percent modulation is obtained by combining out-of-phase carrier voltage with partially modulated signal in cancellation circuit. Uses exalted-carrier detector in overall feedback circuit. Regulated oscillator insures constant output amplitude

By ERNEST S. SAMPSON

A LOW-DISTORTION amplitude-modulated signal source is essential for such jobs as adjusting a-m station monitors and testing high-quality broadcast receivers. With the signal generator described, audio distortions of better than 0.1 percent at 100 percent modulation are obtained by the use of several special circuits not commonly found in commercial testing equipment.

Referring to the block diagram in Fig. 1 and the circuit diagram in Fig. 2, it may be seen that the outputs of the a-f amplifier and r-f oscillator are combined in the modulator to produce an r-f signal which is about 75 percent modulated. One hundred percent modulation is effectively obtained by

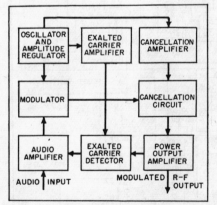

FIG. 1—Block diagram shows how high percent modulation is accomplished with low distortion

adding an out of phase component of the carrier signal through the cancellation amplifier. Negative feedback is employed in both the audio amplifier and modulator, and an exalted-carrier detector is used in an overall feedback circuit.

Circuit Details

The two-stage audio amplifier, whose function is to raise the level of the audio input signal to a value suitable for driving the modulator, employs about 25 db negative feedback from the plate of the second tube to the grid of the first. The amplifier distortion is less than 0.1 percent, and its gain is about 100 with 10 volts rms output.

The tunable broadcast-frequency oscillator which supplies the carrier component to the modulator and drives the exalted amplifier and the cancellation amplifier is a Hartley oscillator. Its output is regulated at 80 volts rms by the 6AG7 regulator circuit which eliminates the need for an amplitude control.

Modulator

A portion of the oscillator signal and the output of the audio amplifier are impressed on the control grid of the 829B modulator tube. The action is very similar to that of an ordinary grid-modulated amplifier.

The constants of the circuit were chosen to give a 75 percent modulated signal at the output of the modulator without the necessity of driving the grid positive. This eliminates the necessity of a low-impedance grid driving source and greatly reduces a source of modulation distortion.

The cathode circuit of the modulator is unique in that it provides a large amount of degeneration which effectively reduces the modulation distortion.

The cathode circuit not only furnishes a d-c bias voltage for the correct operation of the modulator but its action is much the same as that of an ordinary peak detector. The R-C time constant is long enough to maintain the peak r-f

voltage between the r-f current pulses. It is important to make this time constant short enough to prevent audio negative peak clipping. Since a maximum of only 75 percent modulation is required from the modulator, the design of this circuit to prevent peak clipping is simple. Once the resistance R is determined by the value of d-c bias required for the modulator the following equation may be used to determine the capacitance C:

$$C = \frac{\sqrt{1 - K^2}}{R\,\omega\,K}$$

where K is the maximum percent modulation divided by 100, $\omega_a = 2\pi f_a$ and f_a is the highest audio modulation frequency in cps.

The above equation is derived in the following manner: From Fig. 3, let $e_a = E \sin \omega_a t$, where e_a is the modulation signal. Then the envelope of the peak r-f voltages applied across the R-C circuit will be represented by the equation

$$E' = \frac{E}{K} + E \sin\omega t$$

Differentiating the equation of the modulating signal to find its slope

$$\frac{de_a}{dt} = \omega E \cos\omega t$$

The slope of the voltage decay across the R-C circuit at the beginning of each decay period is $-E'/RC$. It is assumed that the voltage decay is linear for the short period between the r-f pulses. In order to prevent distortion due to negative peak clipping, it is necessary that the slope of the R-C circuit voltage decay always be equal to or slightly greater than the slope of the modulation envelope. Therefore,

$$-\frac{\frac{1}{K} + sin\omega t}{RC} = \omega cos\omega t$$

Since there is only one instant during the audio cycle that the above equation can be true, that

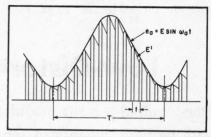

FIG. 3—Modulator cathode waveform showing the modulation envelope

time may be determined by differentiating with respect to t, then

$$RC = \frac{cos\omega t}{\omega sin\omega t}$$

Substituting this in the previous equation and solving for C, we obtain

$$sin\omega t = -K$$
$$cos\omega t = \sqrt{1 - K^2}$$
$$C = \frac{\sqrt{1 - K^2}}{KR\omega}$$

Cancellation Amplifier

The modulator output signal is added to the output signal of the cancellation amplifier in the cancellation circuit. The addition of these two signals results in a sum signal which has its modulation percentage increased to 100 percent from the 75 percent level at the modulator. The cancellation amplifier signal has a 180 degree phase relation with respect to the

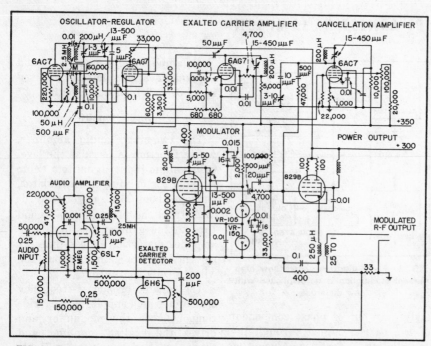

FIG. 2—Circuit diagram of signal generator. Value of cathode capacitor for modulator is determined by formula derived in text

carrier of the modulator output signal.

This 180-degree phase relation is very accurately controlled by the tunable capacitor in the parallel resonant circuit which is the load impedance of the cancellation amplifier. To adjust accurately the phase of this amplifier, it is necessary to view the generator output waveform with an oscilloscope with slightly more audio applied to the generator input than is necessary for 100 percent modulation. This procedure will produce on the oscilloscope a picture which is similar to that of Fig. 4A. Perfect phase relationship reveals two sharp crossover points in the trough of the modulated signal as shown in Fig. 4B.

Since the voltage gain of the cancellation amplifier is not constant over the tunable frequency band, it is necessary to control the screen grid voltage of the amplifier for this purpose. Approximately the correct phase for proper cancellation is obtained at the amplifier output by driving its grid from the grid circuit of the oscillator. Good r-f waveshape is obtained not only by using the highly frequency selective tuned circuit in the plate circuit of the 6AC7 amplifier, but also by operating the amplifier class A with degeneration in the cathode circuit. Figure 4C shows a 100-percent modulated signal with perfect cancellation phase.

Power Output Amplifier

The power output amplifier is driven by the cancellation circuit and is a cathode follower. The 829B tube was chosen because of its high current-conducting capacity and its high transconductance. The grid input capacitance is greatly reduced by driving the screen grid at the same a-c potential as the cathode through the 0.01-μf screen to cathode capacitor. Expressed by an equation, the gain of a cathode follower amplifier is:

$$G = \frac{g_m\, r_k}{g_m\, r_k + 1}$$

where g_m is the transconductance

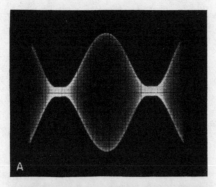
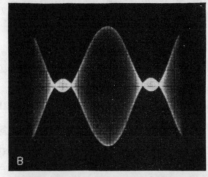
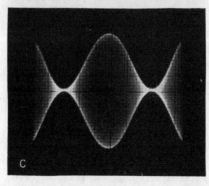

FIG. 4—Output waveform of a-m signal generator for (A) incorrect cancellation phase, (B) correct cancellation phase with overmodulation, and (C) correct cancellation phase and 100 percent modulation

of the tube and r_k is the equivalent cathode resistance. The grid input capacitance will be

$$C_i = C_o\,(1 - G)$$

where C_i is the new input capacitance and C_o is the input capacitance with the cathode and screen at ground potential. The grid input capacitance to the 829B is reduced from 29 $\mu\mu f$ to 3 $\mu\mu f$ with the above mentioned arrangement.

The power output amplifier drives an air-core r-f transformer which is used to reduce the peak to peak amplifier current swing by a factor of 2.5 to 1. The air-core type

of transformer was used because it made possible an impedance transformation without r-f waveform distortion which would result from an iron-core transformer. A tuned transformer could have been used but it would have meant an additional tuning control. The primary winding of the transformer is wound in a single layer on a cylindrical 1.5-inch diameter Bakelite coilform. The secondary winding is wound directly on top of the primary winding. The wire used for the secondary coil has a diameter 2.5 times that of the primary coil. This makes the coils equal in length which provides the maximum possible coefficient of coupling.

Exaltation Circuit

The exaltation amplifier is driven from the grid of the oscillator tube in order to obtain the correct phase for its output which drives the exalted carrier detector. The correct phase for the detector is obtained by adjusting the variable tuning capacitor in the plate circuit of the exaltation amplifier.

The exalted carrier type of detector makes it possible to detect a 100 percent modulated r-f signal without introducing audio negative peak clipping. Negative peak clipping is eliminated by adding a large unmodulated r-f signal in phase with the modulated r-f signal at the detector. This effectively reduces the percent modulation. If the ratio of unmodulated to modulated signals is made large, the phase relation between the two signals does not have to be adjusted accurately. Improper phase relation introduces audio distortion but of small magnitude when a ratio of voltages of 30 to 1 is used in this generator detector. A 10-degree phase relation for the specified conditions will introduce 0.02 percent second harmonic component and zero third harmonic component for a 100 percent modulated signal.

The output of the modulation detector is applied to the input of the audio amplifier through an r-f filter circuit. The overall negative feedback is approximately 20 db and serves to reduce noise and distortion by that factor.

Operation and Performance

In aligning the signal generator to a particular frequency an oscilloscope must be used for viewing the modulated output. There are six controls that must be adjusted for alignment to a particular carrier frequency. The oscillator is adjusted to the desired r-f frequency.

The modulator tuning control is adjusted to give maximum oscilloscope deflection, while the modulator bias control sets the desired output level. Cancellation tuning is set to give minimum r-f output level at the correct phase, and the cancellation gain is adjusted to give approximately 25 percent reduction in output level due to the cancellation amplifier. The exaltation tuning adjustment is set to give a minimum modulation while maintaining a fixed audio input level.

The r-f output level is variable between 6 and 8 volts rms across a termination of 60 to 100 ohms.

The writer acknowledges the important contributions of H. R. Summerhayes, Jr. of the General Electric Company in connection with the development of this signal generator.

REFERENCE

C. A. Cady, Methods of Obtaining Low Distortion at High Modulation Levels, *General Radio Experimenter*, April, 1943.

Blower Selection for Forced-Air Cooled Tubes

How to determine requirements for industrial and communications applications. Charts supplied here, and examples showing how to use them, simplify the job and help to insure trouble-free performance of equipment

By A. G. NEKUT

FORCED-AIR-COOLED power tubes have found wide acceptance in industrial and communications applications because of their convenience and economy. Although forced air is used to cool glass-to-metal seals, bulbs and metal headers of tubes the most important single use is in cooling the external anode.

When a fan or blower is selected for a particular application two factors must be known, the air-flow required by the tube and the static pressure at the blower outlet. Although these factors apply generally to cooling any part of an electron tube, attention is directed in this article to the problem of selecting a blower for cooling the radiator or cooler of an external-anode tube, particularly when duct work is used. The results obtained are equally applicable to the problem of selecting a blower for cooling any other part of a tube.

Factors Involved in Selection

The air flow (Q) required by a tube depends upon the amount of anode dissipation and upon the maximum ambient or incoming air

temperature expected in a given application. For a specified amount of anode dissipation the amount of air flow required to limit the temperature rise of the anode to a safe value may be obtained from tube data. This value of air flow is usually based upon tests made at room temperature and normal barometric pressures, corrected for the rated

maximum ambient or incoming air temperature for the tube (usually 45 C). For applications in which the blower uses air having a density appreciably different from 0.075 lb per ft^3, corrections must be made.

The static pressure (P_s) at the blower outlet depends upon the pressure-versus-airflow characteristics of the system into which the

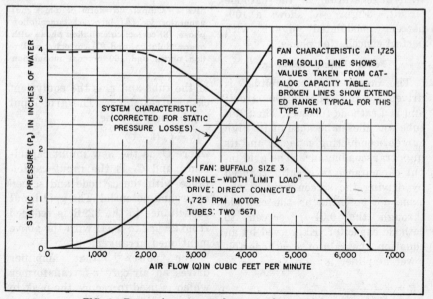

FIG. 1—Fan performance and system characteristic curves

blower must deliver the required volume of air. A typical system characteristic is shown in Fig. 1. The value of static pressure is determined by the following factors:

(1) The static pressure rating of the tube cooler when the required air flow is passing through it. This rating is given in tube data as a function of air flow when the cooler is operating at its maximum rated temperature. When the outlet of a blower discharges into free air, as is the case when the blower-outlet air flow is directed at a tube header, bulb or seal, the static pressure at the blower outlet is zero provided no ducts, constrictions or nozzles are used. Airflow rating of a blower for zero static pressure at the blower outlet is usually called the free-delivery rating of the blower.

(2) The friction losses in ductwork and other components such as elbows, interlock vanes and air filters. Standard tables of duct-pressure loss[1] available in most blower

catalogs may be used for estimating duct friction if the effective duct length is large.

(3) The change in static pressure in a duct due to changes in cross-sectional area which increase or decrease the velocity of the air in the duct. Whenever there is any change in cross-sectional area between the blower outlet and the tube inlet a correction for velocity changes must be added algebraically to the static pressure at the blower outlet. This correction, which is positive for a contraction in area and negative for the expansion in area, is given[2] by the relation

$$\Delta P_s = \frac{V_2{}^2 - V_1{}^2}{(4,000)^2} \qquad (1)$$

where V_1 is the velocity of the air before the change in area and V_2 is the velocity of the air after the change. These velocities in feet per minute may be found from the expression

$$V = Q/A \qquad (2)$$

where A is the cross-sectional area

at the place of measurement in square feet and Q is the air flow in cubic feet per minute. The factor 4,000 of Eq. 1 is the velocity constant for air of standard density of 0.075 lb per ft³. The relationship given in Eq. 1 is shown in graph form in Fig. 2.

A change in cross-sectional area also causes friction losses. Such losses are small and can be ignored

Definitions of Terms	
A	= cross-sectional area of air flow in ft²
D	= diameter of air duct in ft
d	= density of air in lb per ft³
P_s	= static pressure in inches of water
ΔP_s	= change in static pressure in inches of water
Q	= volume of air delivered per unit time in ft³ per min
rpm	= speed of blower in revolutions per min
T_i	= air temperature at inlet in deg C
T_o	= air temperature at outlet in deg C
ΔT	= change in air temperature in deg C
V	= velocity of air in ft per min
W_f	= filament power in watts
W_m	= blower-shaft horsepower
W_p	= plate dissipation in watts
w	= power dissipated per unit air flow in watts per ft³ per min

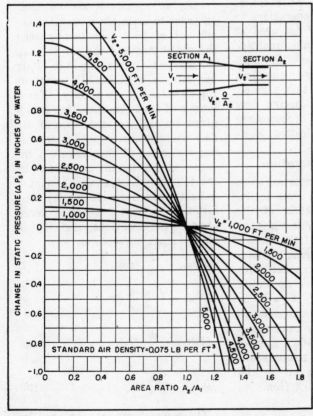

FIG. 2—Change in static pressure due to gradual change in air-flow cross-section

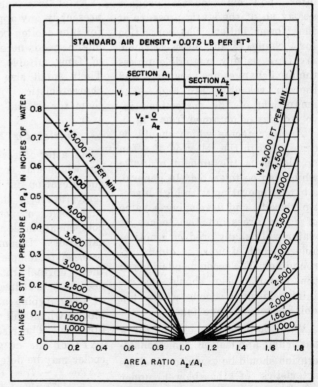

FIG. 3—Change in static pressure due to abrupt change in air-flow cross-section

when the change in cross-sectional area is gradual and occurs over a duct length of more than six duct diameters. When, however, the change is more abrupt, a correction for friction losses must be made in addition to the correction made for velocity changes in the duct. Corrections for friction losses, whether due to either a contraction or expansion in duct area, are always positive and are added to the system static pressure.

A sudden contraction increases the static pressure at the blower outlet[2] according to the relation

$$\Delta P_s = \frac{K_c V_2^2}{(4,000)^2} \qquad (3)$$

where K_c is a constant which depends upon the amount of contraction and is included in a plot of Eq. 3 in Fig. 3.

A sudden expansion increases the static pressure[2] at the blower outlet according to the relation

$$\Delta P_s = \frac{(V_1 - V_2)^2}{(4,000)^2} \qquad (4)$$

The static pressure rating of the cooler and the friction losses in air filters and exit louvers produce nearly all of the static pressure at the blower outlet. The correction for changes in cross-sectional area are usually negligible unless the area changes are very large and the air velocities are high. The magnitude of the corrections involved may be obtained from Fig. 3.

Another factor which should be considered in the selection of a fan or blower is the amount of noise which can be tolerated. In general, a blower operating with high blade-tip velocity and developing a value of P_s in excess of two inches of water will usually produce a noticeable amount of noise in quiet surroundings. The recommendations of the manufacturer should be obtained in applications where low noise output is important.[3]

When a blower is chosen for a particular application, some consideration should be given to the characteristics of the blower under varying load conditions. A satisfac-

tory and widely used type of centrifugal blower is one using an impeller wheel having a multitude of small vanes or blades located at the rim of the wheel and curved in the direction of rotation. Such a blower will develop a given static pressure at lower blade-tip velocity than other types of centrifugal blower, with a resultant economy in blower size. If, however, prolonged operation is contemplated with a tube removed from its socket and thus with reduced static pressure at the blower outlet, a centrifugal blower having backwardly curved blades is recommended, since such a blower has a nonoverloading characteristic. In such a blower the shaft horsepower reaches a maximum somewhere in the middle of its operating range and remains substantially constant for a constant blower speed as the static pressure at the blower outlet is reduced to zero. In the larger sizes, this type of blower often has the further advantage of permitting direct drive from a 1,750-rpm, 60-cycle a-c motor because of its inherently higher speed of operation.

Axial flow fans are not used at present in any appreciable quantity for tube cooling because of the high motor speeds necessary in the sizes of fans suitable for this service. Their small size and in-line flow characteristics may recommend them for special application, however.

Outlet-Air Temperature

A matter of lesser importance but one which may require some design consideration is the effect of the temperature of the air leaving the tube cooler on some of the circuit components such as filament bypass capacitors. If some components are exposed to temperatures exceeding their normal ratings it will be necessary to reduce the temperature of the outgoing air by selecting a blower which will provide a greater air flow. The rise in temperature (ΔT) of the outgoing air in the cooler may be determined from

$$\Delta T = T_o - T_i = \frac{(T_i + 273)(W_p + W_f)}{164\, Q} \qquad (5)$$

where T_i is the temperature of the incoming air in degrees centigrade, W_p is the plate dissipation in watts, W_f is the filament power in watts, and Q is the airflow in cubic feet per minute. For incoming air at room temperature (25 C) this relation may be simplified to

$$\Delta T = \frac{1.82\,(W_p + W_f)}{Q} \qquad (6)$$

The calculated value of ΔT will usually be higher than the measured value because some of the heat produced by the plate and by the filament will be carried away by conduction in the filament leads and cooler support. A further reason is that the heated outgoing air, because of its relatively high velocity, mixes immediately with the surrounding air. Figure 4 is a plot of Eq. 5.

High-Altitude Operation

Tube operation at high altitudes or under conditions where the blower uses air having a density appreciably lower than standard density is sometimes encountered. In order to maintain a constant coefficient of heat transfer between the cooler fins and the air stream, the mass rate of air flow in lb of air per minute must be held constant for all values of air density. For a blower of fixed size operating into a given system, the mass rate of air flow can be held constant by increasing the speed of the blower in inverse ratio of the air densities. In the following fan laws, subscript 1 indicates standard air-density conditions, subscript 2 indicates lower air-density conditions, and W_m is blower-shaft horsepower

$$(\text{rpm})_2 = \frac{d_1}{d_2}\,(\text{rpm})_1 \qquad (7)$$

$$(W_m)_2 = \left(\frac{d_1}{d_2}\right)^2 (W_m)_1 \qquad (8)$$

$$(P_s)_2 = \frac{d_1}{d_2}\,(P_s)_1 \qquad (9)$$

$$Q_2 = \frac{d_1}{d_2}\,Q_1 \qquad (10)$$

These equations may be used in selecting a blower for operation

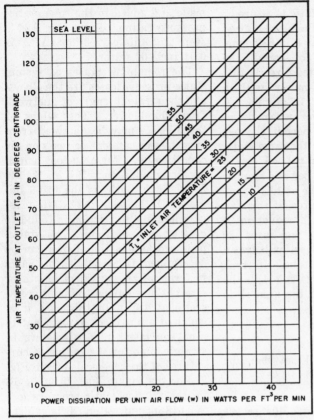

FIG. 4—Change in air temperature due to tube power dissipation

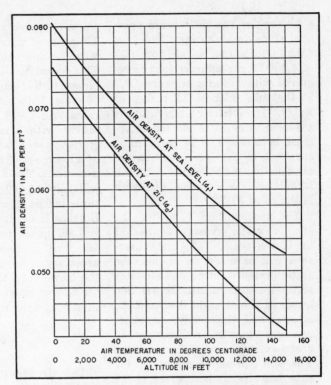

FIG. 5—Change in air density with altitude and temperature of the air

where lower than standard air density prevails by first computing the air flow and static pressure at the blower under standard density conditions and then correcting for the different air density. The variation of air density with altitude and temperature is plotted in Fig. 5. To find the air density from this figure at any temperature and altitude, the following relation is used:

$$d = 13.3\, d_a\, d_t \qquad (11)$$

Testing the System

After the system has been installed, the static-pressure (P_s) rating for the tube may be used to determine whether sufficient air is being supplied to the cooler. A simple U-tube manometer may be constructed as shown in Fig. 6, using water as the manometer liquid. The value of P_s may be read directly as the difference in height of the liquid levels.

To make this measurement a small hole (No. 40 drill size) is drilled in the air-supply duct at some suitable place at least three inches below the cooler. Care should be taken that the hole is free from burrs and is located in a smooth section of air duct at least three inches away from any joints, air-flow interlock vanes or other obstructions. The inlet of the manometer is connected to this hole by means of a suitable length of rubber tubing. The outlet of the manometer is connected to some point in the tube enclosure space or equipment cabinet which is maintained at the static pressure into which the tube air flow must discharge under normal service conditions. This measurement is normally made by inserting the rubber tubing connected to the manometer outlet through a louvre or other opening in the cabinet wall into a region in the cabinet where the air velocity is negligibly small. All doors and other openings normally closed in operation must, of course, be closed.

The value of P_s thus obtained should be equal to or greater than the value given in the tube data for the air flow and dissipation required.

It is desirable to make this measurement with the equipment operating at full rated output, because the static pressure required for a given air flow through a tube cooler increases with cooler temperature. This increase in static pressure varies approximately from 2 to 15 percent, depending upon the tube, as the temperature rise of the cooler is increased from zero to the maximum allowable temperature rise. When many tubes are supplied from a common plenum chamber it is usually sufficiently accurate to measure the static pressure in the plenum chamber and assume that this pressure is the actual static pressure present at the tube inlet.

Standard methods of testing blowers and fans have been published[4].

Example

By way of illustration, let us assume that it is required to select a blower for two 5671 tubes operated at maximum ratings. The tube data indicate that an air flow (Q) of 1,800 ft³ per min per tube is required with a static pressure (P_s) at the tube inlet of 2.2 inches of water. The inlet air temperature is assumed to be 21 C and the equipment is assumed to be operated at sea level, so that no correction for air density need be made. A typical layout for the required ductwork is shown in Fig. 7.

The problem here is to find the effective static pressure required at the blower outlet. This static pressure will be made up of the tube static pressure rating, the air-filter static-pressure rating, the friction losses in the straight duct and the elbows, and the change in static pressure due to any changes in cross-sectional area of the air ducts. The static-pressure rating of the tube has already been given as 2.2 inches of water at 1,800 ft³ per min. An air filter of proper design and adequate air flow cross-section should have a static pressure rating of about 0.25 inch of water.

Before evaluating the remaining static pressure contributions of the system, it is necessary to make a tentative blower selection in order to fix its outlet area. Since the air-flow paths of the two tubes are in parallel, the blower is required to deliver cooling air at a rate of:

$$Q = 2\,(1,800) = 3,600 \text{ ft}^3 \text{ per min}$$

The static pressure due to the tubes and air filter is approximately

$$P_s = 2.2 + 0.25 \cong 2.5 \text{ inches of water}$$

The cross-sectional area (A) of the tube air inlet may now be obtained from the tube dimensional outline. For the 5671, the diameter (D) of the air-inlet duct is approximately 1 foot. The tube air-inlet area is $A = \pi D^2/4 = 0.78$ ft² per tube or 1.56 ft² for the two tubes.

An examination of blower catalogs shows that the Buffalo Forge Company size 2¾, single-inlet single-width Limit Load fan has an outlet area of 1.56 ft² and would apparently be a suitable selection. However, in order to deliver 3,600 ft³

per min against a static pressure of 2.5 inches of water the blower speed must be approximately 1,880 rpm. This speed would not permit the blower to be connected directly to a 60-cycle induction motor with a rated load speed of 1,725 rpm. A blower with a larger wheel diameter, however, will permit the use of a lower speed for the same static pressure. The Limit Load size 3 will deliver 3,600 ft³ per min against three inches of water at 1,720 rpm. Because the outlet area of this fan is 1.86 square feet, a reduction in air flow cross-sectional area is necessary in the connection between the blower and the tube. If A_1 is the blower outlet area and A_2 is the tube inlet area then the area ratio

$$\frac{A_2}{A_1} = \frac{1.56}{1.86} = 0.84$$

The air velocity V_2 at the tube inlet is

$$V_2 = \frac{Q}{A_2} = \frac{3,600}{1.56} = 2,310 \text{ ft per min}$$

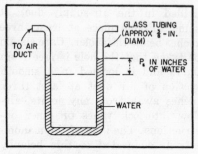

FIG. 6—Simple U-tube manometer, useful for system tests

From Fig. 2, the change in static pressure (ΔP_s) in going from section 2 to section 1 is + 0.14 inch of water. Since this value is positive, it must be added to the tube static-pressure rating. This static-pressure value is based upon the assumption that the change in air-flow cross-sectional area was made gradually. In most cases, however, a gradual change is not practical. For the duct layout shown in Fig. 7 a further correction for a sudden contraction in duct area must also be

made and added to the tube static-pressure rating. From Fig. 3 it is seen that this correction (ΔP_s) is 0.04 inch of water.

The remaining causes of system static-pressure losses are the elbows and the straight length of ductwork from the blower. The values of these losses may be obtained from most blower catalogs or texts on air conditioning. For a 10-foot length of rectangular duct 19⅝ in. × 14⅛ in., to fit the outlet of the size 3 single-width blower, the static-pressure loss due to friction is found to be 0.02 inch of water. The static-pressure loss in the elbows can be determined from published charts in terms of an equivalent length of straight pipe having the same cross-sectional area. In this case it is equal to a length of approximately nine equivalent pipe diameters in straight pipe for the radius of curvatures of the bend scaled from Fig. 7. For the square duct 13 in. × 13 in. the friction static-pressure loss is 0.018 inch of water. It is evident from the above that unless abnormally small duct sizes are used for a given air flow the correction for elbows, etc, are small.

When we collect and add up all the contributions of static pressure in inches of water, we obtain

5671 tubes	2.20
Air filter	0.25
Duct contraction	0.14
Correction due to sudden duct contraction	0.04
Elbow and duct friction	0.04
	2.67

The sum of all the static pressures obtained above is known as the system static pressure at the blower outlet at the rated flow of 3,600 ft³ per min. Since all of these items vary approximately as the square of the velocity, and hence Q, at the blower outlet, the system static pressure curve may be plotted from the relation

$$(P_s)_x = P_s \left(\frac{Q_x}{Q}\right)^2$$
$$= 2.67 \left(\frac{Q_x}{3,600}\right)^2 \qquad (12)$$
$$(P_s)_x = 2.06 \times 10^{-7}\,(Q_x)^2$$

where $(P_s)_x$ is the static pressure of the system measured at the blower outlet for any value of air flow Q_x. This equation is plotted in Fig. 1.

The intersection of the fan characteristic curve and the system characteristic curve in Fig. 1 indicates the operating point of the combination and shows that 3,700 ft³ per min will be delivered to the tubes with a static pressure at the blower outlet of 2.85 inches of water. The catalog ratings show that 2.4 horsepower is required. Since the maximum horsepower for this blower at 1,725 rpm is shown as 2.7 horsepower a three-horsepower motor would be a logical choice.

From Fig. 4, the air temperature at the tube outlet may be obtained. The power dissipated, in watts per ft³ per min, is

$$w = \frac{2(W_p + W_f)}{Q} = \frac{2(25,000 + 3,140)}{3,700} =$$

15 watts per ft³ per min.

For an inlet air temperature of 21 C, the tube outlet air temperature is found from Fig. 4 to be 48 C. This value is generally of interest to the equipment designer in order to predict the maximum temperature to which various components located in the outlet air stream will be exposed.

High-Altitude Example

The preceding example considered the selection of a blower for a cooling system operating under normal conditions of temperature and atmospheric pressure. If this same system were to be operated at an altitude of 5,000 feet above sea level and with an inlet air temperature of 45 C a correction for the reduced air density would be necessary.

From Fig. 5, at an altitude of 5,000 feet and a temperature of 21 C the density $d_a = 0.062$ lb per ft³; at sea level and a temperature of 45 C the density $d_t = 0.069$ lb per ft³. From Eq. 11 the actual air density $d = 13.3 d_a d_t = 13.3(0.062)(0.069) = 0.057$ lb per ft³. The blower selected in the previous example may be used to deliver the same mass rate of air flow when handling

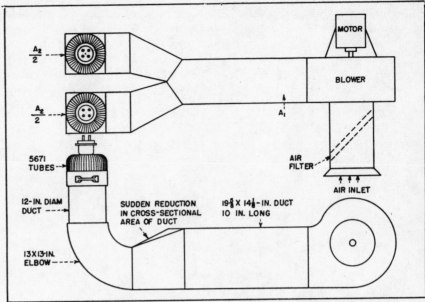

FIG. 7—Typical duct arrangement for cooling two power triodes

lower-density air by increasing its speed in accordance with Eq. 7

$$(\text{rpm})_2 = \frac{d_1}{d_2}(\text{rpm})_1 = \frac{0.075}{0.057}(1,720) =$$

2,260 rpm

The blower-shaft horsepower rating given in the first example must be corrected in accordance with Eq. 8

$$(W_m)_2 = \left(\frac{d_1}{d_2}\right)^2 (W_m)_1 = \left(\frac{0.075}{0.057}\right)^2 (2.4)$$

$$= 4.16 \text{ horsepower}$$

The static pressure measured at the blower outlet when the blower is handling the lower density air is

$$(P_s)_2 = \frac{d_1}{d_2}(P_s)_1 = \frac{0.075}{0.057}(2.9) =$$

3.8 inches of water

The air flow under these conditions may be found from Eq. 10, although there is no particular need for the value found. The outlet air temperature is the same as found in the first example because the mass rate of air flow has been held constant.

The two examples given illustrate the procedure to be followed in selecting blowers to supply the required air flow to the external-anode coolers of typical power tubes. The same procedure can be used to cal-

culate the effective static pressures at the blower outlet, or inlet for suction systems, for any air system which may be used to cool the seals, bulbs or headers of vacuum tubes.

In general, unless the air system is long and has many sharp bends and large abrupt changes in air flow cross-section and unless the air velocity is abnormally high in ducts of small cross-section the corrections for duct friction and area changes are small. The largest contributors to the static pressure at the blower outlet are the tubes themselves and the air filtering systems. One major exception to this last statement, however, is the presence of inadequately designed air exit louvres or openings in the enclosing cabinet. These openings should be designed with adequate area so that the air velocity through them is kept as low as possible.

REFERENCES

(1) "Heating, Ventilating, Air Conditioning Guide," American Society of Heating and Ventilating Engineers.
(2) W. H. McAdams, "Heat Transmission", Second Edition, McGraw-Hill Book Co., New York, 1942.
(3) Sound Measurements Test Code for Centrifugal and Axial Fans, National Association of Fan Manufacturers, Bulletin No. 104.
(4) Standard Test Code for Centrifugal and Axial Fans, National Association of Fan Manufacturers, Bulletin No. 103.

AUTHOR INDEX

INDEX

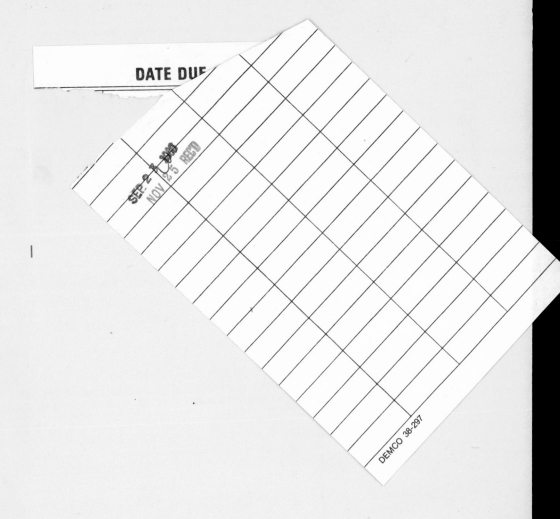